nature

The Living Record of Science
《自然》百年科学经典

英汉对照版　套装共十卷

第九卷
1998-2001

总顾问：李政道 （Tsung-Dao Lee）

英方主编：Sir John Maddox
　　　　　Sir Philip Campbell

中方主编：路甬祥

外语教学与研究出版社 · 麦克米伦教育 · 自然科研

FOREIGN LANGUAGE TEACHING AND RESEARCH PRESS · MACMILLAN EDUCATION · NATURE RESEARCH

北京 BEIJING

图书在版编目（CIP）数据

《自然》百年科学经典 : 套装共十卷 . 第九卷 : 英汉对照 ／（英）约翰·马多克斯（John Maddox），（英）菲利普·坎贝尔（Philip Campbell），路甬祥主编 . —— 北京 : 外语教学与研究出版社，2020.9
　　ISBN 978-7-5213-2021-3

　　Ⅰ . ①自… Ⅱ . ①约… ②菲… ③路… Ⅲ . ①自然科学－文集－英、汉 Ⅳ . ①N53

中国版本图书馆 CIP 数据核字（2020）第 155153 号

地图审图号：GS（2020）5244 号

出 版 人　徐建忠
项目统筹　章思英
项目负责　刘晓楠　黄小斌
责任编辑　王丽霞
责任校对　黄小斌
封面设计　高 蕾
版式设计　孙莉明
插图设计　麦克米伦提供原图扫描版
出版发行　外语教学与研究出版社
社　　址　北京市西三环北路 19 号（100089）
网　　址　http://www.fltrp.com
印　　刷　北京华联印刷有限公司
开　　本　787×1092　1/16
印　　张　51
版　　次　2021 年 1 月第 1 版　2021 年 1 月第 1 次印刷
书　　号　ISBN 978-7-5213-2021-3
定　　价　8000.00 元

购书咨询：（010）88819926　电子邮箱：club@fltrp.com
外研书店：https://waiyants.tmall.com
凡印刷、装订质量问题，请联系我社印制部
联系电话：（010）61207896　电子邮箱：zhijian@fltrp.com
凡侵权、盗版书籍线索，请联系我社法律事务部
举报电话：（010）88817519　电子邮箱：banquan@fltrp.com
物料号：320210001

《自然》百年科学经典（英汉对照版）

总顾问：李政道（Tsung-Dao Lee）

英方主编：Sir John Maddox

Sir Philip Campbell

中方主编：路甬祥

编审委员会

英方编委

Philip Ball

Vikram Savkar

David Swinbanks

中方编委（以姓氏笔画为序）

许智宏

赵忠贤

滕吉文

本卷审稿专家（以姓氏笔画为序）

于 军	万渝生	石锦卫	卢 磊	田立德	巩克瑞	刘守偈
许家喜	杜江峰	李 然	李军刚	李崇银	肖景发	狄增如
汪筱林	宋心琦	张颖奇	陈 阳	陈尔强	陈捷胤	周天军
周礼勇	赵凌霞	胡松年	俞永强	郭建栋	姬书安	曹 俊
彭小忠	韩汝珊	曾长青	解彬彬	黎 卓		

编译委员会

本卷翻译工作组稿人（以姓氏笔画为序）

王丽霞	王晓蕾	王耀杨	刘明	刘晓楠	关秀清	何铭
沈乃澂	周家斌	郭红锋	黄小斌	蔡迪	蔡则怡	

本卷翻译人员（以姓氏笔画为序）

王海纳	王耀杨	毛晨晖	卢皓	吕静	任奕	刘项琨
刘振明	刘皓芳	齐红艳	李梅	杨晶	肖莉	余恒
沈乃澂	张玉光	金世超	周家斌	姜克	高如丽	崔宁
董培智	蔡则怡					

本卷校对人员（以姓氏笔画为序）

马昊	王晓蕾	王德孚	牛慧冲	龙娉娉	卢皓	田晓阳
吉祥	任奕	刘本琼	刘立云	刘项琨	刘琰璐	许静静
阮玉辉	李龙	李平	李景	李婷	李志军	李若男
李照涛	李霄霞	杨晶	杨学良	吴茜	邱珍琳	邱彩玉
何敏	张亚盟	张茜楠	张美月	张瑶楠	陈秀	陈贝贝
陈思原	周晔	周少贞	郑旭峰	郑婧澜	赵凤轩	胡海霞
娄研	洪雅强	贺舒雅	顾海成	徐玲	黄小斌	第文龙
蒋世仰	韩少卿	焦晓林	蔡则怡	裴琳	潘卫东	薛陕

Eric Leher（澳）

Contents
目录

Volume IX

(1998-2001)

Discovery of a Supernova Explosion at Half the Age of the Universe

S. Perlmutter *et al.*

Editor's Note

In the early 1990s it became possible to use type Ia supernovae as "standard candles" to determine astronomical distances. Using this approach, Saul Perlmutter and coworkers here report a supernova at a redshift of 0.83 that is fainter than expected. Although they initially interpreted the faintness as evidence that the universe has a lower average density than was thought, it was soon realized that the best explanation is that the universe is expanding at an accelerating rate. This is now the accepted view, although the reason is unclear and represents one of the central puzzles in contemporary cosmology. One interpretation is that the universe is pervaded by "dark energy" that creates a repulsive force, counteracting gravitational attraction.

The ultimate fate of the Universe, infinite expansion or a big crunch, can be determined by using the redshifts and distances of very distant supernovae to monitor changes in the expansion rate. We can now find[1] large numbers of these distant supernovae, and measure their redshifts and apparent brightnesses; moreover, recent studies of nearby type Ia supernovae have shown how to determine their intrinsic luminosities[2-4]—and therefore with their apparent brightnesses obtain their distances. The > 50 distant supernovae discovered so far provide a record of changes in the expansion rate over the past several billion years[5-7]. However, it is necessary to extend this expansion history still farther away (hence further back in time) in order to begin to distinguish the causes of the expansion-rate changes—such as the slowing caused by the gravitational attraction of the Universe's mass density, and the possibly counteracting effect of the cosmological constant[8]. Here we report the most distant spectroscopically confirmed supernova. Spectra and photometry from the largest telescopes on the ground and in space show that this ancient supernova is strikingly similar to nearby, recent type Ia supernovae. When combined with previous measurements of nearer supernovae[2,5], these new measurements suggest that we may live in a low-mass-density universe.

SN1997ap was discovered by the Supernova Cosmology Project collaboration on 5 March 1997 UT, during a two-night search at the Cerro Tololo Interamerican Observatory (CTIO) 4-m telescope that yielded 16 new supernovae. The search technique finds such sets of high-redshift supernovae on the rising part of their light curves and guarantees the date of discovery, thus allowing follow-up photometry and spectroscopy of the transient supernovae to be scheduled[1]. The supernova light curves were followed

在宇宙年龄一半处发现的超新星爆发

珀尔马特等

编者按

在 20 世纪 90 年代的早期，使用 Ia 型超新星作为"标准烛光"测定天文学距离已成为可能。使用这种方法，索尔·珀尔马特以及他的合作者们在这里报道了在红移 0.83 处比预期的暗淡的一颗超新星。尽管他们最初把这颗超新星的暗淡解释为宇宙的平均密度比普遍认为的要低的证据，但是很快他们意识到最好的解释是宇宙的膨胀在加速。现在这个观点已经被普遍认可，尽管原因尚不知晓，这也是当代宇宙学最主要的难题之一。一种解释是宇宙中充斥着暗能量，产生排斥力，与引力相抗衡。

宇宙的命运最终是无限膨胀还是大挤压，可以通过测量遥远超新星的红移和距离，进而监测宇宙膨胀速率的变化来确定。我们现在发现了大量遥远的超新星[1]，并且测定了它们的红移和视亮度；而对较近 Ia 型超新星的研究已经找到了测定本征光度[2-4]的方法，通过它们的视亮度就能得到距离。至今已发现的 50 多个远距离 Ia 型超新星记录了过去几十亿年间宇宙膨胀速率的变化[5-7]。不过我们还需要进一步追溯更远（即时间上更早）的宇宙膨胀历史，从而找出宇宙膨胀速率变化的原因——是在宇宙质量密度的引力影响下变慢，或是由宇宙学常数的反作用而加速[8]。我们在此报道一颗已获光谱确认的最遥远的超新星。来自地面和空间中最大望远镜的光谱和测光数据表明这颗古老的超新星和较近的 Ia 型超新星非常相似。结合以前对较近距离的 Ia 型超新星的观测数据[2,5]，这些新测量表明我们可能生活在一个质量密度偏低的宇宙之中。

SN1997ap 于世界时（UT）1997 年 3 月 5 日被超新星宇宙学项目团队发现。位于智利的托洛洛山美洲天文台（CTIO）4 米望远镜在两个晚上的搜寻中总共发现了 16 颗新的超新星。搜寻技术能够在这些高红移超新星处于光变曲线上升阶段的时候发现它们，这就保证了发现的日期。因此我们可以安排对这些暂现的超新星进行进一步的测光和光谱观测[1]。利用 CTIO、WIYN、ESO 3.6 米和 INT 的望远镜，我们按

with scheduled R-, I- and some B-band photometry at the CTIO, WIYN, ESO 3.6-m, and INT telescopes, and with spectroscopy at the ESO 3.6-m and Keck II telescopes. (Here WIYN is the Wisconsin, Indiana, Yale, NOAO Telescope, ESO is the European Southern Observatory, and INT is the Isaac Newton Telescope.) In addition, SN1997ap was followed with scheduled photometry on the Hubble Space Telescope (HST).

Figure 1 shows the spectrum of SN1997ap, obtained on 14 March 1997 UT with a 1.5-h integration on the Keck II 10-m telescope. There is negligible ($\leqslant 5\%$) host-galaxy light contaminating the supernova spectrum, as measured from the ground- and space-based images. When fitted to a time series of well-measured nearby type Ia supernova spectra[9], the spectrum of SN1997ap is most consistent with a "normal" type Ia supernova at redshift $z = 0.83$ observed 2 ± 2 supernova-restframe days (~4 observer's days) before the supernova's maximum light in the rest-frame B band. It is a poor match to the "abnormal" type Ia supernovae, such as the brighter SN1991T or the fainter SN1986G. For comparison, the spectra of low-redshift, "normal" type Ia supernovae are shown in Fig. 1 with wavelengths redshifted as they would appear at $z = 0.83$. These spectra show the time evolution from 7 days before, to 2 days after, maximum light.

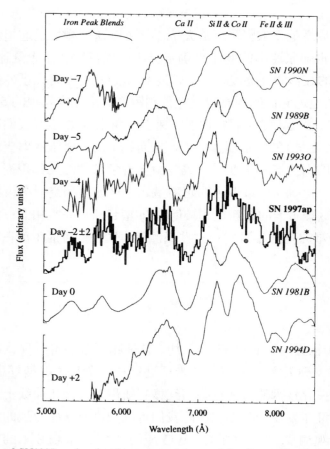

Fig. 1. Spectrum of SN1997ap placed within a time sequence of five "normal" type Ia supernovae. The

计划在 R、I 及 B 波段对超新星进行了测光从而得到光变曲线，同时还用 ESO 3.6 米和凯克 II 望远镜拍摄了光谱。（这里的 WIYN 是指威斯康星大学–印第安纳大学–耶鲁大学–美国国家光学天文台望远镜；ESO 是指欧洲南方天文台；INT 是指艾萨克·牛顿望远镜。）此外，我们还安排哈勃空间望远镜（HST）对 SN1997ap 进行测光。

图 1 是 SN1997ap 的光谱，它是由凯克 II 10 米天文望远镜于 1997 年 3 月 14 日 UT 持续 1.5 小时的观测数据积分而成。地面以及空间望远镜测量到的图像显示，寄主星系对超新星光谱的污染可以忽略不计（≤ 5%）。我们把 SN1997ap 的光谱与一系列较近且已充分测量过的 Ia 型超新星光谱做时间序列拟合，发现它的光谱与红移 $z = 0.83$、在 B 波段极大亮度前 2±2 日（超新星静止系，约为 4 个观测者日）观测的"正常" Ia 型超新星最为一致。SN1997ap 的光谱与其他"非正常" Ia 型超新星（例如较亮的 SN1991T 或较暗的 SN1986G）的光谱并不匹配。图 1 中为了方便比较，低红移的"正常" Ia 型超新星的光谱被红移到 $z = 0.83$ 处。这些光谱显示了超新星从最大亮度的前 7 天到后 2 天的时间演化。

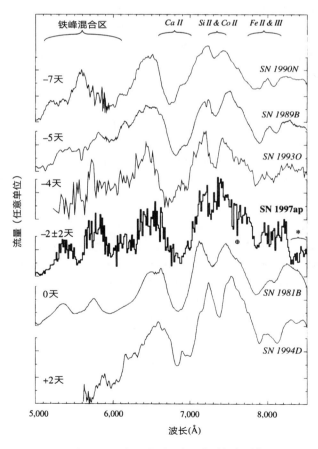

图 1. SN1997ap 的光谱与五个"正常" Ia 型超新星光谱放在一个时间序列中。SN1997ap 的光谱以 12.5 Å data for SN1997ap have been binned by 12.5 Å ; the time series of spectra of the other supernovae[17-21] (the spectrum of SN1993O was provided courtesy of the Calán/Tololo Supernova Survey) are given as they would appear redshifted to $z = 0.83$. The spectra show the evolution of spectral features between 7 rest-frame days before, and 2 days after, rest-frame B-band maximum light. SN1997ap matches best at 2 ± 2 days before maximum light. The symbol $\oplus$ indicates an atmospheric absorption line and * indicates a region affected by night-sky line subtraction residuals. The redshift of $z = 0.83 \pm 0.005$ was determined from the supernova spectrum itself, as there were no host galaxy lines detected.

Figure 2 shows the photometry data for SN1997ap, with significantly smaller error bars for the HST observations (Fig. 2a) than for the ground-based observations (Fig. 2b and c). The width of the light curve of a type Ia supernova has been shown to be an excellent indicator of its intrinsic luminosity, both at low redshift[2-4] and at high redshift[5]: the broader and slower the light curve, the brighter the supernova is at maximum. We characterize this width by fitting the photometry data to a "normal" type Ia supernova template light curve that has its time axis stretched or compressed by a linear factor, called the "stretch factor"[1,5]; a "normal" supernova such as SN1989B, SN1993O or SN1981B in Fig. 1 thus has a stretch factor of $s \approx 1$. To fit the photometry data for SN1997ap, we use template U- and B-band light curves that have first been $1+z$ time-dilated and wavelength-shifted ("K-corrected") to the R- and I-bands as they would appear at $z = 0.83$ (see ref. 5 and P.N. *et al.*, manuscript in preparation). The best-fit stretch factor for all the photometry of Fig. 2 indicates that SN1997ap is a "normal" type Ia supernova: $s = 1.03 \pm 0.05$ when fitted for a date of maximum at 16.3 March 1997 UT (the error-weighted average of the best-fit dates from the light curve, 15.3 ± 1.6 March 1997 UT, and from the spectrum, 18 ± 3 March 1997 UT).

It is interesting to note that we could alternatively fit the $1+z$ time dilation of the event while holding the stretch factor constant at $s = 1.0^{+0.05}_{-0.14}$ (the best fit value from the spectral features obtained in ref. 10). We find that the event lasted $1+z = 1.86^{+0.31}_{-0.09}$ times longer than a nearby $s = 1$ supernova, providing the strongest confirmation yet of the cosmological nature of redshift[9,11,12].

The best-fit peak magnitudes for SN1997ap are $I = 23.20 \pm 0.07$ and $R = 24.10 \pm 0.09$. (All magnitudes quoted or plotted here are transformed to the standard Cousins[13] R and I bands.) These peak magnitudes are relatively insensitive to the details of the fit: if the date of maximum is left unconstrained or set to the date indicated by the best-match spectrum, or if the ground- and space-based data are fitted alone, the peak magnitudes still agree well within errors.

为区间合并；其他超新星的光谱[17-21](SN1993O 的光谱数据由 Calán/Tololo 超新星巡天提供)都被红移到 $z = 0.83$ 处。这些光谱反映了静止系 B 波段光强达到峰值的 7 天前至 2 天后之间的光谱特征变化。SN1997ap 的数据与最大亮度前 2±2 天的光谱数据最吻合。符号 ⊕ 表示大气吸收线，* 表示受夜天光抵扣残余影响的区域。红移 $z = 0.83 \pm 0.005$ 得自超新星光谱，我们并没有检测到寄主星系的谱线。

图 2 显示的是超新星 SN1997ap 的测光数据。哈勃空间望远镜的观测(图 2a)误差显著小于地面望远镜的观测(图 2b 和 2c)。Ia 型超新星光变曲线的宽度被证明是"本征光度"的绝佳表征，无论是在低红移[2-4]还是在高红移[5]处：超新星的光变曲线越宽、变化越慢，那么最大亮度就越高。我们通过将测光数据与"正常"Ia 型超新星的光变曲线模板进行拟合来得到这个宽度，其中模板的时间轴由一个称为"伸展因子"[1,5]的线性参数进行"拉伸"或"压缩"。图 1 中的"正常"超新星 SN1989B、SN1993O 及 SN1981B 的伸展因子 s 约等于 1。为了拟合 SN1997ap 的测光数据，我们使用 U 和 B 波段的光变曲线作为模板，将其经过 $1+z$ 倍的时间拉伸和波长平移(即"K 修正")之后移动到 R 和 I 波段，就像它们在红移 0.83 处一样(见参考文献 5 和纽金特等人正在撰写的文章)。利用图 2 中所有测光数据对延展因子进行拟合得到 $s = 1.03 \pm 0.05$，这表明 SN1997ap 是一个"正常"的 Ia 型超新星：拟合的亮度极大值日期为 1997 年 3 月 16.3 日 UT(根据光变曲线得到的误差加权平均值为 1997 年 3 月 15.3±1.6 日 UT，根据光谱得到的结果为 1997 年 3 月 18±3 日 UT)。

值得一提的是，我们也可以保持伸展因子 $s = 1.0^{+0.05}_{-0.14}$ 不变(这个最佳拟合值来自文献 10 中的光谱数据)，然后对事件的时间膨胀因子 $1+z$ 进行拟合。我们发现 SN1997ap 爆发事件的持续时间是一颗较近超新星($s = 1$)的 $1+z = 1.86^{+0.31}_{-0.09}$ 倍，这一点为红移的宇宙学属性提供了迄今最强的确认[9,11,12]。

超新星 SN1997ap 的峰值星等最佳拟合值为 $I = 23.20 \pm 0.07$ 以及 $R = 24.10 \pm 0.09$。(在本文中，所有提到和绘出的星等都已转换为标准的库森[13]R 和 I 波段星等。)这些峰值星等对拟合的细节并不敏感：如果我们不限制最大值日期或是以最佳匹配光谱来设定最大值日期，或者是只用地面观测数据或空间观测数据来单独拟合，拟合的星等峰值仍然在误差以内。

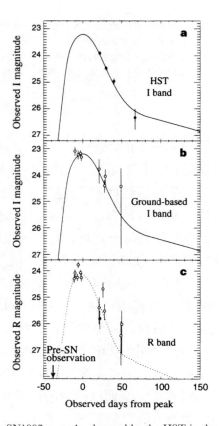

Fig. 2. Photometry points for SN1997ap. **a**, As observed by the HST in the F814W filter; **b**, as observed with ground-based telescopes in the Harris I filter; and **c**, as observed with the ground-based telescopes in the Harris R filter (open circles) and the HST in the F675W filter (filled circle); with all magnitudes corrected to the Cousins I or R systems[13]. The solid line shown in both **a** and **b** is the simultaneous best fit to the ground- and space-based data to the K-corrected, $(1+z)$ time-dilated Leibundgut B-band type Ia supernova template light curve[22], and the dotted line in **c** is the best fit to a K-corrected, time-dilated U-band type Ia supernova template light curve. The ground-based data was reduced and calibrated following the techniques of ref. 5, but with no host-galaxy light subtraction necessary. The HST data was calibrated and corrected for charge-transfer inefficiency following the prescriptions of refs 23, 24. K-corrections were calculated as in ref. 25, modified for the HST filter system. Correlated zero-point errors are accounted for in the simultaneous fit of the light curve. The errors in the calibration, charge-transfer inefficiency correction and K-corrections for the HST data are much smaller (~4% total) than the contributions from the photon noise. No corrections were applied to the HST data for a possible ~4% error in the zero points (P. Stetson, personal communication) or for nonlinearities in the WFPC2 response[26], which might bring the faintest of the HST points into tighter correspondence with the best-fit light curve in **a** and **c**. Note that the individual fits to the data in **a** and **b** agree within their error bars, providing a first-order cross-check of the HST calibration.

The ground-based data show no evidence of host-galaxy light, but the higher-resolution HST imaging shows a marginal detection (after co-adding all four dates of observation) of a possible $I = 25.2 \pm 0.3$ host galaxy 1 arcsec from the supernova. This light does not contaminate the supernova photometry from the HST and it contributes negligibly to the ground-based photometry. The projected separation is ~6 kpc (for $\Omega_M = 1$, $\Omega_\Lambda = 0$ and $h_0 = 0.65$, the dimensionless cosmological parameters describing the mass density,

图 2. SN1997ap 的测光数据点。(**a**)哈勃空间望远镜使用 F814W 滤镜观测的结果；(**b**)地面望远镜使用哈里斯 I 波段滤镜的观测结果；(**c**)地面望远镜使用哈里斯 R 波段滤镜所观测的结果（空心点）和哈勃空间望远镜使用 F675W 滤镜所观测的结果（实心点）；所有星等已被转换到库森 I 或 R 波段[13]。图 **a** 和图 **b** 中的实线是同时将地面和空间的观测数据对经 K 修正和 $1+z$ 倍时间延展的 Ia 型超新星 Leibundgut B 波段光变曲线模板[22]拟合的最佳结果；图 **c** 中的点线是对经 K 修正和 $1+z$ 倍时间延展的 Ia 型超新星 U 波段光变曲线模板拟合的最佳结果。地面观测的数据使用参考文献 5 中的方法进行处理和校准，但没有扣除寄主星系背景光的必要。哈勃空间望远镜的观测数据根据参考文献 23 和 24 中的方法进行了电荷迁移低效率的处理和修正。K 修正使用了参考文献 25 中的方法计算，并根据哈勃空间望远镜的滤镜系统做了调整。在对光变曲线的同步拟合中，我们考虑了零点误差。在哈勃空间望远镜数据的校正、电荷迁移低效率修正和 K 修正中的误差（共约 4%）远小于光子噪声的贡献。对于哈勃空间望远镜数据潜在的约 4% 的零点误差（斯特森，个人交流）和 WFPC2 响应的非线性[26]没有做任何修正。这可能会使哈勃空间望远镜最暗的数据点与图 **a** 和图 **c** 中的最佳拟合曲线吻合得更好。注意图 **a** 和图 **b** 的每个数据点都在各自误差范围内与拟合结果一致，这提供了对哈勃空间望远镜校准的一阶交叉检验。

 地面望远镜观测的数据没有显示寄主星系的光存在的证据，但是在分辨率更高的哈勃空间望远镜所拍摄的图像中有微弱的迹象（在叠加全部四次观测之后）表明，在距离该超新星 1 角秒的地方可能存在一个 $I = 25.2 \pm 0.3$ 的寄主星系。这些光并没有污染到哈勃空间望远镜的超新星测光结果，同时对地面望远镜测光的影响也微不足道。寄主星系到 SN1997ap 的投影距离约为 6 kpc（条件为 $\Omega_M = 1$、$\Omega_\Lambda = 0$ 和

vacuum energy density and Hubble constant, respectively) and the corresponding B-band rest-frame magnitude is $M_B \approx -17$ and its surface brightness is $\mu_B \approx 21$ mag arcsec^{-2}, consistent with properties of local spiral galaxies. We note that the analysis will need a final measurement of any host-galaxy light after the supernova has faded, in the unlikely event that there is a very small knot of host-galaxy light directly under the HST image of SN1997ap.

We compare the K-corrected $R-I$ observed difference of peak magnitudes (measured at the peak of each band, not the same day) to the $U-B$ colour found for "normal" low-redshift type Ia supernovae. We find that the rest-frame colour of SN1997ap [$(U-B)_{\text{SN1997ap}} = -0.28 \pm 0.11$] is consistent with an unreddened "normal" type Ia supernova colour, $(U-B)_{\text{normal}} = -0.32 \pm 0.12$ (see ref. 14 and also P.N. *et al.*, manuscript in preparation). In this region of the sky, there is also no evidence for Galactic reddening[15]. Given the considerable projected distance from the putative host galaxy, the supernova colour, and the lack of galaxy contamination in the supernova spectra, we proceed with an analysis under the hypothesis that the supernova suffers negligible host-galaxy extinction, but with the following caveat.

Although correcting for $E(U-B) \approx 0.04$ of reddening would shift the magnitude by only one standard deviation, $A_{\text{B}} = 4.8E(U-B) = 0.19 \pm 0.78$, the uncertainty in this correction would then be the most significant source of uncertainty for this one supernova. This is because of the large uncertainty in the $(U-B)_{\text{SN1997ap}}$ measurement, and the sparse low-redshift U-band reference data. HST J-band observations are currently planned for future $z > 0.8$ supernovae, to allow a comparison with the restframe $B-V$ colour, a much better indicator of reddening for type Ia supernovae. Such data will thus provide an important improvement in extinction correction uncertainties for future supernovae and eliminate the need for assumptions regarding host-galaxy extinction. In the following analysis, we also do not correct the lower-redshift supernovae for possible host-galaxy extinction, so any similar distribution of extinction would partly compensate for this possible bias in the cosmological measurements.

The significance of type Ia supernovae at $z = 0.83$ for measurements of the cosmological parameters is illustrated on the Hubble diagram of Fig. 3. To compare with low-redshift magnitudes, we plot SN1997ap at an effective rest-frame B-band magnitude of $B = 24.50 \pm 0.15$, derived, as in ref. 5, by adding a K-correction and increasing the error bar by the uncertainty due to the (small) width-luminosity correction and by the intrinsic dispersion remaining after this correction. By studying type Ia supernovae at twice the redshift of our first previous sample at $z \approx 0.4$, we can look for a correspondingly larger magnitude difference between the cosmologies considered. At the redshift of SN1997ap, a flat $\Omega_M = 1$ universe is separated from a flat $\Omega_M = 0.1$ universe by almost one magnitude, as opposed to half a magnitude at $z \approx 0.4$. For comparison, the uncertainty in the peak magnitude of SN1997ap is only 0.15 mag, while the intrinsic dispersion amongst stretch-calibrated type Ia supernovae is ~0.17 mag (ref. 5). Thus, at such redshifts even individual type Ia supernovae become powerful tools for discriminating amongst various world models, provided observations are obtained, such as those presented here, where the

$h_0 = 0.65$，这些无量纲宇宙学参数分别表示质量密度、真空能密度和哈勃常数），对应的 B 波段静止系星等为 $M_B \approx -17$，它的面亮度 $\mu_B \approx 21 \ mag \cdot arcsec^{-2}$，这个属性与较近的旋涡星系的一致。需要指出的是，通常需要在超新星逐渐暗淡后，才能最终测量寄主星系的亮度，以免哈勃空间望远镜拍摄的 SN1997ap 图像正下方正好有个寄主星系的非常小的亮结，不过这种情况不太可能发生。

我们将 K 修正之后的 $R-I$ 峰值星等差（分别观测每个波段的亮度峰值，并非在同一天）和低红移"正常" Ia 型超新星的 $U-B$ 颜色结果作比较。发现 SN1997ap 的静止系颜色 $[(U-B)_{SN1997ap} = -0.28 \pm 0.11]$ 与未红化的"正常" Ia 型超新星的颜色 $[(U-B)_{normal} = -0.32 \pm 0.12]$（见参考文献 14 以及纽金特等人正在撰写的文章）相一致。在这片天区中，我们也没有发现"银河红化"[15]的证据。考虑到假定的寄主星系相当远的投影距离、超新星的颜色，以及光谱并没有受到寄主星系光的污染，我们后面的分析都假定寄主星系对该超新星的消光可以忽略。不过下面几点需要注意。

尽管 $E(U-B) \approx 0.04$ 的红化修正只会让星等偏移一个标准差，$A_B = 4.8E(U-B) = 0.19 \pm 0.78$，这个修正的不确定性是这颗超新星最主要的误差来源。这是因为 $(U-B)_{SN1997ap}$ 的测量有很大的不确定性，而且还缺乏低红移处的 U 波段参考数据。哈勃空间望远镜计划对未来 $z > 0.8$ 的超新星进行 J 波段的观测，以便能够对比静止系 $B-V$ 颜色，它可以作为 Ia 型超新星更好的红化表征。这些数据可以帮助减小未来超新星消光修正的不确定性，并消除有关寄主星系消光的假定。在接下来的分析中，我们也没有对较低红移超新星进行可能的寄主星系的消光修正，所以任何相似的消光分布对宇宙学测量可能造成的偏差会部分地抵消。

红移 $z = 0.83$ 的 Ia 型超新星对宇宙参数测量的意义在图 3 的哈勃图中已经标示出。为了和低红移星等进行对比，我们将 SN1997ap 的数据画在有效静止系下 $B = 24.50 \pm 0.15$ 处，这个值的推导和文献 5 中一样，经过了 K 修正，并考虑了由（小的）宽度–光度修正的不确定性和修正之后遗留的内禀弥散度所引起的误差棒增加。通过研究我们此前 $z \approx 0.4$ 的第一个样本红移的两倍处的超新星，我们可以寻找不同宇宙学模型之间相应更大的星等差。在 SN1997ap 的红移处，$\Omega_M = 1$ 的平坦宇宙与 $\Omega_M = 0.1$ 的平坦宇宙模型相差将近一个星等，而在红移值 $z \approx 0.4$ 处，仅相差半个星等。相比之下，SN1997ap 的峰值星等的不确定性仅有 0.15 星等，然而 Ia 型超新星在延展修正后的内禀弥散度约为 0.17 星等（参考文献 5）。因此，在这样的红移处，只要观测能够提供本文这样的测光误差低于内禀弥散度的数据，即使是单个 Ia photometric errors are below the intrinsic dispersion of type Ia supernova.

Fig. 3. SN1997ap at $z = 0.83$ plotted on the Hubble diagram from ref. 5. Also plotted are the 5 of the first 7 high-redshift supernovae that could be width-luminosity corrected, and the 18 of the lower-redshift supernovae from the Calán/Tololo Supernova Survey that were observed earlier then 5 d after maximum light[3]. Magnitudes have been K-corrected, and also corrected for the width-luminosity relation. The inner error bar on the SN1997ap point corresponds to the photometry error alone, while the outer error bar includes the intrinsic dispersion of type Ia supernovae after stretch correction (see text). The solid curves are theoretical m_B for $(\Omega_M, \Omega_\Lambda) = (0, 0)$ on top, $(1, 0)$ in middle and $(2, 0)$ on bottom. The dotted curves are for the flat-universe case, with $(\Omega_M, \Omega_\Lambda) = (0, 1)$ on top, $(0.5, 0.5)$, $(1, 0)$ and $(1.5, -0.5)$ on bottom.

By combining such data spanning a large range of redshift, it is also possible to distinguish between the effects of mass density Ω_M and cosmological constant Λ on the Hubble diagram[8]. The blue contours of Fig. 4 show the allowed confidence region on the Ω_Λ ($\equiv \Lambda/(3H_0^2)$) versus Ω_M plane for the $z \approx 0.4$ supernovae[5]. The yellow contours show the confidence region from SN1997ap by itself, demonstrating the change in slope of the confidence region at higher redshift. The red contours show the result of the combined fit, which yields a closed confidence region in the Ω_M–Ω_Λ plane. This fit corresponds to a value of $\Omega_M = 0.6 \pm 0.2$ if we constrain the result to a flat universe ($\Omega_\Lambda + \Omega_M = 1$), or $\Omega_M = 0.2 \pm 0.4$ if we constrain the result to a $\Lambda = 0$ universe. These results are preliminary evidence for a relatively low-mass-density universe. The addition of SN1997ap to the previous sample of lower-redshift supernovae decreases the best-fit Ω_M by approximately 1 standard deviation compared to the earlier results[5].

型超新星也能成为区分各种宇宙模型的有力工具。

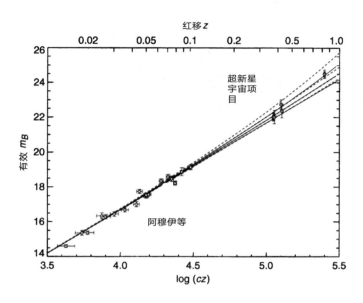

图 3. 红移 $z = 0.83$ 的 SN1997ap 标注在参考文献 5 中的哈勃图上。图上还画出首次能做宽度-光度修正的 7 颗高红移超新星中的 5 个，和 18 颗由 Calán/Tololo 超新星巡天观测到的较低红移超新星，它们是在亮度极大前后五天的区间内被观测到的 [3]。星等已经经过 K 修正和宽度-光度关系修正。SN1997ap 数据点上的内侧误差棒只表示测光误差，而外侧误差棒则包含了经过伸展修正后的 Ia 型超新星内禀弥散度（见正文）。实线对应不同宇宙模型的理论 m_B：上，$(\Omega_M, \Omega_\Lambda) = (0, 0)$；中，$(\Omega_M, \Omega_\Lambda) = (1, 0)$；下，$(\Omega_M, \Omega_\Lambda) = (2, 0)$。虚线对应平坦宇宙模型：上，$(\Omega_M, \Omega_\Lambda) = (0, 1)$；下，$(\Omega_M, \Omega_\Lambda) = (0.5, 0.5)$、$(1, 0)$ 和 $(1.5, -0.5)$。

综合这些大范围红移的数据，我们还有可能在哈勃图中区分质量密度 Ω_M 和宇宙学常数 Λ 的影响 [8]。图 4 中的蓝色等值线显示了 $z \approx 0.4$ 的超新星所允许的 Ω_Λ（$\equiv \Lambda / (3H_0^2)$）与 Ω_M 平面的置信区域 [5]。黄色等值线显示的是 SN1997ap 独立限制的 Ω_Λ 和 Ω_M 置信区域，表明在较高红移处置信区域的斜率有所变化。红色等值线显示的是综合所有超新星进行拟合的结果，得到了一个 Ω_M-Ω_Λ 的封闭置信区域。如果我们限定宇宙是平坦的（$\Omega_\Lambda + \Omega_M = 1$），拟合可以得到 $\Omega_M = 0.6 \pm 0.2$；如果我们限定于 $\Lambda = 0$ 的宇宙，可以得到 $\Omega_M = 0.2 \pm 0.4$。这些结果是宇宙质量密度偏低的初步证据。将超新星 SN1997ap 的数据加入以往较低红移的超新星样本中，我们所得的最佳拟合值比以前的结果减少了大约一个标准差 [5]。

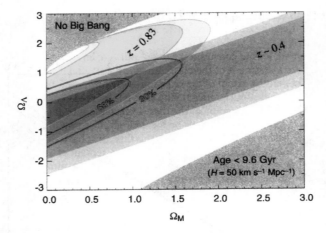

Fig. 4. Contour plot of the best fit confidence regions in the Ω_Λ versus Ω_M plane for SN1997ap and the five supernovae at $z \approx 0.4$ (see ref. 5). The 68% (1σ) and 90% confidence regions for (blue shading) the supernovae at $z \approx 0.4$, (yellow shading) SN1997ap at $z = 0.83$ by itself, and (red contours) all of these supernovae taken together. The two labelled corners of the plot are ruled out because they imply: (upper left corner) a "bouncing" universe with no Big Bang[27], or (lower right corner) a universe younger than the oldest heavy elements, $t_0 < 9.6$ Gyr (ref. 28), for any value of $H_0 \geqslant 50$ km s^{-1} Mpc^{-1}.

Our data for SN1997ap demonstrate: (1) that type Ia supernovae at $z > 0.8$ exist; (2) that they can be compared spectroscopically with nearby supernovae to determine supernova ages and luminosities and check for indications of supernova evolution; and (3) that calibrated peak magnitudes with precision better than the intrinsic dispersion of type Ia supernovae can be obtained at these high redshifts. The width of the confidence regions in Fig. 4 and the size of the corresponding projected measurement uncertainties show that with additional type Ia supernovae having data of quality comparable to that of SN1997ap, a simultaneous measurement of Ω_Λ and Ω_M is now possible. It is important to note that this measurement is based on only one supernova at the highest ($z > 0.8$) redshifts, and that a larger sample size is required to find a statistical peak and identify any "outliers". In particular, SN1997ap was discovered near the search detection threshold and thus may be drawn from the brighter tail of a distribution ("Malmquist bias"). There is similar potential bias in the lower-redshift supernovae of the Calán/Tololo Survey[2], making it unclear which direction such a bias would change Ω_M.

Several more supernovae at comparably high redshift have already been discovered by the Supernova Cosmology Project collaboration, including SN1996cl, also at $z = 0.83$. SN1996cl can be identified as a very probable type Ia supernova, as a serendipitous HST observation (M. Donahue *et al.*, personal communication) shows its host galaxy to be an elliptical or S0. Its magnitude and colour, although much more poorly constrained by photometry data, agree within uncertainty with those of SN1997ap. The next most distant spectroscopically confirmed type Ia supernovae are at $z = 0.75$ and $z = 0.73$ (ref. 16; these supernovae are awaiting final calibration data). In the redshift range $z = 0.3$–0.7, we have discovered over 30 additional spectroscopically confirmed type Ia supernovae, and followed them with two-filter photometry. (The first sample of supernovae with $z \approx 0.4$

14

图 4. 由 SN1997ap 和 5 个 $z \approx 0.4$ 的超新星（参考文献 5）限制的 Ω_M–Ω_Λ 平面的最佳拟合置信区域等值线图。图中画出了 68%（1 个标准差）和 90% 的置信区域：蓝色为五个 $z \approx 0.4$ 超新星的结果，黄色为 $z = 0.83$ 的 SN1997ap 单独限制的结果，红色等值线为所有超新星的结果。图中有标注的两角是被排除的区域：左上角表示一个没有大爆炸的反弹宇宙[27]，右下角表示了一个比最老的重元素年轻的宇宙，在哈勃常数 $H_0 \geqslant 50 \ \mathrm{km \cdot s^{-1} \cdot Mpc^{-1}}$ 时，$t_0 < 96$ 亿年（参考文献 28）。

我们的 SN1997ap 观测数据说明：（1）存在红移值 $z > 0.8$ 的 Ia 型超新星；（2）与较近超新星的光谱做对比可以确定超新星的年龄和光度，并检查超新星演化的迹象；（3）在高红移处，可以获得比 Ia 型超新星内禀弥散度更加精确的校准后峰值星等。图 4 中置信区域的宽度与其对应的投影测量的不确定性的大小表明，通过增加与 SN1997ap 数据质量相当的 Ia 型超新星数据，现在是可能同时测量 Ω_Λ 和 Ω_M 的。需要特别指出的是：这一测量只依赖于一颗最高红移超新星（$z > 0.8$），需要更大的超新星数据样本来得到统计峰值并排除虚假的源。特别是，超新星 SN1997ap 的发现接近搜寻探测极限，可能来自亮度分布的明亮尾段（所谓"马姆奎斯特偏差"）。在 Calán/Tololo 巡天观测的较低红移超新星中存在相似的潜在偏差[2]，我们不清楚这些偏差对 Ω_M 的测量的影响。

超新星宇宙学观测项目已经发现了其他几颗相对高红移的超新星。其中有 SN1996cl，红移值也是 $z = 0.83$，它很可能是一颗 Ia 型超新星。哈勃空间望远镜偶然发现它的寄主星系可能是一个椭圆星系或者是 S0 星系（多纳休等，个人交流）。SN1996cl 的星等和颜色，尽管测光数据限定得不太好，但与 SN1997ap 的数据在误差范围内是一致的。距离上居次的已由光谱确定的两颗 Ia 型超新星的红移值分别为 $z = 0.75$ 和 $z = 0.73$（参考文献 16；正等待这两颗超新星的最后校准数据）。在红移值 $z = 0.3$ 到 0.7 区间，我们已经发现了 30 多颗额外的经光谱确认的 Ia 型超新星，并继以双色测光。（第一组 $z \approx 0.4$ 的超新星样本不是全部经过光谱确认和双色测光的[5]）

were not all spectroscopically confirmed and observed with two-filter photometry[5].) These new supernovae will improve both the statistical and systematic uncertainties in our measurement of Ω_M and Ω_Λ in combination. A matching sample of $\geqslant 6$ type Ia supernovae at $z > 0.7$ is to be observed in two filters in Hubble Space Telescope observations due to start on 5 January 1998. SN1997ap demonstrates the efficacy of these complementary higher-redshift measurements in separating the contribution of Ω_M and Ω_Λ to the total mass-energy density of the Universe.

(**391**, 51-54; 1998)

S. Perlmutter[1,2], G. Aldering[1], M. Della Valle[3], S. Deustua[1,4], R. S. Ellis[5], S. Fabbro[1,6,7], A. Fruchter[8], G. Goldhaber[1,2], A. Goobar[9], D. E. Groom[1], I. M. Hook[1,10], A. G. Kim[1,11], M. Y. Kim[1], R. A. Knop[1], C. Lidman[12], R. G. McMahon[5], P. Nugent[1], R. Pain[1,6], N. Panagia[13], C. R. Pennypacker[1,4], P. Ruiz-Lapuente[14], B. Schaefer[15] & N. Walton[16]

[1] E. O. Lawrence Berkeley National Laboratory, 1 Cyclotron Road, MS 50-232, Berkeley, California 94720, USA

[2] Center for Particle Astrophysics, University of California, Berkeley, California 94720, USA

[3] Dipartimento di Astronomia, Universita' di Padova, Vicolo Osservatorio 5, 35122, Padova, Italy

[4] Space Sciences Laboratory, University of California, Berkeley, California 94720, USA

[5] Institute of Astronomy, Madingley Road, Cambridge CB3 0HA, UK

[6] LPNHE, Universites Paris VI & VII, T33 Rdc, 4, Place Jussieu, 75252 Paris Cedex 05, France

[7] Observatoire de Strasbourg, 11, Rue de l'Universite, 67000 Strasbourg, France

[8] Space Telescope Science Institute, 3700 San Martin Drive, Baltimore, Maryland 21218, USA

[9] Physics Department, Stockholm University, Box 6730, S-11385 Stockholm, Sweden

[10] European Souther Observatory, Karl-Schwarzschild-Strasse 2, D-85748 Garching bei Munchen, Germany

[11] Physique Corpusculaire et Cosmologie, Collège de France, 11, Place Marcelin-Berthelot, 75231 Paris, France

[12] European Southern Observatory, Alonso de Cordova, 3107, Vitacura, Casilla 19001, Santiago, 19, Chile

[13] Space Telescope Science Institute, 3700 San Martin Drive, Baltimore, Maryland 21218, USA; affiliated with the Astrophysics Division, Space Science Department of ESA

[14] Department of Astronomy, Faculty of Physics, University of Barcelona, Diagonal 647, E-08028 Barcelona, Spain

[15] Department of Physics, Yale University, 260 Whitney Avenue, JWG 463, New Haven, Connecticut 06520, USA

[16] Isaac Newton Group, Apartado 321, 38780 Santa Cruz de La Palma, The Canary Islands, Spain

Received 7 October; accepted 18 November 1997.

References:

1. Perlmutter, S. *et al.* in *Thermonuclear Supernovae* (eds Ruiz-Lapuente, P. *et al.*) 749-763 (Kluwer, Dordrecht, 1997).

2. Phillips, M. M. The absolute magnitudes of Type Ia supernovae. *Astrophys. J.* **413**, L105-L108 (1993).

3. Hamuy, M. *et al.* The absolute luminosities of the Calán/Tololo Type Ia supernovae. *Astron. J.* **112**, 2391-2397 (1996).

4. Riess, A. G., Press, W. H. & Kirshner, R. P. Using Type Ia supernova light curve shapes to measure the Hubble constant. *Astrophys. J.* **438**, L17-L20 (1995).

5. Perlmutter, S. *et al.* Measurements of the cosmological parameters Ω and Λ from the first seven supernovae at $z \geqslant 0.35$. *Astrophys. J.* **483**, 565-581 (1997).

6. Perlmutter, S. *et al. IAU Circ.* No. 6621 (1997).

7. Schmidt, B. *et al. IAU Circ.* No. 6646 (1997).

8. Goobar, A. & Perlmutter, S. Feasibility of measuring the cosmological constant Λ and mass density Ω using Type Ia supernovae. *Astrophys. J.* **450**, 14-18 (1995).

9. Riess, A. G. *et al.* Time dilation from spectral feature age measurements of Type Ia supernovae. *Astron. J.* **114**, 722-729 (1997).

10. Nugent, P. *et al.* Evidence for a spectroscopic sequence among Type Ia supernovae. *Astrophys. J.* **455**, L147-L150 (1993).

11. Goldhaber, G. *et al.* in *Thermonuclear Supernovae* (eds Ruiz-Lapuente, P. *et al.*) 777-784 (Kluwer, Dordrecht, 1997).

12. Leibundgut, B. *et al.* Time dilation in the light curve of the distant Type Ia supernova SN 1995K. *Astrophys. J.* **466**, L21-L44 (1996).

13. Bessell, M. S. UBVRI passbands. *Publ. Astron. Soc. Pacif.* **102**, 1181-1199 (1990).

14. Branch, D., Nugent, P. & Fisher, A. in *Thermonuclear Supernovae* (eds Ruiz-Lapuente, P. *et al.*) 715-734 (Kluwer, Dordrecht, 1997).

15. Burstein, D. & Heiles, C. Reddenings derived from H I and galaxy counts—accuracy and maps. *Astron. J.* **87**, 1165-1189 (1982).

16. Perlmutter, S. *et al. IAU Circ.* No. 6540 (1997).

这些新的超新星有利于在把 Ω_M 和 Ω_Λ 结合在一起测量时减小统计误差和系统误差。哈勃空间望远镜从 1998 年 1 月 5 日起将开始使用两片滤镜观测至少 6 颗 $z > 0.7$ 的 Ia 型超新星匹配样本。SN1997ap 表明，我们可以有效地使用额外的较高红移超新星的数据区分 Ω_M 和 Ω_Λ 在宇宙总质能密度中的贡献。

（余恒 翻译；陈阳 审稿）

17. Leibundgut, B. *et al.* Premaximum observations of the type Ia SN 1990N. *Astrophys. J.* **371,** L23-L26 (1991).

18. Wells, L. A. *et al.* The type Ia supernova 1989B in NGC 3627 (M66). *Astron. J.* **108,** 2233-2250 (1994).

19. Branch, D. *et al.* The type I supernova 1981b in NGC 4536: the first 100 days. *Astrophys. J.* **270,** 123-139 (1983).

20. Patat, F. *et al.* The Type Ia supernova 1994D in NGC 4526: the early phases. *Mon. Not. R. Astron. Soc.* **278,** 111-124 (1996).

21. Cappellaro, E., Turatto, M. & Fernley, J. in *IUE—ULDA Access Guide No. 6: Supernovae* (eds Cappellaro, E., Turatto, M. & Fernley, J.) 1-180 (ESA, Noordwijk, 1995).

22. Leibundgut, B., Tammann, G., Cadonau, R. & Cerrito, D. Supernova studies. VII. An atlas of light curves of supernovae type I. *Astron. Astrophys. Suppl. Ser.* **89,** 537-579 (1991).

23. Holtzman, J. *et al.* The photometric performance and calibration of WFPC2. *Publ. Astron. Soc. Pacif.* **107,** 1065-1093 (1995).

24. Whitmore, B. & Heyer, I. *New Results on Charge Transfer Efficiency and Constraints on Flat-Field Accuracy* (Instrument Sci. Rep. WFPC2 97-08, Space Telescope Science Institute, Baltimore, 1997).

25. Kim, A., Goobar, A. & Perlmutter, S. A generalized K-corrections for Type Ia supernovae: comparing R-band photometry beyond $z = 0.2$ with B, V, and R-band nearby photometry. *Publ. Astron. Soc. Pacif.* **108,** 190-201 (1996).

26. Stiavelli, M. & Mutchler, M. *WFPC2 Electronics Verification* (Instrument Sci. Rep. WFPC2 97-07, Space Telescope Science Institute, Baltimore, 1997).

27. Carrol, S., Press, W. & Turner, E. The cosmological constant. *Annu. Rev. Astron. Astrophys.* **30,** 499-542 (1992).

28. Schramm, D. in *Astrophysical Ages and Dating Methods* (eds Vangioni-Flam, E. *et al.*) 365-384 (Editions Frontières, Gif sur Yvette, 1990).

Acknowledgements. The authors are members of the Supernova Cosmology Project. We thank CTIO, Keck, HST, WIYN, ESO and the ORM–La Palma observatories for a generous allocation of time, and the support of dedicated staff in pursuit of this project; D. Harmer, P. Smith and D. Willmarth for their help as WIYN queue observers; and G. Bernstein and A. Tyson for developing and supporting the Big Throughput Camera which was instrumental in the discovery of this supernova.

Correspondence and requests for materials should be addressed to S.P. (e-mail: saul@lbl.gov).

An Exceptionally Well-preserved Theropod Dinosaur from the Yixian Formation of China

Pei-ji Chen *et al.*

Editor's Note

The first sign that the palaeontological world was about to be turned upside down at the 1996 meeting of the Society of Vertebrate Paleontology in New York came when Pei-Ji Chen showed snapshots of a dinosaur from the hitherto obscure Yixian Formation of Liaoning Province, PRC. A dinosaur—with feathers. The relationship between dinosaurs and birds had long been suspected. Indeed, *Archaeopteryx*, the earliest known bird, looked like a feathered dinosaur. However, there had been no hard evidence for feathers in non-flying dinosaurs. To be sure, Chen's *Sinosauropteryx* had more of a fringe of feather-like fibrils than true feathers, but more was to come, and soon. Fossils of feathered dinosaurs began to pour from Liaoning to capture the world's imagination.

Two spectacular fossilized dinosaur skeletons were recently discovered in Liaoning in northeastern China. Here we describe the two nearly complete skeletons of a small theropod that represent a species closely related to *Compsognathus*. *Sinosauropteryx* has the longest tail of any known theropod, and a three-fingered hand dominated by the first finger, which is longer and thicker than either of the bones of the forearm. Both specimens have interesting integumentary structures that could provide information about the origin of feathers. The larger individual also has stomach contents, and a pair of eggs in the abdomen.

THE Jehol biota[1] was widely distributed in eastern Asia during latest Jurassic and Early Cretaceous times. These freshwater and terrestrial fossils include macroplants, palynomorphs, charophytes, flagellates, conchostracans, ostracods, shrimps, insects, bivalves, gastropods, fish, turtles, lizards, pterosaurs, crocodiles, dinosaurs, birds and mammals. In recent years, the Jehol biota has become famous as an abundant source of remains of early birds[2,3]. Dinosaurs are less common in the lacustrine beds, but the specimens described here consist of two nearly complete skeletons of a small theropod discovered by farmers in Liaoning. The skeletons are from the basal part of the Yixian Formation, from the same horizon as the fossil birds *Confuciusornis* and *Liaoningornis*[3]. Both are remarkably well preserved, and include fossilized integument, organ pigmentation and abdominal contents. One of the two was split into part and counterpart, and the sections were deposited in two different institutions. One side (in the National Geological Museum of China, Beijing) became the holotype of *Sinosauropteryx prima*, a supposed bird[4].

在中国义县组发现的一具保存异常完美的兽脚类恐龙

陈丕基等

编者按

当陈丕基在 1996 年纽约举办的古脊椎动物学会会议上展示了来自中国辽宁省义县组（年代还没有研究透彻）的一只恐龙的照片时，古生物学世界被震撼了。一只带羽毛的恐龙！恐龙与鸟类之间的关联一直被怀疑。的确，始祖鸟——已知最早的鸟类——看上去非常像一只带羽毛的恐龙。然而，之前并未发现不会飞的恐龙长有羽毛的确凿证据。诚然，陈丕基命名的中华龙鸟具有的更像是羽毛状的纤维，而不是真的羽毛，但很快就有更多的发现。带羽毛恐龙化石开始在辽宁大量出现，吸引了全世界的目光。

最近在中国东北部的辽宁省发现了两具非常吸引人的恐龙骨架化石。在本文中我们描述了这两具近乎完整的小型兽脚类恐龙骨架，它们代表了一种与美颌龙具有密切关系的恐龙。中华龙鸟是已知的兽脚类恐龙中尾巴最长的，前肢具有三指，由第一指主导运动，第一指要比前肢的任何骨骼都长且粗壮。两件标本都保存了吸引人的皮肤衍生物结构，这些结构能够为羽毛的起源提供信息。较大个体的腹腔中还保存着胃容物以及一对蛋化石。

热河生物群[1] 广泛地分布在东亚地区的侏罗纪末到早白垩世地层中，这里发现的淡水陆相化石包括大型植物、孢粉类、轮藻类、鞭毛虫、叶肢介、介形类、虾、昆虫、双壳类、腹足类、鱼类、龟鳖类、蜥蜴、翼龙、鳄类、恐龙、鸟和哺乳动物。在最近几年里，热河生物群成了著名的早期鸟类化石的丰富产地[2,3]。恐龙化石在湖相地层较少，但是本文记述的两具接近完整的小型兽脚类恐龙骨架是由在辽宁的农民发现的。这两具标本发现自义县组的基部，与孔子鸟和辽宁鸟[3] 层位相同。这两件标本都保存完好，并且包括了石化的皮肤衍生物结构、器官色素沉着和腹容物。两者中有一件标本分离成为正体和负体两块，这两块标本保存在两个不同的机构，一面作为原始中华龙鸟（曾被误认为是鸟类[4]）的正模标本（保存于中国地质博物馆，北京），而负体则和第二件较大的标本一起保存于中国科学院南京地质古

The counterpart and the second larger specimen are in the collections of the Nanjing Institute of Geology and Palaeontology.

The Yixian Formation is mainly composed of andesites, andesite-breccia, agglomerates and basalts, but has four fossil-bearing sedimentary intercalations that are rich in tuffaceous materials. The Jianshangou (formerly Jianshan[5,6]) intercalated bed (60 m thick) is the basal part of this volcanic sedimentary formation, and is made up of greyish–white, greyish–yellow and greyish–black sandstones, siltstones, mudstones and shales. These sediments are rich in fossils of mixed Jurassic–Cretaceous character. The primitive nature of the fossil birds of the Jianshangou fossil group has led to suggestions that the beds could be as early as Tithonian in age[2]. But although *Confuciusornis* and the other birds[3] are more advanced than *Archaeopteryx* in a number of significant features, we can only conclude that the beds that the fossils came from are probably younger than the Solnhofen Lithographic Limestones (Early Tithonian). The presence of *Psittacosaurus* in the same beds is more consistent with an Early Cretaceous age[7], as are the palynomorphs[8] and a recent radiometric date of the formation[9], but other radiometric dating attempts have indicated older ages[10].

Dinosauria OWEN 1842

Theropoda MARSH 1881

Coelurosauria VON HUENE 1914

Compsognathidae MARSH 1882

Sinosauropteryx prima JI and JI 1996

Holotype. Part (National Geological Museum of China, GMV 2123) and counterpart (Nanjing Institute of Geology and Palaeontology, NIGP 127586) slabs of a complete skeleton.

Referred specimen. Nanjing Institute of Geology and Palaeontology NIGP 127587. Nearly complete skeleton, lacking only the distal half of the tail.

Locality and horizon. Jianshangou-Sihetun area of Beipiao, Liaoning, People's Republic of China. Yixian Formation, Jehol Group, Upper Jurassic or Lower Cretaceous (Fig. 1; Fig. 1 has been omitted in this edited version).

Diagnosis. Compsognathid with longest tail known for any theropod (64 caudals). Skull 15% longer than femur, and forelimb (humerus plus radius) only 30% length of leg (femur plus tibia), in contrast with *Compsognathus* where skull is same length as femur, and forelimb length is 40% leg length. Within the Compsognathidae, forelimb length (compared to femur length) is shorter in *Sinosauropteryx* (61–65%) than it is in *Compsognathus* (90–99%). In contrast with all other theropods, ungual phalanx II–2 is longer than the radius. Haemal spines simple and spatulate, whereas those of *Compsognathus* taper distally.

生物研究所。

义县组的主要岩性组成为安山岩、安山角砾岩、集块岩和玄武岩，但是有四个富含凝灰质的含化石沉积岩夹层。尖山沟(以前称"尖山"[5,6])夹层(60米厚)位于火山岩沉积构造的基部，组成层序是：灰白色、灰黄色和灰黑色的砂岩、粉砂岩、泥岩和页岩。这段沉积富含混合侏罗纪–白垩纪特征的化石。尖山沟化石群含有的鸟类化石的原始特征表明该层位可能与提塘阶年代相当[2]。尽管孔子鸟和其他鸟类[3]在许多重要特征上比始祖鸟更加进步，我们仅能推断该化石层位可能要比德国索伦霍芬石印灰岩的层位(早提塘阶)靠上。发现于相同层位的鹦鹉嘴龙生存时代为早白垩世[7]，这与孢粉测年[8]和最近对该地层进行的放射性同位素测年[9]的结果相一致，但是其他的放射性测年显示该地层的年代更古老[10]。

恐龙总目 Dinosauria OWEN 1842
兽脚亚目 Theropoda MARSH 1881
虚骨龙类 Coelurosauria VON HUENE 1914
美颌龙科 Compsognathidae MARSH 1882
原始中华龙鸟 *Sinosauropteryx prima* JI and JI 1996

正模标本 正体(中国地质博物馆，标本编号 GMV 2123)和负体(南京地质古生物研究所，NIGP 127586)完整骨骼的板状化石。

归入标本 南京地质古生物研究所，NIGP 127587。近乎完整的骨骼，仅缺少尾部的远端一半。

产地与层位 中国辽宁省北票市尖山沟–四合屯地区。上侏罗统或下白垩统，热河群，义县组(图1；该图显示中华龙鸟和孔子鸟产地，此版本中省略)。

鉴别特征 一种美颌龙科恐龙，具有已知兽脚类中最长的尾(64个尾椎)。头骨比股骨长15%，前肢(肱骨+桡骨)仅是后肢(股骨+胫骨)长度的30%，而美颌龙头骨与股骨等长，前肢长是后肢长的40%。在美颌龙科成员中，中华龙鸟的前肢与股骨的长度比例为61%～65%，短于美颌龙(90%～99%)。不同于其他兽脚类恐龙，中华龙鸟的第二指爪比桡骨长。脉弧简单且呈片状，而美颌龙的则是锥形。

Description

Sinosauropteryx is comparable in size and morphology to known specimens of *Compsognathus*[11,12] from Germany and France. The smaller Chinese specimen (Fig. 2) is 0.68 m long (snout to end of tail) and has a femur length of 53.2 mm, whereas the second specimen (Fig. 3) has a femur length of 86.4 mm. The former is smaller than the type specimen of *Compsognathus longipes* (femur length about 67 mm) and the latter is smaller than the second specimen of *Compsognathus* from Canjuers (France), which has a femur length of 110 mm and an estimated length of 1.25 m. Although size and body proportions indicate that the smaller specimen was younger when it died, well-ossified limb joints and tarsals suggest that it was approaching maturity.

Fig. 2. *Sinosauropteryx prima* Ji and Ji. **a**, NIGP 127586, the counterpart of holotype (GMV 2123). **b**, Skeletal reconstruction of NIGP 127586. The integumentary structures are along the dorsal side and tail and dark pigmentation in the abdominal region might be some soft tissues of viscera.

描　述

中华龙鸟在大小和形态上同德国、法国已知的美颌龙标本[11,12]相近。中国标本中较小的一块（图 2）为 0.68 米长（从吻到尾巴末端），股骨长为 53.2 毫米，而第二件标本（图 3）的股骨长为 86.4 毫米。前者比模式种长足美颌龙（股骨长约 67 毫米）小，而后者比另一件来自法国 Canjuers 的美颌龙（股骨长为 110 毫米，估计全长 1.25 米）小。尽管大小和身体比例反映出小的标本死时比较年轻，但它死亡后保存下来的完全骨化的肢骨关节和跗骨表明它已经接近成熟。

图 2. 原始中华龙鸟。**a**，NIGP 127586，是正模（GMV 2123）的负体。**b**，标本 NIGP 127586 的骨骼复原。皮肤衍生物结构沿着背部到尾部，腹部区域的黑色沉着可能是一些内脏软体组织残留。

Fig. 3. *Sinosauropteryx prima* Ji and Ji, NIGP 127587, an adult individual from the same locality as holotype.

Sinosauropteryx and *Compsognathus* share several characteristics that indicate close relationship. These can be used to diagnose the Compsognathidae and include unserrated premaxillary but serrated maxillary teeth, a powerful manual phalanx I–1 (shaft diameter is greater than that of the radius), fan-shaped neural spines on the dorsal vertebrae, limited anterior expansion of the pubic boot and a prominent obturator process of the ischium.

Other characteristics were used to diagnose *Compsognathus*, including the presence of a relatively large skull and short forelimbs. In *Compsognathus*, skull length is 30% of that of the presacral vertebral column, whereas this same ratio is 40% in the new specimen NIGP 127586 and 36% in NIGP 127587. Unfortunately, relative skull length is highly variable in theropods. Comparing skull length with femur length, which is less variable than vertebral length, most theropods have skulls 100–119% the length of the femur[13]. The *Compsognathus* skulls are 99–100% and *Sinosauropteryx* skulls are 113–117%. Compsognathids have short forelimbs[11], 40% of the length of the hindlimb in *Compsognathus*. In *Sinosauropteryx*, the lengths of humerus plus radius divided by the sum of femur and tibia lengths produces a figure of less than 30% (Table 1). Unfortunately, such ratios are dependent on the absolute size of the animal, mostly because of negative allometry experienced by the tibia during growth or interspecific size increase. Comparing the lengths of humerus plus radius with femur length produces more useful results. The resulting figures fall within the range of most theropods (60–110%). The abelisaurid *Carnosaurus* and all tyrannosaurs have relatively shorter arms. Within the Compsognathidae, however, arm length is shorter in *Sinosauropteryx* (61–65%) than it is in *Compsognathus* (90–99%).

图 3. 原始中华龙鸟，NIGP 127587，一个成年个体，与正模标本来自同一产地

　　中华龙鸟和美颌龙具有几个共同的特征，显示出它们之间存在密切的关系。这些特征通常能够用于鉴别美颌龙科，包括无锯齿的前颌骨齿和有锯齿的上颌骨齿，强有力的第一指第一骨（直径要比桡骨大），背椎上扇形的神经棘，耻骨靴状突前端有限的扩展以及坐骨明显的闭孔突。

　　其他鉴定美颌龙的特征包括相对较大的头骨和短小的前肢。美颌龙头骨的长度占荐前椎总长的 30%，然而在新标本 NIGP 127586 和 NIGP 127587 中，该比率分别为 40% 和 36%。不巧的是，相对头骨长度在兽脚类恐龙中是一个非常易变的变量。头骨和股骨的长度的比值相对于与椎体的长度比值在兽脚类恐龙中变化较小，大部分兽脚类恐龙的头骨是股骨的长度的 100%～119%[13]。其中美颌龙的该值为 99%～100%，中华龙鸟为 113%～117%。美颌龙科具有较短的前肢[11]，其中美颌龙前肢长度是后肢的 40%。在中华龙鸟中，肱骨加上桡骨的长度与股骨和胫骨的总和相比小于 30%（表 1）。不过，这个比率取决于动物的绝对大小，主要是由生长或种间大小增长的过程中胫骨的异速生长造成的。肱骨加上桡骨的长度与股骨长度的比值更加可靠。该比例在大多数兽脚类的范围内（60%～110%）。在阿贝力龙类和暴龙类中，前肢相对较短。在美颌龙类中，中华龙鸟的前肢长度比值（61%～65%）要比美颌龙的（90%～99%）小。

Table 1. Comparison of size and proportions of *Sinosauropteryx* and *Compsognathus*

Species	Specimen	Skull	Humerus	Radius	Femur	Tibia	Skull/femur	Arm/leg
Compsognathus sp.	BSP ASI	70	39	24.7	71	87.6	0.99	0.40
Compsognathus sp.	MNHN	110	67	42	110		1.00	
Sinosauropteryx primus	NIGP 127586	62.5	20.3	12.4	53.2	61	1.17	0.29
Sinosauropteryx primus	NIGP 127587	97.2	35.5	21	86.4	97	1.13	0.31

Length measurements are given in millimetres. Data about *Compsognathus* are from ref. 11.

Both specimens of *Sinosauropteryx* have 10 cervical and 13 dorsal vertebrae. The posterior cervical vertebrae have biconcave centra. We could not determine the number of sacrals. The tail is extremely long. In the smaller specimen it is almost double the snout–vent length, and there are 59 caudal vertebrae exposed with an estimated five more than have been lost from the middle of the tail of NIGP 127586 (but present in GMV 2123). Only the first 23 vertebrae are preserved in the larger specimen, but this section is longer than the summed lengths of the cervical, dorsal and sacral vertebrae. Neither of the European specimens has a complete tail, but in both cases the tail was clearly longer than the body. When vertebral lengths are normalized (divided by the average lengths of caudal vertebrae 2–5), there are no significant differences between vertebral lengths in any of the four tails. As in *Compsognathus*, the dorsal neural spines are peculiar in that they are anteroposteriorly long but low, and often are fan-shaped.

The caudal centra increase in length over the first six segments, but posteriorly decrease progressively in length and all other dimensions. The first 10 tail vertebrae have neural spines, most of which slope posterodorsally. There are at least four pairs of caudal ribs in NIGP 127586, and more distal caudals have low bumps in this region that could also be interpreted as transverse processes. This could be another way to distinguish the Asian and European compsognathids, because the German specimen of *Compsognathus* apparently lacks caudal ribs and transverse processes[11]. Haemal spines are found on at least the first 47 caudals of NIGP 127586, and the anterior ones are simple spatulate structures that curve gently posteroventrally. The haemal spines are oriented more posteriorly than ventrally, and are more strongly curved.

Both specimens have 13 pairs of dorsal ribs. The ribs indicate a high but narrow body. The distal ends of the first two pairs of ribs are expanded and end in cup-like depressions that suggest the presence of a cartilaginous sternum. The gastralia are well preserved with two gastralia on each side of a segment. The median gastralia cross to form the interconnected "zig-zag" pattern characteristic of all theropods[14] and primitive birds like *Archaeopteryx* and *Confuciusornis*.

The front limb is relatively short and stout. Both NIGP 127586 and NIGP 127587 have articulated hands, something that is lacking in the two European specimens. What has been interpreted by some as the first metacarpal[11] in *Compsognathus* is the first phalanx of

表 1. 中华龙鸟和美颌龙个体大小和比例的相互比较

种类	标本编号	头骨	肱骨	桡骨	股骨	胫骨	头骨/股骨	前肢/后肢
美颌龙未定种	BSP ASI	70	39	24.7	71	87.6	0.99	0.40
美颌龙未定种	MNHN	110	67	42	110		1.00	
原始中华龙鸟	NIGP 127586	62.5	20.3	12.4	53.2	61	1.17	0.29
原始中华龙鸟	NIGP 127587	97.2	35.5	21	86.4	97	1.13	0.31

长度测量的单位是毫米，美颌龙资料来源于参考文献 11。

　　中华龙鸟的两件标本均有 10 节颈椎和 13 节背椎。后部的颈椎是双凹型椎体。不过我们不能确定荐椎的数量。尾巴特别长。在较小的标本 (NIGP 127586) 中，尾长差不多是吻肛距的两倍，有 59 节尾椎暴露，估计尾巴中段至少缺失 5 节以上的椎体 (但在 GMV 2123 中存在)。在较大的标本中只有前 23 节尾椎椎体保存，但是这一段比颈椎、背椎和荐椎的总长要长。而欧洲的两个标本都没有保存完整的尾巴，但二者的尾巴明显要比身体长。当脊椎的长度进行标准化计算 (除以第 2～5 节尾椎的平均长度) 后，这四件标本的尾巴长度没有明显的差异。和美颌龙一样，中华龙鸟背神经棘很奇特，其前后向长但高度略低，且多呈现为扇形。

　　前六节尾椎的椎体长度递增，而后面尾椎的长度和其他尺寸都逐渐递减。前十节尾椎上有神经棘，多数向后背侧倾斜。在 NIGP 127586 中至少有 4 对尾肋，且很多末端尾椎在肋骨着生的部位有较低的突起，可以看作是横突。这可以作为区分亚洲和欧洲的美颌龙类的另一个方法，因为德国的美颌龙标本明显缺少尾肋和尾椎横突 [11]。NIGP 127586 至少前 47 节尾椎上都具有脉弧，前面的脉弧呈轻微向后腹侧弯曲的简单的片状结构。脉弧向后的幅度比向腹部大，且弯曲得更加强烈。

　　两件标本均有 13 对背肋。肋骨的形态揭示了该个体的身躯高而窄。前面两对肋骨的最末端膨大，且末端具有杯状的回陷，揭示了软骨质胸骨的存在。腹膜肋保存较好，在每一节两侧都各有两个腹膜肋。中间的腹膜肋像所有兽脚类恐龙 [14] 和原始鸟类 (如始祖鸟和孔子鸟) 中一样交叉连通呈"之"字形排列。

　　前肢相对短而粗壮，NIGP 127586 和 NIGP 127587 两件标本均保存着有关节的手部，这在欧洲的两标本中是缺乏的。美颌龙中被其他人鉴定为是第一掌骨 [11] 的

digit I, as was originally proposed by von Huene[15]. The first metacarpal is short (4.2 mm long in NIGP 127586, and double that length in 127587), and is probably the element identified as a carpal in the French specimen[12]. As is typical of all theropods, the collateral ligament pits of the first phalanx are much closer to the extensor surface of the bone than they are to the flexor surface. Both phalanx I–1 and the ungual that it supports are relatively large, each being as long as the radius, and thicker than the shafts and the distal ends of either the radius or the ulna. This unusual character seems to have been partially developed in at least phalanx I–1 of *Compsognathus*. Relative to the length of the radius, both these elements are longer in *Sinosauropteryx* than in any other known theropod except for *Mononykus*[16]. As indicated by the proposed phylogenetic placement[16] of *Mononykus*, there are too many anatomical differences between compsognathids and *Mononykus* to suggest a close relationship, and the similarities probably represent convergence.

The long (39 mm in NIGP 127586, 67.5 mm in NIGP 127587), low (22.2 mm high at both pubic and ischial peduncles in NIGP 127587) ilium is shallowly convex on the dorsal side in lateral aspect. The pubis, which is 82.8 mm long in NIGP 127587, is oriented anteroventrally, but is closer to vertical than it is in most non-avian theropods. The distal end expands into a pubic boot as in most tetanuran theropods. In the larger specimen, this expansion is 17.7 mm. As in *Archaeopteryx*[17], *Compsognathus*[11] and dromaeosaurs[18], the boot expands posteriorly from the shaft of the pubis, and the anterior expansion is moderate. The lack of the significant anterior expansion of the pubic boot may be correlated with the inclination of the shaft. The ischium is only two-thirds the length of the pubis in NIGP 127587. It tapers distally into a narrow shaft (3.2 mm in diameter), and like *Compsognathus*, there is a slight expansion at the end (6 mm in NIGP 127587). The prominent obturator process is also found in *Compsognathus*.

The shaft of the femur is gently curved. Both tibia and fibula are elongate. The astragalus and calcaneum are present in both specimens, although not clearly seen in either. There are five metatarsals, but as in other theropods and early birds, the first is reduced to a distal articular condyle, and the fifth is reduced to a proximal splint (Fig. 2b). Metatarsals II, III and IV are closely appressed and elongate, but are not co-ossified. The second and fourth metatarsals do not contact each other. Pedal phalanges are conservative in number (2–3–4–5–0) and morphology.

Inclusions within the Body Cavity

Like the German *Compsognathus*, the larger Chinese specimen has stomach contents preserved within the rib cage. This consists of a semi-articulated skeleton of a lizard, complete with skull (Fig. 4a, b). Numerous lizard skeletons have been recovered from these beds, but have yet to be described. Low in the abdomen of NIGP 127587, anterior to and slightly above the pubic boot, lies a pair of small eggs (37 × 26 mm) (Fig. 4a, c), one in front of the other. Additional eggs may lie underneath. Gastralia lie over the exposed surfaces of the eggs, and the left femur protrudes from beneath them, so there can be no doubt that

骨骼实际上是第一指的第一节，与最早由许纳[15]鉴别的一致。第一掌骨较短（NIGP 127586 中长 4.2 毫米，NIGP 127587 中长度为前者的两倍），它可能就是法国标本[12]中鉴定为腕骨的成分。像典型的兽脚类恐龙一样，第一指骨的侧韧带凹更靠近伸肌面而非屈肌面。第一指的第一节和其支撑的爪相对巨大，都像桡骨一样长，而且比桡骨或尺骨的骨干和末端都要粗。在美颌龙中，至少第一指的第一节有类似的特征。中华龙鸟第一指第一节及爪的长度与桡骨的长度比要比除单爪龙[16]外其他所有已知兽脚类恐龙都大。之前的系统发育结果表明[16]，美颌龙类和单爪龙之间存在许多解剖学的差异，不可能是相近的类群，二者的相似性可能为趋同所致。

髂骨长而低（NIGP 127586 中长 39 毫米，NIGP 127587 中长 67.5 毫米；NIGP 127587 中髂骨在耻骨和坐骨柄处高度均为 22.2 毫米），侧视上背部略微突起。NIGP 127587 的耻骨长 82.8 毫米，指向前腹侧，但比很多非鸟兽脚类恐龙的更接近垂直。像大多数坚尾龙类兽脚类恐龙一样，耻骨末端膨大呈靴状。在较大的标本中，这个膨大有 17.7 毫米。类似始祖鸟[17]、美颌龙[11]和驰龙类[18]，靴状突从耻骨柄向后膨大，前部适度膨大。耻骨突缺少明显的前突可能与耻骨柄的倾斜有关。NIGP 127587 的坐骨只是耻骨长度的三分之二。坐骨向远端变尖形成一个狭窄的骨干（直径 3.2 毫米），且跟美颌龙一样，在末端存在微小的膨大（NIGP 127587 中为 6 毫米）。在美颌龙中也发现了明显的闭孔突。

股骨柄略微弯曲。胫骨和腓骨相对较长。两件标本都保存了距骨和跟骨，尽管保存得都不清晰。具有 5 个跖骨，但和其他兽脚类恐龙和早期鸟类一样，第一跖骨退化为一个末端关节髁，第五跖骨退化成近端的一小块（图 2b）。第 Ⅱ、Ⅲ、Ⅳ 跖骨细长并紧密排列，但没有联合骨化。第 Ⅱ、Ⅳ 跖骨不互相接触。脚趾骨在数量（2–3–4–5–0）和形态学上相对保守。

体腔内含物

同德国的美颌龙一样，中国发现的中华龙鸟标本中较大的一块的腹腔中有胃容物保存。胃容物包括一具部分关节保存的蜥蜴骨骼，头骨完整（图 4a 和 4b）。发现中华龙鸟化石的地层已经发现过众多的蜥蜴骨骼，但还没有进行过描述研究。在 NIGP 127587 的腹部下方，耻骨靴状突的前面略上方，有一对小型的蛋化石（37 毫米 ×26 毫米）（图 4a 和 4c），一个在前一个在后。其余的蛋可能分布在下面。腹膜肋排

they were within the body cavity. It is possible that the eggs were eaten by the dinosaur. However, given their position in the abdomen behind and below the stomach contents, and the fact that they are in the wrong part of the body cavity for the egg shell to be intact, it is more likely that these were unlaid eggs of the compsognathid. Eggs have also been reported in the holotype of *Compsognathus*[19], but they are more numerous and are only 10 mm in diameter. As they were also found outside the body cavity, their identification as *Compsognathus* eggs has not been widely accepted. The presence of fewer but larger eggs in *Sinosauropteryx* casts additional doubt on this identification.

Fig. 4. Body of NIGP 127587. **a**, Stomach contents are preserved within the rib cage, and include a small lizard and a pair of eggs. **b**, A close-up of the lizard skull. **c**, A close-up of a pair of the eggs.

列在蛋化石表面，左股骨从它们下面伸出，因此它们毫无疑问处于体腔之内。蛋有可能是被恐龙吃下去的。但是，考虑到蛋的位置在腹部胃容物后侧和下面，而且如果它们是食物的话，在这个位置蛋壳不可能是完整的，因此这更像是美颌龙类还未产出的蛋。蛋化石也在美颌龙的正模标本中有过报道[19]，但是蛋的数量很多，直径却仅有10毫米。由于这些蛋都在体腔外面发现，把它们鉴定为美颌龙的蛋并没有被广泛接受。中华龙鸟腹腔内少而更大型的蛋对之前美颌龙蛋化石的鉴定提出了新的质疑。

图 4. 标本 NIGP 127587 整体。**a**，保存在腹腔中的胃容物，包括一只小的蜥蜴和一对蛋化石。**b**，蜥蜴头骨的特写。**c**，成对蛋化石的特写。

Although more than two eggs may have been present in the larger specimen of *Sinosauropteryx*, it does not seem as though many could have been held within the abdomen. It may well be that these dinosaurs laid fewer eggs than most (some species are known to have produced in excess of 40)[20]. However, it is more likely that their presence demonstrates paired ovulation, as has been suggested for *Oviraptor*[21], *Troodon*[22] and other theropods. *Sinosauropteryx* therefore probably laid eggs in pairs, with a delay for ovulation between each pair.

Integumentary Structures

One of the most remarkable features of both Chinese specimens is the preservation of integumentary structures. In the larger specimen, these structures can be seen along the dorsal surface of the neck and back, and along the upper and lower margins of the tail, but in the smaller specimen the integumentary structures are clearer (Fig. 5). They cover the top of the back half of the skull, the neck, the back, the hips and the tail. They also extend along the entire ventral margin of the tail. Small patches can be seen on the side of the skull (behind the quadrate and over the articular), behind the right humerus, and in front of the right ulna. With the exception of a small patch outside the left ribs of NIGP 127587 and several areas on the left side of the tail (lateral to the vertebrae), integumentary structures cannot be seen along the sides of the body. The structures were probably present in the living animals, as indicated by the density of the covering dorsal to the body, and by the few random patches of integumentary structures that can be seen elsewhere.

Fig. 5. Integumentary structures in the neck and dorsal sides of NIGP 127586.

尽管在大的中华龙鸟标本中可能存在多于两个蛋化石，但看上去腹腔内蛋化石的数量不会很多。很可能这些恐龙要比多数恐龙产蛋少（一些我们了解的种类产蛋会超过 40 枚）[20]。不过，这些蛋化石的出现再次证实了双排卵现象，如同在窃蛋龙[21]、伤齿龙[22] 和其他兽脚类恐龙中发现的那样。因此，中华龙鸟很可能每次产一对卵，每次排卵之间需要延迟一段时间。

皮肤衍生物结构

两件中国化石标本最显著的特点之一就是保存了皮肤衍生物结构。在较大的标本中，这些结构沿着颈部和背部的背面以及尾巴的上下缘分布，而在较小的标本中皮肤衍生物的结构更清晰（图 5）。它们覆盖头骨背侧的后半部、颈部、背部、臀部和尾巴，同时沿着整个尾巴的腹侧扩展。头骨（方骨后和关节骨上）、右肱骨后侧和右尺骨前侧都能够看出小片的皮肤衍生物。而在 NIGP 127587 上，除了左肋外的一小片和尾巴左侧的几个区域（椎体侧面），身体侧面的其他位置并不能观察到皮肤衍生物。这种结构可能在现生动物中也存在，类似身体背部的浓密毛发和身体其他部位可见的少量皮肤衍生物。

图 5. NIGP 127586 的颈部和背部的皮肤衍生物结构

Fig. 6. Integumentary structures over caudal 27 of NIGP 127587.

In the two theropods, the distances separating the integumentary structures from the underlying bones are directly proportional to the amount of skin and muscle that would have been present. As in modern animals, the integument closely adheres to the tops of the skull and hips, and becomes progressively closer to the caudal vertebrae towards the tip of the tail. In the posterior part of the neck, over the shoulders, and at the base of the tail, the integumentary structures are more distant from the underlying skeletal elements, and in life would have been separated by greater thicknesses of muscle and other soft tissues.

The orientation and frequently sinuous lines of the integumentary structures suggest they were soft and pliable, and semi-independent of each other. They frequently cross each other, and are tangled in some areas. There is an apparent tendency for the integumentary structures to clump along the tail of the smaller specimen, but this is an artefact of the splitting plane between NIGP 127586 (Fig. 2a) and GMV 2123. As both individuals were lying in the water of a lake when they were buried, it is clear that we are not looking at the normal orientation of the integumentary structures in the fossils. Under magnification, the margins of the larger structures are darker along the edges, but lighter medially, which indicates that they might have been hollow. Overall, the integumentary structures are rather coarse for such a small animal, and the thickest strands are much thicker than the hairs of the vast majority of small mammals[23]. In NIGP 127586, integumentary structures are first seen on the dorsal surface of the skull in front of the orbit. The skull is semidisarticulated, and sediment still covers the snout region, so it is possible that the integumentary structures extended more anteriorly. The most rostral integumentary structures are 5.5 mm long, and

图 6. NIGP 127587 的第 27 节尾椎上方的皮肤衍生物结构

在这两个兽脚类恐龙中，皮肤衍生物与下覆骨骼的间距与活着时存在的皮肤和肌肉量呈正比。像现生动物一样，皮肤衍生物紧密黏附在头骨和臀部顶部，并逐渐靠近尾巴末端的尾椎。在颈部后侧、肩部之上和尾巴的基部，皮肤衍生物距离下面的骨骼更远，可能是因为这些区域在动物活着时被非常厚的肌肉和其他软组织与骨骼分隔开。

皮肤衍生物的方向和错综复杂的排列表明它们柔软而易弯曲，相互间较为分离。它们彼此频繁交叉，在某些区域又比较紊乱。在较小的标本中，皮肤衍生物明显的趋向是沿着尾部丛生，但这是 NIGP 127586(图 2a) 和 GMV 2123 之间分割面上的假象。因为两个个体被掩埋时都是在湖水中死亡，因此很显然我们在化石中看到的并非皮肤衍生物的正常方向。当放大一定倍数后，大的结构边缘是暗色的，但是中间是亮的，这显示它们中间可能有空洞。总的来说，这种小型动物皮肤衍生物结构比较粗糙，毛发最浓密部分其浓密程度超过大多数小型哺乳动物的毛发[23]。在 NIGP 127586 上，皮肤衍生物结构首先是在眼眶之前的头骨背部表面看到。头骨是半脱离的，沉积物依然覆盖在吻部，因此皮肤衍生物结构可能会更向前扩展。最靠近吻端的皮肤衍生物有 5.5 毫米长，在头骨上方又延伸了约 4 毫米。它们在肩胛骨远端的上

extend about 4 mm above the skull. They quickly lengthen to at least 21 mm above the distal ends of the scapulae. This axial length seems to stay constant along most of the back, but decreases sharply to 16 mm dorsal to the ilium. The longest integumentary structures seem to have been above the base of the tail, although it is impossible to measure any single structure. More distally along the tail, integumentary structures decrease more rapidly on the lower side of the tail than on the upper. By caudal 47, the ventral structures are 4.2 mm long, about half the length of the dorsal structures in that region.

The size distribution of the integumentary structures of NIGP 127587 follow the same general pattern as in the smaller specimen. Although the integument tends to look thinner on this specimen, it is simply because the integumentary structures are lying closer to the body. Individual measurements are consistently larger than those of NIGP 127586. The integumentary structures are 13 mm long above the skull, 23.5 mm above the fourth cervical, at least 35 mm over the scapulae, at least 40 mm over caudal 27 (Fig. 6), and at least 35 mm below caudal 25. Integumentary structures on the left side of the body are largely covered by ribs, gastralia, stomach contents and matrix, so it is only possible to say that each is more than 5 mm long. Those associated with the right ulna are 14 mm long.

Integumentary structures have also been reported in the theropod *Pelecanimimus*[24] from the Lower Cretaceous of Spain. These consist of subparallel fibres arranged perpendicular to the bones, with a less conspicuous secondary system parallel to them. As described, they seem to be similar to the integumentary structures of *Sinosauropteryx*.

Skin impressions have been found on most main types of dinosaurs, including sauropods, ankylosaurs, ornithopods, stegosaurs, ceratopsians, and several genera of large theropods. In all of these animals, there is no evidence of integumentary structures, and the skin usually has a "pebbly" surface texture. Integumentary structures have been claimed for both specimens of *Compsognathus*[11,25] though the interpretations have been questioned in both cases[11]. In the German specimen, there was supposedly a patch of skin over the abdominal region. The French specimen included some strange markings in the region of the forearm, that were originally identified as a swimming appendage formed either of dermal bone or of thick skin[12], but it is clearly not well enough preserved to be positively identified. The identification of these structures as integumentary is questionable[11], and there is nothing on the Chinese specimens to support the presence of such structures in compsognathids. Evidence of feathers in *Compsognathus* was sought[11] without success, but this lack of evidence on the German specimen of *Compsognathus* does not eliminate the possibility that they might have existed.

Discussion

The integumentary structures of *Sinosauropteryx* are extremely interesting regardless of whether they are referred to as feathers, protofeathers, or some other structure. Unfortunately, they are piled so thick that we have been unable to isolate a single one for

方迅速延长至至少 21 毫米。这个长度似乎在背部大部分区域是恒定的，但是在髂骨背侧迅速递减到 16 毫米。最长的皮肤衍生物可能在尾巴基部的上方，尽管不可能去测量所有单个结构。顺着尾巴向远端延伸，皮肤衍生物结构在尾巴下方要比在上方递减更快。到第 47 节尾椎，腹侧的结构是 4.2 毫米长，约是背部相同区域长度的一半。

NIGP 127587 的皮肤衍生物的大小分布与小的标本遵循相同的普遍模式。这件标本中的皮肤衍生物趋向是逐渐变稀，这仅仅是因为皮肤衍生物更贴近身体。每一个部位皮肤衍生物的测量尺寸都要比标本 NIGP 127586 的大。头骨上的皮肤衍生物结构长 13 毫米，第四颈椎上的长 23.5 毫米，肩胛骨上的至少 35 毫米长，在第 27 节尾椎上的至少 40 毫米长 (图 6)，在第 25 尾椎下的至少 35 毫米长。身体左侧的皮肤衍生物基本被肋骨、腹膜肋、胃容物和围岩所覆盖，因此，只能推测皮肤衍生物可能长于 5 毫米。附着在右侧尺骨上的皮肤衍生物是 14 毫米长。

从西班牙下白垩统发现的兽脚类恐龙似鹈鹕龙标本 [24] 同样报道过皮肤衍生物。它们是由与骨骼垂直的近似平行排列的纤维组成的，具有不显著的次级结构与之平行排列。正如描述所说，它们似乎与中华龙鸟的皮肤衍生物结构相似。

皮肤印痕在很多主要类型的恐龙中曾被发现，包括蜥脚类、甲龙类、鸟脚类、剑龙类、角龙类和一些大型兽脚类恐龙属。但是在所有的这些恐龙中都没有皮肤衍生物存在的证据，它们的皮肤表面通常具有卵纹状的纹理。虽然关于两件标本的皮肤衍生物的解释都存在质疑 [11]，但皮肤衍生物确实在两个美颌龙标本中都存在 [11,25]。在德国的标本中，推测腹部区域上方有一块皮肤。在法国的标本中，前肢区域包括一些奇怪的痕迹，最初被鉴定为游泳的附肢，可能是膜质骨或者厚的皮肤 [12]，但由于保存得不够完好而无法确切地下结论。这些结构被鉴定为皮肤衍生物是存在问题的 [11]，中国的标本没有为美颌龙存在这样的结构提供支持依据。美颌龙存在羽毛的证据并没有寻找 [11] 成功，但是仅凭德国美颌龙标本缺少羽毛证据这一事实并不能排除美颌龙存在皮肤衍生物的可能性。

讨　　论

不论中华龙鸟的皮肤衍生物是羽毛、原始羽毛还是一些其他的结构，它们都是特别引人瞩目的。不巧的是，它们堆积得太厚，使我们不能单独将其分离开来

examination. Comparison with birds from the same locality shows that the same problem exists with identifying individual feathers (other than the flight feathers) and components of feathers in avian specimens. The morphological characteristics that we describe suggest that the integumentary structures seem to resemble most closely the plumules of modern birds, having relatively short quills and long, filamentous barbs. The absence of barbules and hooklets is uncommon in modern birds, but has been noted in Cretaceous specimens[26].

It has been proposed that the feathers of another recently discovered animal from the same locality in Liaoning are structurally intermediate between the integumentary structures of *Sinosauropteryx* and the feathers of *Archaeopteryx*[27]. The clearly preserved feathers of *Protarchaeopteryx robusta* are symmetrical, which indicates that the animal was not capable of flight. This is confirmed by the relatively short length of the forelimb. Both *Sinosauropteryx* and *Protarchaeopteryx* had been identified as birds because of the presence of feathers[27], but much more work needs to be done to prove that the integumentary structures of *Sinosauropteryx* have any structural relationship to feathers, and phylogenetic analysis of the skeleton clearly places compsognathids far from the ancestry of birds. Despite arguments to the contrary[28], cladistic analysis favours the notion that the bird lineage originated within theropod dinosaurs[29,30]. If this phylogenetic framework is accepted, the integumentary structures of *Sinosauropteryx* could shed light on some of the many hypotheses concerning feather origins. Three main functions have been suggested for the initial development of feathers—display, aerodynamics and insulation.

The integumentary structures of *Sinosauropteryx* have no apparent aerodynamic characteristics, but might be representative of what covered the ancestral stock of birds. It is highly unlikely that something as complex as a bird feather could evolve in one step, and many animals glide and fly with much simpler structures. Even birds secondarily simplify feathers when airborne flight ceases to be their main method of locomotion, and produce structures that are intermediate between reptilian scales and feathers[31]. The multi-branched integumentary structures of the Chinese compsognathids are relatively simple, but are suitable for modification into the more complex structures required for flight.

Feathers may have appeared first as display structures[31], but the density, distribution, and relatively short lengths of the integumentary structures of *Sinosauropteryx* suggest that they were not used for display. It is conceivable that both specimens are female, and that the males had more elaborate integumentary structures for display. It is also possible that the integumentary structures were coloured to serve a display function. Therefore, the existing *Sinosauropteryx* specimens do not support the hypothesis that feathers evolved primarily for display, but do not disprove it either.

The dense, pliable integumentary structures of the Chinese compsognathids would not have been appropriate as heat shields to screen and shade the body from the Sun's rays[32]. Although they may have been effective in protecting the body from solar radiation in warm weather, they would also have been effective in preventing an ectothermic

进行检测。和同一产地的鸟类化石相比发现，在鸟类标本中鉴别单独的羽毛（除了翼羽）和羽毛的组成时也存在同样的问题。根据我们描述的形态学特征，该皮肤衍生物结构似乎最接近现代鸟类的绒羽，具有相对较短的羽轴和长的纤维状的羽枝。现代鸟类很少缺失羽小枝和羽小钩，但这种现象在白垩纪的鸟类[26]中是较为常见的。

最近在辽宁同一产地发现的另外一种动物的羽毛被认为是介于中华龙鸟的皮肤衍生物和始祖鸟羽毛之间的中间结构[27]。粗壮原始祖鸟清晰保存的羽毛是对称的，反映出这种动物是不具飞行能力的，这一点同时也根据它的前肢长度相对较短得以证明。中华龙鸟和原始祖鸟都曾经因为羽毛的存在被鉴定为鸟类[27]，但是还有很多工作需要去做来证明中华龙鸟的皮肤衍生物同鸟类羽毛之间存在结构上的联系，而且基于骨骼形态的系统发育分析结果显示美颌龙距离鸟类的祖先很远。尽管存在反对的论断[28]，但系统发育分析仍主张鸟类起源于兽脚类恐龙[29,30]。如果这个系统发生的结果能够被接受的话，那么中华龙鸟的皮肤衍生物结构能阐明关于羽毛起源的很多假说。羽毛的早期起源被认为主要与三个方面的功能有关：展示、空气动力学和保温。

中华龙鸟的皮肤衍生物结构没有明显的空气动力学特征，可能代表鸟类体表覆盖物的原始状态。像鸟类羽毛这种复杂的结构，其演化进程基本上是不可能一步发展到位的，很多动物是利用更为简单的结构进行滑翔和飞行。甚至当一些鸟类不再有飞行的习性时，它们的羽毛会发生次生简化，形成一种介于爬行动物的鳞甲和羽毛中间的结构[31]。中国美颌龙类多分枝的皮肤衍生物结构是相对简单的，但是适合修饰成更复杂的鸟类飞行结构。

羽毛最初出现时可能是作为展示的结构[31]，但中华龙鸟皮肤衍生物的密度、分布和相对短的长度显示它们不是用来展示的。可以想象这两件标本都属于雌性个体，雄性应该具有更为精细的皮肤衍生物用来展示。皮肤衍生物也可能是色彩斑斓的，以适合展示。因此，现存的中华龙鸟标本不支持羽毛原始演化是为了展示的假说，但也不能反驳这种假说。

中国美颌龙类浓密且柔软的皮肤衍生物不适合作为保暖层以及遮蔽太阳辐射[32]。但这些皮肤衍生物在温暖的天气保护身体避免太阳辐射可能是有效的，同时也可以有效预防外温的兽脚类恐龙在太阳直射中吸收外部热量而使体温迅速升高。

theropod from rapidly warming up by basking in the sunshine. If small theropods were endothermic, they would have needed insulation to maintain high body temperatures[33-35]. The presence of dense integumentary structures may suggest that *Sinosauropteryx* was endothermic, and that heat retention was the primary function for the evolution of integumentary structures[36-38]. Recently published histological studies suggest at least some early birds were not truly endothermic[39], although they may have been physiologically intermediate between poikilothermic ectotherms and homeothermic endotherms[40].

The Chinese compsognathids have integumentary structures consisting of vertical fibres running from the base of the head along the back and around the tail extending forwards almost to the legs. There are no structures showing the fundamental morphological features of modern bird feathers, but they could be previously unidentified protofeathers which are not as complex as either down feathers or even the hair-like feathers of secondarily flightless birds. Their simplicity would not have made them ineffective for insulation when wet any more than it negates the insulatory capabilities of mammalian hair. We cannot determine whether or not the integumentary structures were arranged in pterylae, but they were long enough to cover apteria, if they existed, and could therefore still have been effective in thermoregulation. Continuous distribution is not essential to be effective in this function[28], especially if the apteria are part of a mechanism for dispersing excess heat. Finally, the aerodynamic capabilities of bird feathers are not comprised by the previous evolution of less complex protofeathers that had some other function, such as insulation.

In addition to the integumentary structures, there is dark pigmentation over the eyes of both specimens. A second region of dark pigmentation in the abdominal region of the smaller specimen might represent some soft tissues of viscera.

Multidisciplinary and multinational research is just beginning on these unique small theropods. Techniques developed to study fossil feathers[38,41] will be useful research tools as work progresses. In the meantime, the integumentary structures of *Sinosauropteryx* suggest that feathers evolved from simpler, branched structures that evolved in non-avian theropod dinosaurs, possibly for insulation.

(391, 147-152; 1998)

Pei-ji Chen[*], **Zhi-ming Dong**[†] **& Shuo-nan Zhen**[‡]

[*] Nanjing Institute of Geology and Palaeontology, Academia Sinica, 39 East Beijing Road, Nanjing 210008, People's Republic of China

[†] Institute of Vertebrate Paleontology and Paleoanthropology, Academia Sinica, PO Box 643, Beijing 100044, People's Republic of China

[‡] Beijing Natural History Museum, 126 Tien Qiao Street, Beijing 100050, People's Republic of China

Received 14 January; accepted 18 September 1997.

References:

1. Chen, P. J. Distribution and migration of Jehol fauna with reference to nonmarine Jurassic–Cretaceous boundary in China. *Acta Palaeontol. Sin.* **27**, 659-683 (1988).

如果小型兽脚类恐龙是内温的，它们需要隔绝外界来维持较高的体温[33-35]。稠密的皮肤衍生物表明中华龙鸟可能是内温动物，而保暖性是皮肤衍生物结构演化的最初功能[36-38]。最近发表的组织学研究提出，至少一些早期的鸟类不是真正的内温动物[39]，不过它们可能在生理学上介于变温外温动物与恒温内温动物之间[40]。

中国美颌龙类具有的皮肤衍生物结构由垂直的纤维组成，从头部基部开始沿着背部延伸，包围尾部，同时沿尾部向前延伸，几乎到达腿部。它们没有现代鸟类羽毛的基本形态结构，但是可以被看作是一种未被确认的原始羽毛，其复杂程度低于绒羽甚至次级失去飞行能力的鸟类毛发状的羽毛。它们简单的构造在潮湿情况下能有效隔热，比哺乳动物毛发潮湿情况下的保温能力要强。我们不能确定皮肤衍生物结构是否按羽区排列，但如果它们存在，它们长到足够覆盖裸区，就能有效地进行温度调节。皮肤衍生物连续分布对于这个功能的有效性并不是必不可少的[28]，尤其是如果裸区是用来分散多余热量的机制的一部分。最后，鸟类羽毛的空气动力学功能并不为这些处于演化早期的、结构不很复杂的原始羽毛所拥有，它们有另外的功能，如保暖。

除皮肤衍生物结构外，在两件标本眼部的上方都存在深色色素沉着。此外，在较小标本的腹部也保存有深色色素沉着，可能意味着存在一些内脏的软组织。

对于这些独特的小型兽脚类恐龙进行的多学科和多国合作研究只是刚刚开始。羽毛化石研究的技术发展[38,41]为加快研究进展提供了有益的研究工具。同时，中华龙鸟的皮肤衍生物结构揭示了羽毛的演化是从简单、多分枝结构开始的，这种结构在非鸟兽脚类恐龙中出现可能是用于保温的。

（张玉光 翻译；汪筱林 审稿）

2. Hou, L.-H., Zhang, J.-Y., Martin, L. D. & Feduccia, A. A beaked bird from the Jurassic of China. *Nature* **377**, 616-618 (1995).

3. Hou, L.-H., Martin, L. D., Zhang, J.-Y. & Feduccia, A. Early adaptive radiation of birds: evidence from fossils from northeastern China. *Science* **274**, 1164-1167 (1996).

4. Ji, Q. & Ji, S. A. On discovery of the earliest bird fossil in China and the origin of birds. *Chinese Geol.* **233**, 30-33 (1996).

5. Chen, P. J. *et al.* Studies on the Late Mesozoic continental formations of western Liaoning. *Bull. Nanjing Inst. Geol. Palaeontol.* **1**, 22-25 (1980).

6. Chen, P. J. Nonmarine Jurassic strata of China. *Bull. Mus. N. Arizona* **60**, 395-412 (1996).

7. Dong, Z. M. Early Cretaceous dinosaur faunas in China: an introduction. *Can. J. Earth Sci.* **30**, 2096-2100 (1993).

8. Li, W. B. & Liu, Z. S. The Cretaceous palynofloras and their bearing on stratigraphic correlation in China. *Cretaceous Res.* **15**, 333-365 (1994).

9. Smith, P. E. *et al.* Dates and rates in ancient lakes: ^{40}Ar-^{39}Ar evidence for an Early Cretaceous age for the Jehol Group, northeast China. *Can. J. Earth Sci.* **32**, 1426-1431 (1995).

10. Wang, D. F. & Diao, N. C. Geochronology of Jura-Cretaceous volcanics in west Liaoning, China. *Scientific papers on geology for international exchange* **5**, 1-12 (Geological Publishing House, Beijing, 1984).

11. Ostrom, J. H. The osteology of *Compsognathus longipes* Wagner. *Zitteliana* **4**, 73-118 (1978).

12. Bidar, A., Demay, L. & Thomel, G. *Compsognathus corallestris* nouvelle espèce de dinosaurien théropode du Portlandiend de Canjuers (sud-est de la France). *Ann. Mus. d'Hist. Nat. Nice* **1**, 3-34 (1972).

13. Currie, P. J. & Zhao, X. J. A new large theropod (Dinosauria, Theropoda) from the Jurassic of Xinjiang, People's Republic of China. *Can. J. Earth Sci.* **30**, 2037-2081 (1993).

14. Claesseus, L. Dinosaur gastralia and their function in respiration. *J. Vert. Palaeontol.* **16**, 28A (1996).

15. von Huene, F. The carnivorous Saurischia in the Jura and Cretaceous formations principally in Europe. *Revista Museo Plata* **29**, 35-167 (1926).

16. Perle, A., Chiappe, L. M., Barsbold, R., Clark, J. M. & Norell, M. Skeletal morphology of *Mononykus olecranus* (Theropoda: Avialae) from the Late Cretaceous of Mongolia. *Am. Mus. Novit.* **3105**, 1-29 (1994).

17. Wellnhofer, P. Das siebte Exemplar von *Archaeopteryx* aus den Solnhofener Schichten. *Archaeopteryx* **11**, 1-48 (1993).

18. Barsbold, R. Carnivorous dinosaurs from the Cretaceous of Mongolia. *Sovmestnaya Sovetsko-Mongol'skaya Paleontol. Ekspiditsiya, Trudy* **19**, 5-119 (1983).

19. Griffiths, P. The question of *Compsognathus* eggs. *Rev. Paleobiol.* Spec. issue **7**, 85-94 (1993).

20. Carpenter, K., Hirsch, K. F. & Horner, J. R. *Dinosaur Eggs and Babies* (Cambridge Univ. Press, 1994).

21. Dong, Z. M. & Currie, P. J. On the discovery of an oviraptorid skeleton on a nest of eggs at Bayan Mandahu, Inner Mongolia, People's Republic of China. *Can. J. Earth Sci.* **33**, 631-636 (1996).

22. Varricchio, D. J., Jackson, F., Borkowski, J. J. & Horner, J. R. Nest and egg clutches of the dinosaur *Troodon formosus* and the evolution of avian reproductive traits. *Nature* **385**, 247-250 (1997).

23. Meng, J. & Wyss, A. R. Multituberculate and other mammal hair recovered from Palaeogene excreta. *Nature* **385**, 712-714 (1997).

24. Pérez-Moreno, B. P. *et al.* A unique multitoothed ornithomimosaur dinosaur from the Lower Cretaceous of Spain. *Nature* **370**, 363-367 (1994).

25. von Huene, F. Der Vermuthliche Hautpanzer des *Compsognathus longipes* Wagner. *Neues Jb. F. Min.* **1**, 157-160 (1901).

26. Grimaldi, D. & Case, G. R. A feather in amber from the Upper Cretaceous of New Jersey. *Am. Mus. Novit.* **3126**, 1-6 (1995).

27. Ji, Q. & Ji, S. A. *Protarchaeopteryx*, a new genus of Archaeopterygidae in China. *Chinese Geol.* **238**, 38-41 (1997).

28. Feduccia, A. *The Origin and Evolution of Birds* (Yale Univ. Press, New Haven, 1996).

29. Gauthier, J. in *The Origin of Birds and the Evolution of Flight* (ed. Padian, K.) 1-55 (California Acad. Sci., San Francisco, 1986).

30. Fastovsky, D. E. & Weishampel, D. B. *The Evolution and Extinction of the Dinosaurs* (Cambridge Univ. Press, 1996).

31. McGowan, C. Feather structure in flightless birds and its bearing on the question of the origin of feathers. *J. Zool. (Lond.)* **218**, 537-547 (1989).

32. Paul, G. S. *Predatory Dinosaurs of the World* (Simon and Schuster, New York, 1988).

33. Ewart, J. C. The nestling feathers of the mallard, with observations on the composition, origin, and history of feathers. *Proc. Zool. Soc. Lond.* 609-642 (1921).

34. Van Tyne, J. & Berger, A. J. *Fundamentals of Ornithology* (Wiley, New York, 1976).

35. Young, J. Z. *The Life of Vertebrates* (Oxford Univ. Press, **1950**).

36. Chinsamy, A., Chiappe, L. M. & Dodson, P. Growth rings in Mesozoic birds. *Nature* **368**, 196-197 (1994).

37. Chiappe, L. M. The first 85 million years of avian evolution. *Nature* **378**, 349-355 (1995).

38. Brush, A. H. in *Avian Biology* vol. 9 (eds Farner, D. S., King, J. R. & Parkes, K. C.) 121-162 (Academic, London, 1993).

39. Regal, P. J. The evolutionary origin of feathers. *Quart. Rev. Biol.* **50**, 35-66 (1975).

40. Ostrom, J. H. Reply to "Dinosaurs as reptiles". *Evolution* **28**, 491-493 (1974).

41. Davis, P. G. & Briggs, D. E. G. Fossilization of feathers. *Geology* **23**, 783-786 (1995).

Acknowledgements. This study was supported by NSFC. We thank L.-s. Chen and P. J. Currie (Royal Tyrrell Museum of Palaeontology) for helping to prepare the fossil materials and manuscript; M.-m. Zhang, X.-n. Mu, G. Sun, J. H. Ostram, A. Brush, L. Martin, P. Wellnhofer, N. J. Mateer, E. B. Koppelhus, D. B. Brinkman, D. A. Eberth, J. A. Ruben, L. Chiappe, S. Czerkas, R. O'Brien, D. Rimlinger, M. Vickaryous and D. Unwin for assistance and comments; and L. Mazzatenta and M. Skrepnick for help producing the photographs and drawings.

Correspondence and requests for materials should be addressed to P-j.C. (e-mail: lpsnigp@nanjing.jspta.chinamail.sprint.com).

Softening of Nanocrystalline Metals at Very Small Grain Sizes

J. Schiøtz *et al.*

Editor's Note

One of the most useful handles that metallurgists have on the properties of metals is the manipulation of the size and shape of the crystalline grains that typically form a metal's mosaic-like microstructure. It was long known that a metal's hardness increases as its grain size gets smaller—a phenomenon known as the Hall–Petch effect. This seems to stem from the way that defects called dislocations, imperfections in the crystalline packing of metal atoms that can induce ductility by moving through the crystal lattice, get stopped at grain boundaries. The Hall–Petch effect implies that nanocrystalline metals, where the grains are of nanometre scale, should be particularly hard. That expectation is generally borne out, and has led to an interest in nanocrystalline metals as very hard and strong engineering materials. But in this paper, Jakob Schiøtz and colleagues at the Technical University of Denmark suggest that the hardening process will have a fundamental limit: the Hall–Petch effect will reverse when the grains get extremely small, making the metals softer. The work relies on an ability, then relatively recent, to conduct computer simulations for huge numbers of atoms—here about 100,000, providing a block of material that contains several nanoscale grains. The softening is a result of the fact that layers of atoms at grain boundaries slide rather easily; this effect begins to dominate dislocation motions as the grains become so small that a significant fraction of the atoms are situated at their surfaces.

Nanocrystalline solids, in which the grain size is in the nanometre range, often have technologically interesting properties such as increased hardness and ductility. Nanocrystalline metals can be produced in several ways, among the most common of which are high-pressure compaction of nanometre-sized clusters and high-energy ball-milling[1-4]. The result is a polycrystalline metal with the grains randomly orientated. The hardness and yield stress of the material typically increase with decreasing grain size, a phenomenon known as the Hall–Petch effect[5,6]. Here we present computer simulations of the deformation of nanocrystalline copper, which show a softening with grain size (a reverse Hall–Petch effect[3,7]) for the smallest sizes. Most of the plastic deformation is due to a large number of small "sliding" events of atomic planes at the grain boundaries, with only a minor part being caused by dislocation activity in the grains; the softening that we see at small grain sizes is therefore due to the larger fraction of atoms at grain boundaries. This softening will ultimately impose a limit on how strong nanocrystalline metals may become.

纳米晶金属在极小晶粒尺寸时的软化现象

希厄茨等

编者按

冶金学家对金属性能最有用的一个控制手段就是改变晶体晶粒的大小和形状，通常情况下，晶粒形成了金属马赛克状的微观结构。长期以来众所周知，金属的硬度随着晶粒尺寸的减小而增加，这个现象就是霍尔–佩奇效应。这似乎来源于金属原子晶体堆积中称作位错的缺陷（沿晶格运动可产生延性）在晶界处停止运动。霍尔–佩奇效应暗示纳米晶金属——具有纳米尺度的晶粒——应该特别硬。这种预测普遍得到了证实，并使得纳米晶金属作为非常硬且强的工程材料引起了人们的兴趣。但是在本文中丹麦技术大学的雅各布·希厄茨与同事指出，其硬化过程有一个基本的限制：当晶粒极小时，金属将变软，霍尔–佩奇效应将颠倒过来。此工作依赖于当时对包含纳米尺度晶粒材料单元实施大规模原子（本文中约 100,000 个）计算机模拟的能力。软化的结果基于晶界处原子层易于滑移的事实；这一结果开始主导位错运动；这是因为随晶粒变得极小，相当大部分的原子将处于晶粒表面。

纳米晶固体——其晶粒尺寸在纳米数量级——从技术角度常常具有值得关注的性能，例如增加的硬度和延性。纳米晶金属可以通过多种方式制备，其中最常用的是纳米尺寸原子簇的高压成型与高能球磨法[1-4]。其所得产物为具有随机取向晶粒的多晶金属。材料的硬度和屈服应力普遍随着晶粒尺寸的减小而增加，这就是我们所谓的霍尔–佩奇效应[5,6]。本文我们要介绍的是有关纳米晶铜形变的计算机模拟，它显示晶粒达到极小尺寸时材料表现出软化（一种反霍尔–佩奇效应[3,7]）。其塑性形变主要归因于晶界处大量原子平面的微小"滑移"，仅有一小部分是由于晶粒中的位错运动而产生的；因此我们在小晶粒尺寸时看到的软化现象归因于晶界原子所占比例更高。这种软化现象最终决定了纳米晶金属的极值强度。

To simulate the behaviour of nanocrystalline metals with the computer, we construct nanocrystalline "samples" with structures similar to those observed experimentally: essentially equiaxed dislocation-free grains separated by narrow straight grain boundaries[1]. Each sample contains 8–64 grains in a 10.6-nm cube of material, resulting in grain sizes from 3.3 to 6.6 nm. The grains are produced by a Voronoi construction[8]: a set of grain centres are chosen at random, and the part of space closer to a given centre than to any other centre is filled with atoms in an f.c.c. (face-centred cubic) lattice with a randomly selected crystallographic orientation. A typical "sample" is shown in Fig. 1a. To mimic the system's being deep within the bulk of a large sample, the system is replicated infinitely in all three spatial directions (periodic boundary conditions). The forces between the atoms are calculated with the effective-medium theory[9,10], which suitably describes many-atom interactions in metals. The metal chosen for these simulations is copper; very similar results were obtained with palladium. Before deforming the system we "anneal" it by running a 50-ps molecular dynamics simulation at 300 K, allowing unfavourable configurations in the grain boundaries to relax. Doubling the duration of annealing does not have any significant effect, nor does an increase in the temperature to 600 K.

Fig. 1. A simulated nanocrystalline copper sample before (**a**) and after (**b**) 10% deformation. The system contains 16 grains and ~100,000 atoms, giving an average grain diameter of 5.2 nm. Atoms in the grain boundaries are coloured blue, atoms at stacking faults are coloured red. We clearly see stacking faults left behind by partial dislocations that have run through the grains during the deformation processes. Such stacking faults would be removed if a second partial dislocation followed the path of the first, but this is not observed in the present simulations. In the left side of the system, a partial dislocation on its way through a grain is seen (green arrow in **b**).

The main part of the simulation is a slow uniaxial deformation while minimizing the energy with respect to all atomic coordinates. The deformation is applied by expanding the simulation cell in one direction, while the size is allowed to relax in the two perpendicular directions.

The initial and final configurations of such a simulation with a total strain of 10% are shown in Fig. 1. We see how the grain boundaries have become thicker, indicating that significant activity has taken place there. In the grains a few stacking faults have appeared.

为了用计算机模拟纳米晶金属的力学行为，我们构建了类似于实验中所观测到的纳米晶"样品"：基本上等轴的无位错的晶粒被窄而直的晶界所分隔[1]。每个样品是一个包含 8～64 个晶粒的立方体，边长为 10.6 nm，因此其晶粒尺寸为 3.3 nm 到 6.6 nm。晶粒是用沃罗诺伊过程[8]制备的：随机选定一组晶粒中心，在距离一个给定中心比任何其他中心都更近的空间区域中，以具有随机选择的晶体取向的 fcc（面心立方）晶格形式填入原子。一个典型的"样品"如图 1a 所示。为了模拟系统深入块体样品内部的情况，将该系统在全部三个空间方向上无限地复制（周期性边界条件）。原子间作用力用有效介质理论[9,10]来计算，该理论恰当地描述了金属中多原子的相互作用。本研究模拟的金属是铜；在钯中得到了极为类似的结果。在系统形变之前，我们通过在 300 K 时运行 50 ps 的分子动力学模拟来使其"退火"，使晶界上的不利构型得以松弛。将退火的持续时间加倍没有产生任何显著影响，将温度提高到 600 K 也没有影响。

图 1. 在 10% 形变之前（a）和之后（b）的模拟的纳米晶铜样品。体系中包含 16 个晶粒，大约 100,000 个原子，平均晶粒直径为 5.2 nm。晶界上的原子标记为蓝色，堆垛层错处的原子则标记为红色。我们清楚地看到形变过程中穿过晶粒的不全位错留下的堆垛层错。如果有第二个不全位错沿第一个的路径行进，这些堆垛层错将会消失，但在当前模拟过程中并没有观测到这一点。在体系的左边，可以看到一个正在穿过晶粒的不全位错（b 中的绿色箭头）。

模拟的主要部分是在使能量相对于所有原子坐标最小化的前提下进行一次缓慢的单轴形变。形变是通过在一个方向上拉伸模拟晶胞来进行的，同时允许其尺寸在两个垂直方向上弛豫。

图 1 中显示了总应变为 10% 的模拟的初始和最终构型。我们看到晶界是怎样逐渐变厚的，它表明晶界处发生了重要的活动。晶粒中出现了少量的堆垛层错。它们

They are the signature of dislocation activity within the grains.

To facilitate the analysis of the simulations, we identify which atoms are located at grain boundaries and which are inside the grains, by determining the local crystalline order[11,12]. Atoms in local f.c.c. order are considered to be "inside" the grains; atoms in local h.c.p. (hexagonal close-packed) order are classified as stacking faults. All other atoms are considered as belonging to the grain boundaries. Unlike conventional materials, where the volume occupied by the grain boundaries is very small, a significant fraction (30–50%) of the atoms are in the grain boundaries, in agreement with theoretical estimates[2].

As the deformation takes place, we calculate the average stress in the sample as a function of the amount of deformation. For each grain size we simulated the deformation of seven different initial configurations. Fig. 2a shows the obtained average deformation curves. We see a linear elastic region with a Young's modulus around 90–105 GPa (increasing with increasing grain size), compared with 124 GPa in macrocrystalline Cu (ref. 13). This is caused by the large fraction of atoms in the grain boundaries having a lower Young's modulus[14,15]. A similar reduction is seen in simulations where the nanocrystalline metal is grown from a molten phase[16]. The elastic region is followed by plastic yielding at around 1 GPa, and finally the plastic deformation saturates at a maximal flow stress around 3 GPa. The theoretical shear stress of a perfect single crystal is approximately 6 GPa for the potential used.

Fig. 2. The effect of grain size on deformation. **a**, The average stress in the direction of the stretch (σ_{zz}) versus strain for each grain size. Each curve is the average over seven simulations. The curves show the response of the material to mechanical deformation. In the linear part of the curve (low strains) the deformation is mainly elastic: if the tensile load is removed, the material will return to the original configuration. As the deformation is increased, irreversible plastic deformation becomes important. For large deformations plastic processes relieve the stress, and the curves level off. We see a clear grain-size dependence, which is summarized to the right. **b** and **c**, The maximal flow stress and the yield stress as a function of grain size. The yield stress decreases with decreasing grain size, resulting in a reverse Hall–Petch effect. (The maximal flow stress is the stress at the flat part of the stress–strain curves; the yield stress is defined as the stress where the strain departs 0.2% from linearity.)

是晶粒内位错活动的标志。

为了改善对模拟过程的分析，我们通过确定局部晶体有序度辨别出哪些原子位于晶界处，哪些处于晶粒内部[11,12]。我们认为具有局部 fcc 晶序的原子是位于晶粒"内部"的，具有局部 hcp(六方密堆积)晶序的原子则归为堆垛层错。其他所有原子被视为属于晶界。不同于传统材料——其晶界所占据体积很小，所模拟的材料中处于晶界上的原子占有很大比例(30% ~ 50%)，这与理论估计是一致的[2]。

随着形变发生，我们计算了样品中的平均应力随形变量的变化。对于每一晶粒尺寸，我们模拟了七种具有不同初始构型的形变。图 2a 所示为所得到的平均形变曲线。我们看到一个杨氏模量约为 90 ~ 105 GPa(随着晶粒尺寸的增加而增大)的线性弹性区域。与之相比，粗晶铜的杨氏模量为 124 GPa(参考文献 13)。这是由于晶界处的大量原子具有较低的杨氏模量[14,15]。在对从熔融相中生长出来的纳米晶金属的模拟中也看到了类似的模量降低[16]。弹性区域后，塑性屈服出现在 1 GPa 左右，最终塑性形变在流变应力达到最大值——约为 3 GPa 时达到饱和。在所用势能的条件下，完美单晶的理论剪切应力大约为 6 GPa。

图 2. 晶粒尺寸对于形变的影响。**a**，对于每个晶粒尺寸，拉伸方向上的平均应力(σ_{zz})与应变的关系。每条曲线都是七次模拟过程的平均。曲线表示出材料对于机械形变的反应。曲线的线性部分(低应变)主要是弹性形变：如果将拉伸载荷卸载，材料会恢复其初始构型。随着形变增大，不可逆的塑性形变变得更为重要。对于大的形变，塑性过程减缓了应力，因而曲线变得平稳。我们看到一个明显的晶粒尺寸效应，并将其总结于右侧。**b** 和 **c**，极值流变应力和屈服应力随晶粒尺寸的变化函数。屈服应力随着晶粒尺寸的减小而减小，导致反霍尔-佩奇效应。(极值流变应力是位于应力-应变曲线中平坦部分的应力；屈服应力则定义为应变偏离线性 0.2% 时的应力。)

The main deformation mode is illustrated in Fig. 3b, where the relative motions of the atoms is shown. We see that most of the deformation occurs in the grain boundaries in the form of a large number of small sliding events, where only a few atoms (or sometimes a few tens of atoms) move with respect to each other. Occasionally a partial dislocation is nucleated at a grain boundary and moves through a grain. Such events are responsible for a minor part of the total deformation, but in the absence of diffusion they are required to allow for deformations of the grains, as they slide past each other. No dislocation motion is seen in Fig. 3, as none occurred at that time of the simulation. As the grain size is reduced a larger fraction of the atoms belongs to the grain boundaries, and grain-boundary sliding becomes easier. This leads to a softening of the material as the grain size is reduced (Fig. 2).

Fig. 3. Snapshot of grain structure, displacements and stresses at 8% deformation. **a**, The position of the grain boundaries (blue) and stacking faults (red) at this point in the simulation. **b**, The relative motion of the atoms in the z direction (up, in the plane of the paper) during the preceding 0.4% deformation. The green atoms move up, red atoms move down. We see many small, independent slip events in the grain boundaries; this is the main deformation mode. **c**, The stress field (the σ_{33} component) in the grains. Shades of red indicate tensile stress, shades of blue compressive stress (dark colours correspond to high stresses). The stress in the grain boundaries is seen to vary considerably on the atomic scale, and the average stress is ~10–20% lower than in the grains.

The observed deformation mode is in some ways similar to the manner in which grain boundaries carry most of the deformation in superplastic deformation[17,18]. This is consistent with recent simulations of flow speed in nanocrystalline metals[25]. However, in superplasticity the grain-boundary sliding is thermally activated, whereas here it occurs at zero temperature driven by the high stress.

In conventional metals an increase in hardness and yield strength with decreasing grain size is observed. This is called the Hall–Petch effect, and is generally considered to be caused by the grain boundaries, impeding the generation and/or motion of dislocations as the grains get smaller; this behaviour extends far into the nanocrystalline regime[3,19]. The grain sizes in the present simulations correspond to the smallest grain sizes that can be obtained experimentally. In that regime the Hall–Petch effect is often seen to cease or even to reverse, but the results depend strongly on the sample history and on the method used to vary the grain size. Many mechanisms have been proposed for this reverse Hall–Petch effect:

图 3b 描绘出主要的形变模式，其中显示了原子的相对运动。我们看到大多数形变发生在晶界处，其形式为大量的只有几个原子（或有时候是几十个原子）相对彼此运动的微小滑移事件。偶尔会有不全位错在晶界成核，并且穿过一个晶粒。这些情况只是总形变中一小部分形变的原因，但是在没有扩散存在时，需要有这种微小相互滑移才能使晶粒得以发生形变。图 3 中未看到位错运动，因为在模拟时没有发生。随着晶粒尺寸减小，晶界处的原子分数越来越大，从而使晶界的滑动变得更加容易。这导致了晶粒尺寸减小时材料的软化（图 2）。

图 3. 形变 8% 时，晶粒结构、位移和应力的快照。**a**，模拟过程中该点处的晶界（蓝色）和堆垛层错（红色）的位置。**b**，在形变的前 0.4% 过程中，原子在 z 方向上（向上，纸平面中）的相对运动。绿色原子向上运动，红色原子向下运动。我们看到晶界中有很多微小独立滑动，这是主要的形变模式。**c**，晶粒中的应力场（σ_{33} 分力）。红色阴影表示拉伸应力，蓝色阴影表示压缩应力（深色对应于高应力）。可以看到，晶界处的应力在原子尺度上有相当的变化，且平均应力比晶粒内部的约低 10% ~ 20%。

在某种意义上，上述已观察到的形变模式类似于超塑性形变中晶界承担大部分形变的方式 [17,18]。这与最近对于纳米晶金属中流变速度的模拟结果 [25] 是一致的。但是在超塑性中，晶界滑动是热激活的，而在本文中，它发生在零度，受高应力所驱动。

在普通金属中，硬度和屈服强度随着晶粒尺寸减小而增加，这就是所谓的霍尔–佩奇效应。一般认为，强度增加是由于随着晶粒逐渐减小，晶界阻碍了位错的产生和（或）运动；这种行为可以推广到纳米晶体材料体系 [3,19]。当前模拟过程中的晶粒尺寸相当于用实验方法所能获得的最小晶粒尺寸。在这个范围内，经常可以看到霍尔–佩奇效应失效甚至反转，但是其结果强烈地依赖于样品的制备历史和改变晶粒尺寸的方法。对于这种反霍尔–佩奇效应已经提出了很多种机制：小晶粒尺寸

increased porosity at small grain sizes[3], suppression of dislocation pile-ups[20], dislocation motion through multiple grains[21], sliding in the grain boundaries[22], and enhanced diffusional creep in the grain boundaries[7]. Direct measurements of the creep rates seem to rule out the last mechanism[19,20], but otherwise no consensus has been reached. The present simulations indicate that the behaviour characteristic of a reverse Hall–Petch effect is possible even in the absence of porosity, and that it may be caused by sliding in the grain boundaries even in the absence of thermally activated processes. We cannot, however, see a cross-over from this "reverse" behaviour to the normal Hall–Petch regime at larger grain sizes in our simulations, because they become too computationally expensive at these larger sizes. For the same reason, we cannot provide a direct comparison with the behaviour of the bulk metal.

A direct quantitative comparison between the simulations and the experimental results should be done with caution. The main difference between the simulated strain–stress curves and experimental curves is the level of the yield stress, which is approximately twice what is observed in experiments on low-porosity samples (400 MPa)[23]. This value is, however, obtained for a grain size of around 40 nm; extrapolation to 7-nm grains gives a yield strength around 800 MPa (ref. 23), assuming that the Hall–Petch behaviour persists to these grain sizes. Experimentally produced nanocrystalline samples typically contain voids and surface defects, reducing the strength of the material. Surface defects alone have been shown to be able to reduce the strength of nanocrystalline palladium by at least a factor of five[19,24].

Another difference is the absence of thermally activated processes in the simulations. These processes give rise to a strain-rate dependence of the mechanical properties, leading to higher yield stresses at higher strain rates where there is less time available for the activated processes to occur. Thermally activated processes are not included in the simulations because the energy minimization procedure quickly removes all thermal energy. No timescale or strain rate can be directly defined in the simulations, but in a sense the procedure corresponds to a slow strain at very low temperatures: thermally activated processes are excluded but the energy created by the work is carried away fast. The above-mentioned creep measurements[19,20] indicate that diffusion does not play a major role during deformation.

During the later part of the simulated deformation larger average stresses build up within the grains than in the grain boundaries (10–20%), and larger stresses build up in the larger grains (see Fig. 3c). This results in a larger variation in the maximal flow stress than in the yield stress (Fig. 2b): when the grain size is increased the maximal flow stress increases, both because the stresses in the grains increase and because the number of atoms within the grains becomes a larger fraction of the total number of atoms.

(**391**, 561-563; 1998)

时大量增加的孔洞[3]、位错堆积的抑制作用[20]、穿过多晶粒的位错运动[21]、晶界中的滑移[22]，以及晶界处增加的扩散蠕变[7]等。对于蠕变速率的直接测量似乎排除了最后一种机制[19,20]，但除此之外再未能达成任何共识。目前的模拟过程指出，反霍尔-佩奇效应所特有的行为特征甚至可能在缺乏孔洞时出现，并且它甚至可能是在没有热激活的条件下由晶界中的滑移造成的。然而，在我们的模拟过程中，并没有看到从这一"反常"行为向较大晶粒尺寸时的正常霍尔-佩奇情况的过渡，因为对于计算来说，对这些较大尺寸进行模拟的代价太大了。出于同样的理由，我们未能提供与块体金属行为的直接比较。

应该谨慎地直接定量比较模拟与实验的结果。模拟应变-应力曲线与实验所得曲线之间的主要差别是屈服应力水平，模拟值大约是低孔隙率样品实验所测数据（400 MPa)[23]的两倍。不过，400 MPa 这个数值是从晶粒尺寸约 40 nm 的样品得到的；外推到晶粒 7 nm 时，其屈服强度约为 800 MPa(参考文献 23)（假定霍尔-佩奇效应对于这些晶粒尺寸仍然适用)。实验中制备的纳米晶样品中通常包含孔隙和表面缺陷，它们减弱了材料的强度。已经知道仅是表面缺陷就能使纳米晶钯的强度减小为原来的五分之一或更低[19,24]。

另一个差别是在模拟中没有热激活过程。这种热激活造成力学性能对应变速率的依赖性，导致在较高应变速率时有较高的屈服应力，因为可供激活过程发生的时间变少了。模拟中不包括热激活过程是因为能量最小化过程很快地移除了所有热能。模拟中无法直接定义任何时间尺度或应变速率，但是在某种意义上，该程序对应于极低温度时的缓慢应变：热激活过程被排除，但是变形产生的能量被快速带走。前面提到过的蠕变测量实验[19,20]表明扩散在形变过程中并不起主要作用。

在模拟形变的后期，晶粒内部积累了比晶界处更大的平均应力(10% ~ 20%)，而且晶粒越大积累的应力越大（参见图 3c)。这使得最大流变应力比屈服应力有更大的波动（图 2b)：当晶粒尺寸增加时，最大流变应力增大，这既是由于晶粒中的应力增大，也是由于晶粒内部原子的数量在总原子数量中所占比例增加。

（王耀杨 翻译；卢磊 审稿）

Jakob Schiøtz, Francesco D. Di Tolla* & Karsten W. Jacobsen
Center for Atomic-scale Materials Physics and Department of Physics, Technical University of Denmark, DK2800 Lyngby, Denmark
* Present address: SISSA, Via Beirut 2-4, I-34014 Grignano (TS), Italy.

Received 23 June; accepted 29 October 1997.

References:

1. Siegel, R. W. in *Encyclopedia of Applied Physics* Vol. 11, 173-199 (VCH, New York, 1994).

2. Siegel, R. W. What do we really know about the atomic-scale structure of nanophase materials? *J. Phys. Chem. Solids* **55**, 1097-1106 (1994).

3. Siegel, R. W. & Fougere, G. E. in *Nanophase Materials: Synthesis—Properties—Applications* (eds Hadjipanayis, G. C. & Siegel, R. W.) 233-261 (NATO-ASI Ser. E, Vol. 260, Kluwer, Dordrecht, 1994).

4. Gleiter, H. in *Mechanical Properties and Deformation Behavior of Materials Having Ultra-Fine Microstructures* (ed. Nastasi, M.) 3-35 (Kluwer, Dordrecht, 1993).

5. Hall, E. O. The deformation and ageing of mild steel: III Discussion of results. *Proc. Phys. Soc. Lond. B* **64**, 747-753 (1951).

6. Petch, N. J. The cleavage of polycrystals. *J. Iron Steel Inst.* **174**, 25-28 (1953).

7. Chokshi, A. H., Rosen, A., Karch, J. & Gleiter, H. On the validity of the Hall–Petch relationship in nanocrystalline materials. *Scripta Metall.* **23**, 1679-1684 (1989).

8. Voronoi, G. *Z. Reine Angew. Math.* **134**, 199 (1908).

9. Jacobsen, K. W., Nørskov, J. K. & Puska, M. J. Interatomic interactions in the effective-medium theory. *Phys. Rev. B* **35**, 7423-7442 (1987).

10. Jacobsen, K. W., Stoltze, P. & Nørskov, J. K. A semi-empirical effective medium theory for metals and alloys. *Surf. Sci.* **366**, 394-402 (1996).

11. Jónsson, H. & Andersen, H. C. Icosahedral ordering in the Lennard–Jones liquid and glass. *Phys. Rev. Lett.* **60**, 2295-2298 (1988).

12. Clarke, A. S. & Jónsson, H. Structural changes accompanying densification of random-sphere packings. *Phys. Rev. E* **47**, 3975-3984 (1993).

13. Gschneidner, K. A. Physical properties and interrelationships of metallic and semimetallic elements. *Solid State Phys.* **16**, 275-426 (1964).

14. Shen, T. D., Koch, C. C., Tsui, T. Y. & Pharr, G. M. On the elastic moduli of nanocrystalline Fe, Cu, Ni, and Cu-Ni alloys prepared by mechanical milling/alloying. *J. Mater. Res.* **10**, 2892-2896 (1995).

15. Kluge, M. D., Wolf, D., Lutsko, J. F. & Phillpot, S. R. Formalism for the calculation of local elastic constants at grain boundaries by means of atomistic simulation. *J. Appl. Phys.* **67**, 2370-2379 (1990).

16. Phillpot, S. R., Wolf, D. & Gleiter, H. Molecular-dynamics study of the synthesis and characterization of a fully dense, three-dimensional nanocrystalline material. *J. Appl. Phys.* **78**, 847-860 (1995).

17. Chokshi, A. H., Mukherjee, A. K. & Langdon, T. G. Superplasticity in advanced materials. *Mater. Sci. Eng. R* **10**, 237-274 (1993).

18. Ridley, N. (ed.) *Superplasticity: 60 years after Pearson* (Institute of Metals, London, 1995).

19. Nieman, G. W., Weertman, J. R. & Siegel, R. W. Mechanical behavior of nanocrystalline Cu and Pd. *J. Mater. Res.* **6**, 1012-1027 (1991).

20. Nieh, T. G. & Wadsworth, J. Hall–Petch relation in nanocrystalline solids. *Scripta Met. Mater.* **25**, 955-958 (1991).

21. Lian, J., Baudelet, B. & Nazarov, A. A. Model for the prediction of the mechanical behaviour of nanocrystalline materials. *Mater. Sci. Eng. A* **172**, 23-29 (1993).

22. Langdon, T. G. The significance of grain boundaries in the flow of polycrystalline materials. *Mater. Sci. Forum* **189-190**, 31-42 (1995).

23. Suryanarayanan, R. *et al.* Mechanical properties of nanocrystalline copper produced by solution-phase synthesis. *J. Mater. Res.* **11**, 439-448 (1996).

24. Weertman, J. R. Hall–Petch strengthening in nanocrystalline metals. *Mater. Sci. Eng. A* **166**, 161-167 (1993).

25. Van Swygenhoven, H. & Caro, A. Plastic behavior of nanophase Ni: A molecular dynamics computer simulation. *Appl. Phys. Lett.* **71**, 1652-1654 (1997).

Acknowledgements. We thank J. K. Nørskov, T. Leffers, O. B. Pedersen, A. E. Carlsson and J. P. Sethna for discussions. The Center for Atomic-scale Materials Physics is sponsored by the Danish National Research Foundation.

Correspondence and requests for materials should be addressed to J.S. (e-mail: schiotz@fysik.dtu.dk).

56

Extraordinary Optical Transmission through Sub-wavelength Hole Arrays

T. W. Ebbesen *et al.*

Editor's Note

Light rays are generally considered to be blocked by apertures smaller than the light's wavelength. This limits the resolution of optical microscopes. But here Thomas Ebbesen of the NEC Corporation in Princeton and colleagues report the surprising ability of light to "squeeze through" an array of sub-wavelength-sized holes in a thin metal sheet. The effect stems from the interaction of light with mobile electrons on the surface of the metal, which can be excited into wavelike motions called plasmons. A plasmon wave can pass through the hole and then re-radiate light on the far side. This paper stimulated interest in the topic now called plasmonics, which takes advantage of light-plasmon applications to achieve a range of unusual effects, including "invisibility shields".

The desire to use and control photons in a manner analogous to the control of electrons in solids has inspired great interest in such topics as the localization of light, microcavity quantum electrodynamics and near-field optics[1-6]. A fundamental constraint in manipulating light is the extremely low transmittivity of apertures smaller than the wavelength of the incident photon. While exploring the optical properties of submicrometre cylindrical cavities in metallic films, we have found that arrays of such holes display highly unusual zero-order transmission spectra (where the incident and detected light are collinear) at wavelengths larger than the array period, beyond which no diffraction occurs. In particular, sharp peaks in transmission are observed at wavelengths as large as ten times the diameter of the cylinders. At these maxima the transmission efficiency can exceed unity (when normalized to the area of the holes), which is orders of magnitude greater than predicted by standard aperture theory. Our experiments provide evidence that these unusual optical properties are due to the coupling of light with plasmons—electronic excitations—on the surface of the periodically patterned metal film. Measurements of transmission as a function of the incident light angle result in a photonic band diagram. These findings may find application in novel photonic devices.

A variety of two-dimensional arrays of cylindrical cavities in metallic films were prepared and analysed for this study. Typically, a silver film of thickness $t = 0.2$ μm was first deposited by evaporation on a quartz substrate. Arrays of cylindrical holes were fabricated through the film by sputtering using a Micrion focused-ion-beam (FIB) System 9500 (50 keV Ga ions, 5 nm nominal spot diameter). The individual hole diameter d was varied between 150 nm and 1 μm and the spacing between the holes (that is, the periodicity) a_0, was between 0.6 and 1.8 μm. The zero-order transmission spectra, where the incident

通过亚波长孔洞阵列的超常光透射现象

埃贝森等

编者按

一般认为，当孔径小于光束波长时，光线将被阻碍，从而使光学显微镜的分辨率受到限制。但在本文中，普林斯顿日本电气公司研究所的托马斯·埃贝森及其同事报道了光具有"挤过"金属薄膜中亚波长尺寸孔洞阵列的惊人能力。该效应源于光与金属表面可迁移电子间的相互作用，使其激发成为与等离子体激元类似的波的运动。等离子体激元波可以通过孔洞，进而在远端发生光的再辐射。本文诱发了对目前名为等离子体光子学领域的兴趣，该领域旨在利用光-等离子体激元来实现包括"隐形盾"在内的一系列不寻常的效应。

通过与控制固体中电子类似的方式来应用和控制光子的愿望，激起了人们对于光定域化、微腔量子电动力学和近场光学等主题的强烈兴趣[1-6]。调制光时遇到的基本限制就是当孔隙小于入射光子波长时透射率将非常低。但是，在探索金属薄膜中亚微米级圆柱形谐振腔的光学性质时，我们发现，当波长大于阵列周期时，这些孔洞阵列呈现出极不寻常的零级透射光谱（入射光与所探测的光二者共线），并且没有发生衍射。更为特别的是，在波长为圆柱直径的 10 倍处观测到尖锐的透射峰。而且在极大值处透射率可以超过 1（按孔面积归一化后），这比标准孔隙理论的预期值高出几个数量级。我们的实验为下列说法提供了证据：这些不寻常的光学性质源自有周期性排列孔洞的金属薄膜表面上光与等离子体激元的耦合——电子激发作用。以透射作为光线入射角函数的观测获得了光子带图。这些发现可能会在新型光子器件中获得应用。

在这项研究中，我们制备了具有多种二维阵列的圆柱形谐振腔的金属薄膜，并对实验结果进行了分析。典型的一例是，首先通过蒸镀在石英基质上沉积一层 $t = 0.2\ \mu m$ 厚的银膜。继而用 Micrion 聚焦离子束系统 9500（50 keV 镓离子，5 nm 标称点直径）进行溅镀，并在薄膜上加工出圆柱形孔洞阵列。单个孔直径 d 在 150 nm 到 1 μm 之间，孔洞之间的距离 a_0（亦即周期）则在 0.6 μm 和 1.8 μm 之间。零级透射

and detected light are collinear, were recorded with a Cary 5 ultraviolet–near infrared spectrophotometer with an incoherent light source, but the arrays were also studied on an optical bench for transmission, diffraction and reflection properties using coherent sources.

Figure 1 shows a typical zero-order transmission spectrum for a square array of 150 nm holes with a period a_0 of 0.9 µm in a 200 nm thick Ag film. The spectrum shows a number of distinct features. At wavelength $\lambda = 326$ nm the narrow bulk silver plasmon peak is observed which disappears as the film becomes thicker. The most remarkable part is the set of peaks which become gradually stronger at longer wavelengths, increasingly so even beyond the minimum at the periodicity a_0. There is an additional minimum at $\lambda = a_0 \sqrt{\varepsilon}$ corresponding to the metal–quartz interface (where ε is the dielectric constant of the substrate). For $\lambda > a_0 \sqrt{\varepsilon}$, there is no diffraction from the array nor from the individual holes. As expected, the first-order diffraction spots can be seen to be grazing the surface (that is, the diffraction angle approaches 90°) as the wavelength approaches the period from below (this might, in fact, enhance the coupling to be discussed in the next paragraphs). The maximum transmitted intensity occurs at 1,370 nm, nearly ten times the diameter of an individual hole in the array. Even more surprising is that the absolute transmission efficiency, calculated by dividing the fraction of light transmitted by the fraction of surface area occupied by the holes, is $\geqslant 2$ at the maxima. In other words, more than twice as much light is transmitted as impinges directly on the holes. Furthermore, the transmittivity of the array scales linearly with the surface area of the holes. This is all the more remarkable considering that the transmission efficiency of a single sub-wavelength aperture is predicted by Bethe[7] to scale as $(r/\lambda)^4$ where r is the hole radius; accordingly for a hole of 150 nm diameter one expects a transmission efficiency on the order of 10^{-3}. In addition, the intensity (I) of the zero-order transmission from a grating is expected to decrease monotonically at larger wavelengths ($I \propto \lambda^{-1}$) (ref. 8). Therefore our results must imply that the array itself is an active element, not just a passive geometrical object in the path of the incident beam.

Fig. 1. Zero-order transmission spectrum of an Ag array ($a_0 = 0.9$ µm, $d = 150$ nm, $t = 200$ nm).

光谱——其中入射光和所探测的光共线——是用一台具有非相干光源的 Cary 5 型紫外–近红外分光光度计记录的，也用相干光源对光具座上的阵列就透射、衍射和反射性质进行了研究。

图 1 显示了在 200 nm 厚的银膜中，周期 a_0 为 0.9 μm 的 150 nm 孔洞方形阵列典型零级透射光谱。光谱呈现出很多不同的特征。在波长 $\lambda = 326$ nm 处可以看到本底银狭窄的等离子体峰，当薄膜厚度增加时它会消失。最值得关注的部分是在波长较长处逐渐变强的一组峰，甚至增加到超过位于周期 a_0 处的最小值。在 $\lambda = a_0\sqrt{\varepsilon}$ 处有一个额外的最小值，它对应于金属–石英界面（其中 ε 是基质的介电常数）。在 $\lambda > a_0\sqrt{\varepsilon}$ 处，阵列和单个孔洞都没有产生衍射。如同预期的那样，当波长由低处趋近周期值时，可以看到一级衍射点随之掠向表面（即衍射角接近 90°）的现象（实际上，它可能增强我们在下面段落中将要讨论到的耦合作用）。最大透射强度出现在 1,370 nm 处，这一波长大约是阵列中单独一个孔洞的直径的 10 倍。更令人吃惊的是绝对透射率——由光的透射部分除以孔洞占据的表面积即可算出——在最大处 $\geqslant 2$。换句话说，透射出的光强比直接撞击孔洞的光强要高出一倍以上。此外，阵列的透射率随着孔洞表面积呈线性变化。如果考虑到贝特[7]关于单个亚波长孔道透射率与 $(r/\lambda)^4$ 成比例的推断——其中 r 是孔洞半径，这一点就更加值得注意；据此推断，对于直径 150 nm 的孔洞来说，可以预期具有 10^{-3} 数量级的透射率。另外，预期光栅产生的零级透射强度 (I) 会在较大波长 ($I \propto \lambda^{-1}$) 处单调地下降（参考文献 8）。因此我们的结果必然意味着阵列本身就是一个有源元件，而不只是入射光束路径上的一个无源几何体。

图 1. 一个银阵列 ($a_0 = 0.9$ μm，$d = 150$ nm，$t = 200$ nm) 的零级透射光谱

To understand the origin of this phenomenon, we tested the dependence on all the possible variables such as hole diameter, periodicity, thickness and type of metal. It is beyond the scope of this Letter to describe the details of all these experiments. Instead we summarize our observations and illustrate some of the key factors that determine the shape of these spectra. To begin with, the periodicity of the array determines the position of the peaks. The positions of the maxima scale exactly with the periodicity, as shown in Fig. 2a, independent of metal (Ag, Cr, Au), hole diameter and film thickness. The width of the peaks appears to be strongly dependent on the aspect ratio (t/d or depth divided by diameter) of the cylindrical holes (Fig. 2a). For $t/d = 0.2$, the peaks are very broad and just discernible and when the ratio reaches ~ 1, the maximum sharpness is obtained. Further narrowing might depend on the quality of the individual holes. The thickness dependence of the spectra is displayed in Fig. 2b for 0.2 and 0.5 µm Ag films. While the intensity of the bulk plasmon peak decreases rapidly in this range, that of the longer-wavelength peaks decreases approximately linearly with thickness. The spectra change significantly with the type of lattice, for example whether the array is a square or a triangular lattice.

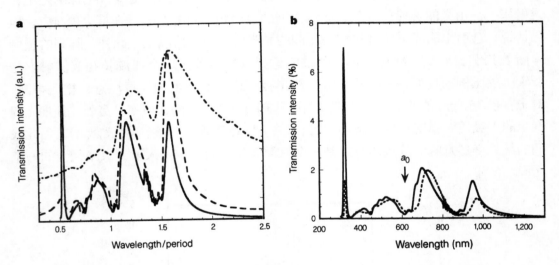

Fig. 2. Effects of parameters on zero-order transmission spectra. **a**, Spectra for various square arrays as a function of λ/a_0. Solid line: Ag, $a_0 = 0.6$ µm, $d = 150$ nm, $t = 200$ nm; dashed line: Au, $a_0 = 1.0$ µm, $d = 350$ nm, $t = 300$ nm; dashed-dotted line: Cr, $a_0 = 1.0$ µm, $d = 500$ nm, $t = 100$ nm. **b**, Spectra for two identical Ag arrays with different thicknesses. Solid line: $t = 200$ nm; dashed line: $t = 500$ nm (this spectrum has been multiplied by 1.75 for comparison). For both arrays: $a_0 = 0.6$ µm; $d = 150$ nm.

Two important clues relating this phenomenon to surface plasmons (SPs) come from the following observations. One is the absence of enhanced transmission in hole arrays fabricated in Ge films which points to the importance of the metallic film. The other clue is the angular dependence of the spectra in metallic samples. The zero-order transmission spectra change in a marked way even for very small angles, as illustrated in Fig. 3 where the spectra were recorded every 2°. The peaks change in intensity and split into new peaks which move in opposite directions. This is exactly the behaviour observed when light couples with SPs in reflection gratings[9-14]. SPs are oscillations of surface charges at the metal

为理解这种现象的来由，我们检测了它对于诸如孔洞直径、周期、金属膜厚度和类型等所有可能变量的依赖性。由于本快报篇幅有限，无法描述所有实验的细节，因此我们总结了观察结果并说明了决定这些光谱的形状的一些关键因素。首先，阵列的周期决定了峰的位置。如图 2a 所示，最大值的位置严格地与周期成比例，而不依赖于所用金属（银、铬、金）、孔洞直径和薄膜厚度。峰的宽度显然强烈地依赖于圆柱形谐振腔的纵横比（t/d，或厚度除以直径）（图 2a）。当 $t/d = 0.2$ 时，峰很宽而且刚刚可以分辨出来，而当该比值达到约 1 时具有最高清晰度。进一步的变窄可能和单个孔洞的性质有关。图 2b 中显示出光谱对于薄膜厚度的依赖性，其中银膜厚度分别为 0.2 μm 和 0.5 μm。本底等离子体激元峰的强度在这个范围内快速下降，而较长波长处的峰强度随着厚度变化大致呈线性下降。光谱随着栅格类型——例如阵列究竟是方形还是三角形栅格——发生显著变化。

图 2. 参数对于零级透射光谱的影响。**a**，作为 λ/a_0 的函数的各种方形阵列的光谱。实线：银，$a_0 = 0.6$ μm，$d = 150$ nm，$t = 200$ nm；虚线：金，$a_0 = 1.0$ μm，$d = 350$ nm，$t = 300$ nm；点划线：铬，$a_0 = 1.0$ μm，$d = 500$ nm，$t = 100$ nm。**b**，只有厚度不同的两个相同银阵列的光谱。实线：$t = 200$ nm；虚线：$t = 500$ nm（为便于比较，此光谱已乘以倍数 1.75）。对两个阵列同时有：$a_0 = 0.6$ μm；$d = 150$ nm。

将这种现象与表面等离子体激元（SP）联系起来的两条重要线索来自下面的观测结果。其一是，由锗薄膜加工制成的孔洞阵列中不存在透射增强现象，表明了薄膜金属的重要性。另一条线索是在金属样品中光谱的角度依赖性。如图 3 所示，即使角度变化很小时，零级透射光谱也会发生明显的变化。图 3 是角度间隔为 2° 时记录下来的光谱。谱峰强度发生变化，并且分裂成向相反方向移动的新谱峰。这正是光与反射光栅中表面等离子体激元耦合时观测到的行为 [9-14]。表面等离子体激元是金属

interface and are excited when their momentum matches the momentum of the incident photon and the grating as follows:

$$k_{sp} = k_x \pm nG_x \pm mG_y$$

where k_{sp} is the surface plasmon wavevector, $k_x = (2\pi/\lambda)\sin\theta$ is the component of the incident photon's wavevector in the plane of the grating and $G_x = G_y = 2\pi/a_0$ are the grating momentum wavevectors for a square array. Therefore if the angle of incidence θ is varied, the incident radiation excites different SP modes and by recording the peak energies as a function of k_x we obtain the dispersion relation shown in Fig. 4. This figure reveals the band structure of SP in the two-dimensional array and it clearly demonstrates the presence of gaps with energies around 30 to 50 meV; these are due to the lifting of the degeneracy by SPs interacting with the lattice. An extrapolation of the dispersion curves yields an intercept with the k-axis at a value which is within the experimental error (~10%) of that expected from the periodicity $(2\pi/a_0)$. The results of Figs 3 and 4 are also sensitive to polarization as expected, but a clear assignment has not yet been possible because of inherent structure of the grains in the metal film.

Fig. 3. Zero-order transmission spectra as a function of incident angle of the light. Spectra were taken every 2° up to 24° for a square Ag array ($a_0 = 0.9$ μm, $d = 150$ nm, $t = 200$ nm). The individual spectra are offset vertically by 0.1% from one another for clarity.

界面上表面电荷的振荡，当它们的动量与入射光子以及光栅的动量满足如下表达式时将受到激发：

$$k_{sp} = k_x \pm nG_x \pm mG_y$$

其中 k_{sp} 是表面等离子体激元波矢，$k_x = (2\pi/\lambda)\sin\theta$ 是入射光子波矢在光栅平面内的分量，而 $G_x = G_y = 2\pi/a_0$ 是方形阵列的光栅动量波矢。因此，如果入射角 θ 变化，入射辐射将激发不同的表面等离子体激元模式；通过记录作为 k_x 的函数的峰值能量，我们得到了图 4 中所显示的色散关系。这幅图揭示了二维阵列中表面等离子体激元的带结构，而且它清楚地阐明了具有约 30 meV 到 50 meV 能量的带隙的存在；它们来源于表面等离子体激元与栅格相互作用导致的简并提升。色散曲线的外推得到在 k 轴上的截距，其数值在依据周期 $(2\pi/a_0)$ 预期的实验误差（约 10%）之内。如同预期，图 3 和图 4 中的结果也对极化很敏感，但是由于金属薄膜中晶粒内在结构间的差异，目前还不能做出明确的归属。

图 3. 作为光线入射角函数的零级透射光谱。对一个方形银阵列每隔 2° 测一次谱图，一直测到 24°（$a_0 = 0.9$ μm，$d = 150$ nm，$t = 200$ nm）。为清晰起见，各个谱之间在垂直方向上错开 0.1%。

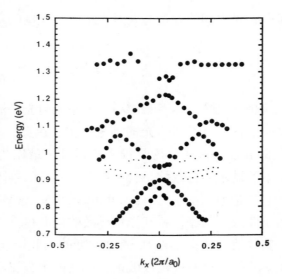

Fig. 4. Dispersion curves (solid circles) along the [10] direction of the array. These curves are extracted from the energy of the transmission peaks of Fig. 3. The momentum k_x is in the plane of the array and is given by $k_x = (2\pi/\lambda) \sin\theta$ where θ is the incident angle of the beam (the units are normalized to $2\pi/a_0$). The curves with the smaller dots correspond to peaks whose amplitudes are much weaker and may or may not be related to the band structure as they do not shift significantly with momentum.

In our experiments the coupling of light with SPs is observed in transmission rather than reflection, in contrast with previous work on SPs on reflection gratings. In those studies the coupling of light to SPs is observed as a redistribution of intensity between different diffracted orders. Even in transmission studies of wire gratings by Lochbihler[15], the effect of SPs is observed through dips in zero-order transmitted light. There is an extensive literature on the infrared properties of wire grids which show a broad transmission centred at $\lambda \approx 1.2a_0$; this has been interpreted in terms of induction effects, in analogy with electric circuits[16,17]. Our results demonstrate the strong enhancement of transmitted light due to coupling of the light with the SP of the two-dimensional array of sub-wavelength holes. Furthermore our results indicate a number of unique features that cannot be explained with existing theories. The SP modes on the metal–air interface are distinctly different from those at the metal–quartz interface. However, the spectra are identical regardless of whether the sample is illuminated from the metal or quartz side. At present we do not understand the detailed mechanism of the coupling between the SP on the front and back surfaces which results in larger than unity transmission efficiency of the holes. The thickness dependence (see Fig. 2b) suggests that the holes play an important part in mediating this coupling and that nonradiative SP modes are transferred to radiative modes by strong scattering in the holes.

In photonic bandgap arrays[2,4], the material is passive and translucent at all wavelengths except at the energies within the gap. In the present arrays, the material plays an active role (through the plasmons) and it is opaque at all wavelengths except those for which coupling occurs. The combination, or integration, of these two types of phenomena might lead to

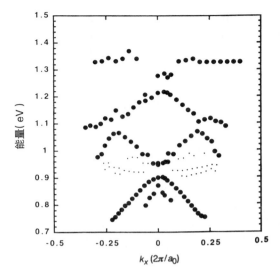

图 4. 沿阵列 [10] 方向的色散曲线（实心圆点）。这些曲线是利用图 3 中透射峰的能量得到的。动量 k_x 位于阵列平面内，由 $k_x = (2\pi/\lambda)\sin\theta$ 给出，其中 θ 是光束的入射角（单位归一化为 $2\pi/a_0$）。由较小的点组成的曲线所对应的峰，其幅度要弱很多，由于随动量变化发生的偏移并不明显，因此与带结构的关联不能确定。

在我们的实验中，光与表面等离子体激元的耦合是在透射中而不是在反射中观测到的，这与此前对反射光栅上的表面等离子体激元的研究相反。在那些研究中，光与表面等离子体激元的耦合是作为强度在不同衍射级之间的重新分配观测到的。即使是在洛赫比勒对线光栅的透射研究中 [15]，表面等离子体激元的影响也是通过零级透射光中的凹陷观测到的。关于线栅的红外性质，已经有大量文献表明它有一个以 $\lambda \approx 1.2a_0$ 为中心的宽透射；可以用类似于电路的感应效应对此进行解释 [16,17]。我们的结果表明，由于光与亚波长孔洞二维阵列的表面等离子体激元耦合，透射光将明显增强。此外，我们的结果还指出了很多用现有理论无法解释的独特性状。位于金属–空气界面上的表面等离子体激元模式明显不同于位于金属–石英界面上的。但是，无论是从金属一侧还是石英一侧对样品进行光照，所得光谱都是一样的。目前，我们还不了解导致孔洞透射效率大于 1 的前后表面上等离子体激元之间耦合的详细机制。厚度依赖性（参见图 2b）意味着孔洞对于调制这类耦合起着重要的作用，也意味着通过孔洞中的强烈散射，非辐射表面等离子体激元模式将转化为辐射模式。

在光子带隙阵列中 [2,4]，材料在除去能隙中的能量之外的所有波长处都是无源、半透明的。在当前的阵列中，材料起到有源的作用（通过等离子体激元），并且在除去发生耦合的那些波长之外的所有波长处都是不透明的。这两种现象的结合或整合

optical features that are very interesting from both fundamental and technological points of view. The demonstration of efficient light transmission through holes much smaller than the wavelength and beyond the inter-hole diffraction limit might, for example, inspire designs for novel nearfield scanning optical microscopes[6], or sub-wavelength photolithography. Theoretical analysis of the results would also be useful for gaining better insight into this extraordinary transmission phenomenon. Perhaps only then can we expect to grasp the full implications of these findings.

(**391**, 667-669; 1998)

T. W. Ebbesen[*†], H. J. Lezec[‡], H. F. Ghaemi[*], T. Thio[*] & P. A. Wolff[*§]

[*] NEC Research Institute, 4 Independence Way, Princeton, New Jersey 08540, USA

[†] ISIS, Louis Pasteur University, 67000 Strasbourg, France

[‡] Micrion Europe GmbH, Kirchenstraße 2, 85622 Feldkirchen, Germany

[§] Department of Physics, Massachusetts Institute of Technology, Cambridge, Massachusetts 02139, USA

Received 15 July; accepted 24 November 1997.

References:

1. John, S. Localization of light. *Phys. Today* 32 (May 1991).

2. Yablonovitch, E. & Leung, K. M. Hope for photonic bandgaps. *Nature* **351,** 278 (1991).

3. Dalichaouch, R., Armstrong, J. P., Schultz, S., Platzman, P. M. & McCall, S. L. Microwave localization by two-dimensional random scattering. *Nature* **354,** 53-55 (1991).

4. J. D. Joannopoulos, Meade R. D. & Winn, J. N. *Photonic Crystals* (Princeton Univ. Press, Princeton, 1995).

5. Haroche, S. & Kleppner, D. Cavity quantum electrodynamics. *Phys. Today* 24 (January 1989).

6. Betzig, E. & Trautman, J. K. Near-field optics: Microscopy, spectroscopy, and surface modification beyond the diffraction limit. *Science* **257,** 189-194 (1992).

7. Bethe, H. A. Theory of diffraction by small holes. *Phys. Rev.* **66,** 163-182 (1944).

8. Born, M. & Wolf, E. *Principles of Optics* (Pergamon, Oxford, 1980).

9. Ritchie, R. H., Arakawa, E. T., Cowan, J. J. & Hamm, R. N. Surface-plasmon resonance effect in grating diffraction. *Phys. Rev. Lett.* **21,** 1530-1533 (1968).

10. Raether, H. *Surface Plasmons* (Springer, Berlin, 1988).

11. Chen, Y. J., Koteles, E. S., Seymour, R. J., Sonek, G. J. & Ballantyne, J. M. Surface plasmons on gratings: coupling in the minigap regions. *Solid State Commun.* **46,** 95-99 (1983).

12. Kitson, S. C., Barnes, W. L. & Sambles, J. R. Full photonic band gap for surface modes in the visible. *Phys. Rev. Lett.* **77,** 2670-2673 (1996).

13. Watts, R. A., Harris, J. B., Hibbins, A. P., Preist, T. W. & Sambles, J. R. Optical excitations of surface plasmon polaritons on 90 and 60 bi-gratings. *J. Mod. Opt.* **43,** 1351-1360 (1996).

14. Derrick, G. H., McPhedran, R. C., Maystre, D. & Neviere, M. Crossed gratings: a theory and its applications. *Appl. Phys.* **18,** 39-52 (1979).

15. Lochbihler, H. Surface polaritons on gold-wire gratings. *Phys. Rev. B* **50,** 4795-4801 (1994).

16. Ulrich, R. Far-infrared properties of metallic mesh and its complimentary structure. *Infrared Phys.* **7,** 37-55 (1967).

17. Larsen, T. A survey of the theory of wire grids. *I.R.E. Trans. Microwave Theory Techniques* **10,** 191-201 (1962).

Acknowledgements. We thank S. Kishida, G. Bugmann and J. Giordmaine for their encouragement, and R. Linke, R. McDonald, M. Treacy, J. Chadi and C. Tsai for discussions. We also thank G. Lewen, G. Seidler, A. Krishnan, A. Schertel, A. Dziesiaty and H. Zimmermann for assistance.

Correspondence should be addressed to T.W.E.

可能产生无论从基础原理还是技术性角度来讲都极为有趣的光学特性。光能有效地透过比波长小很多的孔洞并突破孔洞间衍射的限制，对这一点的证明可以对诸如新型近场扫描光学显微镜 [6] 或者亚波长光刻法的设计等有所启发。对这些结果的理论分析可能会有助于对这种超强透射现象有更深入的理解。也许只有到那时我们才有望掌握这些发现的全部意义。

（王耀杨 翻译；宋心琦 审稿）

Potent and Specific Genetic Interference by Double-stranded RNA in *Caenorhabditis elegans*

A. Fire *et al.*

Editor's Note

Here American biologists Andrew Fire and Craig Mello describe a fundamental form of gene regulation called RNA interference, where snippets of double-stranded RNA instruct the cell to destroy genetically identical messenger RNA molecules, and so effectively silence the corresponding gene. The process occurs naturally in plants and animals, where it helps regulate gene expression and is a vital part of the immune response to viruses and other foreign genetic material. It is widely used in the laboratory to study gene function, and holds promise as a therapeutic tool for thwarting viruses and controlling the expression of aberrant, disease-causing genes. This demonstration of RNA interference in the nematode worm earned Fire and Mello a Nobel Prize eight years later.

Experimental introduction of RNA into cells can be used in certain biological systems to interfere with the function of an endogenous gene[1,2]. Such effects have been proposed to result from a simple antisense mechanism that depends on hybridization between the injected RNA and endogenous messenger RNA transcripts. RNA interference has been used in the nematode *Caenorhabditis elegans* to manipulate gene expression[3,4]. Here we investigate the requirements for structure and delivery of the interfering RNA. To our surprise, we found that double-stranded RNA was substantially more effective at producing interference than was either strand individually. After injection into adult animals, purified single strands had at most a modest effect, whereas double-stranded mixtures caused potent and specific interference. The effects of this interference were evident in both the injected animals and their progeny. Only a few molecules of injected double-stranded RNA were required per affected cell, arguing against stochiometric interference with endogenous mRNA and suggesting that there could be a catalytic or amplification component in the interference process.

DESPITE the usefulness of RNA interference in *C. elegans*, two features of the process have been difficult to explain. First, sense and antisense RNA preparations are each sufficient to cause interference[3,4]. Second, interference effects can persist well into the next generation, even though many endogenous RNA transcripts are rapidly degraded in the early embryo[5]. These results indicate a fundamental difference in behaviour between native RNAs (for example, mRNAs) and the molecules responsible for interference. We sought to test the possibility that this contrast reflects an underlying difference in RNA

秀丽隐杆线虫体内双链 RNA 强烈而特异性的基因干扰作用

法厄 等

编者按

在本文中，美国生物学家安德鲁·法厄和克雷格·梅洛描述了基因调控的一种基本形式——称为 RNA 干扰，即小片段的双链 RNA 导致细胞内基因（序列）相同的信使RNA（mRNA）分子被破坏，从而有效地沉默相应靶基因的表达。这个过程在植物和动物体内自然发生，它有助于调控基因表达，并且也是机体对病毒和其他外来遗传物质进行免疫应答的重要组成部分。RNA 干扰在实验室中被广泛应用于基因功能的研究，并且有望成为抗病毒和控制异常基因与致病基因表达的一种治疗工具。本文中对线虫体内 RNA 干扰机制的阐述令法厄和梅洛于 8 年后获得诺贝尔奖。

在特定生物系统中，用实验方法将 RNA 导入细胞可以干扰内源基因的功能 [1,2]。研究人员认为这种干扰效应源于一种简单的反义机制，该机制依赖于导入的 RNA 与内源信使 RNA 转录本之间的杂交。RNA 干扰已经被用于操控秀丽隐杆线虫基因的表达 [3,4]。在此我们研究了干扰 RNA 结构和释放的必要条件。我们惊奇地发现，双链 RNA 产生的干扰作用比其中的任意一条单链都要强。将纯化的单链导入成年动物体内后最多只产生中等强度的干扰作用，而双链混合物的导入则能产生强烈而特异性的干扰。这种干扰作用在被注射的动物及其后代中都很明显。与内源 mRNA 产生干扰的剂量不同，仅需要几个双链 RNA 分子就可以对细胞产生干扰，这表明，在该干扰过程中可能存在具有催化或放大作用的组分。

虽然 RNA 干扰在秀丽隐杆线虫中非常有效，但是该过程的两个特征却难以得到解释。首先，单独制备的正义 RNA 链或反义 RNA 链都足以产生干扰作用 [3,4]。其次，尽管许多内源 RNA 转录本都在胚胎早期迅速地降解了，但是干扰作用却能够持续到下一代 [5]。这些结果表明产生干扰效应的 RNA 分子和天然分子（如 mRNA）在性质上具有本质差别。我们认为可能是 RNA 的根本结构差异导致了它们具有不同的

structure. RNA populations to be injected are generally prepared using bacteriophage RNA polymerases[6]. These polymerases, although highly specific, produce some random or ectopic transcripts. DNA transgene arrays also produce a fraction of aberrant RNA products[3]. From these facts, we surmised that the interfering RNA populations might include some molecules with double-stranded character. To test whether double-stranded character might contribute to interference, we further purified single-stranded RNAs and compared interference activities of individual strands with the activity of a deliberately prepared double-stranded hybrid.

The *unc-22* gene was chosen for initial comparisons of activity. *unc-22* encodes an abundant but nonessential myofilament protein[7-9]. Several thousand copies of *unc-22* mRNA are present in each striated muscle cell[3]. Semiquantitative correlations between *unc-22* activity and phenotype of the organism have been described[8]: decreases in *unc-22* activity produce an increasingly severe twitching phenotype, whereas complete loss of function results in the additional appearance of muscle structural defects and impaired motility.

Purified antisense and sense RNAs covering a 742-nucleotide segment of *unc-22* had only marginal interference activity, requiring a very high dose of injected RNA to produce any observable effect (Table 1). In contrast, a sense-antisense mixture produced highly effective interference with endogenous gene activity. The mixture was at least two orders of magnitude more effective than either single strand alone in producing genetic interference. The lowest dose of the sense-antisense mixture that was tested, ~60,000 molecules of each strand per adult, led to twitching phenotypes in an average of 100 progeny. Expression of *unc-22* begins in embryos containing ~500 cells. At this point, the original injected material would be diluted to at most a few molecules per cell.

Table 1. Effects of sense, antisense and mixed RNAs on progeny of injected animals

Gene	segment	Size (kilobases)	Injected RNA	F1 phenotype
unc-22				*unc-22*-null mutants: strong twitchers[7,8]
unc22A*	Exon 21–22	742	Sense	Wild type
			Antisense	Wild type
			Sense + antisense	Strong twitchers (100%)
unc22B	Exon 27	1,033	Sense	Wild type
			Antisense	Wild type
			Sense + antisense	Strong twitchers (100%)
unc22C	Exon 21–22†	785	Sense + antisense	Strong twitchers (100%)
fem-1				*fem-1*-null mutants: female (no sperm)[13]
fem1A	Exon 10‡	531	Sense	Hermaphrodite (98%)
			Antisense	Hermaphrodite (> 98%)
			Sense + antisense	Female (72%)
fem1B	Intron 8	556	Sense + antisense	Hermaphrodite (> 98%)
unc-54				*unc-54*-null mutants: paralysed[7,11]
unc54A	Exon 6	576	Sense	Wild type (100%)
			Antisense	Wild type (100%)
			Sense + antisense	Paralysed (100%)§

功能，并希望证实这个观点。通常情况下，用于导入的 RNA 分子都是利用噬菌体的 RNA 聚合酶来获得的[6]。这些聚合酶尽管具有很高的特异性，但也会产生随机突变或者异位突变。DNA 转基因阵列同样也会产生一定比例的异常 RNA 分子[3]。基于这些事实，我们总结出了干扰 RNA 分子中可能包含一些有双链特征的分子。为了验证双链分子是否可以导致干扰效应，我们进一步纯化了单链 RNA 分子，并将各个单链的干扰活性与特意准备的杂交双链分子进行了比较。

我们选择 unc-22 基因来进行初步的活性比较。unc-22 编码一种大量却非必需的肌丝蛋白[7-9]。每个横纹肌细胞中都有数千拷贝的 unc-22 mRNA[3]。unc-22 的活性与机体表型的半定量关系已有报道[8]：unc-22 活性降低会加剧肌肉抽搐这一表型，而 unc-22 完全丧失功能则进一步导致肌肉结构缺陷且运动能力受损。

包含 unc-22 上 742 个核苷酸的正义链和反义链 RNA 纯化片段只有微小的干扰活性，需要注射很高剂量的 RNA 才能产生可见效应（表 1）。相反，正义链–反义链混合物对内源基因活性产生高效的干扰作用。混合物产生的遗传性基因干扰比任何一条单链所产生的至少高两个数量级。实验证明，正义链–反义链混合物的最低剂量（即每个成年动物中每条单链为 60,000 个分子左右）平均可在 100 个后代中导致抽搐表型。unc-22 的表达始于包含约 500 个细胞的胚胎。此时，初始的注射物被稀释为每个细胞最多只含有几个分子。

表 1. 动物注射 RNA 分子正义链、反义链及其混合物后对后代的影响

基因	片段	大小(kb)	注射的 RNA 链	子一代表型
unc-22				unc-22 无效突变体：剧烈抽搐[7,8]
unc22A*	外显子 21~22	742	正义链	野生型
			反义链	野生型
			正义链 + 反义链	剧烈抽搐(100%)
unc22B	外显子 27	1,033	正义链	野生型
			反义链	野生型
			正义链 + 反义链	剧烈抽搐(100%)
unc22C	外显子 21~22†	785	正义链 + 反义链	剧烈抽搐(100%)
fem-1				fem-1 无效突变体：雌体（无精子）[13]
fem1A	外显子 10‡	531	正义链	雌雄同体(98%)
			反义链	雌雄同体(>98%)
			正义链 + 反义链	雌体(72%)
fem1B	内含子 8	556	正义链 + 反义链	雌雄同体(>98%)
unc-54				unc-54 无效突变体：瘫痪[7,11]
unc54A	外显子 6	576	正义链	野生型(100%)
			反义链	野生型(100%)
			正义链 + 反义链	瘫痪(100%)§

Continued

Gene	segment	Size (kilobases)	Injected RNA	F1 phenotype
unc54B	Exon 6	651	Sense	Wild type (100%)
			Antisense	Wild type (100%)
			Sense+antisense	Paralysed (100%)§
unc54C	Exon 1–5	1,015	Sense+antisense	Arrested embryos and larvae (100%)
unc54D	Promoter	567	Sense+antisense	Wild type (100%)
unc54E	Intron 1	369	Sense+antisense	Wild type (100%)
unc54F	Intron 3	386	Sense+antisense	Wild type (100%)
hlh-1				*hlh-1*-null mutants: lumpy-dumpy larvae[16]
hlh1A	Exons1–6	1,033	Sense	Wild type (< 2% lpy-dpy)
			Antisense	Wild type (< 2% lpy-dpy)
			Sense+antisense	Lpy-dpy larvae (>90%)‖
hlh1B	Exons1–2	438	Sense+antisense	Lpy-dpy larvae (>80%)‖
hlh1C	Exons4–6	299	Sense+antisense	Lpy-dpy larvae (>80%)‖
hlh1D	Intron 1	697	Sense+antisense	Wild type (< 2% lpy-dpy)
myo-3-driven GFP transgenes¶				Makes nuclear GFP in body muscle
myo-3::NLS:: gfp:: lacZ		730	Sense	Nuclear GFP–LacZ pattern of parent strain
gfpG	Exons 2–5		Antisense	Nuclear GFP–LacZ pattern of parent strain
			Sense+antisense	Nuclear GFP–LacZ absent in 98% of cells
lacZL	Exon 12–14	830	Sense+antisense	Nuclear GFP–LacZ absent in > 95% of cells
myo-3::MtLS:: gfp				Makes mitochondrial GFP in body muscle
gfpG	Exons 2–5	730	Sense	Mitochondrial-GFP pattern of parent strain
			Antisense	Mitochondrial-GFP pattern of parent strain
			Sense+antisense	Mitochondrial-GFP absent in 98% of cells
LacZL	Exon 12–14	830	Sense+antisense	Mitochondrial-GFP pattern of parent strain

Each RNA was injected into 6–10 adult hermaphrodites (0.5×10^6–1×10^6 molecules into each gonad arm). After 4–6 h (to clear prefertilized eggs from the uterus), injected animals were transferred and eggs collected for 20–22 h. Progeny phenotypes were scored upon hatching and subsequently at 12–24-h intervals.

* to obtain a semiquantitative assessment of the relationship between RNA dose and phenotypic response, we injected each *unc22A* RNA preparation at a series of different concentrations (see figure in Supplementary information for details). At the highest dose tested (3.6×10^6 molecules per gonad), the individual sense and antisense *unc22A* preparations produced some visible twitching (1% and 11% of progeny, respectively). Comparable doses of double-stranded *unc22A* RNA produced visible twitching in all progeny, whereas a 120-fold lower dose of double-stranded *unc22A* RNA produced visible twitching in 30% of progeny.

† *unc22C* also carries the 43-nucleotide intron between exons 21 and 22.

‡ *fem1A* carries a portion (131 nucleotides) of intron 10.

§ Animals in the first affected broods (layed 4–24 h after injection) showed movement defects indistinguishable from those of *unc-54*-null mutants. A variable fraction of these animals (25%–75%) failed to lay eggs (another phenotype of *unc-54*-null mutants), whereas the remainder of the paralysed animals did lay eggs. This may indicate incomplete interference with *unc-54* activity in vulval muscles. Animals from later broods frequently show a distinct partial loss-of-function phenotype, with contractility in a subset of body-wall muscles.

‖ Phenotypes produced by RNA-mediated interference with *hlh-1* included arrested embryos and partially elongated L1 larvae (the *hlh-1*-null phenotype). These phenotypes were seen in virtually all progeny after injection of double-stranded *hlh1A* and in about half of the affected animals produced after injection of double-stranded *hlh1B* and double-stranded *hlh1C*. A set of less severe defects was seen in the remainder of the animals produced after injection of double-stranded *hlh1B* and double-stranded *hlh1C*. The less severe phenotypes are characteristic of partial loss of function of *hlh-1* (B. Harfe and A.F., unpublished observations).

¶ the host for these injections, strain PD4251, expresses both mitochondrial GFP and nuclear GFP-LacZ (see Methods). This allows simultaneous assay for interference with *gfp* (seen as loss of all fluorescence) and with *lacZ* (loss of nuclear fluorescence). The table describes scoring of animals as L1 larvae. Double-stranded *gfpG* caused a loss of GFP in all but 0–3 of the 85 body muscles in these larvae. As these animals mature to adults, GFP activity was seen in 0–5 additional body-wall muscles and in the 8 vulval muscles. Lpy-dpy, lumpy-dumpy.

基因	片段	大小(kb)	注射的 RNA 链	子一代表型
unc-54B	外显子 6	651	正义链	野生型 (100%)
			反义链	野生型 (100%)
			正义链 + 反义链	瘫痪 (100%)§
unc54C	外显子 1~5	1,015	正义链 + 反义链	幼虫及胚胎发育停滞 (100%)
unc54D	启动子	567	正义链 + 反义链	野生型 (100%)
unc54E	内含子 1	369	正义链 + 反义链	野生型 (100%)
unc54F	内含子 3	386	正义链 + 反义链	野生型 (100%)
hlh-1				*hlh-1* 无效突变体：矮胖粗笨幼虫[16]
hlh1A	外显子 1~6	1,033	正义链	野生型 (<2% lpy-dpy)
			反义链	野生型 (<2% lpy-dpy)
			正义链 + 反义链	Lpy-dpy 幼虫 (>90%)‖
hlh1B	外显子 1~2	438	正义链 + 反义链	Lpy-dpy 幼虫 (>80%)‖
hlh1C	外显子 4~6	299	正义链 + 反义链	Lpy-dpy 幼虫 (>80%)‖
hlh1D	内含子 1	697	正义链 + 反义链	野生型 (<2% lpy-dpy)
myo-3 驱动 *GFP* 转移基因¶				
myo-3::NLS:: gfp::lacZ				肌肉产生核 GFP
gfpG	外显子 2~5	730	正义链	亲代核 GFP-LacZ 模式
			反义链	亲代核 GFP-LacZ 模式
			正义链 + 反义链	98% 细胞缺失核 GFP-LacZ
lacZL	外显子 12~14	830	正义链 + 反义链	95% 以上细胞缺失核 GFP-LacZ
myo-3::MtLS:: gfp				肌肉产生线粒体 GFP
gfpG	外显子 2~5	730	正义链	亲代线粒体 GFP 模式
			反义链	亲代线粒体 GFP 模式
			正义链 + 反义链	98% 细胞缺失线粒体 GFP
lacZL	外显子 12~14	830	正义链 + 反义链	亲代线粒体 GFP 模式

每种 RNA 分子被注入 6~10 个雌雄同体的成虫中(每个生殖腺臂注入 0.5×10^6~1×10^6 个分子)。4~6 小时后(这段时间用于清除子宫中受精前的卵子),移出被注射动物并于 20~22 小时收集其卵子。孵育之后即记录后代的表型,且每隔 12~24 小时记录一次。

* 为了测定 RNA 剂量和表型反应之间的半定量关系,我们以一系列的浓度梯度注射 *unc22A* RNA(细节详见补充信息图)。在测试的最高剂量(每个生殖腺 3.6×10^6 个分子)时,单独制备的正义链和反义链 *unc22A* 产生一些可见的抽搐(分别占后代的 1% 和 11%)。相等剂量的双链 *unc22A* RNA 在所有后代中都产生了可见的抽搐,而 1/120 剂量的双链 *unc22A* RNA 在 30% 的后代中产生可见抽搐。

† *unc22C* 同时携带了外显子 21 和 22 之间的含 43 个核苷酸的内含子。

‡ *fem1A* 携带内含子 10 的一部分 (131 个核苷酸)。

§ 首先受影响的一批动物(注射后 4~24 小时产卵)表现出的行动缺陷与 *unc-54* 无效突变体难以区分。这些动物中的一部分(25%~75%)不能产卵(*unc-54* 无效突变体的另一个表型),而剩余的瘫痪动物确实产下了卵。这可能说明在外阴肌肉中对 *unc-54* 活性的干扰不完全。更晚的一批动物表现出明显的部分功能缺失表型,部分体壁肌肉有收缩性。

‖ 通过 RNA 介导的对 *hlh-1* 的干扰,产生的表型包括胚胎发育停滞和 L1 幼虫局部不能延长(*hlh-1* 无效表型)。这些表型在注射双链 *hlh1A* 后的所有后代中及注射双链 *hlh1B* 和双链 *hlh1C* 后受影响的一半动物中都可以见到。其余注射双链 *hlh1B* 和双链 *hlh1C* 的动物中看到不太严重的缺陷。不太严重的缺陷表型源自部分缺失 *hlh-1* 的功能(哈弗和法厄,未发表的观察结果)。

¶ 这些注射的宿主,品系为 PD4251,既表达线粒体 GFP 也表达核 GFP-LacZ(见方法部分)。这允许同时测定对 *gfp* (可见所有荧光丧失)和 *lacZ*(核荧光丧失)的干扰作用。这个表描述了 L1 幼虫的情况。双链 *gfpG* 引起这些幼虫中除 0~3 个以外的 85 个全身肌群中 GFP 缺失。在这些动物长到成虫时,可以在 0~5 条其他的体壁肌肉和 8 条外阴肌肉中观测到 GFP 活性。Lpy-dpy,粗笨-矮胖。

The potent interfering activity of the sense-antisense mixture could reflect the formation of double-stranded RNA (dsRNA) or, conceivably, some other synergy between the strands. Electrophoretic analysis indicated that the injected material was predominantly double-stranded. The dsRNA was gel-purified from the annealed mixture and found to retain potent interfering activity. Although annealing before injection was compatible with interference, it was not necessary. Mixing of sense and antisense RNAs in low-salt concentrations (under conditions of minimal dsRNA formation) or rapid sequential injection of sense and antisense strands were sufficient to allow complete interference. A long interval (> 1 h) between sequential injections of sense and antisense RNA resulted in a dramatic decrease in interfering activity. This suggests that injected single strands may be degraded or otherwise rendered inaccessible in the absence of the opposite strand.

A question of specificity arises when considering known cellular responses to dsRNA. Some organisms have a dsRNA-dependent protein kinase that activates a panic-response mechanism[10]. Conceivably, our sense-antisense synergy might have reflected a nonspecific potentiation of antisense effects by such a panic mechanism. This is not the case: co-injection of dsRNA segments unrelated to *unc-22* did not potentiate the ability of single *unc-22*-RNA strands to mediate inhibition (data not shown). We also investigated whether double-stranded structure could potentiate interference activity when placed in *cis* to a single-stranded segment. No such potentiation was seen: unrelated double-stranded sequences located 5' or 3' of a single-stranded *unc-22* segment did not stimulate interference. Thus, we have only observed potentiation of interference when dsRNA sequences exist within the region of homology with the target gene.

The phenotype produced by interference using *unc-22* dsRNA was extremely specific. Progeny of injected animals exhibited behaviour that precisely mimics loss-of-function mutations in *unc-22*. We assessed target specificity of dsRNA effects using three additional genes with well characterized phenotypes (Fig. 1, Table 1). *unc-54* encodes a body-wall-muscle heavy-chain isoform of myosin that is required for full muscle contraction[7,11,12]; *fem-1* encodes an ankyrin-repeat-containing protein that is required in hermaphrodites for sperm production[13,14]; and *hlh-1* encodes a *C. elegans* homologue of myoD-family proteins that is required for proper body shape and motility[15,16]. For each of these genes, injection of related dsRNA produced progeny broods exhibiting the known null-mutant phenotype, whereas the purified single RNA strands produced no significant interference. With one exception, all of the phenotypic consequences of dsRNA injection were those expected from interference with the corresponding gene. The exception (segment *unc54C* which led to an embryonic- and larval-arrest phenotype not seen with *unc-54-null* mutants) was illustrative. This segment covers the highly conserved myosin-motor domain, and might have been expected to interfere with activity of other highly related myosin heavy-chain genes[17]. The *unc54C* segment has been unique in our overall experience to date: effects of 18 other dsRNA segments (Table 1; and our unpublished observations) have all been limited to those expected from previously characterized null mutants.

正义链–反义链混合物的强干扰活性可以反映双链 RNA(dsRNA)的形成，或者可以想象为，反映了链之间的一些协同作用。电泳分析显示注射的物质主要是双链。dsRNA 是从退火的混合物中凝胶纯化得到的，并且保留了强干扰活性。虽然在注射前退火与干扰不矛盾，但并不是必需的。在低盐浓度下混合正义链和反义链的 RNA（此条件下形成的 dsRNA 最少）或快速连续注射正义和反义链都可以产生完全干扰。连续注射正义链和反义链 RNA 之间的长时间间隔（＞1 小时）会导致干扰活性显著下降。这表明已注射的单链可能被降解或因缺少互补链而难以实施干扰效应。

当考虑到已知的细胞对 dsRNA 的反应时，就产生了一个特殊问题。一些有机体具有 dsRNA 依赖性蛋白激酶，它活化一个恐慌反应机制 [10]。可以想象，我们的正义–反义协同作用可能反映了由这一恐慌机制引起的反义效应的非特异性增强。事实并非如此：共同注射与 unc-22 无关的 dsRNA 片段不能增强单链 unc-22-RNA 介导的抑制作用（数据未显示）。我们也研究了将 cis 放入一个单链片段后双链结构是否可以增强干扰能力。并未观察到这种增强作用：位于一个单链 unc-22 片段 5′ 或 3′ 的无关双链序列不能激发干扰。因此，只有 dsRNA 序列位于与目标基因同源的区域内时才能观察到对干扰的增强作用。

用 unc-22 dsRNA 干扰产生的表型非常特殊。注射动物的后代表现出的行为非常类似于 unc-22 功能缺失突变体。我们用表型明确的其他三个基因来评价 dsRNA 效应的目标特异性（图 1 和表 1）。unc-54 编码的体壁肌肉重链同工型肌球蛋白是完整肌肉收缩所必需的 [7,11,12]；fem-1 编码的锚定蛋白重复包含蛋白在雌雄同体动物中是产生精子所必需的 [13,14]；hlh-1 编码的 myoD 家族蛋白的秀丽隐杆线虫同源物是维持适当的身体形状和运动能力所必需的 [15,16]。对于每个基因来说，注射与之相关的 dsRNA 后，后代表现出已知的无效突变体表型，而提纯的单链 RNA 不能产生显著干扰。dsRNA 注射产生的所有表型皆符合对应基因干扰所预期的表型，仅有一个例外。对此例外（unc54C 片段导致胚胎及幼虫发育阻碍，这在 unc-54 无效突变体中未曾见过）作以下说明：这个片段覆盖高度保守的肌球蛋白分子马达结构域，因此预计它会干扰其他高度相关的肌球蛋白重链基因 [17]。该 unc54C 片段也是我们所有实验数据中唯一出现的例外，其他 18 个 dsRNA 片段所出现的效应均可见于先前已知的无效突变表型中（表 1 和我们未发表的结果）。

Fig. 1. Genes used to study RNA-mediated genetic interference in *C. elegans*. Intron-exon structure for genes used to test RNA-mediated inhibition are shown (grey and filled boxes, exons; open boxes, introns; patterned and striped boxes, 5' and 3' untranslated regions. *unc-22*. ref. 9, *unc*-54, ref. 12, *fem-1*, ref. 14, and *hlh-1*, ref. 15). Each segment of a gene tested for RNA interference is designated with the name of the gene followed by a single letter (for example, *unc22C*). These segments are indicated by bars and upper-case letters above and below each gene. Segments derived from genomic DNA are shown above the gene; segments derived from cDNA are shown below the gene. NLS, nuclear-localization sequence; MtLS, mitochondrial localization sequence.

The pronounced phenotypes seen following dsRNA injection indicate that interference effects are occurring in a high fraction of cells. The phenotypes seen in *unc-54* and *hlh-1* null mutants, in particular, are known to result from many defective muscle cells[11,16]. To examine interference effects of dsRNA at a cellular level, we used a transgenic line expressing two different green fluorescent protein (GFP)-derived fluorescent-reporter proteins in body muscle. Injection of dsRNA directed to *gfp* produced marked decreases in the fraction of fluorescent cells (Fig. 2). Both reporter proteins were absent from the affected cells, whereas the few cells that were fluorescent generally expressed both GFP proteins.

Fig. 2. Analysis of RNA-interference effects in individual cells. Fluorescence micrographs show progeny of injected animals from GFP-reporter strain PD4251. **a-c**, Progeny of animals injected with a control RNA (double-stranded (ds)-*unc22A*). **a**, Young larva, **b**, adult, **c**, adult body wall at high magnification. These GFP patterns appear identical to patterns in the parent strain, with prominent fluorescence in nuclei (nuclear-localized GFP-LacZ) and mitochondria (mitochondrially targeted GFP). **d-f**, Progeny of

图 1. 用于研究秀丽隐杆线虫中 RNA 介导的遗传性干扰的基因。显示了用于测试 RNA 介导的抑制作用的基因内含子–外显子结构(灰色及填充的方框,外显子;空白的方框,内含子;有图案和条纹的方框,5′ 和 3′ 非翻译区。unc-22,参考文献 9;unc-54,参考文献 12;fem-1,参考文献 14;hlh-1,参考文献 15)。用于测试 RNA 干扰的基因片段用基因名加一个字母表示(如 unc22C)。这些片段用横条标出,并且在每个基因上部或下部用大写字母表示。从基因组 DNA 得到的片段在基因上方显示;从 cDNA 得到的片段在基因下方显示。NLS,核定位序列;MtLS,线粒体定位序列。

dsRNA 注射后所观察到的明显表型说明在大量细胞中发生了干扰效应。特别是已经知道在 unc-54 和 hlh-1 无效突变体中见到的表型是源自众多缺陷型肌细胞[11,16]。为了在细胞水平上检验 dsRNA 的干扰效果,我们使用了一个转基因株,它可以在肌肉中表达两种绿色荧光蛋白(GFP)衍生的荧光报告蛋白。注射 dsRNA 直接导致在表达绿色荧光的细胞(图 2)内 gfp 荧光强度的显著下降。两个报告蛋白从受影响的细胞中消失,而少量有荧光的细胞基本都表达两种 GFP 蛋白。

图 2. 在单个细胞中分析 RNA 干扰效应。荧光显微图显示了注射 GFP 报告品系 PD4251 的动物后代。a~c,注射对照 RNA(双链(ds)-unc22A)的动物后代。a,年轻幼虫,b,成虫,c,高倍放大的成虫体壁。这些子代的 GFP 表达情况与亲本一致,核(核定位 GFP-LacZ)和线粒体(线粒体靶标 GFP)中均具有显著的荧光。d~f,注射 ds-gfpG 的动物后代。d 中幼虫只可见一个活性细胞,而 e、f 中的成虫的

animals injected with ds-*gfp*G. Only a single active cell is seen in the larva in **d**, whereas the entire vulval musculature expresses active GFP in the adult animal in **e. f**, Two rare GFP-positive cells in an adult: both cells express both nuclear-targeted GFP-LacZ and mitochondrial GFP. **g-i**, Progeny of animals injected with *ds-lacZ*L RNA: mitochondrial-targeted GFP seems unaffected, while the nuclear-targeted GFP-LacZ is absent from almost all cells (for example, see larva in **g**). **h**, A typical adult, with nuclear GFP-LacZ lacking in almost all body-wall muscles but retained in vulval muscles. Scale bars represent 20 μm.

The mosaic pattern observed in the *gfp*-interference experiments was nonrandom. At low doses of dsRNA, we saw frequent interference in the embryonically derived muscle cells that are present when the animal hatches. The interference effect in these differentiated cells persisted throughout larval growth: these cells produced little or no additional GFP as the affected animals grew. The 14 postembryonically derived striated muscles are born during early larval stages and these were more resistant to interference. These cells have come through additional divisions (13–14 divisions versus 8–9 divisions for embryonic muscles[18,19]). At high concentrations of *gfp* dsRNA, we saw interference in virtually all striated body-wall muscles, with occasional lone escaping cells, including cells born during both embryonic and postembryonic development. The non-striated vulval muscles, which are born during late larval development, appeared to be resistant to interference at all tested concentrations of injected dsRNA.

We do not yet know the mechanism of RNA-mediated interference in *C. elegans*. Some observations, however, add to the debate about possible targets and mechanisms.

First, dsRNA segments corresponding to various intron and promoter sequences did not produce detectable interference (Table 1). Although consistent with interference at a post-transcriptional level, these experiments do not rule out interference at the level of the gene.

Second, we found that injection of dsRNA produces a pronounced decrease or elimination of the endogenous mRNA transcript (Fig. 3). For this experiment, we used a target transcript (*mex-3*) that is abundant in the gonad and early embryos[20], in which straightforward *in situ* hybridization can be performed[5]. No endogenous *mex-3* mRNA was observed in animals injected with a dsRNA segment derived from *mex-3*. In contrast, animals into which purified *mex-3* antisense RNA was injected retained substantial endogenous mRNA levels (Fig. 3d).

Third, dsRNA-mediated interference showed a surprising ability to cross cellular boundaries. Injection of dsRNA (for *unc-22*, *gfp* or *lacZ*) into the body cavity of the head or tail produced a specific and robust interference with gene expression in the progeny brood (Table 2). Interference was seen in the progeny of both gonad arms, ruling out the occurrence of a transient "nicking" of the gonad in these injections. dsRNA injected into the body cavity or gonad of young adults also produced gene-specific interference in somatic tissues of the injected animal (Table 2).

整个外阴肌肉都表达活性 GFP，成虫中仅有两个 GFP 活性细胞：两个细胞都表达活性核靶标 GFP-LacZ 和线粒体靶标 GFP。g~i，注射 ds-*lacZL* RNA 的动物代代：线粒体靶标 GFP 好像不受影响，而核靶标 GFP-LacZ 在几乎所有细胞中都缺失了（例如，见 g 中的幼虫）。h，一个典型的成虫，其核靶标 GFP-LacZ 几乎在所有体壁肌肉都缺失但仍存在于外阴肌肉中。比例尺代表 20 μm。

gfp 干扰实验中观察到的镶嵌状图像不是随机的。在低剂量 dsRNA 时，我们经常看到动物孵化时会出现胚胎源的肌肉细胞发生干扰。不同分化细胞中的干扰效应在整个幼虫成长过程中持续发生：这些细胞在受影响动物的生长过程中很少产生或不产生额外的 GFP。14 个源自胚胎后期的横纹肌在幼虫早期阶段产生并且更能抵抗干扰。这些细胞进行额外的分裂（13~14 次分裂，胚胎源肌肉为 8~9 次分裂 [18,19]）。在高浓度 *gfp* dsRNA 作用时，我们在所有体壁横纹肌中都看到了干扰，只有个别漏网的细胞，包括在胚胎发育和胚胎后期发育过程中出现的细胞。出现于幼虫发育晚期的外阴非横纹肌，似乎在所有检测的 dsRNA 注射浓度下都不发生干扰。

我们还不知道秀丽隐杆线虫中 RNA 介导的干扰机理。然而，一些观察结果增加到对可能靶标和机制方面的讨论中。

第一，对应于各种内含子和启动子序列的 dsRNA 片段没有产生可检测到的干扰效应（表 1）。虽然这支持了干扰发生在转录后水平的观点，但这些实验不能排除基因水平上的干扰。

第二，我们发现注射 dsRNA 导致内源 mRNA 转录本明显减少或消失（图 3）。在这个实验中，我们选用目标转录本（*mex-3*），它在生殖腺和早期胚胎中含量很丰富 [20]，在早期胚胎中可以直接进行原位杂交 [5]。在注射了来自 *mex-3* 的 dsRNA 片段的动物体内没有观察到内源性的 *mex-3* mRNA。相反，注射了纯化的 *mex-3* 反义 RNA 的动物维持基本的内源 mRNA 水平（图 3d）。

第三，dsRNA 介导的干扰显示了穿过细胞边界的惊人能力。头部或尾部体腔内注射 dsRNA（*unc-22*、*gfp* 或 *lacZ*）对孵化后代基因表达产生了特异的、稳定的干扰（表 2）。干扰主要出现在具两个性腺的后代中，且排除了在这些注射中发生短暂的"切口"的可能性。将 dsRNA 注射到年轻成虫的体腔或生殖腺后，在被注射动物的体壁组织内也产生了基因特异性干扰（表 2）。

Fig. 3. Effects of *mex-3* RNA interference on levels of the endogenous mRNA. Interference contrast micrographs show *in situ* hybridization in embryos. The 1,262-nt *mex-3* cDNA clone[20] was divided into two segments, *mex-3A* and *mex-3B*, with a short (325-nt) overlap (similar results were obtained in experiments with no overlap between interfering and probe segments). *mex-3B* antisense or dsRNA was injected into the gonads of adult animals, which were fed for 24 h before fixation and *in situ* hybridization (ref. 5; B. Harfe and A.F., unpublished observations). The *mex-3B* dsRNA produced 100% embryonic arrest, whereas > 90% of embryos produced after the antisense injections hatched. Antisense probes for the *mex-3A* portion of *mex-3* were used to assay distribution of the endogenous *mex-3* mRNA (dark stain). Four-cell-stage embryos are shown; similar results were observed from the one to eight cell stage and in the germ line of injected adults. **a**, Negative control showing lack of staining in the absence of the hybridization probe. **b**, Embryo from uninjected parent (showing normal pattern of endogenous *mex-3* RNA[20]). **c**, Embryo from a parent injected with purified *mex-3B* antisense RNA. These embryos (and the parent animals) retain the *mex-3* mRNA, although levels may be somewhat less than wild type. **d**, Embryo from a parent injected with dsRNA corresponding to *mex-3B*; no *mex-3* RNA is detected. Each embryo is approximately 50 μm in length.

Table 2. Effect of site of injection on interference in injected animals and their progeny

dsRNA	Site of injection	Injected-animal phenotype	Progeny phenotype
None	Gonad or body cavity	No twitching	No twitching
None	Gonad or body cavity	Strong nuclear and mitochondrial GFP expression	Strong nuclear and mitochondrial GFP expression
unc22B	Gonad	Weak twitchers	Strong twitchers
unc22B	Body-cavity head	Weak twitchers	Strong twitchers
unc22B	Body-cavity tail	Weak twitchers	Strong twitchers
gfpG	Gonad	Lower nuclear and mitochondrial GFP expression	Rare or absent nuclear and mitochondrial GFP expression
gfpG	Body-cavity tail	Lower nuclear and mitochondrial GFP expression	Rare or absent nuclear and mitochondrial GFP expression
lacZL	Gonad	Lower nuclear GFP expression	Rare or absent nuclear-GFP expression
lacZL	Body-cavity tail	Lower nuclear GFP expression	Rare or absent nuclear-GFP expression

The GFP-reporter strain PD4251, which expresses both mitochondrial GFP and nuclear GFP-LacZ, was used for injections. The use of this strain allowed simultaneous assay for interference with *gfp* (fainter overall fluorescence), *lacZ* (loss of nuclear fluorescence) and *unc-22* (twitching). Body-cavity injections into the tail region were carried out to minimize accidental injection of the gonad; equivalent results have been observed with injections into the anterior body cavity. An equivalent set of injections was also performed into a single gonad arm. The entire progeny broods showed phenotypes identical to those described in Table 1. This included progeny of both injected and uninjected gonad arms. Injected animals were scored three days after recovery and showed somewhat less dramatic phenotypes than their progeny. This could be partly due to the persistence of products already present in the injected adult.

图 3. *mex-3* RNA 对内源性 mRNA 水平的干扰作用。干扰对比显微照片显示胚胎中的原位杂交结果。将 1,262 个核苷酸的 *mex-3* cDNA 克隆 [20] 分为两个片段，即 *mex-3A* 和 *mex-3B*，两者有一小段（325 个核苷酸）重叠（在干扰片段和探针片段之间无重叠的实验中也得到相似的结果）。将 *mex-3B* 反义链或 dsRNA 注射到成年动物生殖腺内，并在固定和进行原位杂交前饲养 24 小时（参考文献 5；哈弗和法厄，未发表的观察结果）。*mex-3B* dsRNA 可产生 100% 的胚胎抑制，然而大于 90% 的注射了反义链的胚胎都可以孵化。*mex-3* 的部分片段 *mex-3A* 的反义探针用于分析内源性 *mex-3* mRNA（深染色）的分布。四细胞期的胚胎被显示出来。在单细胞期到八细胞期和注射的成虫生殖系中都观察到相似结果。**a**，阴性对照显示无杂交探针时不染色。**b**，来自未注射亲本的胚胎（显示正常内源 *mex-3* RNA 模式 [20]）。**c**，亲本注射了纯化的 *mex-3B* RNA 反义链产生的胚胎。这些胚胎（和亲本动物）保留了 *mex-3* mRNA，但水平相对野型有一定程度降低。**d**，亲本注射了对应 *mex-3B* 的 dsRNA 产生的胚胎；未检测到 *mex-3* RNA。每个胚胎长度大约为 50 μm。

表 2. 在注射动物及其后代中注射位置对干扰的影响

dsRNA	注射位置	注射动物的表型	后代表型
无 无	生殖腺或体腔 生殖腺或体腔	不抽搐 核 GFP 及线粒体 GFP 的高表达	不抽搐 核 GFP 及线粒体 GFP 的高表达
unc22B *unc22B* *unc22B*	生殖腺 头部体腔 尾部体腔	弱抽搐 弱抽搐 弱抽搐	强烈抽搐 强烈抽搐 强烈抽搐
gfpG *gfpG*	生殖腺 尾部体腔	核 GFP 及线粒体 GFP 的低表达 核 GFP 及线粒体 GFP 的低表达	很少或无核 GFP 及线粒体 GFP 表达 很少或无核 GFP 及线粒体 GFP 表达
lacZL *lacZL*	生殖腺 尾部体腔	核 GFP 的低表达 核 GFP 的低表达	很少或无核 GFP 表达 很少或无核 GFP 表达

GFP 报告品系 PD4251 中既可以表达线粒体 GFP 又可以表达核 GFP-LacZ，因此被用于注射。使用这个品系可以同时分析 *gfp*（昏暗的整体荧光），*lacZ*（缺失核荧光）和 *unc-22*（抽搐）的干扰作用。注射到体腔尾部区域以最大限度减少偶然注射到生殖腺的情况；注射到前部体腔也观察到了相同的结果。还有相同的一组只注射到单个生殖腺臂。所有孵化后代呈现的表型与表 1 所描述的相同。包含了注射和未注射生殖腺臂的后代。注射的动物恢复三天后统计的表型一定程度上不如其后代明显。这可以部分归因于被注射的成年动物体内已有产物的持久性。注射双链 *unc22B* 后，部分注射动物在标准饲养条件下产生微弱抽搐（21 个动物中有 10 个）。左旋咪唑的处理导致这些动物发生

After injection of double-stranded *unc22B*, a fraction of the injected animals twitch weakly under standard growth conditions (10 out of 21 animals). Levamisole treatment led to twitching of 100% (21 out of 21) of these animals. Similar effects (not shown) were seen with double-stranded *unc22A*. Injections of double-stranded *gfpG* or double-stranded *lacZL* produced a dramatic decrease (but not elimination) of the corresponding GFP reporters. In some cases, isolated cells or parts of animals retained strong GFP activity. These were most frequently seen in the anterior region and around the vulva. Injections of double-stranded *gfpG* and double-stranded *lacZL* produced no twitching, whereas injections of double-stranded *unc22A* produced no change in the GFP-fluorescence pattern.

The use of dsRNA injection adds to the tools available for studying gene function in *C. elegans*. In particular, it should now be possible functionally to analyse many interesting coding regions[21] for which no specific function has been defined. Although the effects of dsRNA-mediated interference are potent and specific we have observed several limitations that should be taken into account when designing RNA-interference-based experiments. First, a sequence shared between several closely related genes may interfere with several members of the gene family. Second, it is likely that a low level of expression will resist RNA-mediated interference for some or all genes, and that a small number of cells will likewise escape these effects.

Genetic tools are available for only a few organisms. Double-stranded RNA could conceivably mediate interference more generally in other nematodes, in other invertebrates, and, potentially, in vertebrates. RNA interference might also operate in plants: several studies have suggested that inverted-repeat structures or characteristics of dsRNA viruses are involved in transgene-dependent co-suppression in plants[22,23].

There are several possible mechanisms for RNA interference in *C. elegans*. A simple antisense model is not likely: annealing between a few injected RNA molecules and excess endogenous transcripts would not be expected to yield observable phenotypes. RNA-targeted processes cannot, however, be ruled out, as they could include a catalytic component. Alternatively, direct RNA-mediated interference at the level of chromatin structure or transcription could be involved. Interactions between RNA and the genome, combined with propagation of changes along chromatin, have been proposed in mammalian X-chromosome inactivation and plant-gene co-suppression[22,24]. If RNA interference in *C. elegans* works by such a mechanism, it would be new in targeting regions of the template that are present in the final mRNA (as we observed no phenotypic interference using intron or promoter sequences). Whatever their target, the mechanisms underlying RNA interference probably exist for a biological purpose. Genetic interference by dsRNA could be used by the organism for physiological gene silencing. Likewise, the ability of dsRNA to work at a distance from the site of injection, and particularly to move into both germline and muscle cells, suggests that there is an effective RNA-transport mechanism in *C. elegans*.

Methods

RNA synthesis and microinjection. RNA was synthesized from phagemid clones by using T3

100% 的抽搐（21 个中有 21 个）。在双链 unc22A 实验中出现了类似结果（未显示）。注射双链 gfpG 或双链 lacZL 产生的相应 GFP 报告物明显减少（但未消失）。在某些情况下分离的细胞或部分动物体仍有很强的 GFP 活性，这在前部区域和外阴周围最为常见。注射双链 gfpG 和双链 lacZL 不产生抽搐，而注射双链 unc22A 后荧光模式不发生改变。

dsRNA 注射的使用为研究秀丽隐杆线虫基因功能增加了可利用的工具。特别是它可以用于针对许多研究者感兴趣但具体功能尚未确定的编码区的功能分析。虽然 dsRNA 介导的干扰效应很强并具有特异性，但我们也观察到在设计以 RNA 干扰为基础的实验时应考虑的一些局限性。第一，几个紧密相关的基因之间共享的一段序列可以干扰这个基因家族的几个成员。第二，似乎低水平表达可以使部分或全部基因对抗 RNA 介导的干扰，而且少量细胞也可借此逃避 RNA 干扰作用。

遗传工具仅对很少的生物体适用。可以想象双链 RNA 可以更普遍地在其他线虫、无脊椎动物，甚至也可能在脊椎动物中介导干扰效应。RNA 干扰在植物中也可以操作：一些研究提示植物中依赖于转基因的共抑制涉及反向重复结构或 dsRNA 病毒特征 [22,23]。

秀丽隐杆线虫的 RNA 干扰存在几种可能的机制。而简单的反义链模型也似乎不大可能：少量注射的 RNA 分子和过量的内源转录本之间发生退火，估计不能产生可观察到的表型。然而，不能排除以 RNA 为目标的过程中可能包括催化组分。也许，RNA 直接介导的干扰也包括了发生在染色质和转录水平的作用。RNA 和基因组之间的相互作用，伴随着染色质的增殖变化，被认为与哺乳动物 X 染色体失活和植物基因共抑制有关 [22,24]。如果秀丽隐杆线虫研究中的 RNA 干扰是这样的机制，在最终的 mRNA 中表现的应该是新的模板靶标区域（因为我们用内含子和启动子序列时没有观察到表型干扰）。不管它们的目标是什么，RNA 干扰机制的存在可能具有某种生物学目的。dsRNA 产生的遗传干扰可被有机体用于生理基因沉默。同样，dsRNA 能够在距注射位置一定距离处产生作用，尤其是能进入生殖腺和肌肉细胞，这表明秀丽隐杆线虫体内存在有效的 RNA 转移机制。

方　法

RNA 合成和微量注射　使用 T3 和 T7 聚合酶从噬菌粒中合成了 RNA[6]。然后通过两个

and T7 polymerase[6]. Templates were then removed with two sequential DNase treatments. When sense-, antisense-, and mixed-RNA populations were to be compared, RNAs were further purified by electrophoresis on low-gelling-temperature agarose. Gel-purified products appeared to lack many of the minor bands seen in the original "sense" and "antisense" preparations. Nonetheless, RNA species comprising < 10% of purified RNA preparations would not have been observed. Without gel purification, the "sense" and "antisense" preparations produced notable interference. This interference activity was reduced or eliminated upon gel purification. In contrast, sense-plus-antisense mixtures of gel-purified and non-gel-purified RNA preparations produced identical effects.

Sense/antisense annealing was carried out in injection buffer (ref. 27) at 37 °C for 10–30 min. Formation of predominantly double-stranded material was confirmed by testing migration on a standard (nondenaturing) agarose gel: for each RNA pair, gel mobility was shifted to that expected for dsRNA of the appropriate length. Co-incubation of the two strands in a lower-salt buffer (5 mM Tris-Cl, pH 7.5, 0.5 mM EDTA) was insufficient for visible formation of dsRNA *in vitro*. Non-annealed sense-plus-antisense RNAs for *unc22B* and *gfpG* were tested for RNA interference and found to be much more active than the individual single strands, but twofold to fourfold less active than equivalent preannealed preparations.

After preannealing of the single strands for *unc22A*, the single electrophoretic species, corresponding in size to that expected for the dsRNA, was purified using two rounds of gel electrophoresis. This material retained a high degree of interference activity.

Except where noted, injection mixes were constructed so that animals would receive an average of 0.5×10^6 to 1.0×10^6 RNA molecules. For comparisons of sense, antisense, and double-stranded RNA activity, equal masses of RNA were injected (that is, dsRNA was used at half the molar concentration of the single strands). Numbers of molecules injected per adult are approximate and based on the concentration of RNA in the injected material (estimated from ethidium bromide staining) and the volume of injected material (estimated from visible displacement at the site of injection). It is likely that this volume will vary several-fold between individual animals; this variability would not affect any of the conclusions drawn from this work.

Analysis of phenotypes. Interference with endogenous genes was generally assayed in a wild-type genetic background (N2). Features analysed included movement, feeding, hatching, body shape, sexual identity, and fertility. Interference with *gfp* (ref. 25) and *lacZ* activity was assessed using *C. elegans* strain PD4251. This strain is a stable transgenic strain containing an integrated array (ccIs4251) made up of three plasmids: pSAK4 (*myo-3* promoter driving mitochondrially targeted GFP); pSAK2 (*myo-3* promoter driving a nuclear-targeted GFP-LacZ fusion); and a *dpy-20* subclone[26] as a selectable marker. This strain produces GFP in all body muscles, with a combination of mitochondrial and nuclear localization. The two distinct compartments are easily distinguished in these cells, allowing easy distinction between cells expressing both, either, or neither of the original GFP constructs.

Gonadal injection was done as described[27]. Body-cavity injections followed a similar procedure, with needle insertion into regions of the head and tail beyond the positions of the two gonad arms. Injection into the cytoplasm of intestinal cells is also effective, and may be the least disruptive to the

连续的 DNase 处理将模板除去。当正义链、反义链和双链混合物进行比较时，通过低凝胶温度琼脂糖电泳进一步纯化 RNA。凝胶纯化产物似乎缺少在最初"正义链"和"反义链"制备物中看到的许多小条带。然而，包含 <10% 的纯化 RNA 制备物的 RNA 物质无法被观察到。不经过凝胶纯化时，"正义链"和"反义链"制备物会产生明显的干扰。这种干扰活性可被凝胶纯化降低或消除。相反，凝胶纯化的和未经凝胶纯化的正义链加反义链混合物能产生相同的作用。

37℃ 下在注射缓冲液 (参考文献 27) 中进行正义链/反义链退火 10~30 分钟。通过测试在标准 (非变性) 琼脂糖凝胶上的迁移来确定主要双链物质的形成：对每对 RNA，凝胶迁移到预期的 dsRNA 的适当位置。在低盐缓冲液 (5 mM Tris-Cl，pH 7.5，0.5 mM EDTA) 中共同孵育两条链，这不足以在体外形成可见的 dsRNA。用未经退火的 unc22B 和 gfpG 的有义链和反义链混合 RNA 测试 RNA 干扰，发现比单独用一个链的活性高很多，但比提前退火的制备物活性低 1/2 到 1/4。

unc22A 的单链提前退火后，将对应于预期的 dsRNA 大小的单一的电泳条带通过两轮凝胶电泳纯化。这种物质仍保持高度干扰活性。

除了特别指出的地方，构建的注射混合物能使动物平均接受 0.5×10^6 到 1.0×10^6 个 RNA 分子。为比较正义链、反义链和双链 RNA 活性，进行了等量的 RNA 注射 (即 dsRNA 的摩尔浓度为单链 RNA 的一半)。每个成虫注射的分子数量相互接近，分子数量取决于注射物中 RNA 的浓度 (通过溴化乙锭染色来确定) 和注射物体积 (通过注射位置的可见位移来确定)。这个体积在不同个体之间可能有几倍的变化；这一变化不影响本研究中得出的任何结论。

表型分析 内源基因的干扰一般在野生型遗传背景 (N2) 中分析。特征分析包括运动、进食、孵化、身体形态、性别特征和生殖能力。gfp (参考文献 25) 和 lacZ 的干扰活性用秀丽隐杆线虫品系 PD4251 进行评价。这个品系是稳定的转基因品系，包含一个融合序列 (ccIs4251)，由三个质粒组成：pSAK4 (myo-3 启动子启动以线粒体为靶标的 GFP)，pSAK2 (myo-3 启动子启动以核为靶标的 GFP-LacZ 融合子) 和一个 dpy-20 亚克隆 [26] 作为选择性标记。这个品系在全身肌肉中产生 GFP，并结合线粒体和核定位。这两个清楚的部位在这些细胞中很容易区分，在表达两种、表达其中一种和不表达初始 GFP 结构的细胞中都易于区分。

按照文献描述进行了生殖腺注射 [27]。按相似的步骤进行体腔注射，用针插入位于两个生殖腺臂上方的头部和尾部区域。注射到肠细胞的细胞质内也有效，同时可能对动物造成的

animal. After recovery and transfer to standard solid media, injected animals were transferred to fresh culture plates at 16-h intervals. This yields a series of semisynchronous cohorts in which it was straightforward to identify phenotypic differences. A characteristic temporal pattern of phenotypic severity is observed among progeny. First, there is a short "clearance" interval in which unaffected progeny are produced. These include impermeable fertilized eggs present at the time of injection. Second, after the clearance period, individuals that show the interference phenotype are produced. Third, after injected animals have produced eggs for several days, gonads can in some cases "revert" to produce incompletely affected or phenotypically normal progeny.

(**391**, 806-811; 1998)

Andrew Fire[*], **SiQun Xu**[*], **Mary K. Montgomery**[*], **Steven A. Kostas**[*†], **Samuel E. Driver**[‡] & **Craig C. Mello**[‡]

[*] Carnegie Institution of Washington, Department of Embryology, 115 West University Parkway, Baltimore, Maryland 21210, USA

[†] Biology Graduate Program, Johns Hopkins University, 3400 North Charles Street, Baltimore, Maryland 21218, USA

[‡] Program in Molecular Medicine, Department of Cell Biology, University of Massachusetts Cancer Center, Two Biotech Suite 213, 373 Plantation Street, Worcester, Massachusetts 01605, USA

Received 16 September; accepted 24 November 1997.

References:

1. Izant, J. & Weintraub, H. Inhibition of thymidine kinase gene expression by antisense RNA: a molecular approach to genetic analysis. *Cell* **36**, 1007-1015 (1984).
2. Nellen, W. & Lichtenstein, C. What makes an mRNA anti-sense-itive? *Trends Biochem. Sci.* **18**, 419-423 (1993).
3. Fire, A., Albertson, D., Harrison, S. & Moerman, D. Production of antisense RNA leads to effective and specific inhibition of gene expression in *C. elegans* muscle. *Development* **113**, 503-514 (1991).
4. Guo, S. & Kemphues, K. *par-1*, a gene required for establishing polarity in *C. elegans* embryos, encodes a putative Ser/Thr kinase that is asymmetrically distributed. *Cell* **81**, 611-620 (1995).
5. Seydoux, G. & Fire, A. Soma-germline asymmetry in the distributions of embryonic RNAs in *Caenorhabditis elegans*. *Development* **120**, 2823-2834 (1994).
6. Ausubel, F. *et al. Current Protocols in Molecular Biology* (Wiley, New York, 1990).
7. Brenner, S. The genetics of *Caenorhabditis elegans*. *Genetics* **77**, 71-94 (1974).
8. Moerman, D. & Baillie, D. Genetic organization in *Caenorhabditis* elegans: fine structure analysis of the *unc-22 gene*. *Genetics* **91**, 95-104 (1979).
9. Benian, G., L'Hernault, S. & Morris, M. Additional sequence complexity in the muscle gene, *unc-22*, and its encoded protein, twitchin, of *Caenorhabditis elegans*. *Genetics* **134**, 1097-1104 (1993).
10. Proud, C. PKR: a new name and new roles. *Trends Biochem. Sci.* **20**, 241-246 (1995).
11. Epstein, H., Waterston, R. & Brenner, S. A mutant affecting the heavy chain of myosin in *C. elegans. J. Mol. Biol.* **90**, 291-300 (1974).
12. Karn, J., Brenner, S. & Barnett, L. Protein structural domains in the *C. elegans unc-54* myosin heavy chain gene are not separated by introns. *Proc. Natl Acad. Sci. USA* **80**, 4253-4257 (1983).
13. Doniach, T. & Hodgkin, J. A. A sex-determining gene, *fem-1*, required for both male and hermaphrodite development in *C. elegans. Dev. Biol.* **106**, 223-235 (1984).
14. Spence, A., Coulson, A. & Hodgkin, J. The product of *fem-1*, a nematode sex-determining gene, contains a motif found in cell cycle control proteins and receptors for cell-cell interactions. *Cell* **60**, 981-990 (1990).
15. Krause, M., Fire, A., Harrison, S., Priess, J. & Weintraub, H. CeMyoD accumulation defines the body wall muscle cell fate during *C. elegans* embryogenesis. *Cell* **63**, 907-919 (1990).
16. Chen, L., Krause, M., Sepanski, M. & Fire, A. The *C. elegans* MyoD homolog *HLH-1* is essential for proper muscle function and complete morphogenesis. *Development* **120**, 1631-1641(1994).
17. Dibb, N. J., Maruyama, I. N., Krause, M. & Karn, J. Sequence analysis of the complete *Caenorhabditis elegans* myosin heavy chain gene family. *J. Mol. Biol.* **205**, 603-613 (1989).
18. Sulston, J., Schierenberg, E., White, J. & Thomson, J. The embryonic cell lineage of the nematode *Caenorhabditis elegans. Dev. Biol.* **100**, 64-119 (1983).
19. Sulston, J. & Horvitz, H. Postembyonic cell lineages of the nematode *Caenorhabditis elegans. Dev. Biol.* **82**, 41-55 (1977).
20. Draper, B. W., Mello, C. C., Bowerman, B., Hardin, J. & Priess, J. R. *MEX-3* is a KH domain protein that regulates blastomere identity in early *C. elegans* embryos. *Cell* **87**, 205-216 (1996).

损害最小。恢复并转移到标准固体培养基上后，注射的动物每间隔 16 小时转移到新鲜的培养平板上。这样产生的一系列半同步同生群可以直接用于鉴定表型差异。在后代中观察到表型严重的暂时性特征样式。首先，在一个短暂的"间隙"中产生不受影响的后代。这包括在注射时已出现的不透水的受精卵。第二，在这个间隙之后产生显示干扰表型的个体。第三，注射的动物产卵几天后生殖腺在某些情况下又"恢复"产生不完全受影响或表型正常的后代。

(高如丽 李梅 翻译；彭小忠 审稿)

21. Sulston, J. *et al.* The *C. elegans* genome sequencing project: a beginning. *Nature* **356**, 37-41 (1992).

22. Matzke, M. & Matzke, A. How and why do plants inactivate homologous (*trans*) genes? *Plant Physiol.* **107**, 679-685 (1995).

23. Ratcliff, F., Harrison, B. & Baulcombe, D. A similarity between viral defense and gene silencing in plants. *Science* **276**, 1558-1560 (1997).

24. Latham, K. X chromosome imprinting and inactivation in the early mammalian embryo. *Trends Genet.* **12**, 134-138 (1996).

25. Chalfie, M., Tu, Y., Euskirchen, G., Ward, W. & Prasher, D. Green fluorescent protein as a marker for gene expression. *Science* **263**, 802-805 (1994).

26. Clark, D., Suleman, D., Beckenbach, K., Gilchrist, E. & Baillie, D. Molecular cloning and characterization of the *dpy-20* gene of *C. elegans. Mol. Gen. Genet.* **247**, 367-378 (1995).

27. Mello, C. & Fire, A. DNA transformation. *Methods Cell Biol.* **48**, 451-482 (1995).

Supplementary information is available on *Nature*'s World-Wide Web site (http://www.nature.com) or as paper copy from Mary Sheehan at the London editorial office of *Nature*.

Acknowledgements. We thank A. Grishok, B. Harfe, M. Hsu, B. Kelly, J. Hsieh, M. Krause, M. Park, W. Sharrock, T. Shin, M. Soto and H. Tabara for discussion. This work was supported by the NIGMS (A.F.) and the NICHD (C.M.), and by fellowship and career awards from the NICHD (M.K.M.), NIGMS (S.K.), PEW charitable trust (C.M.), American Cancer Society (C.M.), and March of Dimes (C.M.).

Correspondence and requests for materials should be addressed to A.F. (e-mail: fire@mail1.ciwemb.edu).

Total Synthesis of Brevetoxin A

K. C. Nicolaou *et al.*

Editor's Note

The synthesis of "natural products" with complex molecular structures has long been a goal of organic chemists, partly to make pharmaceutically useful new substances but also to refine the synthetic tools at the chemist's disposal. Here K. C. Nicolaou of the Scripps Research Institute in California and his collaborators scale a new peak of the art, assembling the neurotoxin brevetoxin A that is produced by the algae responsible for the poisonous blooms known as red tides. This molecule has a carbon framework containing many ring structures, and contains 22 of the stereogenic centres—molecular groups with two mirror-image forms—that pose a particular challenge to organic chemists.

Brevetoxin A is the most potent neurotoxin secreted by *Gymnodinium breve Davis*, a marine organism often associated with harmful algal blooms known as "red tides"[1-3]. The compound, whose mechanism of action involves binding to and opening of sodium channels[4-7], is sufficiently toxic to kill fish at concentrations of nanograms per ml (refs 3, 4) and, after accumulation in filter-feeding shellfish, to poison human consumers. The precise pathway by which nature constructs brevetoxin A is at present unknown[8,9], but strategies for its total synthesis have been contemplated for some time. The synthetic challenge posed by brevetoxin A reflects the high complexity of its molecular structure: 10 oxygen atoms and a chain of 44 carbon atoms are woven into a polycyclic macromolecule that includes 10 rings (containing between 5 and 9 atoms) and 22 stereogenic centres. Particularly challenging are the 7-, 8- and 9-membered rings which allow the molecule to undergo slow conformational changes and force a 90° twist at one of its rings[1-6]. Here we describe the successful incorporation of methods that were specifically developed for the construction of these rings[10,11] into an overall strategy for the total synthesis of brevetoxin A in its naturally occurring form. The convergent synthesis reported here renders this scarce neurotoxin synthetically available and, more importantly, allows the design and synthesis of analogues for further biochemical studies.

FIGURE 1 shows the synthetic strategy for the construction of brevetoxin A (**1**, Fig. 1a) in bond disconnection (Fig. 1b) and retrosynthetic (Fig. 1c) formats. This analysis led to the expectation of using D-glucose (**4**, Fig. 1c) and D-mannose (**5**, Fig. 1c) as starting materials for the construction of the requisite BCDE (**2**, Fig. 1c) and GHIJ (**3**, Fig. 1c) advanced intermediates, respectively. The union of **2** and **3** under Horner–Wittig conditions was expected to furnish, in a highly convergent manner and after ring closure, the basic ring skeleton of the target molecule, from which brevetoxin A could be

短裸甲藻毒素 A 的全合成

尼科拉乌等

编者按

合成具有复杂分子结构的天然产物一直以来都是有机化学家的目标，这不仅是为了制造出药用的新物质，而且还可以更新供化学家使用的合成工具。在本篇文章中，加利福尼亚斯克里普斯研究所的尼科拉乌和他的同事们攀登上该领域的一座新高峰，合成出神经毒素短裸甲藻毒素 A。它是由恶性繁殖而引发赤潮的藻类产生的。这个分子具有包含很多环状结构的碳骨架，含有 22 个立体异构源中心——具有 2 种镜像形式的分子团——这对有机化学家们特别具有挑战性。

短裸甲藻毒素 A 是由短裸甲藻分泌的毒性最强的神经毒素，短裸甲藻是一种海洋生物，常与被称为"赤潮"的有害的藻华有关 [1-3]。短裸甲藻毒素 A 在浓度为纳克每毫升级别时就足以毒死鱼类（参考文献 3 和 4），它的作用机制涉及结合并开启钠离子通道 [4-7]。它经滤食性贝类积累后也可使人类食用者中毒。目前还不清楚自然界生成短裸甲藻毒素 A 的精确途径 [8,9]，但是我们对其全合成策略的深入探讨已经有一段时间了。短裸甲藻毒素 A 带来的合成挑战反映了其分子结构的高度复杂性：由 10 个氧原子和一条 44 个碳原子的链组成了一个含有 10 个环（含 5 到 9 个原子）和 22 个立体异构源中心的多环大分子。最富挑战性的是 7 元、8 元和 9 元环，它们使得分子进行缓慢的构象变化并迫使其中一个环发生了 90°的扭转 [1-6]。现在我们将阐述一种成功的方法组合，这是特别为全合成以天然形式存在的短裸甲藻毒素 A 而开发的构建环的整体策略 [10,11]。下面介绍的汇聚合成使得这种稀有神经毒素的合成得以实现，更重要的是可以为进一步的生物化学研究设计和合成类似物。

图 1 以键的切断（图 1b）和逆合成（图 1c）反应式的形式显示了短裸甲藻毒素 A（**1**，图 1a）的合成策略。这个分析提示我们可以用 D–葡萄糖（**4**，图 1c）和 D–甘露糖（**5**，图 1c）作为合成的起始原料，分别构建必需的 BCDE（**2**，图 1c）和 GHIJ（**3**，图 1c）高级中间体。经环的闭合后，以高度汇聚的方式将结构 **2** 和 **3** 在霍纳–维蒂希条件下连接有望提供目标分子的基本环状骨架，再通过去保护和官能团转化可以得到短裸甲藻毒素 A。在计划的开始阶段，我们通过分析可以明显地看到，虽

fashioned through deprotections and functional-group manipulations. At the outset of this project, it was also evident from this analysis that although the 5- and 6-membered rings of the target molecule could be derived via well-developed synthetic methods[12], the three larger rings were not easily accessible through conventional techniques. Thus, to construct the 7-, 8- and 9-membered rings we used two important reactions, namely the silver-promoted hydroxydithioketal cyclization reaction[10] (rings F and G) and the palladium-catalysed functionalization of lactones via coupling of their cyclic ketene acetal phosphates[11] (rings B, D and E), that were specifically developed for this purpose.

Fig. 1. Molecular structure (**a**), strategic bond disconnections (**b**), and retrosynthetic analysis (**c**) of brevetoxin A (**1**). Abbreviations for chemical groups: Me, methyl; Ph, phenyl; Tr, trityl; TBDPS, *t*-butyldiphenylsilyl; Et, ethyl; TBS, *t*-butyldimethylsilyl.

The synthesis of the BCDE ring system **2** (Figs 1c and 4) of brevetoxin A began with D-glucose (**4**, Fig. 2) and proceeded via intermediates **16** (Fig. 2) and **26** (Fig. 3). Thus, the D-glucose-derived bis(acetonide) **6**[13] (Fig. 2) was selectively cleaved with H_5IO_6 (ref. 14; for abbreviations see legends in figures) to afford the corresponding aldehyde, which reacted with MeMgBr leading to the expected secondary alcohol (84% overall yield). Swern oxidation of this alcohol, followed by reaction with allylmagnesium bromide in the presence of Ti(*i*-PrO)$_4$, led to the stereoselective formation of tertiary alcohol **7** (76.5% overall yield from **6**). Cleavage of the second acetonide moiety in **7** with EtSH-ZnCl$_2$ led to an open-chain thioketal, whose dibenzylation with NaH-BnBr and ring closure in the presence of I$_2$-aq.NaHCO$_3$ led smoothly to the 6-membered ring lactol **8** in 64.5% overall yield. Olefination of **8** with the appropriate stabilized Wittig reagent, followed by exposure to CSA

然目标分子中的 5 元和 6 元环能够用很成熟的合成方法得到[12]，但是采用传统技术制备三个更大的环就不那么容易了。因此，为了构建 7 元、8 元和 9 元环，我们特地发明并使用了下面两种重要的反应：银促进的羟基二硫缩酮环化反应[10]（F 和 G 环）和钯催化的经环状烯酮缩醛的磷酸酯的偶联反应对内酯的官能团化[11]（B、D 和 E 环）。

图 1. 短裸甲藻毒素 A(**1**)的分子结构(**a**)，键切断策略(**b**)和逆合成分析(**c**)。化学基团的缩略语：Me，甲基；Ph，苯基；Tr，三苯甲基；TBDPS，叔丁基二苯基硅基；Et，乙基；TBS，叔丁基二甲基硅基。

从 D–葡萄糖(**4**，图 2)开始，经由中间体 **16**(图 2)和中间体 **26**(图 3)合成短裸甲藻毒素 A 中的 BCDE 环系 **2**(图 1c 和图 4)。其过程是，用高碘酸选择性裂解由 D–葡萄糖衍生的双缩丙酮化合物 **6**[13]（图 2）得到相应的醛(参考文献 14；缩写请见图中示例)，该醛接着与甲基溴化镁发生反应得到预期的仲醇(总收率为 84%)。此醇经过斯文氧化反应后，在四异丙氧基钛存在的条件下与烯丙基溴化镁反应，立体选择性地形成叔醇化合物 **7**(从 **6** 开始的总收率为 76.5%)。用乙硫醇–氯化锌裂解 **7** 上的第二个丙酮缩合部位得到一个开链的硫缩酮，再用氢化钠–溴化苄进行双苄基化，接着在碘–碳酸氢钠水溶液存在的条件下进行闭环，以 64.5% 的总收率顺利地得到了六元环的内半缩醛 **8**。用适当稳定化的维蒂希试剂对 **8** 进行烯化，接着用

furnished, stereoselectively, the tetrahydropyran system **9** (81% for two steps). Condensation of ketone **9** with $CH_2=C(OMe)OTBS$ (ref. 15) in the presence of $ZnBr_2$ gave compound **10** as a mixture of diastereoisomers (inconsequential) in 93% yield. The terminal olefin in **10** was then converted to a methyl ketone via an oxymercuration-palladation procedure[16] (90% yield), and thence to a vinyl triflate by reaction with NaHMDS-PhNTf$_2$ furnishing intermediate **11** (93% yield). The latter compound (**11**) was coupled[17] with the zinc reagent $IZnCH_2CH_2CO_2Me$ in the presence of $Pd(Ph_3P)_4$ catalyst to extend the "left-hand" side-chain (85% yield). The product was then sequentially deprotected (LiOH; then Li-in liquid NH_3) to afford the dihydroxydicarboxylic acid **12**. Yamaguchi[18] bis(lactonization) of **12** allowed the formation of bis(lactone) **13** (78.5% yield for three steps). Desilylation of **13** with HF·pyridine, followed by dehydration in the presence of Martin's sulphurane ($[PhC(CF_3)_2O]_2SPh_2$) (ref. 19), furnished the doubly unsaturated crystalline bis(lactone) **14** in 81% overall yield. (The melting point of **14** was 158–159 °C (ether/hexane)). An X-ray crystallographic analysis confirmed the structure of **14**. Sequential hydrogenation of the two olefinic bonds in **14**, first with Wilkinson's catalyst [(Ph$_3$P)$_3$RhCl] (**15**, 99% yield, ~4:1 ratio)[20] and then with Pd/C (**16**, 95% yield, ~19:1 ratio), established the two methyl groups in their correct stereochemical arrangement. Compound **16** was separated from its minor diastereoisomers by silica-gel flash chromatography.

Fig. 2. Construction of the BCD bis-lactone system **16**. Reagents and conditions as follows. (a) See ref. 13; (b) H_5IO_6 (1.2 equiv.), EtOAc, 25 °C, 1 h; (c) MeMgBr (5.0 equiv.), Et$_2$O, 0 °C, 2 h, 84% for two

10–樟脑磺酸进行处理，得到立体选择性的四氢吡喃类化合物 **9**(两步收率为 81%)。在溴化锌存在的条件下用 1–甲氧基乙烯基叔丁基二甲基硅基醚(参考文献 15)与酮 **9** 进行缩合，以 93% 的收率得到非对映异构体(无关紧要)的混合物 **10**。**10** 中的末端烯烃经羟汞化–钯化过程转化为甲基酮[16](收率为 90%)，接着与六甲基二硅基氨基钠和 N–苯基双三氟甲磺酰亚胺反应再转换成三氟甲磺酸乙烯酯，从而得到中间体 **11**(收率为 93%)。化合物 **11** 在催化剂四(三苯基膦)钯存在的条件下与锌试剂 2–甲氧羰基乙基碘化锌发生偶联反应[17]得到"左手"侧链延长的产物(收率为 85%)。接着对这个产物依次去保护(先是氢氧化锂，然后是锂的液氨溶液)，得到二羟基二羧酸化合物 **12**。对化合物 **12** 进行山口[18]双内酯化反应得到双内酯化合物 **13**(三步收率为 78.5%)。用氟化氢·吡啶对双内酯化合物 **13** 进行脱硅基化，然后在马丁硫烷([PhC(CF₃)₂O]₂SPh₂)的存在下脱水(参考文献 19)，得到双不饱和的双内酯化合物 **14** 的晶体(总收率为 81%)。**14** 的熔点为 158～159℃(乙醚/己烷)，由 X–射线晶体分析确定了其结构。依次对 **14** 的两个烯键加氢：先用威尔金森催化剂 [(Ph₃P)₃RhCl] 得到化合物 **15**(收率为 99%，比例约为 4∶1)[20]，再用钯/碳得到化合物 **16**(收率为 95%，比例约为 19∶1)，实现了两个甲基在立体化学上的正确排列。化合物 **16** 通过硅胶快速色谱法与其含量较少的非对映异构体分离开。

图 2. BCD 双内酯系 16 的构建过程。所用试剂和反应条件如下。(a) 参见文献 13；(b) 高碘酸(1.2 当量)，乙酸乙酯，25℃，1 h；(c) 甲基溴化镁(5.0 当量)，乙醚，0℃，2 h，两步收率为 84%；(d) 草酰

steps; (d) oxalyl chloride (1.8 equiv.), DMSO (2.2 equiv.), Et₃N (5.0 equiv.), CH₂Cl₂, −78 °C, 1 h, 85%; (e) AllylMgBr (1.5 equiv.), Ti(i-PrO)₄ (1.5 equiv.), THF, −78 °C, 2 h, 90%; (f) EtSH (20.0 equiv.), ZnCl₂ (5.0 equiv.), CH₂Cl₂, 0 °C, 1 h, 94%; (g) NaH (3.0 equiv.), BnBr (2.0 equiv.), n-Bu₄N⁺I⁻ (cat), THF, 0 °C, 5 h, 80%; (h) I₂ (3.3 equiv.), NaHCO₃ (6.5 equiv.), acetone, 25 °C, 1 h, 86%; (i) Ph₃P=CHCOMe (1.5 equiv.), toluene, 110 °C, 4 h; (j) CSA (0.1 equiv.), CHCl₃, 25 °C, 1 h, 81% for two steps; (k) CH₂=C(OMe)OTBS (1.5 equiv.), ZnBr₂ (0.5 equiv.), Et₂O, −78 °C, 2 h, 93%; (l) Hg(OAc)₂ (1.1 equiv.), MeOH, 25 °C, 2 h; (m) PdCl₂ (0.1 equiv.), LiCl (0.2 equiv.), CuCl₂ (3.0 equiv.), MeOH, 70 °C, 2 h, 90% for two steps; (n) NaHMDS (1.2 equiv.), PhNTf₂ (1.2 equiv.), THF, −78 °C, 1 h, 93%; (o) IZn(CH₂)₂CO₂Me (2.0 equiv.), Pd(Ph₃P)₄ (0.05 equiv.), DMA:benzene (1:10), 25 °C, 2 h, 85%; (p) LiOH (10.0 equiv.), THF:H₂O:MeOH (3:1:1), 65 °C, 3 h, 96%; (q) Li (12.0 equiv.), NH₃ (liq.), EtOH, −78 °C, 15 min; (r) 2,4,6-trichlorobenzoyl chloride (2.2 equiv.), Et₃N (4.0 equiv.), THF, 0 °C, 30 min; then 4-DMAP (6.0 equiv.), benzene, 75 °C, 4 h, 82% for two steps; (s) HF · pyridine (3.0 equiv.), CH₂Cl₂, 0 °C, 3 h; (t) [PhC(CF₃)₂O]₂SPh₂ (1.5 equiv.), CH₂Cl₂, 0 °C, 15 min, 81% for two steps; (u) H₂, (Ph₃P)₃RhCl (0.1 equiv.), benzene, 25 °C, 5 h, 99%, ~4:1 ratio; (v) H₂, 10% Pd/C (0.1 equiv.), EtOAc, 25 °C, 12 h, 95%, ~19:1 ratio. CSA, 10-camphorsulphonic acid; DMA, N,N-dimethylacetamide; 4-DMAP, 4-N-dimethylaminopyridine; DMF, N,N-dimethylformamide; DMSO, dimethylsulphoxide; NMO, 4-methylmorpholine-N-oxide; TBS, t-BuMe₂Si; THF, tetrahydrofuran; Tf, triflate. NaHMDS, sodium hexamethyldisilazide; PhNTf₂, N-phenyltrifluoromethanesulphonimide. For selected physical data for compound **14**, see Supplementary Information.

Fig. 3. Construction of the BCDE lactone **26**. Reagents and conditions as follows. (a) KHMDS (4.0 equiv.), (PhO)₂P(O)Cl (6.0 equiv.), HMPA (6.0 equiv.), THF, −78 °C, 1 h, 80%; (b) Me₃SnSnMe₃ (8.0 equiv.), LiCl (6.0 equiv.), Pd(Ph₃P)₄ (0.1 equiv.), THF, 70 °C, 2 h, 81%; (c) n-BuLi (1.55 M in hexanes, 4.0 equiv.), Cu-C≡C-n-Pr (4.4 equiv.), HMPT (8.8 equiv.), THF, −78 → −30 °C, 2 h; (d) TfOCH₂CH₂OBn (7.0 equiv.), THF, −78 → −30 °C, 12 h, 65% for two steps; (e) thexylborane (4.0 equiv.), THF, −30 → 0 °C, 3 h; then H₂O₂ (20.0 equiv.), NaOH (20.0 equiv.), H₂O, 0 °C, 2 h, 80%; (f) t-BuPh₂SiCl (1.3 equiv.), imidazole (3.0 equiv.), DMF, 25 °C, 8 h, 90% (five recycles); (g) 10% Pd/C (10% wt. equiv.), H₂, MeOH, 25 °C, 2 h, 93%; (h) cyclohexanone dimethylketal (1.3 equiv.), PPTS (0.1 equiv.), CH₂Cl₂, 25 °C, 2 h, 85%; (i) PivCl (1.3 equiv.), 4-DMAP (1.4 equiv.), CH₂Cl₂, 25 °C, 0.5 h, 99%; (j) CSA (0.1 equiv.), MeOH:CH₂Cl₂ (2:1), 25 °C, 0.5 h, 88%; (k) TrCl · 4-DMAP (4.0 equiv.), CH₂Cl₂, 40 °C, 12 h, 95%; (l) Ac₂O (1.5 equiv.), 4-DMAP (0.5 equiv.), CH₂Cl₂, 25 °C, 15 min, 99%; (m) TFA (1.5 equiv.), MeOH (10 equiv.), CH₂Cl₂, 25 °C, 30 min, 90%; (n) TPAP (0.1 equiv.), NMO (2.0 equiv.), CH₂Cl₂, 25 °C, 30 min, 97%; (o) ⁻Br⁺PPh₃(CH₂)₃CO₂Me (2.5 equiv.), KHMDS (2.0 equiv.), THF, −78 °C, 1 h, 83%; (p) LiOH (10.0 equiv.), THF:H₂O:MeOH

氯（1.8 当量），二甲基亚砜（2.2 当量），三乙胺（5.0 当量），二氯甲烷，−78℃，1 h，收率为 85%；(e)
烯丙基溴化镁（1.5 当量），四异丙氧基钛（1.5 当量），四氢呋喃，−78℃，2 h，收率为 90%；(f) 乙硫
醇（20.0 当量），氯化锌（5.0 当量），二氯甲烷，0℃，1 h，收率为 94%；(g) 氢化钠（3.0 当量），溴化苄
（2.0 当量），碘化四正丁基铵（催化剂），四氢呋喃，0℃，5 h，收率为 80%；(h) 碘（3.3 当量），碳酸氢
钠（6.5 当量），丙酮，25℃，1 h，收率为 86%；(i) 2−氧代亚丙基三苯基膦（1.5 当量），甲苯，110℃，
4 h；(j) 10−樟脑磺酸（0.1 当量），三氯甲烷，25℃，1 h，两步收率为 81%；(k) 1−甲氧基乙烯基叔丁
基二甲基硅基醚（1.5 当量），溴化锌（0.5 当量），乙醚，−78℃，2 h，收率为 93%；(l) 乙酸汞（1.1 当
量），甲醇，25℃，2 h；(m) 氯化钯（0.1 当量），氯化锂（0.2 当量），氯化铜（3.0 当量），甲醇，70℃，2
h，两步收率为 90%；(n) 六甲基二硅基氨基钠（1.2 当量），N−苯基双三氟甲磺酰胺（1.2 当量），四
氢呋喃，−78℃，1 h，收率为 93%；(o) 2−甲氧羰基乙碘化锌（2.0 当量），四（三苯基膦）钯（0.05 当
量），N,N−二甲基乙酰胺：苯（1:10），25℃，2 h，收率为 85%；(p) 氢氧化锂（10.0 当量），四氢呋喃：
水：甲醇（3:1:1），65℃，3 h，收率为 96%；(q) 锂（12.0 当量），液氨，乙醇，−78℃，15 min；(r) 2,4,6−三
氯苯甲酰氯（2.2 当量），三乙胺（4.0 当量），四氢呋喃，0℃，30 min；接着 4−二甲氨基吡啶（6.0 当
量），苯，75℃，4 h，两步收率为 82%；(s) 氟化氢·吡啶（3.0 当量），二氯甲烷，0℃，3 h；(t) 二（双三
氟甲基苄氧基）二苯基硫烷（1.5 当量），二氯甲烷，0℃，15 min，两步收率为 81%；(u) 氢气，三（三苯基
膦）氯化铑（0.1 当量），苯，25℃，5 h，收率为 99%，比例约 4:1；(v) 氢气，10% 钯/碳（0.1 当量），乙
酸乙酯，25℃，12 h，收率为 95%，比例约 19:1。CSA，10−樟脑磺酸；DMA，N,N−二甲基乙酰胺；
4−DMAP，4−二甲氨基吡啶；DMF，N,N−二甲基甲酰胺；DMSO，二甲基亚砜；NMO，4−甲基吗
啉−N−氧化物；TBS，叔丁基二甲基硅基；THF，四氢呋喃；Tf，三氟甲磺酰基。NaHMDS，六甲基二
硅基氨基钠；PhNHTf₂，N−苯基双三氟甲磺酰亚胺。关于化合物 14 的重要物理数据，请参见补充信息。

图 3. BCDE 内酯 26 的构建过程。所用试剂和反应条件如下。(a) 六甲基二硅基氨基钾（4.0 当量），二苯
氧基磷酰氯（6.0 当量），六甲基磷酰胺（6.0 当量），四氢呋喃，−78℃，1 h，收率为 80%；(b) 六甲基二
锡（8.0 当量），氯化锂（6.0 当量），四（三苯基膦）钯（0.1 当量），四氢呋喃，70℃，2 h，收率为 81%；
(c) 正丁基锂（1.55 M 的己烷溶液，4.0 当量），正戊炔基铜（4.4 当量），六甲基磷酰三胺（8.8 当量），四氢
呋喃，−78℃→−30℃，2 h；(d) 三氟甲磺酸（2−苄氧基）乙基酯（7.0 当量），四氢呋喃，−78℃→−30℃，
12 h，两步收率为 65%；(e) 2,3−二甲基−2−丁基硼烷（4.0 当量），四氢呋喃，−30℃→0℃，3 h；接着双
氧水（20.0 当量），氢氧化钠（20.0 当量），水，0℃，2 h，收率为 80%；(f) 叔丁基二苯基氯硅烷（1.3 当
量），咪唑（3.0 当量），N,N−二甲基甲酰胺，25℃，8 h，收率为 90%（循环五次）；(g) 10% 钯/碳（10%
重量当量），氢气，甲醇，25℃，2 h，收率为 93%；(h) 环己酮二甲缩酮（1.3 当量），对甲苯磺酸吡啶
盐（0.1 当量），二氯甲烷，25℃，2 h，收率为 85%；(i) 2,2−二甲基丙酰氯（1.3 当量），4−二甲氨基吡
啶（1.4 当量），二氯甲烷，25℃，0.5 h，收率为 99%；(j) 10−樟脑磺酸（0.1 当量），甲醇：二氯甲烷
（2:1），25℃，0.5 h，收率为 88%；(k) 三苯甲基氯·4−二甲氨基吡啶（4.0 当量），二氯甲烷，40℃，
12 h，收率为 95%；(l) 乙酸酐（1.5 当量），4−二甲氨基吡啶（0.5 当量），二氯甲烷，25℃，15 min，收

(3:2:1), 0 °C, 4 h; then 4-DMAP (4.0 equiv.), benzene, 80 °C, 2 h, 89% for two steps. 4-DMAP, 4-*N*-dimethylaminopyridine; DMF, *N*,*N*-dimethylformamide; KHMDS, potassium hexamethyldisilazide; HMPT, hexamethylphosphorous triamide; NMO, 4-methyl-morpholine-*N*-oxide; Piv, pivalate; PPTS, pyridinium *p*-toluenesulphonate; TPAP, tetra-*n*-propylammonium perruthenate; TBDPS, *t*-BuPh$_2$Si; Tr, trityl. For selected physical data for compound **26**, see Supplementary Information.

Fig. 4. Construction of the BCDE phosphine oxide **2**. Reagents and conditions as follows. (a) KHMDS (3.0 equiv.), (PhO)$_2$P(O)Cl (5.0 equiv.), THF, −78 °C, 1 h; (b) (*n*-Bu)$_3$SnCH=CH$_2$ (3.0 equiv.), LiCl (5.0 equiv.), Pd(Ph$_3$P)$_4$ (0.1 equiv.), THF, 75 °C, 2 h, 81% for two steps; (c) O$_2$, TPP (0.01 equiv.), CCl$_4$, 25 °C, 0.3 h; (d) Al(Hg) (excess), H$_2$O:THF (1:29), 25 °C, 2 h, 58% for two steps; (e) *t*-Bu$_2$SiCl (1.5 equiv.), imidazole (10.0 equiv.), CH$_2$Cl$_2$, 25 °C, 1 h, 91%; (f) TPAP (0.1 equiv.), NMO (2.0 equiv.), 4-Å MS, CH$_2$Cl$_2$, 25 °C, 1 h, 82%; (g) [(Ph$_3$P)CuH]$_6$ (2.0 equiv.), benzene, 25 °C, 72 h, 70%; (h) DIBAL (2.5 equiv.), CH$_2$Cl$_2$, −78 °C, 30 min, 95%, ~5:1 ratio; (i) TrCl·4-DMAP (15.0 equiv.), CH$_2$Cl$_2$, 40 °C, 24 h, 75% pure trityl ether after silica-gel chromatography; (j) POCl$_3$ (0.01 equiv.), CH$_2$=CMe(OMe) (solvent), 25 °C, 6 h, 95%; (k) neutral alumina-1% H$_2$O activated by heating (excess), hexane, 25 °C, 2 h, 96%; (l) MsCl (2.0 equiv.), Et$_3$N (4.0 equiv.), CH$_2$Cl$_2$, 0 °C, 15 min, 99%; (m) Ph$_2$PLi (3.0 equiv.), HMPA (3.0 equiv.), THF, 0 °C, 30 min; then 5% aq. H$_2$O$_2$ (excess), 93%. DIBAL, diisobutylaluminium hydride; 4-DMAP, 4-*N*-dimethylaminopyridine; HMPA, hexamethylphosphoramide; KHMDS, potassium hexamethyldisilazide; MS, molecular sieves; NMO, 4-methylmorpholine-*N*-oxide; TBDPS, *t*-BuPh$_2$Si; TBS, *t*-BuMe$_2$Si; THF, tetrahydrofuran; TPAP, tetra-*n*-propylammonium perruthenate; TPP, tetraphenylporphyrin; Tr, trityl. Ms, CH$_3$SO$_2$ or methanesulphonyl; imid., imidazole. For selected physical data for compound **2**, see Supplementary Information.

The conversion of bis(lactone) **16** to the tetracyclic 9-membered ring lactone **26** relied on a two-directional approach similar to that previously reported from these laboratories[21] and on a newly developed method for the transformation of lactones to cyclic ethers involving cyclic ketene acetal phosphates[11]. Figure 3 summarizes the sequence for this

率为 99%；（m）三氟乙酸（1.5 当量），甲醇（10.0 当量），二氯甲烷，25℃，30 min，收率为 90%；（n）四正丙基过钌酸铵（0.1 当量），4-甲基吗啉-N-氧化物（2.0 当量），二氯甲烷，25℃，30 min，收率为 97%；（o）溴化三苯基-3-甲氧羰基正丙基磷鎓盐（2.5 当量），六甲基二硅基氨基钾（2.0 当量），四氢呋喃，-78℃，1 h，收率为 83%；（p）氢氧化锂（10.0 当量），四氢呋喃：水：甲醇（3:2:1），0℃，4 h；接着 4-二甲氨基吡啶（4.0 当量），苯，80℃，2 h，两步收率为 89%。4-DMAP，4-二甲氨基吡啶；DMF，N,N-二甲基甲酰胺；KHMDS，六甲基二硅基氨基钾；HMPT，六甲基磷酰三胺；NMO，4-甲基吗啉-N-氧化物；Piv，2,2-二甲基丙酰基；PPTS，对甲苯磺酸吡啶盐；TPAP，四正丙基过钌酸铵；TBDPS，叔丁基二苯基硅基；Tr，三苯甲基。关于化合物 26 的重要物理数据，请参见补充信息。

图 4. BCDE 膦氧化物 2 的构建过程。所用试剂和反应条件如下。（a）六甲基二硅基氨基钾（3.0 当量），二苯氧基磷酰氯（5.0 当量），四氢呋喃，-78℃，1 h；（b）三正丁基乙烯基锡（3.0 当量），氯化锂（5.0 当量），四（三苯基膦）钯（0.1 当量），四氢呋喃，75℃，2 h，两步收率为 81%；（c）氧气，四苯基卟啉（0.01 当量），四氯化碳，25℃，0.3 h；（d）铝汞齐（过量），水：四氢呋喃（1:29），25℃，2 h，两步收率为 58%；（e）二叔丁基氯硅烷（1.5 当量），咪唑（10.0 当量），二氯甲烷，25℃，1 h，收率为 91%；（f）四正丙基过钌酸铵（0.1 当量），4-甲基吗啉-N-氧化物（2.0 当量），4 Å 分子筛，二氯甲烷，25℃，1 h，收率为 82%；（g）三苯基膦氢化铜六聚物（2.0 当量），苯，25℃，72 h，收率为 70%；（h）二异丁基氢化铝（2.5 当量），二氯甲烷，-78℃，30 min，收率为 95%，比例约为 5:1；（i）三苯甲基氯·4-二甲氨基吡啶（15.0 当量），二氯甲烷，40℃，24 h，硅胶色谱法纯化后收率为 75% 纯三苯甲基醚；（j）三氯氧磷（0.01 当量），2-甲氧基丙烯（溶剂），25℃，6 h，收率为 95%；（k）含有 1% 水分的中性氧化铝（加热活化，过量），己烷，25℃，2 h，收率为 96%；（l）甲磺酰氯（2.0 当量），三乙胺（4.0 当量），二氯甲烷，0℃，15 min，收率为 99%；（m）二苯基膦锂（3.0 当量），六甲基磷酰胺（3.0 当量），四氢呋喃，0℃，30 min；接着 5% 双氧水溶液（过量），收率为 93%。DIBAL，二异丁基氢化铝；4-DMAP，4-二甲氨基吡啶；HMPA，六甲基磷酰胺；KHMDS，六甲基二硅基氨基钾；MS，分子筛；NMO，4-甲基吗啉-N-氧化物；TBDPS，叔丁基二苯基硅基；TBS，叔丁基二甲基硅基；THF，四氢呋喃；TPAP，四正丙基过钌酸铵；TPP，四苯基卟啉；Tr，三苯甲基。Ms，甲磺酰基；imid.，咪唑。关于化合物 2 的重要物理数据，请参见补充信息。

由双内酯化合物 16 到含有 9 元环内酯的四环化合物 26 的转化依赖于一个双向的反应方法（类似于一些实验室先前报道的方法[21]）和一个新开发的使用环状烯酮缩醛的磷酸酯将内酯转换为环醚的方法[11]。图 3 中总结了这个转化的顺序。将双内酯

conversion. The bis(lactone) **16** was added to a solution of KHMDS and $(PhO)_2P(O)Cl$, furnishing bis(phosphate) **17** (80% yield), which was coupled with $Me_3SnSnMe_3$ in the presence of $Pd(Ph_3P)_4$ catalyst and LiCl to afford the bis(vinylstannane) **18** (81% yield). Reaction of **18** with n-BuLi, followed by addition of n-PrC $\equiv$ CCu·2HMPT (ref. 22) and $TfOCH_2CH_2OBn$, led to bis(vinylether) **20** in 65% overall yield via mixed cuprate **19**. Hydroboration of **20** with thexylborane, followed by basic hydrogen peroxide work-up (80% yield) and selective monosilylation (90% yield, five recycles) as previously described[21], led to compound **22** via **21**. Having simultaneously functionalized bis(lactone) **16** on both sides, and then successfully differentiating the two ends, we were now in a position to resume the stepwise manipulation of the molecule towards the 9-membered ring lactone **26**. Thus, hydrogenolysis of the two benzyl ethers in **22** (H_2, 10% Pd/C, 93% yield) and ketalization with cyclohexanone dimethylketal in the presence of PPTS (85% yield), followed by pivalate formation (PivCl, 4-DMAP, 99% yield) at the remaining primary alcohol, gave compound **23**. The ketal was then disassembled under acidic conditions (CSA, 88% yield), and the two hydroxyl groups so released were differentiated by trityl ether formation (TrCl·4-DMAP, primary alcohol, 95% yield), acetylation (Ac_2O, 4-DMAP, secondary alcohol, 99% yield) and trityl ether cleavage (TFA, 90% yield) to afford hydroxy acetate **24**. The 9-membered ring lactone was then built on the "right side" of the molecule by (1) TPAP-NMO oxidation[23] of the primary alcohol to the corresponding aldehyde (97% yield); (2) olefination with the ylide derived from $Br^{\ominus}Ph_3P^{\oplus}(CH_2)_3CO_2Me$ and KHMDS (83% yield); (3) saponification of both the methylester and the acetate groups (LiOH) to afford hydroxyacid **25**; and (4) Yamaguchi[18] lactonization, furnishing the targeted intermediate **26** (89% for two steps).

The functionalization of the 9-membered ring lactone to the desired E ring ether functionality was achieved via sequential application of the cyclic ketene acetal phosphate-palladium coupling technology[11] and a selective[24] singlet oxygen 4+2 cycloaddition reaction of a constructed conjugated diene system. Figure 4 outlines the chemistry leading from **26** to the targeted phosphine oxide **2**. Conversion of **26** to its ketene acetal phosphate by reaction with KHMDS and $(PhO)_2P(O)Cl$, followed by palladium-catalysed coupling with tri-n-butylvinyltin, resulted, via **27**, in the formation of conjugated diene **28** (81% overall yield), thus accomplishing the crucial transformation of a lactone to a cyclic ether[11]. The selective functionalization of the diene system in **28** in the presence of the additional double bond within the 9-membered ring, was achieved by a novel 4+2 cycloaddition reaction[24] involving singlet O_2, generated by light in the presence of tetraphenylporphyrin (TPP) as a sensitizer. The formed endoperoxide **29** (~1:1 ratio of diastereoisomers, inconsequential) was then converted to the corresponding diol (58% yield for two steps) by reductive cleavage of the O—O bond with Al(Hg) in $THF-H_2O$.

化合物 **16** 加入到六甲基二硅基氨基钾和二苯氧基磷酰氯的溶液中得到双磷酸酯化合物 **17**(收率为 80%),接着在四(三苯基膦)钯催化剂和氯化锂的存在下与六甲基二锡进行偶联得到双乙烯基锡烷化合物 **18**(收率为 81%)。用正丁基锂与化合物 **18** 反应,接着加入正戊炔基铜·二(六甲基磷酰三胺)(参考文献 22)和三氟甲磺酸(2-苄氧基)乙基酯,经过一个混合的铜盐化合物 **19** 以 65% 的总收率得到双烯醚化合物 **20**。用 2,3-二甲基-2-丁基硼烷对化合物 **20** 进行硼氢化反应,接着用碱性过氧化氢处理(收率为 80%)并以先前报道的方式进行选择性单硅烷化反应[21](收率 90%,循环五次),经过化合物 **21** 得到化合物 **22**。我们已经对双内酯化合物 **16** 的两个侧链同时进行了官能化,并成功地区分了两个末端,现在处于为了得到 9 元环内酯化合物 **26** 继续对分子进行逐步操作的过程中。于是,对化合物 **22** 中的两个苄基醚进行氢解(H$_2$,10% 钯/碳,收率为 93%),然后在对甲苯磺酸吡啶盐存在的条件下用环己酮二甲缩酮进行缩酮化反应(收率为 85%),接着在剩余的伯醇上用 2,2-二甲基丙酰氯和 4-二甲氨基吡啶进行 2,2-二甲基丙酰化(收率为 99%),得到化合物 **23**。在酸性条件下缩酮进行分解(10-樟脑磺酸,收率 88%),释放出的两个羟基经以下反应得到区分:用三苯甲基氯·4-二甲氨基吡啶进行伯醇的三苯甲基醚化(收率为 95%),用乙酸酐和 4-二甲氨基吡啶进行仲醇的乙酰化(收率为 99%),然后用三氟乙酸脱掉三苯甲基(收率为 90%)。最后得到羟基乙酸酯化合物 **24**。接下来在这个分子的"右侧"进行 9 元环内酯的构建:(1)在伯醇上用四正丙基过钌酸铵和 4-甲基吗啉-N-氧化物进行氧化[23]得到相应的醛(收率为 97%);(2)用叶立德(由溴化三苯基-3-甲氧羰基正丙基磷鎓盐和六甲基二硅基氨基钾得到)进行烯化反应(收率为 83%);(3)用氢氧化锂对甲酯和乙酸酯基团进行皂化反应得到羟基酸化合物 **25**;(4)通过山口[18]内酯化,得到目标中间产物 **26**(两步收率为 89%)。

对 9 元环内酯进行官能化以便获得醚化的 E 环是通过如下反应实现的:依次使用环烯酮缩醛的磷酸酯-钯偶联技术[11]和在所构建的共轭二烯上进行选择性[24]单重态氧的 4+2 环加成反应。图 4 概述了从化合物 **26** 到目标膦氧化物 **2** 的化学过程。将 **26** 转化为它的烯酮缩醛磷酸酯是通过与六甲基二硅基氨基钾和二苯氧基磷酰氯反应,经过化合物 **27**,接着在钯催化下与三正丁基乙烯基锡偶联,形成了共轭二烯 **28**(总收率为 81%),从而完成了内酯到环醚的关键性转化[11]。在 9 元环中多余双键存在的情况下,通过一种新的单重态氧参与的 4+2 环加成反应[24]实现了对化合物 **28** 的双烯系统的选择性官能化,其中单重态氧是以四苯基卟啉作为敏化剂经光照生成的。生成的内过氧化物 **29**(非对映异构体的比例约为 1∶1,无关紧要)经 O—O 键在四氢呋喃和水中被铝汞齐还原断裂,转化成相应的二醇化合物(两步的收率为 58%)。用叔丁基二甲基氯硅烷和咪唑对所得二醇中的伯羟基进行选择性硅烷化(收率为

The primary hydroxyl group of the resulting diol was selectively silylated with TBSCl-imid. (91% yield), and the secondary alcohol was oxidized with TPAP-NMO (ref. 23; 82% yield), leading to enone **30**.

The proper functionality and stereochemistry was established on ring E by sequential reduction of the double bond ([(Ph$_3$P)CuH]$_6$, 70% yield)[25] and of the carbonyl group (DIBAL). The DIBAL reduction also cleaved the pivalate group, furnishing diol **31** (95% yield, ~5:1 ratio of diastereoisomers, separated at a later stage). The resulting diol (**31**) was protected by sequential formation of a trityl ether at the primary position (TrCl · 4-DMAP, separation of diastereoisomers with silica-gel flash chromatography, 75% pure trityl ether) and of a mixed methoxyketal at the secondary position [CH$_2$ = CMe(OMe), POCl$_3$ catalyst], before selective removal of the TBS group (alumina)[26] to afford primary alcohol **32** (91% yield for two steps). Finally, mesylation of **32** (MsCl, Et$_3$N), followed by displacement with LiPPh$_2$ and oxidation with hydrogen peroxide, furnished the desired phosphine oxide **2** (BCDE ring system) in 92% overall yield.

The construction of the other requisite advanced intermediate, GHIJ ring system **3**, is shown in Fig. 5. Thus, D-mannose (**5**) was converted to tricyclic dithioketal-aldehyde **33** by a modification of our previously published[27] multi-step sequence (full details will be published elsewhere). Generation of the ylide from phosphonium salt **34**[27] (n-BuLi) and coupling with aldehyde **33** (THF, HMPA, −78 °C) resulted, after selective removal of the TBS group, in the stereoselective formation of Z-olefin **35** in 73% overall yield. Hydroxydithioketal cyclization[10] of **35**, facilitated by AgClO$_4$ in the presence of NaHCO$_3$, SiO$_2$, 4-Å MS in MeNO$_2$, resulted in the formation of the mixed 8-membered ring thioketal **36** in 92% yield. The introduction of the α-methyl group at the fusion of rings G and H was accomplished by oxidation of **36** to sulphone **37** (mCPBA, 93% yield) followed by reaction with AlMe$_3$ to afford **38** (94% yield). The well-defined conformation of the intermediate oxonium species in the latter reaction is presumed to be responsible for the observed stereochemical control. The benzylidene group in **38** was then removed by exposure to EtSH in the presence of Zn(OTf)$_2$ and NaHCO$_3$ (92% yield), and the resulting diol was differentiated by silylation (TBSCl-imid., primary silylether, 92% yield), followed by acetylation (Ac$_2$O, pyridine, secondary acetate, 95% yield), leading to compound **39**. Hydrogenation of the double bond in **39** in the presence of Pd(OH)$_2$/C resulted in concomitant debenzylation, furnishing the corresponding saturated alcohol in 90% yield. The newly liberated secondary hydroxyl group was then protected as a TBS ether (TBSOTf-2,6-lutidine, 87% yield), and the acetate group on ring G was cleaved by the action of K$_2$CO$_3$ in MeOH (93% yield). The resulting secondary alcohol was then oxidized to ketone **40** with TPAP-NMO (ref. 23) in 94% yield. Finally, exposure of **40** to EtSH in the presence of Zn(OTf)$_2$ led to the corresponding dithioketal with concomitant desilylation of the neighbouring oxygen (92% yield), and was followed by oxidation (SO$_3$ · pyridine, DMSO, Et$_3$N)[28] to afford the targeted GHIJ ring system **3**, in 87% overall yield.

91%），再用四正丙基过钌酸铵和 4–甲基吗啉–*N*–氧化物对仲醇进行氧化（参考文献 23；收率为 82%），得到烯酮化合物 **30**。

通过依次还原双键（三苯基膦氢化铜六聚物，收率 70%）[25] 和羰基（二异丁基氢化铝）在 E 环上建立起正确的官能团和立体化学。二异丁基氢化铝同样也会脱除 2,2–二甲基丙酰基，并得到二醇化合物 **31**（收率为 95%，非对映异构体的比例约为 5:1，在后面的阶段进行分离）。依次对所得二醇 **31** 进行保护，在伯醇上进行三苯甲基醚化（三苯甲基氯·4–二甲氨基吡啶，用硅胶快速色谱法分离非对映异构体，得到 75% 纯的三苯甲基醚），在仲醇上进行混合甲氧基缩酮化（2–甲氧基丙烯，三氯氧磷作催化剂），接着用氧化铝选择性地脱除叔丁基二甲基硅基 [26]，得到伯醇化合物 **32**（两步的收率为 91%）。最后用甲磺酰氯/三乙胺对 **32** 进行甲磺酰化，接着用二苯基膦化锂置换甲磺酰基，再用过氧化氢氧化，得到预期的膦氧化物 **2**（BCDE 环系，总收率为 92%）。

图 5 列出了另一个必需的高级中间体（GHIJ 环系 **3**）的构建过程。其过程是，D–甘露糖（**5**）通过改进的我们先前报道 [27] 的多步连续反应方式转化成二硫缩酮–醛的三环化合物 **33**（合成细节将另行报道）。鏻盐 **34**[27] 与正丁基锂反应生成的叶立德与醛化合物 **33** 在 −78℃、六甲基磷酰胺和四氢呋喃的条件下进行偶联，然后选择性脱去叔丁基二甲基硅基，立体选择性地得到 *Z* 构型烯烃化合物 **35**（总收率为 73%）。在碳酸氢钠、二氧化硅、4 Å 分子筛的硝基甲烷溶液中用高氯酸银对 **35** 进行羟基二硫缩酮的环化反应 [10]，结果形成了含有 8 元环的混合硫缩酮化合物 **36**（收率为 92%）。用间氯过氧苯甲酸对化合物 **36** 进行氧化得到砜化物 **37**（收率为 93%），接着再与三甲基铝反应得到化合物 **38**（收率为 94%），从而在 G 环和 H 环的连接处引入了 *α*–甲基。在后面的反应中形成的氧鎓中间体具有明确的构象，我们推测是它控制着所观察到的立体化学。接着在三氟甲磺酸锌和碳酸氢钠的存在下用乙硫醇处理使化合物 **38** 脱掉苯亚甲基得到二醇（收率为 92%），两个羟基发生不同反应，其中伯羟基用叔丁基二甲基氯硅烷和咪唑进行硅烷基化（伯硅醚收率为 92%），接着用乙酸酐和吡啶进行仲羟基的乙酰化（仲乙酸酯收率为 95%），得到化合物 **39**。在氢氧化钯/碳存在的条件下，化合物 **39** 的双键进行氢化并伴随着脱苄基化，以 90% 的收率得到相应的饱和醇，然后对新产生的仲羟基用叔丁基二甲基硅基三氟甲磺酸酯和 2,6–二甲基吡啶进行保护形成叔丁基二甲基硅醚（收率为 87%），接着在碳酸钾的甲醇溶液中脱去 G 环上的乙酸酯（收率为 93%）。再用四正丙基过钌酸铵和 4–甲基吗啉–*N*–氧化物（参考文献 23）对得到的仲醇进行氧化，得到酮化合物 **40**（收率为 94%）。最后，在三氟甲磺酸锌的条件下用乙硫醇处理化合物 **40** 得到相应的二硫缩酮化合物并伴随着邻近氧原子的脱硅烷化（收率为 92%），用三氧化硫·吡啶在三乙胺和二甲基亚砜条件下进行氧化 [28] 得到了目标的 GHIJ 环系化合物 **3**（总收率为 87%）。

Fig. 5. Construction of the GHIJ ring system **3**. Reagents and conditions as follows. (a) See ref. 27; (b) add *n*-BuLi (1.55 M in hexanes, 1.0 equiv.) to **34** (1.0 equiv.) and HMPA (10.0 equiv.) in THF; then add **33**, THF, −78 °C, 1 h; then 25 °C, 1.5 h, 88%; (c) TBAF (1.1 equiv.), THF, 25 °C, 7 h, 83%; (d) AgClO₄ (3.0 equiv.), NaHCO₃ (3.0 equiv.), SiO₂, 4-Å MS, MeNO₂, 25 °C, 3 h, 92%; (e) *m*CPBA (2.0 equiv.), CH₂Cl₂, 0 °C, 2 h, 93%; (f) AlMe₃ (3.0 equiv.), CH₂Cl₂, −78 °C, 1 h, 94%; (g) EtSH (20 equiv.), Zn(OTf)₂ (0.3 equiv.), NaHCO₃ (0.5 equiv.), CH₂Cl₂, 25 °C, 4 h, 92%; (h) TBSCl (1.1 equiv.), imidazole (1.5 equiv.), CH₂Cl₂, 25 °C, 1 h, 92%; (i) Ac₂O (1.1 equiv.), 4-DMAP (1.3 equiv.), CH₂Cl₂, 25 °C, 2.5 h, 95%; (j) H₂, 10% Pd(OH)₂/C (0.15 equiv.), AcOH, 25 °C, 5 h, 90%; (k) TBSOTf (2.5 equiv.), 2,6-lutidine (3.0 equiv.), CH₂Cl₂, 0 °C, 0.5 h, 87%; (l) K₂CO₃ (0.5 equiv.), MeOH, 25 °C, 4 h, 93%; (m) TPAP (0.05 equiv.), NMO (2.0 equiv.), CH₂Cl₂, 25 °C, 1 h, 94%; (n) EtSH (20.0 equiv.), Zn(OTf)₂ (0.3 equiv.), CH₂Cl₂, 25 °C, 2.5 h, 92%; (o) SO₃ · pyridine (3.0 equiv.), DMSO (10.0 equiv.), Et₃N (10.0 equiv.), CH₂Cl₂, 0 °C, 1.5 h, 87%. 4-DMAP, 4-*N*-dimethylaminopyridine; DMF, *N,N*-dimethylformamide; DMSO, dimethyl sulphoxide; HMPA, hexamethyphosphoramide; *m*CPBA, *m*-chloroperbenzoic acid; NMO, 4-methylmorpholine-*N*-oxide; TBAF, tetra-*n*-butylammonium fluoride; TBDPS, *t*-BuPh₂Si; TBS, *t*-BuMe₂Si; Tf, triflate; THF, tetrahydrofuran; TPAP, tetra-*n*-propylammonium perruthenate; imid., imidazole. For selected physical data for compound **3**, see Supplementary Information.

The union of fragments **2** and **3** and the final stages of the total synthesis of brevetoxin A (**1**) are depicted in Fig. 6. Thus, generation of the anion of phosphine oxide **2** with *n*-BuLi (THF, −78 °C), followed by addition of aldehyde **3**, gave a mixture of two diastereomeric hydroxyphosphine oxides (**41a** and **41b**, ~1:1 ratio, 75% total yield). Treatment of this mixture (**41a**+**41b**) with KH in DMF, followed by acidic cleavage of the mixed ketal, resulted in the formation of the desired *Z*-olefin **42** as a single isomer and in 72% yield. The choice of the phosphine oxide (Horner–Wittig reaction)[29] as opposed to the more commonly used phosphonium salt for fragment **2** was necessitated by the inability of the latter to react, via its ylide, with the sterically hindered aldehyde **3**. Furthermore, the placement of the mixed methoxyketal on ring E of the fragment **2** was crucial for the exclusive *Z*-stereoselectivity observed in the coupling reaction. It is presumed that the two oxygens of this group act synergistically with the E-ring oxygen in complexing the lithium atom in a well-defined structure, which leads to the exclusive formation of only the *anti* adducts **41a** and **41b**. Both

图 5. GHIJ 环系化合物 **3** 的构建过程。所用试剂和反应条件如下。(a) 参见文献 27；(b) 将正丁基锂（1.55 M 的己烷溶液，1.0 当量）加入到化合物 **34**（1.0 当量）和六甲基磷酰胺（10.0 当量）的四氢呋喃溶液中；接着加入化合物 **33**，四氢呋喃，−78℃，1 h；然后 25℃，1.5 h，收率为 88%；(c) 四正丁基氟化铵（1.1 当量），四氢呋喃，25℃，7 h，收率为 83%；(d) 高氯酸银（3.0 当量），碳酸氢钠（3.0 当量），二氧化硅，4 Å 分子筛，硝基甲烷，25℃，3 h，收率为 92%；(e) 间氯过氧苯甲酸（2.0 当量），二氯甲烷，0℃，2 h，收率为 93%；(f) 三甲基铝（3.0 当量），二氯甲烷，−78℃，1 h，收率为 94%；(g) 乙硫醇（20.0 当量），三氟甲磺酸锌（0.3 当量），碳酸氢钠（0.5 当量），二氯甲烷，25℃，4 h，收率为 92%；(h) 叔丁基二甲基氯硅烷（1.1 当量），咪唑（1.5 当量），二氯甲烷，25℃，1 h，收率为 92%；(i) 乙酸酐（1.1 当量），4-二甲氨基吡啶（1.3 当量），二氯甲烷，25℃，2.5 h，收率为 95%；(j) 氢气，10% 氢氧化钯/碳（0.15 当量），乙酸，25℃，5 h，收率为 90%；(k) 叔丁基二甲基硅基三氟甲磺酸酯（2.5 当量），2,6-二甲基吡啶（3.0 当量），二氯甲烷，0℃，0.5 h，收率为 87%；(l) 碳酸钾（0.5 当量），甲醇，25℃，4 h，收率为 93%；(m) 四正丙基过钌酸铵（0.05 当量），4-甲基吗啉-N-氧化物（2.0 当量），二氯甲烷，25℃，1 h，收率为 94%；(n) 乙硫醇（20.0 当量），三氟甲磺酸锌（0.3 当量），二氯甲烷，25℃，2.5 h，收率为 92%；(o) 三氧化硫·吡啶（3.0 当量），二甲基亚砜（10.0 当量），三乙胺（10.0 当量），二氯甲烷，0℃，1.5 h，收率为 87%。4-DMAP，4-二甲氨基吡啶；DMF，N,N-二甲基甲酰胺；DMSO，二甲基亚砜；HMPA，六甲基磷酰胺；mCPBA，间氯过氧苯甲酸；NMO，4-甲基吗啉-N-氧化物；TBAF，四正丁基氟化铵；TBDPS，叔丁基二苯基硅基；TBS，叔丁基二甲基硅基；Tf，三氟甲磺酰基；THF，四氢呋喃；TPAP，四正丙基过钌酸铵；imid.，咪唑。关于化合物 **3** 的重要物理数据，请参见补充信息。

　　图 6 中列出的是片断 **2** 和 **3** 的整合及短裸甲藻毒素 A（**1**）全合成的最后几步反应。也就是，用正丁基锂在 −78℃，四氢呋喃作为溶剂的条件下与膦氧化物 **2** 反应生成阴离子，接着与醛化物 **3** 加成，得到两个非对映异构的羟基膦氧化物的混合物 **41a** 和 **41b**（比例约为 1:1，总收率为 75%）。用含氢化钾的 N,N-二甲基甲酰胺溶液处理此混合物（**41a**+**41b**），接着酸性裂解该混合缩酮，得到了预期的 Z-型烯烃 **42** 的单一异构体（收率为 72%）。之所以选择霍纳-维蒂希反应[29] 的膦氧化物，而不选择更常用的鏻盐来合成片断 **2**，是因为后者形成的叶立德不能与具有空间位阻的醛化物 **3** 发生反应。此外，片断 **2** 中 E 环上的混合甲氧基缩酮的位置对偶联反应中专一的 Z-型立体选择性具有决定作用。我们推测，这个基团上的两个氧原子与 E 环上的氧原子在与锂原子形成具有明确结构的复合物时发生协同作用，使得仅生成反

diastereoisomers furnish the same *Z*-olefin (whereas the *syn* diastereoisomers would form the *E*-olefin). Ring closure of hydroxydithioketal[10] **42**, induced by AgClO$_4$, furnished the 8-membered ring mixed thioketal in 80% yield. Oxidation of this mixed thioketal with *m*CPBA led to the corresponding sulphone (85% yield), which upon exposure to BF$_3$ · Et$_2$O in the presence of Et$_3$SiH (ref. 10) at −78 °C, resulted in the reductive removal of the ethyl sulphone moiety and concomitant cleavage of the trityl ether, furnishing the **BCDEFGHIJ** ring skeleton (compound **43**, 80% yield) of brevetoxin A. The stereochemistry of the newly

Fig. 6. Total synthesis of brevetoxin A (**1**). Reagents and conditions as follows. (a) Add *n*-BuLi (1.55 M in hexanes, 1.0 equiv.) to **2** (1.0 equiv.) in THF at −78 °C, then **3**, 20 min, 75%; (b) KH (2.0 equiv.), DMF, 25 °C, 0.5 h; (c) 20% aq. AcOH, THF, 25 °C, 6 h, 72% for two steps; (d) AgClO$_4$ (3.0 equiv.), NaHCO$_3$ (3.0 equiv.), SiO$_2$, 4-Å MS, MeNO$_2$, 25 °C, 2 h, 80%; (e) *m*CPBA (2.2 equiv.), CH$_2$Cl$_2$, 0 °C, 1 h, 85%; (f) BF$_3$ · Et$_2$O (3.0 equiv.), Et$_3$SiH, CH$_2$Cl$_2$, −78 °C, 30 min, 80%; (g) TPAP (0.1 equiv.), NMO (2.0 equiv.), CH$_2$Cl$_2$, 25 °C, 30 min; (h) NaClO$_2$ (2.0 equiv.), NaH$_2$PO$_4$ (3.0 equiv.), 2-methyl-2-butene (5.0 equiv.), *t*-BuOH:H$_2$O (5:1), 25 °C, 30 min; (i) CH$_2$N$_2$, Et$_2$O, 25 °C, 15 min, 80% for three steps; (j) HF · pyridine (10.0 equiv.), CH$_2$Cl$_2$, 0 °C, 2 h, 90%; (k) Dess–Martin periodinane (1.5 equiv.), CH$_2$Cl$_2$, 25 °C, 1 h, 80%; (l) CH$_2$=N$^{\oplus}$Me$_2$I$^{\ominus}$(10.0 equiv.), Et$_3$N (15.0 equiv.), CH$_2$Cl$_2$, 25 °C, 5 h, 90%. DMF, *N*,*N*-dimethylformamide; *m*CPBA, *m*-chloroperbenzoic acid; NMO, 4-methylmorpholine-*N*-oxide; TBDPS, *t*-BuPh$_2$Si; TBS, *t*-BuMe$_2$Si; THF, tetrahydrofuran; TPAP, tetra-*n*-propylammonium perruthenate; Tr, trityl. Selected physical data for synthetic brevetoxin A (**1**): retention factor $R_f = 0.45$ (silica, 1:1 ethyl acetate:hexane); specific rotation$[\alpha]_D^{22}$ +75.5 (*c* 0.2, CH$_2$Cl$_2$); infrared spectra (pure compound) ν_{max} 3,425.1, 2,920.5, 2,849.2,

式加成产物 **41a** 和 **41b**。这两种非对映异构体具有同样的 *Z*-型烯键(而顺式加成的非对映异构体则会形成 *E*-型烯键)。用高氯酸银引导羟基二硫缩酮化合物 **42** 进行闭环反应 [10],以 80% 的收率得到 8 元环的混合硫缩酮产物。然后用间氯过氧苯甲酸氧化该混合硫缩酮得到相应的砜化物(收率为 85%),接着在 −78℃、三乙基硅烷存在的条件下(参考文献 10),用三氟化硼·乙醚还原去除其乙基砜的部分,并伴随着三苯甲基醚键的断裂,生成短裸甲藻毒素 A 的 BCDEFGHIJ 环系骨架(化合物 **43**,收

图 6. 短裸甲藻毒素 A(**1**)的全合成。所用试剂和反应条件如下。(a)在 −78℃ 下,将正丁基锂(1.55 M 的己烷溶液,1.0 当量)加入到化合物 **2**(1.0 当量)的四氢呋喃溶液中,接着加入化合物 **3**,20 min,收率为 75%;(b)氢化钾(2.0 当量),*N,N*-二甲基甲酰胺,25℃,0.5 h;(c)20% 的乙酸水溶液,四氢呋喃,25℃,6 h,两步收率 72%;(d)高氯酸银(3.0 当量),碳酸氢钠(3.0 当量),二氧化硅,4 Å 分子筛,硝基甲烷,25℃,2 h,收率为 80%;(e)间氯过氧苯甲酸(2.2 当量),二氯甲烷,0℃,1 h,收率为 85%;(f)三氟化硼·乙醚(3.0 当量),三乙基硅烷,二氯甲烷,−78℃,30 min,收率为 80%;(g)四正丙基过钌酸铵(0.1 当量),4-甲基吗啉-*N*-氧化物(2.0 当量),二氯甲烷,25℃,30 min;(h)亚氯酸钠(2.0 当量),磷酸二氢钠(3.0 当量),2-甲基-2-丁烯(5.0 当量),叔丁醇:水(5:1),25℃,30 min;(i)重氮甲烷,乙醚,25℃,15 min,三步收率为 80%;(j)氟化氢·吡啶(10.0 当量),二氯甲烷,0℃,2 h,收率为 90%;(k)戴斯-马丁氧化剂(1.5 当量),二氯甲烷,25℃,1 h,收率为 80%;(l)*N,N*-二甲基亚甲基碘化铵(10.0 当量),三乙胺(15.0 当量),二氯甲烷,25℃,5 h,收率为 90%。DMF,*N,N*-二甲基甲酰胺;*m*CPBA,间氯过氧苯甲酸;NMO,4-甲基吗啉-*N*-氧化物;TBDPS,叔丁基二苯基硅基;TBS,叔丁基二甲基硅基;THF,四氢呋喃;TPAP,四正丙基过钌酸铵;Tr,三苯甲基。关于合

1,788.2, 1,689.5, 1,455.1, 1,378.7, 1,314, 1,265.7, 1,208.3, 1,079.9, 897.1, 737.0 cm^{-1}; ^{1}H NMR (C$_6$D$_6$, 600 MHz, 45 °C) δ 9.29 (s, 1 H), 5.90 (s, 1 H), 5.87 (dd, J = 10.8, 5.2 Hz, 1 H), 5.78–5.67 (bm, 2 H), 5.71–5.64 (m, 1 H), 5.43 (s, 1 H), 4.55 (dd, J = 8.0, 5.4 Hz, 1 H), 3.98–3.91 (m, 3 H), 3.74 (b, 1 H), 3.59–3.54 (m, 1 H), 3.52 (ddd, J = 10.6, 7.9, 2.3 Hz, 1 H), 3.46–3.34 (m, 4 H), 3.29 (bd, J = 8.5 Hz, 1 H), 3.19–3.10 (m, 3 H), 2.94 (ddd, J = 12.0, 8.0, 4.1 Hz, 1 H), 2.89 (ddd, J = 11.9, 9.2, 4.5 Hz, 1 H), 2.80 (dd, J = 11.9, 4.6 Hz, 1 H), 2.78 (dd, J = 9.6, 2.7 Hz, 1 H), 2.72–2.40 (bm, 4 H), 2.65 (dd, J = 10.7, 10.7 Hz, 1 H), 2.40 (ddd, J = 15.2, 10.8, 4.0 Hz, 1 H), 2.36 (dd, J = 16.9, 8.2 Hz, 1 H), 2.31 (dd, J = 11.6, 4.2 Hz, 1 H), 2.25–2.21 (m, 1 H), 2.24–2.20 (m, 1 H), 2.21 (dd, J = 16.9, 10.3 Hz, 1 H), 2.18–2.10 (m, 1 H), 2.05–1.92 (m, 6 H), 1.92–1.86 (m, 1 H), 1.86–1.74 (m, 3 H), 1.72–1.52 (m, 7 H), 1.44–1.38 (m, 1 H), 1.37–1.24 (m, 1 H), 1.24 (s, 3 H), 1.20 (d, J = 7.1 Hz, 3 H), 0.98–0.95 (m, 1 H), 0.96 (s, 3 H), 0.77 (d, J = 6.8 Hz, 3 H); ^{13}C NMR (C$_6$D$_6$, 150 MHz, 45 °C) δ 193.5, 171.0, 148.9, 139.0, 134.4, 128.5, 127.4, 124.8, 92.0, 88.5, 86.7, 85.1, 84.7, 84.1, 83.8, 82.2, 82.0, 80.4, 79.9, 78.9, 77.8, 76.7, 76.2, 71.9, 71.1, 69.6, 66.3, 62.4, 52.9, 45.6, 43.3, 38.2, 37.5, 36.9, 36.2, 35.9, 33.8, 32.3, 31.4, 29.0, 27.6, 27.2, 21.4, 19.7, 16.8, 15.0 (carbons 17, 20 and 28 were observed at best as weak broad signals at 34.5, 34.5 and 30.9, respectively, as previously reported[30,31]; mass spectra: calculated for C$_{49}$H$_{70}$O$_{13}$ (M+Na$^+$) 889.4714, found 889.4747. For selected physical data for compounds **42** and **43**, see Supplementary Information.

generated stereocenter at the FG ring junction of **43** was confirmed by comparison of its NMR data to those of brevetoxin A[1,3,30,31] and of a model system[24]. The fusion of ring A onto the rest of the brevetoxin A framework was accomplished by stepwise oxidation of the primary alcohol in **43** to the corresponding aldehyde (TPAP-NMO)[23] and carboxylic acid (NaClO$_2$-NaH$_2$PO$_4$, 2-methyl-2-butene)[32], followed by methyl ester formation (CH$_2$N$_2$, 80% for three steps) and exposure to HF·pyridine. The latter reaction resulted in the removal of all three silyl groups and spontaneous ring closure to form the γ-lactone ring, furnishing the ABCDEFGHIJ ring system **44** (90% yield) of brevetoxin A. Finally, exposure of diol **44** to carefully controlled amounts of Dess–Martin[33] reagent gave, selectively, the corresponding hydroxy aldehyde (80% yield), whose reaction with CH$_2$ = N$^{\oplus}$Me$_2$I$^{\ominus}$ (ref. 34) proceeded smoothly to afford brevetoxin A (**1**) in 90% yield. Synthetic brevetoxin A was identical in all respects with naturally occurring brevetoxin A (as determined by thin-layer chromatography, high-performance liquid chromatography, ^{1}H and ^{13}C NMR, optical rotation $[\alpha]_D^{22}$, infrared spectroscopy and mass spectrometry)[1-3,30,31].

The total synthesis of brevetoxin A (**1**) became possible only after a long campaign which involved several thwarted strategies and the development of a number of new synthetic technologies. Particularly rewarding were the solutions found to the synthetic challenges posed by the 7-, 8- and 9-membered rings of the target molecule[10,11] and the convergent strategy finally developed to reach the complex and aesthetically pleasing structure of brevetoxin A. Through the described chemistry, brevetoxin A (**1**) joins brevetoxin B[35-38] in yielding to total synthesis. The work described here opens up the possibility of preparing suitable molecular probes that may contribute to the development of sensing devices[39] for this and related biotoxins of the "red tides"[40-45] and enhance our understanding of this phenomenon.

(**392**, 264-269; 1998)

成的短裸甲藻毒素 A(**1**)的重要物理数据如下：薄层保留系数 $R_f = 0.45$(硅胶，乙酸乙酯：己烷 = 1:1)；比旋光度 $[\alpha]_D^{22} + 75.5$(c 0.2，二氯甲烷)；红外光谱(纯化合物)ν_{max} 3,425.1，2,920.5，2,849.2，1,788.2，1,689.5，1,455.1，1,378.7，1,314，1,265.7，1,208.3，1,079.9，897.1，737.0 cm^{-1}；^{1}H 核磁共振谱(氘代苯，600 MHz，45 ℃)δ 9.29(s, 1 H)，5.90 (s, 1 H)，5.87 (dd, $J = 10.8$, 5.2 Hz, 1 H)，5.78 ~ 5.67 (bm, 2 H)，5.71 ~ 5.64 (m, 1 H)，5.43 (s, 1 H)，4.55 (dd, $J = 8.0$, 5.4 Hz, 1 H)，3.98 ~ 3.91 (m, 3 H)，3.74 (b, 1 H)，3.59 ~ 3.54 (m, 1 H)，3.52 (ddd, $J = 10.6$, 7.9, 2.3 Hz, 1 H)，3.46 ~ 3.34 (m, 4 H)，3.29 (bd, $J = 8.5$ Hz, 1 H)，3.19 ~ 3.10 (m, 3 H)，2.94 (ddd, $J = 12.0$, 8.0, 4.1 Hz, 1 H)，2.89 (ddd, $J = 11.9$, 9.2, 4.5 Hz, 1 H)，2.80 (dd, $J = 11.9$, 4.6 Hz, 1 H)，2.78 (dd, $J = 9.6$, 2.7 Hz, 1 H)，2.72 ~ 2.40 (bm, 4 H)，2.65 (dd, $J = 10.7$, 10.7 Hz, 1 H)，2.40 (ddd, $J = 15.2$, 10.8, 4.0 Hz, 1 H)，2.36 (dd, $J = 16.9$, 8.2 Hz, 1 H)，2.31 (dd, $J = 11.6$, 4.2 Hz, 1 H)，2.25 ~ 2.21 (m, 1 H)，2.24 ~ 2.20 (m, 1 H)，2.21 (dd, $J = 16.9$, 10.3 Hz, 1 H)，2.18 ~ 2.10 (m, 1 H)，2.05 ~ 1.92 (m, 6 H)，1.92 ~ 1.86 (m, 1 H)，1.86 ~ 1.74 (m, 3H)，1.72 ~ 1.52 (m, 7 H)，1.44 ~ 1.38 (m, 1 H)，1.37 ~ 1.24 (m, 1 H)，1.24 (s, 3 H)，1.20 (d, $J = 7.1$ Hz, 3 H)，0.98 ~ 0.95 (m, 1 H)，0.96 (s, 3 H)，0.77 (d, $J = 6.8$ Hz, 3 H)；^{13}C 核磁共振谱(氘代苯，150 MHz，45 ℃)δ 193.5，171.0，148.9，139.0，134.4，128.5，127.4，124.8，92.0，88.5，86.7，85.1，84.7，84.1，83.8，82.2，82.0，80.4，79.9，78.9，77.8，76.7，76.2，71.9，71.1，69.6，66.3，62.4，52.9，45.6，43.3，38.2，37.5，36.9，36.2，35.9，33.8，32.3，31.4，29.0，27.6，27.2，21.4，19.7，16.8，15.0(正如先前的报道[30,31]，碳 17，20 和 28 分别在 34.5，34.5 和 30.9 处峰型最佳，为弱的宽峰)；质谱：$C_{49}H_{70}O_{13}$(M+Na$^+$)的计算值为 889.4714，测定值为 889.4747。关于化合物 **42** 和 **43** 的重要物理数据，请参见补充信息。

率为 80%)。在化合物 **43** 中 FG 环的连接处形成了新的立构中心，其立体化学是通过将它的核磁共振数据与短裸甲藻毒素 A 的[1,3,30,31]和一个模型系统[24]中的核磁共振数据进行比较而得到证实的。经过下面的过程将 A 环结合到短裸甲藻毒素 A 骨架的其余部分上：对化合物 **43** 上的伯醇进行逐步氧化，先用四正丙基过钌酸铵和 4-甲基吗啉-N-氧化物氧化成相应的醛[23]，再用亚氯酸钠-磷酸二氢钠和 2-甲基-2-丁烯进一步氧化成羧酸[32]，然后用重氮甲烷进行甲酯化(三步的收率为 80%)，接着再用氟化氢·吡啶处理以脱去三个甲硅烷基，并同时发生闭环反应形成 γ-内酯环，得到短裸甲藻毒素 A 的 ABCDEFGHIJ 环系化合物 **44**(收率为 90%)。最后，用严格控制加入量的戴斯-马丁[33]试剂选择性地氧化二醇化合物 **44**，得到相应的羟基醛化合物(收率为 80%)，再与 N,N-二甲基亚甲基碘化铵(参考文献 34)顺利地发生反应，以 90% 的收率得到短裸甲藻毒素 A(**1**)。合成的短裸甲藻毒素 A 与天然存在的短裸甲藻毒 A 在各方面的性质都是一致的(经薄层色谱，高效液相色谱，^{1}H 和 ^{13}C 核磁共振谱，比旋光度 $[\alpha]_D^{22}$，红外光谱和质谱验证)[1-3,30,31]。

只有经过长期努力(其间经历了数次失败的策略和若干新合成技术的发展)，才实现了短裸甲藻毒素 A(**1**)的全合成。尤其有意义的是找到了应对目标分子中 7 元、8 元和 9 元环的合成挑战的方法[10,11]，以及最终开发出的构建了短裸甲藻毒素 A 这一复杂而美观结构的汇聚式合成策略。通过前述的化学合成，短裸甲藻毒素 A(**1**)和短裸甲藻毒素 B[35-38]都可以通过全合成得到。这里发表的研究工作为制备适当的分子探针开拓了可行性，这些探针可能有助于开发出传感设备[39]，用于检测与"赤潮"相关的生物毒素[40-45]，并增进我们对该现象的理解。

(刘振明 翻译；许家喜 审稿)

K. C. Nicolaou, Zhen Yang, Guo-qiang Shi, Janet L. Gunzner, Konstantinos A. Agrios & Peter Gärtner

Department of Chemistry and The Skaggs Institute for Chemical Biology, The Scripps Research Institute, 10550 North Torrey Pines Road, La Jolla, California 92037, USA and Department of Chemistry and Biochemistry, University of California, San Diego, 9500 Gilman Drive, La Jolla, California 92093, USA

Received 24 November 1997; accepted 19 January 1998.

References:

1. Shimizu, Y., Chou, H.-N. & Bando, H. Structure of brevetoxin A (GB-1 toxin), the most potent toxin in the Florida red tide organism *Gymnodinium breve* (*Ptychodiscus brevis*). *J. Am. Chem. Soc.* **108,** 514-515 (1986).

2. Shimizu, Y., Bando, H., Chou, H.-N., Van Duyne, G. & Clardy, J. C. Absolute configuration of brevetoxins. *J. Chem. Soc., Chem. Commun.* 1656-1658 (1986).

3. Pawlak, J. *et al.* Structure of brevetoxin A as constructed from NMR and MS data. *J. Am. Chem. Soc.* **109,** 1144-1150 (1987).

4. Rein, K. S., Baden, D. G. & Gawley, R. E. Conformational analysis of the sodium channel modulator, brevetoxin A, comparison with brevetoxin B conformations, and a hypothesis about the common pharmacophore of the "site 5" toxins. *J. Org. Chem.* **59,** 2101-2106 (1994).

5. Rein, K. S., Lynn, B., Baden, D. G. & Gawley, R. E. Brevetoxin B: chemical modifications, synaptosome binding, toxicity, and an unexpected conformational effect. *J. Org. Chem.* **59,** 2107-21013 (1994).

6. Yasumoto, T. & Murata, M. Marine toxins. *Chem. Rev.* **93,** 1897-1909 (1993).

7. Gawley, R. E. *et al.* The relationship of brevetoxin "length" and A-ring functionality to binding and activity in neuronal sodium channels. *Chem. Biol.* **2,** 533-541 (1995).

8. Chou, H.-N. & Shimizu, Y. Biosynthesis of brevetoxins. Evidence for the mixed origin of the backbone carbon chain and the possible involvement of dicarboxylic acids. *J. Am. Chem. Soc.* **109,** 2184-2185 (1987).

9. Lee, M. S., Qin, G.-W., Nakanishi, K. & Zagorski, M. G. Biosynthesis studies on brevetoxins, potent neurotoxins produced by the dinoflagellate *Gymnodinium breve*. *J. Am. Chem. Soc.* **111,** 6234-6241 (1989).

10. Nicolaou, K. C., Prasad, C. V. C., Hwang, C.-K., Duggan, M. E. & Veale, C. A. Cyclizations of hydroxydithioketals. New synthetic technology for the construction of oxocenes and related medium ring systems. *J. Am. Chem. Soc.* **111,** 5321-5330 (1989).

11. Nicolaou, K. C., Shi, G.-Q., Gunzner, J. L., Gärtner, P. & Yang, Z. Palladium-catalyzed functionalization of lactones via their cyclic ketene acetal phosphates. Efficient new synthetic technology for the construction of medium and large cyclic ethers. *J. Am. Chem. Soc.* **119,** 5467-5468 (1997).

12. Nicolaou, K. C., Prasad, C. V. C., Somers, P. K. & Hwang, C.-K. Activation of 6-*endo* over 5-*exo* hydroxy epoxide openings. Stereo- and ringselective synthesis of tetrahydrofuran and tetrahydropyran systems. *J. Am. Chem. Soc.* **111,** 5330-5334 (1989).

13. Freeman, J. P. in *Organic Syntheses (Collective Vol. VII)* 139-141 (Wiley, New York, 1990).

14. Xie, M., Beges, D. A. & Robins, M. J. Efficient "dehomologation" of di-*O*-isopropylidenehexofuranose derivatives to give *O*-isopropylidenepentofuranose by sequential treatment with periodic acid in ethyl acetate and sodium borohydride. *J. Org. Chem.* **61,** 5178-5179 (1996).

15. Mukaiyama, T., Banno, K. & Narasaka, K. New cross-aldol reactions. Reactions of silyl enol ethers with carbonyl compounds activated by titanium tetrachloride. *J. Am. Chem. Soc.* **96,** 7503-7509 (1974).

16. Rodeheaver, G. T. & Hunt, D. F. Conversion of olefins into ketones with mercuric acetate and palladium chloride. *Chem. Commun.* 818-819 (1971).

17. Tamura, Y., Ochiai, H., Nakamura, T. & Yoshida, Z. Arylation and vinylation of 2-carboethoxyethylzinc iodide and 3-carboethoxypropylzinc iodide catalyzed by palladium. *Tetrahedr. Lett.* **27,** 955-958 (1986).

18. Inanaga, J., Hirata, K., Saeki, H., Katsuki, T. & Yamaguchi, M. A rapid esterification by mixed anhydride and its application to large-ring lactonization. *Bull. Chem. Soc. Jpn* 52, 1989-1993 (1979).

19. Arhart, R. J. & Martin, J. C. Sulfuranes, V. The chemistry of sulfur (IV) compounds. Dialkoxydiarylsulfuranes. *J. Am. Chem. Soc.* **94,** 4997-5003 (1972).

20. Hoveyda, A. H., Evans, D. A. & Fu, G. C. Substrate-directable chemical reactions. *Chem. Rev.* **93,** 1307-1370 (1993).

21. Nicolaou, K. C., McGarry, D. G. & Sommers, P. K. New synthetic strategies for the construction of medium-size cyclic ethers. Stereocontrolled synthesis of the BCD ring framework of brevetoxin A. *J. Am. Chem. Soc.* **112,** 3696-3697 (1990).

22. Corey, E. J. & Beames, D. J. Mixed cuprate reagents of type R1R2CuLi which allow selective group transfer. *J. Am. Chem. Soc.* **94,** 7210-7211 (1972).

23. Ley, S. V., Norman, J., Griffith, W. P. & Marsden, S. P. Tetrapropylammonium perruthenate, Pr4N+RuO4, TPAP: a catalytic oxidant for organic synthesis. *Synthesis* 639-666 (1994).

24. Nicolaou, K. C. *et al.* New synthetic technology for the construction of 9-membered ring cyclic ethers. Construction of the EFGH ring skeleton of brevetoxin A. *J. Am. Chem. Soc.* **119,** 8105-8106 (1997).

25. Mahoney, W. S., Brestensky, D. M. & Stryker, J. M. Selective hydride-mediated conjugate reduction of α,β-unsaturated carbonyl compounds using [(Ph3P)CuH]6. *J. Am. Chem. Soc.* **119,** 8105-8106 (1997).

26. Feixas, J., Capdevila, A. & Guerrero, A. Utilization of neutral alumina as a mild reagent for the selective cleavage of primary and secondary silyl ethers. *Tetrahedron* **50,** 8539-8550 (1994).

27. Nicolaou, K. C. *et al.* Novel strategies for the construction of complex polycyclic ether frameworks. Stereocontrolled synthesis of the FGHIJ ring system of brevetoxin A. *Angew. Chem. Int. Edn. Engl.* **30,** 299-303 (1991).

28. Parikh, J. R. & Doering, W. von E. Sulfur trioxide in the oxidation of alcohols by dimethyl sulfoxide. *J. Am. Chem. Soc.* **89,** 5505-5507 (1967).

29. Clayden, J. & Warren, S. Stereocontrol in organic synthesis using the diphenylphosphoryl group. *Angew. Chem. Int. Edn. Engl.* **35,** 241-270 (1996).

30. Zagorski, M. G., Nakanishi, K., Qin, G.-W. & Lee, M. S. Assignment of ^{13}C NMR peaks of brevetoxin A: application of two-dimensional Hartmann-Hahn spectroscopy. *J. Org. Chem.* **53,** 4156-4157 (1988).

31. Lee, M. S., Nakanishi, K. & Zagorski, M. G. Full proton assignment of BTX-A, $C_{49}H_{70}O_{13}$. *New J. Chem.* **11,** 753-756 (1987).

32. Klindgren, B. O. & Nilsson, T. Preparation of carboxylic acids from aldehydes (including hydroxylated benzaldehydes) by oxidation with chlorite. *Acta Chem. Scand.* **27,** 888-890 (1973).

33. Dess, D. B. & Martin, J. C. Readily accessible 12-I-5 oxidant for the conversion of primary and secondary alcohols to aldehydes and ketones. *J. Org. Chem.* **48,** 4155-4156 (1983).

34. Schreiber, J., Maag, H., Hashimoto, N. & Eschenmoser, A. Dimethyl(methylene)ammonium iodide. *Angew. Chem. Int. Edn. Engl.* **10,** 330-331 (1971).

35. Nicolaou, K. C. *et al.* Total synthesis of brevetoxin B. 1. First generation strategies and new approaches to oxepane systems. *J. Am. Chem. Soc.* **117,** 10227-10238 (1995).

36. Nicolaou, K. C. *et al.* Total synthesis of brevetoxin B. 2. Second generation strategies and construction of the dioxepane region [DEFG]. *J. Am. Chem. Soc.* **117,** 10239-10251 (1995).

37. Nicolaou, K. C. *et al.* Total synthesis of brevetoxin B. 3. Final strategy and completion. *J. Am. Chem. Soc.* **117,** 10252-10263 (1995).

38. Nicolaou, K. C. The total synthesis of brevetoxin B: a twelve year odyssey in organic synthesis. *Angew. Chem. Int. Edn. Engl.* **35,** 589-607 (1996).

39. Homaka, Y. Recent methods for detection of seafood toxins: recent immunological method for ciguatoxin and related polyethers. *Food Addit. Contam.* **10,** 71-82 (1993).

40. Anderson, D. M. Turning back the harmful red tide. *Nature* **388,** 513-514 (1997).

41. Barker, R. *And the Waters Turned to Blood* (Simon & Schuster, New York, 1997).

42. Anderson, D. M. Red tides. *Sci. Am.* **271,** 62-68 (1994).

43. Hall, S. & Strichartz, G. (eds) (American Chemical Society, Washington DC, 1990).

44. Okaichi, T., Anderson, D. M. & Nemoto, T. (eds) *Red Tides. Biology, Environmental Science, and Toxicology* (Elsevier, New York, 1989).

45. Anderson, D. M. & White, A. W. Marine biotoxins at the top of the food chain. *Oceanus* **35,** 55-61 (1992).

Supplementary Information is available on *Nature*'s World-Wide Web site (http://www.nature.com) and as paper copy from Mary Sheehan at the London editorial office of *Nature*.

Acknowledgements. We are indebted to those of our collaborators whose early contributions on this project made its success possible; their names will appear in the full account of this work. We thank K. Nakanishi and Y. Shimizu for samples of natural brevetoxin A, and D. H. Huang, G. Siuzdak and R. Chadha for the NMR, mass spectroscopic and X-ray crystallographic assistance, respectively. This work was supported by the National Institutes of Health USA (GM), The Skaggs Institute for Chemical Biology, Novartis, Merck, Hoffmann-La Roche, Schering Plough, DuPont Merck, the American Chemical Society (graduate fellowship sponsored by Aldrich to J.L.G.) and the Foundation for the Promotion of Scientific Investigations (postdoctoral fellowship to P.G.). Z.Y. and G.S. contributed equally to this project.

Correspondence and requests for materials should be addressed to K.C.N. at The Scripps Research Institute (e-mail: kcn@scripps.edu).

Global-scale Temperature Patterns and Climate Forcing over the Past Six Centuries

M. E. Mann *et al.*

Editor's Note

To understand current climate change, we need to know how it compares with changes in the historical past, which would have had natural rather than human causes. Here Michael Mann and his coworkers use a wide range of different climate indicators in the geological and biological records to reconstruct global climate over the past 600 years. They conclude that the average temperature in the Northern Hemisphere fluctuated only slightly before an abrupt twentieth-century increase. This "hockey-stick" graph (Figure 5b) became notorious when it was later found to have been derived from flawed calculations. But although climate sceptics have implied that it undermines the case for global warming, many other lines of evidence in fact show it to be real.

Spatially resolved global reconstructions of annual surface temperature patterns over the past six centuries are based on the multivariate calibration of widely distributed high-resolution proxy climate indicators. Time-dependent correlations of the reconstructions with time-series records representing changes in greenhouse-gas concentrations, solar irradiance, and volcanic aerosols suggest that each of these factors has contributed to the climate variability of the past 400 years, with greenhouse gases emerging as the dominant forcing during the twentieth century. Northern Hemisphere mean annual temperatures for three of the past eight years are warmer than any other year since (at least) AD 1400.

KNOWING both the spatial and temporal patterns of climate change over the past several centuries remains a key to assessing a possible anthropogenic impact on post-industrial climate[1]. In addition to the possibility of warming due to increased concentrations of greenhouse gases during the past century, there is evidence that both solar irradiance and explosive volcanism have played an important part in forcing climate variations over the past several centuries[2,3]. The unforced "natural variability" of the climate system may also be quite important on multidecadal and century timescales[4,5]. If a faithful empirical description of climate variability could be obtained for the past several centuries, a more confident estimation could be made of the roles of different external forcings and internal sources of variability on past and recent climate. Because widespread instrumental climate data are available for only about one century, we must use proxy climate indicators combined with any very long instrumental records that are available to obtain such an empirical description of large-scale climate variability during past centuries. A variety of studies have sought to use a "multiproxy" approach to understand long-term climate variations, by analysing a widely distributed set of proxy and instrumental

过去六个世纪全球尺度上的
气温分布型与气候强迫

曼等

编者按

为理解当前的气候变化，我们需要把其与历史上自然的而非人为因素导致的变化进行比较。本文中，迈克尔·曼和他的同事们运用一系列不同的地质记录和生物记录的气候指标重建了过去 600 年间的全球气候。他们认为，北半球的平均温度在二十世纪突然升高，但在此之前的变化都只是轻微的波动。后来，这种"曲棍球棍"图（图5b）因被发现是一种错误的计算结果而变得臭名昭著。然而，尽管气候怀疑论者已经暗示它削弱了全球变暖的论据，但仍有许多其他的证据表明它是真实存在的。

利用广泛分布的高分辨率气候代用指标的多变量校正结果，本文对过去六个世纪中每年的地表温度分布型在空间上进行了全球恢复重建。重建结果与代表温室气体浓度、太阳辐照度以及火山气溶胶变化的时间序列记录之间的时间相关性表明，上述各因子对过去 400 年中发生的气候变化都有影响，其中温室气体从二十世纪开始成为最主要的影响因素。在北半球，过去八年中有三年的年均气温均创造了（至少）从公元 1400 年以来的最高纪录。

认识过去几个世纪中气候变化的空间和时间模态仍然是评估后工业化时代人类对气候影响的关键所在 [1]。有证据显示，除了在过去的一个世纪中温室气体浓度的增加导致了气候变暖以外，在过去的几个世纪中，太阳辐照度与火山爆发在影响气候变化中也起着重要作用 [2,3]。气候系统的非强迫"自然变率"也可能在数十年乃至上百年的时间尺度上具有重要意义 [4,5]。倘若能够对过去几个世纪中的气候变化做出较可靠的经验描述，那么就可据此对引起过去和近期气候变化的各外部强迫及内在因素所起的作用给出一个更为可信的评估。由于采用大范围仪器进行气候观测仅开展了约一个世纪的时间，我们必须将气候代用指标与已有的较长期的仪器观测资料相结合，以获得过去几个世纪中大尺度气候变化的经验性描述。已有大量研究试图采用"多种代用资料"法来推断长期的气候变化，通过分析广泛分布的各类代用资料和仪器观测的气候指标 [1,5-8] 来深入研究全球的长期气候变化。在上述前人研究的基础

climate indicators[1,5-8] to yield insights into long-term global climate variations. Building on such past studies, we take a new statistical approach to reconstructing global patterns of annual temperature back to the beginning of the fifteenth century, based on the calibration of multiproxy data networks by the dominant patterns of temperature variability in the instrumental record.

Using these statistically verifiable yearly global temperature reconstructions, we analyse the spatiotemporal patterns of climate change over the past 500 years, and then take an empirical approach to estimating the relationship between global temperature changes, variations in volcanic aerosols, solar irradiance and greenhouse-gas concentrations during the same period.

Data

We use a multiproxy network consisting of widely distributed high-quality annual-resolution proxy climate indicators, individually collected and formerly analysed by many palaeoclimate researchers (details and references are available: see Supplementary Information). The network includes (Fig. 1a) the collection of annual-resolution dendroclimatic, ice core, ice melt, and long historical records used by Bradley and Jones[6] combined with other coral, ice core, dendroclimatic, and long instrumental records. The long instrumental records have been formed into annual mean anomalies relative to the 1902–80 reference period, and gridded onto a 5°×5° grid (yielding 11 temperature grid-point series and 12 precipitation grid-point series dating back to 1820 or earlier) similar to that shown in Fig. 1b. Certain densely sampled regional dendroclimatic data sets have been represented in the network by a smaller number of leading principal components (typically 3–11 depending on the spatial extent and size of the data set). This form of representation ensures a reasonably homogeneous spatial sampling in the multiproxy network (112 indicators back to 1820).

Potential limitations specific to each type of proxy data series must be carefully taken into account in building an appropriate network. Dating errors in a given record (for example, incorrectly assigned annual layers or rings) are particularly detrimental if mutual information is sought to describe climate patterns on a year-by-year basis. Standardization of certain biological proxy records relative to estimated growth trends, and the limits of constituent chronology segment lengths (for example, in dendroclimatic reconstructions), can restrict the maximum timescale of climate variability that is recorded[9], and only a limited subset of the indicators in the multiproxy network may thus "anchor in" the longest-term trends (for example, variations on timescales greater than 500 years). However, the dendroclimatic data used were carefully screened for conservative standardization and sizeable segment lengths. Moreover, the mutual information contained in a diverse and widely distributed set of independent climate indicators can more faithfully capture the consistent climate signal that is present, reducing the compromising effects of biases and weaknesses in the individual indicators.

116

上，我们采用了一种新的统计方法重建了十五世纪以来全球气温的年际变化分布型，其中多代用数据网的校正，是根据（近期的）器测资料反映的主要气温变化模态来进行的。

本文利用上述经统计学验证的年际全球气温重建资料，分析了过去 500 年中气候变化的时空模态，之后又利用经验方法研究了同时期内全球温度变化与火山气溶胶、太阳辐照度以及温室气体浓度变化之间的相互关系。

数　据

我们所采用的是由广泛分布的高质量年际分辨率气候代用指标组成的多种代用资料网，而这些代用指标都是许多古气候学家各自收集和之前分析过的（详细内容及参考文献见补充信息）。该资料网包括（图 1a）布拉德利和琼斯[6]所采用的年际分辨率的年轮气候学、冰芯、冰融体以及长期历史记录，同时还结合了其他学者关于珊瑚、冰芯、年轮气候学以及长期的仪器观测记录的资料。其中长期的仪器观测记录均处理为相对于 1902 ~ 1980 年间的年平均值的距平值，并插值为 5°×5° 的网格（形成 11 个温度格点序列和 12 个降雨量格点序列，一直追溯到 1820 年甚至更早），如图 1b 所示。在数据网络中，对于某些取样较为密集的区域性年轮气候学数据库就通过主成分信息进行稀疏化处理（根据空间范围和数据库的大小一般取代表性的 3 ~ 11 个点不等）来表示。这样就保证了所形成的多种代用资料网在空间取样上的合理均匀性（其中 112 个指标可回溯至 1820 年）。

在建立合适的数据网的过程中，必须仔细考虑到每种代用指标数据序列的潜在局限性。倘若通过寻找共有信息以得出逐年的气候分布型，那么存在于给定记录中的测年误差（比如，年层或年轮的判定错误）将极具破坏性。基于生长趋势估计的某类生物代用记录的标准化处理以及（用以在）年代学中使用的指标片段的（时间）长度（例如树轮重建），限制了我们在记录中能看到的最长时间尺度的气候变化特征[9]，因此在多种代用资料网中只有非常有限的一部分代用指标能用于"锚定"长尺度（例如时间尺度大于 500 年）的气候。不过我们所用的年轮数据均已经过严格的筛选，以实现守恒标准化以及较长的分割长度。此外，各类气候指标库分布广泛且相互独立，它们所包含的共有信息更能准确地获取已有的一致性的气候信号，进而降低因单个指标的偏差和不足而带来的相互影响。

Fig. 1. Data used in this study. **a**, Distribution of annual-resolution proxy indicators used in this study. Dendroclimatic reconstructions are indicated by "tree" symbols, ice core/ice melt proxies by "star" symbols and coral records by "C" symbols. Long historical records and instrumental "grid-points" series are shown by squares (temperature) or diamonds (precipitation). Groups of "+" symbols indicate principal components of dense tree-ring sub-networks, with the number of such symbols indicating the number of retained principal components. Sites are shown dating back to at least 1820 (red), 1800 (blue-green), 1750 (green), 1600 (blue) and 1400 (black). Certain sites (for example, the Quelccaya ice core) consist of multiple proxy indicators (for example, multiple cores, and both $\delta^{18}O$ isotope and accumulation measurements). **b**, Distribution of the 1,082 nearly continuous available land air/sea surface temperature grid-point data available from 1902 onward, indicated by shading. The squares indicate the subset of 219 grid-points with nearly continuous records extending back to 1854 that are used for verification. Northern Hemisphere (**NH**) and global (**GLB**) mean temperature are estimated as areally weighted (that is, cosine latitude) averages over the Northern Hemisphere and global domains respectively.

Monthly instrumental land air and sea surface temperature[10] grid-point data (Fig. 1b) from the period 1902–95 are used to calibrate the proxy data set. Although there are notable spatial gaps, this network covers significant enough portions of the globe to form reliable estimates of Northern Hemisphere mean temperature, and certain regional indices of particular importance such as the "NINO3" eastern tropical Pacific surface temperature index often used to describe the El Niño phenomenon. The NINO3 index is constructed from the eight grid-points available within the conventional NINO3 box (5° S to 5° N, 90–150° W).

118

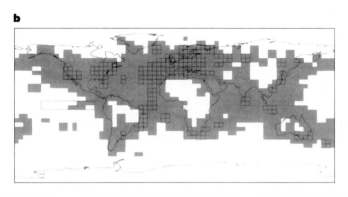

图 1. 本研究所采用的数据。**a**, 本研究中年分辨率代用指标的分布。年轮气候重建以"树形"符号表示，冰芯/冰融体代用指标以"星状"符号表示，而珊瑚记录则用"C"表示。长期记录和仪器记录的"格点"序列则分别以方框（温度）和菱形（降雨量）表示。"+"群表示密集的树木年轮子网络的主成分，其数量代表所保留下来的主成分的数目。图中还给出了可分别回溯到 1820 年（红）、1800 年（蓝绿）、1750 年（绿）、1600 年（蓝）和 1400 年（黑）的站位分布。有些观测站（例如魁尔克亚冰芯）包含多个代用指标（如，多个岩芯，同时测定 $\delta^{18}O$ 同位素和加积速率两项指标）。**b**, 1902 年以后的所有 1,082 个近乎连续的陆地气温/海表温度格点数据的分布，在图中以阴影表示。方框表示由 219 个格点组成的子库，是检验过程中所采用的可回溯到 1854 年的连续记录。北半球（NH）和全球（GLB）平均气温是分别根据北半球和全球范围内的面积加权（即纬度的余弦值）平均值估算而来的。

　　利用 1902～1995 年间仪器记录的陆地气温和海表温度[10]的月际格点数据（图1b）对代用指标数据库作了校正。尽管空间上还存明显的空白，但该数据网络已对全球所有重要区域实现了覆盖，由此得出的北半球平均气温是可靠的，而某些区域性指标则具有特殊意义，比如，"NINO3"赤道东太平洋表层温度指数常用来描述厄尔尼诺现象。NINO3 指数是从传统 NINO3 区（南纬 5°到北纬 5°，西经 90°到西经 150°）中抽出的 8 个格点构成的。

Multiproxy Calibration

Although studies have shown that well chosen regional paleoclimate reconstructions can act as surprisingly representative surrogates for large-scale climate[11-13], multiproxy networks seem to provide the greatest opportunity for large-scale palaeoclimate reconstruction[6] and climate signal detection[1,5]. There is a rich tradition of multivariate statistical calibration approaches to palaeoclimate reconstruction, particularly in the field of dendroclimatology where the relative strengths and weaknesses of various approaches to multivariate calibration have been well studied[14,15]. Such approaches have been applied to regional dendroclimatic networks to reconstruct regional patterns of temperature[16,17] and atmospheric circulation[18-20] or specific climate phenomena such as the Southern Oscillation[21]. Largely because of the inhomogeneity of the information represented by different types of indicators in a true "multiproxy" network, we found conventional approaches (for example, canonical correlation analysis, CCA, of the proxy and instrumental data sets) to be relatively ineffective. Our approach to climate pattern reconstruction relates closely to statistical approaches which have recently been applied to the problem of filling-in sparse early instrumental climate fields, based on calibration of the sparse sub-networks against the more widespread patterns of variability that can be resolved in shorter data sets[22,23]. We first decompose the twentieth-century instrumental data into its dominant patterns of variability, and subsequently calibrate the individual climate proxy indicators against the time histories of these distinct patterns during their mutual interval of overlap. One can think of the instrumental patterns as "training" templates against which we calibrate or "train" the much longer proxy data (that is, the "trainee" data) during the shorter calibration period which they overlap. This calibration allows us to subsequently solve an "inverse problem" whereby best estimates of surface temperature patterns are deduced back in time before the calibration period, from the multiproxy network alone.

Implicit in our approach are at least three fundamental assumptions. (1) The indicators in our multiproxy trainee network are linearly related to one or more of the instrumental training patterns. In the relatively unlikely event that a proxy indicator represents a truly local climate phenomenon which is uncorrelated with larger-scale climate variations, or represents a highly nonlinear response to climate variations, this assumption will not be satisfied. (2) A relatively sparse but widely distributed sampling of long proxy and instrumental records may nonetheless sample most of the relatively small number of degrees of freedom in climate patterns at interannual and longer timescales. Regions not directly represented in the trainee network may nonetheless be indirectly represented through teleconnections with regions that are. The El Niño/Southern Oscillation (ENSO), for example, shows global-scale patterns of climatic influence[24], and is an example of a prominent pattern of variability which, if captured, can potentially describe variability in regions not directly sampled by the trainee data. (3) Patterns of variability captured by the multiproxy network have analogues in the patterns we resolve in the shorter instrumental data. This last assumption represents a fairly weak "stationarity" requirement—we do not require that the climate itself be stationary. In fact, we expect that some sizeable trends

多代用指标的校正

虽然研究显示仔细筛选出的区域性古气候重建出乎意料地可以代替大尺度的气候变化[11-13]，但多代用资料网似乎才是最有可能完成大尺度古气候重建[6]和气候信号探测[1,5]的方法。多元统计校正法用于古气候重建已有许多先例，特别是在年轮气候学领域，各种多元校正法的优缺点已有详细研究[14,15]。此类方法也已应用到区域性年轮气候指标网络以重建区域性温度分布型[16,17]、大气环流[18-20]以及特殊的气候现象（如南方涛动）[21]等。不过我们发现，主要由于在真正的"多代用"数据网中不同类型指标所反映的信息是不一致的，从而传统方法（例如，代用指标和仪器数据库的典型相关分析，即 CCA）的效果相对较差。而我们所采用的气候分布型重建方法则与统计方法紧密相关，该统计方法近来已在解决早期仪器气候记录稀疏地方的插值问题方面得到了应用，其原理是，根据分布更为广泛的短期数据库所反映的变化模式[22,23]对稀疏的子网络加以校正。首先，我们将二十世纪的仪器观测数据分解，得出其主要变化模式。然后根据不同分布型的时间序列，对各个气候代用指标加以校正，校正在各指标共同的重叠区间上进行。我们可以将仪器记录下的分布型看作"训练"模板，我们利用它来校正或"训练"相互重叠的更短的校正期间内的长期代用指标数据（即"训练"数据）。接下来我们可以利用该校正来解决一个"反向问题"，从而仅仅根据多代用指标就可推出校正期间以前的表层温度分布型。

该方法包括至少三项基本前提假设。(1)多代用训练数据网中的指标与所采用的一个或多个仪器训练分布型呈线性相关。为数极少的情况，即代用指标代表的是真实的局部气候现象（与大尺度气候变化并不相关），或者代表的是对气候变化的强烈非线性响应时，是不能满足上述假设条件的。(2)相对稀疏但分布广泛的长期代用指标还是能获取年际或更长时间尺度上的气候分布型中自由度较小的大部分数据。训练数据网中无法直接表示的区域可以通过与其他区域的遥相关间接表示。例如，厄尔尼诺和南方涛动（ENSO）对气候分布型的影响是全球范围的[24]，也是主要的变化模态的一个实例，倘若找到了它的变化，就可以大致得出未能通过训练数据进行直接取样区域的变化情况。(3)利用多代用指标网得到的变化模态与我们根据短期器测数据从分布型得出的结果相似。最后这一项假设代表了一种比较低的"稳定"要求——我们并不是要求气候本身固定不变。事实上，我们希望通过重建找出那些较大的气候变化。不过，我们确实也假定上世纪气候的基本空间变化模态与前几个世

in the climate may be resolved by our reconstructions. We do, however, assume that the fundamental spatial patterns of variation which the climate has shown during the past century are similar to those by which it has varied during past recent centuries. Studies of instrumental surface-temperature patterns suggest that such a form of stationarity holds up at least on multidecadal timescales, during the past century[23]. The statistical cross-validation exercises we describe later provide the best evidence that these key underlying assumptions hold.

We isolate the dominant patterns of the instrumental surface-temperature data through principal component analysis[25] (PCA). PCA provides a natural smoothing of the temperature field in terms of a small number of dominant patterns of variability or "empirical eigenvectors". Each of these eigenvectors is associated with a characteristic spatial pattern or "empirical orthogonal function" (EOF) and its characteristic evolution in time or "principal component" (PC). The ranking of the eigenvectors orders the fraction of variance they describe in the (standardized) multivariate data during the calibration period. The first five of these eigenvectors describe a fraction $\beta = 0.93$ (that is, 93%) of the global-mean (GLB) temperature variations, 85% of the Northern Hemisphere-mean (NH) variations, 67% of the NINO3 index, and 76% of the non-trend-related (DETR) NH variance (see Methods for a description of the β statistic used here as a measure of resolved variance). A sizeable fraction of the total multivariate spatiotemporal variance (MULT) in the raw (instrumental) data (27%) is described by these five eigenvectors, or about 30% of the standardized variance (no. 1 = 12%, no. 2 = 6.5%, no. 3 = 5%, no. 4 = 4%, no. 5 = 3.5%). Figure 2 shows the EOFs of the first five eigenvectors. The associated PCs and their reconstructed counterparts (RPCs) are discussed in the next section. The first eigenvector, associated with the significant global warming trend of the past century, describes much of the variability in the global (GLB = 88%) and hemispheric (NH = 73%) means. Subsequent eigenvectors, in contrast, describe much of the spatial variability relative to the large-scale means (that is, much of the remaining MULT). The second eigenvector is the dominant ENSO-related component, describing 41% of the variance in the NINO3 index. This eigenvector shows a modest negative trend which, in the eastern tropical Pacific, describes a "La Niña"-like cooling trend[26], which opposes warming in the same region associated with the global warming pattern of the first eigenvector. The third eigenvector is associated largely with interannual-to-decadal scale variability in the Atlantic basin and carries the well-known temperature signature of the North Atlantic Oscillation (NAO)[27] and decadal tropical Atlantic dipole[28]. The fourth eigenvector describes a primarily multidecadal timescale variation with ENSO-scale and tropical/subtropical Atlantic features, while the fifth eigenvector is dominated by multidecadal variability in the entire Atlantic basin and neighbouring regions that has been widely noted elsewhere[29-34].

We calibrate each of the indicators in the multiproxy data network against these empirical eigenvectors at annual-mean resolution during the 1902–80 training interval. Although the seasonality of variability is potentially important—many extratropical proxy indicators, for example, reflect primarily warm-season variability[6,7]—we seek in the present study to resolve only annual-mean conditions, exploiting the seasonal climate persistence, and the fact that the mutual information from data reflecting various seasonal windows should

纪是相似的。对器测地表温度时空分布模态的研究显示，在上世纪，这样的稳定形态至少在数十年的时间尺度上是成立的[23]。后文我们将会给出统计交叉验证结果，而它正是上述暗含的关键假设成立的最好证据。

　　利用主成分分析法[25]（PCA）将器测地表温度数据显示的主要分布型从中提取出来。PCA 提供一个自然平滑的温度场，它以少数几个主变化模态或"经验特征向量"的形式表示。每个特征向量都对应着一个与之相关的特征空间分布型（或"经验正交函数"，EOF）及其时间演化特征（或"主成分"，PC）。在（标准化）多元数据分析中，特征向量的级别表示其在校正期间内贡献的方差的大小。前五个特征向量反映的依次是：全球平均（GLB）温度变化 $\beta = 0.93$（即 93%），北半球（NH）的平均温度变化 85%，NINO3 指数 67%，北半球非趋势相关（DETR）方差 76%（这里 β 用来衡量解释方差，其统计学意义见方法部分）。这五个特征向量就可以表示出原始（仪器观测）数据中总多元时空方差（MULT）（27%）的大部分，约贡献标准方差的 30%（no.1 = 12%，no.2 = 6.5%，no.3 = 5%，no.4 = 4%，no.5 = 3.5%）。图 2 所示为前五个特征向量的经验正交函数。相关的多个主成分及其对应的重建主成分（RPC）将在下节讨论。第一个特征向量，与上世纪全球显著变暖的趋势相关，体现了全球（GLB = 88%）和半球（NH = 73%）平均值的主要变化。而后面的特征向量则表示了不同地区相对于大尺度平均值的主要空间变化（即主要剩余 MULT）。第二个特征向量主要是与 ENSO 相关的分量，占 NINO3 指数方差的 41%。该特征向量表现出轻微的负相关变化趋势，在热带东太平洋地区，代表了类似于拉尼娜现象的变冷趋势[26]，这与反映全球变暖分布型的第一个特征向量在同一地区显示出的变暖趋势相反。第三个特征向量主要反映了大西洋海盆在年际、十年尺度上的变化，带有众所周知的北大西洋涛动（NAO）的温度变化[27]和十年际热带大西洋偶极子[28]等特征。第四个特征向量反映的主要是 ENSO 和热带、副热带大西洋在数十年尺度上的变化，而第五个特征向量则反映了整个大西洋海盆及其邻近地区数十年尺度上的变化，这在其他文章中[29-34]已得到了广泛的关注。

　　利用上述经验特征向量对多代用数据网中的每个指标在 1902～1980 年间的值逐一作了年均分辨率尺度上的校正。虽然季节性尺度的变化具有潜在的重要意义（例如，许多温带代用指标主要反映了暖季变化性[6,7]），但在本研究中我们借助季节性气候的持续性，仅关注年均变化情况，而反映了不同季节性气候的数据的共有信息

Fig. 2. Empirical orthogonal functions (EOFs) for the five leading eigenvectors of the global temperature data from 1902 to 1980. The gridpoint areal weighting factor used in the PCA procedure has been removed from the EOFs so that relative temperature anomalies can be inferred from the patterns.

provide complementary information regarding annual mean climate conditions[10]. Following this calibration, we apply an overdetermined optimization procedure to determine the best combination of eigenvectors represented by the multiproxy network back in time on a year-by-year basis, with a spatial coverage dictated only by the spatial extent of the instrumental training data. From the RPCs, spatial patterns and all relevant averages or indices can be readily determined. The details of the entire statistical approach are described in the Methods section.

图 2. 1902～1980 年间全球温度数据的五个主要特征向量的经验正交函数（EOF）。主成分分析中所采用的格点面积加权因子已从经验正交函数中剔除，因而可从其分布型上推断出相对温度距平值。

也可为年均气候的相关情况提供补充信息 [10]。根据这一校正方法，我们用一个超定优选方案来确定特征向量的最优组合，并以多代用数据网中的逐年数据表示，其空间尺度仅取决于仪器记录的训练数据的空间范围。从数个 RPC 中可以确定出空间分布型和所有相关的平均值或指标。整个统计方法的详细描述见方法部分。

The skill of the temperature reconstructions (that is, their statistical validity) back in time is established through a variety of complementary independent cross-validation or "verification" exercises (see Methods). We summarize here the main results of these experiments (details of the quantitative results of the calibration and verification procedures are available; see Supplementary Information).

(1) In the reconstructions from 1820 onwards based on the full multiproxy network of 112 indicators, 11 eigenvectors are skilfully resolved (nos 1–5, 7, 9, 11, 14–16) describing ~70–80% of the variance in NH and GLB mean series in both calibration and verification. (Verification is based here on the independent 1854–1901 data set which was withheld; see Methods.) Figure 3 shows the spatial patterns of calibration β, and verification β and the squared correlation statistic r^2, demonstrating highly significant reconstructive skill over widespread regions of the reconstructed spatial domain. 30% of the full spatiotemporal variance in the gridded data set is captured in calibration, and 22% of the variance is verified in cross-validation. Some of the degradation in the verification score relative to the calibration score may reflect the decrease in instrumental data quality in many regions before the twentieth century rather than a true decrease in resolved variance. These scores thus compare favourably to the 40% total spatiotemporal variance that is described by simply filtering the raw 1902–80 instrumental data with 11 eigenvectors used in calibration, suggesting that the multiproxy calibrations are describing a level of variance in the data reasonably close to the optimal "target" value. Although a verification NINO3 index is not available from 1854 to 1901, correlation of the reconstructed NINO3 index with the available Southern Oscillation index (SOI) data from 1865 to 1901 of $r = -0.38$ ($r^2 = 0.14$) compares reasonably with its target value given by the correlation between the actual instrumental NINO3 and SOI index from 1902 to 1980 ($r = -0.72$). Furthermore, the correspondence between the reconstructed NINO3 index warm events and historical[35] El Niño chronology back to 1820 (see Methods) is significant at the 98% level.

(2) The calibrations back to 1760, based on 93 indicators, continue to resolve at least nine eigenvectors (nos 1–5, 7, 9, 11, 15) with no degradation of calibration or verification resolved variance in NH, and only slight degradation in MULT (calibration ~27%, verification ~17%). Our reconstructions are thus largely indistinguishable in skill back to 1760.

(3) The network available back to 1700 of 74 indicators (including only two instrumental or historical indicators) skilfully resolves five eigenvectors (nos 1, 2, 5, 11, 15) and shows some significant signs of decrease in reconstructive skill. In this case, ~60–70% of NH variance is resolved in calibration and verification, ~14–18% of MULT in calibration, and 10–12% of MULT in verification. The verification r of NINO3 with the SOI is in the range of $r \approx -0.25$ to -0.35, which is statistically significant (as is the correspondence with the historical[35] chronology back to 1700) but notably inferior to the later calibrations. In short, both spatial patterns and large-scale means are skilfully resolved, but with significantly less resolved variance than in later calibrations.

　　向回追溯的温度重建方法的可行性（即其统计有效性）是通过各种补充的独立交叉验证或"检验"练习（见方法）确定的。在此我们总结了上述实验的主要结果（校正和检验过程中详细的定量结果见补充信息）。

　　(1) 根据 112 个指标组成的完整多代用数据网得到的可追溯至 1820 年的重建结果，可分辨出 11 个特征向量（nos 1～5，7，9，11，14～16），在 NH 和 GLB 平均值序列的校正和检验中方差贡献率约为 70%～80%。（本文检验是根据 1854～1901 年保留下来的独立数据库进行的，见方法部分。）图 3 所示为校正 β，检验 β 以及平方相关系数 r^2 的空间分布型，证明在重建的空间范围所覆盖的广大区域上该方法均具有很高的可行性。校正范围覆盖了网格数据库中总时空变化的 30%，且有 22% 通过了交叉验证法的检验。检验得分相对于校正得分的降低可能反映了二十世纪以前仪器测定数据质量较低而非解释方差的真正降低。由此，上述得分与 40% 的总时空方差就顺利对应起来了，其中总时空方差以校正中所用的 11 个特征向量对 1902～1980 年仪器测定的原始数据进行简单筛选后的结果来表示，说明多代用指标校正反映了数据方差水平，与理想"目标"值非常接近。虽然没有 1854～1901 年间 NINO3 指数的检验结果，但重建 NINO3 指数与 1865～1901 年间南方涛动指数（SOI）的相关系数 $r = -0.38$（$r^2 = 0.14$），与 1902～1980 年间实际仪器记录中 NINO3 和 SOI 指数的相关系数（$r = -0.72$）给出的目标值是可比的。另外，重建 NINO3 指数变暖事件与历史上[35]自 1820 年以来发生的厄尔尼诺现象（见方法）之间相关性显著，置信水平为 98%。

　　(2) 基于 93 项指标可回溯至 1760 年的校正结果，仍可分辨出至少 9 个特征向量（nos 1～5，7，9，11，15），而北半球的校正方差和检验方差都没有下降，并且 MULT 也只有微弱的下降（校正方差约 27%，检验方差约为 17% 左右）。因此，我们所得到的自 1760 年以来的重建结果从效果上来说没有很大区别。

　　(3) 由 74 个指标（仅包含两个仪器测定或历史指标）组成的、可回溯到 1700 年的数据网，可分辨出 5 个特征向量（nos 1，2，5，11，15），在重建效果上则表现出明显的下降迹象。此时，校正和检验过程中北半球的方差约占 60%～70%，而 MULT 的校正方差约占 14%～18%，检验方差为 10%～12%。根据 SOI 得到的 NINO3 的检验系数 r 约在 -0.25 到 -0.35 之间，具有统计学意义（回溯到历史上[35]1700 年的也是如此），但明显低于后续的校正结果。总之，空间分布型和大尺度平均值都可很好地解译出来，但与后来的校正结果相比，解释方差较小。

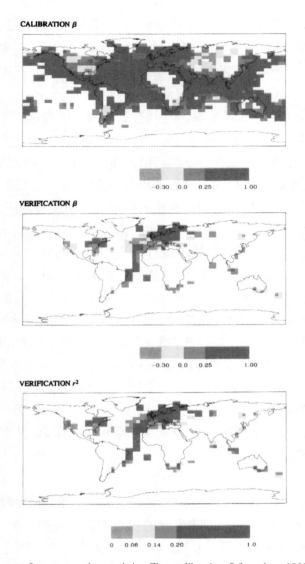

Fig. 3. Spatial patterns of reconstruction statistics. Top, calibration β (based on 1902–80 data); middle, verification (based on 1854–1901 data) β; bottom, verification r^2 (also based on 1854–1901 data). For the β statistic, values that are insignificant at the 99% level are shown in grey negative; but 99% significant values are shown in yellow, and significant positive values are shown in two shades of red. For the r^2 statistic, statistically insignificant values (or any grid-points with unphysical values of correlation $r < 0$) are indicated in grey. The colour scale indicates values significant at the 90% (yellow), 99% (light red) and 99.9% (dark red) levels (these significance levels are slightly higher for the calibration statistics which are based on a longer period of time). A description of significance level estimation is provided in the Methods section.

(4) The network of 57 indicators back to 1600 (including one historical record) skilfully resolves four eigenvectors (nos 1, 2, 11, 15). 67% of NH is resolved in calibration, and 53% in verification. 14% of MULT is resolved in calibration, and 12% of MULT in verification. A significant, but modest, level of ENSO-scale variability is resolved in the calibrations.

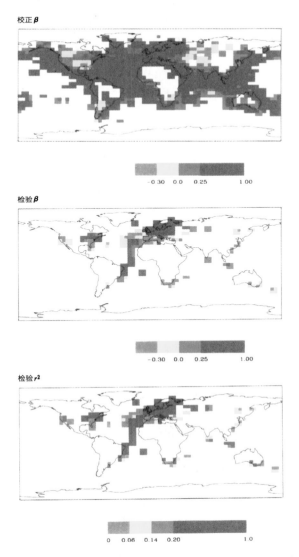

图 3. 重建数据的空间分布型。上图，校正 β（以 1902～1980 年的数据为基础）；中图，检验 β（以 1854～1901 年的数据为基础）；下图，检验 r^2（同样以 1902～1980 年的数据为基础）。对 β 来说，置信水平为 99% 时，不具有显著性的值以灰色的负数表示，具有显著性的值以黄色表示，而显著相关的正值则以两种红色色调来表示。对于 r^2，不具有统计学意义的值（或 $r<0$ 的非自然值格点）以灰色表示。彩色图例分别表示置信水平为 90%（黄色）、99%（浅红色）和 99.9%（深红色）时显著相关的值（对于在长时间尺度上得到的校正数据来说，上述显著性水平略高）。有关显著性水平估计的详细描述见方法部分。

（4）可回溯到 1600 年的 57 个指标（包括一个历史记录）组成的数据网则可分辨出 4 个特征向量（nos 1，2，11，15）。北半球的校正方差贡献为 67%，检验方差为 53%。校正 MULT 为 14%，检验 MULT 为 12%。校正过程中发现 ENSO 变化的影响很显著，但贡献不是很大。

(5) The network of 24 proxy indicators back to 1450 resolves two eigenvectors (nos 1, 2) and ~40–50% of NH in calibration and verification. Only ~10% of MULT is resolved in calibration and ~5% in verification. There is no skilful reconstruction of ENSO-scale variability. Thus spatial reconstructions are of marginal usefulness this far back, though the largest-scale quantities are still skilfully resolved.

(6) The multiproxy network of 22 indicators available back to 1400 resolves only the first eigenvector, associated with 40–50% of resolved variance in NH in calibration and verification. There is no useful resolution of spatial patterns of variability this far back. The sparser networks available before 1400 show little evidence of skill in reconstructing even the first eigenvector, terminating useful reconstruction at the initial year AD 1400.

(7) Experiments using trainee networks containing only proxy (that is, no instrumental or historical) indicators establish the most truly independent cross-validation of the reconstruction as there is in this case neither spatial nor temporal dependence between the calibration and verification data sets. Such statistically significant verification is demonstrated at the grid-point level (calibration and verification resolved variance ~15% for the MULT statistic), at the largest scales (calibration and verification resolved variance ~60–65% for NH) and the NINO3-scale (90–95% statistical significance for all verification diagnostics). In contrast, networks containing only the 24 long historical or instrumental records available back to 1820 resolve only ~30% of NH in calibration or verification, and the modest multivariate calibration and verification resolved variance scores of MULT (~10%) are artificially inflated by the high degree of spatial correlation between the instrumental "multiproxy" predictor and instrumental predictand data. No evidence of skilful ENSO-scale reconstruction is evident in these latter reconstructions. In short, the inclusion of the proxy data in the "multiproxy" network is essential for the most skilful reconstructions. But certain sub-components of the proxy dataset (for example, the dendroclimatic indicators) appear to be especially important in resolving the large-scale temperature patterns, with notable decreases in the scores reported for the proxy data set if all dendroclimatic indicators are withheld from the multiproxy network. On the other hand, the long-term trend in NH is relatively robust to the inclusion of dendroclimatic indicators in the network, suggesting that potential tree growth trend biases are not influential in the multiproxy climate reconstructions. The network of all combined proxy and long instrumental/historical indicators provide the greatest cross-validated estimates of skilful reconstruction, and are used in obtaining the reconstructions described below.

Temperature Reconstructions

The reconstructions discussed here are derived using all indicators available, and using the optimal eigenvector subsets determined in the calibration experiments described above (11 from 1780–1980, 9 from 1760–1779, 8 from 1750–1759, 5 from 1700–1749, 4

（5）可回溯到 1450 年的 24 个代用指标解出了 2 个特征向量（nos 1，2），其中北半球的校正方差和检验方差贡献均在 40%～50% 左右。校正过程中仅有约 10% 的 MULT 可解释，而检验过程中则仅为 5% 左右。在 ENSO 尺度的变化方面没有获得有效的重建结果。因此，回溯到这一时期所获得的空间重建结果的用处不大，不过所得出的最大尺度还是有效的。

（6）可回溯到 1400 年的 22 个指标组成的多代用数据网仅能解出第一个特征向量，其中，北半球的校正和检验方差贡献为 40%～50%。关于这一时期的空间变化分布型没有得出更多有效信息。1400 年以前的数据网则更稀疏，即便对第一个特征向量也未能在其中找到有效证据，因此可以认为有效的重建结果止于最初的公元 1400 年。

（7）利用仅包含代用指标（即没有仪器记录和历史记录）的训练数据网进行实验建立的交叉验证结果的独立性最好，因为在这种情况下，校正和检验数据库之间无论是时间上还是空间上都没有相关性。此类显著性检验在格点水平上（MULT 统计结果的校正和检验解释方差约为 15%），最大尺度上（北半球的校正和检验解释方差贡献率约为 60%～65%），以及 NINO3 尺度（所有方差检验在置信水平为 90%～95% 时都具有统计学意义）都得到了验证。相反，可回溯至 1820 年的仅包含 24 个长期历史记录和仪器记录的数据网中，北半球通过校正和检验的置信水平仅为 30% 左右，而 MULT 在多元校正和检验下的方差得分则更低（约 10%），而且其中还存在人为增大的因素，因为仪器"多代用"预报因子和仪器预报值之间在空间上具有高度的相关性。在后一种重建结果中，没有找到 ENSO 尺度变动的有效证据。总而言之，要获得最佳重建结果，"多代用"网中代用指标数据所包含的内容是最重要的。但某些代用指标组成的子库（例如树木年轮指标）在解决大尺度温度分布型时显得尤为重要。比如，倘若将树木年轮指标从多代用网络中都剔除掉，代用指标数据库的得分将显著下降。另一方面，对于数据网中包含树木年轮指标的情况来说，北半球的长期趋势则具有一定的稳健性，这说明，在多代用指标气候重建中，树木生长趋势中可能存在的偏差带来的影响并不大。利用由所有混合代用指标和长期仪器/历史指标组成的数据网所得到的重建结果具有最佳的交叉验证有效性。下文将要讨论的重建结果就是由此获得的。

温 度 重 建

这里所讨论的重建是利用所有可用指标得出的，另外还采用了前述校正实验确定出的最优特征向量子集（1780～1980 年为 11 个，1760～1779 年 9 个，1750～1759 年 8 个，1700～1749 年 5 个，1600～1699 年 4 个，1450～1599 年 2 个，1400～1449 年 1

from 1600–1699, 2 from 1450–1599, 1 from 1400–1449). To better illustrate the workings and effectiveness of the proxy pattern reconstruction procedure, we show as an example (Fig. 4) the actual, the EOF-filtered, and the reconstructed temperature patterns for a year (1941) during the calibration interval. This year was a known ENSO year, associated with a warm eastern tropical Pacific and a cold central North Pacific. Pronounced cold anomalies were also found over large parts of Eurasia. The proxy-reconstructed pattern captures these features, although in a relatively smoothed sense (describing ~30% of the full variance in that pattern), and is remarkably similar to the raw data once it has been filtered by retaining only the 11 eigenvectors (nos 1–5, 7, 9, 11, 14–16) used in pattern reconstruction. It is thus visually apparent that the multiproxy network is quite capable of resolving much of the structure resolved by the eigenvectors retained in the calibration process.

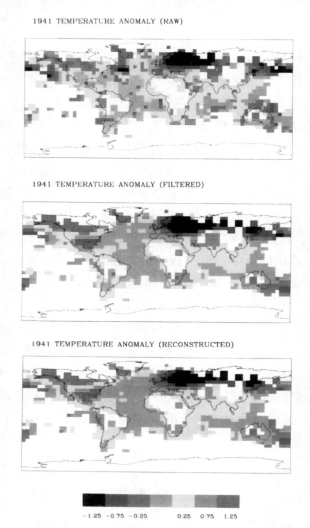

1941 TEMPERATURE ANOMALY (RAW)

1941 TEMPERATURE ANOMALY (FILTERED)

1941 TEMPERATURE ANOMALY (RECONSTRUCTED)

−1.25   −0.75   −0.25   0.25   0.75   1.25

Fig. 4. Comparison of the proxy-based spatial reconstructions of the anomaly pattern for 1941 versus the raw data. Comparisons based on actual (top), EOF-filtered (middle), and proxy-reconstructed (bottom) data. Anomalies (relative to 1902–80 climatology) are indicated by the colour scale shown in °C.

个）。为了更好地阐释多代用指标分布型重建方法的运作方式及其有效性，作为示例，图 4 分别给出了校正区间内 1941 年的三种温度分布型：原始数据、EOF 过滤结果和重建结果。这一年是显著的 ENSO 年，东赤道太平洋非常暖，而中北部太平洋则较冷。欧亚地区大部也出现了显著的异常变冷现象。而根据代用指标重建出的气温分布型也恰反映出了上述特征，只是其变化趋势相对平滑一些（贡献了分布型总方差的 30% 左右）。而且，如果利用分布型重建中采用的 11 个特征向量（nos 1～5，7，9，11，14～16）对原始数据加以筛选，所剩下的数据与重建结果亦极为相似。因此，显然多数经校正过程中保留下来的特征向量解出的结构都可用多代用数据网解决。

1941 温度距平值（原始数据）

1941 温度距平值（EOF 过滤结果）

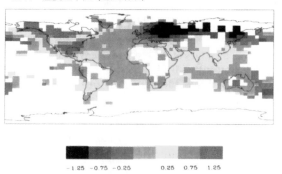

1941 温度距平值（重建结果）

图 4. 在 1941 年的异常分布型下，根据代用指标得到的空间重建结果与原始数据的对比。图示分别为原始数据（上图）、EOF 筛选后的数据（中图）以及代用指标重建结果（下图）。距平值（相对于 1902～1980 年间的气候）以彩色图例标出，单位为℃。

We consider the temporal variations in the first five RPCs (Fig. 5a). The positive trend in RPC no. 1 during the twentieth century is clearly exceptional in the context of the long-term variability in the associated eigenvector, and indeed describes much of the unprecedented warming trend evident in the NH reconstruction. The negative trend in RPC no. 2 during the past century is also anomalous in the context of the longer-term evolution of the associated eigenvector. The recent negative trend is associated with a pattern of cooling in the eastern tropical Pacific (superimposed on warming associated with the pattern of eigenvector no. 1) which may be a modulating negative feedback on global warming[26]. RPC no. 5 shows notable multidecadal variability throughout both the modern and pre-calibration interval, associated with the wavelike trend of warming and subsequent cooling of the North Atlantic this century discussed earlier[29-33] and the longer-term multidecadal oscillations in this region detected in a previous analysis of proxy climate networks[5]. This variability may be associated with ocean–atmosphere processes related to the North Atlantic thermohaline circulation[4,34].

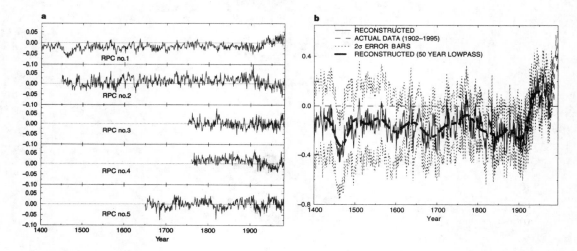

Fig. 5. Time reconstructions (solid lines) along with raw data (dashed lines). **a**, For principal components (RPCs) 1–5; **b**, for Northern Hemisphere mean temperature (NH) in °C. In both cases, the zero line corresponds to the 1902–80 calibration mean of the quantity. For **b** raw data are shown up to 1995 and positive and negative 2σ uncertainty limits are shown by the light dotted lines surrounding the solid reconstruction, calculated as described in the Methods section.

The long-term trends in the reconstructed annual mean NH series (Fig. 5b) are quite similar to those of decadal Northern Hemisphere summer temperature reconstructions[6], showing pronounced cold periods during the mid-seventeenth and nineteenth centuries, and somewhat warmer intervals during the mid-sixteenth and late eighteenth centuries, with almost all years before the twentieth century well below the twentieth-century climatological mean. Taking into account the uncertainties in our NH reconstruction (see Methods), it appears that the years 1990, 1995 and now 1997 (this value recently calculated and not shown) each show anomalies that are greater than any other year back to 1400 at 3 standard errors, or roughly a 99.7% level of certainty. We note that hemispheric mean

　　我们来看一下前 5 个 RPC 随时间的变化（图 5a）。在二十世纪，RPC no.1 在该特征向量长期变化的背景下的正变化趋势是异常明显的，这实际上反映了北半球重建结果中表现出的空前变暖的趋势。而上世纪 RPC no.2 在相关特征向量上的长期演化背景下的负相关变化也是异常的。最近的负相关变化趋势则可能与东赤道太平洋的变冷有关（叠加于特征向量 no.1 的变暖趋势之上），它可能是全球变暖的一种负反馈调制[26]。RPC no.5 在整个现代（器测）时期以及（器测）之前的时期都表现出显著的以数十年为周期的变化特征，这可能与本世纪北大西洋的波状变暖及之后的变冷现象相关，这一点前人已有研究[29-33]，前人根据代用指标气候网分析发现该区长期存在周期为数十年的振荡变化[5]。该变化可能反映了与北大西洋温盐循环有关的海－气相互作用过程[4,34]。

图 5. 时间序列的重建结果（实线）及原始数据（虚线），**a**，主成分因子（RPC）1～5；**b**，北半球平均温度（NH），单位℃。两图中的零线均对应 1902～1980 年间的校正平均值。**b** 图所示为直到 1995 的原始数据，其不确定界限为 ±2σ，以实线周围的浅色点虚线表示，计算过程详见方法部分。

　　年均北半球序列重建结果中的长期变化趋势（图 5b）与北半球夏季温度重建结果的十年平均值变化[6]相似，在十七世纪中期和十九世纪均表现为显著冷期，而十六世纪中期和十八世纪后期则有一段时间相对较暖，另外二十世纪之前的结果均低于二十世纪的气候平均值。如果考虑我们的 NH 重建结果中的不确定性（见方法），那么，1990 年、1995 年以及现在的 1997 年（该值是新计算出的，文中未列出）的距平值呈现异常，比 1400 年以来的任何年份都高，其置信水平为 99.7%（相当于三个标准差）。我们注意到，半球的平均值与全球或半球的均一趋势并不一致。图 6 上图为

values are not associated with globally or hemispherically uniform trends. An example of the global pattern for an historically documented[35] "very strong" El Niño year (1791) is shown in Fig. 6 top panel, demonstrating the classic warm eastern tropical Pacific and cold central North Pacific sea surface temperature patterns. Analysis of ENSO variability in these reconstructions is discussed in more detail elsewhere[36]. We also show the reconstructed pattern for 1816 (Fig. 6 bottom panel). Quite anomalous cold is evident throughout much of the Northern Hemisphere (even relative to this generally cold decade) but with a quadrupole pattern of warmth near Newfoundland and the Near East, and enhanced cold in the eastern United States and Europe consistent with the anomalous atmospheric circulation associated with the NAO pattern. Such a pattern is indeed observed in empirical[37] and model-based studies[38] of the atmospheric response to volcanic forcing. We infer in the 1816 temperature pattern a climatic response to the explosive Tambora eruption of April 1815 based on both the anomalous hemispheric coolness and the superimposed NAO-like pattern. Reconstructed time series RPCs nos 1–5, the NH series, the NINO3 index and reconstructions for specific grid-points can be obtained through the NOAA palaeoclimatology Web site (http://www.ngdc.noaa.gov/paleo/paleo.html).

1791 TEMPERATURE ANOMALY PATTERN

1816 TEMPERATURE ANOMALY PATTERN

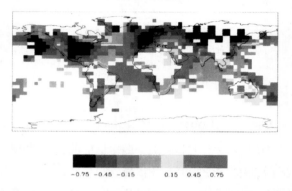

−0.75 −0.45 −0.15   0.15 0.45 0.75

Fig. 6. Reconstructed annual temperature patterns for two example years. Top, 1791; bottom, 1816. The colours indicate regions which exceeded (either positively or negatively) the threshold indicated in °C. The zero baseline is defined by the 1902–80 climatological mean for each grid-point.

前人已证实的"超强"厄尔尼诺年(1791)的全球温度分布型[35]，显示了典型的东赤道太平洋暖、中北部太平洋冷的海表温度分布型。根据上述重建分析出的ENSO的变化在其他文章中有更为详细的讨论[36]。我们还给出了重建的1816年全球温度分布型(图6下图)。北半球大部分地区都表现为明显的异常寒冷(即使相对于总体较冷的这个十年来说也是如此)，但在纽芬兰岛附近和近东地区则呈现四极子增暖模态，而美国东部和欧洲地区则更冷一些，这与NAO模态有关的大气异常环流有关。关于大气对火山强迫响应的研究，无论是经验观测[37]还是模式研究[38]，都证实了这种分布型的存在。根据北半球的异常变冷现象和叠加其上的类NAO模态，我们推断在1816年的温度分布型是对1815年4月爆发的坦博拉火山喷发的一种气候响应。重建的时间序列RPC nos 1~5、NH序列、NINO3指数以及特定格点的重建结果都可从美国国家海洋和大气局(NOAA)的古气候网站找到(网址http://www.ngdc.noaa.gov/paleo/html)。

1791　温度距平值分布型

1816　温度距平值分布型

图6. 两个典型年份上重建的年际温度分布型。上图为1791年；下图为1816年。彩色部分表示超出界限的区域(不管是正向的还是负向的)，单位℃。零基线是根据1902~1980年间每个格点的气候平均值得到的。

Attribution of Climate Forcings

We take an empirical approach to detecting the possible effects of external forcings on the climate. The reconstructed NH series is taken as a diagnostic of the global climate, and we examine its relationship with three candidate external forcings during the period 1610–1995 including (1) CO_2 measurements[39] as a proxy for total greenhouse-gas changes, (2) reconstructed solar irradiance variations[2] and (3) the weighted historical "dust veil index" (DVI) of explosive volcanism (see Fig. 31.1 in ref. 40) updated with recent data[41]. While we warn that historical series for these forcing agents are imperfectly known or measured, they do nonetheless represent our best estimates of the time-histories of the corresponding forcings. More detailed discussions of the estimation of, and potential sources of uncertainty or bias in, these series are available[2,39,40]. Industrial-aerosol forcing of the climate has also been suggested as an important forcing of recent climate[42,43], but its physical basis is still controversial[44], and difficult to estimate observationally. Noting that in any case, this forcing is not believed to be important before about 1940, its omission should be inconsequential in our long-term detection approach. Our empirical signal detection is complementary to that of model-based "finger-print" signal detection studies[42,43,45]; while our empirical approach relies on the faithfulness of the reconstructed forcing series and on the assumption of a linear and contemporaneous response to forcings, it does not suffer the potential weaknesses of incomplete representations of internal feedback processes[26], poorly constrained parametrizations of climatic responses[44], and underestimated natural variability[1] in model-based studies. To the extent that the response to forcing is not contemporaneous, but rather is delayed owing to the inertia of the slow-response components of the climate system (for example, the ocean and cryosphere), our detection approach will tend to underestimate the response to forcings, making the approach a relatively conservative one.

We estimate the response of the climate to the three forcings based on an evolving multivariate regression method (Fig. 7). This time-dependent correlation approach generalizes on previous studies of (fixed) correlations between long-term Northern Hemisphere temperature records and possible forcing agents[2,3]. Normalized regression (that is, correlation) coefficients r are simultaneously estimated between each of the three forcing series and the NH series from 1610 to 1995 in a 200-year moving window. The first calculated value centred at 1710 is based on data from 1610 to 1809, and the last value, centred at 1895, is based on data from 1796 to 1995—that is, the most recent 200 years. A window width of 200 yr was chosen to ensure that any given window contains enough samples to provide good signal-to-noise ratios in correlation estimates. Nonetheless, all of the important conclusions drawn below are robust to choosing other reasonable (for example, 100-year) window widths.

气候强迫的影响因素

本文采用了经验方法研究了外部强迫可能对气候产生的影响。对全球气候的诊断是采用重建的 NH 序列来进行的，同时对它与 1610～1995 年间三个候选的气候强迫之间的关系作了评估，其中包括：(1) 作为所有温室气体变化代用指标的 CO_2 的测定结果[39]，(2) 重建的太阳辐照度变化[2]，(3) 火山喷发作用的历史权重"尘幕指数"(DVI)(见文献 40 中的图 31.1)，并且已更新至最新数据[41]。但是我们还要注意一点，那就是，我们对这些强迫因素的历史序列的了解和测定都存在一定缺陷，不过尽管如此，它们仍然代表了我们对相应气候强迫的历史变化的最佳估计。前人已有关于这些序列估计值及其潜在不确定性和偏差来源的详细讨论[2,39,40]。工业气溶胶对气候的影响也被认为是近年来气候的重要强迫因子[42,43]，不过关于其物理基础仍存在争议[44]，而且也很难通过观测做出评估。不管怎样，在 1940 年以前这一强迫的影响不是那么重要，但在我们的长期探测法中漏掉它也是不合理的。我们采用的经验信号探测法是对基于模式的"指纹"信号探测研究[42,43,45]的一种补充，同时我们采用的经验方法依赖于重建的强迫序列的准确性以及这些强迫的同期响应呈线性的假定，它不受模式研究中存在的内在反馈过程[26]的不完整性、气候响应参数化的低约束性[44]以及对自然变化的低估[1]等潜在缺陷的影响。从某种程度上来说，气候对影响因素的响应并不是同期的，它会因气候体系中缓慢响应组分(如海洋以及冰冻圈等)的惯性而被延迟，因此本文采用的探测方法可能会低估气候对上述强迫的响应，也就是说这是一种相对较为保守的研究方法。

我们利用改进的多元回归法研究了气候对三个强迫因子的响应情况(图 7)。该依时相关法是根据前人关于北半球气温的长期记录与潜在影响因素之间的(固定的)相关性研究[2,3]概括而来的。同时还求出了各强迫序列与 1610 到 1995 年间 NH 序列之间的标准化回归(即相关性)系数 r，其中以 200 年作为滑动窗口。由此得到的第一个以 1710 年为中心的计算值就是根据 1610 到 1809 年之间的数据得到的，而最后一个值，以 1895 年为中心，是根据 1796 到 1995 年，即最近 200 年的数据得出的。之所以将窗口宽度选为 200 年是为了保证每个给定窗口中包含足够多的样本来为相关性研究提供最佳信噪比。不过，在选择其他合理的窗口宽度(比如 100 年)时，下文将要得出的那些重要结论是同样成立的。

Fig. 7 Relationships of Northern Hemisphere mean (NH) temperature with three candidate forcings between 1610 and 1995. Panels, (top to bottom) as follows. "NH", reconstructed NH temperature series from 1610–1980, updated with instrumental data from 1981–95. "Solar", reconstructed solar irradiance. "log CO_2", greenhouse gases represented by atmospheric CO_2 measurements. "DVI", weighted volcanic dust veil index. Bottom panel, evolving multivariate correlation of NH series with the three forcings NH, Solar, log CO_2. The time axis denotes the centre of a 200-year moving window. One-sided (positive) 90%, 95%, 99% significance levels (see text) for correlations with CO_2 and solar irradiance are shown by horizontal dashed lines, while the one-sided (negative) 90% significance threshold for correlations with the DVI series is shown by the horizontal dotted line. The grey bars indicate two difference 200-year windows of data, with the long-dashed vertical lines indicating the centre of the corresponding window.

We test the significance of the correlation coefficients (r) relative to a null hypothesis of random correlation arising from natural climate variability, taking into account the reduced degrees of freedom in the correlations owing to substantial trends and low-frequency variability in the NH series. The reduced degrees of freedom are modelled in terms of first-order markovian "red noise" correlation structure of the data series, described by the lag-one autocorrelation coefficient ρ during a 200-year window. This parameter ranges from 0.48 in the first window (1610–1809) to 0.77 in the final window (1796–1995) of the moving correlation, the considerably larger recent value associated with the substantial global warming trend of the past century. This latter trend has been shown to be inconsistent with red noise[46] and could thus itself be argued as indicative of externally forced variability. An argument could in this sense, be made for using the smaller pre-industrial value $\rho = 0.48$ of the NH series in estimating the statistical degrees of freedom appropriate for the null hypothesis of natural variability. Nonetheless, we make the conservative choice of adopting the largest value $\rho = 0.77$ as representative of the natural serial correlation in the series. We use Monte Carlo simulations to estimate the likelihood of chance spurious correlations of such serially correlated noise with each of the three actual forcing series. The associated confidence limits are approximately constant between sliding 200-year windows. For

图 7. 1610～1995 年北半球平均（NH）气温与三个强迫因子之间的关系。从上到下依次为："NH"，1610～1980 年北半球温度序列的重建结果，同时利用 1981～1995 年间的仪器测定信息得到的更新结果；"Solar"，太阳辐照度的重建结果；"log CO_2"，以大气 CO_2 浓度的测定值表示的温室气体情况；"DVI"，火山尘幕指数的加权平均值；底图为 NH 序列与三个强迫因子（NH、Solar、log CO_2）之间多元回归相关系数的变化。时间轴上标出了各滑动窗口（200 年）的中心年份。单边（正向）检验条件下，气温与 CO_2 和太阳辐照度之间相关系数的显著性水平为 90%、95%、99%（见正文），显著性水平在图中以水平划线标出；而 DVI 序列单边（负向）检测条件下，气温与 CO_2 和太阳辐照度之间相关系数的显著性水平为 90%，显著性水平在图中以水平点线表示。灰色条带所示为两个不同的 200 年滑动窗口内的数据，垂向长划线所示为相应滑动窗口的中心位置。

　　我们检验相关系数（r）相对于原（零）假设相关系数的显著性，其中原（零）假设相关系数是由气候自然变化产生的随机序列得到的，该过程考虑了由 NH 序列的明显趋势和低频变化所导致的相关性中自由度的降低。自由度的降低是通过数据序列的一阶马尔可夫"红噪声"相关性结构的形式模拟出的，上述红噪声通过计算 200 年滑动窗口中滞后 1 年的自相关系数 ρ 来描述。该参数变化范围为 0.48（滑动相关的第一个窗口（1610～1809））到 0.77（滑动相关的最后一个窗口（1796～1995）），距今最近的值要大得多，这与过去一个世纪中全球呈显著变暖有关。而后一种趋势与红噪声结果[46] 相矛盾，所以可以认为它本身就是衡量外部因素引起的变化的一个指标。从这个意义上来讲，我们就可以认为利用工业化以前 NH 序列的较小值 $\rho = 0.48$ 来估计统计自由度也是适合自然变化的无效假设的。尽管如此，我们还是保守地选择了最大值，即 $\rho = 0.77$ 来作为序列中自然序列的相关系数。我们采用蒙特卡罗模拟法对序列相关噪声与三个实际影响因素序列之间为偶然虚假相关的可能性作了评估。在各个 200 年间隔的滑动窗口之间，其置信区间基本不变。对于与 CO_2 和太阳辐照

(positive) correlations with both CO_2 and solar irradiance, the confidence levels are both approximately 0.24 (90%), 0.31 (95%), 0.41 (99%), while for the "whiter" relatively trendless, DVI index, the confidence levels for (negative) correlations are somewhat lower (-0.16, -0.20, -0.27 respectively). A one-sided significance test is used in each case because the physical nature of the forcing dictates a unique expected sign to the correlations (positive for CO_2 and solar irradiance variations, negative for the DVI fluctuations).

The correlation statistics indicate highly significant detection of solar irradiance forcing in the NH series during the "Maunder Minimum" of solar activity from the mid-seventeenth to early eighteenth century which corresponds to an especially cold period. In turn, the steady increase in solar irradiance from the early nineteenth century through to the mid-twentieth century coincides with the general warming over the period, showing peak correlation during the mid-nineteenth century. The regression against solar irradiance indicates a sensitivity to changes in the "solar constant" of ~ 0.1 K W^{-1} m^{-2}, which is consistent with recent model-based studies[42]. Greenhouse forcing, on the other hand, shows no sign of significance until a large positive correlation sharply emerges as the moving window slides into the twentieth century. The partial correlation with CO_2 indeed dominates over that of solar irradiance for the most recent 200-year interval, as increases in temperature and CO_2 simultaneously accelerate through to the end of 1995, while solar irradiance levels off after the mid-twentieth century. It is reasonable to infer that greenhouse-gas forcing is now the dominant external forcing of the climate system. Explosive volcanism exhibits the expected marginally significant negative correlation with temperature during much of 1610–1995 period, most pronounced in the 200-year window centred near 1830 which includes the most explosive volcanic events.

A variety of general circulation[42,47] and energy-balance model experiments[43,45,48] as well as statistical comparisons of twentieth-century global temperatures with forcing series[49] suggest that, although both solar and greenhouse-gas forcings play some role in explaining twentieth-century climate trends, greenhouse gases appear to play an increasingly dominant role during this century. Such a proposition is consistent with the results of this study.

As larger numbers of high-quality proxy reconstructions become available in diverse regions of the globe, it may be possible to assimilate a more globally representative multiproxy data network. Given the high level of skill possible in large-scale reconstruction back to 1400 with the present network, it is reasonable to hope that it may soon be possible to faithfully reconstruct mean global temperatures back over the entire millennium, resolving for example the enigmatic[7] medieval period. Geothermal measurements from boreholes[50] recover long-term temperature trends without many of the complications of traditional proxy indicators and, in combination with traditional multiproxy networks, may prove helpful in better resolving trends over many centuries. With a better knowledge of how the climate has varied before the twentieth century, we will be able to place even better constraints on the importance of natural and anthropogenic factors governing the climate of the past few centuries, factors which will no doubt continue to affect climate variability in the future, in addition to any anthropogenic effects.

度之间的（正）相关性，其置信水平分别约为 0.24(90%)、0.31(95%)、0.41(99%)，而对于趋势性不太明显的"更白的"尘幕指数，其（负）相关性的置信水平则低一些（分别为 −0.16、−0.20 和 −0.27）。所有情况采用的都是单边显著性检验，因为强迫因子的物理性质已决定了相关关系的唯一的期望符号（与 CO_2 和太阳辐照度的变化之间为正，与 DVI 指数的波动之间为负）。

相关性统计量表明，从十七世纪中期到十八世纪早期，即太阳活动处于"蒙德极小期"时，NH 序列中太阳辐照度强迫的影响非常明显，而此时又正是异常寒冷的一段时期。反过来，从十九世纪早期到二十世纪中期太阳辐照度的稳步增强与该时期总体变暖的趋势一致，其中十九世纪中期时两者相关性最高。太阳辐照度回归分析结果表明"太阳常数"变化约 $0.1 \ K \cdot W^{-1} \cdot m^{-2}$ 时较为敏感，这与近期的模式研究结果[42]是一致的。另一方面，温室效应强迫，只在滑动窗移至二十世纪时才突然表现出很强的正相关性，而之前没有任何明显的信号。在最近 200 年里，气候与 CO_2 的相关性实际上已经超过气候与太阳辐照度的相关性，变成了最主要的因素，主要表现为温度和 CO_2 浓度同步加速升高，直到 1995 年底仍是如此，而太阳辐照度水平则自二十世纪中期以后持续平稳。由此我们可以断定，温室气体强迫是如今气候系统中最主要的外部强迫。正如我们所料，从 1610～1995 年间的大多数时间里火山喷发与温度变化呈略显著的负相关关系，而最显著的时期是 1830 年前后的 200 年，因为多数火山喷发事件都发生在这一时期。

各种大气环流[42,47]与能量平衡模式实验[43,45,48]以及二十世纪全球温度与其强迫因子序列之间的统计比较结果[49]表明，虽然太阳辐射和温室气体都能在一定程度上解释二十世纪气候的变化趋势，但本世纪中温室气体的作用似乎日益显著。这一点与本文的研究结果也是一致的。

随着全球各个地区越来越多的高质量代用指标重建结果的出现，人们将可以得到一个更具有全球代表性的多代用数据网。基于目前该网得到的自 1400 年以来的大尺度重建结果的高水准性，我们有理由期待近千年来全球平均温度的可靠重建结果很快就可以实现，从而能够解开中世纪的谜团[7]。根据钻孔[50]得到的地热测量结果可以恢复出长期的温度变化趋势，而无须借助复杂的传统代用指标，并且将它与传统的多代用指标网相结合，说不定还可以更好地推断出数个世纪上的变化趋势。倘若能够对二十世纪以前气候的变化情况了解得更多一些，我们将可以对过去几个世纪中影响气候变化的自然因素和人为因素所起到的重要性进行限定，除人为因素以外，未来这些因素无疑还会持续影响气候变化。

Methods

Statistics. We use as our primary diagnostic of calibration and verification reconstructive skill the conventional "resolved variance" statistic;

$$\beta = 1 - \frac{\sum (y_{\text{ref}} - \hat{y})^2}{\sum y_{\text{ref}}^2}$$

where y_{ref} is the reference series (the raw data in the case of calibration or the verification dataset in the case of verification) and $\hat{y}$ is the series being compared to it (the proxy-reconstructed data for either calibration or verification). We compute β for each grid-point, and for the NH, GLB and MULT quantities. The sum extends over the time interval of comparison, and for the multivariate case (MULT), over all gridpoints as well. We also computed a calibration β statistic for the detrended NH series (DETR) to distinguish between explanatory variance associated with the notable trend of the twentieth century, and that related to departures from the trend.

β is a quite rigorous measure of the similarity between two variables, measuring their correspondence not only in terms of the relative departures from mean values (as does the correlation coefficient r) but also in terms of the means and absolute variance of the two series. For comparison, correlation (r) and squared-correlation (r^2) statistics are also determined. The expectation value for two random series is $\beta = -1$. Negative values of β may in fact be statistically significant for sufficient temporal degrees of freedom. Nonetheless, the threshold $\beta = 0$ defines the simple "climatological" model in which a series is assigned its long-term mean. In this sense, statistically significant negative values of β might still be considered questionable in their predictive or reconstructive skill. Owing to the more rigorous "match" between two series sought by β, highly significant values of β are possible even when r^2 is only marginally significant.

Significance levels were determined for r^2 from standard one-sided tables, accounting for decreased degrees of freedom owing to serial correlation. Significance levels for β were estimated by Monte Carlo simulations, also taking serial correlation into account. Serial correlation is assumed to follow from the null model of AR(1) red noise, and degrees of freedom are estimated based on the lag-one autocorrelation coefficients (ρ) for the two series being compared. Although the values of ρ differ from grid-point to grid-point, this variation is relatively small, making it simplest to use the ensemble average values of ρ over the domain ($\rho \approx 0.2$).

Calibration. With the spatial sampling of $M = 1,082$ continuous monthly grid-point surface temperature anomaly (that is, de-seasonalized) data used (Fig. 1b), the $N = 1,128$ months of data available from 1902 to 1995 were sufficient for a unique, overdetermined eigenvector decomposition (note that $N' = 94$ years of the annual mean data would, in contrast, not be sufficient).

For each grid-point, the mean was removed, and the series was normalized by its standard deviation. A standardized data matrix $\boldsymbol{T}$ of the data is formed by weighting each grid-point by the cosine of its central latitude to ensure areally proportional contributed variance, and a conventional Principal Component Analysis (PCA) is performed,

方　法

统计量　我们把传统的"解释方差"统计量作为校正和检验重建效果的主要诊断方法：

$$\beta = 1 - \frac{\sum (y_{\text{ref}} - \hat{y})^2}{\sum y_{\text{ref}}^2}$$

其中，y_{ref} 为参考序列（校正过程中的原始数据或检验过程中的检验数据库），$\hat{y}$ 为与之相比较的序列（校正或检验时的多代用指标重建数据）。我们对每个格点以及 NH、GLB 和 MULT 序列的 β 值都做了计算。求和的范围是整个对比区间，而在多元情形（MULT）下，则对所有格点求和。我们还计算了 NH 降趋势序列（DETR）的校正 β 值，以区分与二十世纪的显著变化趋势有关的解释性方差和与之背离趋势相关的方差。

β 可以相当精确地衡量两个变量之间的相似性，它不仅可以衡量与平均值的相对偏离（如相关系数 r），还能表示出两序列之间的平均值和绝对方差。为了对比起见，我们还确定出了相关系数 r 及其平方值。两个随机序列的期望值为 $\beta = -1$。β 为负值时实际上表示它在足够的时间自由度下具有统计学意义。不管怎样，临界值 $\beta = 0$ 时，可定义出一个简单的"气候"模式，从中可指定某序列的长期平均值。从这个角度来讲，当 β 为显著负值时，所得的预测和重建结果仍值得商榷。由于根据 β 得到的两个序列之间"匹配"更精确，因此，即使当 r^2 仅略微显著时，β 值会表现出高度的显著性。

根据标准单边表确定出的 r^2 的显著性水平结果显示，自由度的下降是由序列间的相关性引起的。利用蒙特卡罗模拟法对 β 的显著性水平做了研究，同时也考虑到了序列相关性的影响。假设序列相关性服从 AR(1) 红噪声的原假设模型，其自由度根据两个对比序列滞后为 1 个单位的自相关系数 (ρ) 进行估算。虽然格点与格点之间的 ρ 值不同，但这个变化相对较小，因而取定义域内 ρ 的集合平均值是一种最简便的方法 $(\rho \approx 0.2)$。

校正　采用 $M = 1{,}082$ 个空间格点的逐月温度距平值（消除季节性变化后）（图 1b），由此，1902～1995 年间 $N = 1{,}128$ 个月份上的可用数据足以获得唯一的超定的特征向量分解（相反，$N' = 94$ 年时的年均数据则无法满足）。

去除每个格点的平均值，并以其标准偏差对序列作标准化。以格点中心纬度的余弦值来取各格点的加权平均值从而形成标准化数据矩阵 **T**，以确定因面积不同而引起的变化，然后进行传统的主成分分析（PCA），其中：

$$T = \sum_{k=1}^{K} \lambda_k \mathbf{u}_k^t \mathbf{v}_k$$

decomposing the dataset into its dominant spatiotemporal eigenvectors. The M-vector or empirical orthogonal function (EOF) $\mathbf{v}_k$ describes the relative spatial pattern of the kth eigenvector, the N-vector $\mathbf{u}_k$ or principal component (PC) describes its variation over time, and the scalar λ_k describes the associated fraction of resolved (standardized and weighted) data variance.

In a given calibration exercise, we retain a specified subset of the annually averaged eigenvectors, the annually averaged PCs denoted by $\bar{u}_n^k$, where $n = 1, ..., \bar{N}, \bar{N} = 79$ is the number of annual averages used of the N-month length data set. In practice, only a small subset N_{eofs} of the highest-rank eigenvectors turn out to be useful in these exercises from the standpoint of verifiable reconstructive skill. An objective criterion was used to determine the particular set of eigenvectors which should be used in the calibration as follows. Preisendorfer's[25] selection rule "rule N" was applied to the multiproxy network to determine the approximate number N_{eofs} of significant independent climate patterns that are resolved by the network, taking into account the spatial correlation within the multiproxy data set. Because the ordering of various eigenvectors in terms of their prominence in the instrumental data, and their prominence as represented by the multiproxy network, need not be the same, we allowed for the selection of non-contiguous sequences of the instrumental eigenvectors. We chose the optimal group of N_{eofs} eigenvectors, from among a larger set (for example, the first 16) of the highest-rank eigenvectors, as the group of eigenvectors which maximized the calibration explained variance. It was encouraging from a consistency standpoint that this subset typically corresponded quite closely to the subset which maximized the verification explained variance statistics (see below), but the objective criterion was, as it should be, independent of the verification process. We emphasize, furthermore, that statistical significance was robustly established, as neither the measures of statistical skill nor the reconstructions themselves were highly sensitive to the precise criterion for selection. In addition to the above means of cross-validation, we also tested the network for sensitivity to the inclusion or elimination of particular trainee data (for example, instrumental/historical records, noninstrumental/historical records, or dendroclimatic proxy indicators).

These N_{eofs} eigenvectors were trained against the N_{proxy} indicators, by finding the least-squares optimal combination of the N_{eofs} PCs represented by each individual proxy indicator during the $\bar{N} = 79$ year training interval from 1902 to 1980 (the training interval is terminated at 1980 because many of the proxy series terminate at or shortly after 1980). The proxy series and PCs were formed into anomalies relative to the same 1902–80 reference period mean, and the proxy series were also normalized by their standard deviations during that period. This proxy-by-proxy calibration is well posed (that is, a unique optimal solution exists) as long as $\bar{N} > N_{eofs}$ (a limit never approached in this study) and can be expressed as the least-squares solution to the overdetermined matrix equation, $\boldsymbol{U}\mathbf{x} = \mathbf{y}^{(p)}$, where

$$U = \begin{vmatrix} \bar{u}_1^{(1)} & \bar{u}_1^{(2)} & \cdots & \bar{u}_1^{(N_{eofs})} \\ \bar{u}_2^{(1)} & \bar{u}_2^{(2)} & \cdots & \bar{u}_2^{(N_{eofs})} \\ \vdots & & & \\ \bar{u}_{\bar{N}}^{(1)} & \bar{u}_{\bar{N}}^{(2)} & \cdots & \bar{u}_{\bar{N}}^{(N_{eofs})} \end{vmatrix}$$

is the matrix of annual PCs, and

146

$$T = \sum_{k=1}^{K} \lambda_k \mathbf{u}_k^{\dagger} \mathbf{v}_k$$

将数据库分解为主要的时空特征向量。M 向量或称经验正交函数（EOF）$\mathbf{v}_k$ 表示第 k 个特征向量的相对空间分布型，N 向量 $\mathbf{u}_k$ 或称主成分（PC），则反映了其随时间的变化，标量 λ_k 与解出（标准值和加权平均值）数据的方差有关。

在特定的校正过程中，我们保留了由特征向量年均值组成的子集，年均主成分以 $\bar{u}_n^k$ 表示，其中 $n = 1, \cdots, \bar{N}$，$\bar{N} = 79$ 是长度为 N 月的数据库的年平均值。从可检测的重建效果来看，在实际操作中，仅最高阶特征向量组成的较小的子集 N_{eofs} 被证明是有用的。我们采用了一项客观标准来确定特征向量的组合，如后文所示这些特征向量将用于校正过程。将普赖森多费尔[25]的选择定则"N 定则"用于多代用数据网来确定数据网所解释的显著独立气候分布型中的大致个数 N_{eofs}，同时还考虑了多代用数据库中的空间相关性。由于仪器测量数据的突出特征所反映出的特征向量的级别与多代用数据网络表示的特征之间不必完全相同，所以我们也考虑到了所选出的仪器记录特征向量为不连续序列的情况。我们从最高阶特征向量组成的较大子集（比如，前 16 个特征向量）中选出 N_{eofs} 向量的最优组合来作为校正过程中方差贡献率最大的特征向量组。令人鼓舞的是，尽管所采用的客观标准与检验过程是相互独立的（本就应该独立），从一致性角度来看，该子集与检验过程中方差贡献率最大的子集非常相近（见下文）。此外，需要强调的是，该数据的统计学意义是稳健的，统计效果的测量和重建方法本身对选择的确切标准都不是非常敏感。除上述交叉验证手段以外，我们还测试了数据网络对引入或消除特殊训练数据（例如，仪器/历史记录、非仪器/历史记录、年轮气候代用指标等）的敏感度。

利用 N_{proxy} 指标来训练 N_{eofs} 特征向量，从中找出从 1902～1980 年的 $\bar{N} = 79$ 年的训练区间上各代用指标所代表的 N_{eofs} 主成分的最小二乘方优化组合（训练区间截止于 1980 年是因为许多代用指标序列均终止于 1980 年或略晚）。从代用指标序列和各个主成分中减去 1902～1980 年间的平均值，同时利用该时段上的标准偏差对代用指标进行标准化。只要 $\bar{N} > N_{\text{eofs}}$（该界限在本研究中均未被打破）代用指标的逐个校正就是适定的（即存在唯一的优化解），可以表示为超定矩阵方程 $\mathbf{U}\mathbf{x} = \mathbf{y}^{(\text{P})}$ 的最小二乘方解，其中

$$U = \begin{vmatrix} \bar{u}_1^{(1)} & \bar{u}_1^{(2)} & \cdots & \bar{u}_1^{(N_{\text{eofs}})} \\ \bar{u}_2^{(1)} & \bar{u}_2^{(2)} & \cdots & \bar{u}_2^{(N_{\text{eofs}})} \\ & & \vdots & \\ \bar{u}_{\bar{N}}^{(1)} & \bar{u}_{\bar{N}}^{(2)} & \cdots & \bar{u}_{\bar{N}}^{(N_{\text{eofs}})} \end{vmatrix}$$

是由各年的主成分组成的矩阵，并且

$$\mathbf{y}^{(p)} = \begin{vmatrix} y_1^{(p)} \\ y_2^{(p)} \\ \vdots \\ y_{\tilde{N}}^{(p)} \end{vmatrix}$$

is the time series $\tilde{N}$-vector for proxy record p.

The N_{eofs}-length solution vector $\mathbf{x} = \mathbf{G}^{(p)}$ is obtained by solving the above overdetermined optimization problem by singular value decomposition for each proxy record $p = 1, \ldots, P$. This yields a matrix of coefficients relating the different proxies to their closest linear combination of the N_{eofs} PCs;

$$\mathbf{G} = \begin{vmatrix} G_1^{(1)} & G_2^{(2)} & \cdots & G_{N_{\text{eofs}}}^{(1)} \\ G_1^{(2)} & G_2^{(2)} & \cdots & G_{N_{\text{eofs}}}^{(2)} \\ \vdots & & & \\ G_1^{(P)} & G_2^{(P)} & \cdots & G_{N_{\text{eofs}}}^{(P)} \end{vmatrix}$$

This set of coefficients will not provide a single consistent solution, but rather represents an overdetermined relationship between the optimal weights on each on the N_{eofs} PCs and the multiproxy network.

Proxy-reconstructed patterns are thus obtained during the pre-calibration interval by the year-by-year solution of the overdetermined matrix equation, $\mathbf{Gz} = \mathbf{y}_{(j)}$, where $\mathbf{y}_{(j)}$ is the predictor vector of values of each of the P proxy indicators during year j. The predictand solution vector $\mathbf{z} = \hat{\mathbf{U}}$ contains the least-squares optimal values of each of the N_{eofs} PCs for a given year. This optimization is overdetermined (and thus well constrained) as long as $P > N_{\text{eofs}}$ which is always realized in this study. It is noteworthy that, unlike conventional palaeoclimate transfer function approaches, there is no specific relationship between a given proxy indicator and a given predictand (that is, reconstructed PC). Instead, the best common choice of values for the small number of N_{eofs} predictands is determined from the mutual information present in the multiproxy network during any given year. The reconstruction approach is thus relatively resistant to errors or biases specific to any small number of indicators during a given year.

This yearly reconstruction process leads to annual sequences of the optimal reconstructions of the retained PCs, which we term the reconstructed principal components or RPCs and denote by $\hat{\mathbf{u}}^k$. Once the RPCs are determined, the associated temperature patterns are readily obtained through the appropriate eigenvector expansion,

$$\hat{\mathbf{T}} = \sum_{k=1}^{N_{\text{eofs}}} \lambda_k \hat{\mathbf{u}}_k^{\dagger} \mathbf{v}_k$$

while quantities of interest (for example, NH) are calculated from the appropriate spatial averages, and appropriate calibration and verification resolved variance statistics are calculated from the raw and reconstructed data.

$$\mathbf{y}^{(p)} = \begin{vmatrix} y_1^{(p)} \\ y_2^{(p)} \\ \vdots \\ y_{\tilde{N}}^{(p)} \end{vmatrix}$$

是代用指标记录 p 的时间序列的 $\tilde{N}$ 维向量。

通过解答上述超定的最优化问题可得到 N_{eofs} 长度解向量 $\mathbf{x} = \mathbf{G}^{(P)}$，方法是对每个代用指标记录 $p = 1$，$\cdots$，P 作奇异值分解。从而形成一个由相关系数组成的矩阵，将不同的代用指标与与之最相近的 N_{eofs} 主成分的线性组合联系起来：

$$\mathbf{G} = \begin{vmatrix} G_1^{(1)} & G_2^{(1)} & \cdots & G_{N_{\text{eofs}}}^{(1)} \\ G_1^{(2)} & G_2^{(2)} & \cdots & G_{N_{\text{eofs}}}^{(2)} \\ & \vdots & & \\ G_1^{(P)} & G_2^{(P)} & \cdots & G_{N_{\text{eofs}}}^{(P)} \end{vmatrix}$$

该组相关系数并不能解译为单个连续解，而是代表了每个 N_{eofs} 主成分的最优加权和多代用数据网之间的超定关系。

这样，利用超定矩阵方程 $\mathbf{Gz} = \mathbf{y}_{(j)}$ 在各年上的解就可获得由代用资料在器测资料校正之前的时期重建的模态，方程中 $\mathbf{y}_{(j)}$ 为 j 年每个 P 代用指标值的预测向量。预测解向量 $\mathbf{z} = \hat{\mathbf{U}}$ 包含给定年份上所有 N_{eofs} 主成分最优值的最小二乘方。只要 $P > N_{\text{eofs}}$，这种优化方法就是超定的（因而受到很好的限制），而在本研究中该条件是始终都可以保证的。值得注意的是，与传统的古气候转换函数法不同，本方法中给定的代用指标和给定的预测对象（即重建的主成分）之间并没有特殊的关系。相反，对于为数较少的 N_{eofs} 预测对象来说，一般其最优选择值是由给定年份中多代用数据网络显示的共有信息决定的。因此，该重建方法对于给定年份上少数指标带来的误差和偏差具有一定的抵抗力。

逐年重建过程可以得到每年的残余主成分理想重建结果序列，我们将其称为重建主成分，即 RPC，以 $\hat{\mathbf{u}}^k$ 表示。一旦确定出各个 RPC，就可通过适当的特征向量扩展得出相关的温度分布型：

$$\hat{\mathbf{T}} = \sum_{k=1}^{N_{\text{eofs}}} \lambda_k \hat{\mathbf{u}}_k^{\dagger} \mathbf{v}_k$$

我们所要研究的量（比如 NH）可通过适当的空间平均值计算得到，利用原始数据和重建数据可计算出合适的校正和检验方差。

Several checks were performed to ensure a reasonably unbiased calibration procedure. The histograms of calibration residuals were examined for possible heteroscedasticity, but were found to pass a χ^2 test for gaussian characteristics at reasonably high levels of significance (NH, 95% level; NINO3, 99% level). The spectra of the calibration residuals for these quantities were, furthermore, found to be approximately "white", showing little evidence for preferred or deficiently resolved timescales in the calibration process. Having established reasonably unbiased calibration residuals, we were able to calculate uncertainties in the reconstructions by assuming that the unresolved variance is gaussian distributed over time. This variance increases back in time (the increasingly sparse multiproxy network calibrates smaller fractions of variance), yielding error bars which expand back in time.

Verification. Verification resolved variance statistics (β) were determined based on two distinct verification data sets including (1) the sparse subset of the gridded data ($M' = 219$ grid-points) for which independent values are avail-able from 1854 to 1901 (see Fig. 1b) and (2) the small subset of 11 very long instrumental estimated temperature grid-point averages (10 in Eurasia, 1 in North America—see Fig. 1a) constructed from the longest available station measurements. Each of these "grid-point" series shared at least 70% of their variance with the corresponding temperature grid-point available from 1854–1980, providing verification back to at least 1820 in all cases (and back through the mid and early eighteenth century in many cases). Note that this latter verification data set is only temporally, but not spatially, independent of the multiproxy network itself, which contains these long instrumental grid-point series as a small subset of the network. In case (1), NH and GLB verification statistics are computed as well as the multivariate (MULT) grid-point level verification statistic, although these quantities represent different spatial samplings from those in the full calibration data set owing to the sparser sampling of the verification period. Case (2) provides a longer-term, albeit an even less spatially representative, multivariate verification statistic (MULTb). In this case, the spatial sampling does not permit meaningful estimates of NH or GLB mean quantities. In any of these diagnostics, a positive value of β is statistically significant at $> 99\%$ confidence as established from Monte Carlo simulations. Verification skills for the NINO3 reconstructions are estimated by other means, as the actual NINO3 index is not available far beyond the beginning of the calibration period. The (negative) correlation r of NINO3 with the SOI annual-mean from 1865 to 1901 (P. D. Jones, personal communication), and a squared congruence statistic g^2 measuring the categorical match between the distribution of warm NINO3 events and the distribution of warm episodes according to the historical[35] chronology (available back to the beginning of 1525), were used for statistical cross-validation based on one-sided tables and Monte Carlo simulations, respectively. The results of all calibration and verification experiments are available; see Supplementary Information.

($\mathbf{392}$, 779-787; 1998)

Michael E. Mann[*], Raymond S. Bradley[*] & Malcolm K. Hughes[†]

[*] Department of Geosciences, University of Massachusetts, Amherst, Massachusetts 01003-5820, USA
[†] Laboratory of Tree Ring Research, University of Arizona, Tucson, Arizona 85721, USA

Received 9 May 1997; accepted 27 February 1998.

为了保证校正过程的合理性和公正性，我们作了多次核对。同时对校正残差柱状图的异方差性作了检验，但结果发现，其高斯分布特征可通过 χ^2 检验，且显著性的置信水平较高（NH，95%；NINO3，99%）。另外研究还发现，这些量的校正残差的频率谱基本是白噪音，很难从中找出校正过程对时间尺度有偏好或有未充分解释的时间尺度的证据。确定出公正合理的校正残差以后，并假定未解释方差随时间呈高斯分布，那么就可从中计算出重建结果的不确定性。该方差随时间的向前追溯而逐渐变大（随着多代用数据网越来越稀疏，能校正的差异越来越小），误差范围也逐渐增大。

检验 检验解释方差 (β) 是根据两个不同的检验数据库确定出的，这两个数据库分别为：(1) 格点数据较稀疏 ($M' = 219$ 个格点) 的子集，从中可以得到 1854～1901 年间的独立值（见图 1b）；(2) 利用历史最悠久的站位记录构建的 11 个较长的仪器温度记录的格点平均值（欧亚地区 10 个，北美 1 个，见图 1a）。假设所有情况下检验时间均至少可回溯到 1820 年（有些情况下还可以回溯到十八世纪中期或十八世纪初），那么从 1854 到 1980 年，上述每个"格点"序列与相应的温度格点解释了至少 70% 的方差。需要注意的是，后一种检验数据库仅是时间上的而并非空间上的，与多代用数据网本身是独立的，这些长期仪器格点序列仅是多代用数据网所包含的一个小的子网。第 (1) 种情形中，计算了 NH 和 GLB 检验统计量以及多元（MULT）格点水平上的检验统计量，只是与全部校正数据库相比它们代表的空间取样间隔不同，因为检验期内的取样较稀疏。第 (2) 种情形是一种长期的多元检验统计量（MULTb），只是其空间代表性略差。在这种情形下，所用空间采样方法并不能保证 NH 或 GLB 平均量的估计值有意义。根据蒙特卡罗模拟法，在上述所有情形中，当置信水平 > 99% 时，正值 β 均具有统计学意义。NINO3 重建结果的检验效果是通过其他途径得出的，因为在校正周期开始后的很长一段时间都没有可用的实际 NINO3 指数。1865～1901 年间 NINO3 与 SOI 年均值的（负）相关系数 r（琼斯，个人交流），以及用来衡量 NINO3 变暖事件的分布与由历史[35] 年表（可回溯到 1525 年初期）得到的变暖事件的分布情况之间的类型匹配度的平方同余数 g^2，分别根据单边检验表和蒙特卡罗模拟进行了交叉验证。校正和检验的结果见补充信息。

（齐红艳 翻译；俞永强 审稿）

References:

1. Barnett, T. P., Santer, B., Jones, P. D., Bradley, R. S. & Briffa, K. R. Estimates of low frequency natural variability in near-surface air temperature. *Holocene* **6,** 255-263 (1996).

2. Lean, J., Beer, J. & Bradley, R. S. Reconstruction of solar irradiance since 1610: Implications for climate change. *Geophys. Res. Lett.* **22,** 3195-3198 (1995).

3. Crowley, T. J. & Kim, K. Y. Comparison of proxy records of climate change and solar forcing. *Geophys. Res. Lett.* **23,** 359-362 (1996).

4. Delworth, T. D., Manabe, S. & Stouffer, R. J. Interdecadal variations of the thermohaline circulation in a coupled ocean–atmosphere model. *J. Clim.* **6,** 1993-2011 (1993).

5. Mann, M. E., Park, J. & Bradley, R. S. Global interdecadal and century-scale oscillations during the past five centuries. *Nature* **378,** 266-270 (1995).

6. Bradley, R. S. & Jones, P. D. "Little Ice Age" summer temperature variations: their nature and relevance to recent global warming trends. *Holocene* **3,** 367-376 (1993).

7. Hughes, M. K. & Diaz, H. F. Was there a "Medieval Warm Period" and if so, where and when? *Clim. Change* **26,** 109-142 (1994).

8. Diaz, H. F. & Pulwarty, R. S. An analysis of the time scales of variability in centuries-long ENSO-sensitive records in the last 1000 years. *Clim. Change* **26,** 317-342 (1994).

9. Cook, E. R., Briffa, K. R., Meko, D. M., Graybill, D. A. & Funkhouser, G. The "segment length" curse in long tree-ring chronology development for paleoclimatic studies. *Holocene* **5,** 229-237 (1995).

10. Jones, P. D. & Briffa, K. R. Global surface air temperature variations during the 20th century: Part 1—Spatial, temporal and seasonal details. *Holocene* **1,** 165-179 (1992).

11. Bradley, R. S. in *Climatic Variations and Forcing Mechanisms of the Last 2000 Years* (eds Jones, P. D., Bradley, R. S. & Jouzel, J.) 603-624 (Springer, Berlin, 1996).

12. Jacoby, G. C. & D'Arrigo, R. Reconstructed Northern Hemisphere annual temperature since 1671 based on high-latitude tree-ring data from North America. *Clim. Change* **14,** 39-59 (1989).

13. Jacoby, G. C., D'Arrigo, R. D. & Tsevegyn, D. Mongolian tree rings and 20th-century warming. *Science* **9,** 771-773 (1996).

14. Fritts, H. C., Blasing, T. J., Hayden, B. P. & Kutzbach, J. E. Multivariate techniques for specifying tree-growth and climate relationships and for reconstructing anomalies in paleoclimate. *J. Appl. Meteorol.* **10,** 845-864 (1971).

15. Cook, E. R., Briffa, K. R. & Jones, P. D. Spatial regression methods in dendroclimatology: a review and comparison of two techniques. *Int. J. Climatol.* **14,** 379-402 (1994).

16. Briffa, K. R., Jones, P. D. & Schweingruber, F. H. Tree-ring density reconstructions of summer temperature pattern across western North American since 1600. *J. Clim.* **5,** 735-753 (1992).

17. Schweingruber, F. H., Briffa, K. R. & Jones, P. D. Yearly maps of summer temperatures in western Europe from A.D. 1750 to 1975 and Western North American from 1600 to 1982. *Vegetatio* **92,** 5-71 (1991).

18. Fritts, H. *Reconstructing Large-scale Climatic Patterns from Tree Ring Data* (Univ. Arizona Press, Tucson, 1991).

19. Guiot, J. The combination of historical documents and biological data in the reconstruction of climate variations in space and time. *Palaeoklimaforschung* **7,** 93-104 (1988).

20. D'Arrigo, R. D., Cook, E. R., Jacoby, G. C. & Briffa, K. R. NAO and sea surface temperature signatures in tree-ring records from the North Atlantic sector. *Quat. Sci. Rev.* **12,** 431-440 (1993).

21. Stahle, D. W. & Cleaveland, M. K. Southern Oscillation extremes reconstructed from tree rings of the Sierra Madre Occidental and southern Great Plains. *J. Clim.* **6,** 129-140 (1993).

22. Smith, T. M., Reynolds, R. W., Livezey, R. E. & Stokes, D. C. Reconstruction of historical sea surface temperatures using empirical orthogonal functions. *J. Clim.* **9,** 1403-1420 (1996).

23. Kaplan, A. *et al.* Analyses of global sea surface temperature 1856-1991. *J. Geophys. Res.* (in the press).

24. Halpert, M. S. & Ropelewski, C. F. Surface temperature patterns associated with the Southern Oscillation. *J. Clim.* **5,** 577-593 (1992).

25. Preisendorfer, R. W. *Principal Component Analysis in Meteorology and Oceanography* (Elsevier, Amsterdam, 1988).

26. Cane, M. *et al.* Twentieth-century sea surface temperature trends. *Science* **275,** 957-960 (1997).

27. Hurrell, J. W. Decadal trends in the North Atlantic Oscillation, regional temperatures and precipitation. *Science* **269,** 676-679 (1995).

28. Chang, P., Ji, L. & Li, H. A decadal climate variation in the tropical Atlantic Ocean from thermodynamic air–sea interactions. *Nature* **385,** 516-518 (1997).

29. Folland, C. K., Parker, D. E. & Kates, F. E. Worldwide marine temperature fluctuations 1856-1981. *Nature* **310,** 670-673 (1984).

30. Kushnir, Y. Interdecadal variations in North Atlantic sea surface temperature and associated atmospheric conditions. *J. Clim.* **7,** 141-157 (1994).

31. Schlesinger, M. E. & Ramankutty, N. An oscillation in the global climate system of period 65-70 years. *Nature* **367,** 723-726 (1994).

32. Mann, M. E. & Park, J. Global-scale modes of surface temperature variability on interannual to century timescales. *J. Geophys. Res.* **99,** 25819-25833 (1994).

33. Mann, M. E. & Park, J. Joint spatiotemporal modes of surface temperature and sea level pressure variability in the northern hemisphere during the last century. *J. Clim.* **9,** 2137-2162 (1996).

34. Delworth, T. D., Manabe, S. & Stouffer, R. J. Multidecadal climate variability in the Greenland Sea and surrounding regions: a coupled model simulation. *Geophys. Res. Lett.* **24,** 257-260 (1997).

35. Quinn, W. H. & Neal, V. T. in *Climate Since A.D. 1500* (eds Bradley, R. S. & Jones, P. D.) 623-648 (Routledge, London, 1992).

36. Mann, M. E., Bradley, R. S. & Hughes, M. K. in *El Niño and the Southern Oscillation: Multiscale Variability and its Impacts on Natural Ecosystems and Society* (eds Diaz, H. F. & Markgraf, V.) (Cambridge Univ. Press, in the press).

37. Kelly, P. M., Jones, P. D. & Pengqun, J. The spatial response of the climate system to explosive volcanic eruptions. *Int. J. Climatol.* **16,** 537-550 (1996).

38. Kirchner, I. & Graf, H. F. Volcanoes and El Niño: signal separation in Northern Hemisphere winter. *Clim. Dyn.* **11,** 341-358 (1995).

39. Raynaud, D., Barnola, J. M., Chappellaz, J. & Martinerie, P. in *Climatic Variations and Forcing Mechanisms of the Last 2000 Years* (eds Jones, P. D., Bradley, R. S. & Jouzel, J.) 547-562 (Springer, Berlin, 1996).

40. Bradley, R. S. & Jones, P. D. in *Climate Since A.D. 1500* (eds Bradley, R. S. & Jones, P. D.) 606-622 (Routledge, London, 1992).

41. Robock, A. & Free, M. P. Ice cores as an index of global volcanism from 1850 to the present. *J. Geophys. Res.* **100,** 11549-11567 (1995).

42. Hegerl, G. C. *et al.* Multi-fingerprint detection and attribution analysis of greenhouse gas, greenhouse gas-plus-aerosol and solar forced climate change. *Clim. Dyn.* **13,** 613-634 (1997).

43. North, G. R. & Stevens, M. J. Detecting climate signals in the surface temperature record. *J. Clim.* (in the press).

44. Hansen, J., Sato, M. & Ruedy, R. The missing climate forcing. *Phil. Trans. R. Soc. Lond. B* **352,** 231-240 (1997).

45. Stevens, M. J. & North, G. R. Detection of the climate response to the solar cycle. *J. Clim.* (in the press).

46. Mann, M. E. & Lees, J. Robust estimation of background noise and signal detection in climatic time series. *Clim. Change* **33,** 409-445 (1996).

47. Rind, D. & Overpeck, J. Hypothesized causes of decadal-to-century climate variability: climate model results. *Quat. Sci. Rev.* **12,** 357-374 (1993).

48. Wigley, T. M. L. & Raper, S. C. B. Natural variability of the climate system and detection of the greenhouse effect. *Nature* **344,** 324-327 (1990).

49. Thomson, D. J. Dependence of global temperatures on atmospheric CO_2 and solar irradiance. *Proc. Natl Acad. Sci. USA* **94,** 8370-8377 (1997).

50. Pollack, H. N. & Chapman, D. S. Underground records of changing climate. *Sci. Am.* **268,** 44-50 (1993).

Supplementary Information is available on *Nature*'s World-Wide Web site (http://www.nature.com) or as paper copy from Mary Sheehan at the London editorial office of *Nature*.

Acknowledgements. This work benefited from discussions with M. Cane, E. Cook, M. Evans, A. Kaplan and collaborators at the Lamont Doherty Earth Observatory. We acknowledge discussions with K. Briffa, T. Crowley, P. Jones, S. Manabe, R. Saravanan and K. Trenberth, as well as the comments of G. Hegerl. We thank R. D'Arrigo, D. Fisher, G. Jacoby, J. Lean, A. Robock, D. Stahle, C. Stockton, E. Vaganov, R. Villalba and the numerous contributors to the International Tree-Ring Data Bank and other palaeoclimate researchers who have made their data available to us for use in this study; we also thank F. Keimig, M. Munro, R. Holmes and C. Aramann for their technical assistance. This work was supported by the NSF and the US Department of Energy. M.E.M. acknowledges support through the Alexander Hollaender Distinguished Postdoctoral Research Fellowship program of the Department of Energy. This work is a contribution to the NSF- and NOAA-sponsored Analysis of Rapid and Recent Climatic Change (ARRCC) project.

Correspondence and requests for materials should be addressed to M.E.M. (e-mail: mann@snow.geo.umass.edu).

Identification of a Host Galaxy at Redshift $z=3.42$ for the γ-ray Burst of 14 December 1997

S. R. Kulkarni *et al.*

Editor's Note

Gamma-ray bursts were first discovered by a satellite launched to look for detonations of nuclear weapons. The first counterparts at other wavelengths were found in 1997 by the BeppoSAX satellite, after which it became clear that the bursts were happening in distant and faint galaxies. But the energy release could not be calibrated without knowing just how far away they are. Here Shrinivas Kulkarni at the California Institute of Technology and coworkers determine that a gamma-ray burst of 14 December 1997 happened in a galaxy at a redshift of 3.42. This meant that if it was radiated uniformly, the energy released as gamma rays alone would be more than 10^{53} erg, or about 1,000 times greater than a supernova. Astronomers now believe that the burst is beamed through a small angle, reducing the total energy to about 10^{51} erg, or about ten times that of a normal supernova.

Knowledge of the properties of γ-ray bursts has increased substantially following recent detections of counterparts at X-ray, optical and radio wavelengths. But the nature of the underlying physical mechanism that powers these sources remains unclear. In this context, an important question is the total energy in the burst, for which an accurate estimate of the distance is required. Possible host galaxies have been identified for the first two optical counterparts discovered, and a lower limit obtained for the redshift of one of them, indicating that the bursts lie at cosmological distances. A host galaxy of the third optically detected burst has now been identified and its redshift determined to be $z = 3.42$. When combined with the measured flux of γ-rays from the burst, this large redshift implies an energy of 3×10^{53} erg in the γ-rays alone, if the emission is isotropic. This is much larger than the energies hitherto considered, and it poses a challenge for theoretical models of the bursts.

EVER since their discovery nearly three decades ago[1], it was understood that progress in solving the puzzle of γ-ray bursts (GRBs) depends on their identification at other—preferably optical—wavelengths, so that the distances could be measured using standard spectroscopic techniques. From distances and flux measurements one can then infer luminosities and other physical parameters, which can then be used to test theoretical models of the bursts and their origins.

A recent breakthrough in this field was the precise localization of bursts by the BeppoSAX

1997 年 12 月 14 日的伽马射线暴在红移 3.42 处的寄主星系的证认

库尔卡尼等

编者按

伽马射线暴最早是被一个探测核武器爆炸的卫星所发现的。1997 年，贝波 X 射线天文卫星首次探测到伽马射线暴在其他波段上的对应体。自那以后，人们逐渐意识到这些暴发生于遥远的暗弱星系当中。然而，如果我们不知道它们到底离我们有多远，我们就没办法确定它们释放的能量。这里，根据加州理工学院的什里尼沃斯·库尔卡尼与他的合作者的研究结果得知，1997 年 12 月 14 日发现的伽马射线暴产生于一个红移为 3.42 的星系当中。这意味着如果它各向均匀地向外辐射，那么单以 γ 射线形式释放的能量就将超过 10^{53} erg，大约是一个超新星能量的 1,000 倍。当前天文学家相信伽马射线暴是在一个小角度范围内定向爆发，这样使得该伽马射线暴所释放的能量降至大约 10^{51} erg，对应一个普通超新星能量的十倍左右。

随着近来对伽马射线暴在 X 射线、光学以及射电波段对应体的观测，我们对这种天体特征的认知大大地获得增加。然而我们对于提供暴能源的底层物理机制仍不清楚。这其中，一个重要的问题就是，要确定整个暴的总能量，需要精确地测量它相对我们的距离。到目前为止，人们已经辨认出了最先发现的两个光学对应体的可能寄主星系，并定出了其中一个星系的红移下限，这表明伽马射线暴发生在宇宙学距离上。在这里，我们也证认出了第三个从光学上探测到对应体的暴的寄主星系，并定出其红移为 3.42。根据实际探测到的 γ 射线流量，如果辐射是各向同性的，那么如此高的红移就意味着单 γ 射线上释放的能量就达到 3×10^{53} erg。这比先前考虑的能量都要大得多，因此对伽马射线暴的理论模型提出了挑战。

自三十年前发现伽马射线暴 [1] 起，人们就知道，要解决伽马射线暴（GRB）的谜团需要证认出其他波段——尤其是可见光波段的对应体，这样才能通过标准的光谱方法来确定它们的距离。由距离和流量我们就能推算出它的光度和其他物理量，用以验证伽马射线暴机制和起源的理论模型。

这个领域最新的突破是 BeppoSAX 卫星对暴的精确定位 [2]，它帮助我们首次在

satellite[2], which has led to the first identifications of GRBs at other wavelengths: X-rays[3], optical[4] and radio[5]. This has further led to the determination of the distance scale of GRBs, with the detection of intergalactic absorption lines[6] in the optical transient[7,8] (OT) of GRB970508 (refs 9, 10). Apparent host galaxies have been detected for the first two optical afterglows found[11-14].

Here we report follow-up studies of the OT[15] of a relatively bright burst, GRB971214 (refs 16–18). As the OT faded away, we found an extended object with a red-band magnitude $R = 25.6 \pm 0.15$ at the position of the OT. Based on the excellent positional coincidence, 0.06 ± 0.06 arcsec, we argue here that this is the host galaxy of GRB971214. Spectroscopic observations show that the host is a typical star-forming galaxy[19-21] at a redshift $z = 3.418$.

Given this high redshift, the γ-ray energy release of this burst is unexpectedly large, about 3×10^{53} erg, assuming isotropic emission, corresponding to about 16% of the rest-mass energy of our Sun. Energy released in other forms of radiation, for example, neutrinos or gravity waves, is not included in this energy budget. Nonetheless, the inferred energy release in γ-rays alone is so substantial that it may present difficulties for some of the currently popular theoretical models for the origin of the bursts (coalescence of neutron stars). We may be forced to consider even more energetic possibilities[22,23] or to find ways of extracting more electromagnetic energy in coalescence models.

The Optical Transient

Our follow-up at the Keck Observatory began on the night of 1997 December 15 UT, approximately 13 h after the burst. The only available imager was a "guide" camera with a small field-of-view and relatively low sensitivity; consequently, these data were not used in the analysis described below. For the subsequent nights we used the Low Resolution Imaging Spectrograph[24] (LRIS) mounted at the Cassegrain focus of the Keck II 10-m telescope. Our early observations were made in the I band. This choice was driven by the presence of a bright Moon in the sky. Later observations were done under darker sky conditions and with a R-band filter (OG570+KG3). In Table 1 we give a summary of our observations as well as other reported measurements[25-29].

Figure 1 shows an I-band image obtained on 1997 December 16.52 UT, when the OT[26] was still bright. I-band and R-band magnitudes of the OT are given in Table 1 and shown in Fig. 2. In order to establish consistency between our measurements and the earlier measurements reported by others, we measured instrumental magnitudes of a number of "secondary" stars in the general vicinity of the OT and then used them to define the zero-point of our instrumental magnitudes for all of our data sets. We calibrated the instrumental magnitudes by using observations of the standard star PG0231+051 (for which we assume I-band magnitude $I = 16.639$ mag; ref. 30) obtained on 1997 December 22 UT. We then derived the magnitudes for stars H1 and H2 (identified in Fig. 1) as 16.1 ± 0.1 mag and 18.6 ± 0.2 mag, respectively. For these two stars, Halpern et al.[15] obtained 15.93 mag and 18.46 mag.

其他波段（X 射线 [3]、光学波段 [4]、射电波段 [5]）证认出 GRB 的对应体。据此，我们可以进一步确定 GRB 的距离尺度，比如对 GRB970508 的光学暂现源 [7,8]（OT）的星系际吸收线 [6] 进行探测以确定 GRB970508（参考文献 9 和 10）的距离。到目前为止，人们已经探测到最早发现的两个光学余辉所对应的寄主星系 [11-14]。

这里我们要报道的是对一个较亮的 GRB971214（参考文献 16 ~ 18）的 OT[15] 的后续研究。在 OT 消失以后，我们在原来的位置上发现了一个 R 波段星等为 25.6±0.15 的延展天体。由于位置上惊人的一致——相差仅 0.06±0.06 角秒，我们推测这就是 GRB971214 的寄主星系。光谱分析表明这个星系是一个典型的恒星形成星系 [19-21]，红移为 3.418。

如此之高的红移意味着这个伽马射线暴所释放的 γ 射线的能量相当大，如果辐射是各向同性的，那么释放的能量约为 3×10^{53} erg，相当于 16% 的太阳静质能。这其中还不包括其他形式的辐射，比如中微子和引力波等。然而，单是这推算出的 γ 射线波段的能量如此之大就已经给目前流行的伽马射线暴爆发起源理论模型（中子星并合）带来了挑战。我们不得不考虑其他可以产生更高能量的理论模型 [22,23]，或者在并合模型中找到可以提取更多电磁能量的方式。

光学暂现源

我们于世界时 1997 年 12 月 15 日夜里（大约是伽马射线暴爆发后的 13 小时）在凯克观测站开始进行后续观测。唯一可用的成像设备是一个小视场、相对低灵敏度的导星相机，因此这批数据没有用于下面的分析。接下来的几个夜里我们使用装在 10 米凯克望远镜 II 卡塞格林焦点上的低分辨率成像摄谱仪 [24]（LRIS）。前期的观测由于有月光干扰，因此只在 I 波段进行。在天空背景变暗后我们采用 R 波段滤光片（OG570+KG3）进行后续的观测。在表 1 中我们对我们的观测条件以及其他已有的测量结果 [25-29] 进行了简单的总结。

图 1 显示的是世界时 1997 年 12 月 16.52 日获得的 I 波段图像，图像中 OT[26] 还非常明亮，我们将 OT I 波段和 R 波段的星等列于表 1 中并标示于图 2 中。为了使所得数据格式同前人的测量结果相一致，我们测量了 OT 附近一系列二级标准星的仪器星等，用以确定我们所有数据集的仪器星等的零点。然后我们通过世界时 1997 年 12 月 22 日对标准星 PG0231+051（取其 I 波段星等为 16.639 星等；参考文献 30）的观测对仪器星等进行定标。这样，我们得到恒星 H1 和 H2（在图 1 中标出）的绝对星等分别为 16.1±0.1 星等和 18.6±0.2 星等。相应地，哈尔彭等人 [15] 给出的结果是 15.93 星等和 18.46 星等，两者在误差范围内一致，于是我们可以将我们 I 波段的测

Within errors, these two sets of measurements agree and thus allow us to link our I-band magnitudes to those of Halpern *et al.*[26]. The zero point for our R-band magnitudes was set by assuming $R = 20.1 \pm 0.1$ for object 2 of Henden *et al.*[29]; see also Fig. 1. Our R-band magnitude is in excellent agreement with that obtained by Diercks *et al.*[28] at about the same epoch.

Fig. 1. Images of the field of the optical transient of GRB971214 and the associated host galaxy. **a**, I-band image of the field of the optical transient (OT) of GRB971214. The image is 3.5 arcmin by 3.0 arcmin and has been smoothed by a gaussian of full-width at half-maximum (FWHM) of 0.53 arcsec. The numbered stars are "secondary" stars used for achieving consistency within our various data sets. Stars H1 and H2 allow us to link our photometry with that of Halpern *et al.*[26] and Henden *et al.*[29]. The "rays" are light from the bright star (6.7 mag) SAO15663 diffracted by the telescope structure; this bright star is ~1 arcmin northeast of the OT. The rays rotate as the telescope tracks the source. In **b**, the left panel is an I-band image of the OT obtained from data taken on 1997 December 16 UT. The image is a square of side 1

量结果与他们的结果 [26] 联合起来使用。R 波段的零点是在假定亨登等人 [29] 的 2 号天体 R 波段星等为 20.1±0.1 的情况下而确定的；参见图 1。这样，我们获得的 R 波段数据与迪克斯等人 [28] 在同时期的测量结果相当吻合。

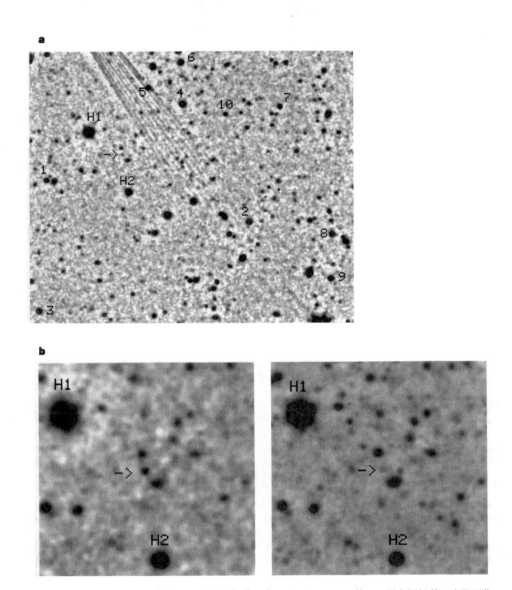

图 1. GRB971214 的 OT 及其寄主星系所在视场的图像。**a**. GRB971214 的 OT 所在视场的 I 波段图像。图像为 3.5 角分 ×3.0 角分，已做半峰全宽为 0.53 角秒的高斯平滑处理。已编号的恒星是用以同其他批次数据进行定标的二级标准星。恒星 H1 和 H2 使我们的测光数据得以同哈尔彭等人 [26] 和亨登等人 [29] 的数据进行比较。图中的"射线状特征"是被望远镜结构衍射的亮星 SAO15663（6.7 星等）的星光；这颗亮星位于 OT 东北约 1 角分处。随着望远镜跟踪目标时的视场旋转，射线也相应转动。**b**. 左图是世界时 1997 年 12 月 16 日时拍摄的 OT 的 I 波段图像。图像大小为 1 角分见方，经半峰全宽为 0.53 角秒的

arcmin, and has been smoothed by a guassian with FWHM of 0.53 arcsec. The OT is marked. The right panel is an R-band image of the field of OT obtained from data taken on 1998 January 10 UT. The image is a square of side 1 arcmin, and has been smoothed by a gaussian with FWHM of 0.53 arcsec. An extended object is seen at the position of the OT. We suggest that this is the host galaxy of GRB971214. For all three images, North is to the top and East to the left. In all three images the optical transient is marked by an arrow. We have also obtained the spectrum of the galaxy ~4.5 arcsec to the northeast of the OT. The spectrum shows a prominent [O $_{II}$] 3,727 emission line and the usual absorption features at a redshift of 0.5023.

Fig. 2. The R- and I-band light curve of the OT of GRB971214. The OT is identified in Fig.1. The x-axis is $\log(t - t_0)$ where t is the UT date of the observation and t_0 is the UT date of the GRB. All times are measured in units of days. The GRB took place on 1997 December 14.9727 (ref.16). At I band the OT is well detected for the first three nights. Upper limits exist for the nights of UT 1997 December 20 and December 22. The dotted line is a linear least-squares fit to the I-band data but restricted to these first three nights. The assumed model is $I(t - t_0) = I_1 + s \log(t - t_0)$; here I is the magnitude at time t, s is the slope and I_1 the offset. The fits yield $I_1 = 22.22 \pm 0.18$ and $s = 3.09 \pm 0.52$. For reasons discussed in the text it is reasonable to assume that the R-band light curve has the same slope, s. The solid line is parallel to the dotted line but goes through our R-band magnitude of 1997 December 16.63 UT. This line describes adequately the R-band light curve for the first three nights. Clearly, the December 15.50 point of Henden et al.[29] is not well accounted for by this model. The R-band measurements of 1998 January 10 and February 24 lie well above the extrapolation of the dotted line. We attribute this excess over the decaying optical transient as arising from galaxy K shown in Fig. 1. In both the January 10 and February 24 images, the full width at half maximum (FWHM) of K is 1.07 arcsec which is larger than the same estimated from stars in the vicinity of K (Table 1). The rough size of K is thus ~0.65 arcsec.

The decay of previous OTs associated with GRBs appears to be well characterized by a power law: $S(t) \propto t^{-a}$, where $S(t)$ is the flux of the OT and t is the time since the γ-ray burst. Accepting this parametric form and considering only the time interval December 15–17,

高斯平滑处理。图中标出了 OT 的位置。右图是世界时 1998 年 1 月 10 日获得的 OT 所在视场的 R 波段图像，也是 1 角分见方，同样经半峰全宽为 0.53 角秒的高斯平滑处理。在 OT 原来的位置上可以看见一个延展天体，我们认为那就是 GRB971214 的寄主星系。所有的三幅图片均为上北左东，OT 由箭头标出。我们也获得了 OT 东北约 4.5 角秒处的星系的光谱，光谱中有明显的 [O II] 3,727 发射线和红移 0.5023 处常见的吸收线。

图 2. GRB971214 光学暂现源 R 和 I 波段的光变曲线。OT 已在图 1 中标出。x 轴是 $\log(t-t_0)$，其中 t 是观测的世界时，t_0 是 GRB 的世界时，均以天为单位。GRB 发生于 1997 年 12 月 14.9727 日（参考文献 16）。在 I 波段前三个晚上的探测都可得到很确切的结果，在 12 月 20 日和 22 日都只能得到上限。图中的虚线是 I 波段数据的线性最小二乘法拟合，不过仅限于对前三天的观测进行拟合。假定的模型是 $I(t-t_0)=I_1+s\log(t-t_0)$，其中 I 是时间 t 时的星等，s 是斜率，I_1 是偏置。拟合的结果为 $I_1=22.22\pm0.18$，$s=3.09\pm0.52$。由于正文中提到的原因，有理由相信 R 波段光变曲线有着同样的斜率 s。图中实线与虚线平行，且过世界时 1997 年 12 月 16.63 日测得的 R 波段星等，同前三天的 R 波段光变数据基本吻合。亨登等人 [29] 12 月 15.50 日的数据点显然不满足这个模型。1998 年 1 月 10 日和 2 月 24 日的 R 波段测量结果都在虚线的外推之上，我们认为这种对衰减的光学暂现源的亮度超出是由图 1 中显示的星系 K 引起的，在 1 月 10 日和 2 月 24 日的图像中 K 的半峰全宽为 1.07 角秒，这个值比它邻近的恒星的估值大得多（见表 1）。由此估计 K 的角直径约为 0.65 角秒。

之前提到的与 GRB 相关的 OT 的光度衰减可以按幂律形式进行描述，即 $S(t)\propto t^{-a}$，其中 $S(t)$ 为 OT 的流量，t 是从伽马射线暴爆发算起的时间。基于这个参数表达式且仅考虑 12 月 15～17 日的数据，我们可以得到 $I(t)=(22.22\pm0.18)+(3.09\pm0.52)\log(t)$， we obtain $I(t) = (22.22 \pm 0.18) + (3.09 \pm 0.52) \log (t)$: here t is in days. As magnitudes are defined to be $-2.5 \log(S) +$ constant, the value of a is 1.22 ± 0.2—remarkably similar to those reported for previous OTs[31-33].

From the data in Fig. 2 we see that initially the R-band flux appears to decrease in approximately the same fashion as the I-band flux. Such broad-band decay has been noted in previous OTs[32,33] and indeed is an expectation of simple fireball models[31,34]. Accepting that all optical bands decay with the same a, we obtain $R(t) = (23.0 \pm 0.22) + (3.09 \pm 0.52) \log(t)$. In arriving at this equation we have used our 16 December R-band measurement (Table 1) to set the zero point.

Identifying the Host Galaxy

Using the above decay formula we predict $R = 27.4 \pm 0.8$ mag on 1998 January 10 UT. In contrast, we find at the same epoch an object at the position of the OT with $R = 25.6 \pm 0.17$ mag (see Fig. 1). Furthermore, this object, which we will call "K", is extended in comparison to stars in the same field. We suggest that K is the host galaxy of the GRB and has become apparent now that the OT has dimmed.

It is important to assess how well K coincides with the OT. To this end, we determined the location of the OT relative to 15 "tertiary" stars in the vicinity of the OT in the December 16.52 I-band image, and likewise for K in the January 10 R-band image. The error in the measured angular difference between the OT and K is determined by two factors, as follows. (1) The error in determining the centroid of K, which primarily arises from the small number of signal photons and the sky background. We estimate this to be 0.20 pixel (r.m.s.); each LRIS pixel is a square of side 0.211 arcsec. The similar error for the OT is negligible because the OT is much brighter than K in the December 16 image that we used. (2) Errors due to coordinate transformation between the two images which are of different orientations. We determined a coordinate transformation between the frames using the measurements of the tertiary stars, and then transformed the centroid of the OT into the frame of January 10 image. This error turns out to be negligible compared to the error discussed in (1). The difference between the position of the OT in the transformed image and that of K is $\Delta X = 0.24 \pm 0.20$ pixel $= 0.05 \pm 0.04$ arcsec and $\Delta Y = 0.14 \pm 0.20$ pixel $= 0.03 \pm 0.04$ arcsec, corresponding to a radial separation of 0.06 ± 0.06 arcsec.

One may argue that the density of galaxies as faint as K is sufficiently high that the coincidence of the OT with a background galaxy is not improbable. The cumulative surface density[35] of galaxies with $R \leqslant 25.5$ mag is 3.9×10^5 per degree². Considering angular offsets up to the apparent radius of the galaxy, 0.35 arcsec (see Fig. 1), the chance coincidence probability is reasonably small ($\sim 10^{-3}$). We therefore suggest that galaxy K is the host of the OT and thus is the host of GRB971214.

其中 t 的单位是天。由于星等值的定义可以表示为 $-2.5 \log(S) +$ 常数，因此 a 的值为 1.22 ± 0.2，这个结果同以前 OT 的研究结果[31-33] 很接近。

从图 2 中的数据可以看出初始阶段 R 波段的流量衰减特征几乎与 I 波段的情况相同，这一宽波段的衰减现象也曾在以前对 OT 的观测[32,33] 中被人们注意到，与此同时这个现象也符合简单火球模型的理论预言[31,34]。如果所有光学波段的衰减的幂指数都对应相同的 a 值，那么 $R(t) = (23.0 \pm 0.22) + (3.09 \pm 0.52) \log(t)$。此处我们采用了 12 月 16 日 R 波段的测量结果 (见表 1) 来标定星等零点。

寄主星系证认

利用上面的衰减公式我们估计出世界时 1998 年 1 月 10 日的 OT R 波段星等为 27.4 ± 0.8，然而相比之下，我们在同一时期 OT 的位置上发现一个 R 波段星等为 25.6 ± 0.17 的天体 (见图 1)。此外，该天体 (称为 "K") 相比于同视场的恒星而言是一个展源。因此我们推断 K 可能是这个 GRB 的寄主星系，正是在 OT 变得暗淡之后才得以显现出来。

明确天体 K 与 OT 的一一对应的关系是非常重要的。为此，我们在 12 月 16.52 日的 I 波段图像上确定了 OT 相对于它附近 15 个三级标准星的相对位置，并在 1 月 10 日的 R 波段图像上对天体 K 进行同样的操作。这里有两个因素决定 OT 和 K 之间角度差异的误差。(1) K 天体形心的定位误差，这个误差主要来源于过少数量的信号光子以及天空背景。我们估计其误差大小为 0.20 个像素 (均方根)，而 LRIS 望远镜的每个像素为长 0.211 角秒的方格。相比之下，OT 的此类误差则可以忽略，因为在选取的 12 月 16 日的图像中 OT 比 K 亮很多。(2) 将方位角不同的两幅图像进行坐标变换所引入的误差。我们通过测量三级标准星来对两个图像系统进行坐标变换，然后依此把 OT 的形心位置变换到 1 月 10 日的图像中去。相比于前面讨论的因素 (1)，这个误差可以忽略不计。转换后的图像中 OT 与 K 的位置差别为 $\Delta X = 0.24 \pm 0.20$ 像素 $= 0.05 \pm 0.04$ 角秒，$\Delta Y = 0.14 \pm 0.20$ 像素 $= 0.03 \pm 0.04$ 角秒，这对应它们的径向距离为 0.06 ± 0.06 角秒。

有人也许会怀疑，像 K 这样暗淡的星系其分布密度相当高，OT 有可能刚好与一个背景星系位置相重合。但是所有 R 波段星等小于等于 25.5 的星系累积面密度[35] 为每平方度 3.9×10^5 个。即使考虑到这个星系视半径的角度偏移 (也只有 0.35 角秒，见图 1)，这种意外重合的可能性也相当小 (约为 10^{-3})。因此我们认为星系 K 是 OT 的寄主星系，也是 GRB971214 的寄主星系。

Determining the Redshift

Spectroscopic observations of the OT and its host galaxy were obtained using LRIS[24]. Our initial attempt to obtain the spectrum of the OT on 1997 December 17 UT was unsuccessful, largely due to the bright moonlight. Subsequent observations were obtained under much better sky conditions, and after the OT had faded and object K dominated the light. Almost all spectra were obtained with the slit position angle close to the parallactic angle, and the wavelength-dependent slit losses are not important for the discussion below. The log and the technical details of the spectroscopic observations can be found in Table 2.

The spectrum, shown in Fig. 3, shows a prominent emission line at 5,382.1 Å with a clear continuum drop immediately on the blue (short-wavelength) side of the line. No other emission line is detected. The continuum rises slightly towards the red and is undetectable at about 4,000 Å.

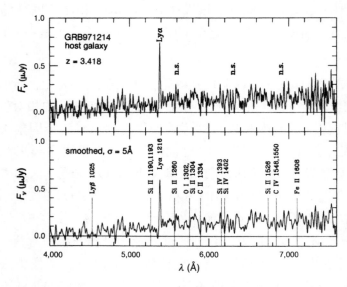

Fig. 3. The composite Keck spectrum of the host galaxy of GRB971214. The top panel shows the original data, with the locations of the prominent night sky (n.s.) emission lines indicated. The bottom panel shows the same spectrum smoothed with a gaussian with $\sigma = 5$ Å, which is approximately equal to the effective instrumental resolution. Locations of several absorption features commonly seen in the spectra of $z \approx 3$ galaxies are indicated. The redshift, $z = 3.418$, has been derived from the mean point of the Lyα emission and absorption features, as described in the text. The log of the observations and the details of the spectrograph settings can be found in Table 2. The "lower" resolution data were reduced completely independently by two of the authors (S.G.D. and K.L.A.), using independent reduction packages. The results are in an excellent mutual agreement. The "higher" resolution data are also fully consistent with them, showing essentially the same spectroscopic features. The useful wavelength range spanned by the lower-resolution data is ~4,000–7,600 Å, and the higher-resolution data spans ~4,900–7,300 Å. All of the spectra have been averaged with appropriate signal-to-noise weighting, after suitable resampling.

确 定 红 移

我们通过 LRIS[24] 获得了 OT 及其寄主星系的光谱观测结果。在世界时 1997 年 12 月 17 日，我们初次尝试拍摄 OT 光谱，但主要由于月光太亮而没能成功。后续观测的天气状况较好，且当时 OT 已减弱，亮度主要由天体 K 主导。在拍摄所有光谱时基本上狭缝位置角都接近于星位角，从而波长依赖的狭缝损失在下文中的讨论并不重要。我们在表 2 中给出了一些光谱观测日志和技术细节。

在图 3 显示的光谱中，我们在波长 5,382.1 Å 处发现了一条很强的发射线，并在紧挨该发射线的蓝（短波）端发现连续谱有明显的下降。同时并没有探测到其他的发射线。另外，连续谱朝着红端有轻微上升，并在大约 4,000 Å 处已不能被测到。

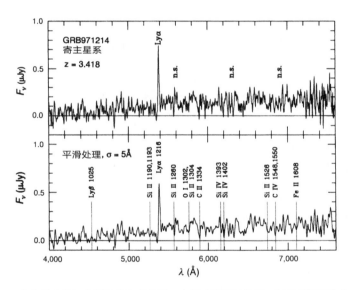

图 3. GRB971214 寄主星系的凯克望远镜合成光谱。上部分是原始数据，标出了明显的夜晚天光 (ns) 发射线的位置。下部分是经 σ = 5 Å 的高斯平滑处理之后所得到的光谱，与仪器的有效分辨率接近。图中标出了红移在 3 左右的星系中常见的吸收线，如正文中所述，通过 Lyα 发射线的中心和吸收线特征得出该星系的红移 z = 3.418。观测日志和光谱细节可以在表 2 中看到。"较低"分辨率数据由作者中的两位（乔尔戈夫斯基和阿德尔贝格尔）用完全不同的测光包各自独立处理得出，结果相当一致。"较高"分辨率的数据也与之吻合，显现出相同的光谱特征。低分辨率数据的有效波长范围约为 4,000～7,600 Å，高分辨率数据约为 4,900～7,300 Å。全部光谱都经适当重采样后对信噪比加权进行了平均操作。

There are only two plausible interpretations of this prominent emission line. All other choices would require a presence of other, stronger emission lines which are not seen in our spectrum. First, the line could be [O II] 3,727 at $z = 0.444$. We would then expect to see comparably strong [O III] 5,007 and 4,959 lines at 7,230 Å and 7,160 Å, Hβ 4,861 Å at 7,020 Å, and perhaps also other Balmer lines. Yet none of these lines are seen in our data, even though they fall in a reasonably clean part of the spectrum. It would be also hard to understand the abrupt drop in the continuum blueward of the emission line.

The alternative interpretation, and the interpretation which we favour, is that the emission line is Lyα 1,215.7 Å at a redshift $z_{em} = 3.428$. The overall appearance of the spectrum is typical of the known, star-forming galaxies at comparable redshifts[19-21]. In the absence of an active nucleus, no other strong emission lines would be expected within the wavelength range probed by our spectrum.

Additional arguments in favour of the large-redshift interpretation include:

(1) The drop across the Lyα line, due to the absorption by intervening hydrogen, is characteristic of objects at such high redshifts. The measured drop amplitude[36] $D_A = 0.35 \pm 0.05$ is exactly the mean value seen in the spectra of quasars at this redshift[37].

(2) We expect no flux blueward of 4,030 Å, the redshifted Lyman continuum break. Additionally, we expect a relatively flat, star-formation-powered continuum redward of the Lyα line. Our spectrum is consistent with these expectations. The expected suppression of blue light is also supported by our imaging observations in the B band (Table 1); this band covers the range 3,900–4,800 Å. Our 3σ upper limit on the B magnitude of galaxy K is 26.8 mag, corresponding to a B-band flux of < 84 nJy. We find that the red portion of the spectrum can be approximated by $F_\nu = 174(\nu/\nu_R)^\alpha$ nJy with $\alpha = -0.7 \pm 0.2$; here F_ν is the spectral density at frequency ν and $\nu_R = 4.7 \times 10^{14}$ Hz, the centre frequency of the R band. The extrapolation of this spectrum to the B band ($\nu_B = 6.8 \times 10^{14}$ Hz) is 134 nJy, above our upper limit.

(3) We plot in Fig. 3 the expected locations of some of the commonly observed interstellar gas absorption lines seen in the spectra of star-forming galaxies at high redshifts[19-21]. We note several coincidences with dips in the observed spectrum.

Table 1. Summary of R- and I-band measurements

Epoch (UT)	Band	Magnitude	Notes and refs*
1997 Dec.15.47	I	21.27 ± 0.30	Ref. 26
1997 Dec.16.52	I	22.85 ± 0.33	9 × 120 s, 0.9″, R.G.
1997 Dec.17.45	I	23.34 ± 0.31	9 × 120 s, 1.1″, R.G. †
1997 Dec.17.60	I	23.55 ± 0.26	11 × 120 s, 0.8″, R.G.
1997 Dec.17.63	I	23.57 ± 0.40	11 × 120 s, 0.63″, R.G.‡

对于这条显著的发射线的解释只有两种可能，因为所有其他的解释都还要求存在其他更强的发射线，但它们未在我们光谱中出现。首先一种可能是这条谱线是红移为 0.444 的 [O II] 3,727。如果是这样，我们还将期待在 7,230 Å 和 7,160 Å 处看到差不多强的 [O III] 5,007 和 4,959 线，以及在 7,020 Å 处的 Hβ 4,861 Å，也许还有其他的巴耳末谱线。但是我们的数据中却并没有出现这些谱线，即使它们落在光谱中相对干净的一块区域。与此同时，这种解释也很难解释发射线蓝端连续谱的突降。

因此我们更倾向于另一种可能，即这条显著的发射线其实是红移 3.428 的 Lyα 1,215.7 Å。整个光谱的特征同具有差不多红移的已知恒星形成星系的典型光谱特征相一致 [19-21]。因为没有活跃的星系核，在我们所观测的光谱范围内不会看到其他更强的谱线。

支持高红移的其他理由还包括：

（1）由传播过程中的氢吸收所导致的跨 Lyα 线的流量陡降是这类高红移天体的普遍特征。测量到的下降幅度 [36] $D_A = 0.35 \pm 0.05$，正是这个红移处观测类星体光谱所得到的平均值 [37]。

（2）我们预期在 4,030 Å（即红移后的莱曼连续谱跳变）的更蓝端测不到流量。另外，我们期待在 Lyα 线的红端看到一个相对平坦的由恒星形成活动所贡献的连续谱。我们的光谱结果与这些预期相吻合。我们所预期的蓝光的压低也在 B 波段（3,900 ~ 4,800 Å，见表 1）的成像观测中得到了证实。天体 K 的 B 波段 3σ 置信度的星等上限为 26.8，对应的 B 波段流量小于 84 nJy。我们发现光谱红端部分的谱密度近似满足公式 $F_v = 174(v/v_R)^a$ nJy，其中 F_v 为频率 v 处的谱密度，$\alpha = -0.7 \pm 0.2$，$v_R = 4.7 \times 10^{14}$ Hz 为 R 波段的中央频率；将此光谱外推到 B 波段（$v_B = 6.8 \times 10^{14}$ Hz），那么对应的流量值为 134 nJy，这将高于我们测得的流量上限。

（3）我们在图 3 中标出了通常能在高红移的恒星形成星系中观测到的星际气体吸收线的位置 [19-21]，我们注意到它们与观测到的光谱中的几处凹陷区域相对应。

表 1. R 和 I 波段测量数据汇总

时期（世界时）	波段	星等	注释和参考文献 *
1997 年 12 月 15.47 日	I	21.27 ± 0.30	参考文献 26
1997 年 12 月 16.52 日	I	22.85 ± 0.33	9 × 120 s, 0.9″, 古德里奇
1997 年 12 月 17.45 日	I	23.34 ± 0.31	9 × 120 s, 1.1″, 古德里奇 †
1997 年 12 月 17.60 日	I	23.55 ± 0.26	11 × 120 s, 0.8″, 古德里奇
1997 年 12 月 17.63 日	I	23.57 ± 0.40	11 × 120 s, 0.63″, 古德里奇 ‡

Continued

Epoch (UT)	Band	Magnitude	Notes and refs*
1997 Dec. 20.53	I	> 24	10 × 360 s, A.V.F.1.4″ §
1997 Dec. 22.63	I	> 24.5	2 × 400 s, 0.9″, M.D. ‖
1997 Dec.15.50	R	21.7 ± 0.10	Ref. 29
1997 Dec.15.51	R	22.1 ± 0.10	Ref. 28
1997 Dec.16.46	R	23.3 ± 0.17	6 × 180 s, 0.86″, R.G.
1997 Dec.16.63	R	23.7 ± 0.10	3 × 180 s, 0.56″, R.G. ‡
1997 Dec.16.52	R	23.7 ± 0.30	Ref. 28
1997 Dec.17.51	R	24.4 ± 0.50	Ref. 25
1998 Jan.10.62	R	25.6 ± 0.17	12 × 300 s, 0.86″, J. Aycock¶
1998 Feb. 24.52	R	25.6 ± 0.15	10 × 300 s, 0.87″, S.R.K.
1998 Feb. 24.58	B	> 26.8	6 × 300, 3 × 600,1.00″, S.R.K.#

* The entries in the last column are: (for Keck observations) the number of frames obtained, the integration time, the seeing specified as full-width at half-maximum (FWHM), the observer or the reference (for observations reported in the literature). Additional notes are indicated by a letter. The log of the December 15 "guide" camera observations is not included here as we did not use those data in any quantitative analysis. (The OT was detected in those data, though.) Successive frames are displaced by 5–15 arcsec and the final image is obtained by registering the frames and then adding. All the imaging analysis was carried out with IRAF, a software package supplied by the National Optical Astronomy Observatories.

† Rhoads[27] reports $I = 22.9 ± 0.4$ on 1997 Dec 17.37 UT. This is consistent, within errors, with our measurement of the same night. However, due to the large error bars, this is not included in our compilation (above).

‡ This observation was affected by light diffracted by the telescope structure contaminating the region in the vicinity of the OT (see Fig.1). The diffracted pattern was ∼15 pixels wide and long. An image was formed by assigning each pixel a value equal to the median of a box 75×5 pixels, aligned along the diffraction spikes. All features smaller than this box disappear in the resultant image, leaving only the diffracted rays. This median image was then subtracted from the original image leaving an image free from the diffracted pattern. Photometry of the OT, reported in this table, was then performed on this subtracted image.

§ The data were taken in the polarimetric mode of LRIS and hence the light is split into two orthogonal polarization components—we call this the top and bottom channels. The images from each of the channels were reduced separately, averaged together and the two resultant images were co-added to give the final image. The seeing as estimated by observations of the standard star SA 104 440 (ref. 30) was exceptionally bad, ∼1.4 arcsec. No object was found in the final image at the position of the OT. We do not have a good estimate of the true point-spread function in the final image as the useful field is only 25 arcsec across and there are no bright stars within this. Based on noise statistics within an aperture of radius 1.5 arcsec we set a 3σ detection limit of $I = 24$ mag for this data. Analysis of artificial stars with FWHM of 1.4 arcsec using the IRAF task DAOFIND led to a detection limit of 23 mag. However, visual inspection of the artificial stars knowing the position of the object results in a more stringent limit, closer to the $I = 24$ mag obtained above.

‖ 3σ upper limit estimated from the detection statistics of artificial stars which have the same point-spread function as that of nearby stars and embedded in the general vicinity of the OT. This observation suffered from high sky brightness (19.1 mag per square arcsec) and also lack of numerous exposures.

¶ The first four exposures suffered from brighter sky as the Moon was still up in the sky. The image shown in Fig. 1 is the sum of the next eight exposures.

3σ upper limit. See footnote ‖ for details of the procedure of deriving the upper limit.

If this interpretation is correct, a better estimate of the galaxy's redshift can be obtained as follows. The Lyα emission line tends to be shifted systematically to the red in such galaxies, due to resonant scattering and absorption in the ambient gas. In any given case,

168

时期（世界时）	波段	星等	注释和参考文献 *
1997 年 12 月 20.53 日	I	>24	10×360 s，菲力片科 1.4″§
1997 年 12 月 22.63 日	I	>24.5	2×400 s，0.9″，戴维斯‖
1997 年 12 月 15.50 日	R	21.7±0.10	参考文献 29
1997 年 12 月 15.51 日	R	22.1±0.10	参考文献 28
1997 年 12 月 16.46 日	R	23.3±0.17	6×180 s，0.86″，古德里奇
1997 年 12 月 16.63 日	R	23.7±0.10	3×180 s，0.56″，古德里奇 ‡
1997 年 12 月 16.52 日	R	23.7±0.30	参考文献 28
1997 年 12 月 17.51 日	R	24.4±0.50	参考文献 25
1998 年 1 月 10.62 日	R	25.6±0.17	12×300 s，0.86″，艾科克 ¶
1998 年 2 月 24.52 日	R	25.6±0.15	10×300 s，0.87″，库尔卡尼
1998 年 2 月 24.58 日	B	>26.8	6×300，3×600，1.00″，库尔卡尼 #

* 最后一列的内容分别是：（对于凯克的观测数据来说）观测帧数、积分时间、以半峰全宽表示的视宁度、观测者或参考文献（对于文章报道的观测）。额外的注释由符号标出。12 月 15 日的导星照相机的观测数据没有用于任何定量分析，因此这里没有给出日志（尽管其中观测数据也已探测到 OT）。相邻各帧之间位移了 5～15 角秒，通过对齐和叠加来获得最终的图像。所有的图像分析工作都使用美国国家光学天文台开发的 IRAF 软件包完成。

† 罗兹 [27] 给出世界时 1997 年 12 月 17.37 日 $I=22.9±0.4$。这与我们同天的结果在误差范围内一致。但是这个结果由于误差棒过大，所以没有列入上面的列表中。

‡ 望远镜结构造成的衍射光污染了 OT 邻近视场（见图 1），观测结果受到一定影响。衍射花纹长宽各大概 15 像素。我们给每一个像素赋值，该值取为 75×5 像素的方框区域内的中值，而该方框沿着衍射峰成直线。如此得到的图像中所有小于此方框的特征都会消失，只剩衍射线。将此图像从原始图像中减去，便可除去衍射花纹。表中所给出的 OT 的测光值，便是在相减后的图像上得到的。

§ 这些数据是由 LRIS 在偏振模式下获得的，因此光被分解为两个正交的极化分量，分别称为上、下通道。各通道的图像分开进行处理，求平均，然后将得到的两幅图像进行叠加得到最后的图像。视宁度是通过观测标准星 SA 104 440（参考文献 30）估计出来的，结果异常地差，约为 1.4 角秒。在最后的图像中 OT 的位置上并未出现任何天体。由于有效视场跨度只有 25 角秒，而且其中没有亮星，我们无法较好地估计最后的图像中的点扩展函数。根据孔径 1.5 角秒内的噪声统计，我们估计数据在 3σ 内的探测极限为 $I=24$ 星等。用软件 IRAF 的 DAOFIND 函数包分析半峰全宽为 1.4 角秒的虚拟假星，所获得的探测极限可达 23 星等。不过若考虑假星的位置已知，按上述方法我们可以得到一个更加严格的限制，更接近上面得到的 24 星等。

‖ 我们对与邻近恒星具有同样点扩展函数且落在 OT 附近的假星进行探测统计所获得的 3σ 上限。此观测受到明亮天光的影响（每平方角秒 19.1 星等），且曝光次数也不够。

¶ 由于有月亮在天上，前四次曝光受到明亮天光的影响。图 1 中的图像是由随后八次曝光叠加而成。

\# 3σ 上限。处理细节参看脚注 ‖。

　　如果这个解释正确，就可以用下面的方法更好地估计星系的红移值。在此类星系中 Lyα 发射线会因为环境气体的共振散射和吸收而系统地向红端移动。在任何特

the bias thus introduced in the centring of the peak of the Lyα emission depends on the exact geometry and kinematics of the gas and dust, which are not known; but on average the effect is to shift the peak of the Lyα emission to the red, relative to the systemic redshift of the galaxy[19-21]. We measure the wavelength of the apparent absorption dip immediately on the high-frequency side of the emission line as: $\lambda_{obs,air} = 5,356.1$ Å. Taking the mean of this wavelength and that of the emission line, and applying the standard air-to-vacuum correction, we obtain for the systemic redshift of this galaxy, $z_K = 3.418 \pm 0.010$.

As discussed above the continuum slope of the observed spectrum redward of the emission line is $F_v \propto v^a$ with $a = -0.7 \pm 0.2$. Unobscured star-forming galaxies have $a \approx 0.0$ to -0.5, depending on the initial mass function and the history of star formation. The slightly steeper slope of our spectrum suggests a modest amount of rest-frame extinction for the galaxy as a whole. This of course does not constrain the extinction along any particular line of sight, such as the direction to the OT itself. We note that similar extinctions are inferred for star-forming galaxies at comparable redshift[19].

Two corrections must be taken into account before a quantitative interpretation of the spectrum can be done. First, the Galactic reddening in this direction is estimated[33] to be $E_{B-V} \approx 0.016$ mag, implying a Galactic extinction correction to the observed fluxes of about 6% at the wavelength of the emission line, and about 4% in the R band. Second, by comparing the spectrum to our measured R-band photometry of the galaxy, we estimate the loss due to the finite size of the slit to be a factor of 1.48.

The Nature of the Host Galaxy

We now discuss the physical properties and nature of this galaxy. Assuming a standard Friedman model cosmology with $H_0 = 65$ km s^{-1} Mpc^{-1} and $\Omega_0 = 0.3$, we derive a luminosity distance (d_L) of 9.7×10^{28} cm (changing the cosmological parameters to $H_0 = 50$ km s^{-1} Mpc^{-1} and $\Omega_0 = 1$ yields $d_L = 8.6 \times 10^{28}$ cm). (H_0, the Hubble constant, is the expansion rate of the Universe at the present time. Ω_0 is the ratio of the mean density of the Universe to the closure density.) Assuming that the intrinsic spectrum F_v is $\propto v^{-0.7}$ and scaling from the observed R-band magnitude corrected for the Galactic extinction, we find the restframe B-band flux to be ~0.45 μJy. The corresponding absolute B magnitude is $M_B \approx -20.9$, and is about equal to the absolute magnitude of a typical, L_* galaxy today. Given its high redshift, this galaxy probably has yet to produce most of its stars, and even with some evolutionary fading of its present-day luminosity it may evolve to an L_* galaxy.

The observed Lyα emission line flux is $F_{Ly\alpha} = (3.8 \pm 0.4) \times 10^{-18}$ erg cm^{-2} s^{-1}. Correcting for the flux calibration zero-point and the Galactic extinction, this becomes $F_{Ly\alpha} = (6.2 \pm 0.7) \times 10^{-18}$ erg cm^{-2} s^{-1}. For our assumed cosmology, the implied Lyα line luminosity is $L_{Ly\alpha} = (7.3 \pm 0.8) \times 10^{41}$ erg s^{-1}. Estimates of conversion of the Lyα line luminosity to the implied unobscured star-formation rate (SFR) are in the range $L_{Ly\alpha} = (7 \pm 4) \times 10^{41}$ erg s^{-1} for SFR = 1 $M_\odot$ yr^{-1} (where $M_\odot$ is the solar mass), depending on the stellar initial mass

定情况下，定位 Lyα 发射线的峰所引入的偏差都与具体的然而未知的气体和尘埃几何和动力学特征有关，但是平均来讲这些效应都会使 Lyα 发射线的峰相对星系的系统性红移更偏向红端[19-21]。我们测量了紧挨着发射线的高频端的明显吸收凹陷的波长为 5,356.1 Å。取此值和发射线波长的平均值，再应用标准大气–真空修正关系，我们可以得到此星系的系统性红移为 $z_K = 3.418 \pm 0.010$。

正如前文提到过的，观测上发射线红端的连续谱斜率满足 $F_v \propto v^\alpha$，其中 $\alpha = -0.7 \pm 0.2$。对于没有被遮挡的恒星形成星系，α 约为 $0.0 \sim -0.5$，这依赖于星系的初始质量函数和恒星形成历史。我们光谱数据中略陡的斜率表明该星系从总体来说受到了中等程度的静止参照系消光。这当然不能限制任何特定方向上的消光，比如 OT 的方向上。我们也注意到具有差不多红移的其他恒星形成星系也存在类似的消光[19]。

在对光谱进行定量解释之前还要做两个修正。首先，该方向上的银河系红化可以近似估计[33]为 $E_{B-V} \approx 0.016$ 星等，由此可推算出在发射线波长处应对流量进行 6% 的银河系消光修正，而在 R 波段进行 4% 的修正。其次，通过把光谱和我们得到的 R 波段的星系测光结果相比较，我们估计由狭缝尺度有限导致的光损失因子为 1.48。

寄主星系性质

下面来讨论这个星系的物理特征和性质。在 $H_0 = 65$ km · s^{-1} · Mpc^{-1}(H_0 是哈勃常数，指宇宙现在的膨胀速率)，$\Omega_0 = 0.3$(Ω_0 是宇宙平均密度与闭合密度的比值)的标准弗里德曼宇宙学模型下，我们可以得到该星系的光度距离为 9.7×10^{28} cm(如果将宇宙学参量改变为 $H_0 = 50$ km · s^{-1} · Mpc^{-1}，$\Omega_0 = 1$，则 $d_L = 8.6 \times 10^{28}$ cm)。假定本征光谱满足 $F_v \propto v^{-0.7}$，并由改正了银河系消光后的 R 波段星等进行推算，我们求得静止参照系中 B 波段的流量约为 0.45 μJy，对应的 B 波段绝对星等 $M_B \approx -20.9$，基本和目前典型的 L_* 型星系的绝对星等相同。考虑到它是一个高红移的星系，大部分恒星应该还没有产生，甚至它现在的光度受一些演化过程影响而变暗，它可能正向一个 L_* 型星系演化。

观测到的 Lyα 发射线的流量为 $F_{Ly\alpha} = (3.8 \pm 0.4) \times 10^{-18}$ erg · cm^{-2} · s^{-1}，经零点修正和银河系消光修正后变为 $F_{Ly\alpha} = (6.2 \pm 0.7) \times 10^{-18}$ erg · cm^{-2} · s^{-1}。在我们所采用的宇宙学模型框架下，我们可以推算出 Lyα 谱线的光度为 $L_{Ly\alpha} = (7.3 \pm 0.8) \times 10^{41}$ erg · s^{-1}。从谱线光度和暗示的未遮挡恒星形成率(SFR)之间的转换关系来看，对应 SFR $= 1$ $M_\odot$ · yr^{-1}(其中 $M_\odot$ 为太阳质量)的区间是 $L_{Ly\alpha} = (7 \pm 4) \times 10^{41}$ erg · s^{-1}，具体依赖于恒星的初始质

function (IMF)[39,40]. We thus estimate the unobscured star-formation rate in this galaxy to be approximately $(1.0 \pm 0.5)\, M_\odot\, \mathrm{yr}^{-1}$.

Table 2. Summary of spectroscopic observations

Epoch (UT)	Grating (lines per mm)	Slit width (arcsec)	Int. time (s)	Notes
1997 Dec. 28	300	1.5	2×1800 s	T.K.
1998 Feb. 3	300	1.0	5×1800 s	S.R.K
1998 Feb. 22	600	1.0	2×1800 s	S.R.K.
1998 Feb. 23	600	1.0	6×1800 s	S.R.K.

Entries (from left to right) are: the UT date of the observation, the grating used, the slit width in arcsec, the number of exposures and the integration time per exposure, and the name of the principal observer. The 300 lines per mm grating is blazed to 5,000 Å and the blaze wavelength of the 600 lines per mm grating is 7,500 Å. The centre wavelength of the 300 lines per mm spectra (hereafter "lower" resolution data) is ~6,400 Å and the dispersion is ~2.45 Å per pixel. The centre wavelength of the 600 lines per mm spectra, the "higher resolution" data, is 6,100 Å and the dispersion is 1.25 Å per pixel. In both cases, the spectral resolution as parametrized by the FWHM is ~5 pixels. The spectrum of the standard star HZ 44 (ref. 45) obtained on February 3 was used to flux calibrate the lower-resolution spectra, and the spectrum of GD 153 (ref. 46), observed on February 22, was used to calibrate the higher-resolution spectra. The zero-point uncertainty of the flux calibration is estimated to be ~10%, judging by the internal agreement, but the slit losses are likely to be higher. Wavelength calibration was derived from arc lamp spectra taken immediately after the observations of the target. The random errors in the wavelength calibration are 0.3 Å and the estimated systematic errors due to instrument flexure are of the same order. Both these uncertainties are unimportant for our redshift determination discussed in the text.

However, the Lyα emission line is probably attenuated by resonant scattering in neutral hydrogen and by absorption by dust. An independent, and perhaps more robust, estimate of the star-formation rate can be obtained from the rest-frame continuum luminosity at 1,500 Å (ref. 41). We note that the observed flux at a wavelength of $1,500(1+z_K)$ Å is 0.22 µJy. This translates to a star-formation rate, under the usual assumption of a Salpeter IMF, of $5.2\, M_\odot\, \mathrm{yr}^{-1}$. These numbers should be regarded as lower limits given the unknown extinction in the rest-frame of galaxy K.

On the whole, the properties of galaxy K are typical of the known systems at comparable redshifts[19-21], thus giving us some confidence that our redshift interpretation is indeed correct.

The fluence of this GRB[17] above the observed photon energy of 20 keV is $F = 1.1 \times 10^{-5}$ erg cm^{-2}. The γ-ray fluence as observed by the Gamma-ray Burst Monitor (GRBM) on board BeppoSAX is $(0.9 \pm 0.9) \times 10^{-5}$ erg cm^{-2} s^{-1} (above 40 keV). The burst was also observed by the All Sky Monitor on board the X-ray satellite XTE (ref. 42). D. A. Smith (personal communication) estimates the fluence in the 2–12 keV band to be $1.8(\pm 0.03) \times 10^{-7}$ erg cm^{-2}. Thus the isotropic energy loss in γ-rays alone at the distance to the host is $4\pi d_L^2 F/(1+z) \approx 3 \times 10^{53}$ erg.

The currently favoured model[43] for GRBs is coalescence of neutron stars. The coalescence is expected to release most of the energy in neutrinos (as in type II supernovae) and about

量函数 (IMF)[39,40]。我们据此估计该星系的未遮挡恒星形成率约为 (1.0 ± 0.5) $M_{\odot} \cdot yr^{-1}$。

表 2. 光谱观测数据汇总

时期（世界时）	光栅（每毫米线数）	狭缝宽度（角秒）	积分时间（秒）	注释
1997 年 12 月 28 日	300	1.5	2×1800 秒	昆迪茨
1998 年 2 月 3 日	300	1.0	5×1800 秒	库尔卡尼
1998 年 2 月 22 日	600	1.0	2×1800 秒	库尔卡尼
1998 年 2 月 23 日	600	1.0	6×1800 秒	库尔卡尼

表头从左到右依次为：观测的标准世界时，所用光栅，缝宽（角秒为单位），曝光次数和每次曝光时间，主要观测者的名字。每毫米 300 线光栅的闪耀波长为 5,000 Å，每毫米 600 线的光栅闪耀波长则为 7,500 Å。300 线光栅光谱（以下称低分辨率数据）的中央波长约为 6,400 Å，色散为每像素 2.45 Å。600 线光栅光谱（高分辨率数据）的中央波长为 6,100 Å，色散为每像素 1.25 Å。两种情况下由半峰全宽参数化表示的光谱分辨率约为 5 像素，2 月 3 日获得的标准星 HZ 44 的光谱（参考文献 45）用于低分辨率光谱流量校准，而 2 月 22 日获得的 GD 153 的光谱（参考文献 46）用于高分辨率光谱流量校准。流量校准时零点的不确定性，通过内部符合判断，约为 10%，但狭缝损失率可能会更高。波长修正是从观测目标后立即拍摄的弧光灯光谱中得到的，随机误差为 0.3 Å，仪器弯沉也会带来同量级的系统误差。所有这些误差对文中所讨论的红移的确定并不重要。

但是，Lyα 发射线的强度可能被中性氢的共振散射和尘埃吸收所减弱。利用静止参考系下连续谱在 1,500 Å 处的光度可以对恒星形成率给出另一个独立的、更稳健的估计（参考文献 41）。我们注意到在波长 $1,500(1+z_K)$ Å 处的观测流量为 0.22 μJy，如果采用萨尔皮特初始质量函数的通常假定，得出的恒星形成率为 5.2 $M_{\odot} \cdot yr^{-1}$。鉴于星系 K 在静止参考系中的消光情况未知，这些结果应视为恒星形成率的下限。

总的来说，星系 K 的性质在已知的同等红移的星系[19-21]中非常典型，这使我们更加确信自己的红移推算是正确的。

这个 GRB[17] 在 20 keV 的光子能量以上的能流为 $F = 1.1 \times 10^{-5}$ erg $\cdot$ cm^{-2}。由装在 BeppoSAX 卫星上的伽马射线暴监测器（GRBM）观测到的 γ 射线流量（40 keV 以上）则为 $(0.9 \pm 0.9) \times 10^{-5}$ erg $\cdot$ cm$^{-2} \cdot$ s^{-1}。X 射线时变探测器（参考文献 42）上的全天探测器同样观测到这次暴，史密斯（个人交流）估计该暴在 $2 \sim 12$ keV 能段的能流为 $1.8(\pm 0.03) \times 10^{-7}$ erg $\cdot$ cm^{-2}。因此在这个距离上各向同性释放的 γ 射线能量为 $4\pi d_L^2 F/(1+z) \approx 3 \times 10^{53}$ erg。

目前倾向于用中子星并合模型[43]来解释 GRB。并合过程中大部分能量应以中微子的形式放出（与 II 型超新星相同），有大约 10^{51} erg 的能量以电磁能的形式释放。

10^{51} erg is supposed to be in the form of electromagnetic energy. The measured fluence of GRB971214 when combined with our proposed redshift for the GRB appears to be inconsistent with the expectations of the neutron-star merger model in its simplest form; however, it is possible that more elaborate versions of this model could be made to fit these observations. Non-spherical emission could reduce the strain on the energy budget but will not alter the fact that this fairly bright burst originated from such a large redshift.

The most significant implication of our hypothesis that K is the host galaxy of GRB971214 is the implied extreme energetics. The energy budget for GRBs goes up from the traditional 10^{51} erg to perhaps the entire energy available in the coalescence of neutron-star mergers[43]. Other energetic models, ranging from the death of an extremely massive star[23] to coalescence of black-hole neutron star binaries[22] may then become more attractive. In the latter models, GRBs are directly related to the formation rate of massive stars. If that is the case, then the typical redshift of GRBs is approximately 2 (ref. 44), consistent with the suggested high redshift for GRB971214. Moreover, this burst evidently did not originate in a highly obscured star-forming region in its host galaxy.

Regardless of the details of their genesis, GRBs appear to be the brightest known objects in the Universe, albeit over the limited duration of the burst. The term "hypernova"[23] can be justifiably used to describe these most extreme events, especially their after-glow. GRB971214 was not a particularly faint event, and thus statistically we expect many fainter events to arise from larger redshifts. The high brightness of GRBs and their optical transients offer us exciting and new opportunities to probe the Universe at high redshifts.

(**393**, 35-39; 1998)

S. R. Kulkarni[*], S. G. Djorgovski[*], A. N. Ramaprakash[*†], R. Goodrich[‡], J. S. Bloom[*], K. L. Adelberger[*], T. Kundic[*], L. Lubin,[*], D. A. Frail[§], F. Frontera[‖#], M. Feroci[¶], L. Nicastro[⋆], A. J. Barth[**], M. Davis[**], A. V. Filippenko[**] & J. Newman[**]

[*] Palomar Observatory 105-24, California Institute of Technology, Pasadena, California 91125, USA

[†] Inter-University Centre for Astronomy and Astrophysics, Ganeshkhind, Pune 411 007, India

[‡] W. M. Keck Observatory, 65-0120 Mamalahoa Highway, Kamuela, Hawaii 96743, USA

[§] National Radio Astronomy Observatory, Socorro, New Mexico 8801, USA

[‖] Istituto Tecnologie Studio delle Radiazioni Extraterrestri, CNR, via Gobetti 101, Bologna I-40129, Italy

[#] Dipartimento di Fisica, Universita Ferrara, Via Paradiso 12, I-44100, Italy

[¶] Istituto di Astrofisica Spaziale, CNR, via Fosso del Cavaliere, Roma I-00133, Italy

[⋆] Istituto Fisica Cosmica App. Info., CNR, via U. La Malfa 153, Palermo I-90146, Italy

[**] Department of Astronomy, University of California, Berkeley, California 94720, USA

Received 18 March; accepted 14 April 1998.

References:

1. Klebesadel, R. W., Strong, I. B. & Olson, R. A. Observations of gamma-ray bursts of cosmic origin. *Astrophys. J.* **182**, L85-L88 (1973).

2. Boella, G. *et al.* BeppoSAX, the wide band mission for x-ray astronomy. *Astron. Astrophys. Suppl. Ser.* **122**, 299-399 (1997).

3. Costa, E. *et al.* Discovery of an X-ray afterglow associated with the γ-ray burst of 28 February 1997. *Nature* **387**, 783-785 (1997).

4. van Paradijs, J. *et al.* Transient optical emission from the error box of the γ-ray burst of 28 February 1997. *Nature* **386**, 686-689 (1997).

5. Frail, D. A., Kulkarni, S. R., Nicastro, L., Feroci, M. & Taylor, G. B. The radio afterglow from the γ-ray burst of 8 May 1997. *Nature* **389**, 261-263 (1997).

而在 GRB971214 中，结合推算出的红移以及测量到的能量，我们发现结果与最简单的中子星并合模型预言不符，然而对模型作更细致的调整也许能使模型与观测数据相吻合。非球对称的辐射也会缓解释放能量不足的问题，但是仍很难解释在这样高的红移处有如此亮的爆发。

在 K 是 GRB971214 的寄主星系的前提下，最富意义的暗示就是所推算出的巨大能量。GRB 的能量需求从传统的 10^{51} erg 增加到了大概中子星并合事件所能释放的全部能量 [43]。诸如极大质量恒星死亡 [23]，黑洞–中子星并合事件 [22] 等其他模型因此变得更有吸引力。在后面的这两个模型中，GRB 将与大质量恒星的形成率直接相关，如果是这样，GRB 的典型红移应为 2 左右（参考文献 44），这与 GRB971214 给出的高红移的结果相一致。此外，这个暴很明显地并没有发生在该寄主星系被严重遮蔽的恒星形成区中。

不论它们的具体起源是什么，GRB 是宇宙中已知的最亮的天体，尽管只是在有限的持续时间之内。术语"极超新星"[23] 可以用来形容这类极端事件，特别是它们的余辉。GRB971214 并不是一个特别暗的事件，因此我们可以期望统计上在更高红移处会探测到很多更暗的事件。GRB 及其光学暂现源的巨大亮度为我们探索高红移处的宇宙提供了令人兴奋的新机会。

（余恒 翻译；黎卓 审稿）

6. Metzger, M. R. *et al.* Spectral constraints on the redshift of the optical counterpart to the γ-ray burst of 8 May 1997. *Nature* **387,** 878-880 (1997).

7. Bond, H. E. *et al. IAU Circ.* No. 6665 (1997).

8. Djorgovski, S. G. *et al.* The optical counterpart to the γ-ray burst 970508. *Nature* **387,** 876-878 (1997).

9. Costa, E. *et al. IAU Circ.* No. 6649 (1997).

10. Piro, L. *et al. IAU Circ.* No. 6656 (1997).

11. Bloom, J. S., Kulkarni, S. R., Djorgovski, S. G. & Frail, D. A. *GCN Note* No. 30 (1998).

12. Zharikov, S. V., Sokolov, V. V. & Baryshev, Y. V. *GCN Note* No. 31 (1998.).

13. Galama, T. J. *et al.* Optical followup of GRB 970508. *Astrophys. J.* (submitted).

14. Sahu, K. C. *et al.* Observations of GRB 970228 and GRB 970508 and the neutron star merger mode. *Astrophys. J.* **489,** L127-L131 (1997).

15. Halpern, J. P., Thorstensen, J. R., Helfand, D. J. & Costa, E. Optical afterglow of the γ-ray burst of 14 December 1997 *Nature* **393,** 41-43 (1998).

16. Heise, J. *et al. IAU Circ.* No. 6787 (1997).

17. Kippen, R. M. *et al. IAU Circ.* No. 6789 (1997).

18. Antonelli, L. A. *et al. IAU Circ.* No. 6792 (1997).

19. Steidel, C. C., Giavalisco, M., Pettini, M., Dickinson, M. & Adelberger, K. Spectroscopic confirmation of a population of normal star-forming galaxies at redshifts $z > 3$. *Astrophys. J.* **462,** L17-L21 (1996).

20. Steidel, C. C., Giavalisco, M., Dickinson, M. & Adelberger, K. L. Spectroscopy of Lyman break galaxies in the Hubble Deep Field. *Astron. J.* **112,** 352-358 (1996).

21. Steidel, C. C. *et al.* A large structure of galaxies at redshift $z \sim 3$ and its cosmological implications. *Astrophys. J.* **492,** 428-438 (1998).

22. Meszáros, P. & Rees, M. J. Poynting jets from black holes and cosmological gamma-ray bursts. *Astrophys. J.* **482,** L29-L31 (1997).

23. Paczyński, B. Are gamma-ray bursts in star-forming regions? *Astrophys. J.* **492,** L45-L48 (1998).

24. Oke, J. B. *et al.* The Keck low-resolution imaging spectrometer. *Publ. Astron. Soc. Pacif.* **107,** 375-385 (1995).

25. Castander, F. J. *et al. GCN Note* No. 1! (1997).

26. Halpern, J., Thorstensen, J., Helfand, D. & Costa, E. *IAU Circ.* No. 6788 (1997).

27. Rhoads, J. *IAU Circ.* No. 6793 (1997).

28. Diercks, A. *et al. IAU Circ.* No. 67921 (1997).

29. Henden, A. A., Luginbuhl, C. B. & Vrba, F. J. *GCN Note.* No. 16 (1997).

30. Landolt, A. U. UBVRI photometric standard stars in the magnitude range $11.5 < V < 16.0$ around the celestial equator. *Astron. J.* **104,** 340-371 (1992).

31. Wijers, R. A. M. J., Rees, M. J. & Meszáros, P. Shocked by GRB 970228: the afterglow of a cosmological fireball. *Mon. Not. R. Astron Soc.* **288,** L51-L56 (1997).

32. Sokolov, V. V. *et al.* BVR_cI_c photometry of GRB 970508 optical remnant: May–August, 1997. *Astron. Astrophys.* (in the press); preprint http://xxx.lanl.gov, astro-ph/0902341 (1998).

33. Galama, T. J. *et al.* Optical follow-up of GRB 970508. *Astrophys. J.* (in the press); preprint http:// xxx.lanl.gov, astro-ph/9802160 (1998).

34. Waxman, E. Gamma-ray-burst afterglow: supporting the cosmological fireball model, constraining parameters, and making predictions. *Astrophys. J.* **485,** L5-L8 (1997).

35. Hogg, D. W. *et al.* Counts and colors of faint galaxies in the U and R bands. *Mon. Not. R. Astron. Soc.* **288,** 404-410 (1997).

36. Oke, J. B. & Korycansky, D. Absolute spectrophotometry of very large redshift quasars. *Astrophys. J.* **255,** 11-19 (1996).

37. Kennefick, J. D., Djorgovski, S. G. & de Carvalho, R. R. The luminosity function of $z > 4$ quasars from the second Palomar sky survey. *Astron. J.* **110,** 2553-2565 (1995).

38. Schlegel, D. J., Finkbeiner, D. P. & Davis, M. Maps of dust IR emission for use in estimation of reddening and CMBR foregrounds. *Astrophys. J.* (in the press); preprint http://xxx.lanl.gov, astro-ph/0910327.

39. Thompson, D., Djorgovski, S. & Trauger, J. A narrow-band imaging survey for primeval galaxies. *Astron. J.* **110,** 963-981 (1995).

40. Charlot, S. & Fall, S. M. Lyman-alpha emission from galaxies. *Astrophys. J.* **415,** 580-588 (1993).

41. Leitherer, C., Robert, C. & Heckman, T. M. Atlas of synthetic ultraviolet-spectra of massive star populations. *Astrophys. J. Suppl.* **99,** 173-187 (1995).

42. Doty, J. P. The All Sky Monitor for the X-ray Timing Explorer. *Proc. SPIE* **982,** 164-172 (1988).

43. Narayan, R., Pacsyński, B. & Piran, T. Gamma-ray bursts as the death throes of massive binary stars. *Astrophys. J.* **395,** L83-L86 (1992).

44. Wijers, R. A. M. J., Bloom, J., Bagla, J. S. & Natarajan, P. Gamma-ray bursts from stellar remnants: probing the universe at high redshift. *Mon. Not. R. Astron. Soc.* **294,** L13-L17 (1998).

45. Massey, P., Strobel, K., Barnes, J. & Anderson, E. Spectrophotometric standards. *Astrophys. J.* **328,** 315-333 (1988).

46. Bohlin, R., Colina, L. & Finley, D. White dwarf standard stars: G191-B2B, GD 71, GD 153, HZ 43. *Astron. J.* **110,** 1316-1325 (1995).

Acknowledgements. The observations reported here were obtained at the W. M. Keck Observatory, which is operated by the California Association for Research in Astronomy, a scientific partnership among California Institute of Technology, the University of California and NASA. It was made possible by the financial support from W. M. Keck Foundation. We thank W. Sargent, Director of the Palomar Observatory, F. Chaffee, Director of the Keck Observatory and our colleagues for continued support of our GRB program. We thank J. C. Clemens and M. H. van Kerkwijk for help with observations and exchange of dark time. S.R.K.'s research is supported by the NSF and NASA. S.G.D. acknowledges partial support from the Bressler Foundation. A.N.R. is grateful to the International Astronomical Union for a travel grant.

Correspondence and requests for materials should be addressed to S.R.K. (e-mail: srk:surya.caltech.edu).

1997 年 12 月 14 日的伽马射线暴在红移 3.42 处的寄主星系的证认

A Silicon-based Nuclear Spin Quantum Computer

B. E. Kane

Editor's Note

In the 1980s, physicists began trying to build computing devices that exploit quantum effects, which could be much more powerful than classical devices, at least for certain computational tasks. The practical development of such machines was immensely challenging because of their inherent sensitivity to disruption from the environment. Here Australian physicist Bruce Kane proposes a scheme for implementing a quantum computer by storing its information in the relatively isolated spins of nuclei of dopant atoms inserted into silicon electronic devices. Logical operations, he suggests, could be performed on these spins with external electric fields, and measurements made with currents of spin-polarized electrons. Practical quantum computers are now being developed, and this strategy remains one of many being explored.

Quantum computers promise to exceed the computational efficiency of ordinary classical machines because quantum algorithms allow the execution of certain tasks in fewer steps. But practical implementation of these machines poses a formidable challenge. Here I present a scheme for implementing a quantum-mechanical computer. Information is encoded onto the nuclear spins of donor atoms in doped silicon electronic devices. Logical operations on individual spins are performed using externally applied electric fields, and spin measurements are made using currents of spin-polarized electrons. The realization of such a computer is dependent on future refinements of conventional silicon electronics.

ALTHOUGH the concept of information underlying all modern computer technology is essentially classical, physicists know that nature obeys the laws of quantum mechanics. The idea of a quantum computer has been developed theoretically over several decades to elucidate fundamental questions concerning the capabilities and limitations of machines in which information is treated quantum mechanically[1,2]. Specifically, in quantum computers the ones and zeros of classical digital computers are replaced by the quantum state of a two-level system (a qubit). Logical operations carried out on the qubits and their measurement to determine the result of the computation must obey quantum-mechanical laws. Quantum computation can in principle only occur in systems that are almost completely isolated from their environment and which consequently must dissipate no energy during the process of computation, conditions that are extraordinarily difficult to fulfil in practice.

Interest in quantum computation has increased dramatically in the past four years because of two important insights: first, quantum algorithms (most notably for prime factorization[3,4]

硅基核自旋量子计算机

编者按

20世纪80年代，物理学家开始尝试构建利用量子效应的计算设备，至少对于某些计算任务而言，它可能比传统设备性能强大得多。由于其对来自环境的干扰具有内在的敏感性，这类机器的实际研发极具挑战性。本文中，澳大利亚物理学家布鲁斯·凯恩提出了一种实现量子计算机的方案，将其信息存储在硅电子器件中内嵌掺杂原子的相对孤立的核自旋中。他建议，逻辑运算可以在外部电场辅助下用这些自旋进行，并用自旋极化电子的电流进行测量。可行的量子计算机正在开发中，该方案仍然是许多正在被探索的策略之一。

量子计算机的计算效率可能会超过传统经典计算机，因为量子算法允许用更少的步骤来执行某些任务。但是这些机器的实际研发仍然是一个艰巨的挑战。这里我将提出一种构建基于量子力学的计算机的方法。计算信息被编码在掺杂硅的电子器件中施主原子的核自旋上。单个自旋的逻辑运算用外部施加电场来实现，而自旋测量基于自旋极化电子的电流。这样一个计算机的实现依赖于传统硅器件未来的精密程度。

尽管所有现代计算机所依赖的信息概念本质上都是基于经典理论的，然而物理学家知道自然界遵从量子力学定律。量子计算机的概念在理论上已经发展了几十年，旨在阐明使用量子力学来处理信息的计算机的能力和极限等基本问题[1,2]。具体而言，在量子计算机中，经典计算机中的0和1被一个二能级系统的量子态（量子比特）所取代。在量子比特上进行的逻辑运算及用来决定计算结果的测量必须遵守量子力学定律。量子计算理论上只能发生在与外界环境几乎完全隔离的系统中，这样在计算过程中不会存在能量的耗散，这样的苛刻条件在现实中很难满足。

在过去四年中，两个重大的突破使人们对量子计算的兴趣与日俱增。第一个是量子算法（尤其值得一提的是质因子分解[3,4]和穷举搜索[5]）的开发，而且这些算法

and for exhaustive search[5]) have been developed that outperform the best known algorithms doing the same tasks on a classical computer. These algorithms require that the internal state of the quantum computer be controlled with extraordinary precision, so that the coherent quantum state upon which the quantum algorithms rely is not destroyed. Because completely preventing decoherence (uncontrolled interaction of a quantum system with its surrounding environment) is impossible, the existence of quantum algorithms does not prove that they can ever be implemented in a real machine.

The second critical insight has been the discovery of quantum error-correcting codes that enable quantum computers to operate despite some degree of decoherence and which may make quantum computers experimentally realizable[6,7]. The tasks that lie ahead to create an actual quantum computer are formidable: Preskill[8] has estimated that a quantum computer operating on 10^6 qubits with a 10^{-6} probability of error in each operation would exceed the capabilities of contemporary conventional computers on the prime factorization problem. To make use of error-correcting codes, logical operations and measurement must be able to proceed in parallel on qubits throughout the computer.

The states of spin 1/2 particles are two-level systems that can potentially be used for quantum computation. Nuclear spins have been incorporated into several quantum computer proposals[9-12] because they are extremely well isolated from their environment and so operations on nuclear spin qubits could have low error rates. The primary challenge in using nuclear spins in quantum computers lies in measuring the spins. The bulk spin resonance approach to quantum computation[11,12] circumvents the single-spin detection problem essentially by performing quantum calculations in parallel in a large number of molecules and determining the result from macroscopic magnetization measurements. The measurable signal decreases with the number of qubits, however, and scaling this approach above about ten qubits will be technically demanding[37].

To attain the goal of a 10^6 qubit quantum computer, it has been suggested that a "solid state" approach[13] might eventually replicate the enormous success of modern electronics fabrication technology. An attractive alternative approach to nuclear spin quantum computation is to incorporate nuclear spins into an electronic device and to detect the spins and control their interactions electronically[14]. Electron and nuclear spins are coupled by the hyperfine interaction[15]. Under appropriate circumstances, polarization is transferred between the two spin systems and nuclear spin polarization is detectable by its effect on the electronic properties of a sample[16,17]. Electronic devices for both generating and detecting nuclear spin polarization, implemented at low temperatures in $GaAs/Al_xGa_{1-x}As$ heterostructures, have been developed[18], and similar devices have been incorporated into nanostructures[19,20]. Although the number of spins probed in the nanostructure experiments is still large ($\sim 10^{11}$; ref. 19), sensitivity will improve in optimized devices and in systems with larger hyperfine interactions.

在执行相同任务时优于经典计算机上最著名的算法。这些算法要求量子计算机的内部状态被准确无误地控制，这样量子算法所依赖的相干量子态就不会被破坏。因为完全阻止量子退相干（量子系统和外界环境之间非受控的相互作用）是不可能的，所以量子算法的存在并不能保证它们可以在真实的计算机上面得以实现。

第二个重大的突破是量子纠错码的发现，它可以使量子计算机运行时容忍一定程度的量子退相干，这使得量子计算机在实验上的实现成为可能[6,7]。眼下制造一台真正的量子计算机的任务是艰巨的：据普雷斯基尔[8]估计，一台使用 10^6 个量子比特且每次运算误码率为 10^{-6} 的量子计算机可以在质因子分解问题上超过同时代的传统计算机。为了利用纠错码，逻辑运算和测量必须能够在整个计算机的量子比特上并行进行。

自旋为 1/2 的粒子的状态是二能级系统，具备应用于量子计算的潜质。核自旋已经被纳入数个量子计算机提案[9-12]中，因为它们与外界环境间被很好地隔离，因此利用核自旋比特来运算，误码率可能很低。在量子计算机中使用核自旋的主要挑战在于测量自旋。量子计算的系综自旋共振方法[11,12]基本上是通过在大量分子上的并行量子计算并由宏观磁化测量确定结果来绕开单个自旋的测量问题。然而可测量信号随着量子比特数目的增多而减少，因此将这种方法扩展到 10 个量子比特以上将会对技术要求极为苛刻[37]。

为了实现 10^6 量子比特计算机，有人建议使用"固态"方法[13]，这种方法也许可以最终复制现代电子器件微加工技术的巨大成功。核自旋量子计算的一种有吸引力的替代方法是将核自旋融合到电子器件中，并且通过电学方式来测量自旋以及控制其之间的相互作用[14]。电子和核自旋被超精细相互作用耦合在一起[15]。在适当情况下，极化可以在两个自旋系统中转移，核自旋极化可以通过其对样品的电子性质的影响来测量[16,17]。用来产生和探测核自旋极化的电子器件也已经在低温砷化镓（GaAs）/铝镓砷（$Al_xGa_{1-x}As$）异质结构中实现[18]，类似的器件也已经被整合到纳米结构中[19,20]。尽管在纳米结构试验中研究的自旋数目仍然很大（约为 10^{11}；文献 19），但在经过优化的器件中以及更强的超精细相互作用系统中，灵敏度会得到进一步的改善。

Here I present a scheme for implementing a quantum computer on an array of nuclear spins located on donors in silicon, the semiconductor used in most conventional computer electronics. Logical operations and measurements can in principle be performed independently and in parallel on each spin in the array. I describe specific electronic devices for the manipulation and measurement of nuclear spins, fabrication of which will require significant advances in the rapidly moving field of nanotechnology. Although it is likely that scaling the devices proposed here into a computer of the size envisaged by Preskill[8] will be an extraordinary challenge, a silicon-based quantum computer is in a unique position to benefit from the resources and ingenuity being directed towards making conventional electronics of ever smaller size and greater complexity.

Quantum Computation with a ^{31}P Array in Silicon

The strength of the hyperfine interaction is proportional to the probability density of the electron wavefunction at the nucleus. In semiconductors, the electron wavefunction extends over large distances through the crystal lattice. Two nuclear spins can consequently interact with the same electron, leading to electron-mediated or indirect nuclear spin coupling[15]. Because the electron is sensitive to externally applied electric fields, the hyperfine interaction and electron-mediated nuclear spin interaction can be controlled by voltages applied to metallic gates in a semiconductor device, enabling the external manipulation of nuclear spin dynamics that is necessary for quantum computation.

The conditions required for electron-coupled nuclear spin computation and single nuclear spin detection can arise if the nuclear spin is located on a positively charged donor in a semiconductor host. The electron wavefunction is then concentrated at the donor nucleus (for s orbitals and energy bands composed primarily of them), yielding a large hyperfine interaction energy. For shallow-level donors, however, the electron wavefunction extends tens or hundreds of ångströms away from the donor nucleus, allowing electron-mediated nuclear spin coupling to occur over comparable distances. The quantum computer proposed here comprises an array of such donors positioned beneath the surface of a semiconductor host (Fig. 1). A quantum mechanical calculation proceeds by the precise control of three external parameters: (1) gates above the donors control the strength of the hyperfine interactions and hence the resonance frequency of the nuclear spins beneath them; (2) gates between the donors turn on and off electron-mediated coupling between the nuclear spins[13]; (3) a globally applied a.c. magnetic field B_{ac} flips nuclear spins at resonance. Custom adjustment of the coupling of each spin to its neighbours and to B_{ac} enables different operations to be performed on each of the spins simultaneously. Finally, measurements are performed by transferring nuclear spin polarization to the electrons and determining the electron spin state by its effect on the orbital wavefunction of the electrons, which can be probed using capacitance measurements between adjacent gates.

这里我将介绍一种利用位于硅材料施主上面的核自旋阵列来实现量子计算机的方法，硅材料是大多数传统计算机电子学中使用的半导体。理论上逻辑运算和测量可以在阵列中的各个自旋上独立且并行执行。我将介绍特定的电子器件来实现核自旋的控制和测量，其制造需要迅猛发展的纳米科技领域的重大突破。把这里提出的器件缩放到普雷斯基尔[8]设想的尺寸的计算机中，这也许是一个巨大的挑战，然而，由于人们为了将传统电子器件做得更小且更加复杂的过程中积累了资源和聪明才智，硅基量子计算机仍然具有独特的地位。

使用硅中 ^{31}P 阵列的量子计算

超精细相互作用的强度正比于原子核处电子波函数的概率密度。在半导体中，电子波函数在晶格上延展很长的距离。两个核自旋因此可以和同一个电子相互作用，这就导致了电子介导的或者间接的核自旋耦合[15]。由于电子对于外加电场的敏感，超精细相互作用以及电子介导的核自旋相互作用可以通过调节施加在半导体器件中金属栅极上的电压来控制，这使量子计算所要求的核自旋动力学的外部调制成为了可能。

如果核自旋位于半导体宿主中带正电的施主上面，电子耦合核自旋计算以及单核自旋检测所需的条件会被满足。电子波函数将会集中于施主的原子核（对于 s 轨道和主要由它们组成的能带），产生大的超精细相互作用能。然而对于浅能级施主来说，电子波函数从原子核向外扩展了几十甚至几百埃，从而允许电子介导核自旋耦合在相对远的距离发生。本文提出的量子计算机包括在半导体宿主表面下方的一系列这样的施主（如图 1）。量子力学计算通过精确控制三个外部参数来进行：（1）施主上方的栅极控制超精细相互作用的强度，因此也就控制了栅极下方的核自旋的共振频率；（2）施主之间的栅极可以用来开通和关闭核自旋之间的电子介导耦合[13]；（3）一个对全体施加的交变磁场 B_{ac} 用来翻转与磁场共振的核自旋。单独调节每个自旋之间的耦合以及自旋与外加磁场 B_{ac} 的耦合，使每个自旋上的不同运算可以同时进行。最后，通过转移核自旋极化到电子身上进而影响电子轨道波函数，最终通过测试其对相邻的栅极之间的电容的改变来测得自旋态。

Fig. 1. Illustration of two cells in a one-dimensional array containing ³¹P donors and electrons in a Si host, separated by a barrier from metal gates on the surface. "A gates" control the resonance frequency of the nuclear spin qubits; "J gates" control the electron-mediated coupling between adjacent nuclear spins. The ledge over which the gates cross localizes the gate electric field in the vicinity of the donors.

An important requirement for a quantum computer is to isolate the qubits from any degrees of freedom that may lead to decoherence. If the qubits are spins on a donor in a semiconductor, nuclear spins in the host are a large reservoir with which the donor spins can interact. Consequently, the host should contain only nuclei with spin $I = 0$. This simple requirement unfortunately eliminates all III–V semiconductors as host candidates, because none of their constituent elements possesses stable $I = 0$ isotopes[21]. Group IV semiconductors are composed primarily $I = 0$ isotopes and can in principle be purified to contain only $I = 0$ isotopes. Because of the advanced state of Si materials technology and the tremendous effort currently underway in Si nanofabrication, Si is the obvious choice for the semiconductor host.

The only $I = 1/2$ shallow (group V) donor in Si is ³¹P. The Si:³¹P system was exhaustively studied 40 years ago in the first electron–nuclear double-resonance experiments[22,23]. At sufficiently low ³¹P concentrations at temperature $T = 1.5$ K, the electron spin relaxation time is thousands of seconds and the ³¹P nuclear spin relaxation time exceeds 10 hours. It is likely that at millikelvin temperatures the phonon limited ³¹P relaxation time is of the order of 10^{18} seconds (ref. 24), making this system ideal for quantum computation.

The purpose of the electrons in the computer is to mediate nuclear spin interactions and to facilitate measurement of the nuclear spins. Irreversible interactions between electron and nuclear spins must not occur as the computation proceeds: the electrons must be in a non-degenerate ground state throughout the computation. At sufficiently low temperatures, electrons only occupy the lowest energy-bound state at the donor, whose twofold spin degeneracy is broken by an applied magnetic field B. (The valley degeneracy of the Si conduction band is broken in the vicinity of the donor[25]. The lowest donor excited state is approximately 15 meV above the ground state[23].) The electrons will only occupy the lowest energy spin level when $2\mu_B B \gg kT$, where μ_B is the Bohr magneton. (In Si, the Landé

图 1. 硅宿主中 ^{31}P 施主和电子的一维阵列中的两个单元的示意图，图中的势垒层将该阵列与表面的金属栅极隔离开。"A 栅极"用来控制核自旋量子比特的共振频率。"J 栅极"用来控制相邻核自旋的电子介导耦合。栅极末端的台阶状设计使得加在施主附近的电场局域化。

对于量子计算机来说，一个重要的要求是量子比特应该与可能导致退相干的任何自由度隔离开来。如果量子比特是在半导体中的施主上的自旋，施主自旋可以和宿主材料中其他大量核自旋构成的群体相互作用。因此宿主应该只含有自旋 $I = 0$ 的原子核。这个简单的要求遗憾地排除了所有 III–V 半导体作为宿主的可能性，因为他们中的任何元素都没有稳定的 $I = 0$ 的同位素 [21]。而 IV 半导体主要包含 $I = 0$ 同位素，而且理论上可以被提纯到只含有 $I = 0$ 的同位素。由于硅材料技术的领先状态以及现阶段人们对硅纳米加工方面的巨大投入，硅理所当然地成为半导体宿主的选择。

硅中唯一的 $I = 1/2$ 浅施主（第五主族）是 ^{31}P。在 40 年以前人们发现的第一个电子–原子核双共振的试验中 [22,23]Si:^{31}P 系统已经得到了深入的研究。温度 $T = 1.5$ K 时，当 ^{31}P 的浓度足够低时，电子自旋的弛豫时间是几千秒，^{31}P 的核自旋弛豫时间超过 10 小时。这样的话，在毫开尔文的温度下，声子散射受限的 ^{31}P 的弛豫时间在 10^{18} 秒的量级（文献 24），使得这种系统成为量子计算的理想选择。

该计算机利用电子来促成核自旋之间的相互作用以及核自旋的测量。电子和核自旋之间不可逆的相互作用必须在计算过程中避免：电子必须在整个计算过程中处于非简并基态。在足够低的温度下，通过外加磁场 B 打破电子基态的双重自旋简并度，这样电子只占据施主的最低能量束缚态。（硅的导带的谷简并在施主附近被破坏了 [25]。施主的最低激发态大概是基态上方 15 meV[23]。）当 $2\mu_B B \gg kT$ 时，电子仅占据最低自旋能级，其中 μ_B 是波尔磁子。（在硅中，朗德 g 因子非常接近 +2，所以在我

g-factor is very close to $+2$, so $g = 2$ is used throughout this discussion.) The electrons will be completely spin-polarized $(n_\uparrow / n_\downarrow < 10^{-6})$ when $T \lesssim 100$ mK and $B \gtrsim 2$ tesla. A quantum-mechanical computer is non-dissipative and can consequently operate at low temperatures. Dissipation will arise external to the computer from gate biasing and from eddy currents caused by B_{ac}, and during polarization and measurement of the nuclear spins. These effects will determine the minimum operable temperature of the computer. For this discussion, I will assume $T = 100$ mK and $B = 2$ T. Note that these conditions do not fully polarize the nuclear spins, which are instead aligned by interactions with the polarized electrons.

Magnitude of Spin Interactions in Si:^{31}P

The size of the interactions between spins determines both the time required to do elementary operations on the qubits and the separation necessary between donors in the array. The hamiltonian for a nuclear spin–electron system in Si, applicable for an $I = 1/2$ donor nucleus and with $B \| z$ is $H_{en} = \mu_B B \sigma_z^e - g_n \mu_n B \sigma_z^n + A \sigma^e \cdot \sigma^n$, where σ are the Pauli spin matrices (with eigenvalues ± 1), μ_n is the nuclear magneton, g_n is the nuclear g-factor (1.13 for ^{31}P; ref. 21), and $A = \frac{8}{3} \pi \mu_B g_n \mu_n |\Psi(0)|^2$ is the contact hyperfine interaction energy, with $|\Psi(0)|^2$, the probability density of the electron wavefunction, evaluated at the nucleus. If the electron is in its ground state, the frequency separation of the nuclear levels is, to second order

$$h\nu_A = 2 g_n \mu_n B + 2A + \frac{2A^2}{\mu_B B} \qquad (1)$$

In Si:^{31}P, $2A/h = 58$ MHz, and the second term in equation (1) exceeds the first term for $B < 3.5$ T.

An electric field applied to the electron–donor system shifts the electron wavefunction envelope away from the nucleus and reduces the hyperfine interaction. The size of this shift, following estimates of Kohn[25] of shallow donor Stark shifts in Si, is shown in Fig. 2 for a donor 200 Å beneath a gate. A donor nuclear spin–electron system close to an "A gate" functions as a voltage-controlled oscillator: the precession frequency of the nuclear spin is controllable externally, and spins can be selectively brought into resonance with B_{ac}, allowing arbitrary rotations to be performed on each nuclear spin.

们的讨论中使用 $g=2$。）当 $T \leqslant 100$ mK 且 $B \geqslant 2$ T 的时候，电子将会被完全自旋极化（$n_\uparrow/n_\downarrow < 10^{-6}$）。量子力学计算机是无耗散的，因此可以在低温状态下运行。然而当栅极偏压出现以及 B_{ac} 引起的涡电流出现时，计算机外部的功耗会上升，这在核自旋的极化和测量时也会出现。这些效应决定了计算机的最低工作温度。为了讨论这些问题，我们假设 $T=100$ mK 且 $B=2$ T。注意这些条件并不是完全极化了核自旋，核自旋是通过和极化电子的作用来对齐的。

在 Si:^{31}P 中的自旋相互作用的量级

自旋相互作用的大小决定了量子比特基本运算所需的时间以及阵列中施主之间需要的间隔。硅中的核自旋–电子系统的哈密顿量，在施主原子核 $I=1/2$、磁场 B 方向平行于 z 方向时，为 $H_{en}=\mu_B B\sigma e_z - g_n\mu_n B\sigma e_z + A\sigma^e \cdot \sigma^n$，这里 σ 是泡利自旋矩阵（本征值为 ± 1），μ_n 是核磁子，g_n 是原子核的 g 因子（对于 ^{31}P 而言，g 因子为 1.13；文献 21），$A=\frac{8}{3}\pi\mu_B g_n\mu_n|\Psi(0)|^2$ 是接触超精细相互作用能，其中 $|\Psi(0)|^2$ 是电子波函数在原子核的概率密度。如果电子处于基态，那么原子核能级的频率间隔（取到二阶）是，

$$h\nu_A = 2g_n\mu_n B + 2A + \frac{2A^2}{\mu_B B} \tag{1}$$

在 Si:^{31}P 中，$2A/h=58$ MHz；在 $B<3.5$ T 的时候，等式（1）中的第二项大于第一项。

一个施加于电子–施主系统的外加电场会使得电子波函数的包络线向远离原子核的方向平移从而减少超精细相互作用。根据科恩[25]对硅中浅施主斯塔克位移的估测，图 2 给出了栅极下方 200 Å 处施主上述位移的大小。靠近"A 栅极"的施主核自旋–电子系统起到电压控制振荡器的作用：这样核自旋的进动频率就可以外部控制了，自旋也可以选择性地与 B_{ac} 共振，这就使得每一个核自旋可以任意地旋转。

Fig. 2. An electric field applied to an *A* gate pulls the electron wavefunction away from the donor and towards the barrier, reducing the hyperfine interaction and the resonance frequency of the nucleus. The donor nucleus–electron system is a voltage-controlled oscillator with a tuning parameter α of the order of 30 MHz V^{-1}.

Quantum mechanical computation requires, in addition to single spin rotations, the two-qubit "controlled rotation" operation, which rotates the spin of a target qubit through a prescribed angle if, and only if, the control qubit is oriented in a specified direction, and leaves the orientation of the control qubit unchanged[26,27]. Performing the controlled rotation operation requires nuclear-spin exchange between two donor nucleus–electron spin systems[13], which will arise from electron-mediated interactions when the donors are sufficiently close to each other. The hamiltonian of two coupled donor nucleus–electron systems, valid at energy scales small compared to the donor–electron binding energy, is $H = H(B) + A_1\sigma^{1n} \cdot \sigma^{2e} + A_2\sigma^{2n} \cdot \sigma^{2e} + J\sigma^{1e} \cdot \sigma^{2e}$, where $H(B)$ are the magnetic field interaction terms for the spins. A_1 and A_2 are the hyperfine interaction energies of the respective nucleus–electron systems. $4J$, the exchange energy, depends on the overlap of the electron wavefunctions. For well separated donors[28]

$$4J(r) \cong 1.6 \frac{e^2}{\epsilon a_{\mathrm{B}}} \left(\frac{r}{a_{\mathrm{B}}} \right)^{\frac{5}{2}} \exp\left(\frac{-2r}{a_{\mathrm{B}}} \right) \tag{2}$$

where r is the distance between donors, ϵ is the dielectric constant of the semiconductor, and a_{B} is the semiconductor Bohr radius. This function, with values appropriate for Si, is plotted in Fig. 3. Equation (2), originally derived for H atoms, is complicated in Si by its valley degenerate anisotropic band structure[29]. Exchange coupling terms from each valley interfere, leading to oscillatory behaviour of $J(r)$. In this discussion, the complications introduced by Si band structure will be neglected. In determining $J(r)$ in Fig. 3, the

图 2. 施加于 A 栅极的电场使得电子波函数远离施主而朝向势垒，这就减少了超精细相互作用以及原子核的共振频率。施主的原子核–电子系统是一个电压调节的振荡器，调谐参数 α 量级为 30 MHz·V^{-1}。

除了单个自旋的旋转，量子力学计算需要双量子比特的"控制旋转"操作，当且仅当控制量子比特的取向在特定方向时，该操作将会使目标量子比特的自旋按照指定的角度旋转，从而使得控制量子比特的取向不变[26,27]。要实现这种控制旋转操作需要两个施主原子核–电子自旋系统中的核自旋交换[13]，当两个施主足够接近的时候，这将会由于电子介导相互作用而发生。当能量尺度与施主–电子结合能相比较小的时候，两个耦合的施主原子核–电子系统的哈密顿量可以表示为 $H = H(B) + A_1\sigma^{1n} \cdot \sigma^{2e} + A_2\sigma^{2n} \cdot \sigma^{2e} + J\sigma^{1e} \cdot \sigma^{2e}$。其中 $H(B)$ 为自旋的磁场相互作用项。A_1 和 A_2 为两个原子核–电子系统中各自的超精细相互作用能量。$4J$ 为依赖于电子波函数重叠的交换能。对于足够隔离的施主[28]而言，

$$4J(r) \cong 1.6\frac{e^2}{\epsilon a_B}\left(\frac{r}{a_B}\right)^{\frac{5}{2}}\exp\left(\frac{-2r}{a_B}\right) \qquad (2)$$

其中 r 是施主之间的距离，ϵ 是半导体的介电常数，a_B 是半导体的玻尔半径。根据硅来选取适当的参数，这个函数的图像如图 3 所示。起初由氢原子推导出来的等式 (2) 在硅中是非常复杂的，这是因为硅的谷简并各向异性能带结构[29]。每一个谷干涉的交换耦合项都会导致 $J(r)$ 的振荡行为。在这里的讨论中，我们将忽略由于硅的能带结构导致的复杂问题。为了在图 3 中确定 $J(r)$，采用硅的横质量（$\cong 0.2m_e$）， transverse mass for Si ($\cong 0.2m_e$) has been used, and $a_B = 30$ Å. Because J is proportional to the electron wave function overlap, it can be varied by an electrostatic potential imposed by a "J-gate" positioned between the donors[13]. As shall be seen below, significant coupling between nuclei will occur when $4J \approx \mu_B B$, and this condition approximates the necessary separation between donors of 100–200 Å. Whereas actual separations may be considerably larger than this value because the J gate can be biased positively to reduce the barrier between donors, the gate sizes required for the quantum computer are near the limit of current electronics fabrication technology.

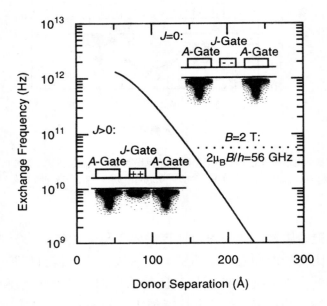

Fig. 3. J gates vary the electrostatic potential barrier V between donors to enhance or reduce exchange coupling, proportional to the electron wavefunction overlap. The exchange frequency ($4J/h$) when $V = 0$ is plotted for Si.

For two-electron systems, the exchange interaction lowers the electron singlet ($|\uparrow\downarrow - \downarrow\uparrow\rangle$) energy with respect to the triplets[30]. (The $|\uparrow\downarrow\rangle$ notation is used here to represent the electron spin state, and the $|01\rangle$ notation the nuclear state; in the $|\downarrow\downarrow 11\rangle$ state, all spins point in the same direction. For simplicity, normalization constants are omitted.) In a magnetic field, however, $|\downarrow\downarrow\rangle$ will be the ground state if $J < \mu_B B/2$ (Fig. 4a). In the $|\downarrow\downarrow\rangle$ state, the energies of the nuclear states can be calculated to second order in A using perturbation theory. When $A_1 = A_2 = A$, the $|10 - 01\rangle$ state is lowered in energy with respect to $|10 + 01\rangle$ by:

$$h\nu_J = 2A^2 \left(\frac{1}{\mu_B B - 2J} - \frac{1}{\mu_B B} \right) \tag{3}$$

The $|11\rangle$ state is above the $|10 + 01\rangle$ state and the $|00\rangle$ state below the $|10 - 01\rangle$ state by an energy $h\nu_A$, given in equation (1). For the Si:^{31}P system at $B = 2$ T and for $4J/h = 30$ GHz, equation (3) yields $\nu_J = 75$ kHz. This nuclear spin exchange frequency approximates the rate at which binary operations can be performed on the computer (ν_J can be increased

$a_B = 30$ Å。因为 J 正比于电子波函数的重叠，它会通过施主之间的"J 栅极"所产生的静电势而变化[13]。如下所示，当 $4J \approx \mu_B B$ 的时候，核之间会产生显著的耦合，这个已经逼近了施主之间的最小要求间距 $100 \sim 200$ Å。然而实际上的间距可能远大于这个值，因为 J 栅极可以被施加正偏压来减少施主之间的势垒，量子计算机所需要的栅极的尺寸已经接近了当今电子学微加工技术的极限。

图 3. J 栅极可以改变施主之间的静电势垒 V，以此来增强或者减弱交换耦合，正比于电子波函数的重叠。当 $V = 0$ 时，硅的交换频率（$4J/h$）如图所示。

对于双电子系统来说，交换作用使得电子的单重态（$|\uparrow\downarrow - \downarrow\uparrow\rangle$）能量相对于三重态能量降低[30]。（$|\uparrow\downarrow\rangle$ 符号被用来代表电子自旋态，$|01\rangle$ 符号表示核自旋态；在 $|\downarrow\downarrow 11\rangle$ 状态下，所有自旋在同一方向。为了简化，归一化的常数被省略）。然而在磁场存在时，当 $J < \mu_B B/2$ 时（如图 4a 所示），$|\downarrow\downarrow\rangle$ 将会是电子的基态。在 $|\downarrow\downarrow\rangle$ 态中，核态的能量可以用微扰理论取到 A 的二阶项来计算。当 $A_1 = A_2 = A$ 时，$|10 - 01\rangle$ 态的能量相比 $|10 + 01\rangle$ 态的能量小了：

$$h\nu_J = 2A^2 \left(\frac{1}{\mu_B B - 2J} - \frac{1}{\mu_B B} \right) \tag{3}$$

$|11\rangle$ 态在 $|10 + 01\rangle$ 态上方距离能量 $h\nu_A$ 处，而 $|00\rangle$ 在 $|10 - 01\rangle$ 下方距离能量 $h\nu_A$ 处，由等式（1）给出。对于 Si:^{31}P 系统，在 $B = 2$ T 且 $4J/h = 30$ GHz 时，等式（3）给出解为 $\nu_J = 75$ kHz。这个核自旋交换频率近似于计算机进行二进制运算的频率（ν_J 可以

by increasing J, but at the expense of also increasing the relaxation rate of the coupled nuclear–electron spin excitations). The speed of single spin operations is determined by the size of B_{ac} and is comparable to 75 kHz when $B_{ac} = 10^{-3}$ T.

Fig. 4. Two qubit quantum logic and spin measurement. **a**, Electron (solid lines) and lowest energy-coupled electron–nuclear (dashed lines) energy levels as a function of J. When $J < \mu_B B/2$, two qubit computations are performed by controlling the $|10-01\rangle - |10+01\rangle$ level splitting with a J gate. Above $J = \mu_B B/2$, the states of the coupled system evolve into states of differing electron polarization. The state of the nucleus at $J = 0$ with the larger energy splitting (controllable by the A gate bias) determines the final electron spin state after an adiabatic increase in J. **b**, Only $|\uparrow\downarrow - \downarrow\uparrow\rangle$ electrons can make transitions into states in which electrons are bound to the same donor (D^- states). Electron current during these transitions is measurable using capacitive techniques, enabling the underlying spin states of the electrons and nuclei to be determined.

Spin Measurements

Measurement of nuclear spins in the proposed quantum computer is accomplished in a two-step process: distinct nuclear spin states are adiabatically converted into states with different electron polarization, and the electron spin is determined by its effect on the symmetry of the orbital wavefunction of an exchange-coupled two-electron system. A procedure for accomplishing this conversion is shown in Fig. 4. While computation is done when $J < \mu_B B/2$ and the electrons are fully polarized, measurements are made when $J > \mu_B B/2$, and $|\uparrow\downarrow - \downarrow\uparrow\rangle$ states have the lowest energy (Fig. 4a). As the electron levels cross, the $|\downarrow\downarrow\rangle$ and $|\uparrow\downarrow - \downarrow\uparrow\rangle$ states are coupled by hyperfine interactions with the nuclei. During an adiabatic increase in J, the two lower-energy nuclear spin states at $J = 0$ evolve into $|\uparrow\downarrow - \downarrow\uparrow\rangle$ states when $J > \mu_B B/2$, whereas the two higher-energy nuclear states remain $|\downarrow\downarrow\rangle$. If, at $J = 0$, $A_1 > A_2$, the orientation of nuclear spin 1 alone will determine whether the system evolves into the $|\uparrow\downarrow - \downarrow\uparrow\rangle$ or the $|\downarrow\downarrow\rangle$ state during an adiabatic increase in J.

通过增加 J 来增加，但是也以增加了耦合原子核–电子自旋激发的弛豫速率为代价）。单个自旋的运算速度是由 B_{ac} 的大小来决定的，当 $B_{ac} = 10^{-3}$ T 时相当于 75 kHz。

图 4. 两个量子比特的逻辑和自旋测量。**a**，电子（实线）和最低能量耦合电子–核自旋（虚线）能级随 J 的变化。当 $J < \mu_B B/2$，两个量子比特计算通过使用 J 栅极控制 $|10-01\rangle - |10+01\rangle$ 能级分裂来实现。在 $J = \mu_B B/2$ 上方，耦合系统的态演化为不同电子极化的态。原子核的具有很大能量分裂的（受 A 栅极偏压的控制）在 $J = 0$ 的态决定了在 J 绝热增加后，电子最终的自旋态。**b**，只有 $|\uparrow\downarrow - \downarrow\uparrow\rangle$ 电子才可以转换成电子与同一个施主结合的态（D^- 态）。这个转换过程的电子电流是可以通过电容技术来测量的，这就使得电子和原子核的基础自旋态可以被探测。

自 旋 测 量

在本文提出的量子计算机中，核自旋测量是分两步来实现的：不同的原子核自旋态绝热转化为不同电子极化的态，且电子自旋是由其对交换耦合双电子系统的轨道波函数对称性的影响来决定的。图 4 展示了如何实现这一转换的过程。当计算完成时 $J < \mu_B B/2$ 且电子被充分地极化，测量在 $J > \mu_B B/2$ 时进行，$|\uparrow\downarrow - \downarrow\uparrow\rangle$ 态有最低的能量（图 4a）。当电子能级交叉时，$|\downarrow\downarrow\rangle$ 态和 $|\uparrow\downarrow - \downarrow\uparrow\rangle$ 态就会通过与原子核产生超精细相互作用耦合。在 J 绝热增加过程中，当 $J > \mu_B B/2$ 时，两个处于 $J = 0$ 的低能量核自旋态演化为 $|\uparrow\downarrow - \downarrow\uparrow\rangle$ 态，然而两个高能级的核自旋态仍然保持 $|\downarrow\downarrow\rangle$ 态。如果在 $J = 0$ 时，$A_1 > A_2$，1 号原子核自旋的取向将独自决定系统在 J 的绝热增加过程中是演化为 $|\uparrow\downarrow - \downarrow\uparrow\rangle$ 态或者是 $|\downarrow\downarrow\rangle$ 态。

A method to detect the electron spin state by using electronic means is shown in Fig. 4b. Both electrons can become bound to the same donor (a D^- state) if the A gates above the donors are biased appropriately. In Si:P, the D^- state is always a singlet with a second electron binding energy of 1.7 meV (refs 31, 32). Consequently, a differential voltage applied to the A gates can result in charge motion between the donors that only occurs if the electrons are in a singlet state. This charge motion is measurable using sensitive single-electron capacitance techniques[33]. This approach to spin measurement produces a signal that persists until the electron spin relaxes, a time that, as noted above, can be thousands of seconds in Si:P.

The spin measurement process can also be used to prepare nuclear spins in a prescribed state by first determining the state of a spin and flipping it if necessary so that it ends up in the desired spin state. As with the spin computation procedures already discussed, spin measurement and preparation can in principle be performed in parallel throughout the computer.

Initializing the Computer

Before any computation, the computer must be initialized by calibrating the A gates and the J gates. Fluctuations from cell to cell in the gate biases necessary to perform logical operations are an inevitable consequence of variations in the positions of the donors and in the sizes of the gates. The parameters of each cell, however, can be determined individually using the measurement capabilities of the computer, because the measurement technique discussed here does not require precise knowledge of the J and A couplings. The A-gate voltage at which the underlying nuclear spin is resonant with an applied B_{ac} can be determined using the technique of adiabatic fast passage[34]: when $B_{ac} = 0$, the nuclear spin is measured and the A gate is biased at a voltage known to be off resonance. B_{ac} is then switched on, and the A gate bias is swept through a prescribed voltage interval. B_{ac} is then switched off and the nuclear spin is measured again. The spin will have flipped if, and only if, resonance occurred within the prescribed A-gate voltage range. Testing for spin flips in increasingly small voltage ranges leads to the determination of the resonance voltage. Once adjacent A gates have been calibrated, the J gates can be calibrated in a similar manner by sweeping J-gate biases across resonances of two coupled cells.

This calibration procedure can be performed in parallel on many cells, so calibration is not a fundamental impediment to scaling the computer to large sizes. Calibration voltages can be stored on capacitors located on the Si chip adjacent to the quantum computer. External controlling circuitry would thus need to control only the timing of gate biases, and not their magnitudes.

Spin Decoherence Introduced by Gates

In the quantum computer architecture outlined above, biasing of A gates and J gates

一种用来探测电子自旋态的方法是使用电子手段，如图 4b 所示。如果施主上方的 A 栅极被施加适当的偏压，两个电子可以都结合到同一个施主（D^- 态）。在 Si:P 中 D^- 态总是具有 1.7 meV 第二电子结合能的单重态[31,32]。因此，施加一个差分电压于栅极 A 上可以导致只有处于单重态的电子可以在施主间产生电荷移动。这种电荷移动可以通过灵敏的单电子电容技术[33] 来测量。这种测量自旋的方法产生的信号持续到电子自旋发生弛豫为止，如前所述，在 Si:P 系统中这种过程可以有几千秒的时间。

自旋的测量过程也可以用来将核自旋初始化到指定的态上：首先确定自旋的态，如果需要的话就翻转它使它停在想要的自旋态上。正如我们已经讨论的自旋计算过程，自旋的测量和准备原则上可以在计算机中并行执行。

初始化计算机

在进行任何计算之前，计算机必须通过定标 A 栅极和 J 栅极来实现初始化。施主位置以及栅极大小的不均匀必然造成不同单元执行逻辑运算所必需的栅极偏压的涨落，不过每个单元的参数都可以通过计算机的测量功能来独自地确定，因为这里讨论的测量技术不需要非常准确地了解 J 栅极和 A 栅极的耦合。A 栅极下面核自旋与外加 B_{ac} 共振时，所需要施加的 A 栅极电压可以通过绝热快速通过技术[34] 来确定：当 $B_{ac} = 0$ 时，核自旋被测量，且 A 栅极被施加一个能消除共振的偏压。B_{ac} 然后被启动，在指定的电压区间内扫描 A 栅极偏压。然后关闭 B_{ac} 并再次测量核自旋。当且仅当共振在指定的 A 栅极电压范围内出现的时候，自旋才会被翻转。在越来越小的电压范围内测试自旋的翻转将能确定出共振的电压。当邻近的 A 栅极被定标之后，J 栅极可以用同样的方法在两个耦合单元的共振区扫描 J 栅极偏压来定标。

这种定标程序可以在多个单元上面并行进行，所以定标问题不是将计算机扩展到大尺寸的主要阻碍。定标电压可以存储在连接到量子计算机上的硅芯片的电容中。因此，外部控制电路只需要控制栅极偏压的时间，而不是他们的大小。

栅极导致的自旋退相干

在上面概述的量子计算机的设计结构中，对 A 类和 J 类栅极施加偏压可以自

enables custom control of the qubits and their mutual interactions. The presence of the gates, however, will lead to decoherence of the spins if the gate biases fluctuate away from their desired values. These effects need to be considered to evaluate the performance of any gate-controlled quantum computer. During the computation, the largest source of decoherence is likely to arise from voltage fluctuations on the A gates. (When $J < \mu_B B/2$, modulation of the state energies by the J gates is much smaller than by the A gates. J exceeds $\mu_B B/2$ only during the measurement process, when decoherence will inevitably occur.) The precession frequencies of two spins in phase at $t = 0$ depends on the potentials on their respective A gates. Differential fluctuations of the potentials produce differences in the precession frequency. At some later time $t = t_\phi$, the spins will be 180° out of phase; t_ϕ can be estimated by determining the transition rate between $|10+01\rangle$ (spins in phase) and $|10-01\rangle$ (spins 180° out of phase) of a two-spin system. The hamiltonian that couples these states is $H_\phi = \frac{1}{4}h\Delta(\sigma_z^{1n} - \sigma_z^{2n})$, where Δ is the fluctuating differential precession frequency of the spins. Standard treatment of fluctuating hamiltonians[34] predicts: $t_\phi^{-1} = \pi^2 S_\Delta(\nu_{st})$, where S_Δ is the spectral density of the frequency fluctuations, and ν_{st} is the frequency difference between the $|10-01\rangle$ and $|10+01\rangle$ states. At a particular bias voltage, the A gates have a frequency tuning parameter $\alpha = d\Delta/dV$. Thus:

$$t_\phi^{-1} = \pi^2 \alpha^2(V) S_V(\nu_{st}) \tag{4}$$

where S_V is the spectral density of the gate voltage fluctuations.

S_V for good room temperature electronics is of order 10^{-18} V^2/Hz, comparable to the room temperature Johnson noise of a 50-Ω resistor. The value of α, estimated from Fig. 2, is 10–100 MHz V^{-1}, yielding $t_\phi = 10$–1,000 s; α is determined by the size of the donor array cells and cannot readily be reduced (to increase t_ϕ) without reducing the exchange interaction between cells. Because α is a function of the gate bias (Fig. 2), t_ϕ can be increased by minimizing the voltage applied to the A gates.

Although equation (4) is valid for white noise, at low frequencies it is likely that materials-dependent fluctuations ($1/f$ noise) will be the dominant cause of spin dephasing. Consequently, it is difficult to give hard estimates of t_ϕ for the computer. Charge fluctuations within the computer (arising from fluctuating occupancies of traps and surface states, for example) are likely to be particularly important, and minimizing them will place great demands on computer fabrication.

Although materials-dependent fluctuations are difficult to estimate, the low-temperature operations of the computer and the dissipationless nature of quantum computing mean that, in principle, fluctuations can be kept extremely small: using low-temperature electronics to bias the gates (for instance, by using on chip capacitors as discussed above) could produce $t_\phi \approx 10^6$ s. Electronically controlled nuclear spin quantum computers thus have the theoretical capability to perform at least 10^5 to perhaps 10^{10} logical operations during t_ϕ, and can probably meet Preskill's criterion[8] for an error probability of 10^{-6} per qubit operation.

定义地控制量子比特以及他们之间的相互作用。然而如果栅极的偏压振荡出期望的范围，栅极的存在将导致自旋退相干。这些效应应该在任何通过栅极控制来实现的量子计算机的性能评价中被考虑到。在计算过程中，导致退相干的主要来源一般是 A 栅极上的电压振荡。（当 $J < \mu_B B/2$ 时，态能量被 J 栅极调制的幅度远小于被 A 栅极调制的幅度。J 超过 $\mu_B B/2$ 只会发生在测量过程，那时退相干是不可避免的。）在 $t = 0$ 时刻同相位中的两个自旋的进动频率取决于他们各自 A 栅极上的电势。这两个电势的差值波动引起进动频率的相对变化。在稍后的 $t = t_\phi$ 时刻，这两个自旋的相位将会相差 180 度（反相位）；t_ϕ 可以通过这个双自旋系统在 $|10+01\rangle$（自旋同相位）和 $|10-01\rangle$（自旋 180 度反相位）两种状态间的转换速率来确定。这些态之间耦合的哈密顿量为 $H_\phi = \frac{1}{4} h\Delta(\sigma_z^{1n} - \sigma_z^{2n})$，其中 Δ 是不同自旋进动频率差值的振荡。对该振荡哈密顿量进行标准处理 [34] 导出：$t_\phi^{-1} = \pi^2 S_\Delta(\nu_{st})$，其中 S_Δ 是频率振荡的频谱密度，ν_{st} 是 $|10-01\rangle$ 和 $|10+01\rangle$ 态之间的频率差。在一个固定的偏压下，A 类栅极有一个频率调谐参数 $\alpha = d\Delta/dV$。因此

$$t_\phi^{-1} = \pi^2 \alpha^2(V) S_V(\nu_{st}) \tag{4}$$

其中 S_V 是栅极电压涨落的频谱密度。

良好的室温电子元件的 S_V 的量级是 10^{-18} V^2/Hz，这和一个 50 Ω 的电阻的室温约翰逊噪音是接近的。从图 2 中估算出的 α 值大概为 $10 \sim 100$ MHz · V^{-1}，导出 $t_\phi = 10 \sim 1,000$ s；α 可以由施主阵列单元的大小来确定，且不能在不减小单元之间的相互作用的情况下被轻易地减小（来增加 t_ϕ）。因为 α 是栅极偏压的函数（图 2），t_ϕ 可以通过最小化 A 类栅极偏压来增加。

虽然等式 4 对白噪声来说是正确的，在低频率条件下，导致自旋退相的主要原因很可能是依赖于材料的波动（$1/f$ 噪音）。因此给出计算机一个准确的预期值 t_ϕ 是非常困难的。计算机内部的电荷涨落（例如由陷阱和表面态的占位数涨落引起）很可能是非常重要的，这就要求在计算机制造中最小化这种电荷涨落。

虽然依赖材料的波动很难预期，在低温条件下的计算机运算以及量子计算无耗散的特征意味着，原则上波动可以被保持得很小：使用低温电子器件来给栅极施加偏压（例如之前讨论中提到的使用芯片电容）可以使得 t_ϕ 约等于 10^6 s。电子器件控制的核自旋量子计算机因此理论上具备了在 t_ϕ 时间内执行 10^5 到 10^{10} 逻辑运算的能力，这样基本上就满足了普雷斯基尔的每个量子比特运算误码率为 10^{-6} 的准则 [8]。

Constructing the Computer

Building the computer presented here will obviously be an extraordinary challenge: the materials must be almost completely free of spin ($I \neq 0$ isotopes) and charge impurities to prevent dephasing fluctuations from arising within the computer. Donors must be introduced into the material in an ordered array hundreds of Å beneath the surface. Finally, gates with lateral dimensions and separations ~ 100 Å must be patterned on the surface, registered to the donors beneath them. Although it is possible that the computer can use SiO_2 as the barrier material (the standard MOS technology used in most current conventional electronics), the need to reduce disorder and fluctuations to a minimum means that heteroepitaxial materials, such as Si/SiGe, may ultimately be preferable to Si/SiO_2.

The most obvious obstacle to building to the quantum computer presented above is the incorporation of the donor array into the Si layer beneath the barrier layer. Currently, semiconductor structures are deposited layer by layer. The δ-doping technique produces donors lying on a plane in the material, with the donors randomly distributed within the plane. The quantum computer envisaged here requires that the donors be placed into an ordered one- or two-dimensional array; furthermore, precisely one donor must be placed into each array cell, making it extremely difficult to create the array by using lithography and ion implantation or by focused deposition. Methods currently under development to place single atoms on surfaces using ultra-high-vacuum scanning tunnelling microscopy[35] or atom optics techniques[36] are likely candidates to be used to position the donor array. A challenge will be to grow high-quality Si layers on the surface subsequent to placement of the donors.

Fabricating large arrays of donors may prove to be difficult, but two-spin devices, which can be used to test the logical operations and measurement techniques presented here, can be made using random doping techniques. Although only a small fraction of such devices will work properly, adjacent conventional Si electronic multiplexing circuitry can be used to examine many devices separately. The relative ease of fabricating such "hybrid"(quantum-conventional) circuits is a particularly attractive feature of Si-based quantum computation.

In a Si-based nuclear spin quantum computer, the highly coherent quantum states necessary for quantum computation are incorporated into a material in which the ability to implement complex computer architectures is well established. The substantial challenges facing the realization of the computer, particularly in fabricating 100-Å-scale gated devices, are similar to those facing the next generation of conventional electronics; consequently, new manufacturing technologies being developed for conventional electronics will bear directly on efforts to develop a quantum computer in Si. Quantum computers sufficiently complex that they can achieve their theoretical potential may thus one day be built using the same technology that is used to produce conventional computers.

(**393**, 133-137; 1998)

构造计算机

构造一个这里讨论的计算机显然将是非常巨大的挑战：选取的材料必须完全没有自旋（$I \neq 0$ 同位素）和电荷杂质，以避免计算机中出现退相位扰动。施主必须作为一个有序的阵列导入材料表面几百埃以下。最后，横向尺寸和间距为 100 Å 左右的栅极被加工在表面，与其下方的施主对应。虽然使用二氧化硅（大多数当前传统电子器件所使用的标准 MOS 技术）作为势垒层材料是可行的，但是由于需要最小化无序和扰动，意味着异质外延材料如硅/硅锗（Si/SiGe）最终可能优于硅/二氧化硅（Si/SiO_2）。

构造上文描述的量子计算机最明显的困难是如何将施主阵列注入势垒层下方的硅层中。现阶段半导体结构是逐层沉积制造的。δ 掺杂技术得到的施主位于材料中的单层中，其中施主是随机分布在这一层中的。我们这里设想的量子计算机要求施主被放置于有序的一维或者二维的阵列中；另外，施主必须被准确地放置在每个阵列单元中，这就使得通过光刻技术和离子注入或者通过聚焦沉积方法都很难制造出这种阵列。目前正在发展的将单原子放在表面的技术是利用超高真空扫描隧道显微镜 [35] 或者原子光学技术 [36] 实现的，这些是可能被用来放置施主阵列的备选方法。接着的一个挑战将是在施主放置处表面上生长高质量的硅层。

制造大的施主阵列也许是非常困难的，但是用来检验此处介绍的逻辑计算和测量技术的双自旋器件可以使用随机掺杂技术来制造。虽然只有一小部分这样的器件可以正常工作，但是相关的传统硅电子学中的复用电路可以用来独立地检测许多器件。制造这种"混合"（量子–传统）电路的相对简易性是硅基量子计算机的独特魅力所在。

在基于硅的核自旋量子计算机中，量子计算所必需的高度相干的量子态被整合到能够实现复杂计算机结构的材料中。实现量子计算机面临的重要挑战，尤其是 100 Å 尺度的栅极器件制造，与下一代传统电子器件面临的挑战类似；因此，正为传统电子器件研发的新制造技术将与开发硅量子计算机的努力直接相关。足够复杂以至于可以实现其理论潜力的量子计算机，也许会在将来的某一天使用传统计算机类似的技术搭建起来。

（姜克 翻译；杜江峰 审稿）

B. E. Kane

Semiconductor Nanofabrication Facility, School of Physics, University of New South Wales, Sydney 2052, Australia

Received 10 November 1997; accepted 24 February 1998.

References:

1. Steane, A. Quantum computing. *Rep. Prog. Phys.* **61,** 117-173 (1998).

2. Bennett, C. H. Quantum information and computation. *Physics Today* 24-30 (Oct. 1995).

3. Shor, P. W. in *Proc. 35th Annu. Symp. Foundations of Computer Science* (ed. Goldwasser, S.) 124-134 (IEEE Computer Society, Los Alamitos, CA, 1994).

4. Ekert, A. & Jozsa, R. Quantum computation and Shor's factoring algorithm. *Rev. Mod. Phys.* **68,** 733-753 (1996).

5. Grover, L. K. Quantum mechanics helps in searching for a needle in a haystack. *Phys. Rev. Lett.* **79,** 325-328 (1997).

6. Calderbank, A. R. & Shor, P. W. Good quantum error correcting codes exist. *Phys. Rev. A* **54,** 1098-1105 (1996).

7. Steane, A. M. Error correcting codes in quantum theory. *Phys. Rev. Lett.* **77,** 793-797 (1996).

8. Preskill, J. Reliable quantum computers. *Proc. R. Soc. Lond. A* **454,** 385-410 (1998).

9. Lloyd, S. A potentially realizable quantum computer. *Science* **261,** 1569-1571 (1993).

10. DiVincenzo, D. P. Quantum computation. *Science* **270,** 255-261 (1995).

11. Gershenfeld, N. A. & Chuang, I. L. Bulk spin-resonance quantum computation. *Science* **275,** 350-356 (1997).

12. Cory, D. G., Fahmy, A. F. & Havel, T. F. Ensemble quantum computing by NMR spectroscopy. *Proc. Natl Acad. Sci. USA* **94,** 1634-1639 (1997).

13. Loss, D. & DiVincenzo, D. P. Quantum computation with quantum dots. *Phys. Rev. A* **57,** 120-126 (1998).

14. Privman, V., Vagner, I. D. & Kventsel, G. Quantum computation in quantum Hall systems. *Phys. Lett. A* **239,** 141-146 (1998).

15. Slichter, C. P. *Principles of Magnetic Resonance* 3rd edn, Ch 4 (Springer, Berlin, 1990).

16. Dobers, M., Klitzing, K. v., Schneider, J., Weimann, G. & Ploog, K. Electrical detection of nuclear magnetic resonance in GaAs-Al$_x$Ga$_{1-x}$As heterostructures. *Phys. Rev. Lett.* **61,** 1650-1653 (1988).

17. Stich, B., Greulich-Weber, S. & Spaeth, J.-M. Electrical detection of electron nuclear double resonance in silicon. *Appl. Phys. Lett.* **68,** 1102-1104 (1996).

18. Kane, B. E., Pfeiffer, L. N. & West, K. W. Evidence for an electric-field-induced phase transition in a spin-polarized two-dimensional electron gas. *Phys. Rev. B* **46,** 7264-7267 (1992).

19. Wald, K. W., Kouwenhoven, L. P., McEuen, P. L., van der Vaart, N. C. & Foxon, C. T. Local dynamic nuclear polarization using quantum point contacts. *Phys. Rev. Lett.* **73,** 1011-1014 (1994).

20. Dixon, D. C., Wald, K. R., McEuen, P. L. & Melloch, M. R. Dynamic polarization at the edge of a two-dimensional electron gas. *Phys. Rev. B* **56,** 4743-4750 (1997).

21. *CRC Handbook of Chemistry and Physics* 77th edn 11-38 (CRC Press, Boca Raton, Florida, 1996).

22. Feher, G. Electron spin resonance on donors in silicon. I. Electronic structure of donors by the electron nuclear double resonance technique. *Phys. Rev.* **114,** 1219-1244 (1959).

23. Wilson, D. K. & Feher, G. Electron spin resonance experiments on donors in silicon. III. Investigation of excited states by the application of uniaxial stress and their importance in relaxation processes. *Phys. Rev.* **124,** 1068-1083 (1961).

24. Waugh, J. S. & Slichter, C. P. Mechanism of nuclear spin-lattice relaxation in insulators at very low temperatures. *Phys. Rev. B* **37,** 4337-4339 (1988).

25. Kohn, W. *Solid State Physics* Vol. 5 (eds Seitz, F. & Turnbull, D.) 257-320 (Academic, New York, 1957).

26. DiVincenzo, D. P. Two-bit gates are universal for quantum computation. *Phys. Rev. A* **51,** 1015-1021 (1995).

27. Lloyd, S. Almost any quantum logic gate is universal. *Phys. Rev. Lett.* **75,** 346-349 (1995).

28. Herring, C. & Flicker, M. Asymptotic exchange coupling of two hydrogen atoms. *Phys. Rev.* **134,** A362–A366 (1964).

29. Andres, K., Bhatt, R. N., Goalwin, P., Rice, T. M. & Walstedt, R. E. Low-temperature magnetic susceptibility of Si:P in the nonmetallic region. *Phys. Rev. B* **24,** 244-260 (1981).

30. Ashcroft, N. W. & Mermin, N. D. in *Solid State Physics* Ch. 32 (Saunders College, Philadelphia, 1976).

31. Larsen, D. M. Stress dependence of the binding energy of D^- centers in Si. *Phys. Rev. B* **23,** 5521-5526 (1981).

32. Larsen, D. M. & McCann, S. Y. Variational studies of two- and three-dimensional D^- centers in magnetic fields. *Phys. Rev. B* **46,** 3966-3970 (1992).

33. Ashoori, R. C. Electrons in artificial atoms. *Nature* **379,** 413-419 (1996).

34. Abragam, A. *Principles of Nuclear Magnetism* (Oxford Univ. Press, London, 1961).

35. Lyding, J. W. UHV STM nanofabrication: progress, technology spin-offs, and challenges. *Proc. IEEE* **85,** 589-600 (1997).

36. Adams, C. S., Sigel, J. & Mlynek, J. Atom optics. *Phys. Rep.* **240,** 143-210 (1994).

37. Warren, W. S. The usefulness of NMR quantum computing. *Science* **277,** 1688-1690 (1997).

Acknowledgements. This work has been supported by the Australian Research Council. I thank R. G. Clark for encouragement and E. Hellman for suggesting that the work in ref. 18 could be relevant to quantum computation.

Correspondence should be addressed to the author (e-mail: kane@newt.phys.unsw.edu.au).

Collective Dynamics of "Small-world" Networks

D. J. Watts and S. H. Strogatz

Editor's Note

We live in a world of networks, from human social networks and biological food webs to neural systems, transportation networks and the modern Internet. In this paper, Duncan Watts and Steven Strogatz demonstrate that these networks often share surprising architectural similarities. Most notably, they are "small worlds", in that only a few steps are needed to move along links from any one point to another, even in networks containing an enormous number of elements. Such networks also tend to be highly "clustered", with many redundant paths, making them connected wholes that are resilient to the removal of links. This paper stimulated an explosion of work on complex networks by providing a new conceptual framework for analysing them.

Networks of coupled dynamical systems have been used to model biological oscillators[1-4], Josephson junction arrays[5,6], excitable media[7], neural networks[8-10], spatial games[11], genetic control networks[12] and many other self-organizing systems. Ordinarily, the connection topology is assumed to be either completely regular or completely random. But many biological, technological and social networks lie somewhere between these two extremes. Here we explore simple models of networks that can be tuned through this middle ground: regular networks "rewired" to introduce increasing amounts of disorder. We find that these systems can be highly clustered, like regular lattices, yet have small characteristic path lengths, like random graphs. We call them "small-world" networks, by analogy with the small-world phenomenon[13,14] (popularly known as six degrees of separation[15]). The neural network of the worm *Caenorhabditis elegans*, the power grid of the western United States, and the collaboration graph of film actors are shown to be small-world networks. Models of dynamical systems with small-world coupling display enhanced signal-propagation speed, computational power, and synchronizability. In particular, infectious diseases spread more easily in small-world networks than in regular lattices.

TO interpolate between regular and random networks, we consider the following random rewiring procedure (Fig. 1). Starting from a ring lattice with n vertices and k edges per vertex, we rewire each edge at random with probability p. This construction allows us to "tune" the graph between regularity ($p = 0$) and disorder ($p = 1$), and thereby to probe the intermediate region $0 < p < 1$, about which little is known.

"小世界"网络的集体动力学

沃茨，斯特罗加茨

编者按

我们生活在一个网络世界里：从人类社会网络和生物食物网到神经系统、运输网络和现代互联网。本文中，邓肯·沃茨和史蒂文·斯特罗加茨证明了这些网络通常具有惊人的结构相似性。最值得注意的是，它们是"小世界"，因为即使在包含大量元素的网络中，也只需要几个步骤就可以沿着链路从一个点移动到另一个点。这种网络也倾向于高度"集群化"，许多冗余路径使得它们连接在一起成为一个整体，从而对链路的移除具有恢复力。本文提供了一个新的概念框架来分析复杂网络，促进了复杂网络研究工作的爆炸式增长。

耦合动力系统网络已被广泛应用于生物振荡[1-4]、约瑟夫森结阵列[5,6]、可激发介质[7]、神经网络[8-10]、空间博弈[11]、基因控制网络[12]以及多种其他自组织系统的建模。通常情况下，其拓扑结构被认为或是完全规则的，或是完全随机的。但是许多生物、技术和社会的网络介于这两种极端状况之间。本文阐述了一种处于这种中间态的简单的网络模型：将规则网络"重新连接"来引入更多无序性。我们发现这些系统可以像有序晶格一样被高度集聚，同时具有很小的特征路径长度，类似随机图。通过与小世界现象[13,14]（人们所熟知的六度分隔[15]）的类比，我们称它们为"小世界"网络。秀丽隐杆线虫的神经网络、美国西部的电力网络以及电影演员的合作图都表现为小世界网络。具有小世界耦合的动力系统模型显示了更强的信号传播速度、计算能力和同步性。特别需要指出的是，传染病在小世界网络中传播要比在规则网络中传播更容易。

为了实现规则网络和随机网络之间的中间状态，我们来考虑以下的随机重连过程（图1）。从一个具有 n 个顶点，每个顶点 k 条边的环形晶格网络开始，我们以概率 p 随机地将每条边重新连接。这种构造允许我们在规则（$p=0$）和无序（$p=1$）之间"调谐"，从而探索目前被了解得很少的 $0<p<1$ 的中间区域。

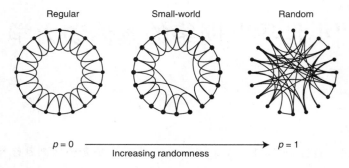

Fig. 1. Random rewiring procedure for interpolating between a regular ring lattice and a random network, without altering the number of vertices or edges in the graph. We start with a ring of n vertices, each connected to its k nearest neighbours by undirected edges. (For clarity, $n = 20$ and $k = 4$ in the schematic examples shown here, but much larger n and k are used in the rest of this Letter.) We choose a vertex and the edge that connects it to its nearest neighbour in a clockwise sense. With probability p, we reconnect this edge to a vertex chosen uniformly at random over the entire ring, with duplicate edges forbidden; otherwise we leave the edge in place. We repeat this process by moving clockwise around the ring, considering each vertex in turn until one lap is completed. Next, we consider the edges that connect vertices to their second-nearest neighbours clockwise. As before, we randomly rewire each of these edges with probability p, and continue this process, circulating around the ring and proceeding outward to more distant neighbours after each lap, until each edge in the original lattice has been considered once. (As there are $nk/2$ edges in the entire graph, the rewiring process stops after $k/2$ laps.) Three realizations of this process are shown, for different values of p. For $p = 0$, the original ring is unchanged; as p increases, the graph becomes increasingly disordered until for $p = 1$, all edges are rewired randomly. One of our main results is that for intermediate values of p, the graph is a small-world network: highly clustered like a regular graph, yet with small characteristic path length, like a random graph. (See Fig. 2.)

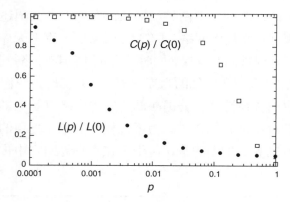

Fig. 2. Characteristic path length $L(p)$ and clustering coefficient $C(p)$ for the family of randomly rewired graphs described in Fig. 1. Here L is defined as the number of edges in the shortest path between two vertices, averaged over all pairs of vertices. The clustering coefficient $C(p)$ is defined as follows. Suppose that a vertex v has k_v neighbours; then at most $k_v(k_v-1)/2$ edges can exist between them (this occurs when every neighbour of v is connected to every other neighbour of v). Let C_v denote the fraction of these allowable edges that actually exist. Define C as the average of C_v over all v. For friendship networks, these statistics have intuitive meanings: L is the average number of friendships in the shortest chain connecting two people; C_v reflects the extent to which friends of v are also friends of each other; and thus C measures the cliquishness of a typical friendship circle. The data shown in the figure are averages over 20 random realizations of the rewiring process described in Fig. 1, and have been normalized by the values $L(0)$, $C(0)$ for a regular lattice. All the graphs have $n = 1,000$ vertices and an average degree of $k = 10$ edges per vertex. We note that a logarithmic horizontal scale has been used to resolve the rapid drop in $L(p)$, corresponding

规则　　　　　　　小世界　　　　　　　随机

$p = 0$ ——————————→ $p = 1$
随机性增加

图1. 随机重新连接来制造处于规则环形晶格网络和随机网络之间的状态，而顶点和边的数量不变。我们从一个具有 n 个顶点的环开始，每个顶点都与最近的 k 个相邻顶点通过无向边相连。（为了表述清晰，图中的例子取 $n = 20$，$k = 4$，但在文中的其他部分我们取了更大的 n 和 k 值。）我们选取一个顶点以及顺时针方向上连接该顶点和最近邻点的边。以概率 p 将这条边重新连接到整个环上随机选取的任一顶点，不允许有重复连接的边；否则保持该边不动。我们沿环的顺时针方向重复这个过程，按顺序考虑到每个顶点直到一圈完成。接下来，我们考虑连接顶点与其顺时针方向第二近邻点的边。像上次操作一样，我们以概率 p 随机地重新连接这些边，然后我们重复这个过程，沿环循环，并在每一圈之后对连接更远近邻点的边继续该操作，直到每条原始网络中的边都被考虑到为止。（因为整个图中共有 $nk/2$ 条边，所以重新连接过程在 $k/2$ 圈后结束。）图中表示了不同 p 时，该过程的三种实现方式。$p = 0$ 时，原始环不变；随 p 增大图形无序性开始增加，到 $p = 1$ 时，所有的边都被随机地重新连接。我们得出的一个主要结论是，对于 p 处于中间值时，图为一小世界网络：像规则图一样高度集聚，又像随机图一样具有很小的特征路径长度。（见图2）

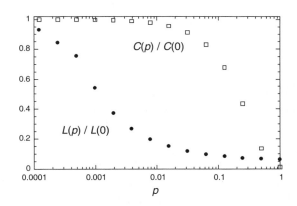

图2. 特征路径长度 $L(p)$ 与图1中所描述的随机重连图形的集聚系数 $C(p)$ 的关系。L 被定义为两顶点之间最短路径上的边的数量，为所有顶点对的平均值。集聚系数 $C(p)$ 按下述定义。假设一顶点 v 有 k_v 个邻点；那么至多有 $k_v(k_v - 1)/2$ 条边连接它们（这种情况发生在 v 的每个邻点都与 v 的所有其他邻点相连）。用 C_v 来表示真正存在的边占这些所有被允许出现的边的比例。定义 C 为所有的顶点 v 对应 C_v 的平均值。对于朋友关系网络，这些统计数据有着直观的含义：L 为两个人之间最短链中朋友关系的平均数；C_v 反映 v 的朋友中有多少互相之间也是朋友；因而 C 测量朋友关系圈的小集团性。图中所示的数据为图1中所描述的20种随机重连过程的平均值，并相对规则晶格网络的 $L(0)$ 和 $C(0)$ 进行了归一化。所有的图形都有 $n = 1,000$ 个顶点，每个顶点平均有 $k = 10$ 条边。我们使用对数横坐标以解决 $L(p)$ 骤降

to the onset of the small-world phenomenon. During this drop, $C(p)$ remains almost constant at its value for the regular lattice, indicating that the transition to a small world is almost undetectable at the local level.

We quantify the structural properties of these graphs by their characteristic path length $L(p)$ and clustering coefficient $C(p)$, as defined in Fig. 2 legend. Here $L(p)$ measures the typical separation between two vertices in the graph (a global property), whereas $C(p)$ measures the cliquishness of a typical neighbourhood (a local property). The networks of interest to us have many vertices with sparse connections, but not so sparse that the graph is in danger of becoming disconnected. Specifically, we require $n \gg k \gg \ln(n) \gg 1$, where $k \gg \ln(n)$ guarantees that a random graph will be connected[16]. In this regime, we find that $L \sim n/2k \gg 1$ and $C \sim 3/4$ as $p \to 0$, while $L \approx L_{random} \sim \ln(n)/\ln(k)$ and $C \approx C_{random} \sim k/n \ll 1$ as $p \to 1$. Thus the regular lattice at $p = 0$ is a highly clustered, large world where L grows linearly with n, whereas the random network at $p = 1$ is a poorly clustered, small world where L grows only logarithmically with n. These limiting cases might lead one to suspect that large C is always associated with large L, and small C with small L.

On the contrary, Fig. 2 reveals that there is a broad interval of p over which $L(p)$ is almost as small as L_{random} yet $C(p) \gg C_{random}$. These small-world networks result from the immediate drop in $L(p)$ caused by the introduction of a few long-range edges. Such "short cuts" connect vertices that would otherwise be much farther apart than L_{random}. For small p, each short cut has a highly nonlinear effect on L, contracting the distance not just between the pair of vertices that it connects, but between their immediate neighbourhoods, neighbourhoods of neighbourhoods and so on. By contrast, an edge removed from a clustered neighbourhood to make a short cut has, at most, a linear effect on C; hence $C(p)$ remains practically unchanged for small p even though $L(p)$ drops rapidly. The important implication here is that at the local level (as reflected by $C(p)$), the transition to a small world is almost undetectable. To check the robustness of these results, we have tested many different types of initial regular graphs, as well as different algorithms for random rewiring, and all give qualitatively similar results. The only requirement is that the rewired edges must typically connect vertices that would otherwise be much farther apart than L_{random}.

The idealized construction above reveals the key role of short cuts. It suggests that the small-world phenomenon might be common in sparse networks with many vertices, as even a tiny fraction of short cuts would suffice. To test this idea, we have computed L and C for the collaboration graph of actors in feature films (generated from data available at http://us.imdb.com), the electrical power grid of the western United States, and the neural network of the nematode worm C. elegans[17]. All three graphs are of scientific interest. The graph of film actors is a surrogate for a social network[18], with the advantage of being much more easily specified. It is also akin to the graph of mathematical collaborations centred, traditionally, on P. Erdös (partial data available at http://www.acs.oakland.edu/~grossman/erdoshp.html). The graph of the power grid is relevant to the efficiency and robustness of power networks[19]. And C. elegans is the sole example of a completely mapped neural network.

的问题，对应小世界现象的开始。在这个骤降过程中，规则晶格网络的 $C(p)$ 基本保持不变，也就意味着网络结构向小世界的转变在局域上是无法探测的。

通过它们的特征路径长度 $L(p)$ 和集聚系数 $C(p)$（图 2 注给出了这两项的定义），我们将这些图形的结构属性进行量化。这里 $L(p)$ 测量图形中两顶点之间的分隔（一种全局属性），而 $C(p)$ 测量近邻顶点间的小集团性（一种局域属性）。我们感兴趣的网络有很多顶点但连接很稀疏，但是没有稀疏到存在使图断开的危险。具体地讲，我们要求 $n \gg k \gg \ln(n) \gg 1$，其中 $k \gg \ln(n)$ 确保了随机图会被连接[16]。在这种机制下，我们发现当 $p \to 0$ 时，$L \sim n/2k \gg 1$，$C \sim 3/4$，而当 $p \to 1$ 时，$L \approx L_{随机} \sim \ln(n)/\ln(k)$，$C \approx C_{随机} \sim k/n \ll 1$。因此在 $p = 0$ 时的规则晶格网络是一高度群聚、L 随 n 线性增加的大世界，而 $p = 1$ 时的随机网络是一低群聚、L 只随 n 对数增长的小世界。这些带有限制性的情况很可能让人们认为大的 C 永远与大 L 相关，而小 C 与小 L 相关。

相反地，图 2 揭示了在 $L(p)$ 小到与 $L_{随机}$ 接近，但 $C(p) \gg C_{随机}$ 时，p 存在一个很宽的跨度。这些小世界网络源于由若干远程边的引入而引起的 $L(p)$ 的骤降。这样的"捷径"连接起了原本要相隔较 $L_{随机}$ 远很多的顶点。对于小的 p 来说，每一条捷径都产生很强的非线性效应作用于 L，不仅仅缩短了它所连接的顶点之间的距离，而且还缩短了它们与直接邻点之间的距离，以及与邻点的邻点之间的距离，等等。相比之下，从群聚的邻点中移除用于制造捷径的一条边，最多产生线性效应作用于 C；因此对于小的 p 即使 $L(p)$ 迅速减小，$C(p)$ 也仍保持不变。这里的一个很重要的启示是，就局部而言（通过 $C(p)$ 所反应的），向小世界的转变几乎无法探测。为了检验这些结果的稳健性，我们测试了多种不同类型的初始规则图，以及随机重连的不同算法，所有的测试都给出性质类似的结果。唯一的要求是重新连接的边通常必须连接原本比 $L_{随机}$ 远很多的顶点。

以上理想的构造揭示了捷径的核心作用。它意味着小世界现象在多顶点的稀疏网络中很普遍，很少的捷径就满足要求。为了验证这个想法，我们计算了故事片电影中演员的合作图（数据由 http://us.imdb.com 提供）、美国西部的电力网络以及秀丽隐杆线虫神经网络[17] 这三个图的 L 和 C。所有这三个图都引起了科学界的兴趣。电影演员合作图是社会网络的代表[18]，具有很容易被细化定义的优势。它也与传统上的、以保罗·埃尔德什为中心的数学合作图相似（部分数据可以在 http://www.acs.oakland.edu/~grossman/erdoshp.html 上获得）。电力网络的图与电力网络的效率和稳定性相关[19]。而秀丽隐杆线虫是完整的神经网络的唯一例子。

Table 1 shows that all three graphs are small-world networks. These examples were not hand-picked; they were chosen because of their inherent interest and because complete wiring diagrams were available. Thus the small-world phenomenon is not merely a curiosity of social networks[13,14] nor an artefact of an idealized model—it is probably generic for many large, sparse networks found in nature.

Table 1. Empirical examples of small-world networks

	L_{actual}	L_{random}	C_{actual}	C_{random}
Film actors	3.65	2.99	0.79	0.00027
Power grid	18.7	12.4	0.080	0.005
C. elegans	2.65	2.25	0.28	0.05

Characteristic path length L and clustering coefficient C for three real networks, compared to random graphs with the same number of vertices (n) and average number of edges per vertex (k). (Actors: $n = 225,226$, $k = 61$. Power grid: $n = 4,941$, $k = 2.67$. C. elegans: $n = 282$, $k = 14$.) The graphs are defined as follows. Two actors are joined by an edge if they have acted in a film together. We restrict attention to the giant connected component[16] of this graph, which includes ~90% of all actors listed in the Internet Movie Database (available at http://us.imdb.com), as of April 1997. For the power grid, vertices represent generators, transformers and substations, and edges represent high-voltage transmission lines between them. For C. elegans, an edge joins two neurons if they are connected by either a synapse or a gap junction. We treat all edges as undirected and unweighted, and all vertices as identical, recognizing that these are crude approximations. All three networks show the small-world phenomenon: $L \gtrsim L_{random}$ but $C \gg C_{random}$.

We now investigate the functional significance of small-world connectivity for dynamical systems. Our test case is a deliberately simplified model for the spread of an infectious disease. The population structure is modelled by the family of graphs described in Fig. 1. At time $t = 0$, a single infective individual is introduced into an otherwise healthy population. Infective individuals are removed permanently (by immunity or death) after a period of sickness that lasts one unit of dimensionless time. During this time, each infective individual can infect each of its healthy neighbours with probability r. On subsequent time steps, the disease spreads along the edges of the graph until it either infects the entire population, or it dies out, having infected some fraction of the population in the process.

Two results emerge. First, the critical infectiousness r_{half}, at which the disease infects half the population, decreases rapidly for small p (Fig. 3a). Second, for a disease that is sufficiently infectious to infect the entire population regardless of its structure, the time $T(p)$ required for global infection resembles the $L(p)$ curve (Fig. 3b). Thus, infectious diseases are predicted to spread much more easily and quickly in a small world; the alarming and less obvious point is how few short cuts are needed to make the world small.

Our model differs in some significant ways from other network models of disease spreading[20-24]. All the models indicate that network structure influences the speed and extent of disease transmission, but our model illuminates the dynamics as an explicit function of structure (Fig. 3), rather than for a few particular topologies, such as random graphs, stars and chains[20-23]. In the work closest to ours, Kretschmar and Morris[24] have shown

表 1 显示所有三个图都是小世界网络。这些例子不是特别挑选出来的；它们之所以被选择是因为它们本身具有吸引力，而且它们的连接完备清晰。因此小世界现象不只是社会网络的奇异现象 [13,14]，也不是一个理想模型的人为性质——它很可能是自然中发现的许多大的、稀疏的网络的普遍现象。

表 1. 小世界网络的实际举例

	$L_{真实}$	$L_{随机}$	$C_{真实}$	$C_{随机}$
电影演员	3.65	2.99	0.79	0.00027
电力网络	18.7	12.4	0.080	0.005
秀丽隐杆线虫	2.65	2.25	0.28	0.05

三个真实网络的特征路径长度 L 和集聚系数 C，与具有相同的顶点数 (n) 及每顶点的平均边数 (k) 的随机图的比较。（电影演员：$n = 225,226$，$k = 61$。电力网络：$n = 4,941$，$k = 2.67$。秀丽隐杆线虫：$n = 282$，$k = 14$。）图的定义如下。两演员如果出演过同一电影，他们即被一边连接。我们仅关注其中的最大连通子集 [16]，其中包含了截至 1997 年 4 月网络电影数据库（源自 http://us.imdb.com）所列出的所有演员的约 90%。对于电力网络，顶点代表发电机、变压器和变电站，边代表他们之间的高压电线。对于秀丽隐杆线虫，如果两神经元通过突触或者缝隙连接相连，则用边将二者连接。我们假设所有的边无方向无加权，所有的顶点都是相同的，所以这只是一种粗糙的近似。所有三个网络显示出小世界现象：$L \geqslant L_{随机}$ 而 $C \gg C_{随机}$。

我们现在来研究以小世界方式连接的动力学系统的功能意义。我们的测试案例是被有意简化的一传染性疾病的传播模型。人口的相互作用结构用图 1 所描述的一系列图给出。在时间 $t = 0$ 时，一感染性个体被引入原本健康的人群。被感染的个体在患病经过一无量纲时间单位后被永久性移除（通过免疫或死亡）。在这段时间内，每个被感染的个体以概率 r 传染每个健康的邻居。在随后的时间段，疾病沿图的边传播直到把疾病传染给所有的人，或者疾病传染一部分人之后消亡。

这里出现了两个结果。首先，考查疾病传染一半人口的临界感染率 $r_{半数}$，在 p 较小时，它迅速减小（图 3a）。其次，无论什么结构，对于足以传染整个人群的疾病，整体感染所需的时间 $T(p)$ 与 $L(p)$ 曲线相似（图 3b）。因此，传染性疾病可能会更容易、更迅速地在小世界中传播；需要注意但不太明显的一点是最少需要多少捷径可以构造这样的小世界。

我们的模型与其他疾病传播的网络模型 [20-24] 有很大程度的不同。其他所有的模型都显示网络结构影响疾病传播的速度和程度，但是我们的模型给出了动力学行为作为结构性质的一个明确函数关系（图 3），而不是只考虑少数的特定拓扑结构，例如随机图、星形网络和链 [20-23]。与我们最接近的研究中，克雷奇马尔和莫里斯 [24] 已

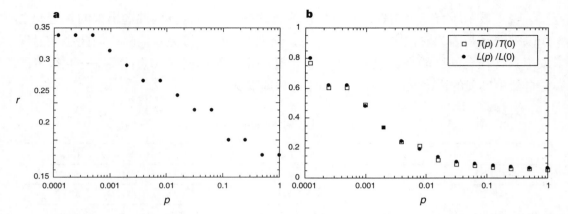

Fig. 3. Simulation results for a simple model of disease spreading. The community structure is given by one realization of the family of randomly rewired graphs used in Fig. 1. **a**, Critical infectiousness r_{half}, at which the disease infects half the population, decreases with p. **b**, The time $T(p)$ required for a maximally infectious disease $(r = 1)$ to spread throughout the entire population has essentially the same functional form as the characteristic path length $L(p)$. Even if only a few per cent of the edges in the original lattice are randomly rewired, the time to global infection is nearly as short as for a random graph.

that increases in the number of concurrent partnerships can significantly accelerate the propagation of a sexually-transmitted disease that spreads along the edges of a graph. All their graphs are disconnected because they fix the average number of partners per person at $k = 1$. An increase in the number of concurrent partnerships causes faster spreading by increasing the number of vertices in the graph's largest connected component. In contrast, all our graphs are connected; hence the predicted changes in the spreading dynamics are due to more subtle structural features than changes in connectedness. Moreover, changes in the number of concurrent partners are obvious to an individual, whereas transitions leading to a smaller world are not.

We have also examined the effect of small-world connectivity on three other dynamical systems. In each case, the elements were coupled according to the family of graphs described in Fig. 1. (1) For cellular automata charged with the computational task of density classification[25], we find that a simple "majority-rule" running on a small-world graph can outperform all known human and genetic algorithm-generated rules running on a ring lattice. (2) For the iterated, multi-player "Prisoner's dilemma"[11] played on a graph, we find that as the fraction of short cuts increases, cooperation is less likely to emerge in a population of players using a generalized "tit-for-tat"[26] strategy. The likelihood of cooperative strategies evolving out of an initial cooperative/non-cooperative mix also decreases with increasing p. (3) Small-world networks of coupled phase oscillators synchronize almost as readily as in the mean-field model[2], despite having orders of magnitude fewer edges. This result may be relevant to the observed synchronization of widely separated neurons in the visual cortex[27] if, as seems plausible, the brain has a small-world architecture.

We hope that our work will stimulate further studies of small-world networks. Their

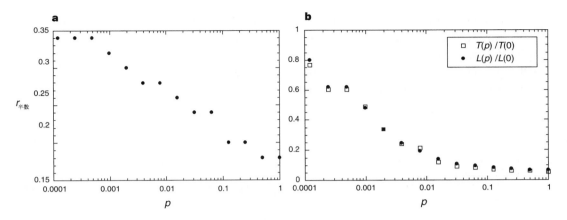

图 3. 一个简单的疾病传播模型的模拟结果。社群结构由图 1 中随机重连图族的一个实现给出。**a**，疾病感染半数人群的临界感染率 $r_{半数}$ 随 p 减小。**b**，最强感染性疾病（$r=1$）传播至整个人群所需的时间 $T(p)$ 具有与特征路径长度 $L(p)$ 相同的函数形式。即使原始晶格网络中只有几个百分比的边被重连，整体感染的时间也与随机图中的一样短。

经指出并行性伴侣关系数目的增加会加速沿图边传播的性疾病的传染。他们所有的图形都是断开的，因为他们设定了每个人的伴侣平均数为 $k=1$。并行性伴侣关系数目的增加会通过增加最大连通集团中顶点的数目引起传播加速。相比而言，我们的图是相连的；因此所预测的传播动态行为上的改变是由于更多的精细结构特征而非连通性的改变。此外，并行性伴侣关系数目的改变对于个体来说影响是明显的，但对整体结构向小世界转变的影响却不明显。

我们也测试了小世界性质在其他三个动态系统中的效应。在每种情况下，元素通过图 1 所描述的系统网络发生耦合。(1) 对于负责密度分类计算的元胞自动机[25]，我们发现一个简单的在小世界图中运行的"多数规则"可以胜过所有已知在环形晶格网络中运行的人为以及遗传算法产生的规则。(2) 对于一个基于网络迭代的、多人的"囚徒困境"[11]，我们发现随捷径数量的增加，运用"以牙还牙"[26]战略的参与者更不容易产生合作。由原始的合作/非合作组合发展产生的合作战略的可行性也随着 p 的增加而降低。(3) 耦合相位振荡的小世界网络的同步几乎与在平均场模型[2]中的一样容易，尽管边的数量少了几个量级。这个结果可能与所观测到的视觉皮层中被广泛分离的神经元的同步性[27]相关，如此看来，大脑似乎也具有小世界体系结构。

我们希望本文可以促进小世界网络更深层次的研究。小世界网络同时具有高聚

distinctive combination of high clustering with short characteristic path length cannot be captured by traditional approximations such as those based on regular lattices or random graphs. Although small-world architecture has not received much attention, we suggest that it will probably turn out to be widespread in biological, social and man-made systems, often with important dynamical consequences.

(**393**, 440-442; 1998)

Duncan J. Watts[*] & **Steven H. Strogatz**

Department of Theoretical and Applied Mechanics, Kimball Hall, Cornell University, Ithaca, New York 14853, USA
[*] Present address: Paul F. Lazarsfeld Center for the Social Sciences, Columbia University, 812 SIPA Building, 420 W118 St, New York, New York 10027, USA.

Received 27 November 1997; accepted 6 April 1998.

References:

1. Winfree, A. T. *The Geometry of Biological Time* (Springer, New York, 1980).

2. Kuramoto, Y. *Chemical Oscillations, Waves, and Turbulence* (Springer, Berlin, 1984).

3. Strogatz, S. H. & Stewart, I. Coupled oscillators and biological synchronization. *Sci. Am.* **269**(6), 102-109 (1993).

4. Bressloff, P. C., Coombes, S. & De Souza, B. Dynamics of a ring of pulse-coupled oscillators: a group theoretic approach. *Phys. Rev. Lett.* **79**, 2791-2794 (1997).

5. Braiman, Y., Lindner, J. F. & Ditto, W. L. Taming spatiotemporal chaos with disorder. *Nature* **378**, 465-467 (1995).

6. Wiesenfeld, K. New results on frequency-locking dynamics of disordered Josephson arrays. *Physica B* **222**, 315-319 (1996).

7. Gerhardt, M., Schuster, H. & Tyson, J. J. A cellular automaton model of excitable media including curvature and dispersion. *Science* **247**, 1563-1566 (1990).

8. Collins, J. J., Chow, C. C. & Imhoff, T. T. Stochastic resonance without tuning. *Nature* **376**, 236-238 (1995).

9. Hopfield, J. J. & Herz, A. V. M. Rapid local synchronization of action potentials: Toward computation with coupled integrate-and-fire neurons. *Proc. Natl Acad. Sci. USA* **92**, 6655-6662 (1995).

10. Abbott, L. F. & van Vreeswijk, C. Asynchronous states in neural networks of pulse-coupled oscillators. *Phys. Rev. E* **48**(2), 1483-1490 (1993).

11. Nowak, M. A. & May, R. M. Evolutionary games and spatial chaos. *Nature* **359**, 826-829 (1992).

12. Kauffman, S. A. Metabolic stability and epigenesis in randomly constructed genetic nets. *J. Theor. Biol.* **22**, 437-467 (1969).

13. Milgram, S. The small world problem. *Psychol. Today* **2**, 60-67 (1967).

14. Kochen, M. (ed.) *The Small World* (Ablex, Norwood, NJ, 1989).

15. Guare, J. *Six Degrees of Separation: A Play* (Vintage Books, New York, 1990).

16. Bollabás, B. *Random Graphs* (Academic, London, 1985).

17. Achacoso, T. B. & Yamamoto, W. S. *AY's Neuroanatomy of C. elegans for Computation* (CRC Press, Boca Raton, FL, 1992).

18. Wasserman, S. & Faust, K. *Social Network Analysis: Methods and Applications* (Cambridge Univ. Press, 1994).

19. Phadke, A. G. & Thorp, J. S. *Computer Relaying for Power Systems* (Wiley, New York, 1988).

20. Sattenspiel, L. & Simon, C. P. The spread and persistence of infectious diseases in structured populations. *Math. Biosci.* **90**, 341-366 (1988).

21. Longini, I. M. Jr A mathematical model for predicting the geographic spread of new infectious agents. *Math. Biosci.* **90**, 367-383 (1988).

22. Hess, G. Disease in metapopulation models: implications for conservation. *Ecology* **77**, 1617-1632 (1996).

23. Blythe, S. P., Castillo-Chavez, C. & Palmer, J. S. Toward a unified theory of sexual mixing and pair formation. *Math. Biosci.* **107**, 379-405 (1991).

24. Kretschmar, M. & Morris, M. Measures of concurrency in networks and the spread of infectious disease. *Math. Biosci.* **133**, 165-195 (1996).

25. Das, R., Mitchell, M. & Crutchfield, J. P. in *Parallel Problem Solving from Nature* (eds Davido, Y., Schwefel, H.-P. & Männer, R.) 344-353 (Lecture Notes in Computer Science 866, Springer, Berlin, 1994).

26. Axelrod, R. *The Evolution of Cooperation* (Basic Books, New York, 1984).

27. Gray, C. M., König, P., Engel, A. K. & Singer, W. Oscillatory responses in cat visual cortex exhibit intercolumnar synchronization which reflects global stimulus properties. *Nature* **338**, 334-337 (1989).

Acknowledgements. We thank B. Tjaden for providing the film actor data, and J. Thorp and K. Bae for the Western States Power Grid data. This work was supported by the US National Science Foundation (Division of Mathematical Sciences).

Correspondence and requests for materials should be addressed to D.J.W. (e-mail: djw24@columbia.edu).

集度与短特征路径长度的独特特征，不能用传统的近似方法例如基于规则晶格网络或者随机图的方法来获得。尽管小世界体系结构还没有引起很大的关注，我们推测它将在生物、社会以及人工系统等广泛存在，并且通常对系统的动力学行为有重要的影响。

（崔宁 翻译；狄增如 审稿）

Deciphering the Biology of *Mycobacterium tuberculosis* from the Complete Genome Sequence

S. T. Cole *et al.*

Editor's Note

This paper reveals the complete genome sequence of the tuberculosis-causing bacterium *Mycobacterium tuberculosis*. The genome, which contains over 4 million base pairs and around 4,000 genes, provides a sequence of every potential drug target and every possible antigen that could be used in a vaccine, making it of huge importance. The data, collected by microbial scientist Stewart T. Cole and colleagues, also shed light on the bacterium's basic biology. For example, the genome contains many genes involved in lipid metabolism, thought to encode the bacterium's complex cell wall. And two new families of proteins are thought to represent a possible source of antigenic variation, perhaps explaining how the pathogen alters its surface proteins to evade the host's immune response.

Countless millions of people have died from tuberculosis, a chronic infectious disease caused by the tubercle bacillus. The complete genome sequence of the best-characterized strain of *Mycobacterium tuberculosis*, H37Rv, has been determined and analysed in order to improve our understanding of the biology of this slow-growing pathogen and to help the conception of new prophylactic and therapeutic interventions. The genome comprises 4,411,529 base pairs, contains around 4,000 genes, and has a very high guanine+cytosine content that is reflected in the biased amino-acid content of the proteins. *M. tuberculosis* differs radically from other bacteria in that a very large portion of its coding capacity is devoted to the production of enzymes involved in lipogenesis and lipolysis, and to two new families of glycine-rich proteins with a repetitive structure that may represent a source of antigenic variation.

DESPITE the availability of effective short-course chemotherapy (DOTS) and the Bacille Calmette-Guérin (BCG) vaccine, the tubercle bacillus continues to claim more lives than any other single infectious agent[1]. Recent years have seen increased incidence of tuberculosis in both developing and industrialized countries, the widespread emergence of drug-resistant strains and a deadly synergy with the human immunodeficiency virus (HIV). In 1993, the gravity of the situation led the World Health Organisation (WHO) to declare tuberculosis a global emergency in an attempt to heighten public and political awareness. Radical measures are needed now to prevent the grim predictions of the WHO becoming reality. The combination of genomics and bioinformatics has the potential to generate the information and knowledge that will

根据全基因组序列破译结核分枝杆菌生物学

这篇文章揭示了引起结核病的细菌——结核分枝杆菌的完整基因组序列。该基因组包含超过 400 万个碱基对和大约 4,000 个基因，为每个潜在的药物靶标和每个可能用于生产疫苗的抗原提供了序列，这使得该基因组的序列尤为重要。由微生物学家斯图尔特·科尔及其同事收集的数据也揭示了该细菌的基本生物学特性。例如，该基因组包含很多参与脂类代谢的基因，这些基因被认为编码细菌复杂的细胞壁。两个新蛋白家族被认为代表了抗原变异的可能来源，这也许能解释病原体是如何改变自身表面蛋白来躲避宿主的免疫反应。

数以百万计的人死于肺结核——一种由结核杆菌引起的慢性传染病。目前研究最清楚的结核分枝杆菌菌株 H37Rv 的完整基因组序列已完成测序和分析，有助于增加我们对这种生长缓慢的病原菌的生物学理解，帮助我们研发新的预防和治疗干预措施。该基因组由 4,411,529 个碱基对组成，包含约 4,000 个基因，鸟嘌呤 + 胞嘧啶含量很高，这在蛋白质的氨基酸含量偏倚上有所反映。结核分枝杆菌与其他细菌的根本不同之处在于，它很大一部分编码能力用于编码脂肪合成和分解的酶，以及两个富含甘氨酸且有重复性结构的蛋白新家族，这两个家族可能是抗原变异的来源。

尽管已有有效的短程化疗（DOTS）和卡介苗（BCG）疫苗可用，相比其他单一传染源，结核杆菌仍然夺走更多人的生命[1]。近年来，结核病发病率在发展中国家和工业化国家都呈上升趋势，耐药菌株普遍出现，并且与人类免疫缺陷病毒（HIV）共同形成致命的双重感染。1993 年，由于势态严重，世界卫生组织（WHO）宣布结核病为全球紧急事件，试图提高公众意识和政治意识。现在需要严格的措施防止世界卫生组织残酷的预言成为现实。基因组学和生物信息学的结合，有望产生新信息和新知识，构思和开发针对该空气传播疾病的新疗法及干预措施，并阐明其病原

enable the conception and development of new therapies and interventions needed to treat this airborne disease and to elucidate the unusual biology of its aetiological agent, *Mycobacterium tuberculosis*.

The characteristic features of the tubercle bacillus include its slow growth, dormancy, complex cell envelope, intracellular pathogenesis and genetic homogeneity[2]. The generation time of *M. tuberculosis*, in synthetic medium or infected animals, is typically ~24 hours. This contributes to the chronic nature of the disease, imposes lengthy treatment regimens and represents a formidable obstacle for researchers. The state of dormancy in which the bacillus remains quiescent within infected tissue may reflect metabolic shutdown resulting from the action of a cell-mediated immune response that can contain but not eradicate the infection. As immunity wanes, through ageing or immune suppression, the dormant bacteria reactivate, causing an outbreak of disease often many decades after the initial infection[3]. The molecular basis of dormancy and reactivation remains obscure but is expected to be genetically programmed and to involve intracellular signalling pathways.

The cell envelope of *M. tuberculosis*, a Gram-positive bacterium with a G+C-rich genome, contains an additional layer beyond the peptidoglycan that is exceptionally rich in unusual lipids, glycolipids and polysaccharides[4,5]. Novel biosynthetic pathways generate cell-wall components such as mycolic acids, mycocerosic acid, phenolthiocerol, lipoarabinomannan and arabinogalactan, and several of these may contribute to mycobacterial longevity, trigger inflammatory host reactions and act in pathogenesis. Little is known about the mechanisms involved in life within the macrophage, or the extent and nature of the virulence factors produced by the bacillus and their contribution to disease.

It is thought that the progenitor of the *M. tuberculosis* complex, comprising *M. tuberculosis*, *M. bovis*, *M. bovis* BCG, *M. africanum* and *M. microti*, arose from a soil bacterium and that the human bacillus may have been derived from the bovine form following the domestication of cattle. The complex lacks interstrain genetic diversity, and nucleotide changes are very rare[6]. This is important in terms of immunity and vaccine development as most of the proteins will be identical in all strains and therefore antigenic drift will be restricted. On the basis of the systematic sequence analysis of 26 loci in a large number of independent isolates[6], it was concluded that the genome of *M. tuberculosis* is either unusually inert or that the organism is relatively young in evolutionary terms.

Since its isolation in 1905, the H37Rv strain of *M. tuberculosis* has found extensive, worldwide application in biomedical research because it has retained full virulence in animal models of tuberculosis, unlike some clinical isolates; it is also susceptible to drugs and amenable to genetic manipulation. An integrated map of the 4.4 megabase (Mb) circular chromosome of this slow-growing pathogen had been established previously and ordered libraries of cosmids and bacterial artificial chromosomes (BACs) were available[7,8].

216

体——结核分枝杆菌独特的生物学机理。

结核杆菌的典型特征包括生长缓慢、休眠、细胞被膜复杂、胞内发病和遗传同质性[2]。在合成培养基或感染的动物中，结核分枝杆菌的代时通常约为 24 小时。这导致这种病本质上是慢性的，必须采取长期的治疗方案，对研究者而言也是一个严重障碍。休眠状态下的结核杆菌在感染组织内保持静态，这可能反映了细胞介导的免疫反应导致了代谢的关闭，这些免疫反应只能抑制感染但不能消除感染。伴随着衰老或免疫抑制引起的免疫力减弱，休眠状态的细菌再次活化，导致疾病通常在最初感染的几十年后爆发[3]。休眠和再次活化的分子基础仍然不清楚，但预计受到遗传调控并且涉及细胞内的信号通路。

结核分枝杆菌是革兰氏阳性细菌，基因组富含 G+C，它的细胞被膜在肽聚糖外还有另外一层，这一层中的罕见脂、糖脂和多糖极其丰富[4,5]。新的生物合成途径产生细胞壁组分，如分枝菌酸、结核蜡酸、苯酚硫代醇、脂阿拉伯甘露聚糖和阿拉伯半乳糖，其中一些可能有助于结核杆菌长期存活，引发宿主炎症反应，并且在致病中发挥作用。目前对它在巨噬细胞内的生存机制了解甚少，对杆菌产生的毒力因子的水平和本质以及它们对疾病的作用也知之甚少。

结核分枝杆菌复合群包含结核分枝杆菌、牛型分枝杆菌、牛型分枝杆菌卡介苗、非洲分枝杆菌和田鼠分枝杆菌，其祖先被认为源自土壤细菌，而人型杆菌可能是在牛驯化后来源于牛型分枝杆菌。复合群菌株缺乏菌株间的遗传多样性，核苷酸变化非常少[6]。就免疫和疫苗研发来说这一点很重要，因为大多数蛋白质在所有菌株中完全相同，所以抗原漂移会受限。基于对大量独立分离株的 26 个位点进行系统序列分析[6]得出的结论是结核分枝杆菌的基因组要么异常不活跃，要么该生物在进化上相对年轻。

自1905 年分离到结核分枝杆菌的 H37Rv 菌株，该菌株已在世界范围的生物医学研究中得到了深入的应用，因为它在肺结核动物模型中保留了全部的毒力，这与有些临床菌株不同；并且它还对药物敏感，易于遗传操作。我们已经建立了该生长缓慢的病原菌的 4.4 Mb 环状染色体的整合图谱，并且规则排序的黏粒和细菌人工染色体（BACs）文库也已建好[7,8]。

Organization and Sequence of the Genome

Sequence analysis. To obtain the contiguous genome sequence, a combined approach was used that involved the systematic sequence analysis of selected large-insert clones (cosmids and BACs) as well as random small-insert clones from a whole-genome shotgun library. This culminated in a composite sequence of 4,411,529 base pairs (bp) (Figs 1, 2; Editorial note: Figure 2, showing a linear map of the chromosome of *M. tuberculosis* H37Rv, was originally included as a fold-out insert. For details, see http://www.sanger.ac.uk/resources/downloads/bacteria/mycobacterium.html), with a G+C content of 65.6%. This represents the second-largest bacterial genome sequence currently available (after that of *Escherichia coli*)[9]. The initiation codon for the *dnaA* gene, a hallmark for the origin of replication, *oriC*, was chosen as the start point for numbering. The genome is rich in repetitive DNA, particularly insertion sequences, and in new multigene families and duplicated housekeeping genes. The G+C content is relatively constant throughout the genome (Fig. 1) indicating that horizontally transferred pathogenicity islands of atypical base composition are probably absent. Several regions showing higher than average G+C content (Fig. 1) were detected; these correspond to sequences belonging to a large gene family that includes the polymorphic G+C-rich sequences (PGRSs).

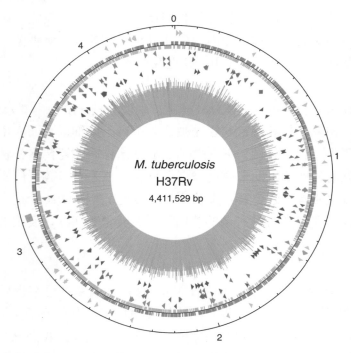

Fig. 1. Circular map of the chromosome of *M. tuberculosis* H37Rv. The outer circle shows the scale in Mb, with 0 representing the origin of replication. The first ring from the exterior denotes the positions of stable RNA genes (tRNAs are blue, others are pink) and the direct repeat region (pink cube); the second ring inwards shows the coding sequence by strand (clockwise, dark green; anticlockwise, light green); the third ring depicts repetitive DNA (insertion sequences, orange; 13E12 REP family, dark pink; prophage, blue);

基因组结构和序列

序列分析 为得到连续的基因组序列，我们采取了一个组合方法，这个方法包括对选定的大插入片段克隆（黏粒和 BACs）和一个全基因组鸟枪文库的随机小插入片段克隆进行系统的序列分析。最终得到 4,411,529 个碱基对（bp）的组合序列（图 1 和图 2；编者注：图 2 显示了结核分枝杆菌 H37Rv 染色体的线性图谱，在原文中是一个折叠插入图。更多的细节请看 http://www.sanger. ac.uk/resources/downloads/bacteria/mycobacterium.html），其中 G+C 含量为 65.6%。这是目前已有的第二大细菌基因组序列（在大肠杆菌之后）[9]。*dnaA* 基因的起始密码子，复制起始位点的标志 *oriC* 被选定为编码的起点。该基因组富含重复 NDA 序列，特别是插入序列，以及新的多基因家族和重复的管家基因。G+C 含量在整个基因组中相对恒定（图 1），这表明可能没有横向转移来的具有非典型碱基组成的致病岛。我们检测到几个 G+C 含量高于平均水平的区域（图 1）；它们对应属于同一个大基因家族的序列，这些序列富含 G+C 且具有多态性（PGRS）。

图 1. 结核分枝杆菌 H37Rv 染色体的环形图。外环单位的刻度为 Mb，0 代表复制起点。从外侧数第一环表示稳定 RNA 基因的位置（tRNA 是蓝色的，其他是粉红色）和正向重复区域（粉红条）；向内第二环按链表示编码序列（顺时针，暗绿色；逆时针，浅绿色）；第三环表示重复 DNA（插入序列，橙色；13E12 REP 家族，深粉色；原噬菌体，蓝色）；第四环表示 PPE 家族成员的位置（绿色）；第五环表示

the fourth ring shows the positions of the PPE family members (green); the fifth ring shows the PE family members (purple, excluding PGRS); and the sixth ring shows the positions of the PGRS sequences (dark red). The histogram (centre) represents G+C content, with < 65% G+C in yellow, and > 65% G+C in red. The figure was generated with software from DNASTAR.

Genes for stable RNA. Fifty genes coding for functional RNA molecules were found. These molecules were the three species produced by the unique ribosomal RNA operon, the 10Sa RNA involved in degradation of proteins encoded by abnormal messenger RNA, the RNA component of RNase P, and 45 transfer RNAs. No 4.5S RNA could be detected. The *rrn* operon is situated unusually as it occurs about 1,500 kilobases (kb) from the putative *oriC*; most eubacteria have one or more *rrn* operons near to *oriC* to exploit the gene-dosage effect obtained during replication[10]. This arrangement may be related to the slow growth of *M. tuberculosis*. The genes encoding tRNAs that recognize 43 of the 61 possible sense codons were distributed throughout the genome and, with one exception, none of these uses A in the first position of the anticodon, indicating that extensive wobble occurs during translation. This is consistent with the high G+C content of the genome and the consequent bias in codon usage. Three genes encoding tRNAs for methionine were found; one of these genes (*metV*) is situated in a region that may correspond to the terminus of replication (Figs 1, 2). As *metV* is linked to defective genes for integrase and excisionase, perhaps it was once part of a phage or similar mobile genetic element.

Insertion sequences and prophages. Sixteen copies of the promiscuous insertion sequence IS*6110* and six copies of the more stable element IS*1081* reside within the genome of H37Rv[8]. One copy of IS*1081* is truncated. Scrutiny of the genomic sequence led to the identification of a further 32 different insertion sequence elements, most of which have not been described previously, and of the 13E12 family of repetitive sequences which exhibit some of the characteristics of mobile genetic elements (Fig. 1). The newly discovered insertion sequences belong mainly to the IS*3* and IS*256* families, although six of them define a new group. There is extensive similarity between IS*1561* and IS*1552* with insertion sequence elements found in *Nocardia* and *Rhodococcus* spp., suggesting that they may be widely disseminated among the actinomycetes.

Most of the insertion sequences in *M. tuberculosis* H37Rv appear to have inserted in intergenic or non-coding regions, often near tRNA genes (Fig. 1). Many are clustered, suggesting the existence of insertional hot-spots that prevent genes from being inactivated, as has been described for *Rhizobium*[11]. The chromosomal distribution of the insertion sequences is informative as there appears to have been a selection against insertions in the quadrant encompassing *oriC* and an overrepresentation in the direct repeat region that contains the prototype IS*6110*. This bias was also observed experimentally in a transposon mutagenesis study[12].

At least two prophages have been detected in the genome sequence and their presence may explain why *M. tuberculosis* shows persistent low-level lysis in culture. Prophages phiRv1 and phiRv2 are both ~10 kb in length and are similarly organized, and some of their

PE 家族成员（紫色，除 PGRS 外）；第六环表示 PGRS 序列的位置（暗红色）。柱状图（中心）代表 G+C 含量，＜65% 的 G+C 含量为黄色，＞65% 的 G+C 含量为红色。此图使用软件 DNASTAR 生成。

编码稳定 RNA 的基因 我们发现了 50 个编码功能性 RNA 分子的基因。这些分子分别是：由独特的核糖体 RNA 操纵子产生的三类分子、参与降解异常信使 RNA 所编码的蛋白质的 10Sa RNA、核糖核酸酶 P（RNase P）的 RNA 组分和 45 个转运 RNA 分子。没有检测到 4.5S RNA。*rrn* 操纵子的位置异常，因为它距假定的 *oriC* 1,500 kb；大多数真细菌在 *oriC* 附近有一个或多个 *rrn* 操纵子，从而利用复制期间得到的基因剂量效应 [10]。这种排列可能与结核分枝杆菌生长缓慢有关。编码 tRNA 的基因分布在基因组中，能识别分散在基因组中 61 个可能的有义密码子中的 43 个，但有一个例外，所有反密码子的第一位都不用 A，表明翻译过程中摆动广泛存在。这与基因组中 G+C 含量高及其导致的密码子偏好相符。我们发现了三个甲硫氨酸 tRNA 编码基因；其中一个基因（*metV*）位于可能对应复制终点的区域（图 1 和图 2）。*metV* 与整合酶和切除酶的缺陷基因相关，或许它曾经是噬菌体或相似的可移动遗传元件的一部分。

插入序列和原噬菌体 H37Rv 基因组中有 16 个拷贝的混杂的 IS*6110* 插入序列和 6 个拷贝的较稳定的 IS*1081* 元件 [8]。其中一个 IS*1081* 拷贝是截短的。仔细查看基因组序列又进一步鉴定了 32 个不同的插入序列元件，其中大部分以前没有描述过，另外还鉴定了 13E12 家族重复序列，该序列具有可移动遗传元件的某些特征（图 1）。新发现的插入序列大多属于 IS*3* 和 IS*256* 家族，但其中 6 个定义了一个新的种类。IS*1561* 和 IS*1552* 与诺卡氏菌属和红球菌属中发现的插入序列元件有广泛的相似性，这表明它们可能在放线菌中广泛传播。

结核分枝杆菌 H37Rv 中的大多数插入序列似乎插到了基因间区或非编码区，通常靠近 tRNA 基因（图 1）。许多插入序列聚集成簇，意味着存在插入热点以防止基因被灭活，这与根瘤菌中所描述的类似 [11]。插入序列在染色体上的分布可以提供有用的信息，因为似乎存在某种选择避免插入到 *oriC* 周围四分之一的区域，并且插入序列似乎在包含 IS*6110* 原型的正向重复区域中出现次数过多。这种倾向在一个研究转座子突变的实验中发现过 [12]。

在基因组序列中至少发现了两个原噬菌体，它们的存在可能解释了为什么结核分枝杆菌在培养中存在持续低水平裂解。原噬菌体 phiRv1 和 phiRv2 长度都约为 10 kb，结构相似，并且它们的一些基因产物与链霉菌和腐生分枝杆菌编码的产物有显著的

gene products show marked similarity to those encoded by certain bacteriophages from *Streptomyces* and saprophytic mycobacteria. The site of insertion of phiRv1 is intriguing as it corresponds to part of a repetitive sequence of the 13E12 family that itself appears to have integrated into the biotin operon. Some strains of *M. tuberculosis* have been described as requiring biotin as a growth supplement, indicating either that phiRv1 has a polar effect on expression of the distal *bio* genes or that aberrant excision, leading to mutation, may occur. During the serial attenuation of *M. bovis* that led to the vaccine strain *M. bovis* BCG, the phiRv1 prophage was lost[13]. In a systematic study of the genomic diversity of prophages and insertion sequences (S.V.G. *et al.*, manuscript in preparation), only IS*1532* exhibited significant variability, indicating that most of the prophages and insertion sequences are currently stable. However, from these combined observations, one can conclude that horizontal transfer of genetic material into the free-living ancestor of the *M. tuberculosis* complex probably occurred in nature before the tubercle bacillus adopted its specialized intracellular niche.

Genes encoding proteins. 3,924 open reading frames were identified in the genome (see Methods), accounting for ~91% of the potential coding capacity (Figs 1, 2). A few of these genes appear to have in-frame stop codons or frameshift mutations (irrespective of the source of the DNA sequenced) and may either use frameshifting during translation or correspond to pseudogenes. Consistent with the high G+C content of the genome, GTG initiation codons (35%) are used more frequently than in *Bacillus subtilis* (9%) and *E. coli* (14%), although ATG (61%) is the most common translational start. There are a few examples of atypical initiation codons, the most notable being the ATC used by *infC*, which begins with ATT in both *B. subtilis* and *E. coli* [9,14]. There is a slight bias in the orientation of the genes (Fig. 1) with respect to the direction of replication as ~59% are transcribed with the same polarity as replication, compared with 75% in *B. subtilis*. In other bacteria, genes transcribed in the same direction as the replication forks are believed to be expressed more efficiently[9,14]. Again, the more even distribution in gene polarity seen in *M. tuberculosis* may reflect the slow growth and infrequent replication cycles. Three genes (*dnaB*, *recA* and Rv1461) have been invaded by sequences encoding inteins (protein introns) and in all three cases their counterparts in *M. leprae* also contain inteins, but at different sites[15] (S.T.C. *et al.*, unpublished observations).

Protein function, composition and duplication. By using various database comparisons, we attributed precise functions to ~40% of the predicted proteins and found some information or similarity for another 44%. The remaining 16% resembled no known proteins and may account for specific mycobacterial functions. Examination of the amino-acid composition of the *M. tuberculosis* proteome by correspondence analysis[16], and comparison with that of other microorganisms whose genome sequences are available, revealed a statistically significant preference for the amino acids Ala, Gly, Pro, Arg and Trp, which are all encoded by G+C-rich codons, and a comparative reduction in the use of amino acids encoded by A+T-rich codons such as Asn, Ile, Lys, Phe and Tyr (Fig. 3). This approach also identified two groups of proteins rich in Asn or Gly that belong to new families, PE and PPE (see below). The fraction of the proteome that has arisen through gene

相似性。phiRv1 的插入位点很有趣，因为它与 13E12 家族的一段重复序列对应，这段序列本身似乎已经整合到生物素操纵子中。有一些结核分枝杆菌菌株被描述为需要生物素作为生长补充，这说明要么 phiRv1 对远端 bio 基因的表达有极性效应，要么可能发生了异常切除，导致基因突变。在牛型分枝杆菌连续衰减产生牛型分枝杆菌卡介苗疫苗株的过程中，phiRv1 原噬菌体丢失[13]。对原噬菌体基因组多样性和插入序列的系统研究（戈登等，稿件准备中）显示，只有 IS1532 显示出显著变化，这表明大多数原噬菌体和插入序列目前处于稳定状态。但是，综合这些观察结果我们可以得出结论，遗传物质向营自由生活的结核分枝杆菌复合群祖先发生水平转移，实际上很可能发生在结核菌采用它独特的细胞内生活方式之前。

基因编码蛋白　从基因组中鉴定到 3,924 个开放读码框（见方法），约占潜在编码能力的 91%（图 1 和图 2）。其中少数基因似乎有读码框内终止密码子或移码突变（不考虑测序 DNA 的来源），这些基因可能在翻译过程中有移码，或是假基因的转录产物。与基因组高 G+C 含量一致，GTG 起始密码子的使用频率（35%）高于枯草芽孢杆菌（9%）和大肠杆菌（14%），尽管 ATG 在翻译起始最常见（61%）。这里有少数非典型起始密码子的例子，最值得注意的是 infC 使用 ATC，而在枯草芽孢杆菌和大肠杆菌中则都使用 ATT[9,14]。相对于复制方向，基因定位有轻微偏好（图 1），约 59% 的转录方向与复制方向相同，而枯草芽孢杆菌中为 75%。在其他细菌中，基因转录与复制叉方向相同并可以更高效地表达[9,14]。同样，结核分枝杆菌基因极性分布更均衡，这可以反映出其生长缓慢和复制周期稀少。三个基因（dnaB、recA 和 Rv1461）都有内含肽（蛋白内含子）编码序列插入，并且这三个基因在麻风分枝杆菌中的同源基因也都包含内含肽，只是插入位点不同[15]（科尔等，未发表的观察结果）。

蛋白质功能、组成和复制　通过使用各种数据库进行比较，我们对约 40% 的预测蛋白的功能有了精确的注释，另外也发现了其他 44% 的蛋白质的一些信息或相似性。其余的 16% 与已知蛋白质没有相似性，可能负责特定的结核杆菌功能。通过对应分析检查结核分枝杆菌的蛋白质组的氨基酸组成[16]，并与其他基因组序列可用的微生物进行比较，统计上显示结核分枝杆菌显著偏好丙氨酸（Ala）、甘氨酸（Gly）、脯氨酸（Pro）、精氨酸（Arg）和色氨酸（Trp）等，这些氨基酸均由富含 G+C 的密码子编码，相对少使用富含 A+T 的密码子编码的氨基酸，如天冬酰胺（Asn）、异亮氨酸（Ile）、赖氨酸（Lys）、苯丙氨酸（Phe）和酪氨酸（Tyr）（见图 3）。这种方法还发现了两组富含天冬酰胺（Asn）或甘氨酸（Gly）的蛋白质新家族，PE 和 PPE（见

duplication is similar to that seen in *E. coli* or *B. subtilis* (~51%; refs 9, 14), except that the level of sequence conservation is considerably higher, indicating that there may be extensive redundancy or differential production of the corresponding polypeptides. The apparent lack of divergence following gene duplication is consistent with the hypothesis that *M. tuberculosis* is of recent descent[6].

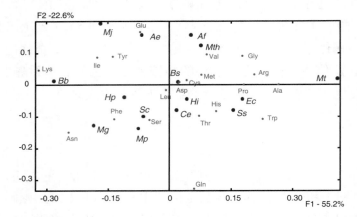

Fig. 3. Correspondence analysis of the proteomes from extensively sequenced organisms as a function of amino-acid composition. Note the extreme position of *M. tuberculosis* and the shift in amino-acid preference reflecting increasing G+C content from left to right. Abbreviations used: *Ae, Aquifex aeolicus*; *Af, Archaeoglobus fulgidis*; *Bb, Borrelia burgdorfei*; *Bs, B. subtilis*; *Ce, Caenorhabditis elegans*; *Ec, E. coli*; *Hi, Haemophilus influenzae*; *Hp, Helicobacter pylori*; *Mg, Mycoplasma genitalium*; *Mj, Methanococcus jannaschi*; *Mp, Mycoplasma pneumoniae*; *Mt, M. tuberculosis*; *Mth, Methanobacterium thermoautotrophicum*; *Sc, Saccharomyces cerevisiae*; *Ss, Synechocystis* sp. strain PCC6803. F1 and F2, first and second factorial axes[16].

General Metabolism, Regulation and Drug Resistance

Metabolic pathways. From the genome sequence, it is clear that the tubercle bacillus has the potential to synthesize all the essential amino acids, vitamins and enzyme co-factors, although some of the pathways involved may differ from those found in other bacteria. *M. tuberculosis* can metabolize a variety of carbohydrates, hydrocarbons, alcohols, ketones and carboxylic acids[2,17]. It is apparent from genome inspection that, in addition to many functions involved in lipid metabolism, the enzymes necessary for glycolysis, the pentose phosphate pathway, and the tricarboxylic acid and glyoxylate cycles are all present. A large number (~200) of oxidoreductases, oxygenases and dehydrogenases is predicted, as well as many oxygenases containing cytochrome P450, that are similar to fungal proteins involved in sterol degradation. Under aerobic growth conditions, ATP will be generated by oxidative phosphorylation from electron transport chains involving a ubiquinone cytochrome *b* reductase complex and cytochrome *c* oxidase. Components of several anaerobic phosphorylative electron transport chains are also present, including genes for nitrate reductase (*narGHJI*), fumarate reductase (*frdABCD*) and possibly nitrite reductase (*nirBD*), as well as a new reductase (*narX*) that results from a rearrangement of a homologue of the *narGHJI* operon. Two genes encoding haemoglobin-like proteins,

下文）。通过基因复制蛋白质组的比例升高，与大肠杆菌或枯草杆菌相似（大约51%；参考文献9和14），但序列的保守水平要高很多，这表明相应的多肽可能存在大量冗余或差异化表达。基因复制后明显缺少分化，这与结核分枝杆菌在进化上属于近代物种的假说是一致的[6]。

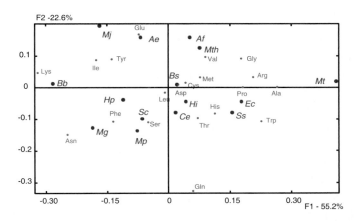

图3. 大量测序的有机蛋白质组作为氨基酸组成的函数的对应分析。注意结核分枝杆菌的极端位置和氨基酸偏好的改变，该改变反映了G+C含量由左至右增加。缩写的使用：*Ae*，风产液菌；*Af*，闪亮古生球菌；*Bb*，伯氏疏螺旋体；*Bs*，枯草芽孢杆菌；*Ce*，秀丽隐杆线虫；*Ec*，大肠杆菌；*Hi*，流感嗜血杆菌；*Hp*，幽门螺杆菌；*Mg*，生殖支原体；*Mj*，詹氏甲烷球菌；*Mp*，肺炎支原体；*Mt*，结核分枝杆菌；*Mth*，嗜热自养甲烷杆菌；*Sc*，酿酒酵母；*Ss*，集胞藻 PCC6803 菌株。F1 和 F2，第一和第二因子轴[16]。

基本代谢、调控及耐药性

代谢途径 从基因组序列可以清楚地看到，尽管结核杆菌一些途径可能不同于在其他细菌中发现的途径，但它有能力合成所有必需氨基酸、维生素和辅酶。结核分枝杆菌可以代谢多种碳水化合物、烃、醇、酮和羧酸[2,17]。基因组检测清楚地显示，除了脂代谢的许多功能，糖酵解、戊糖磷酸途径、三羧酸和乙醛酸循环等所必需的酶也都存在。预测有大量（约 200 种）的氧化还原酶、氧化酶和脱氢酶，还有许多含有细胞色素 P450 的氧化酶，它们和参与固醇降解的真菌蛋白类似。有氧生长条件下，通过电子传递链包括泛醌–细胞色素 *b* 还原酶复合体和细胞色素 *c* 氧化酶，氧化磷酸化产生腺苷三磷酸（ATP）。还存在几个厌氧磷酸化电子传递链组分，这包括硝酸还原酶基因（*narGHJI*）、富马酸还原酶基因（*frdABCD*），可能还有亚硝酸盐还原酶基因（*nirBD*），另外还有一个新的还原酶基因（*narX*），它可能由一个与 *narGHJI* 操纵子同源的基因重排而来。我们还发现两个血红蛋白类似蛋白的编码基因，可能防

which may protect against oxidative stress or be involved in oxygen capture, were found. The ability of the bacillus to adapt its metabolism to environmental change is significant as it not only has to compete with the lung for oxygen but must also adapt to the microaerophilic/anaerobic environment at the heart of the burgeoning granuloma.

Regulation and signal transduction. Given the complexity of the environmental and metabolic choices facing *M. tuberculosis*, an extensive regulatory repertoire was expected. Thirteen putative sigma factors govern gene expression at the level of transcription initiation, and more than 100 regulatory proteins are predicted (Table 1)(Editorial note: this large table, giving a functional classification of all protein-coding genes in *M. tuberculosis*, has been omitted in this edited version. Note that the original version published in *Nature* contained errors, which were corrected in an erratum in *Nature* **396**, 190–198 (1998)). Unlike *B. subtilis* and *E. coli*, in which there are > 30 copies of different two-component regulatory systems[14], *M. tuberculosis* has only 11 complete pairs of sensor histidine kinases and response regulators, and a few isolated kinase and regulatory genes. This relative paucity in environmental signal transduction pathways is probably offset by the presence of a family of eukaryotic-like serine/threonine protein kinases (STPKs), which function as part of a phosphorelay system[18]. The STPKs probably have two domains: the well-conserved kinase domain at the amino terminus is predicted to be connected by a transmembrane segment to the carboxy-terminal region that may respond to specific stimuli. Several of the predicted envelope lipoproteins, such as that encoded by *lppR* (Rv2403), show extensive similarity to this putative receptor domain of STPKs, suggesting possible interplay. The STPKs probably function in signal transduction pathways and may govern important cellular decisions such as dormancy and cell division, and although their partners are unknown, candidate genes for phosphoprotein phosphatases have been identified.

Drug resistance. *M. tuberculosis* is naturally resistant to many antibiotics, making treatment difficult[19]. This resistance is due mainly to the highly hydrophobic cell envelope acting as a permeability barrier[4], but many potential resistance determinants are also encoded in the genome. These include hydrolytic or drug-modifying enzymes such as β-lactamases and aminoglycoside acetyl transferases, and many potential drug–efflux systems, such as 14 members of the major facilitator family and numerous ABC transporters. Knowledge of these putative resistance mechanisms will promote better use of existing drugs and facilitate the conception of new therapies.

Lipid Metabolism

Very few organisms produce such a diverse array of lipophilic molecules as *M. tuberculosis*. These molecules range from simple fatty acids such as palmitate and tuberculostearate, through isoprenoids, to very-long-chain, highly complex molecules such as mycolic acids and the phenolphthiocerol alcohols that esterify with mycocerosic acid to form the scaffold for attachment of the mycosides. Mycobacteria contain examples of every known lipid and

御氧化应激或参与氧捕获。结核分枝杆菌的代谢适应环境变化的能力很有意义，因为它不仅要和肺竞争氧气，还必须适应迅速生长的肉芽瘤中心的微需氧/厌氧环境。

调控和信号传导　鉴于结核分枝杆菌面临的复杂环境和代谢选择，预计会有一套广泛的调控基因集。13 个假定的 σ 因子在转录起始水平控制基因表达，并且预测有 100 多个调节蛋白（表 1）。（编者注：给出结核分枝杆菌所有蛋白编码基因的大表在此版中被删除了。注意发表在《自然》中的版本含有错误，在《自然》1998 年第 396 卷 190～198 页的勘误中得以校正。）与枯草芽孢杆菌和大肠杆菌中有 >30 个拷贝的不同的双组分调控系统 [14] 不同，结核分枝杆菌只有完整的 11 对传感器组氨酸激酶和反应调节子，以及少量单独的激酶和调控基因。环境信号传导通路的相对不足可能通过一个真核样丝氨酸/苏氨酸蛋白激酶（STPK）家族来抵消，这个家族是磷酸传递系统的一部分 [18]。STPK 可能有两个结构域：氨基端为高度保守的激酶结构域，羧基端则可能对一些特定的刺激产生反应，据推测，这两个区域通过一个跨膜片段相连。一些预测的细胞被膜脂蛋白，如 lppR（Rv2403）编码的蛋白，与 STPK 中假定的受体结构域有广泛的相似性，这暗示可能存在相互作用。STPK 可能在信号传导通路中起作用，并可能控制重要的细胞决策，如休眠和细胞分裂，尽管它们的搭档未知，但已经发现磷蛋白磷酸酶的候选基因。

耐药性　结核分枝杆菌自身能抵抗多种抗生素，这使治疗变得困难 [19]。这种抗性的主要原因是细胞被膜高度疏水成为渗透屏障 [4]，但许多潜在的耐药性决定成分也是由基因组编码的。这些成分包括水解酶或药物修饰酶，如 β-内酰胺酶和氨基糖苷乙酰转移酶，以及许多潜在的药物外排系统，如主要协助转运蛋白家族的 14 个成员和大量 ABC 转运体。关于这些假设的耐药机制的知识将促进对现有药物的更好利用并有助于设计新的治疗方案。

脂 质 代 谢

极少数生物体像结核分枝杆菌一样产生一系列不同的亲脂性分子。这些分子包括简单脂肪酸，如棕榈酸酯和结核硬脂酸，以及类异戊二烯和极长链、高度复杂的分子，如分枝菌酸和苯酚结核菌醇，后者酯化结核蜡酸形成供海藻糖苷附着的支架。结核分枝杆菌包含已知的各类脂质和聚酮生物合成系统，包括通常在哺乳动物和植

polyketide biosynthetic system, including enzymes usually found in mammals and plants as well as the common bacterial systems. The biosynthetic capacity is overshadowed by the even more remarkable radiation of degradative, fatty acid oxidation systems and, in total, there are ~250 distinct enzymes involved in fatty acid metabolism in *M. tuberculosis* compared with only 50 in *E. coli*[20].

Fatty acid degradation. *In vivo*-grown mycobacteria have been suggested to be largely lipolytic, rather than lipogenic, because of the variety and quantity of lipids available within mammalian cells and the tubercle[2] (Fig. 4a). The abundance of genes encoding components of fatty acid oxidation systems found by our genomic approach supports this proposition, as there are 36 acyl-CoA synthases and a family of 36 related enzymes that could catalyse the first step in fatty acid degradation. There are 21 homologous enzymes belonging to the enoyl-CoA hydratase/isomerase superfamily of enzymes, which rehydrate the nascent product of the acyl-CoA dehydrogenase. The four enzymes that convert the 3-hydroxy fatty acid into a 3-keto fatty acid appear less numerous, mainly because they are difficult to distinguish from other members of the short-chain alcohol dehydrogenase family on the basis of primary sequence. The five enzymes that complete the cycle by thiolysis of the β-ketoester, the acetyl-CoA C-acetyltransferases, do indeed appear to be a more limited family. In addition to this extensive set of dissociated degradative enzymes, the genome also encodes the canonical FadA/FadB β-oxidation complex (Rv0859 and Rv0860). Accessory activities are present for the metabolism of odd-chain and multiply unsaturated fatty acids.

物以及一般细菌系统中发现的酶。与辐射分布更加显著的脂肪酸氧化降解系统相比，生物合成能力甚至相形见绌，总的来说在结核分枝杆菌中共有约 250 种不同的酶参与脂肪酸代谢，相比之下大肠杆菌中只有 50 种[20]。

脂肪酸的降解 研究发现体内生长的分枝杆菌主要参与脂肪降解，而不是脂肪合成，因为哺乳动物细胞和结节中有大量各种可用的脂类[2]（图 4a）。我们用基因组学方法发现大量脂肪酸氧化系统组分的编码基因支持这一观点，有 36 个酰基辅酶 A 合酶和一个含有 36 种酶，能催化脂肪酸降解第一步的酶家族。有 21 个属于烯脂酰辅酶 A 水合酶/异构酶超家族的同源酶，它们对酯酰辅酶 A 脱氢酶的新生产物进行再水合。有四个酶负责将 3-羟基脂肪酸转化为 3-酮脂肪酸，这个数目似乎少了很多，主要是因为在一维序列水平上难以将它们和短链醇脱氢酶家族的其他成员区分开。乙酰辅酶 A C-乙酰转移酶通过硫解 β-酮酸酯完成循环，该家族确实较小，只有五个成员。除了这一系列数目众多的游离降解酶，基因组也编码典型的 FadA/FadB β-氧化复合体（Rv0859 和 Rv0860），还包括代谢奇数链脂肪酸和多不饱和脂肪酸等辅助活性。

b

Gene	Function
fas	Fatty acid synthase, produces C_{16}-C_{16} acyl-CoA esters
fabD	Malonyl-CoA:AcpM acyltransferase, AcpM loading
acpM	Acyl carrier protein, meromycolate precursor transport
kasA	Ketoacyl acyl carrier protein synthase, chain elongation
kasB	Ketoacyl acyl carrier protein synthase, chain elongation
accD	Acetyl-CoA carboxylase, malonyl-CoA synthesis
mabA	3-oxo-acyl-acyl carrier protein reductase, reduces KasA/B product
inhA	Enoyl-acyl carrier protein reductase
cmaA1	cyclopropane mycolic acid synthase 1, distal-position specific
cmaA2	cyclopropane mycolic acid synthase 2, proximal-position specific

c

Gene	Function
mas	Four rounds extension of $C_{16,18}$ using Me-malonyl CoA
ppsA	Extension of C_{18} with malony CoA, partial reduction
ppsB	Extension with malony CoA, partial reduction
ppsC	Extension with malony CoA, complete reduction
ppsD	Extension with Me-malony CoA, partial reduction
ppsE	Extension with malony CoA, partial reduction, decarboxylation

Fig. 4. Lipid metabolism. **a**, Degradation of host-cell lipids is vital in the intracellular life of *M. tuberculosis*. Host-cell membranes provide precursors for many metabolic processes, as well as potential precursors of mycobacterial cell-wall constituents, through the actions of a broad family of β-oxidative enzymes encoded by multiple copies in the genome. These enzymes produce acetyl CoA, which can be converted into many different metabolites and fuel for the bacteria through the actions of the enzymes of the citric acid cycle and the glyoxylate shunt of this cycle. **b**, The genes that synthesize mycolic acids, the dominant lipid component of the mycobacterial cell wall, include the type I fatty acid synthase (*fas*) and

图 4. 脂质代谢。**a**，宿主细胞脂质的降解对于结核分枝杆菌的胞内生活是至关重要的。在基因组中多拷贝基因编码的 β 氧化酶大家族的作用下，宿主细胞膜为许多代谢过程提供前体，也为分枝杆菌细胞壁成分提供潜在的前体。这些酶产生乙酰辅酶 A，在柠檬酸循环及乙醛酸旁路循环酶的作用下，乙酰辅酶 A 转换成许多不同的代谢物和供细菌生长用的原料。**b**，合成分枝菌酸（分枝杆菌细胞壁的主要脂分）的基因，包括 I 型脂肪酸合酶（*fas*）和独特的 II 型系统，II 型系统依靠扩展一个结合在酰基载体蛋白的前体

a unique type II system which relies on extension of a precursor bound to an acyl carrier protein to form full-length (~80-carbon) mycolic acids. The *cma* genes are responsible for cyclopropanation. **c**, The genes that produce phthiocerol dimycocerosate form a large operon and represent type I (*mas*) and type II (the *pps* operon) polyketide synthase systems. Functions are colour coordinated.

Fatty acid biosynthesis. At least two discrete types of enzyme system, fatty acid synthase (FAS) I and FAS II, are involved in fatty acid biosynthesis in mycobacteria (Fig. 4b). FAS I (Rv2524, *fas*) is a single polypeptide with multiple catalytic activities that generates several shorter CoA esters from acetyl-CoA primers[5] and probably creates precursors for elongation by all of the other fatty acid and polyketide systems. FAS II consists of dissociable enzyme components which act on a substrate bound to an acyl-carrier protein (ACP). FAS II is incapable of *de novo* fatty acid synthesis but instead elongates palmitoyl-ACP to fatty acids ranging from 24 to 56 carbons in length[17,21]. Several different components of FAS II may be targets for the important tuberculosis drug isoniazid, including the enoyl-ACP reductase InhA[22], the ketoacyl-ACP synthase KasA and the ACP AcpM[21]. Analysis of the genome shows that there are only three potential ketoacyl synthases: KasA and KasB are highly related, and their genes cluster with *acpM*, whereas KasC is a more distant homologue of a ketoacyl synthase III system. The number of ketoacyl synthase and ACP genes indicates that there is a single FAS II system. Its genetic organization, with two clustered ketoacyl synthases, resembles that of type II aromatic polyketide biosynthetic gene clusters, such as those for actinorhodin, tetracycline and tetracenomycin in *Streptomyces* species[23]. InhA seems to be the sole enoyl-ACP reductase and its gene is co-transcribed with a *fabG* homologue, which encodes 3-oxoacyl-ACP reductase. Both of these proteins are probably important in the biosynthesis of mycolic acids.

Fatty acids are synthesized from malonyl-CoA and precursors are generated by the enzymatic carboxylation of acetyl (or propionyl)-CoA by a biotin-dependent carboxylase (Fig. 4b). From study of the genome we predict that there are three complete carboxylase systems, each consisting of an α- and a β-subunit, as well as three β-subunits without an α-counterpart. As a group, all of the carboxylases seem to be more related to the mammalian homologues than to the corresponding bacterial enzymes. Two of these carboxylase systems (*accA1*, *accD1* and *accA2*, *accD2*) are probably involved in degradation of odd-numbered fatty acids, as they are adjacent to genes for other known degradative enzymes. They may convert propionyl-CoA to succinyl-CoA, which can then be incorporated into the tricarboxylic acid cycle. The synthetic carboxylases (*accA3*, *accD3*, *accD4*, *accD5* and *accD6*) are more difficult to understand. The three extra β-subunits might direct carboxylation to the appropriate precursor or may simply increase the total amount of carboxylated precursor available if this step were rate-limiting.

Synthesis of the paraffinic backbone of fatty and mycolic acids in the cell is followed by extensive postsynthetic modifications and unsaturations, particularly in the case of the mycolic acids[24,25]. Unsaturation is catalysed either by a FabA-like β-hydroxyacyl-ACP dehydrase, acting with a specific ketoacyl synthase, or by an aerobic terminal mixed function desaturase that uses both molecular oxygen and NADPH. Inspection of the genome revealed no obvious candidates for the FabA-like activity. However, three potential aerobic

形成全长（约 80 碳）分枝菌酸。*cma* 基因负责形成环丙烷。**c**，产生结核菌醇双结核蜡酸酯的基因形成一个大操纵子，代表 I 型（*mas*）和 II 型（*pps* 操纵子）聚酮合酶系统。功能和颜色相对应。

脂肪酸生物合成　至少有两个不同类型的酶系统，脂肪酸合酶（FAS）I 和 FAS II，参与结核分枝杆菌的脂肪酸生物合成（图 4b）。FAS I（Rv2524，*fas*）是一个具有多种催化活性的单一多肽，它能利用乙酰辅酶 A 引物产生一些较短的辅酶 A 酯[5]，并且可能通过所有其他脂肪酸和聚酮系统产生延伸所需的前体。FAS II 由多个可解离的酶组分组成，这些酶组分都作用于一个结合在酰基载体蛋白（ACP）上的底物。FAS II 不能从头合成脂肪酸，但可以将软脂酰-ACP 延伸为长度为 24 到 56 个碳的脂肪酸[17,21]。FAS II 的几个不同组分可能是重要的抗结核病药物异烟肼的靶标，包括烯脂酰-ACP 还原酶 InhA[22]、酮脂酰-ACP 合酶 KasA 和 ACP AcpM[21]。基因组分析表明只有三个潜在酮脂酰合酶：KasA 和 KasB 高度相关，它们的基因与 *acpM* 聚集成簇，而 KasC 则是酮脂酰合酶 III 系统的一个更远源的同源蛋白。酮脂酰合酶和 ACP 基因的数量表明有单一的 FAS II 系统。该系统的遗传结构有两个聚集成簇的酮脂酰酶，类似于 II 型芳香族聚酮生物合成基因簇，如链霉菌中的放线紫红素、四环素、特曲霉素合成基因簇[23]。InhA 似乎是唯一的烯脂酰-ACP 还原酶，其基因与编码 3-氧酰基-ACP 还原酶的 *fabG* 同源基因进行共转录。这两种蛋白质很可能在分枝菌酸合成中起重要作用。

脂肪酸是由丙二酰辅酶 A 合成的，前体由依赖生物素的羧化酶酶促羧化乙酰（或丙酰）-辅酶 A（图 4b）生成。通过对基因组的研究，我们预测出三个完整的羧化酶系统，每一个都包括一个 α 亚基和一个 β 亚基，另外还预测出三个 β 亚基，没有 α 亚基与之配对。整体而言，所有羧化酶和哺乳动物来源的同源蛋白的亲缘关系似乎高于细菌来源的同源酶。羧化酶系统（*accA1*、*accD1* 和 *accA2*、*accD2*）中的两个很可能参与奇数碳原子脂肪酸的降解，因为在基因组上它们与其他已知降解酶基因邻近。他们可能将丙酰辅酶 A 转换为琥珀酰辅酶 A，然后琥珀酰辅酶 A 被纳入三羧酸循环。具有合成作用的羧化酶（*accA3*、*accD3*、*accD4*、*accD5* 和 *accD6*）更难理解。如果这步是限速步骤的话，这三个额外的 β 亚基可能介导适当的前体羧化或只是简单地增加可用的羧化前体总数。

在细胞内合成脂肪酸和分枝菌酸的石蜡骨架后接着进行大量的合成后修饰和不饱和化，特别是在分枝菌酸的合成中[24,25]。不饱和化由一个 FabA 样的 β-羟脂酰-ACP 脱水酶催化，该酶与特定的酮酯酰合酶共同起作用，或者由一个使用分子氧和 NADPH 的需氧末端混合功能去饱和酶催化。检测基因组没有发现明显具有 FabA 样活性的候选基因。然而，很显然，三个潜在的需氧去饱和酶（由 *desA1*、 desaturases (encoded by *desA1*, *desA2* and *desA3*) were evident that show little similarity to related vertebrate or yeast enzymes (which act on CoA esters) but instead resemble plant desaturases (which use ACP esters). Consequently, the genomic data indicate that unsaturation of the meromycolate chain may occur while the acyl group is bound to AcpM.

Much of the subsequent structural diversity in mycolic acids is generated by a family of *S*-adenosyl-L-methionine-dependent enzymes, which use the unsaturated meromycolic acid as a substrate to generate *cis* and *trans* cyclopropanes and other mycolates. Six members of this family have been identified and characterized[25] and two clustered, convergently transcribed new genes are evident in the genome (*umaA1* and *umaA2*). From the functions of the known family members and the structures of mycolic acids in *M. tuberculosis*, it is tempting to speculate that these new enzymes may introduce the *trans* cyclopropanes into the meromycolate precursor. In addition to these two methyltransferases, there are two other unrelated lipid methyltransferases (Ufa1 and Ufa2) that share homology with cyclopropane fatty acid synthase of *E. coli*[25]. Although cyclopropanation seems to be a relatively common modification of mycolic acids, cyclopropanation of plasma-membrane constituents has not been described in mycobacteria. Tuberculostearic acid is produced by methylation of oleic acid, and may be synthesized by one of these two enzymes.

Condensation of the fully functionalized and preformed meromycolate chain with a 26-carbon α-branch generates full-length mycolic acids that must be transported to their final location for attachment to the cell-wall arabinogalactan. The transfer and subsequent transesterification is mediated by three well-known immunogenic proteins of the antigen 85 complex[26]. The genome encodes a fourth member of this complex, antigen 85C′ (*fbpC2*, Rv0129), which is highly related to antigen 85C. Further studies are needed to show whether the protein possesses mycolyltransferase activity and to clarify the reason behind the apparent redundancy.

Polyketide synthesis. Mycobacteria synthesize polyketides by several different mechanisms. A modular type I system, similar to that involved in erythromycin biosynthesis[23], is encoded by a very large operon, *ppsABCDE*, and functions in the production of phenolphthiocerol[5]. The absence of a second type I polyketide synthase suggests that the related lipids phthiocerol A and B, phthiodiolone A and phthiotriol may all be synthesized by the same system, either from alternative primers or by differential postsynthetic modification. It is physiologically significant that the *pps* gene cluster occurs immediately upstream of *mas*, which encodes the multifunctional enzyme mycocerosic acid synthase (MAS), as their products phthiocerol and mycocerosic acid esterify to form the very abundant cell-wall-associated molecule phthiocerol dimycocerosate (Fig. 4c).

Members of another large group of polyketide synthase enzymes are similar to MAS, which also generates the multiply methyl-branched fatty acid components of mycosides and phthiocerol dimycocerosate, abundant cell-wall-associated molecules[5]. Although some of these polyketide synthases may extend type I FAS CoA primers to produce other long-chain methyl-branched fatty acids such as mycolipenic, mycolipodienic and mycolipanolic acids or the phthioceranic and hydroxyphthioceranic acids, or may even show functional overlap[5],

234

desA2 和 *desA3* 编码）与脊椎动物或酵母中的相关酶（作用于辅酶 A 酯）几乎没有相似性，而与植物中的去饱和酶（使用 ACP 酯）相似。因此，基因组数据表明，当酰基结合到 AcpM 上可能使得局部分枝菌酸酯链去饱和。

分枝菌酸许多后来的结构多样性是由 S-腺苷-L-甲硫氨酸依赖的酶家族产生的，它以不饱和的局部分枝菌酸为底物生成顺式-和反式-环丙烷以及其他分枝菌酸。现在已经鉴定和描述了这个家族的六个成员[25]，两个基因簇集中转录的新基因在基因组中很明显（*umaA1* 和 *umaA2*）。从已知家族成员的功能和结核分枝杆菌分枝菌酸的结构推测，这些新酶可能将反式环丙烷引入到局部分枝菌酸前体中。除了这两个甲基转移酶，还有另外两个无关的脂质甲基转移酶（Ufa1 和 Ufa2）与大肠杆菌的环丙烷脂肪酸合酶有同源性[25]。虽然环丙烷化似乎是分枝菌酸的一种相对常见的修饰，但质膜组分的环丙烷化在分枝杆菌中还未见描述。结核硬脂酸通过油酸的甲基化产生，该合成过程可能由这两个酶中的一个完成。

完全功能的预先形成的局部分枝菌酸链和 26 碳 α 分枝缩合产生全长分枝菌酸，分枝菌酸必须转移到最终的位置以结合细胞壁阿拉伯半乳糖。转移和随后的酯交换反应由抗原 85 复合体中三个众所周知的免疫原性蛋白介导[26]。基因组编码这个复合体的第四个成员，抗原 85C′（*fbpC2*，Rv0129）与抗原 85C 高度相关。这个蛋白是否具有分枝酸转移酶活性，以及其明显冗余背后的原因的阐明，都需要进一步的研究。

聚酮合成　分枝杆菌通过几种不同机制合成聚酮。模块化的 I 型系统，类似于参与红霉素生物合成的系统[23]，由一个非常大的操纵子 *ppsABCDE* 编码，并在苯酚结核菌醇的产生中起作用[5]。基因组中不存在第二个 I 型聚酮合酶说明相关的脂质结核菌醇 A 和 B、结核菌二醇 A 和结核菌三醇都可能由同一系统合成，这要么使用了不同的引物，要么合成后进行了不同的修饰。*pps* 基因簇紧邻 *mas* 上游，*mas* 编码多功能酶分枝杆菌结核蜡酸合酶（MAS），这在生理上很重要，因为它们的产物结核菌醇和结核蜡酸酯化形成了非常丰富的细胞壁关联分子结核菌醇双结核蜡酸酯（图 4c）。

另一个聚酮合酶大家族的成员与 MAS 相似，它也产生丰富的细胞壁关联分子——海藻糖苷和结核菌醇双结核蜡酸酯的多种甲基化分枝脂肪酸组分[5]。虽然其中一些聚酮合酶可能延长 I 型 FAS 辅酶 A 引物，产生其他长链甲基化分枝脂肪酸，如霉脂酸、霉脂二烯酸和霉脂羟基酸或分枝菌蜡酸和羟基分枝菌蜡酸，甚至出现功能重叠[5]，但是这些酶的数目比已知代谢物多得多。因此，可能存在只在特定条件

there are many more of these enzymes than there are known metabolites. Thus there may be new lipid and polyketide metabolites that are expressed only under certain conditions, such as during infection and disease.

A fourth class of polyketide synthases is related to the plant enzyme superfamily that includes chalcone and stilbene synthase[23]. These polyketide synthases are phylogenetically divergent from all other polyketide and fatty acid synthases and generate unreduced polyketides that are typically associated with anthocyanin pigments and flavonoids. The function of these systems, which are often linked to apparent type I modules, is unknown. An example is the gene cluster spanning *pks10*, *pks7*, *pks8* and *pks9*, which includes two of the chalcone-synthase-like enzymes and two modules of an apparent type I system. The unknown metabolites produced by these enzymes are interesting because of the potent biological activities of some polyketides such as the immunosuppressor rapamycin.

Siderophores. Peptides that are not ribosomally synthesized are made by a process that is mechanistically analogous to polyketide synthesis[23,27]. These peptides include the structurally related iron-scavenging siderophores, the mycobactins and the exochelins[2,28], which are derived from salicylate by the addition of serine (or threonine), two lysines and various fatty acids and possible polyketide segments. The *mbt* operon, encoding one apparent salicylate-activating protein, three amino-acid ligases, and a single module of a type I polyketide synthase, may be responsible for the biosynthesis of the mycobacterial siderophores. The presence of only one non-ribosomal peptide-synthesis system indicates that this pathway may generate both siderophores and that subsequent modification of a single ε-amino group of one lysine residue may account for the different physical properties and function of the siderophores[28].

Immunological Aspects and Pathogenicity

Given the scale of the global tuberculosis burden, vaccination is not only a priority but remains the only realistic public health intervention that is likely to affect both the incidence and the prevalence of the disease[29]. Several areas of vaccine development are promising, including DNA vaccination, use of secreted or surface-exposed proteins as immunogens, recombinant forms of BCG and rational attenuation of *M. tuberculosis*[29]. All of these avenues of research will benefit from the genome sequence as its availability will stimulate more focused approaches. Genes encoding ~90 lipoproteins were identified, some of which are enzymes or components of transport systems, and a similar number of genes encoding preproteins (with type I signal peptides) that are probably exported by the Sec-dependent pathway. *M. tuberculosis* seems to have two copies of *secA*. The potent T-cell antigen Esat-6 (ref. 30), which is probably secreted in a Sec-independent manner, is encoded by a member of a multigene family. Examination of the genetic context reveals several similarly organized operons that include genes encoding large ATP-hydrolysing membrane proteins that might act as transporters. One of the surprises of the genome project was the discovery of two extensive families of novel glycine-rich proteins, which may be of immunological significance as they are predicted to be abundant and potentially polymorphic antigens.

下，如在感染和疾病时表达的新的脂和聚酮代谢产物。

第四类聚酮合酶与包含查尔酮和二苯乙烯合酶的植物酶超家族[23]有关。这些聚酮合酶在系统发生上与其他所有聚酮和脂肪酸合酶不同，它们产生通常与花青素和黄酮类化合物相关联的非还原聚酮。这些系统的功能未知，经常与一些明显的 I 型模块相连接。一个例子是涵盖 pks10、pks7、pks8 和 pks9 的基因簇，它包括两个查尔酮合酶的类似酶和明显的 I 型系统的两个模块。因为一些聚酮如免疫抑制剂雷帕霉素具有强大的生物活性，所以这些酶产生的未知代谢产物很有趣。

铁载体　非核糖体合成的肽链是通过与聚酮合成相似的过程产生的[23,27]。这些肽包括结构相关的清除铁的铁载体，分枝杆菌素和胞外螯合素[2,28]，它们是通过向水杨酸盐添加丝氨酸（或苏氨酸）、两个赖氨酸和各种脂肪酸和可能的聚酮片段得到的。mbt 操纵子可能负责分枝杆菌铁载体的合成，它编码一个明显的水杨酸盐活化蛋白、三个氨基酸连接酶和 I 型聚酮合酶的一个单一模块。基因组中只有一个非核糖体肽合成系统表明该途径可能产生这两种铁载体，并且一个赖氨酸残基的 ε–氨基的后续修饰可能是铁载体具有不同物理性质和功能的原因[28]。

免疫学特性和致病性

鉴于全球结核病的发生规模，接种疫苗不只是一个优先选择，也可能是对结核病的发病率和流行都发挥作用的唯一实际的公共健康干预措施[29]。疫苗开发的几个领域是有前途的，这包括使用分泌蛋白或表面暴露蛋白作为免疫原的 DNA 疫苗、重组形式的卡介苗和合理减毒的结核分枝杆菌[29]。所有这些研究途径将从基因组序列中受益，基因组序列的获得将促进产生更加聚焦的解决方法。我们鉴定了约 90 个脂蛋白编码基因，其中有些是酶或转运系统组分，还有数量相当的基因编码蛋白质前体（含 I 型信号肽），它们很可能通过 Sec 依赖途径向胞外转运。结核分枝杆菌似乎有两个拷贝的 secA。有效的 T 细胞抗原 Esat-6（参考文献 30）由多基因家族的一个成员编码，很可能以不依赖 Sec 的方式分泌。对基因组邻近区域的检查发现了几个结构相似的操纵子，其中包括编码具有 ATP 水解功能的高分子量膜蛋白基因，而这些膜蛋白可能是转运体。本基因组项目的惊喜之一是发现了新的富含甘氨酸的蛋白质，它们分别属于两个大家族，可能有免疫学意义，因为它们被预测是丰富且潜在的多态性抗原。

The PE and PPE multigene families. About 10% of the coding capacity of the genome is devoted to two large unrelated families of acidic, glycine-rich proteins, the PE and PPE families, whose genes are clustered (Figs 1, 2) and are often based on multiple copies of the polymorphic repetitive sequences referred to as PGRSs, and major polymorphic tandem repeats (MPTRs), respectively[31,32]. The names PE and PPE derive from the motifs Pro–Glu (PE) and Pro–Pro–Glu (PPE) found near the N terminus in most cases[33]. The 99 members of the PE protein family all have a highly conserved N-terminal domain of ~110 amino-acid residues that is predicted to have a globular structure, followed by a C-terminal segment that varies in size, sequence and repeat copy number (Fig. 5). Phylogenetic analysis separated the PE family into several subfamilies. The largest of these is the highly repetitive PGRS class, which contains 61 members; members of the other subfamilies, share very limited sequence similarity in their C-terminal domains (Fig. 5). The predicted molecular weights of the PE proteins vary considerably as a few members contain only the N-terminal domain, whereas most have C-terminal extensions ranging in size from 100 to 1,400 residues. The PGRS proteins have a high glycine content (up to 50%), which is the result of multiple tandem repetitions of Gly– Gly–Ala or Gly–Gly–Asn motifs, or variations thereof.

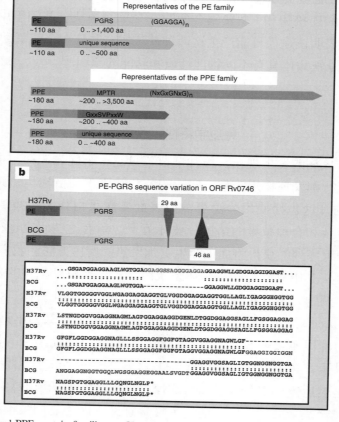

Fig. 5. The PE and PPE protein families. **a**, Classification of the PE and PPE protein families. **b**, Sequence

PE 和 PPE 多基因家族　基因组约 10% 的编码能力用于编码酸性富含甘氨酸但相互之间不相关的两大蛋白家族，PE 和 PPE 家族，它们的基因聚集成簇（图 1 和图 2），且通常分别基于多个拷贝的被称为 PGRS 的多态性重复序列和主要多态性串联重复序列（MPTR）[31,32]。命名为 PE 和 PPE 是因为在大多数情况下靠近 N 端有脯氨酸–谷氨酸（PE）和脯氨酸–脯氨酸–谷氨酸（PPE）基序 [33]。PE 蛋白家族的 99 个成员都有一个高度保守的 N 末端结构域，该结构域含有约 110 个氨基酸残基，预测为球状结构，其后是大小、序列和重复拷贝数都不同的 C 端片段（图 5）。系统发育分析将 PE 家族分为几个亚家族。其中最大的是高度重复的 PGRS 类，包含 61 个成员；其他亚家族成员 C 端结构域的序列相似性很有限（图 5）。PE 蛋白的预测分子量差别很大，因为少数成员只包含 N 端结构域，而大多数成员具有大小从 100 到 1,400 个残基不等的 C 端延伸。PGRS 蛋白甘氨酸含量高（达 50%），这是甘氨酸–甘氨酸–丙氨酸或甘氨酸–甘氨酸–天冬酰氨基序或其他变异基序多次串联重复的结果，或者是由于突变导致的。

图 5. PE 和 PPE 蛋白家族。**a**，PE 和 PPE 蛋白家族的分类。**b**，结核分枝杆菌 H37Rv 和牛分枝杆菌卡介

variation between *M. tuberculosis* H37Rv and *M. bovis* BCG-Pasteur in the PE-PGRS encoded by open reading frame (ORF) Rv0746.

The 68 members of the PPE protein family (Fig. 5) also have a conserved N-terminal domain that comprises ~180 amino-acid residues, followed by C-terminal segments that vary markedly in sequence and length. These proteins fall into at least three groups, one of which constitutes the MPTR class characterized by the presence of multiple, tandem copies of the motif Asn–X–Gly–X–Gly–Asn–X–Gly. The second subgroup contains a characteristic, well-conserved motif around position 350, whereas the third contains proteins that are unrelated except for the presence of the common 180-residue PPE domain.

The subcellular location of the PE and PPE proteins is unknown and in only one case, that of a lipase (Rv3097), has a function been demonstrated. On examination of the protein database from the extensively sequenced *M. leprae*[15], no PGRS- or MPTR-related polypeptides were detected but a few proteins belonging to the non-MPTR subgroup of the PPE family were found. These proteins include one of the major antigens recognized by leprosy patients, the serine-rich antigen[34]. Although it is too early to attribute biological functions to the PE and PPE families, it is tempting to speculate that they could be of immunological importance. Two interesting possibilities spring to mind. First, they could represent the principal source of antigenic variation in what is otherwise a genetically and antigenically homogeneous bacterium. Second, these glycine-rich proteins might interfere with immune responses by inhibiting antigen processing.

Several observations and results support the possibility of antigenic variation associated with both the PE and the PPE family proteins. The PGRS member Rv1759 is a fibronectin-binding protein of relative molecular mass 55,000 (ref. 35) that elicits a variable antibody response, indicating either that individuals mount different immune responses or that this PGRS protein may vary between strains of *M. tuberculosis*. The latter possibility is supported by restriction fragment length polymorphisms for various PGRS and MPTR sequences in clinical isolates[33]. Direct support for genetic variation within both the PE and the PPE families was obtained by comparative DNA sequence analysis (Fig. 5). The gene for the PE–PGRS protein Rv0746 of BCG differs from that in H37Rv by the deletion of 29 codons and the insertion of 46 codons. Similar variation was seen in the gene for the PPE protein Rv0442 (data not shown). As these differences were all associated with repetitive sequences they could have resulted from intergenic or intragenic recombinational events or, more probably, from strand slippage during replication[32]. These mechanisms are known to generate antigenic variability in other bacterial pathogens[36].

There are several parallels between the PGRS proteins and the Epstein–Barr virus nuclear antigens (EBNAs). Members of both polypeptide families are glycine-rich, contain extensive Gly–Ala repeats, and exhibit variation in the length of the repeat region between different isolates. The Gly–Ala repeat region of EBNA1 functions as a *cis*-acting inhibitor of the ubiquitin/proteasome antigen-processing pathway that generates peptides presented in

240

苗-巴斯德开放阅读框（ORF）Rv0746 编码的 PE-PGRS 的序列变异。

    PPE 蛋白家族的 68 个成员（图 5）也有保守的 N 端结构域，由 180 个氨基酸残基组成，其后是序列和长度都有很大差异的 C 端片段。这些蛋白质至少可分为三组，其中一组组成了 MPTR 类，其特点是含有多个天冬酰胺-X-甘氨酸-X-甘氨酸-天冬酰胺-X-甘氨酸基序的串联拷贝。第二组在位置 350 左右包含一个独特的高保守基序，而第三组包含的蛋白，除了都含有长 180 个氨基酸残基的 PPE 结构域外没有其他相关性。

    PE 和 PPE 蛋白的亚细胞定位未知，仅在一个脂酶（Rv3097）的例子中证明是有功能的。对全面测序的麻风分枝杆菌[15] 蛋白数据库进行检测，没有检测到 PGRS 或 MPTR 相关多肽，但发现了少量非 MPTR 亚组的 PPE 蛋白家族。这些蛋白质包括麻风病患者识别的一个主要抗原——富含丝氨酸的抗原[34]。尽管认定 PE 和 PPE 家族有生物学功能还为时过早，但对它们可能有免疫学功能的推测是很吸引人的。我们想到两个有趣的可能性。第一，它们可能代表结核分枝杆菌抗原变异的主要来源，否则结核分枝杆菌将是遗传和抗原均一的细菌。第二，这些富含甘氨酸的蛋白质可能会通过抑制抗原加工干扰免疫应答。

    少量观察数据和结果支持抗原变异与 PE 和 PPE 家族蛋白存在相关的可能性。PGRS 成员 Rv1759 是纤连蛋白结合蛋白，相对分子量为 55,000（参考文献 35），诱导不同的抗体反应，这表明要么不同个体产生了不同的免疫应答，要么结核分枝杆菌不同菌株的 PGRS 蛋白是不同的。后者的可能性得到临床分离株中不同的 PGRS 和 MPTR 序列的限制性片段长度多态性的支持[33]。PE 和 PPE 家族内的遗传变异得到了比较 DNA 序列分析的直接支持（图 5）。BCG 的 PE-PGRS 蛋白 Rv0746 的基因与 H37Rv 中的不同，前者含 29 个密码子的缺失和 46 个密码子的插入。类似的变化在 PPE 蛋白 Rv0442 的基因中也可以看到（数据未显示）。由于这些差异都与重复序列相关，它们可能来自基因间或基因内的重组事件，或者更可能是复制过程中链的滑动引起的[32]。已知其他病原菌可利用这些机制产生抗原变异[36]。

    PGRS 蛋白和 EB 病毒核抗原（EBNAs）之间有一些相似之处。两个多肽家族成员都富含甘氨酸，含有丰富的甘氨酸-丙氨酸重复序列，不同分离株重复区域的长度不同。EBNA1 的甘氨酸-丙氨酸重复区域是泛素/蛋白酶体抗原加工途径的顺式作用抑制剂，这一途径产生的肽出现在主要组织相容性复合物（MHC）I 类分子存在的

the context of major histocompatibility complex (MHC) class I molecules[37,38]. MHC class I knockout mice are very susceptible to *M. tuberculosis*, underlining the importance of a cytotoxic T-cell response in protection against disease[3,39]. Given the many potential effects of the PPE and PE proteins, it is important that further studies are performed to understand their activity. If extensive antigenic variability or reduced antigen presentation were indeed found, this would be significant for vaccine design and for understanding protective immunity in tuberculosis, and might even explain the varied responses seen in different BCG vaccination programmes[40].

Pathogenicity. Despite intensive research efforts, there is little information about the molecular basis of mycobacterial virulence[41]. However, this situation should now change as the genome sequence will accelerate the study of pathogenesis as never before, because other bacterial factors that may contribute to virulence are becoming apparent. Before the completion of the genome sequence, only three virulence factors had been described[41]: catalase-peroxidase, which protects against reactive oxygen species produced by the phagocyte; *mce*, which encodes macrophage-colonizing factor[42]; and a sigma factor gene, *sigA* (aka *rpoV*), mutations in which can lead to attenuation[41]. In addition to these single-gene virulence factors, the mycobacterial cell wall[4] is also important in pathology, but the complex nature of its biosynthesis makes it difficult to identify critical genes whose inactivation would lead to attenuation.

On inspection of the genome sequence, it was apparent that four copies of *mce* were present and that these were all situated in operons, comprising eight genes, organized in exactly the same manner. In each case, the genes preceding *mce* code for integral membrane proteins, whereas *mce* and the following five genes are all predicted to encode proteins with signal sequences or hydrophobic stretches at the N terminus. These sets of proteins, about which little is known, may well be secreted or surface-exposed; this is consistent with the proposed role of Mce in invasion of host cells[42]. Furthermore, a homologue of *smpB*, which has been implicated in intracellular survival of *Salmonella typhimurium*, has also been identified[43]. Among the other secreted proteins identified from the genome sequence that could act as virulence factors are a series of phospholipases C, lipases and esterases, which might attack cellular or vacuolar membranes, as well as several proteases. One of these phospholipases acts as a contact-dependent haemolysin (N. Stoker, personal communication). The presence of storage proteins in the bacillus, such as the haemoglobin-like oxygen captors described above, points to its ability to stockpile essential growth factors, allowing it to persist in the nutrient-limited environment of the phagosome. In this regard, the ferritin-like proteins, encoded by *bfrA* and *bfrB*, may be important in intracellular survival as the capacity to acquire enough iron in the vacuole is very limited.

Methods

Sequence analysis. Initially, ~3.2 Mb of sequence was generated from cosmids[8] and the remainder was obtained from selected BAC clones[7] and 45,000 whole-genome shotgun clones. Sheared

242

条件下^[37,38]。MHC I 类敲除小鼠非常容易感染结核分枝杆菌，这强调了细胞毒性 T 细胞反应在抗病保护中的重要性^[3,39]。鉴于 PPE 和 PE 蛋白质的多种潜在作用，进一步研究了解它们的活性有很重要的意义。如果确实发现大量抗原变异或抗原呈递减少，将对设计疫苗和理解肺结核中保护性免疫有重大意义，甚至可能解释在不同的卡介苗接种方案中看到的不同反应^[40]。

致病性 尽管进行了大量研究，但关于分枝杆菌毒性的分子基础仍知之甚少^[41]。然而，这种情况现在应该会有所改变，因为基因组序列将前所未有地加快致病机制的研究，其他可能与毒力有关的细菌因子正在变得更加清楚。在完成基因组测序之前，只有三个毒力因子被描述过^[41]：过氧化氢酶-过氧化物酶，可以保护其免受巨噬细胞产生的活性氧的伤害；*mce*，编码巨噬细胞集落因子^[42]；一个 σ 因子基因，*sigA*（又名 *rpoV*），该基因的突变可导致减毒^[41]。除了这些单基因毒力因子，结核菌的细胞壁^[4] 在病理学上也很重要，但因其生物合成的复杂性致使鉴定失活导致减毒的关键基因很困难。

检查基因组序列发现，很显然存在 *mec* 的四个拷贝，而且都位于操纵子中，这些操纵子包括 8 个基因，组织形式完全相同。在每个操纵子中，*mec* 前面的基因编码整合膜蛋白，而 *mec* 及其后面的五个基因都被预测编码 N 端有信号肽序列或疏水序列的蛋白质。我们对这些蛋白质知之甚少，它们很可能是分泌或表面暴露的蛋白，这与有人已经提出的 Mce 在侵入宿主细胞中的功能一致^[42]。此外，我们还鉴定了 *smpB* 的一个同源基因，该基因与鼠伤寒沙门菌在细胞内的生存密切相关^[43]。根据基因组序列鉴定的其他分泌蛋白可能作为毒力因子的蛋白包括一系列磷脂酶 C、脂肪酶和酯酶，它们可能攻击细胞膜或者液泡膜，还包括几个蛋白酶。其中一个磷脂酶发挥接触依赖性溶血素的作用（斯托克，个人交流）。芽孢杆菌中存在储存蛋白，例如上述血红蛋白样氧捕捉蛋白，表明其具备储存必需生长因子的能力，使之能够在吞噬小体养分有限的环境中生存。在这点上，*bfrA* 和 *bfrB* 编码的铁蛋白样蛋白，可能对细胞内生存很重要，因为在液泡中获得足够铁的能力是非常有限的。

方　法

序列分析 起初，黏粒测序获得了约 3.2 Mb 的序列^[8]，其余序列是从选定的 BAC 克隆^[7] 和 45,000 个全基因组鸟枪克隆中得到的。将黏粒和 BAC 的打断片段（1.4～2.0 kb）克隆

fragments (1.4–2.0 kb) from cosmids and BACs were cloned into M13 vectors, whereas genomic DNA was cloned in pUC18 to obtain both forward and reverse reads. The PGRS genes were grossly underrepresented in pUC18 but better covered in the BAC and cosmid M13 libraries. We used small-insert libraries[44] to sequence regions prone to compression or deletion and, in some cases, obtained sequences from products of the polymerase chain reaction or directly from BACs[7]. All shotgun sequencing was performed with standard dye terminators to minimize compression problems, whereas finishing reactions used dRhodamine or BigDye terminators (http://www.sanger.ac.uk). Problem areas were verified by using dye primers. Thirty differences were found between the genomic shotgun sequences and the cosmids; twenty of which were due to sequencing errors and ten to mutations in cosmids (1 error per 320 kb). Less than 0.1% of the sequence was from areas of single-clone coverage, and ~0.2% was from one strand with only one sequencing chemistry.

Informatics. Sequence assembly involved PHRAP, GAP4 (ref. 45) and a customized perl script that merges sequences from different libraries and generates segments that can be processed by several finishers simultaneously. Sequence analysis and annotation was managed by DIANA (B.G.B. *et al.*, unpublished). Genes encoding proteins were identified by TB-parse[46] using a hidden Markov model trained on known *M. tuberculosis* coding and non-coding regions and translation-initiation signals, with corroboration by positional base preference. Interrogation of the EMBL, TREMBL, SwissProt, PROSITE[47] and in-house databases involved BLASTN, BLASTX[48], DOTTER (http://www.sanger. ac.uk) and FASTA[49]. tRNA genes were located and identified using tRNAscan and tRNAscan-SE[50]. The complete sequence, a list of annotated cosmids and linking regions can be found on our website (http:// www. sanger.ac.uk) and in MycDB (http://www.pasteur.fr/mycdb/).

(**393**, 537-544; 1998)

S. T. Cole[*], R. Brosch[*], J. Parkhill, T. Garnier[*], C. Churcher, D. Harris, S. V. Gordon[*], K. Eiglmeier[*], S. Gas[*], C. E. Barry III[†], F. Tekaia[‡], K. Badcock, D. Basham, D. Brown, T. Chillingworth, R. Connor, R. Davies, K. Devlin, T. Feltwell, S. Gentles, N. Hamlin, S. Holroyd, T. Hornsby, K. Jagels, A. Krogh[§], J. McLean, S. Moule, L. Murphy, K. Oliver, J. Osborne, M. A. Quail, M.-A. Rajandream, J. Rogers, S. Rutter, K. Seeger, J. Skelton, R. Squares, S. Squares, J. E. Sulston, K. Taylor, S. Whitehead & B. G. Barrell

Sanger Centre, Wellcome Trust Genome Campus, Hinxton CB10 1SA, UK

[*] Unité de Génétique Moléculaire Bactérienne, and [‡] Unité de Génétique Moléculaire des Levures, Institut Pasteur, 28 rue du Docteur Roux, 75724 Paris Cedex 15, France

[†] Tuberculosis Research Unit, Laboratory of Intracellular Parasites, Rocky Mountain Laboratories, National Institute of Allergy and Infectious Diseases, National Institutes of Health, Hamilton, Montana 59840, USA

[§] Center for Biological Sequence Analysis, Technical University of Denmark, Lyngby, Denmark

Received 15 April; accepted 8 May 1998.

References:

1. Snider, D. E. Jr, Raviglione, M. & Kochi, A. in *Tuberculosis: Pathogenesis, Protection, and Control* (ed. Bloom, B. R.) 2-11 (Am. Soc. Microbiol., Washington DC, 1994).

2. Wheeler, P. R. & Ratledge, C. in *Tuberculosis: Pathogenesis, Protection, and Control* (ed. Bloom, B. R.) 353-385 (Am. Soc. Microbiol., Washington DC, 1994).

3. Chan, J. & Kaufmann, S. H. E. in *Tuberculosis: Pathogenesis, Protection, and Control* (ed. Bloom, B. R.) 271-284 (Am. Soc. Microbiol., Washington DC, 1994).

4. Brennan, P. J. & Draper, P. in *Tuberculosis: Pathogenesis, Protection, and Control* (ed. Bloom, B. R.) 271-284 (Am. Soc. Microbiol., Washington DC, 1994).

5. Kolattukudy, P. E., Fernandes, N. D., Azad, A. K., Fitzmaurice, A. M. & Sirakova, T. D. Biochemistry and molecular genetics of cell-wall lipid biosynthesis in mycobacteria. *Mol. Microbiol.* **24,** 263-270 (1997).

到 M13 载体上，将基因组 DNA 克隆到质粒 pUC18 上获得正向和反向可读片段。PGRS 基因在 pUC18 中出现的频率严重低于正常水平，但在 BAC 和黏粒 M13 文库中覆盖得很好。我们使用小插入片段文库 [44] 对易压缩或缺失的区域测序，在某些情况下，从 PCR 反应产物中或直接从 BACs 中获得序列 [7]。所有鸟枪测序采用标准染料终止剂，以尽量减少压缩问题，终止反应用 dRhodamine 或 BigDye 终止剂 (http://www.sanger.ac.uk)。存在问题的区域用染料标记引物验证。在基因组鸟枪测序和黏粒测序的序列之间发现了 30 个差异；其中 20 个是由测序错误引起的，10 个是由黏粒中的突变 (1 个错误/320 kb) 引起的。小于 0.1% 的序列来自单个克隆覆盖的区域，大约 0.2% 来自只有一个测序化学反应的一条链。

信息学　序列组装使用了 PHRAP、GAP4(参考文献 45) 和定制的 perl 脚本，该脚本用于合并不同文库中的序列，并生成可以同时被几个基因组完成工具处理的片段。序列分析和注释由 DIANA(巴雷尔等，未发表) 完成。使用 TB-parse[46] 鉴定蛋白质编码基因，使用马尔可夫模型分析已知的结核分枝杆菌编码和非编码区域及翻译起始信号，通过位置碱基偏好进行验证。综合使用 EMBL、TREMBL、SwissProt、PROSITE[47] 数据库和内部数据库 BLASTN、BLASTX[48]、DOTTER(http://www.sanger.ac.uk) 和 FASTA[49] 等。使用 tRNAscan 和 tRNAscan-SE[50] 定位和鉴定 tRNA 基因。在我们的网站 (http:// www.sanger.ac.uk) 上和 MycDB(http://www.pasteur.fr/mycdb/) 中可找到完整的基因组序列、一系列已注释的黏粒和相连接区域。

(李梅 翻译；解彬彬 审稿)

6. Sreevatsan, S. *et al.* Restricted structural gene polymorphism in the *Mycobacterium tuberculosis* complex indicates evolutionarily recent global dissemination. *Proc. Natl Acad. Sci. USA* **94**, 9869-9874 (1997).

7. Brosch, R. *et al.* Use of a *Mycobacterium tuberculosis* H37Rv bacterial artificial chromosome library for genome mapping, sequencing and comparative genomics. *Infect. Immun.* **66**, 2221-2229 (1998).

8. Philipp, W. J. *et al.* An integrated map of the genome of the tubercle bacillus, *Mycobacterium tuberculosis* H37Rv, and comparison with *Mycobacterium leprae. Proc. Natl Acad. Sci. USA* **93**, 3132-3137 (1996).

9. Blattner, F. R. *et al.* The complete genome sequence of *Escherichia coli* K-12. *Science* **277**, 1453-1462 (1997).

10. Cole, S. T. & Saint-Girons, I. Bacterial genomics. *FEMS Microbiol. Rev.* **14**, 139-160 (1994).

11. Freiberg, C. *et al.* Molecular basis of symbiosis between *Rhizobium* and legumes. *Nature* **387**, 394-401 (1997).

12. Bardarov, S. *et al.* Conditionally replicating mycobacteriophages: a system for transposon delivery to *Mycobacterium tuberculosis. Proc. Natl Acad. Sci. USA* **94**, 10961-10966 (1997).

13. Mahairas, G. G., Sabo, P. J., Hickey, M. J., Singh, D. C. & Stover, C. K. Molecular analysis of genetic differences between *Mycobacterium bovis* BCG and virulent *M. bovis. J. Bacteriol.* **178**, 1274-1282 (1996).

14. Kunst, F. *et al.* The complete genome sequence of the gram-positive bacterium *Bacillus subtilis. Nature* **390**, 249-256 (1997).

15. Smith, D. R. *et al.* Multiplex sequencing of 1.5 Mb of the *Mycobacterium leprae* genome. *Genome Res.* **7**, 802-819 (1997).

16. Greenacre, M. *Theory and Application of Correspondence Analysis* (Academic, London, 1984).

17. Ratledge, C. R. in *The Biology of the Mycobacteria* (eds Ratledge, C. & Stanford, J.) 53-94 (Academic, San Diego, 1982).

18. Av-Gay, Y. & Davies, J. Components of eukaryotic-like protein signaling pathways in *Mycobacterium tuberculosis. Microb. Comp. Genomics* **2**, 63-73 (1997).

19. Cole, S. T. & Telenti, A. Drug resistance in *Mycobacterium tuberculosis. Eur. Resp. Rev.* **8**, 701S-713S (1995).

20. Riley, M. & Labedan, B. in Escherichia coli *and* Salmonella (ed. Neidhardt, F. C.) 2118-2202 (ASM, Washington, 1996).

21. Mdluli, K. *et al.* Inhibition of a *Mycobacterium tuberculosis* β-ketoacyl ACP synthase by isoniazid. *Science* **280**, 1607-1610 (1998).

22. Banerjee, A. *et al.* inhA, a gene encoding a target for isoniazid and ethionamide in *Mycobacterium tuberculosis. Science* **263**, 227-230 (1994).

23. Hopwood, D. A. Genetic contributions to understanding polyketide synthases. *Chem. Rev.* **97**, 2465-2497 (1997).

24. Minnikin, D. E. in *The Biology of the Mycobacteria* (eds Ratledge, C. & Stanford, J.) 95-184 (Academic, London, 1982).

25. Barry, C. E. III *et al.* Mycolic acids: structure, biosynthesis, and physiological functions. *Prog. Lipid Res.* (in the press).

26. Belisle, J. T. *et al.* Role of the major antigen of *Mycobacterium tuberculosis* in cell wall biogenesis. *Science* **276**, 1420-1422 (1997).

27. Marahiel, M. A., Stachelhaus, T. & Mootz, H. D. Modular peptide synthetases involved in nonribosomal peptide synthesis. *Chem. Rev.* **97**, 2651-2673 (1997).

28. Gobin, J. *et al.* Iron acquisition by *Mycobacterium tuberculosis*: isolation and characterization of a family of iron-binding exochelins. *Proc. Natl Acad. Sci. USA* **92**, 5189-5193 (1995).

29. Young, D. B. & Fruth, U. in *New Generation Vaccines* (eds Levine, M., Woodrow, G., Kaper, J. & Cobon, G. S.) 631-645 (Marcel Dekker, New York, 1997).

30. Sorensen, A. L., Nagai, S., Houen, G., Andersen, P. & Anderson, A. B. Purification and characterization of a low-molecular-mass T-cell antigen secreted by *Mycobacterium tuberculosis. Infect. Immun.* **63**, 1710-1717 (1995).

31. Hermans, P. W. M., van Soolingen, D. & van Embden, J. D. A. Characterization of a major polymorphic tandem repeat in *Mycobacterium tuberculosis* and its potential use in the epidemiology of *Mycobacterium kansasii* and *Mycobacterium gordonae. J. Bacteriol.* **174**, 4157-4165 (1992).

32. Poulet, S. & Cole, S. T. Characterisation of the polymorphic GC-rich repetitive sequence (PGRS) present in *Mycobacterium tuberculosis. Arch. Microbiol.* **163**, 87-95 (1995).

33. Cole, S. T. & Barrell, B. G. in *Genetics and Tuberculosis* (eds Chadwick, D. J. & Cardew, G., *Novartis Foundation Symp. 217*) 160-172 (Wiley, Chichester, 1998).

34. Vega-Lopez, F. *et al.* Sequence and immunological characterization of a serine-rich antigen from *Mycobacterium leprae. Infect. Immun.* **61**, 2145-2153 (1993).

35. Abou-Zeid, C. *et al.* Genetic and immunological analysis of *Mycobacterium tuberculosis* fibronectin-binding proteins. *Infect. Immun.* **59**, 2712-2718 (1991).

36. Robertson, B. D. & Meyer, T. F. Genetic variation in pathogenic bacteria. *Trends Genet.* **8**, 422-427 (1992).

37. Levitskaya, J. *et al.* Inhibition of antigen processing by the internal repeat region of the Epstein-Barr virus nuclear antigen-1. *Nature* **375**, 685-688 (1995).

38. Levitskaya, J., Sharipo, A., Leonchiks, A., Ciechanover, A. & Masucci, M. G. Inhibition of ubiquitin/ proteasome-dependent protein degradation by the Gly-Ala repeat domain of the Epstein-Barr virus nuclear antigen 1. *Proc. Natl Acad. Sci. USA* **94**, 12616-12621 (1997).

39. Flynn, J. L., Goldstein, M. A., Treibold, K. J., Koller, B. & Bloom, B. R. Major histocompatibility complex class-I restricted T cells are required for resistance to *Mycobacterium tuberculosis* infection. *Proc. Natl Acad. Sci. USA* **89**, 12013-12017 (1992).

40. Bloom, B. R. & Fine, P. E. M. in *Tuberculosis: Pathogenesis, Protection, and Control* (ed. Bloom, B. R.) 531-557 (Am. Soc. Microbiol., Washington DC, 1994).

41. Collins, D. M. In search of tuberculosis virulence genes. *Trends Microbiol.* **4**, 426-430 (1996).

42. Arruda, S., Bomfim, G., Knights, R., Huima-Byron, T. & Riley, L. W. Cloning of an *M. tuberculosis* DNA fragment associated with entry and survival inside cells. *Science* **261**, 1454-1457 (1993).

43. Baumler, A. J., Kusters, J. G., Stojikovic, I. & Heffron, F. *Salmonella typhimurium* loci involved in survival within macrophages. *Infect. Immun.* **62**, 1623-1630 (1994).

44. McMurray, A. A., Sulston, J. E. & Quail, M. A. Short-insert libraries as a method of problem solving in genome sequencing. *Genome Res.* **8**, 562-566 (1998).

45. Bonfield, J. K., Smith, K. F. & Staden, R. A new DNA sequence assembly program. *Nucleic Acids Res.* **24**, 4992-4999 (1995).

46. Krogh, A., Mian, I. S. & Haussler, D. A hidden Markov model that finds genes in *E. coli* DNA. *Nucleic Acids Res.* **22**, 4768-4778 (1994).

47. Bairoch, A., Bucher, P. & Hofmann, K. The PROSITE database, its status in 1997. *Nucleic Acids Res.* **25**, 217-221 (1997).

48. Altschul, S., Gish, W., Miller, W., Myers, E. & Lipman, D. A basic local alignment search tool. *J. Mol. Biol.* **215,** 403-410 (1990).

49. Pearson, W. & Lipman, D. Improved tools for biological sequence comparisons. *Proc. Natl Acad. USA* **85,** 2444-2448 (1988).

50. Lowe, T. M. & Eddy, S. R. tRNAscan-SE: a program for improved detection of transfer RNA genes in genomic DNA. *Nucleic Acids Res.* **25,** 955-964 (1997).

Acknowledgements. We thank Y. Av-Gay, F.-C. Bange, A. Danchin, B. Dujon, W. R. Jacobs Jr, L. Jones, M. McNeil, I. Moszer, P. Rice and J. Stephenson for advice, reagents and support. This work was supported by the Wellcome Trust. Additional funding was provided by the Association Francaise Raoul Follereau, the World Health Organisation and the Institut Pasteur. S.V.G. received a Wellcome Trust travelling research fellowship.

Correspondence and requests for materials should be addressed to B.G.B. (barrell@sanger.ac.uk) or S.T.C. (stcole@pasteur.fr). The complete sequence has been deposited in EMBL/GenBank/DDBJ as MTBH37RV, accession number AL123456.

Two Feathered Dinosaurs from Northeastern China

Ji Qiang *et al.*

Editor's Note

Sinosauropteryx was soon followed by even more spectacular creatures. This report from Ji and colleagues describes two: *Protarchaeopteryx* and *Caudipteryx* which, like *Sinosauropteryx*, came from Liaoning Province in northeastern PRC. Phylogenetic analysis placed these long-legged, ground-living runners close to the origin of birds, although they were both more primitive than *Archaeopteryx* and presumably incapable of flight. Unlike *Sinosauropteryx*, however, there was no doubting that these creatures had feathers. *Protarchaeopteryx* had a switch of feathers on the end of its tail, and *Caudipteryx* appeared to have feathers fringing its forelimbs. These creatures provided a graphic demonstration that feathers appeared in evolution long before dinosaurs became capable of flight.

Current controversy over the origin and early evolution of birds centres on whether or not they are derived from coelurosaurian theropod dinosaurs. Here we describe two theropods from the Upper Jurassic/Lower Cretaceous Chaomidianzi Formation of Liaoning Province, China. Although both theropods have feathers, it is likely that neither was able to fly. Phylogenetic analysis indicates that they are both more primitive than the earliest known avialan (bird), *Archaeopteryx*. These new fossils represent stages in the evolution of birds from feathered, ground-living, bipedal dinosaurs.

Dinosauria Owen 1842
Theropoda Marsh 1881
Maniraptora Gauthier 1986
Unnamed clade
Protarchaeopteryx robusta Ji & Ji 1997

Holotype. National Geological Museum of China, NGMC 2125 (Figs 1, 2 and 3).

Locality and horizon. Sihetun area near Beipiao City, Liaoning, China. Jiulongsong Member of Chaomidianzi Formation, Jehol Group[1]. This underlies the Yixian Formation, the age of which has been determined to be Late Jurassic to Early Cretaceous[2-4].

Diagnosis. Large straight premaxillary teeth, and short, bulbous maxillary and dentary teeth, all of which are primitively serrated. Rectrices form a fan at the end of the tail.

Description. The skull of *Protarchaeopteryx* is shorter than the femur (Table 1). There are

中国东北地区两类长羽毛的恐龙

季强等

编者按

继中华龙鸟发现之后更多引人注目的生物相继被发现。这篇季强和同事们发表的文章描述了其中两种：原始祖鸟和尾羽龙，它们跟中华龙鸟一样来自中国东北地区的辽宁省。系统发育分析显示这些长腿、陆地生活的擅跑者与鸟类的起源关系密切，尽管它们都比始祖鸟原始，并且可能不会飞行。不过，与中华龙鸟不同的是，它们毫无疑问确实存在羽毛。原始祖鸟尾巴的末端发育一簇羽毛，尾羽龙的前肢边缘也覆盖羽毛。这些生物为羽毛的出现远远早于恐龙变得能够飞行提供了形象的说明。

最近关于鸟类起源及其早期演化的争论集中在鸟类是否起源于兽脚类恐龙的虚骨龙类。本文描述了在中国辽宁省上侏罗统/下白垩统炒米甸子组的两类兽脚类恐龙。虽然这两类都有羽毛，但很可能都不会飞行。系统发育分析表明两者都比已知最早的鸟类——始祖鸟更加原始。这些新的化石代表了从长有羽毛、地面生活和两足行走的恐龙向鸟类演化的阶段。

恐龙总目 Dinosauria Owen 1842

兽脚亚目 Theropoda Marsh 1881

手盗龙类 Maniraptora Gauthier 1986

未命名分类单元 Unnamed clade

粗壮原始祖鸟 *Protarchaeopteryx robusta* Ji & Ji 1997

正模标本 中国地质博物馆，标本编号 NGMC 2125（图 1、2 和 3）。

产地与层位 中国辽宁省北票市四合屯，热河群炒米甸子组九龙松段 [1]。位于义县组之下，义县组时代为晚侏罗世至早白垩世 [2-4]。

鉴定特征 大且直的前颌骨齿，短而呈球状的上颌骨齿和齿骨齿，所有的牙齿都是原始的锯齿状。尾羽在尾部末端形成扇形。

描述 原始祖鸟的头骨比股骨短（表 1）。有四颗带锯齿的前颌骨齿（图 1c），齿

four serrated premaxillary teeth (Fig. 1c), with crown heights of up to 12 mm. Premaxillary teeth of coelophysids[5], compsognathids[6,7] and early birds lack serrations, but premaxillary denticles are present in most other theropods. Six maxillary and seven dentary teeth are preserved (Fig. 1), all of which are less than a quarter the height of the premaxillary teeth. They most closely resemble those of *Archaeopteryx*[8] in shape (Figs 1b, c and 2b, c), but have anterior and posterior serrations (7–10 serrations per mm).

Table 1. Lengths of elements in *Protarchaeopteryx* and *Caudipteryx*

Element	NGMC 2125	NGMC 97-4-A	NGMC 97-9-A
Body length	690	890	725
Skull	70	76	79
Sternal plates	25	36	–
Humerus	88	69	70
Arm (humerus to end of phalange II-2)	297	214	220
Ilium	95	101	–
Ischium	–	77	–
Leg (femur to end of phalange III-4)	450	550	540
Femur	122	147	149
Tibia	160	188	182
Metatarsal III	85	115	117

Length measurements are given in millimetres. NGMC 2125, *Protarchaeopteryx*; NGMC 97-4-A and NGMC 97-9-A, *Caudipteryx*.

Fig. 1. *Protarchaeopteryx robusta.* **a**, NGMC 2125, holotype. Scale bar, 5 cm. **b**, Fourth to sixth left dentary teeth. Scale bar, 1 mm. **c**, Premaxillary teeth showing small serrations. Scale bar, 5 mm.

冠高达 12 毫米。腔骨龙类 [5]、美颌龙类 [6,7] 和早期鸟类的前颌骨齿缺少锯齿，但前颌骨齿的锯齿出现在大多数其他的兽脚类恐龙中。标本保存了六颗上颌骨齿和七颗齿骨齿（图 1），这些牙齿要短于前颌骨齿高度的四分之一。它们在形态上非常接近始祖鸟的牙齿 [8]（图 1b、1c 和图 2b、2c），但其前缘和后缘具有锯齿（每毫米 7～10 个锯齿）。

表 1. 原始祖鸟和尾羽龙骨骼成分的长度

骨骼成分	NGMC 2125	NGMC 97-4-A	NGMC 97-9-A
身长	690	890	725
头骨	70	76	79
胸骨板	25	36	–
肱骨	88	69	70
前臂（肱骨到第 II 指第 2 指骨末端）	297	214	220
髂骨	95	101	–
坐骨	–	77	–
后肢（股骨到第 III 趾第 4 趾骨末端）	450	550	540
股骨	122	147	149
胫骨	160	188	182
第 III 跖骨	85	115	117

长度测量单位是毫米。NGMC 2125 为原始祖鸟，NGMC 97-4-A 和 NGMC 97-9-A 为尾羽龙。

图 1. 粗壮原始祖鸟。**a**，NGMC 2125，正模标本，比例尺为 5 厘米。**b**，左侧第 4 到第 6 齿骨齿，比例尺为 1 毫米。**c**，前颌骨齿的小锯齿，比例尺为 5 毫米。

Fig. 2. *Protarchaeopteryx robusta*. **a**, Outline of the specimen shown in Fig. 1a. **b**, Outline of the left dentary teeth shown in Fig. 1b. **c**, Drawing of the front of the jaws, showing the large size of the premaxillary teeth compared with maxillary and dentary ones. Abbreviations: Co, coracoid; d, dentary; F, femur; f, feathers; Fib, fibula; Fu, furcula; H, humerus; m, maxilla; P, pubis; pm, premaxilla; R, radius; S, scapula; St, sternal plate; T, tibia; U, ulna. Numbers represent tooth positions from front to back.

The amphicoelous posterior cervicals are the same length as the posterior dorsals, which have large pleurocoels. If the lengths of missing segments of the tail are accounted for, there were fewer than 28 caudals. Vertebrae increase in length from proximal to mid-caudals, as in most non-avian coelurosaurs.

There are two thin, flat, featureless sternal plates. The clavicles are fused into a broad, U-shaped furcula (interclavicular angle is about 60°) as in *Archaeopteryx, Confuciusornis* and many non-avian theropods. The forelimb is shorter than the hindlimb. The arm is shorter (compared to the femur) than it is in birds, but is longer than those of long-armed non-avian coelurosaurs such as dromaeosaurids and oviraptorids (Table 2). The better preserved right wrist of NGMC 2125 has a single semilunate carpal capping the first two metacarpals. The hand has the normal theropod phalangeal formula of 2-3-4-x-x. The manus is longer than either the humerus or radius. Compared to femur length, the hand is more elongate than those of any theropods other than *Archaeopteryx*[9] and *Confuciusornis* (Table 2). More advanced birds such as *Cathayornis* have shorter hands[10]. Phalanges III-1 and III-2 in the hand of *Protarchaeopteryx* are almost the same size, and are about half the length of III-3. The unguals are long and sharp, and keratinous sheaths are preserved on two of them.

252

图 2. 粗壮原始祖鸟。**a**, 根据图 1a 绘制的标本轮廓。**b**, 根据图 1b 绘制的左侧齿骨齿轮廓。**c**, 颌部前部素描图, 显示与上颌骨齿和齿骨齿相比较大的前颌骨齿。缩写: Co, 乌喙骨; d, 齿骨; F, 股骨; f, 羽毛; Fib, 腓骨; Fu, 叉骨; H, 肱骨; m, 上颌骨; P, 耻骨; pm, 前颌骨; R, 桡骨; S, 肩胛骨; St, 胸骨板; T, 胫骨; U, 尺骨。数字代表牙齿位置的前后顺序。

双凹型的后部颈椎与后部背椎等长, 背椎具有大的侧凹。如果算上尾巴缺失的片段, 尾椎应该少于 28 节。尾椎的椎体从近端到中部逐渐加长, 这与大多数非鸟虚骨龙类一样。

有两块薄而扁平且没有明显特征的胸骨板。锁骨愈合成宽阔的 U 形叉骨 (锁骨间夹角为 60 度), 类似于始祖鸟、孔子鸟和很多非鸟兽脚类恐龙。前肢比后肢短。前臂 (与股骨相比较) 要比鸟类的对应部位短, 但要比那些非鸟虚骨龙类如驰龙类、窃蛋龙类等较长的前臂长 (表 2)。NGMC 2125 的右腕保存很好, 单一的半月形腕骨覆盖前两个掌骨。手指指式是兽脚类恐龙通常的 2-3-4-x-x。手部比肱骨和桡骨都长。和股骨长度相比较, 手指要比任何兽脚类 (除了始祖鸟 [9] 和孔子鸟) 的都要长 (表 2)。较进步鸟类诸如华夏鸟的手指比较短 [10]。原始祖鸟的第Ⅲ指第 1、2 指骨几乎等长, 大约为第 3 指骨长的一半。指爪长而锋利, 其中两枚指爪上都保存有角质鞘。

Table 2. Relative proportions of elements in relevant avian and non-avian theropods

Element	Drom	Ov	Tro	Cx	Px	Ax	Con
Arm/F	1.8–2.6	1.5–1.8	1.8	1.5	2.4	3.7	3.9
S/H	0.8	1.0–1.2	–	1.1	–	0.6	0.8
R/H	0.7–0.8	0.8–0.9	0.6–0.7	0.9	0.8	0.9	0.8
Manus/H	0.9–1.2	1.2–1.4	1.3	1.2	1.6	1.2	1.3
Manus/F	1.0	0.7–1.0	0.8	0.6	1.2	1.5	1.6
McI/McII	0.4–0.5	0.4–0.6	0.3	0.4	0.4	0.3	0.4
T/F	1.1–1.4	1.2	1.1–1.2	1.2	1.3	1.4	1.1
Leg/F	3.6	3.3	3.8	3.7	3.7	3.8	3.3
Leg/arm	1.4	1.7	2.1	2.5	1.5	1.1	0.8

All data were collected from original specimens by P.J.C. Ax, *Archaeopteryx*; Con, *Confuciusornis*; Cx, *Caudipteryx*; Drom, dromaeosaurids; F, femur; H, humerus; Mc, metacarpal; Ov, oviraptorids; Px, *Protarchaeopteryx*; R, radius; S, scapula; T, tibia; Tro, troodontids.

The preacetabular blade of the ilium is about the same length as the postacetabular blade. The pubic boot expands posteriorly. Anteriorly, the pubis is not exposed.

The tibia is longer than the femur, as it is in most advanced theropods and early birds. It is not known if the fibula extended to the tarsus.

The metatarsals are separate from each other and the distal tarsals. Metatarsal I is centred halfway up the posteromedial edge of the second metatarsal. In perching birds such as *Sinornis*[9], metatarsal I is positioned near the end of metatarsal II and is retroverted. Its condition in *Archaeopteryx* is intermediate. Pedal unguals are smaller than manual unguals.

A clump of at least six plumulaceous feathers is preserved anterior to the chest, with some showing well-developed vanes (Fig. 3a). Evenly distributed plumulaceous feathers up to 27 mm long are associated with ten proximal caudal vertebrae. Twenty-millimetre plumulaceous feathers are preserved along the lateral side of the right femur and the proximal end of the left femur.

Parts of more than twelve rectrices are preserved[11] attached to the distal caudals. One of the symmetrical tail feathers (Fig. 3b) extends 132 mm from the closest tail vertebra, and has a long tapering rachis with a basal diameter of 1.5 mm. The well-formed pennaceous vanes of *Protarchaeopteryx* show that barbules were present. The vane is 5.3 mm wide on either side of the rachis. At midshaft, five barbs come off the rachis every 5 mm (compared with six in *Archaeopteryx*), and individual barbs are 15 mm long. As in modern rectrices, the barbs at the base of the feather are plumulaceous.

表 2. 相关的鸟类和非鸟兽脚类恐龙的骨骼成分比例

骨骼成分	Drom	Ov	Tro	Cx	Px	Ax	Con
Arm/F	1.8~2.6	1.5~1.8	1.8	1.5	2.4	3.7	3.9
S/H	0.8	1.0~1.2	–	1.1	–	0.6	0.8
R/H	0.7~0.8	0.8~0.9	0.6~0.7	0.9	0.8	0.9	0.8
Manus/H	0.9~1.2	1.2~1.4	1.3	1.2	1.6	1.2	1.3
Manus/F	1.0	0.7~1.0	0.8	0.6	1.2	1.5	1.6
McI/McII	0.4~0.5	0.4~0.6	0.3	0.4	0.4	0.3	0.4
T/F	1.1~1.4	1.2	1.1~1.2	1.2	1.3	1.4	1.1
Leg/F	3.6	3.3	3.8	3.7	3.7	3.8	3.3
Leg/arm	1.4	1.7	2.1	2.5	1.5	1.1	0.8

所有数据由菲利普·柯里从原始标本收集。Arm，前臂；Ax，始祖鸟；Con，孔子鸟；Cx，尾羽龙；Drom，驰龙类；F，股骨；H，肱骨；Leg，后肢；Manus，手部；Mc，掌骨；Ov，窃蛋龙类；Px，原始祖鸟；R，桡骨；S，肩胛骨；T，胫骨；Tro，伤齿龙类。

髂骨的前、后髋臼区域大约等长。耻骨的靴状突向后扩展。耻骨前部没有暴露出来。

胫骨比股骨长，这与大多数进步的兽脚类和早期鸟类一样。但不太清楚腓骨是否延伸到跗骨。

跖骨彼此分离，并与跗骨远端分离。第 I 跖骨位于第 II 跖骨后内侧缘的一半位置。在栖禽类如中国鸟中 [9]，第 I 跖骨的位置接近第 II 跖骨末端并向后倾。始祖鸟的情形介于中间。趾爪比指爪小得多。

一丛至少包括 6 枚绒羽的羽毛保存在胸部前方，有一些显示发育很好的羽片（图 3a）。均匀分布的长达 27 毫米的绒羽，与近端 10 节尾椎相关联。20 毫米长的绒羽沿着右股骨侧面及左股骨近端保存。

多于 12 根的部分尾羽保存下来，附着在远端尾椎上 [11]。其中一根对称的尾羽（图 3b）从最近的尾椎延伸 132 毫米，羽轴长而向末端逐渐变尖，羽轴基部直径为 1.5 毫米。原始祖鸟已经成型的羽片保存有羽小枝。在羽轴任一侧的羽片宽 5.3 毫米。在羽轴中部，每隔 5 毫米有 5 个羽枝从羽轴伸出（始祖鸟是 6 个），单个羽枝长 15 毫米。而现生鸟类的尾羽中，羽毛基部的羽枝为似绒羽状。

Fig. 3. *Protarchaeopteryx robusta*, NGMC 2125. **a**, Contour and plumulaceous feathers. Scale bar, 10 mm. **b**, Rectrices. Scale bar, 5 mm.

Maniraptora Gauthier 1986
Unnamed clade

Diagnosis. The derived presence of a short tail (less than 23 caudal vertebrae) and arms with remiges attached to the second digit.

Caudipteryx zoui gen. et sp. nov.

Etymology. "*Caudipteryx*" means "tail feather"; "*zoui*" refers to Zou Jiahua, vice-premier of China and an avid supporter of the scientific work in Liaoning.

Holotype. NGMC 97-4-A (Figs 4 and 5b).

图 3. 粗壮原始祖鸟，NGMC 2125。**a**，廓羽及绒羽，比例尺为 10 毫米。**b**，尾羽，比例尺为 5 毫米。

手盗龙类　Maniraptora Gauthier 1986

未命名分类单元　Unnamed clade

鉴定特征　具有的进步特征为短尾（尾椎少于 23 节）以及前臂飞羽着生于第 II 指上。

邹氏尾羽龙（新属新种）　*Caudipteryx zoui* gen. et sp. nov.

词源　"*Caudipteryx*" 意为"尾羽"；"*zoui*" 指的是时任中国国务院副总理的邹家华，他大力支持辽宁的化石科学研究。

正模标本　NGMC 97-4-A（图 4 和图 5b）。

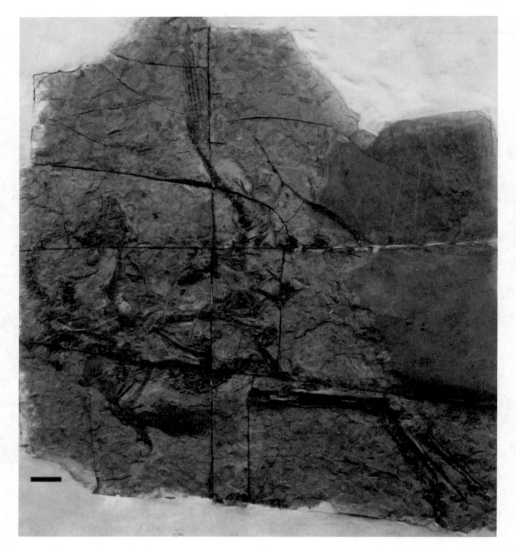

Fig. 4. *Caudipteryx zoui*, holotype, NGMC 97-4-A. Scale bar, 5 cm.

Paratype. NGMC 97-9-A (Fig. 5d).

Locality and horizon. Sihetun area, Liaoning. Jiulongsong Member of the Chaomidianzi Formation.

Diagnosis. Elongate, hooked premaxillary teeth with broad roots; maxilla and dentary edentulous. Tail short (one-quarter of the length of the body). Arm is long for a non-avian theropod; short manual claws. Leg-to-arm ratio, 2.5.

图 4. 邹氏尾羽龙，正模标本，NGMC 97-4-A。比例尺为 5 厘米。

副模标本 NGMC 97-9-A（图 5d）。

产地与层位 辽宁省四合屯，炒米甸子组九龙松段。

鉴定特征 长的钩状前颌骨齿，齿根比较宽；上颌骨和齿骨缺少牙齿。尾巴短（约为身体长度的四分之一）。作为非鸟兽脚类恐龙，其前臂较长；指爪短小。后肢与前臂长度之比为 2.5。

Fig. 5. *Caudipteryx zoui*. **a**, Haemal spines from the fourth, sixth, eighth, eleventh and thirteenth caudal vertebrae (from left to right) of NGMC 97-4-A in left lateral view. **b**, Drawing of the specimen shown in Fig. 4. **c**, Wrist of NGMC 97-4-A. **d**, Drawing of NGMC 97-9-A. **e**, Proximal tarsals of NGMC 97-9-A. Abbreviations: a, astragalus; c, calcaneum; Co, coracoid; F, femur; g, gastroliths; H, humerus; I, ilium; Is, ischium; P, pubis; R, radius; S, scapula; St, sternal plate; T, tibia; U, ulna; ?, possibly fragment of gastralia. Roman numerals represent digit numbers.

Description. The skulls of both specimens of *Caudipteryx* are shorter than the corresponding femora because of a reduction in the length of the antorbital region. The relatively large premaxilla (Figs 6 and 7) borders most of the large external naris. The maxilla and nasal are short, but the frontals and jugals are long. The lacrimal of NGMC 97-4-A is an inverted L-shaped, pneumatic bone. Scleral plates are preserved in the 20-mm-diameter orbits of both specimens. The tall quadratojugal seems to have contacted the squamosal and abutted the lateral surface of the quadrate. The single-headed quadrate is vertical in orientation. The ectopterygoid has a normal theropod hooklike jugal process. There is a broad, beak-like margin at the symphysis of the dentaries. Posteriorly, the dentary bifurcates around a large external mandibular fenestra as in oviraptorids. A well-developed, sliding intramandibular joint is present between dentary and surangular.

图 5. 邹氏尾羽龙。**a**，NGMC 97-4-A 的第 4、6、8、11、13 尾椎相应的脉弧左侧视（从左至右）。**b**，图 4 中标本的素描图。**c**，NGMC 97-4-A 的腕部。**d**，NGMC 97-9-A 的素描图。**e**，NGMC 97-9-A 的近端跗骨。缩写：a，距骨；c，跟骨；Co，乌喙骨；F，股骨；g，胃石；H，肱骨；I，髂骨；Is，坐骨；P，耻骨；R，桡骨；S，肩胛骨；St，胸骨板；T，胫骨；U，尺骨；?，可能的腹膜肋片段。罗马数字表示指/趾的顺序。

描述　　两件尾羽龙标本的头骨长度要比各自的股骨短，这是由眶前区缩短造成的。相对较大的前颌骨（图 6 和图 7）构成较大的外鼻孔的大部分边缘。上颌骨和鼻骨较短，而额骨和轭骨较长。NGMC 97-4-A 标本的泪骨呈倒转的"L"形，为含气骨骼。两件标本的巩膜板均保存在直径 20 毫米的眼眶中。高的方轭骨似乎与鳞骨连接且与方骨的侧面相邻。单头的方骨近于直立。外翼骨具有兽脚类恐龙通常具有的钩状轭骨突。齿骨联合的边缘表面宽阔且呈鸟喙状。像窃蛋龙类一样，齿骨后部围绕着大的外下颌孔分叉。非常发育的、可滑动的颌内关节存在于齿骨与上隅骨之间。

261

Fig. 6. *Caudipteryx zoui*, skull of NGMC 97-9-A in right lateral view. Scale bar, 1 cm.

Fig. 7. *Caudipteryx zoui*. **a**, Sketch of skull shown in Fig. 6. **b**, Premaxillary tooth of NGMC 97-4-A, showing resorption pit and germ tooth. Abbreviations: an, angular; d, dentary; ec, ectopterygoid; eo, exoccipital; f, frontal; h, hyoid; j, jugal; l, lacrymal; m, maxilla; n, nasal; ns, neural spine; p, parietal; pm, premaxilla; po, postorbital; q, quadrate; qj, quadratojugal; sa, surangular; sp, scleral plate; spl, splenial; t, premaxillary teeth.

There are four teeth in each premaxilla. They have elongate, needlelike crowns, and the roots are five times wider than the crowns (Fig. 7b). The lingual wall of the root of the third right tooth has been resorbed for the crown of a replacement tooth. The teeth seem

图 6. 邹氏尾羽龙，NGMC 97-9-A 头骨右侧视。比例尺为 1 厘米。

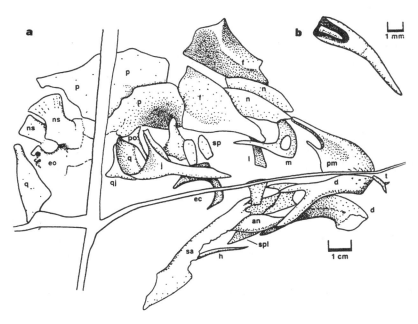

图 7. 邹氏尾羽龙。**a**，图 6 的头骨素描图。**b**，NGMC 97-4-A 的前颌骨齿，显示出再吸收窝和胚齿。缩写：an，隅骨；d，齿骨；ec，外翼骨；eo，外枕骨；f，额骨；h，舌骨；j，轭骨；l，泪骨；m，上颌骨；n，鼻骨；ns，神经棘；p，顶骨；pm，前颌骨；po，眶后骨；q，方骨；qj，方轭骨；sa，上隅骨；sp，巩膜板；spl，夹板骨；t，前颌骨齿。

　　每侧前颌骨上各有 4 颗牙齿。它们具有拉长的、像针一样的齿冠，根部是冠部的 5 倍宽（图 7b）。右侧第 3 颗牙齿齿根的舌面被一颗替换齿的齿冠再吸收。牙齿似

to have been procumbent, with an inflection at the gumline. *Caudipteryx* had no maxillary or dentary teeth.

There are ten amphicoelous cervical vertebrae and five sacrals as in most non-avian theropods and *Archaeopteryx*[8,12]. The tail of NGMC 97-4-A is articulated and well-preserved, and includes 22 vertebrae, as in *Archaeopteryx*. It is shorter than the 30-segment tails of oviraptorids. Most other non-avian theropods have much longer tails. Caudals do not become longer posteriorly, as they do in most non-avian theropods and *Archaeopteryx*. Almost two-thirds of the tail of NGMC 97-4-A is preserved as a straight rod, but the vertebrae are not fused. The first six haemal spines are elongate, rodlike structures. More posterior haemal spines decrease in height, but expand anteriorly and posteriorly (Fig. 5a).

Each segment of gastralia is formed by two pairs of slender, tapering rods, as in all non-avian theropods, *Protarchaeopteryx* and early birds[8,9,13,14].

The paired sternals are similar to those of dromaeosaurids and oviraptorids. *Confuciusornis* had a relatively larger, unkeeled sternum. Some short bones with slight expansions at each end are found near the sternal plates of NGMC 97-9-A, and may be sternal ribs.

The scapula is longer than the humerus, whereas the scapula-to-humerus ratio is less than 1.0 in flying birds (Table 2) because of humerus elongation. The clavicles are fused into a broad, U-shaped furcula in NGMC 97-9-A as in *Archaeopteryx*, *Confuciusornis* and many non-avian theropods.

Compared to the humerus, forearm length is similar to that in oviraptorosaurs (Table 2), *Archaeopteryx* and *Protarchaeopteryx*. In more advanced birds[15,16], the radius is longer than the humerus. The external surface of the ulna, as in *Archaeopteryx*[8], lacks any evidence of quill nodes.

There are three carpals preserved in NGMC 97-4-A, including a large semi-lunate one that caps metacarpals I and II as in dromaeosaurids, oviraptorids, troodontids, *Archaeopteryx*, *Confuciusornis* and other birds. Four carpals have been recognized in *Archaeopteryx*[12]. A large triangular radiale sits between the semi-lunate and the radius. A small carpal articulates with the third metacarpal. A thin wedge of bone at the end of the ulna is probably a fragment of gastralia.

The unfused metacarpals and digits of both specimens are well preserved. The third metacarpal is almost as long as the second, but is more slender. The hand has the normal theropod phalangeal formula of 2-3-4-x-x. The manus is longer than either the humerus or the radius, which is a primitive characteristic shared with most non-avian coelurosaurs, *Archaeopteryx*[9] and *Confuciusornis*. In contrast with *Archaeopteryx*, *Confuciusornis*, *Protarchaeopteryx* and many non-avian theropods (ornithomimids, troodontids, dromaeosaurids and oviraptorids), the manus is relatively short compared with the femur.

264

乎呈平伏状，齿龈有些弯曲。尾羽龙没有上颌骨齿和齿骨齿。

与大多数非鸟兽脚类恐龙和始祖鸟一样 [8,12] 有 10 个双凹型的颈椎和 5 个荐椎。NGMC 97-4-A 尾部骨骼相关节且保存完好，同始祖鸟一样共包括 22 节尾椎。这比窃蛋龙类的 30 节要短。大多数其他非鸟兽脚类恐龙都具有长得多的尾巴。尾椎没有像大多非鸟兽脚类恐龙和始祖鸟一样向后变长。NGMC 97-4-A 几乎三分之二的尾巴呈杆状，但尾椎没有愈合。前 6 个脉弧是伸长的棒状结构。靠后的脉弧高度减小，但前后向都扩展（图 5a）。

每节腹膜肋由两对细长且两端变尖的棒状小骨组成，这与所有非鸟兽脚类恐龙、原始祖鸟以及早期鸟类一样 [8,9,13,14]。

成对的胸骨与驰龙类和窃蛋龙类的相似。孔子鸟具有一个相对较大的、无龙骨突的胸骨。NGMC 97-9-A 的每个胸骨板附近都有一些短小、两端微弱膨大的骨骼，可能是胸肋。

肩胛骨比肱骨长，但在飞行鸟类中，肱骨的加长使其肩胛骨与肱骨的比率小于1.0（表 2）。NGMC 97-9-A 的锁骨愈合成宽阔的 U 形叉骨，就像始祖鸟、孔子鸟和许多非鸟兽脚类恐龙一样。

以肱骨比较，尾羽龙前臂的长度与窃蛋龙类（表 2）、始祖鸟和原始祖鸟的是较为相似的。在较进步的鸟类中 [15,16]，桡骨比肱骨长。尺骨的外表面比较像始祖鸟 [8]，缺乏羽茎节点存在的证据。

NGMC 97-4-A 有三个腕骨保存，包括一块大的覆盖第 Ⅰ、Ⅱ 掌骨的半月形腕骨，这与驰龙类、窃蛋龙类、伤齿龙类、始祖鸟、孔子鸟和其他鸟类一样。始祖鸟保存了四个腕骨 [12]。一块大的三角形桡腕骨位于半月形腕骨和桡骨之间，小的腕骨和第Ⅲ掌骨相关节。尺骨末端有块细小的楔形骨，大概是腹膜肋的碎块。

两件标本中未愈合的掌骨和指骨保存很完整。第Ⅲ掌骨和第Ⅱ掌骨差不多一样长，但较纤细。手指指式是兽脚类恐龙通常的 2-3-4-x-x。手部比肱骨和桡骨都长，这是与大多数非鸟虚骨龙类、始祖鸟 [9] 和孔子鸟共有的原始特征。同始祖鸟、孔子鸟和原始祖鸟及许多非鸟兽脚类恐龙（似鸟龙类、伤齿龙类、驰龙类和窃蛋龙类）相反的是，手部相对股骨而言要短。

The curved second manual ungual is about two-thirds the size of the same element in *Protarchaeopteryx*, and is less than 70% the length of the penultimate phalanx.

Pelvic elements are unfused, as they are in all non-avian theropods (except some ceratosaurs) and the most primitive birds[16]. The acetabulum is large, comprising almost a quarter of the length of the ilium (the ratio of acetabulum-to-ilium length is less than 0.11 in birds[17]). It has a deeper, shorter, more squared-off preacetabular region than that of *Protarchaeopteryx*, and closely resembles the ilium of dromaeosaurids[18]. The tapering postacetabular region is lower and longer than the preacetabular. The pubic peduncle is anteroposteriorly elongated, and has a notch (Figs 4 and 5b) in the ventral margin that divides the suture into two surfaces. This notch and the deep pubic peduncle of the ischium are characteristic of opisthopubic pelves. The ischium has no dorsal process such as that found in *Archaeopteryx* and *Confuciusornis*, and the shaft curves down and back. A well-developed ventromedial flange is present, perhaps indicating contact between elements. In general appearance, the ischium most closely resembles those of non-avian coelurosaurs.

The ratio of hindlimb-to-forelimb length is higher than in other coelurosaurs (Table 2) except alvarezsaurids[19], which had exceptionally short arms. The greater trochanter is separated from the lesser trochanter of the femur by a shallow notch, and forms a raised, semi-lunate rim that is similar to the trochanter femoris of birds, troodontids and avimimids.

None of the fibulae is complete, but NGMC 97-9-A has a socket for the distal end of the fibula formed by the calcaneum, astragalus and tibia. The astragalus is not fused to the tibia. The ascending process of NGMC 97-9-A (Fig. 5e) extends 22% of the distance up the front surface of the tibia, compared with 12% in *Archaeopteryx*[12]. As in *Archaeopteryx*[8], *Confuciusornis*[10] and most non-avian theropods, the calcaneum is retained as a separate, disk-like element. Two distal tarsals are positioned over the third and fourth metatarsals, as in *Archaeopteryx*, *Boluochia*[20] and all non-avian theropods that lack fused tarsometatarsals.

The metatarsals of *Caudipteryx* are not fused; this is the plesiomorphic condition expressed in most non-avian theropods. Metatarsal I is centred about a quarter of the way up the posteromedial corner of the second metatarsal. The third is the longest of the metatarsals, and in anterior view completely separates the second and fourth metatarsals, unlike in the arctometatarsalian condition of many theropods[21]. Nevertheless, at midshaft the third metatarsal is thin anteroposteriorly and is triangular in cross-section. The pedal unguals are triangular in cross-section and are about the same size as the manual unguals.

At least fourteen remiges are attached to the second metacarpal, phalanx II-1, and the base of phalanx II-2 of NGMC 97-4-A (Fig. 8a). Each remex has a well-preserved rachis and vane. The most distal remex is less than 30 mm long. The second most distal remex is 63.5 mm long, is symmetrical, and has 6.5-mm-long barbs on either side of the rachis. The fourth most distal primary remex is 95 mm long and is longer than the humerus. Unfortunately, the distal ends of the remaining remiges are not preserved. In flying birds

弯曲的第Ⅱ指爪长度是原始祖鸟同一骨骼成分的三分之二，也比倒数第2指骨长度的70%短。

腰带各骨骼未愈合，类似于所有的非鸟兽脚类恐龙（一些角鼻龙类除外）和大多数原始的鸟类[16]。髋臼很大，几乎占髂骨长度的四分之一（在鸟类中，髋臼与髂骨的比率小于0.11[17]）。它的前髋臼区域比原始祖鸟的深而短，更接近方形，十分接近驰龙类的髂骨[18]。向后端变窄的后髋臼区域要比前髋臼区域低而长。耻骨柄前后延长，在靠近腹侧边缘发育的凹槽（图4和图5b）将缝合线分开为两面。这个凹槽和深的坐骨的耻骨柄是后伸型耻骨具有的特征。坐骨没有如同始祖鸟和孔子鸟一样的背突，坐骨柄向下向后弯曲。存在发育很好的腹中缘，或许表明两骨骼之间的接触。大体上看，坐骨表现出同非鸟虚骨龙类十分相似的特征。

后肢和前肢长度的比率要比其他的虚骨龙类（除了阿瓦拉慈龙类[19]，其前臂异常短小）的高（表2）。股骨的大转子与小转子被一个浅的凹槽分开，并形成了一个突起的、半月形边缘，形态和鸟类、伤齿龙类以及拟鸟龙类的股骨转子相似。

腓骨都保存不完整，但是NGMC 97-9-A的跟骨、距骨和胫骨形成一个腓骨末端的窝。距骨没有和胫骨愈合。NGMC 97-9-A的上升突（图5e）延伸了胫骨的前表面之上距离的22%，而始祖鸟的则是12%[12]。类似于始祖鸟[8]、孔子鸟[10]和大多数非鸟兽脚类恐龙，跟骨仍保留为一分离的圆盘状骨骼。两个远端跗骨的位置超过第Ⅲ、Ⅳ跖骨，像始祖鸟、波罗赤鸟[20]以及所有缺少愈合的跗跖骨的非鸟兽脚类恐龙一样。

尾羽龙的跖骨没有愈合，这是与大多非鸟兽脚类恐龙相似的近祖性状。第Ⅰ跖骨位于第Ⅱ跖骨后内侧角向上四分之一处。第Ⅲ跖骨是最长的跖骨，从前视上看，完全地将第Ⅱ、Ⅳ跖骨分开，这与很多兽脚类恐龙[21]的窄跖型情形不同。然而，第Ⅲ跖骨的骨干前后向窄细，横截面呈三角形。趾爪的横截面是三角形，大约与指爪的尺寸相同。

NGMC 97-4-A标本中，至少有14根飞羽附着在第Ⅱ掌骨和第Ⅱ指的第1指骨上，以及第Ⅱ指第2指骨的基部（图8a）。每根飞羽上很好地保留着羽轴和羽片。最远端的飞羽长不超过30毫米。第二远端的飞羽长63.5毫米，左右对称，羽轴的两侧有6.5毫米长的羽枝。第四远端的初级飞羽长95毫米，比肱骨都长。遗憾的是，

(even *Archaeopteryx*[12]), each remex is longer than they are in *Caudipteryx*, and the most distal remiges are the longest. For example, the remiges of *Archaeopteryx*[22] are more than double the length of the femur. The barbs on either side of the rachis are symmetrical, contrasting with *Archaeopteryx* and modern flying birds[23].

Fig. 8. Feathers of *Caudipteryx zoui*, NGMC 97-4-A. **a**, Remiges of left arm. Scale bar, 1.75 cm. **b**, Rectrices, showing colour banding. Scale bar, 1 cm.

The holotype preserves ten complete and two partial rectrices. Eleven are attached to the left side of the tail, and were probably paired with another eleven feathers on the right side (only the terminal feather is preserved). Two rectrices are attached to each side of the last five or six caudal vertebrae, but not to more anterior ones. NGMC 97-9-A preserves most of nine rectrices. In *Archaeopteryx*, rectrices are associated with all but the first five or

其他飞羽的远端未能保存下来。在飞行鸟类（甚至始祖鸟[12]）中，每个飞羽都要比尾羽龙的飞羽长，且最远端的飞羽是最长的。例如，始祖鸟[22]的飞羽要长于股骨的两倍。与始祖鸟和现生飞行鸟类[23]不同，尾羽龙羽轴两侧的羽枝是左右对称的。

图 8. 邹氏尾羽龙的羽毛，NGMC 97-4-A。**a**，左臂上的飞羽，比例尺为 1.75 厘米。**b**，尾羽，显示出色带，比例尺为 1 厘米。

正模标本保存了 10 根完整的和 2 根局部的尾羽。其中 11 根羽毛附着在尾巴的左侧，可能右侧存在另外 11 根与之成对的羽毛（只有末端的羽毛保留着）。2 根尾羽附着在最后 5 或 6 节尾椎的两侧，但没有更靠前一些。NGMC 97-9-A 保留着 9 根尾羽的大部分。在始祖鸟中，尾羽和所有尾椎（除了前 5 或 6 节）相互关联[12,22]。每个

six caudals[12,22]. Each rachis has a basal diameter of 0.74 mm and tapers distally. All the feathers appear to be symmetrical (Fig. 8b), although in most cases the tips of the barbs of adjacent feathers overlap. The vane of the sixth feather is 6 mm wide on either side of the rachis.

The body of NGMC 97-4-A, especially the hips and the base of the tail, is covered by small, plumulaceous feathers of up to 14 mm long.

Both specimens have concentrations of small polished and rounded pebbles in the stomach region. These gastroliths are up to 4.5 mm in diameter, although most are considerably less than 4 mm wide.

Phylogenetic analysis

We examined the systematic positions of *Protarchaeopteryx* and *Caudipteryx* by coding these specimens for the 90 characters used in an analysis of avialan phylogeny[24] (for a matrix of these characters, see Supplementary Information). Characters were unordered, and a tree was produced using the branch-and-bound option of PAUP[25]. We rooted the tree with Velociraptorinae[26,27]. A single tree resulted with a length of 110 steps, a retention index of 0.849 and a consistency index of 0.855. Analysis shows *Caudipteryx* to be the sister group to the Avialae, and *Protarchaeopteryx* to be unresolved from the Velociraptorinae root (Fig. 9). The placement of *Protarchaeopteryx* as the sister group to *Caudipteryx*+Avialae, as the sister group to Velociraptorinae, or as the sister group to Velociraptorinae+(*Caudipteryx*+Avialae) are equally well supported by the data. Characters that define the *Caudipteryx*+Avialae clade in the shortest tree include unambiguous (uninfluenced by missing data or optimization) characters 2 and 12 and several more ambiguous ones (characters 4, 5, 10, 11, 15, 19, 24, 37, 85 and 86). *Caudipteryx* is separated from the Avialae by three unambiguous characters (7, 8 and 71) and additional ambiguous ones (characters 5, 6, 9, 10, 11, 18, 24, 39, 40, 56 and 69). The important characteristic of this phylogeny is that the Avialae (not including *Protarchaeopteryx* and *Caudipteryx*) is monophyletic; this placement is supported by the unequivocal presence of a quadratojugal that is joined to the quadrate by a ligament[17] (character 7), the absence of a quadratojugal squamosal contact (character 8) and a reduced or absent process of the ischium (character 71).

羽轴的基部直径是 0.74 毫米，并且末端越来越细。所有的羽毛都是对称的（图 8b），尽管在大多数情况下相邻羽毛的羽枝末梢是相互交叠的。第 6 根羽毛羽轴两侧的羽片均为 6 毫米宽。

在 NGMC 97-4-A 的身体上，特别是臀部和尾巴基部，覆盖着小的绒羽，长度可达 14 毫米。

两件标本在胃部区域具有密集的磨光的圆形小卵石。这些胃石的直径最大可达 4.5 毫米，不过大部分胃石的宽度远小于 4 毫米。

系统发育分析

我们将标本编码到初鸟类包含 90 个特征的系统发育分析中，检验了原始祖鸟和尾羽龙的系统发育位置 [24]（这些特征的矩阵可见补充信息。编者注：本书未收录补充信息）。特征是无序的，系统树是通过 PAUP 程序 [25] 的分支界定计算的。我们以疾走龙类作为系统树的根 [26,27]。运行 110 步得出单一的系统树，保留指数是 0.849，稠度指数是 0.855。分析显示尾羽龙和初鸟类是姊妹群，而原始祖鸟在疾走龙类分支上的位置并未能解决（图 9）。原始祖鸟与尾羽龙 + 初鸟类构成姊妹群，或与疾走龙类构成姊妹群，或与疾走龙类 +（尾羽龙 + 初鸟类）构成姊妹群，这些结果同等程度地被数据所支持。在该最短的树中，定义尾羽龙 + 初鸟类这一分支的特征包括确定的（未受缺失数据或最优化影响）特征 2 和 12，以及另外一些不甚明确的特征（特征 4、5、10、11、15、19、24、37、85 和 86）。尾羽龙可从初鸟类中划分开来，这被三个确定的特征（7、8 和 71）和其他不确定的特征（特征 5、6、9、10、11、18、24、39、40、56 和 69）所支持。这一系统关系树的重要特征是初鸟类（不包括原始祖鸟和尾羽龙）是单系的，它的定位被以下特征所支持：确切存在的方轭骨以及其与方骨以韧带连接 [17]（特征 7），方轭骨和鳞骨不接触（特征 8）以及减弱或缺失的坐骨突（特征 71）。

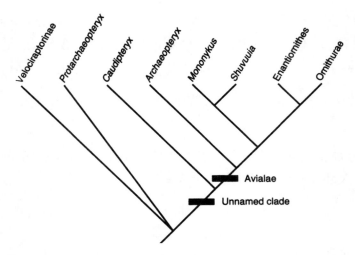

Fig. 9. Cladogram of proposed relationships of *Protoarchaeopteryx* and *Caudipteryx*. This tree is based on 90 characters and has a length of 110 steps.

As characters dealing with feathers cannot be scored relative to outgroup conditions, they were not used in the phylogenetic analysis. However, our analysis indicates that feathers can no longer be used in the diagnosis of the Avialae.

Discussion

The three *Protarchaeopteryx* and *Caudipteryx* individuals were close to maturity at the time of death. The neural spines seem to be fused to cervical and dorsal centra in *Protarchaeopteryx*. Sternal plates ossify late in the ontogeny of non-avian theropods, and are present in both *Caudipteryx* and *Protarchaeopteryx*. Well-ossified sternal ribs, wrist bones and ankle bones in *Caudipteryx* also indicate the maturity of the specimens.

The remiges of *Caudipteryx* and the rectrices of both *Protarchaeopteryx* and *Caudipteryx* have symmetrical veins, whereas even those of *Archaeopteryx* are asymmetrical. Birds with asymmetrical feathers are generally considered to be capable of flight[23], but it is possible that an animal with symmetrical feathers could also fly. Relative arm length of *Protarchaeopteryx* is shorter than that of *Archaeopteryx*, but is longer than in non-avian coelurosaurs. The arms of *Caudipteryx*, in contrast, are shorter than those of most non-avian coelurosaurs; the remiges are only slightly longer than the humerus; and the distal remiges are shorter than more proximal ones. It seems unlikely that this animal was capable of active flight. The relatively long legs of *Protarchaeopteryx* and *Caudipteryx*, both of which have the hallux positioned high and orientated anteromedially, indicate that they were ground-dwelling runners.

Paired rectrices of *Protarchaeopteryx* and *Caudipteryx* are restricted to the end of the tail, whereas in *Archaeopteryx* they extend over more than two-thirds the length of the tail[12].

图 9. 原始祖鸟和尾羽龙系统关系的进化分支图。该系统树基于 90 个特征和 110 步得出。

由于羽毛这一特征不能与外类群中的情形作出量化联系，因此羽毛特征没有用于系统发育分析当中。然而，我们的分析指出羽毛不能再作为鉴定初鸟类的特征指标。

讨 论

这三件原始祖鸟和尾羽龙的标本个体在死亡时都比较接近成熟。原始祖鸟的颈椎与背椎椎体似乎与对应的神经棘已经愈合。在非鸟兽脚类恐龙个体发育过程中，胸骨板的骨化相对较晚，但这些在尾羽龙和原始祖鸟中都是存在的。骨化较好的胸肋、腕骨和踝骨同样显示尾羽龙是成熟个体。

尾羽龙的飞羽、原始祖鸟和尾羽龙的尾羽都具有对称的纹理，但始祖鸟的这些羽毛是不对称的。具有不对称羽毛的鸟类一般被认为能够飞行 [23]，但具有对称羽毛的动物也可能会飞。原始祖鸟前臂的相对长度要比始祖鸟的短一些，但还是要比非鸟虚骨龙类的长。而尾羽龙的前臂则相反，要比大多数非鸟虚骨龙类的短；飞羽仅比肱骨长一点点；远端飞羽短于近端飞羽。这些特征都表明这种动物具备主动飞行能力是不太可能的。原始祖鸟和尾羽龙都具相对较长的腿，它们的拇趾位置比较高且指向前内侧，表明它们是陆地生活的奔跑者。

原始祖鸟和尾羽龙成对的尾羽仅局限于尾的末端，而在始祖鸟中尾羽延伸的长度可超过尾部长度的三分之二 [12]。不管是在什么情况保存下来的，我们发现半羽和

Wherever preservation made it possible, we found semi-plumes and down-like feathers around the periphery of the bodies, suggesting that most of the bodies were feather-covered, possibly like *Archaeopteryx*[28]. Feathers found with *Otogornis*[29] were also apparently plumulaceous. Plumulaceous and downy feathers cover the bodies of *Protarchaeopteryx* and *Caudipteryx*, and possibly that of *Sinosauropteryx* as well[7]. This suggests that the original function of feathers was insulation.

Phylogenetic analysis shows that both *Caudipteryx* and *Protarchaeopteryx* lie outside Avialae and are non-avian coelurosaurs. This indicates that feathers are irrelevant in the diagnosis of birds. It can no longer be certain that isolated down and semi-plume feathers[30-33] discovered in Mesozoic rocks belonged to birds rather than to non-avian dinosaurs. Furthermore, the presence of feathers on flightless theropods suggests that the hypothesis that feathers and flight evolved together is incorrect. Finally, the presence of remiges, rectrices and plumulaceous feathers on non-avian theropods provides unambiguous evidence supporting the theory that birds are the direct descendants of theropod dinosaurs.

(**393**, 753-761; 1998)

Ji Qiang[*], **Philip J. Currie**[†], **Mark A. Norell**[‡] **& Ji Shu-An**[*]

[*] National Geological Museum of China, Yangrou Hutong 15, Xisi, 100034 Beijing, People's Republic of China

[†] Royal Tyrrell Museum of Palaeontology, Box 7500, Drumheller, Alberta T0J 0Y0, Canada

[‡] American Museum of Natural History, Central Park West at 79th Street, New York, New York 10024-5192, USA

Received 19 January; accepted 27 May 1998.

References:

1. Ji, Q. *et al.* On the sequence and age of the protobird bearing deposits in the Sihetun-Jianshangou area, Beipiao, western Liaoning. *Prof. Pap. Strat. Paleo.* (in the press).

2. Hou, L.-H., Zhou, Z.-H., Martin, L. D. & Feduccia, A. A beaked bird from the Jurassic of China. *Nature* **377**, 616-618 (1995).

3. Smith, P. E. *et al.* Dates and rates in ancient lakes: ^{40}Ar-^{39}Ar evidence for an Early Cretaceous age for the Jehol Group, northeast China. *Can. J. Earth Sci.* **32**, 1426-1431 (1995).

4. Smith, J. B., Hailu, Y. & Dodson, P. in *The Dinofest Symposium, Abstracts* (eds Wolberg, D. L. *et al.*) 55 (Academy of Natural Sciences, Philadelphia, 1998).

5. Colbert, E. H. The Triassic dinosaur *Coelophysis*. *Bull. Mus. N. Arizona* **57**, 1-160 (1989).

6. Ostrom, J. H. The osteology of *Compsognathus longipes* Wagner. *Zitteliana* **4**, 73-118 (1978).

7. Chen, P.-j., Dong, Z.-m. & Zhen, S.-n. An exceptionally well-preserved theropod dinosaur from the Yixian Formation of China. *Nature* **391**, 147-152 (1998).

8. Wellnhofer, P. A new specimen of *Archaeopteryx* from the Solnhofen Limestone. *Nat. Hist. Mus. Los Angeles County Sci. Ser.* **36**, 3-23 (1992).

9. Sereno, P. C. & Rao, C. G. Early evolution of avian flight and perching: new evidence from the Lower Cretaceous of China. *Science* **255**, 845-848 (1992).

10. Zhou, Z. H. in *Sixth Symposium on Mesozoic Terrestrial Ecosystems and Biota, Short Papers* (eds Sun, A. & Wang, Y.) 209-214 (China Ocean, Beijing, 1995).

11. Ji, Q. & Ji, S. A. Protarchaeopterygid bird (*Protarchaeopteryx* gen. nov.)—fossil remains of archaeopterygids from China. *Chinese Geol.* **238**, 38-41 (1997).

12. Wellnhofer, P. Das fünfte skelettexemplar von *Archaeopteryx*. *Palaeontogr.* A **147**, 169-216 (1974).

13. Wellnhofer, P. Das siebte Exemplar von *Archaeopteryx* aus den Solnhofener Schichten. *Archaeopteryx* **11**, 1-48 (1993).

14. Hou, L. H. A carinate bird from the Upper Jurassic of western Liaoning, China. *Chinese Sci. Bull.* **42**, 413-416 (1997).

15. Dong, Z. M. A lower Cretaceous enantiornithine bird from the Ordos Basin of Inner Mongolia, People's Republic of China. *Can. J. Earth Sci.* **30**, 2177-2179 (1993).

16. Forster, C. A., Sampson, S. D., Chiappe, L. M. & Krause, D. W. The theropod ancestry of birds: new evidence from the Late Cretaceous of Madagascar. *Science* **279**, 1915-1919 (1998).

17. Chiappe, L. M., Norell, M. A. & Clark, J. M. The skull of a relative of the stem-group bird *Mononykus*. *Nature* **392**, 275-278 (1998).

18. Norell, M. A. & Makovicky, P. Important features of the dromaeosaur skeleton: information from a new specimen. *Am. Mus. Novit.* **3215**, 1-28 (1997).

19. Perle, A., Chiappe, L. M., Barsbold, R., Clark, J. M. & Norell, M. Skeletal morphology of *Mononykus olecranus* (Theropoda: Avialae) from the Late Cretaceous of Mongolia. *Am. Mus. Novit.* **3105**, 1-29 (1994).

20. Zhou, Z. H. The discovery of Early Cretaceous birds in China. *Courier Forschungsinstitut Senckenberg* **181**, 9-22 (1995).

绒羽状的羽毛围绕在身体周围，初步判断身体表面大部分披有羽毛，这些特点大概有些类似于始祖鸟 [28]。在鄂托克鸟 [29] 上发现的羽毛同样很显然是绒羽。绒羽和绒羽状羽毛覆盖原始祖鸟和尾羽龙的身体，也许中华龙鸟也是这样 [7]。这表明羽毛的最初功能是用来保温的。

系统发育分析表明了尾羽龙和原始祖鸟位于初鸟类之外，而属于非鸟虚骨龙类恐龙。这显示羽毛对于定义鸟类是一个毫不相关的特征。发现于中生代岩石中的孤立存在的半羽和绒羽状羽毛 [30-33] 将不再确切地属于鸟类，而可能为非鸟兽脚类恐龙的羽毛。而且，在不会飞的兽脚类恐龙身上存在羽毛表明羽毛和飞行同步演化的假说是不正确的。最后，非鸟兽脚类恐龙身上的飞羽、尾羽和绒羽的存在，为鸟类是兽脚类恐龙直接后裔的理论提供了确凿的证据。

（张玉光 翻译；姬书安 审稿）

21. Holtz, T. R. Jr The phylogenetic position of the Tyrannosauridae: implications for theropod systematics. *J. Paleontol.* **68,** 1100-1117 (1994).

22. deBeer, G. *Archaeopteryx lithographica. Br. Mus. Nat. Hist.* **244,** 1-68 (1954).

23. Feduccia, A. & Tordoff, H. B. Feathers of *Archaeopteryx*: asymmetric vanes indicate aerodynamic function. *Science* **203,** 1021-1022 (1979).

24. Chiappe, L. M. in *The Encyclopedia of Dinosaurs* (eds Currie, P. J. & Padian, K.) 32-38 (Academic, San Diego, 1997).

25. Swofford, D. & Begle, D. P. *Phylogenetic Analysis Using Parsimony. Version 3.1.1.* (Smithsonian Institution, Washington DC, 1993).

26. Gauthier, J. in *The Origin of Birds and the Evolution of Flight* (ed. Padian, K.) 1-55 (Calif. Acad. Sci., San Francisco, 1986).

27. Holtz, T. R. Jr Phylogenetic taxonomy of the Coelurosauria (Dinosauria: Theropoda). *J. Paleontol.* **70,** 536-538 (1996).

28. Owen, R. On the *Archaeopteryx* of von Meyer, with a description of the fossil remains of a long-tailed species, from the Lithographic Stone of Solenhofen. *Phil. Trans., Lond.* **153,** 33-47 (1863).

29. Hou, L. H. A late Mesozoic bird from Inner Mongolia. *Vert. PalAsiatica* **32,** 258-266 (1994).

30. Kurochkin, E. N. A true carinate bird from Lower Cretaceous deposits in Mongolia and other evidence of Early Cretaceous birds in Asia. *Cretaceous Res.* **6,** 271-278 (1985).

31. Sanz, J. L., Bonapart, J. F. & Lacasa, A. Unusual Early Cretaceous birds from Spain. *Nature* **331,** 433- 435 (1988).

32. Kellner, A. W. A., Maisey, J. G. & Campos, D. A. Fossil down feather from the Lower Cretaceous of Brazil. *Palaeontol.* **37,** 489-492 (1994).

33. Grimaldi, D. & Case, G. R. A feather in amber from the Upper Cretaceous of New Jersey. *Am. Mus. Novit.* **3126,** 1-6 (1995).

Supplementary information is available on *Nature*'s World-Wide Web site (http://www.nature.com) or as paper copy from the London editorial office of *Nature*.

Acknowledgements. We thank A. Brush, B. Creisler, M. Ellison, W.-D. Heinrich, N. Jacobsen, E. and R. Koppelhus, P. Makovicky, A. Milner, G. Olshevsky, J. Ostrom and H.-P. Schultze for advice, access to collections and logistic support; and the National Geographic Society, National Science Foundation (USA), the American Museum of Natural History, National Natural Science Foundation of China and the Ministry of Geology for support. Photographs were taken by O. L. Mazzatenta and K. Aulenback; the latter was also responsible for preliminary preparation of the *Caudipteryx* specimens. Line drawings are by P. J. C.

Correspondence and requests for materials should be addressed to P.J.C. (e-mail: pcurrie@mcd.gov.ab.ca).

An Electrophoretic Ink for All-printed Reflective Electronic Displays

B. Comiskey *et al.*

Editor's Note

The printed word retains some advantages over electronic displays. The subliminal flickering of screens tires the eye, and they are fragile, expensive, energy-hungry, and lose contrast in bright ambient light. This has stimulated a quest for "electronic paper" that combines the benefits of printed paper with the convenience and versatility of electronic information systems. Here researchers at MIT's Media Lab report one of the first candidate materials: a layer of transparent microcapsules on a flexible plastic sheet. Each capsule contains white and black pigment particles that can be drawn to the top surface by an electric field. This foundational paper led to a spinoff company, E-Ink, which, in partnership with microelectronics companies, now sells a range of portable display devices.

It has for many years been an ambition of researchers in display media to create a flexible low-cost system that is the electronic analogue of paper. In this context, microparticle-based displays[1-5] have long intrigued researchers. Switchable contrast in such displays is achieved by the electromigration of highly scattering or absorbing microparticles (in the size range 0.1–5 μm), quite distinct from the molecular-scale properties that govern the behaviour of the more familiar liquid-crystal displays[6]. Microparticle-based displays possess intrinsic bistability, exhibit extremely low power d.c. field addressing and have demonstrated high contrast and reflectivity. These features, combined with a near-lambertian viewing characteristic, result in an "ink on paper" look[7]. But such displays have to date suffered from short lifetimes and difficulty in manufacture. Here we report the synthesis of an electrophoretic ink based on the microencapsulation of an electrophoretic dispersion[8]. The use of a microencapsulated electrophoretic medium solves the lifetime issues and permits the fabrication of a bistable electronic display solely by means of printing. This system may satisfy the practical requirements of electronic paper.

PREVIOUS approaches to fabricating particle-based displays have been based on rotating bichromal spheres in glass cavities[1] or elastomeric slabs[2,3], and electrophoresis in glass cavities[4,5]. The advantageous optical and electronic characteristics of microparticle displays, as compared to liquid-crystal displays, result from the ability to electrostatically migrate highly scattering pigments such as titanium dioxide ($n = 2.7$), yielding a difference in optical index of refraction with the surrounding dielectric liquid of $\Delta n = 1.3$ and black pigments with very high absorption and hiding power. This results

一种可用于全印刷反射式电子
显示器的电泳墨水

与电子显示相比，印刷的文字仍然具有一定的优势。电子显示器的轻微闪烁容易使
眼睛疲劳，另外，它们易碎、昂贵、耗能，在明亮的环境光线下对比度下降。因而
刺激了能够兼顾纸质印刷物的优点和电子信息系统的便利性与广泛性的"电子纸张"
的需求。麻省理工学院媒体实验室的研究人员在本文中报道了首选材料之一：置于
软塑料片上的透明微胶囊层。每个胶囊中都含有在电场中可移向顶面的黑、白两种
颜色的微粒。这篇基础性的文章导致一个派生公司——E-Ink 的问世，该公司与微
电子公司合作后，一系列便携式显示设备已进入市场。

长期以来，显示媒介领域的研究人员一直有一种追求，即发明一种柔韧的低成
本系统，也就是实现纸张的电子模拟。在这种情况下，基于微粒的显示器 [1-5] 早已引
起了研究人员们的兴趣。这类显示器中可切换的对比度是通过强散射或强吸收微粒
（尺寸范围为 0.1~5 μm）的电迁移来实现的，完全不同于人们熟知的通过分子的性质
来调控的液晶显示器 [6]。基于微粒的显示器拥有本征双稳态，表现出极低的直流电
场编址，并且具有很高的对比度和反射率。这些特征，再加之近朗伯显示特性，就
能产生"纸上墨迹"的视觉效果 [7]。但是这类显示器却存在着寿命短，制作难度大的
缺点。本文中我们报道了一种基于电泳分散微胶囊化 [8] 的电泳型墨水的合成。使用
微胶囊化的电泳介质解决了寿命问题，并且实现了仅用印刷技术便可制造双稳态电
子显示器的要求。该系统可以达到电子纸张应用于实际的要求。

以往生产基于微粒的显示器的方法是以在玻璃腔 [1] 或弹性板 [2,3] 中的双色拧
转球，和它们在玻璃腔中的电泳 [4,5] 为基础的。与液晶显示器相比，微粒显示器具
有优越的光学和电学特性，基于高散射颜料例如二氧化钛（$n = 2.7$）的静电迁移能
力，使其和周围介电液体及高吸收和遮盖力黑色颜料之间的光学折射率差异较大
（$\Delta n = 1.3$）。从而导致散射长度很短（约 1 μm）而相应的反射率和对比度很高，效果

in a very short scattering length (~1 µm) and a correspondingly high reflectivity and contrast, similar to that of ink on paper. For comparison, typical index differences in a scattering-mode liquid crystal are less than $\Delta n = 0.25$ (ref. 9).

Despite these favourable attributes, microparticle displays at present suffer from a number of shortcomings. These include, in the case of the bichromal sphere system, difficulty in obtaining complete rotation (and thus complete contrast) due to a fall-off in the dipole force close to normal angles and difficulty of manufacture. In the case of electrophoretic systems, the shortcomings include reduced lifetime due to colloidal instability[10]. Finally, bistable display media of all types, to date, are not capable of being manufactured with simple processes such as printing. (Although recent results have been obtained in ink-jetting of electroluminescent doped polymer films for organic light-emitting structures[11], such emissive non-bistable displays do not meet a key criterion of "electronic paper", namely the persistent display of information with zero power consumption.)

To realize a printable bistable display system, we have synthesized an electrophoretic ink by microencapsulating droplets of an electrophoretic dispersion in individual microcapsules with diameters in the range of 30–300 µm. Figure 1a indicates schematically the operation of a system of microencapsulated differently coloured and charged microparticles, in which one or the other species of particles may be migrated towards the viewer by means of an externally applied electric field. Figure 1b shows cross-sectional photomicrographs of a single microcapsule addressed with positive and negative fields.

Fig. 1. Electrophoretic microcapsule. **a**, Schematic illustration of microencapsulated electrophoretic image display (white and black microparticles system). The top transparent electrode becomes positively charged, resulting in negatively-charged white microparticles migrating towards it. Oppositely charged black microparticles move towards the bottom electrode. **b**, Photomicrograph of an individual microcapsule addressed with a positive and negative field.

280

和纸上墨迹相近。相比较而言散射型液晶的典型折射率差值则小于 $\Delta n = 0.25$（参考文献 9）。

　　尽管具有这些有利的属性，现阶段的微粒显示器仍然存在许多缺点。其中包括，在双色拧转球系统中，由于在接近直角时偶极力下降，使其难以完全拧转（从而达到最大反差），此外还有制造上的困难。至于电泳系统，缺点包括胶体不稳定性[10]引起的寿命缩短。总之，至今为止，各种类型的双稳态显示媒体都不可能通过如印刷这样的简单过程来生产。（尽管用喷墨法在掺杂的电致发光聚合物薄膜上制备有机发光结构最近已有进展[11]，但这类发光非双稳态显示器并没有达到"电子纸张"的关键指标，即零能耗时信息的持久显示。）

　　为了实现可印刷的双稳态显示系统，我们合成了一种电泳墨水，通过将电泳分散的液滴微胶囊化，微胶囊的直径范围为 $30 \sim 300$ μm。图 1a 显示了不同颜色的带电微粒微胶囊化系统的操作示意图，在该系统中一种或另一种粒子可以通过外加电场移向观察者。图 1b 显示了用正负电场编址的单一微胶囊的横截面显微照片。

图 1. 电泳微胶囊。**a**，电泳成像显示器微胶囊化的示意图（黑白微粒系统）。上方的透明电极带正电，引起带负电的白色微粒向它迁移。带相反电荷的黑色微粒向下方电极迁移。**b**，用正负电场编址单个微胶囊的显微照片。

The microencapsulated electrophoretic system was synthesized using the following process. The internal phase of the microcapsules was composed of a mixed dispersion of black and white microparticles in a dielectric fluid. To obtain white microparticles, a suspension of rutile titanium dioxide (specific gravity = 4.2) in molten low-molecular-weight polyethylene was atomized. A similar process was used to prepare black microparticles with an inorganic black pigment. The resulting particles were sieved to obtain a dry powder with an average diameter of 5 μm. Alternatively, smaller monodisperse particles, with a diameter less than 1 μm, were prepared chemically. The polyethylene serves to reduce the specific gravity of the particles (typically to ~1.5) and present a modified surface chemistry for charging purposes. The particles in suspension acquire a surface charge due to the electrical double layer[12]. The black and white particles have different zeta potential (and hence different mobility) due to the electroconductivity of the black pigment[13]. These microparticles are then dispersed in a mixture of tetrachloroethylene (specific gravity, 1.6) and an aliphatic hydrocarbon (specific gravity, 0.8) which is specific-gravity-matched to the manufactured particles. In the case where the particles are designed with charges of opposite sign, they are prevented from coagulation by providing a physical polymeric adsorbed layer on the surface of each particle which provides strong inter-particle repulsive forces[10]. Alternatively, a single particle system (white microparticles) dispersed in a dyed (Oil Blue N) dielectric fluid was prepared.

This suspension, which in typical electrophoretic displays would be interposed between two glass electrodes, was then emulsified into an aqueous phase and microencapsulated by means of an *in situ* polycondensation of urea and formaldehyde. This process produces discrete mechanically strong and optically clear microcapsules. The microcapsules are optionally filtered to obtain a desired size range, and are subsequently washed and dried.

Microcapsules (white particle in dye) were prepared and dispersed in a carrier (ultraviolet-curable urethane) and subsequently coated onto a transparent conductive film (indium tin oxide (ITO) on polyester). Rear electrodes printed from a silver-doped polymeric ink were then applied to the display layer. Figure 2 shows a series of microphotographs at different magnifications in which the letter "k" has been electronically addressed in the electronic ink. The sample shown was sieved to have a mean capsule size of 40 ± 10 μm yielding a capsule resolution of ~600 dots per inch. By going to a system using structured top electrodes (or address lines as opposed to a continuous electrode), we were able to fractionally address single microcapsules, yielding an addressable resolution of ~1,200 dots per inch.

微胶囊电泳系统经由以下工序合成。微胶囊的分散相由黑白微粒在介电流体的分散系混合而成。白色微粒是通过金红石型二氧化钛（比重 = 4.2）在熔化的低分子量聚乙烯的悬浮液中雾化而成。黑色微粒可用无机黑色颜料经过类似的过程制备。所得粒子经筛分得到平均直径为 5 μm 的干粉。此外直径小于 1 μm 的较小单分散粒子可用化学方法制备。聚乙烯用来降低粒子的比重（通常降至 1.5 左右）和提供经化学修饰的表面使之能够带电。悬浮液中粒子表面电荷来自双电层作用[12]。黑色颜料的导电性使黑白粒子具有不同的界面电位（进而有不同的迁移率）[13]。这些微粒被分散于四氯乙烯（比重 1.6）和一种脂肪烃（比重 0.8）的混合物中，混合物与所制备粒子的比重相匹配。在粒子按设计分别带有异性电荷的情况下，在粒子表面上通过物理吸附覆盖上一层高聚物，使得粒子间存在强互斥力[10]以避免发生聚沉。此外，还制备了分散在染色（油蓝 N）介电流体中的单粒子系统（白色微粒）。

该悬浮液置于典型电泳显示器的两块玻璃电极之间，在水相中乳化并通过尿素和甲醛的原位缩聚反应实现微胶囊化。该方法可制得高强度、光学性能清晰、分立的微胶囊。筛选后可获得所需尺寸范围的微胶囊，随之进行清洗和干燥。

在载体（紫外光固化的聚氨酯）中制备和分散微胶囊（染料中的白色粒子）后，随即覆以透明导电薄膜（载有氧化铟锡（ITO）的聚酯）。然后，用于显示层的背电极由银掺杂的聚合物墨水印制而成。图 2 显示了不同放大率下的一系列显微照片，为字母"k"在电子墨水中的电子编址。所示样品曾经过筛选，胶囊平均尺寸为 40 ± 10 μm，得到的胶囊分辨率为每英寸约 600 点。通过运用结构化的面电极（或者编址线与连续电极方向相反）系统，我们可对部分单一微胶囊编址，得到的编址分辨率为每英寸约 1,200 点。

Fig. 2. Electrophoretic ink. Photomicrographs of 200-μm-thick film of electronic ink ("white particles in dye" type) with a capsule diameter of 40 ± 10 μm (top view). The electronically addressed letter "k" is white, other areas are blue.

In addition to making a flexible and printable system, microencapsulating the electrophoretic dispersion has solved a longstanding problem with electrophoretic displays, namely limited lifetime due to particle clustering, agglomeration and lateral migration[10]. This is because the dispersion is physically contained in discrete compartments, and cannot move or agglomerate on a scale larger than the capsule size. In ink samples that we have prepared to date, $> 10^7$ switching cycles have been observed with no degradation in performance. We have measured contrast ratios of 7:1 with 35% reflectance and a near-lambertian viewing characteristic. Using the same measurement system, we measured newspaper at 5:1 contrast and 55% reflectance. We have observed image storage times of several months, after which the material may be addressed readily.

In Fig. 3a we show maximum minus minimum reflected optical power (non-normalized contrast) versus drive frequency for several different applied fields; open symbols indicate data taken from low to high frequency, filled symbols show data from high to low frequency. Figure 3b shows plots of contrast versus applied field for different frequencies. The data in Fig. 3 were obtained for a 200-μm film of electronic ink (of the type "white particles in dye"), with capsules of diameter 40 ± 10 μm on ITO polyester with a silver-ink rear electrode.

图 2. 电泳墨水。胶囊直径为 40±10 μm，厚度为 200 μm 的电子墨水（"染料中白色粒子"型）薄膜显微照片（俯视图）。电子编址的字母"k"为白色，其他区域为蓝色。

除了制作灵活的可印刷系统之外，微胶囊电泳分散法解决了电泳显示器的一个存在已久的问题，即由于粒子簇集，聚沉，以及横向迁移带来的寿命受限问题[10]。因为分散被物理地限制在分立的空间中，移动和聚集都不可能超出胶囊的尺寸。目前为止，我们制备的墨水样品，经 10^7 次以上的切换循环，没有观测到性能有所下降。测量得到的对比度为 7:1，反射率为 35%，并且观测到近朗伯显示特性。运用相同的测量系统，我们测得报纸的对比度为 5:1，反射率为 55%。而且经几个月的存放后，该材料仍然可以很容易地编址。

图 3a 中展示了反射光强的最大和最小值之差（对比度未归一化）与不同外加场下驱动频率的关系；空心图形代表频率由低至高时采集的数据，实心图形代表频率由高至低时所采集的数据。图 3b 为不同频率下对比度与外加电场的关系。图 3 中的数据源于 200 μm 的电子墨水（"染料中白色粒子"型）薄膜，在具有银墨水背电极的 ITO 聚酯膜上的胶囊直径为 40±10 μm。

Fig. 3. Properties of a 200-μm-thick film of electronic ink ("white particles in dye" type) with capsule diameter of 40 ± 10 μm. **a**, Maximum minus minimum reflected optical power (contrast) versus drive frequency for several different applied fields (open symbols, data taken from low to high frequency; filled symbols, from high to low frequency). **b**, Plot of contrast versus applied field for different frequencies.

We may calculate the particle mobility, zeta potential and charge per particle as follows. The low-frequency asymptote in Fig. 3a indicates that at sufficiently slow driving frequency there is time for the internal particles to make a full traverse of the capsule, after which there is no further contribution to the contrast. Thus the cusp of the sigmoid in Fig. 3a may be taken to indicate the frequency (5 Hz) at which the particle just traverses a round trip (2×40 μm $= 80$ μm) in the microcapsule yielding a velocity of $v = 400$ μm s^{-1}. The Reynolds number is given by Re $= \rho v r \eta^{-1}$ where ρ is the internal fluid density, r is the particle radius, η is the internal fluid viscosity and v is the particle velocity. For the present system we have $\rho = 1.6 \times 10^{-15}$ kg μm^{-3}, $v = 400$ μm s^{-1}, $r = 0.5$ μm, and $\eta = 0.8 \times 10^{-9}$ kg μm^{-1} s^{-1}; and Re $= 0.0004 \ll 1$ and the flow is laminar[14]. The transient time to establish the laminar flow may be estimated from the Navier–Stokes equation to be $\tau_{ss} = (1/9) r^2 \rho \eta^{-1} = 55$ ns. Thus for time-scales of interest, the particle mobility is given as $\mu = v/E = \epsilon\zeta/6\pi\eta = q/12\pi r\eta$ where ϵ is the dielectric constant of the internal fluid, ζ is the zeta potential of the particles and q is the charge per particle. Thus for our system we have

图 3. 胶囊直径为 40±10 μm，厚度为 200 μm 的电子墨水（"染料中白色粒子"型）薄膜的属性。**a**，反射光强的最大值与最小值之差（对比度）与不同外场下驱动频率的关系（空心图形，频率由低至高采集的数据；实心图形，频率由高至低所采集的数据）。**b**，不同频率下对比度与外场的关系。

　　我们可以通过如下方法计算粒子的迁移率、界面电位和单位粒子的荷电量。图 3a 中低频渐近线意味着当驱动频率足够低时，内部粒子有时间完全横穿胶囊，之后对对比度没有进一步的贡献。因此图 3a 中 S 形的突起点可以视为粒子刚好在胶囊中以 5 Hz 的频率往返一周（2×40 μm = 80 μm）时的速率，为 $v = 400$ μm·s^{-1}。雷诺常数由 Re = $\rho v r \eta^{-1}$ 给出，其中 ρ 为内部流体密度，r 为粒子半径，η 为内部流体黏度，v 为粒子速度。对于现在的系统，有 $\rho = 1.6 \times 10^{-15}$ kg·μm^{-3}，$v = 400$ μm·s^{-1}，$r = 0.5$ μm，$\eta = 0.8 \times 10^{-9}$ kg·μm^{-1}·s^{-1}，Re = 0.0004 ≪ 1，并且流动为层流[14]。确定层流的瞬态时间可以从纳维–斯托克斯方程中估算出来，为 $\tau_{ss} = (1/9)\ r^2 \rho \eta^{-1} = 55$ ns。因此在我们所感兴趣的时间尺度之内，粒子迁移率可以表示为 $\mu = v/E = \epsilon\zeta/6\pi\eta = q/12\pi r\eta$，其中 ϵ 为内部流体的介电常数，ζ 为粒子的界面电位，q 为单位粒子的电量。对于我们的系统，$\mu = 169$ μm^2·V^{-1}·s^{-1}，$\epsilon = 2.5 \times 8.85 \times 10^{-6}$ kg·μm·s^{-2}·V^{-2}，$\zeta = 120$ mV，

$\mu = 169\ \mu m^2\ V^{-1}\ s^{-1}$, $\epsilon = 2.5 \times 8.85 \times 10^{-6}\ kg\ \mu m\ s^{-2}\ V^{-2}$, $\zeta = 120\ mV$, and $q = 2.6 \times 10^{-18}\ C = 16 e^{-}$. The very small charge per particle indicates the mechanism for "field-off" bistability. Particle/capsule-wall and particle/particle binding dominate the particle/particle repulsion coming from the very small charge per particle. Other mechanisms for "field-off" bistability include charge redistribution and minimization.

Figure 3a indicates the compromise between switching speed and contrast; Fig. 3b shows the compromise between applied field and contrast. In both sets of curves, the high-contrast asymptote indicates the regime in which the particles have made full traverse of the capsule, and further time or applied field has no further consequence. Two-particle (black/white particles) systems, as opposed to "single particle in dye" systems, relax these trade-offs due to the absence of exponential light absorption in the dye case due to dye interstitially present between white particles.

In order to efficiently address a large number of pixels, matrix addressing is required. Matrix addressing in turn requires that either the contrast material (passive matrix) or an underlying electronic layer (active matrix) possess a threshold in order to prevent crosstalk between address lines. Typically, the display material may support passive matrix addressing for small numbers of pixels[15]. Larger numbers of pixels require the nonlinearity of an electronic element as implemented in active matrix addressing[16]. Active matrix structures, typically formed from polysilicon on glass, are expensive and would obviate many of the advantages of a flexible low-cost paper-like display. Our group has recently demonstrated an all-printed metal–insulator–metal (MIM) diode structure[17] capable of forming the active matrix for electrophoretic ink, which should enable us to drive high-pixel-count sheets of electrophoretic ink while maintaining the ease of fabrication and low-cost structure provided by the ink material itself. Work by other groups may also be of use in this endeavour[18]. We believe that such systems will open up a new field of research in printable microscopic electro-mechanical systems. Coupled with recent advances in printable logic, such technology offers the prospect of fundamentally changing the nature of printing, from printing form to printing function.

(**394**, 253-255; 1998)

Barrett Comiskey, J. D. Albert, Hidekazu Yoshizawa & Joseph Jacobson
Massachusetts Institute of Technology, The Media Laboratory, 20 Ames Street, Cambridge, Massachusetts 02139-4307, USA

Received 8 December 1997; accepted 18 May 1998.

References:

1. Pankove, J. I. *Color Reflection Type Display Panel* (Tech. Note No. 535, RCA Lab., Princeton, NJ, 1962).

2. Sheridon, N. K. & Berkovitz, M. A. The gyricon–a twisting ball display. *Proc. Soc. Information Display* **18**(3,4), 289-293 (1977).

3. Sheridon, N. K. *et al.* in *Proc. Int. Display Research Conf.* (ed. Jay Morreale) L82–L85 (Toronto, 1997).

4. Ota, I., Honishi, J. & Yoshiyama, M. Electrophoretic image display panel. *Proc. IEEE* **61**, 832-836 (1973).

5. Dalisa, A. L. Electrophoretic display technology. *IEEE Trans. Electron Devices* **ED-24**(7), 827-834 (1977).

6. Castellano, J. A. & Harrison, K. J. in *The Physics and Chemistry of Liquid Crystal Devices* (ed. Sprokel, G. J.) 263-288 (Plenum, New York, 1980).

$q = 2.6 \times 10^{-18}$ C $= 16e^-$。单位粒子带电量极低表示遵守"去场"双稳态机制。粒子/胶囊壁和粒子/粒子间的结合对来自带电量很小的微粒间的粒子/粒子互斥起主导作用。"去场"双稳态的其他机制包括电荷再分布以及最小化。

图 3a 指示出切换速度与对比度之间的制约关系；图 3b 显示了外场与对比度之间的制约关系。在两组曲线中，高对比度渐近线暗示着粒子完全穿越胶囊的机制，随后时间和外场都不再起作用。和"染料中的单粒子系统"不同的是，在双粒子（黑/白粒子）系统中，由于白粒子处于染料之中，而染料对光不发生指数型吸收，因而削弱了这种制约。

大量像素的有效编址要应用矩阵编址。矩阵编址又依次要求对比材料（被动矩阵）或者基本电层（主动矩阵）具有一个阈值以防止编址线之间的串扰。通常，显示材料可以支持少量像素的被动矩阵编址[15]。大量像素要求电子元件在实现主动矩阵编址时具有非线性[16]。主动矩阵结构，通常是由在玻璃上的多晶硅形成，昂贵而且不具备低成本的柔韧性类纸张显示器的许多优点。我们的团队近期提出了一种可印刷的金属-绝缘体-金属（MIM）的二极管结构[17]，可以组成电泳墨水的主动矩阵，应当有可能使驱动电泳墨水的高像素数印刷板成为现实，因为使用了这种墨水材料，保持了制造的简单易行和结构的低成本。其他团队的工作也可能应用到这项研究之中[18]。我们相信这种系统会开创可印刷微观机电系统的一个新研究领域。结合现阶段其他可印刷技术的思路，这种技术预期将从根本上改变印刷的特性，从印刷形式到印刷功能。

（崔宁 翻译；宋心琦 审稿）

7. Fitzhenry-Ritz, B. Optical properties of electrophoretic image displays. *IEEE Trans. Electron Devices* **ED-28**(**6**), 726-735 (1981).

8. Comiskey, B., Albert, J. D. & Jacobson, J. Electrophoretic ink: a printable display material. In *Digest of Tech. Papers* 75-76 (Soc. Information Display, Boston, 1997).

9. Okada, M., Hatano, T. & Hashimoto, K. Reflective multicolor display using cholesteric liquid crystals. In *Digest of Tech. Papers* 1019-1026 (Soc. Information Display, Boston, 1997).

10. Murau, P. & Singer, B. The understanding and elimination of some suspension instabilities in an electrophoretic display. *J. Appl. Phys.* **49**, 4820-4829 (1978).

11. Hebner, T. R., Wu, C. C., Marcy, D., Lu, M. H. & Sturm, J. C. Ink-jet printing of doped polymers for organic light emitting devices. *Appl. Phys. Lett.* **72**, 519-521 (1998).

12. Fowkes, F. M., Jinnai, H., Mostafa, M. A., Anderson, F. W. & Moore, R. J. in *Colloids and Surfaces in Reprographic Technology* (eds Hair, M. & Croucher, M. D.) (Am. Chem. Soc., Washington DC, 1982).

13. Claus, C. J. & Mayer, E. F. in *Xerography and Related Processes* (eds Dessauer, J. H. & Clark, H. E.) 341-373 (Focal, New York, 1965).

14. Landau, L. D. & Lifshitz, E. M. *Fluid Mechanics* (Pergamon, New York, 1959).

15. Ota, I., Sato, T., Tanka, S., Yamagami, T. & Takeda, H. Electrophoretic display devices. In *Laser 75* 145-148 (Optoelectronics Conf. Proc., Munich, 1975).

16. Shiffman, R. R. & Parker, R. H. An electrophoretic image display with internal NMOS address logic and display drivers. *Proc. Soc. Information Display* **25.2**, 105-115 (1984).

17. Park, J. & Jacobson, J. in *Proc. Materials Research Soc.* B8.2 (Mater. Res. Soc., Warrendale, PA, 1998).

18. Service, R. F. Patterning electronics on the cheap. *Science* **278**, 383 (1997).

Correspondence and requests for materials should be addressed to J.J. (e-mail: jacobson@media.mit.edu).

Asynchrony of Antarctic and Greenland Climate Change during the Last Glacial Period

T. Blunier *et al.*

Editor's Note

Clues to the mechanisms of natural climate shifts can be gleaned from looking at whether or not they happen synchronously across the globe. This is particularly pertinent for the rapid climate transitions seen in ice-core records of temperature during the last ice age. Here Thomas Blunier of the University of Bern and his coworkers compare these fast climate fluctuations between Greenland in the Northern Hemisphere and Antarctica in the Southern Hemisphere. They find that the Antarctic events happen about 1,000–2,500 years before those in Greenland. The researchers suspect that ocean circulation links the hemispheric climates: changes that originate in the south are transferred to the north by concomitant changes to circulation in the North Atlantic.

A central issue in climate dynamics is to understand how the Northern and Southern hemispheres are coupled during climate events. The strongest of the fast temperature changes observed in Greenland (so-called Dansgaard–Oeschger events) during the last glaciation have an analogue in the temperature record from Antarctica. A comparison of the global atmospheric concentration of methane as recorded in ice cores from Antarctica and Greenland permits a determination of the phase relationship (in leads or lags) of these temperature variations. Greenland warming events around 36 and 45 kyr before present lag their Antarctic counterpart by more than 1 kyr. On average, Antarctic climate change leads that of Greenland by 1–2.5 kyr over the period 47–23 kyr before present.

GREENLAND ice-core isotopic records[1,2] have revealed 24 mild periods (interstadials) of 1–3 kyr duration during the last glaciation[1] known as Dansgaard–Oeschger (D–O) events[3], where temperature increased by up to 15 °C compared with full glacial values[4,5]. The temperature over Greenland is essentially controlled by heat released from the surface of the North Atlantic Ocean[6]. This heat is brought to the North Atlantic by the thermohaline circulation which is driven by the North Atlantic Deep Water (NADW) formation[7]. NADW strongly influences the deep circulation on a global scale. Therefore climate change related to the North Atlantic thermohaline circulation is not restricted to the North Atlantic region but has global implications[8]. Data correlating with D–O events have been found, for examples in the southern Atlantic[9], the Pacific Ocean[10] and probably also the Indian Ocean[11]. On the continents, related events were found in North America where D–O events are manifested as wetter climate periods[12,13]. Also, the hydrological cycle

末次冰期南极和格陵兰气候变化的非同步性

布鲁尼尔等

编者按

有关自然气候变化机制的线索可以通过考察其是否在全球同步发生来收集。这尤其适合用来研究末次冰期期间冰芯温度记录所展现的气候快速变化问题。本文中，来自伯尔尼大学的托马斯·布鲁尼尔及其合作者比较了北半球格陵兰和南半球南极二者间的这些快速气候波动。他们发现南极的事件比格陵兰的对应事件早发生约1,000~2,500年。研究者们猜测海洋环流联动了两个半球的气候：起源于南半球的变化，通过伴随的北大西洋环流的变化，传递至北半球。

气候动力学的核心问题是弄清在气候事件发生过程中南北半球之间如何耦合。在格陵兰观测到的末次冰期内最强的快速温度变化（所谓丹斯果–厄施格尔事件）和南极温度记录有一定的相似性。对比南极和格陵兰冰芯中记录的全球大气甲烷浓度，可以确定这些温度变化之间的位相关系（超前还是滞后）。距今3.6万年和4.5万年的格陵兰增暖比南极相应的温度变化滞后1,000年以上。总的说来，在距今4.7万年前到2.3万年前期间南极气候变化比格陵兰的超前1,000~2,500年。

格陵兰冰芯的同位素记录[1,2]揭示在末次冰期内[1]有24个时间长度约1,000年到3,000年、称之为丹斯果–厄施格尔事件（简称D–O事件）[3]的温暖时段（间冰阶），当时其温度与整个冰期的温度相比增高达15℃[4,5]。格陵兰的温度基本上受控于北大西洋洋面所释放的热量[6]，这些热量是由北大西洋深层水（NADW）的生成所驱动的温盐环流带到北大西洋洋面的[7]。NADW强烈地影响着全球范围海洋的深层环流，因此，和北大西洋温盐环流有关的气候变化并不局限于北大西洋地区，而是有着全球性的影响[8]。例如在南大西洋[9]、太平洋[10]，可能还包括印度洋[11]，都已发现与D–O事件有关的记录。在大陆上，有关的事件在北美也有发现，该地D–O事件表现为更湿润的气候特征[12,13]。热带水循环的变化似乎也和D–O事件同步出

in the tropics appears to have changed in parallel with D–O events. This is indicated by changes in atmospheric methane concentration, the main source of which is wetlands situated in the tropics during the last glaciation[14].

Temperature variations in Greenland inferred from the $\delta^{18}O$ record are characterized by fast warmings and slow coolings during the last glaciation. Antarctic temperature variations (from $\delta^{18}O$ and δD records) show a different pattern with fewer, less pronounced and rather gradual warming and cooling events over the same period[15,16].

One of the great challenges of climate research is therefore to find a mechanism that is able to reconcile the very different dynamical behaviour of high-latitude Northern and Southern hemispheres and their phase relationship during rapid climate change. A crucial test for our understanding of climate change is the relative phase of events in the two hemispheres. Using the global isotopic signal of atmospheric oxygen, Bender et al.[17] hypothesized that interstadial events start in the north and spread to the south provided that they last long enough (~2 kyr), postulating that northern temperature variations lead those in Antarctica. On the other hand, they did not exclude the possibility that corresponding events are out of phase, as suggested by Stocker et al.[18] on the basis of a simplified ocean–atmosphere model which shows that heat is drawn from the Antarctic region when NADW switches on at the onset of a D–O event. This leads to a cooling of surface air temperatures in the south and a corresponding warming in the north. Charles et al.[9] used stable-isotope ratios of benthic and planktonic foraminifera in a single core from the Southern Ocean to argue that the Northern Hemisphere climate fluctuations lagged those of the Southern Hemisphere by ~1.5 kyr. They conclude that a direct link of high-latitude climate is not promoted by deep-ocean variability.

Conclusive information regarding the phase lag of climate events can come only from high-resolution palaeoarchives which have either absolute or synchronized timescales with uncertainties smaller than 500 yr (for example, to distinguish the Younger Dryas from the Antarctic Cold Reversal[19], hereafter YD and ACR). This prerequisite is at present satisfied only in polar ice cores. Here we use fast variations in methane during the last glaciation for a synchronization that permits a better estimate of the relative timing of events in the two hemispheres.

The CH_4 records from two Antarctic ice cores (Byrd station 80° S, 120° W; Vostok 78.47° S, 106.80° E) and one Greenland core (GRIP ice core, Summit 72.58° N, 37.64° W) have been used to establish coherent timescales for the Antarctic cores with respect to the GRIP timescale over the period from 50 kyr BP to the Holocene epoch. The timescale for the Greenland reference core (GRIP) has been obtained by stratigraphic layer counting[20] down to 14,450 yr BP with an uncertainty of ± 70 yr at 11,550 yr BP (termination of the YD). For older ages, the chronology is based on an ice-flow model[21]. This timescale is not considered to be absolute; for instance, the model-based dating differs from the stratigraphic layer counting in the deeper part of the core by several thousand years. However, our conclusions do not depend on the particular timescale, as explained below.

现。这种末次冰期时热带水循环的改变，以源于热带湿地的大气甲烷浓度的变化为标志 [14]。

从 $\delta^{18}O$ 记录中推断出格陵兰在末次冰期中的温度变化特征表现为快速增暖和缓慢变冷。南极在同一时期的温度变化（从 $\delta^{18}O$ 和 δD 记录推断）则显示出不同的模态：即较少的、不那么显著且较为渐进的增暖和变冷事件 [15,16]。

因此，气候研究的最大挑战之一就是找出一种能够调和高纬度南北半球气候快速变化之间显著不同的动力行为以及位相关系的机制。对两半球发生的事件的相对位相的研究是认识气候变化的重要的检验方法之一。本德等 [17] 分析了全球大气中的氧同位素信息，提出猜想认为如果间冰阶事件持续时间足够长（约 2,000 年），那么这些事件开始于北半球，然后向南半球扩展，即假设北半球温度变化导致了南极温度的变化。另外，这些实验也不排除两半球对应事件异相的可能性，如同施托克尔等 [18] 从一个简化的海洋–大气模式中展示的那样：在 D–O 事件伊始，NADW 开启，热量从南极地区流出。这就使南半球地表气温降低，北半球温度对应升高。查尔斯等 [9] 应用南大洋一个岩芯中底栖和浮游有孔虫的稳定同位素比率资料，提出北半球的气候波动比南半球滞后 1,500 年左右。他们的结论是，两半球高纬度气候的直接联系并非由深海的变化促成。

关于气候事件之间位相滞后的关键信息只能来自高分辨率的古资料，它需要绝对的或同步化的时标，其不确定性要小于 500 年（以便区分如南极转冷期 [19]（ACR）和新仙女木期（YD））。现在只有极地冰芯可以满足这一先决条件。我们应用了末次冰期内的甲烷快速变化以保证同步化的时标，这样就可以对两半球气候事件之间的相对时间有更好的估计。

应用两个南极冰芯（80°S，120°W 的伯德站冰芯和 78.47°S，106.80°E 的东方站冰芯）和一个格陵兰冰芯（72.58°N，37.64°W 的萨米特站的 GRIP 冰芯（GRIP 即格陵兰冰芯计划））的 CH_4 记录，建立距今 5 万年前到全新世时期南极冰芯相对于 GRIP 冰芯的同步时标。应用地层计数法 [20] 已经将格陵兰参考冰芯（GRIP 冰芯）的时标向下标定至距今 14,450 年，在距今 11,550 年（YD 结束时）存在 ±70 年的不确定性。对于更早的时期，其年代由冰流模型确定 [21]。这样确定的时标并不是绝对的，例如，基于模型的定年和用地层计数法得到的冰芯深部年龄有数千年的差异。无论如何，如下所述，我们的结论并不依赖于求得的个别时标。

We are able to show that long-lasting Greenland warming events around 36 and 45 kyr BP (D–O events 8 and 12) lag their Antarctic counterpart by 2–3 kyr (comparing the starting points of corresponding warmings). On average, Antarctic climate change leads that of Greenland by 1–2.5 kyr over the period 47–23 kyr BP. This finding contradicts the hypothesis that Antarctic warmings are responses to events in the Northern Hemisphere[17]. The observed time lag also calls into question a coupling between northern and southern polar regions via the atmosphere, and favours a connection via the ocean. Indeed, climate models[18,22–24] suggest that heat is extracted from the Southern Hemisphere when NADW formation switches on. This interhemispheric coupling is clearly identified in interstadial events 8 and 12, as well as during the termination of the last glaciations.

Synchronization of Ice-core Records

Because the porous firn layer on the surface of the ice sheet exchanges air with the overlying atmosphere, air, which gets enclosed in bubbles at 50–100 m below the surface (present-day conditions), has a mean age which is younger than the surrounding ice[5]. Consequently, a timescale for the ice and a timescale for the air need to be known, both of which depend on local climate characteristics. For GRIP, the difference between the age of the ice and the mean age of the gas at close-off depth (Δage) has been calculated using a dynamic model[5] for firn densification and diffusional mixing of the air in the firn, including the heat transport in the firn and temperature dependence of the close-off density. For Summit, estimates of the main parameters—accumulation rate and temperature[4,25]—allow the calculation of Δage with an uncertainty of only ± 100 yr between 10 and 20 kyr BP, increasing to ± 300 yr back to 50 kyr BP (ref. 5). Temperature was deduced from the δ^{18}O profile as suggested from borehole temperature measurements for the glacial–interglacial transition[4], corresponding roughly to a linear dependence with a slope of 0.33‰ per °C. This relation is in contrast to today's relation[26] with a slope of 0.67‰ per °C. However, there is good evidence that the δ^{18}O–temperature relation was close to the one derived from the borehole temperature profile throughout the past 40 kyr (ref. 5).

The model calculations are confirmed by an independent measurement of Δage on the GISP2 core, drilled 30 km to the west of the GRIP drill site. A Δage of 809 ± 20 yr was determined, on the basis of thermal fractionation of nitrogen at the termination of YD[27]. This is consistent with Δage of 775 ± 100 yr for the YD calculated with the same model used here[5].

Two steps are necessary to synchronize ice cores via a gas record: (1) correlation of the CH$_4$ records, and (2) calculation of the age of the ice by determining Δage. The initial GRIP CH$_4$ profile[14,28] was refined between 9 and 55 kyr BP by an additional 180 samples measured both in the Bern and Grenoble laboratories, resulting in a mean sampling resolution of about 150 yr in the period of interest. A number of new samples were measured on the Antarctic cores from Byrd and Vostok station; 179 and 56, respectively. These measurements cover the time period 9–47 kyr BP on Byrd and 30–43 kyr BP on Vostok,

我们能够说明的是，发生在大约距今 3.6 万年前和 4.5 万年前（D–O 事件 8 和 12）的持续较长的格陵兰增暖事件比南极的相应事件滞后 2,000~3,000 年（由对比相应的增暖事件的开始时间而得）。平均说来，在距今 4.7 万到 2.3 万年前的南极气候变化比格陵兰超前 1,000~2,500 年。这一发现反驳了南极增暖是对北半球对应事件的响应这一假设[17]。所观测到的时间滞后使人们对南北半球极区间的耦合是通过大气来实现的观点产生怀疑，转而支持通过海洋产生关联的观点。实际上气候模式[18,22-24]显示，当 NADW 的形成开启，它将从南半球获得热量。这种半球之间的耦合关系可以从间冰阶事件 8 和 12 以及末次冰期的结束期中被清晰地辨认出来。

冰芯记录的同时化

由于冰盖表面覆盖的透气粒雪层和其上的大气间有空气交换，包裹在冰盖表面（指现代冰盖表面）以下 50~100 m 处气泡中的空气的平均年代比周围冰的年代要晚[5]。因此需要知道冰的时标和空气的时标，它们二者都取决于当地的气候特点。对于 GRIP 冰芯，冰的年代和包裹在深处气泡中的气体的平均年代的差（Δage）已经可以用一个关于雪粒致密化和雪粒中空气扩散混合的动力学模式[5]计算出来，该模式考虑了雪粒中的热量输送与封闭密度对温度的关系。对于萨米特站，通过主要参数（累积率和温度[4,25]）的估计可以算出 Δage，其不确定性在距今 1 万到 2 万年间仅为 ±100 年，到距今 5 万年时不确定性增加到 ±300 年（见参考文献 5）。就像对冰期–间冰期转换期间钻孔温度的测量[4]那样，温度可由 $\delta^{18}O$ 廓线推导出来，二者粗略符合斜率为 0.33‰/℃ 的线性关系。这一关系和现今斜率为 0.67‰/℃ 的关系[26]大不相同。不过，有充分的证据表明 $\delta^{18}O$–温度关系和从过去 4 万年钻孔温度廓线得来的关系是相近的（见参考文献 5）。

模式的计算结果已被 GRIP 冰芯钻孔点西面 30 km 处的 GISP2 冰芯（格陵兰冰盖计划 2）独立测量的 Δage 值证实。根据 YD 结束时氮的热力学分级[27]，Δage 值为 809±20 年。这和应用同一模式对 YD 时期计算得到的 775±100 年的 Δage 值是一致的[5]。

应用气体记录使冰芯资料同时化需要两个步骤：(1) CH_4 记录的相关性计算。(2) 通过求 Δage 计算冰的年代。结合伯尔尼和格勒诺布尔的两个实验室测量的 180 个样本，初始的 GRIP 冰芯 CH_4 廓线[14,28]在距今 9,000 年到 5.5 万年段的精度得以提高，这使得其平均采样分辨率在所关心的时段可达到 150 年左右。在南极伯德站和东方站冰芯测得了大量新的样本，两站样本数分别为 179 和 56。这些观测值涵盖伯德站距今 9,000 年到 4.7 万年时期和东方站距今 3 万到 4.3 万年的时期，其平均采

with a mean sampling resolution of 200 and 250 yr, respectively. For the synchronization of the CH_4 records, a Monte Carlo method was used, searching for a maximal correlation between the records[5]. The fast CH_4 variations allow us to fit the records to ±200 yr. The time period 25–17 kyr BP was excluded from the synchronization because only low CH_4 variations appear during that period, making the correlation uncertain.

The uncertainty in Δage for the Antarctic sites is dominated by the uncertainty in temperature and accumulation. Estimates of the glacial–interglacial temperature difference at Vostok and Byrd station range from 7 to 15 °C (refs 29, 30). This range is covered in our Δage calculations for Byrd station (see Methods). Δage for the Byrd core is one order of magnitude smaller than for the Vostok core, and comparable to the GRIP Δage. This makes the synchronization of isotopes more convincing for Byrd/GRIP than for Vostok/GRIP (see below and Methods).

To validate the resulting timescales, the distinct double peak of the cosmogenic radioisotope ^{10}Be around 40 kyr BP can be used. The GRIP ^{10}Be record[31] is plotted together with that of Byrd[32] on the new synchronized timescale in Fig. 1. Unfortunately, the resolution of the latter is much lower, which does not allow a firm validation. Nevertheless, the two timescales—resulting from assuming 7 °C or 15 °C glacial–interglacial temperature change—are both consistent with the ^{10}Be signal. As they represent extreme positions relative to the GRIP record around the peak position, we are confident that the true Byrd timescale (relative to GRIP) lies within our estimates. The relative uncertainty at the location of the ^{10}Be peak given by the two temperature models is about 300 yr.

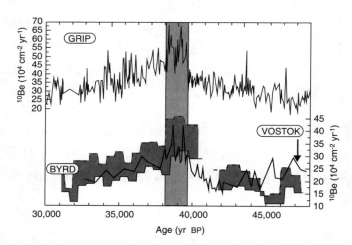

Fig. 1. ^{10}Be fluxes from Byrd[32], Vostok[33] and GRIP[31] ice cores. Values for Byrd were reduced by 15%, accounting for a difference in standards used for the measurements on the Byrd and the GRIP/Vostok cores (J. Beer, personal communication). Dating of the GRIP core is after ref. 21. For Byrd, two dating scenarios were used: lower temperature and accumulation (solid line); higher temperature and accumulation (dashed line; see Methods for details). Vostok was dated as described in Methods. The hatched area indicates the ^{10}Be peak area deduced from the GRIP core.

样分辨率分别为 200 年和 250 年。为了使 CH₄ 记录同时化，应用蒙特卡罗方法寻求记录之间的最大相关性 [5]。CH₄ 的快速变化使得我们拟合记录的精度达到 ±200 年。距今 2.5 万到 1.7 万年段在同时化时被剔除，因为这一时期 CH₄ 的变化较慢，使相关性变得不确定。

南极测站 Δage 值的不确定性来源于温度及累积率的不确定性。东方站和伯德站的冰期-间冰期温度差异范围为 7 ~ 15℃（参考文献 29 和 30），这一差异范围在我们对伯德站 Δage 计算的范围之内（详见方法部分）。伯德站冰芯的 Δage 值比东方站冰芯的值小一个量级，而与 GRIP 冰芯的 Δage 值接近。这就使得对于同位素记录的同时化，伯德站/GRIP 冰芯的对比相比东方站/GRIP 冰芯的对比更具说服力（详见下文和方法部分）。

可以利用宇宙线产生的放射性同位素 ¹⁰Be 在距今 4 万年左右的显著双峰现象来确认所求出的时间标尺的有效性，在图 1 中 GRIP 冰芯的 ¹⁰Be 的记录 [31] 和伯德站冰芯的记录 [32] 一起画在新的同步化时标上。遗憾的是，后者的分辨率很低，因而可用程度不高。不过，从假定的 7℃ 或 15℃ 的冰期-间冰期温度变化得到的两个时标都与 ¹⁰Be 的信号一致。由于它们代表了相对于 GRIP 记录在峰值附近的极端位置，我们可以认为真实的伯德站冰芯时标（相对于 GRIP 冰芯时标）处于我们估计的范围内。两个温度模式给出的 ¹⁰Be 峰值位置的相对不确定性大约为 300 年。

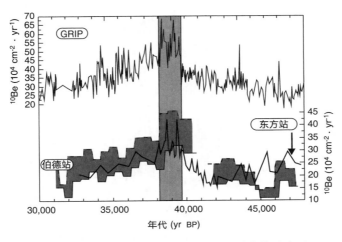

图 1. 伯德站 [32]、东方站 [33] 和 GRIP[31] 冰芯的 ¹⁰Be 通量。伯德站的值减少了 15%，说明伯德站和 GRIP/东方站观测标准有差别（比尔，个人交流）。GRIP 冰芯的年代根据参考文献 21 确定。伯德站的定年运用了两种情景：较低的温度及累积率（实线）；较高的温度及累积率（虚线，详见方法部分）。东方站的定年在方法部分进行了描述。阴影区表示由 GRIP 冰芯推断的 ¹⁰Be 的峰值区。

Main Features of Antarctic Climate

Vostok station has a low accumulation rate and low temperature; the present values are 1.7–2.6 cm of ice per year and −55°C, respectively[16]. This results in a large Δage, and makes Δage extremely sensitive to uncertainties in these parameters. Therefore, the Vostok CH_4 record alone is not well suited to correlate the Northern and the Southern hemispheres on a millennial scale. However, in combination with the detailed [10]Be record[31,33] a reasonable dating relative to Greenland can be achieved (for details, see Methods). The use of Vostok, in view of the relation between Greenland and Antarctic records, is to indicate which features seen in the Byrd core are representative for the climate in Antarctica (we limit our discussion to these features). They include the deglaciation and the ACR, a cold event occurring during the Bølling/Allerød[19,34,35], and warm events centring at 35.5 and 44.5 kyr BP (denoted as A1 and A2 in Fig 2).

Fig. 2. GRIP[1], Byrd[15] and Vostok[16] isotopic and CH_4 records on the common timescale (GRIP timescale in years before 1989). For the data from Byrd, a solid line shows the lower-temperature scenario, and the shaded area indicates the range of Δage for the two temperature scenarios discussed in Methods. The CH_4 scale at lower left corresponds to the GRIP values; Byrd and Vostok values were lowered by 200 and 400 p.p.b.v., respectively, for better visibility. The numbers on top of the GRIP isotopic record

南极气候的主要特征

东方站冰的累积率低，温度也低：当前冰的累积率为每年 1.7～2.6 厘米，温度为 -55℃ [16]。这导致一个大的 Δage 值，且使 Δage 对这些参数的不确定性极端敏感。因此，该站的 CH_4 记录不适合单独表示南北半球千年尺度的气候特征。但是，如果再联合详细的 [10]Be 记录 [31,33] 就能得到相对于格陵兰冰芯记录的合理的年代值（详见方法部分）。鉴于格陵兰和南极记录的关系，应用东方站的资料可以告诉我们从伯德站冰芯中所见的哪些特征对于南极气候是有代表性的（此处讨论仅限于这些特征）。这些气候事件包括冰消期和 ACR，后者是发生在波令/阿勒罗德期间 [19,34,35] 的一个冷事件，前者是中心位于距今 3.55 万和 4.45 万年的暖事件（图 2 中用 A1 和 A2 表示）。

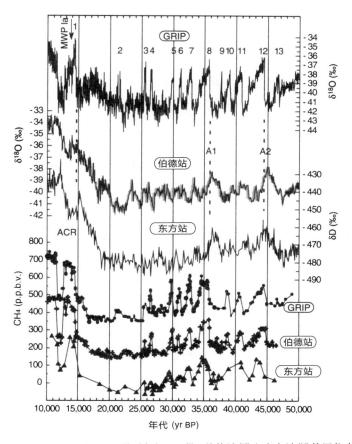

图 2. 同一时标下（1989 年以前的 GRIP 的时标）GRIP[1]、伯德站 [15] 和东方站 [16] 的同位素和 CH_4 记录。对于伯德站的资料，实线表示低温的情景，阴影区域表示方法部分中讨论的两种情景的 Δage 值的范围。左下方的 CH_4 标尺对应 GRIP 的值；伯德站和东方站的值分别在图示中降低 200 ppbv 和 400 ppbv，以使两站的结果看得更清楚。GRIP 的同位素记录顶部的数字表示 D-O 事件的位置；ACR 是茹泽尔等 [34]

indicate the location of Dansgaard–Oeschger events; ACR is the location of the Antarctic Cold Reversal as described by Jouzel *et al.*[34]; Antarctic warmings are indicated by A1 and A2; vertical dashed lines show the location of Greenland warmings 1, 8 and 12 in the Antarctic cores. The Byrd $\delta^{18}O$ variation between 25 and 17 kyr BP shows most likely local climate characteristics because: (1) it is not seen in the Vostok or in the Dome C record[51], and (2) it is not compatible with the climate mechanism seen during events A1, A2 and also the ACR present in all Antarctic records. The arrow marked MWP 1a indicates the position of the first meltwater pulse[45].

Phase Lag

In Fig. 2 the isotopic records from Byrd ($\delta^{18}O$), Vostok (δD) and GRIP ($\delta^{18}O$), which is representative of Greenland[2,21] and clearly registers Northern Hemispheric climate change[36], are plotted on the common timescale (Table 1) based on GRIP. Our synchronization clearly demonstrates that the Antarctic warmings (A1 and A2) are out of phase with the corresponding D–O events (8 and 12). Antarctic temperature variations A1 and A2 are characterized by a gradual rather than abrupt increase and decrease; D–O events by a fast increase and a slow decrease. While the Antarctic temperature is already increasing, Greenland is still cooling. The Antarctic temperature rise is interrupted once Greenland temperature jumps to an interstadial state within only a few decades[2,21]. Subsequently, the temperature decreases in both hemispheres to full glacial level, where Antarctica reaches this level earlier than Greenland.

Table 1. Corresponding depths for the three ice cores

Age of the ice (kyr BP)	Depth GRIP (m)	Depth Byrd*†(m)	Depth Vostok†(m)
12	1638.0	1074.4	261.1
13	1674.0	1124.2	278.6
14	1722.6	1161.4	293.1
15	1770.0	1198.6	307.6
16	1802.2	1235.8	322.8
17	1834.3	1269.5	336.4
18	1867.6	1294.4	348.9
19	1894.5	1319.4	360.1
20	1916.5	1344.3	371.0
21	1937.7	1369.3	381.9
22	1958.8	1394.2	392.9
23	1975.6	1419.1	404.3
24	1993.1	1444.1	415.9
25	2011.1	1469.0	427.3
26	2031.6	1493.9	438.9
27	2051.6	1518.7	451.3
28	2065.1	1539.9	464.2

描述的南极转冷事件；南极增温用 A1 和 A2 表示；垂直虚线表示南极冰芯中对应于格陵兰增温事件 1、8 和 12 的位置。距今 2.5 万到 1.7 万年之间伯德站 δ18O 的变化很可能表示局地气候特征，这是因为：(1) 这些变化并未在东方站或冰穹 C 记录 [51] 中见到；(2) 它与事件 A1 和 A2 中所见的气候机制不兼容，且所有南极记录中都有 ACR 出现。MWP 1a 所示的箭头表示第一次融水脉冲事件 [45] 的位置。

相 位 滞 后

图 2 中给出的来自伯德站 (δ18O)、东方站 (δD) 和 GRIP(δ18O) 三个点的同位素记录共同标注在以 GRIP 冰芯为基础的时标上 (参见表 1)。GRIP 代表格陵兰 [2,21]，清晰地记录了北半球的气候变化 [36]。我们的同时化结果清晰地表明，南极增暖 (A1 和 A2) 和对应的 D–O 事件 (8 和 12) 异相。南极的温度变化事件 A1 和 A2 以渐进变化为特征，而不是突然的增温或降温，而 D–O 事件的特点则是快速增温和缓慢降温。当南极开始增温时，格陵兰仍在降温。一旦格陵兰温度在短短几十年内突然转到间冰阶时 [2,21]，南极的温度上升就被打断了。之后，两半球的温度同时降低，进入完全的冰期状态，不过南极达到这一状态要比格陵兰早一些。

表 1. 三个冰芯的相应深度

冰的年代 (距今千年)	GRIP 深度 (米)	伯德站深度 *† (米)	东方站深度 † (米)
12	1638.0	1074.4	261.1
13	1674.0	1124.2	278.6
14	1722.6	1161.4	293.1
15	1770.0	1198.6	307.6
16	1802.2	1235.8	322.8
17	1834.3	1269.5	336.4
18	1867.6	1294.4	348.9
19	1894.5	1319.4	360.1
20	1916.5	1344.3	371.0
21	1937.7	1369.3	381.9
22	1958.8	1394.2	392.9
23	1975.6	1419.1	404.3
24	1993.1	1444.1	415.9
25	2011.1	1469.0	427.3
26	2031.6	1493.9	438.9
27	2051.6	1518.7	451.3
28	2065.1	1539.9	464.2

Continued

Age of the ice (kyr BP)	Depth GRIP (m)	Depth Byrd*†(m)	Depth Vostok†(m)
29	2079.9	1561.1	477.6
30	2097.5	1582.3	492.0
31	2112.6	1603.5	505.6
32	2129.5	1624.7	516.4
33	2149.9	1645.8	528.5
34	2162.9	1667.0	541.5
35	2182.7	1688.2	553.8
36	2203.6	1709.4	566.4
37	2214.7	1730.6	581.1
38	2227.5	1751.7	593.5
39	2242.8	1772.9	604.2
40	2255.1	1786.5	614.2
41	2272.0	1798.8	623.6
42	2282.6	1811.2	633.4
43	2297.6	1823.5	642.7
44	2315.9	1840.7	653.2
45	2330.2	1858.3	665.8
46	2340.2	1875.8	680.0
47	2353.2	1893.4	694.2

* The indicated depth corresponds to the higher Byrd temperature scenario (see Methods).

† We note that in the new Byrd, as well as in the new Vostok, age–depth relations, rather unrealistic changes in the annual layer thickness appear. They result because the synchronization is based on the GRIP timescale which is, although well dated, not an absolute timescale. Therefore care must be taken when using the Byrd and Vostok timescales with respect to annual layer or accumulation changes. Our conclusions do not depend on an absolute timescale, and are unaffected by such problems (see Methods).

We point out that our synchronization excludes the possibility that Antarctic and Greenland events are in phase. To bring the isotopic records in phase, the Byrd Δage would have to be reduced by more than 1,000 yr. As Δage is only about 500 yr during A1 and A2 (see Fig. 3) this would result in a negative Δage, which is impossible. Further, the relative position of A1 is also confirmed by the [10]Be peak recorded in the ice of the three investigated cores.

Antarctic isotopic events other than A1 and A2 can hardly be allocated individually with D–O events. However, one can calculate the mean time shift required to obtain the best correlation between Greenland and Antarctic isotopic records in the period 45–23 kyr BP. Best correlations are obtained when the Antarctic signal is shifted towards younger ages by 1–2.5 kyr. This, and the timing of the events (A1 and A2), confirms the chronology obtained by deep sea cores[9] and contradicts the hypothesis that long interstadials begin in the Northern Hemisphere and spread to Antarctica, creating a lag of Antarctic climate with respect to Greenland (at least for the past 50 kyr).

冰的年代(距今千年)	GRIP 深度(米)	伯德站深度 *†(米)	东方站深度 †(米)
29	2079.9	1561.1	477.6
30	2097.5	1582.3	492.0
31	2112.6	1603.5	505.6
32	2129.5	1624.7	516.4
33	2149.9	1645.8	528.5
34	2162.9	1667.0	541.5
35	2182.7	1688.2	553.8
36	2203.6	1709.4	566.4
37	2214.7	1730.6	581.1
38	2227.5	1751.7	593.5
39	2242.8	1772.9	604.2
40	2255.1	1786.5	614.2
41	2272.0	1798.8	623.6
42	2282.6	1811.2	633.4
43	2297.6	1823.5	642.7
44	2315.9	1840.7	653.2
45	2330.2	1858.3	665.8
46	2340.2	1875.8	680.0
47	2353.2	1893.4	694.2

* 所示深度对应于较高的伯德站冰芯温度情景(参见方法部分)。

† 我们注意到,在新的伯德站冰芯和东方站冰芯的年代–深度关系中,年层厚度出现了相当不切实际的变化。这是由于同时化是基于 GRIP 冰芯的时标,而这一时标虽然经过了很好的定年,但仍不是绝对的时标。因此,当使用与年层和冰累积量变化有关的伯德站和东方站时标时需要多加小心。我们的结论并不依赖于绝对的时标,也不受这一问题的影响(参见方法部分)。

需要指出,我们的同时化处理排除了南极和格陵兰发生的事件同相的可能性。因为为了使同位素记录同相,伯德站冰芯的 Δage 必须减少 1,000 年以上。而 Δage 在 A1 和 A2 期间大约只有 500 年(参见图 3),这将导致负的 Δage 值,这是不可能的。而且,A1 的相对位置也是由研究所用的三个冰芯中 [10]Be 的峰值所确认的。

南极的同位素事件除 A1 和 A2 以外,很难单独由 D–O 事件确定。然而我们可以通过计算所需的平均时间偏移得到距今 4.5 万到 2.3 万年期间格陵兰和南极同位素记录的最佳相关关系。当南极的信号向现今移动 1,000 ~ 2,500 年时,可以得到最佳相关关系。这与事件 A1 和 A2 的定年结果一起证实了由深海岩芯得到的年表 [9],并且反驳了长间冰阶始于北半球并向南半球扩张,导致南半球的气候变化(至少在过去 5 万年期间)滞后于格陵兰这一假说。

Fig. 3. Plot of Δage versus ice age. The solid line shows data from GRIP[5], the shaded area gives the range of Δage for the Byrd core covered by the temperature scenarios discussed in Methods, calculated with the same model as the GRIP Δage.

Implication for North–South Connection

A connection between the hemispheres can take place over the ocean or over the atmosphere. Charles et al.[9] suggested that both high northern and southern temperature could be driven over the atmosphere or the ocean by tropical temperature. Whereas coupling between Antarctic and tropical temperatures would be immediate, northern temperature would lag a tropical temperature change due to the thermal influence of the ice sheets or by the ice sheets' influence on salt balance of the North Atlantic surface layer. An immediate response of the Southern Hemisphere to tropical temperature would tend to synchronize the CH_4 (mainly related to tropical moisture changes) and the Antarctic isotope signal, whereas we observe a synchronism of CH_4 and Greenland $\delta^{18}O$ (refs 5, 14). This makes a coupling via atmosphere improbable, and points instead to a dominant role of the ocean controlling the past climate of both polar regions.

It is supposed that changes in the Atlantic thermohaline circulation, the direct cause of temperature changes in central Greenland[6], are closely linked to ice-rafting events and associated melt water which occur simultaneously in the North Atlantic region[37]. Melting reduces the deep-water formation and initiates cooling in the North Atlantic region. The cooling then slows the melting and permits re-establishment of the NADW formation, rapidly bringing heat to the North Atlantic[6]. The temperature increase then leads again to a freshwater input into the North Atlantic and to gradual shut down of NADW formation[38]. Model simulations demonstrate the NADW's sensitivity to freshwater input in the North Atlantic[24,39], and they also indicate that the resumption of the "conveyor belt" circulation after a shut-down is a rapid process[39,40].

图 3. Δage 和冰年代的关系图。实线表示 GRIP[5] 的数据，阴影区表示方法部分中讨论的伯德站冰芯的温度情景的 Δage 范围，其计算模式和 GRIP 冰芯的 Δage 计算模式相同。

南北半球联系的启示

两半球间的联系可以通过海洋，也可以通过大气发生。查尔斯等[9]认为，南北半球高纬度地区的温度都可以由热带温度通过大气或海洋驱动。然而南极和热带温度之间的耦合是即时的，由于冰盖的热力影响或冰盖对北大西洋表层盐平衡的影响，北半球的温度变化滞后于热带温度的变化。南半球对热带温度的即时响应致使 CH₄（主要和热带的湿度变化有关）和南极同位素信号的变化同步，而我们观测到了 CH₄ 和格陵兰 δ¹⁸O 变化之间的同步性（参考文献 5 和 14）。这就使得通过大气的耦合不大可能发生，取而代之的是海洋对过去两极气候的控制起主导作用。

可以推测，作为格陵兰中部气温变化直接原因的大西洋温盐环流变化[6]与同时发生在北大西洋地区的冰筏事件和融水事件[37]紧密相连。冰的融化减少了深层水的形成，引起北大西洋地区降温。降温过程的发生减慢了冰的融化，使 NADW 的形成重新建立，并迅速将热量带至北大西洋[6]。而温度的上升又再次导致淡水进入北大西洋，使 NADW 的形成逐渐关闭[38]。模式模拟指出了 NADW 对北大西洋地区淡水输入的敏感性[24,39]，同时也指出，"输送带"环流关闭后的重启是一个快速过程[39,40]。

D–O events and corresponding ice raftings occur more frequently than Antarctic warmings. Therefore, ice-rafting events can only partly, possibly through an increase in sea level, be initiated by Antarctic warmings. For the D–O events that have no counterpart in Antarctica, the trigger mechanism for ice-rafting events thus originates probably from an internal process of one of the ice sheets ablating into the North Atlantic. The Laurentide ice sheet can be excluded as it has a time constant of about 7 kyr (refs 41, 42), longer than the required 2–3 kyr between ice-rafting events[37]. Bond and Lotti[37] proposed instead ice sheets in Greenland, the Barents Sea or Scandinavia as candidates for such a trigger mechanism.

Central to the dynamics that we reconstruct on the basis of the ice cores is the role of the thermohaline circulation in the North Atlantic. Activation of the thermohaline circulation in the North Atlantic tends to cool the Southern Hemisphere[22,43]. This is exactly what happens during D–O events 12 and 8 (corresponding to A1 and A2), but also during D–O event 1, which is followed by the ACR[19]. Further, the YD/ACR out-of-phase relationship between Northern and Southern hemispheres is consistent with model simulations from ref. 18, recently reproduced with a three-dimensional coupled atmosphere–ocean general circulation model[24].

We may speculate that Antarctica is asynchronously coupled to the Northern Hemisphere during the whole glacial period investigated. Indeed, some of the smaller D–O events (for example, events 7 or 11) might have a concomitant cooling in Antarctica. The smaller amplitude of these coolings compared to the main events A1 and A2 might point to a positive correlation between the duration of a D–O event and the amplitude of the successive Antarctic cooling. However, it is also possible that the small Antarctic events may merely be noise in the isotopic records. In that case, the heat would only be drawn from Antarctica when Antarctica is in a warm phase. This leads to the speculation that under full glacial conditions Greenland and Antarctic temperature, and hence also thermohaline circulation and Antarctic circumpolar sea surface temperature[9], are only weakly coupled. A weaker coupling of the hemispheres is achieved when the Atlantic thermohaline circulation exchanges less water with the Southern Ocean, and so has a reduced influence on the heat balance of the southern latitudes. The strength of this circulation also determines its stability to freshwater flux perturbations: a weaker thermohaline circulation is more likely to shut down for a given perturbation[44]. If a weak Atlantic thermohaline circulation switches off, then the north will still experience strong cooling, but with a reduced influence on southern climate. We hypothesize that this is the case during the short D–O events which have no corresponding signal in Antarctic records. D–O events 12 and 8 and the Bølling/Allerød/YD sequence, on the other hand, would be examples of strong coupling between the hemispheres.

Warming in Antarctica tends to reduce sea surface density and hence the density of newly formed deep water. This favours NADW formation[43], and hence brings the ocean circulation closer to its strong mode with a tighter coupling of the circumpolar sea surface temperature to the Atlantic thermohaline circulation. A switch-on of the thermohaline circulation after ice-rafting events leads to the observed cooling in Antarctica, which results

D–O 事件和相应的冰筏事件相比南极增温发生得更为频繁。因此，冰筏事件可能只是部分由北大西洋增温引起的海平面上升导致。在南极，没有类似 D–O 事件的过程，因而触发冰筏事件的机制可能源于一块冰盖融化到北大西洋中的内部过程。可以排除劳伦太德冰盖，因为它的冰筏事件间隔是一个大约 7,000 年的固定时间（参考文献 41 和 42），这一数字比冰筏事件中所需要的 2,000 ～ 3,000 年要长 [37]。邦德和洛蒂 [37] 提出格陵兰、巴伦支海或者斯堪的纳维亚的冰盖可以作为这样一种触发机制。

根据冰芯建立的动力学的核心问题是北大西洋温盐环流的作用。北大西洋温盐环流的激活导致南半球降温 [22,43]。这确实在 D–O 事件 12 和 8（相当于 A1 和 A2）期间发生过，但也同样在 ACR 之前的 D–O 事件 1 期间发生过 [19]。另外，南北半球 YD/ACR 的异相关系和参考文献 18 的模式模拟结果一致，该模拟结果最近由一个三维大气–海洋耦合环流模式重现 [24]。

我们推测，在我们所研究的整个冰期，南极和北半球的耦合是非同步的。某些较小的 D–O 事件（如事件 7 或 11）确实可以在南极出现伴随的降温，这些降温的幅度与主要事件 A1 和 A2 相比要小，这可能指示 D–O 事件的持续时间和随之而来的南极降温幅度之间的正相关。但是，小的南极事件也可能仅仅是同位素记录中的噪音。在这种情况下，当南极处于暖位相时，热量仅来源于南极地区。由此可以推测，在全冰期尺度下，格陵兰和南极的温度以及温盐环流和南极绕极海面温度 [9] 都仅有较弱的耦合。当大西洋的温盐环流和南大洋的海水交换较少并因此对南纬区域热平衡影响减小时，半球之间的耦合就更弱。这一环流的强度也决定了在淡水输入造成扰动的情况下其表现出的稳定性：弱的温盐环流更容易由于扰动的影响而消失 [44]。如果弱的大西洋温盐环流消失了，北半球将仍处于强烈的降温状态，但南半球气候受到的影响会减小。我们猜想，那些在南极记录中缺乏对应信号的短 D–O 事件就属于这种情况。另一方面，D–O 事件 12 和 8 及波令/阿勒罗德/YD 序列则是两半球间强耦合的例子。

南极升温会导致海水密度的减小，并因此使得新形成的深层水的密度减小。这有利于 NADW 的形成 [43]，从而使海洋环流更接近其强模态，在此模态下，绕极海面温度和大西洋温盐环流之间的耦合更紧密。冰筏事件之后温盐环流的开启导致观测到的南极降温，结果再次导致数千年范围内两半球间更弱的耦合。这也和事件

again in a weaker coupling of the hemispheres for several thousand years. This is also consistent with an increased heat transport to high northern latitudes during A1 and A2 leading to the observed prolonged D–O events 8 and 12.

During the deglaciation, the climate system shows very similar behaviour. During the first part of the deglaciation the Antarctic warming is not interrupted as no ice-rafting events in the North Atlantic region are taking place: perhaps the lowered sea level makes it impossible for an ice sheet to initiate significant surging of other North Atlantic ice sheets. Then a sudden temperature increase in Greenland (14.5 kyr BP) initiates the same pattern as in the glaciation, namely a cooling in Antarctica (ACR). The first meltwater pulse (MWP 1A)[45] reduces NADW, at first gradually and then completely, allowing further warming in Antarctica. This makes the deglaciation a complicated process involving Milankovitch forcing, internal ice-sheet processes, and ocean circulation changes.

Further data from Antarctica which are synchronized with the existing records, together with model simulations, will help us disentangle the complicated pattern of climate change between Northern and Southern hemispheres for the entire glacial period. More, and better, data should be available from current European, Japanese and American ice-core drilling programmes.

Methods

To calculate Δage, the accumulation rate and temperature need to be known. The temperature at the time of precipitation can be determined from the $\delta^{18}O$ signal recorded in the ice. Assuming that today's spatial dependence between $\delta^{18}O$ and temperature was also valid in the past, the glacial–interglacial temperature increase in Antarctica is ~7–10 °C (refs 16, 29). On the other hand, recent borehole temperature measurements at Vostok suggest[30] a temperature change of up to 15 °C.

The amount of snow falling over the year depends on the mean temperature of the inversion layer. This temperature (T_I) can be calculated for the surface temperature (T_G) according to[46]:

$$T_I = 0.67\, T_G - 1.2\,°C \qquad (1)$$

where T_I and T_G are in °C. Assuming a linear relation between accumulation rate and the derivative of the water vapour partial pressure (P) with respect to temperature (T) (ref. 16), the accumulation rate which has led to a layer now found at depth z is given by:

$$a(z) = a_0 \left(\left.\frac{\partial P}{\partial T}\right|_{T_0} \right)^{-1} \left.\frac{\partial P}{\partial T}\right|_{T_I(z)} \qquad (2)$$

where T_0 and $T_I(z)$ are the inversion layer temperature for today's accumulation rate a_0 and for the past accumulation rate $a(z)$, respectively.

A1、A2 期间向北半球高纬度热量输送的增加是一致的，热量输送的增加导致了观测到的延长的 D–O 事件 8 和 12。

在冰消期，气候系统表现出非常相似的行为。冰川消退的开始阶段，南极的升温并未中断，因为在北大西洋没有冰筏事件发生：或许最低的海平面使得一个北大西洋冰盖无法令其他北大西洋冰盖发生明显涌动。此后格陵兰的突然增温（距今 1.45 万年）启动了与冰期相同的模态（称为南极转冷事件，即 ACR）。第一次融水脉冲事件（MWP 1A）[45] 减弱了 NADW，一开始逐渐地、之后彻底地引起南极的进一步升温。这就使冰川消退成为涉及米兰科维奇驱动、冰盖内部过程和海洋环流变化的复杂过程。

和已有记录进行过同时化处理的更多资料和模式模拟结果将帮助我们弄清整个冰期南北半球之间气候变化的复杂过程。从现在欧洲、日本和美洲的冰芯钻探计划可以获得更多更好的资料。

方　法

为了计算 Δage 需要知道冰的累积率和温度。降水时的温度可以从冰的 $\delta^{18}O$ 信号求得。假设现今的 $\delta^{18}O$ 和温度的空间关系在过去也是成立的，则南极冰期和间冰期之间的温度增加大约为 7～10℃（参考文献 16 和 29）。另外，由最近东方站的钻孔温度测量得知 [30]，温度变化可以高达 15℃。

年降雪量取决于逆温层的平均温度。这一温度（T_I）可由地表温度（T_G）按下式计算 [46]：

$$T_\mathrm{I} = 0.67\, T_\mathrm{G} - 1.2℃ \tag{1}$$

式中 T_I 和 T_G 的单位用℃表示。假定冰的累积率和水汽分压（P）对温度（T）的导数是线性关系（参考文献 16），则深度 z 的累积率用下式表示：

$$a(z) = a_0 \left(\frac{\partial P}{\partial T}\Big|_{T_0} \right)^{-1} \frac{\partial P}{\partial T}\Big|_{T_\mathrm{I}(z)} \tag{2}$$

其中 T_0 和 $T_\mathrm{I}(z)$ 分别是现今累积率 a_0 情况下和过去累积率 $a(z)$ 情况下逆温层的温度。

Byrd. As the accumulation is calculated from the temperature and present accumulation rate, its uncertainty is essentially linked to the uncertainty in both parameters. For Byrd we have calculated a new age of the ice for two temperature scenarios. For the warmer scenario, the $\delta^{18}O$–temperature relation from ref. 29 was used (equation (3)); for the colder scenario[30] we use the linear relation given in equation (4):

$$T = (1.01\,^{\circ}C \text{ per } \text{‰})\,\delta^{18}O + 6.57\,^{\circ}C \tag{3}$$
$$T = (2.07\,^{\circ}C \text{ per } \text{‰})\,\delta^{18}O + 42.7\,^{\circ}C \tag{4}$$

From the two temperature scenarios, accumulation was calculated according to equations (1) and (2) with $a_0 = 11.2$ cm per yr ice equivalent[47]. Thereafter, Δage was calculated using the dynamical model (Fig. 3) leading, in combination with the CH_4 synchronization, to a timescale for the warmer- and the colder-temperature scenario.

The accumulation rate is calculated from these temperatures and therefore also covers a wide range of possible accumulations (mean accumulation rates for the glacial are 7.9 and 5.5 cm yr^{-1} for the higher- and the lower-temperature scenario, respectively). Alternatively, the accumulation rate can be calculated from the annual layer thickness, if the ice flow pattern is known. The flow pattern in the Byrd station area is very complicated (due to bedrock topography and melting at the bottom), which results in uncertainties in the calculated accumulation rate[15,48]. However, our accumulation range over the glacial is consistent with measured annual layer thickness[47], assuming a linear thinning of annual layers with depth deduced from the Holocene period.

Vostok. As Vostok is a low accumulation site, the ice from the time period considered here is found in the upper 740 m of the ice sheet. There, ice flow is well known and was described by a glaciological model[49]. Thus, it should in principle be possible to get coherency between the timescales for the ice and the occluded gas, accumulation and temperature. In a first approach the ^{10}Be peak around 40 kyr was synchronized between GRIP[31] and Vostok[33]. For this purpose, accumulation rates were calculated from equations (1) and (2) from the isotopic temperature[16]. Δage was obtained using this accumulation and the isotopic temperature where the present-day accumulation rate a_0 was set to 2.1 cm yr^{-1}, within the uncertainty for today's accumulation rate[50]. To obtain a timescale from the accumulation rate, annual layer thickness was calculated using the thinning function from the glaciological model[49]. With this approach the main features in the isotopic record, as well as the Vostok CH_4 signal, appear shifted relative to the Byrd record. Reducing the Vostok temperature (suggested by Salamatin *et al.*[30]) and therefore also accumulation rate would make the match even worse. In order to get the Vostok CH_4 record in agreement with its GRIP and Byrd counterpart, Vostok and/or the GRIP/Byrd timescales must be squeezed and stretched.

In a first case, we consider Vostok as reference timescale and adapt the GRIP/Byrd timescales. Consequently accumulation has to be changed in both cores and with the same amplitude and sign; therefore this does not change the relative phasing of GRIP and Byrd. This scenario brings event A2 in to agreement between Byrd and Vostok, but it creates fluctuations in the annual layer thickness of GRIP, which are not expected from the exponential relation between accumulation and $\delta^{18}O$ (ref. 25).

312

伯德站 由于过去冰的累积率是用温度和现在的累积率计算的，因此其不确定性本质上和这两个参数的不确定性有关。对伯德站，我们用两个温度情景计算了新的冰的年代值。对较暖的情景，$\delta^{18}O$ 和温度的关系取自参考文献 29（即（3）式），对较冷的情景[30]，应用（4）式给出线性关系：

$$T = (1.01℃/‰) \delta^{18}O + 6.57℃ \tag{3}$$

$$T = (2.07℃/‰) \delta^{18}O + 42.7℃ \tag{4}$$

应用这两个温度情景按式（1）和（2）取 $a_0 = 11.2$ 厘米/年（冰当量）[47] 计算了冰的累积率。然后使用经同时化处理的 CH_4 资料应用动力学模式在冷暖两个温度情景下计算了 Δage（见图 3）。

从上述温度情景计算的冰的累积率覆盖了一个较宽的可能累积率范围（冰期平均累积率在高温情景和低温情景下分别为 7.9 厘米/年和 5.5 厘米/年）。另外，如果知道冰流型，也可以从冰的年层厚度计算冰的累积率。然而，由于基岩地形和底部融化，伯德站区域的冰流型非常复杂，这就导致所计算的累积率有相当的不确定性[15,48]。不过，如果假定在全新世时期冰的年层厚度随深度线性减少的话，我们计算的整个冰期累积率的范围和冰的年层厚度的测量结果是一致的[47]。

东方站 由于东方站是一个低累积率站点，这里所讨论的时期内的冰位于冰盖上部 740 米范围。这里冰流的情况已为人们所熟知，并已被冰川学模型所描述[49]。因此，原则上我们有可能得到冰的时标与封闭在其中的气体、冰的累积率和温度的一致性关系。初步结果说明，^{10}Be 在 4 万年附近的峰值同步出现在 GRIP 冰芯[31] 和东方站冰芯[33]。为此，从式（1）和（2）应用同位素温度[16] 计算出冰的累积率。应用这一累积率和同位素温度，求得了 Δage，此处现今累积率 a_0 设为 2.1 厘米/年，该值在现今累积率的不确定性范围内[50]。为了从累积率获得时标，应用从冰川学模型[49] 得到的减薄函数计算了冰的年层厚度。应用这一方法，同位素记录和东方站 CH_4 信号的主要特征表现出相对于伯德站记录的偏移。降低东方站温度（像萨拉马京等人[30] 建议的那样）和累积率后将会使吻合程度变得更差。为了使东方站的 CH_4 记录与 GRIP 冰芯、伯德站冰芯吻合，东方站冰芯和（或）GRIP 冰芯/伯德站冰芯的时标必须缩短或拉长。

在第一种情况下，我们把东方站冰芯当作参考时标，调整 GRIP 冰芯/伯德站冰芯的时标。因此这两个冰芯的冰累积率必须做出正负相同、幅度一致的改变，这样就不会改变 GRIP 冰芯和伯德站冰芯的相对位相。这种情景使得事件 A2 的时间在伯德站和东方站保持一致，但是它会产生 GRIP 冰芯中年层厚度的波动，而这与冰累积率和 $\delta^{18}O$ 之间的指数关系不甚符合（参考文献 25）。

In a second case, we consider GRIP as the reference timescale. The Vostok gas timescale is squeezed and stretched in order to fit the GRIP CH_4 record. The Vostok ice timescale is treated in the same way which is changing the accumulation rate. Thus Δage is re-calculated with the accumulation rates consistent with the modified timescale (using the thinning function from the glaciological model[49]). The resulting change in the gas chronology was found to be negligible; this means that the Vostok CH_4 record is still in agreement with the GRIP CH_4 chronology. This scenario also brings event A2 into agreement between Byrd and Vostok, but now creates unexpected fluctuations in the annual layer thickness of Vostok. $\delta^{18}O$, ^{10}Be and CH_4 data are presented using this chronology in Figs 1 and 2.

In both cases, maintaining consistency between ^{10}Be peaks and CH_4 records, we obtain good correlation between the isotope records of Byrd and Vostok, and are therefore confident that the characteristic features reflect identical climate events. We are left with the unsolved problem of annual layer fluctuation either in the Vostok or in the GRIP ice core. However, the synchronization of the Byrd and GRIP core is robust to this problem.

Three cores from Vostok are involved in this study. The isotopic profile was obtained on the 3G core[16] while ^{10}Be was measured on the 4G core[33]. The occurrence of a dust horizon in both cores at around 550 m depth (J. R. Petit, personal communication) allows an exact synchronization of the cores (4G depth increased by 3.41 m). The CH_4 profile was measured on the 5G core, which is of better quality than the 3G and 4G cores. The dust horizon at 550 m depth was not found in the 5G core. We thus performed additional CH_4 measurements on the 3G core over the CH_4 increase associated with D–O event 5, allowing us to estimate the depth offset between 3G and 5G (5G depth decreased by 3 m).

(**394**, 739-743; 1998)

T. Blunier[*], J. Chappellaz[†], J. Schwander[*], A. Dällenbach[*], B. Stauffer[*], T. F. Stocker[*], D. Raynaud[†], J. Jouzel[‡†], H. B. Clausen[§], C. U. Hammer[§] & S. J. Johnsen[§‖]

[*] Climate and Environmental Physics, Physics Institute, University of Bern, Sidlerstrasse 5, CH-3012 Bern, Switzerland
[†] CNRS Laboratoire de Glaciologie et Géophysique de l'Environnement (LGGE), BP 96, 38402 St Martin d'Hères Cedex, Grenoble, France
[‡] Laboratoire des Sciences du Climat et de l'Environnement, UMR CEA-CNRS 1572, CEA Saclay, Orme des Merisiers, 91191 Gif sur Yvette, France
[§] Department of Geophysics (NBIfAPG), University of Copenhagen, Juliane Maries Vej 30, 2100 Copenhagen O, Denmark
[‖] Science Institute, Department of Geophysics, University of Iceland, Dunhaga 3, Is-107 Reykjavik, Iceland

Received 1 September 1997; accepted 13 February 1998.

References:

1. Dansgaard, W. *et al.* Evidence for general instability of past climate from a 250-kyr ice-core record. *Nature* **364,** 218-220 (1993).
2. Grootes, P. M., Stuiver, M., White, J. W. C., Johnsen, S. & Jouzel, J. Comparison of oxygen isotope records from the GISP2 and GRIP Greenland ice cores. *Nature* **366,** 552-554 (1993).
3. Oeschger, H *et al.* in *Climate Processes and Climate Sensitivity* (eds Hansen, J. E. & Takahashi, T.) 299-306 (Vol. 29, Geophys. Monogr. Ser., Am. Geophys. Union, Washington DC, 1984).
4. Johnsen, S., Dahl-Jensen, D., Dansgaard, W. & Gundestrup, N. Greenland palaeotemperatures derived from GRIP bore hole temperature and ice core isotope profiles. *Tellus B* **47,** 624-629 (1995).
5. Schwander, J. *et al.* Age scale of the air in the summit ice: Implication for glacial-interglacial temperature change. *J. Geophys. Res.* **102,** 19483-19494 (1997).

在第二种情况下，我们把 GRIP 冰芯当作参考时标。将东方站的气体时标缩短或拉长，以适应 GRIP 冰芯的 CH_4 记录。东方站冰的时标也用同一种方法处理，即改变冰的累积率。此时，使用与修正过的时标相符的冰累积率重新计算 Δage（应用冰川学模型 [49] 得到的减薄函数）。我们发现这样做引起的气体年代值的改变是可以忽略的；这就是说，东方站的 CH_4 记录仍然符合 GRIP 冰芯的 CH_4 记录的年代。这种情景也使东方站和伯德站的 A2 事件的年代保持一致，不过它导致了东方站年层厚度的意外波动。我们在图 1、图 2 中给出的 $\delta^{18}O$、^{10}Be 和 CH_4 资料便是用的这种年代计算方法。

在上述两种情况下，我们保持 ^{10}Be 峰值和 CH_4 记录之间的一致性，从而得到了伯德站和东方站同位素记录较好的相关性，也因此可以确信独有的特征反映了相同的气候事件。尚未解决的问题是，要么东方站冰芯，要么 GRIP 冰芯，会出现年层厚度波动的问题。无论如何，伯德站冰芯和 GRIP 冰芯的同时化对于这个问题而言是稳健的。

本研究用了东方站的三个冰芯。同位素廓线来自 3G（第 3 代）冰芯 [16]，而 ^{10}Be 则由 4G 冰芯测得 [33]。在两个冰芯约 550 米深处（珀蒂，个人交流）出现的尘埃层顶提供了冰芯之间的精确同时化（4G 冰芯的厚度增加了 3.41 米）。CH_4 的廓线测量自 5G 冰芯，它比 3G 冰芯和 4G 冰芯的质量要好。但在 550 米深度发现的尘埃面并未出现在 5G 冰芯中。因此我们对 3G 冰芯中与 D–O 事件 5 有关的 CH_4 增长进行了补充测量，使我们可以估计 3G 和 5G 冰芯之间的深度偏差（5G 冰芯的深度减少 3 米）。

（周家斌 翻译；李崇银 审稿）

6. Bond, G. *et al.* Correlations between climate records from North Atlantic sediments and Greenland ice. *Nature* **365**, 143-147 (1993).

7. Roemmich, D. Estimation of meridional heat flux in the North Atlantic by inverse methods. *J. Phys. Oceanogr.* **10**, 1972-1983 (1981).

8. Broecker, W. S. & Denton, G. H. The role of ocean-atmosphere reorganizations in glacial cycles. *Geochim. Cosmochim. Acta* **53**, 2465-2501 (1989).

9. Charles, C. D., Lynch-Stieglitz, J., Ninnemann, U. S. & Fairbanks, R. G. Climate connections between the hemisphere revealed by deep sea sediment core/ice core correlations. *Earth Planet. Sci. Lett.* **142**, 19-27 (1996).

10. Behl, R. J. & Kennett, J. P. Brief interstadial events in the Santa Barbara basin, NE Pacific, during the past 60 kyr. *Nature* **379**, 243-379 (1996).

11. Bard, E., Rostek, F. & Sonzogni, C. Interhemispheric synchrony of the last deglaciation inferred from alkenone palaeothermometry. *Nature* **385**, 707-710 (1997).

12. Grimm, E. C., Jacobson, G. L. Jr, Watts, W. A., Hansen, B. C. S. & Maasch, K. A. A 50,000-year record of climate oscillations from Florida and its temporal correlation with the Heinrich events. *Science* **261**, 198-200 (1993).

13. Benson, L. V. *et al.* Climatic and hydrologic oscillations in the Owens Lake basin and adjacent Sierra Nevada, California. *Science* **274**, 746-749 (1996).

14. Chappellaz, J. *et al.* Synchronous changes in atmospheric CH_4 and Greenland climate between 40 and 8 kyr BP. *Nature* **366**, 443-445 (1993).

15. Johnsen, S. J., Dansgaard, W., Clausen, H. B. & Langway, C. C. Oxygen isotope profiles through the Antarctic and Greenland ice sheets. *Nature* **235**, 429-434 (1972).

16. Jouzel, J. *et al.* Vostok ice core: A continuous isotope temperature record over the last climatic cycle (160,000 years). *Nature* **329**, 403-408 (1987).

17. Bender, M. *et al.* Climate correlations between Greenland and Antarctica during the past 100,000 years. *Nature* **372**, 663-666 (1994).

18. Stocker, T. F., Wright, D. G. & Mysak, L. A. A zonally averaged, coupled ocean-atmosphere model for paleoclimate studies. *J. Clim.* **5**, 773-797 (1992) .

19. Blunier, T. *et al.* Timing of the Antarctic Cold Reversal and the atmospheric CO_2 increase with respect to the Younger Dryas event. *Geophys. Res. Lett.* **24**, 2683-2686 (1997).

20. Hammer, C. U. *et al. Report on the Stratigraphic Dating of the GRIP Ice Core* (Spec. Rep. of the Geophysical Dept, Niels Bohr Institute for Astronomy, Physics and Geophysics, Univ Copenhagen, in the press).

21. Johnsen, S. J. *et al.* Irregular glacial interstadials recorded in a new Greenland ice core. *Nature* **359**, 311-313 (1992).

22. Crowley, T. J. North Atlantic deep water cools the Southern Hemisphere. *Paleoceanography* **7**, 489-497 (1992) .

23. Stocker, T. F. & Wright, D. G. Rapid changes in ocean circulation and atmospheric radiocarbon. *Paleoceanography* **11**, 773-796 (1996).

24. Schiller, A., Mikolajewicz, U. & Voss, R. The stability of the thermohaline circulation in a coupled ocean-atmosphere general circulation model. *Clim. Dyn.* **13**, 325-348 (1997).

25. Dahl-Jensen, D., Johnsen, S. J., Hammer, C. U., Clausen, H. B. & Jouzel, J. in *Ice in the Climate System* (ed. Peltier, W. R.) 517-532 (Springer, Berlin, (1993).

26. Johnsen, S. J., Dansgaard, W. & White, J. W. C. The origin of Arctic precipitation under present and glacial conditions. *Tellus B* **41**, 452-468 (1989).

27. Severinghaus, J. P., Sowers, T., Brook, E. J., Alley, R. B. & Bender, M. L. Timing of abrupt climate change at the end of the Younger Dryas interval from thermally fractionated gases in polar ice. *Nature* **391**, 141-146 (1998).

28. Blunier, T., Chappellaz, J., Schwander, J., Stauffer, B. & Raynaud, D. Variations in atmospheric methane concentration during the Holocene epoch. *Nature* **374**, 46-49 (1995).

29. Robin, G. de Q. in *The Climatic Record in Polar Ice Sheets* (ed. Robin, G. de Q.) 180-184 (Cambridge Univ. Press, London, 1983).

30. Salamatin, A. N. *et al.* Ice core age dating and paleothermometer calibration based on isotope and temperature profiles from deep boreholes at Vostok Station (East Antarctica). *J. Geophys. Res.* **103**, 8963-8978 (1998).

31. Yiou, F. *et al.* Beryllium 10 in the Greenland Ice Core Project ice core at Summit, Greenland. *J. Geophys. Res.* **102**, 26783-26794 (1997).

32. Beer, J. *et al. The Last Deglaciation: Absolute and Radiocarbon Chronologies* (eds Bard, E. & Broecker, W. S.) 141-153 (NATO ASI Ser. I 2, Springer, Berlin, 1992) .

33. Raisbeck, G. M. *et al.* in *The Last Deglaciation: Absolute and Radiocarbon Chronologies* (eds Bard, E. & Broecker, W. S.) 127-140 (NATO ASI Ser. I 2, Springer, Berlin, 1992).

34. Jouzel, J. *et al.* The two-step shape and timing of the last deglaciation in Antarctica. *Clim. Dyn.* **11**, 151-161 (1995).

35. Sowers, T. & Bender, M. Climate records covering the last deglaciation. *Science* **269**, 210-214 (1995).

36. Siegenthaler, U., Eicher, U., Oeschger, H. & Dansgaard, W. Lake sediments as continental $\delta^{18}O$ records from the transition of glacial-interglacial. *Ann. Glaciol.* **5**, 149-152 (1984).

37. Bond, G. C. & Lotti, R. Iceberg discharges into the North Atlantic on millennial time scales during the last deglaciation. *Science* **267**, 1005-1010 (1995).

38. Stocker, T. F. & Wright, D. G. The effect of a succession of ocean ventilation changes on radiocarbon. *Radiocarbon* **40**, 359-366 (1998).

39. Stocker, T. F. & Wright, D. G. Rapid transitions of the ocean's deep circulation induced by changes in surface water fluxes. *Nature* **351**, 729-732 (1991).

40. Wright, D. G. & Stocker, T. F. in *Ice in the Climate System* (ed Peltier, W. R.) 395-416 (NATO ASI Ser .I 12, Springer, Berlin, 1993).

41. MacAyeal, D. R. A low-order model of the Heinrich event cycle. *Paleoceanography* **8**, 767-773 (1993).

42. MacAyeal, D. R. Binge/purge oscillations of the Laurentide ice sheet as a cause of the North Atlantic's Heinrich events. *Paleoceanography* **8**, 775-784 (1993).

43. Stocker, T F., Wright, D. G. & Broecker, W. S. The influence of high-latitude surface forcing on the global thermohaline circulation. *Paleoceanography* **7**, 529-541 (1992).

44. Tziperman, E. Inherently unstable climate behaviour due to weak thermohaline ocean circulation. *Nature* **386**, 592-595 (1997).

45. Bard, E. *et al.* Deglacial sea-level record from Tahiti corals and the timing of global meltwater discharge. *Nature* **382**, 241-244 (1996).

46. Jouzel, J. & Merlivat, L. Deuterium and oxygen 18 in precipitation: modeling of the isotopic effects during snow formation. *J. Geophys. Res.* **89**, 11749-11757 (1984).

47. Hammer, C. U., Clausen, H. B. & Langway, C. C. Jr. Electrical conductivity method (ECM) stratigraphic dating of the Byrd Station ice core, Antarctica. *Ann. Glaciol.* **20**, 115-120 (1994).

48. Whillans, I. M. Ice flow along the Byrd station strain network, Antarctica. *J. Glaciol.* **24,** 15-28 (1979).

49. Ritz, C. *Un Modèle Thermo-Mécanique d'évolution Pour le Bassin Glaciaire Antarctique Vostok-glacier Byrd : Sensiblité aux Valeurs des Paramètres Mal Connus.* Thesis, Univ. J. Fourier (1992).

50. Jouzel, J. *et al.* Extending the Vostok ice-core record of palaeoclimate to the penultimate glacial period. *Nature* **364,** 407-412 (1993).

51. Lorius, C., Merlivat, L., Jouzel, J. & Pourchet, M. A 30,000-yr isotope climatic record from Antarctic ice. *Nature* **280,** 644-648 (1979).

Acknowledgements. This work, in the frame of the Greenland Ice Core Project (GRIP), was supported by the University of Bern, the Swiss National Science Foundation, the Federal Department of Energy (BFE), the Schwerpunktprogramm Umwelt (SPPU) of the Swiss National Science Foundation, the EC program "Environment and Climate 1994-1998", the Fondation de France and the Programm National de Dynamique du Climat of CNRS. We thank F. Finet for the CH_4 measurements on Vostok and part of GRIP, C. Rado and J. R. Petit for ice sampling at Vostok station, C. C. Langway for providing us with additional Byrd samples and F. Yiou, G. Raisbeck and J. Beer for the ^{10}Be data.

Correspondence and requests for materials should be addressed to T.B. (e-mail: blunier@climate.unibe.ch).

317

Energy Implications of Future Stabilization of Atmospheric CO₂ Content

M. I. Hoffert *et al.*

Editor's Note

Mitigating climate change caused by human-induced emissions of greenhouse gases will, if it is not to impede economic growth, require extensive recourse to "clean" energy-generating technologies that reduce or eliminate these emissions. Here Martin Hoffert and his colleagues provide a sobering assessment of the scale of that challenge. They estimate that even relatively modest goals for stabilizing carbon dioxide emissions will demand much more emissions-free energy production than is anticipated for the year 2050 without any governmental intervention. This implies that "massive" investment in the research that could enable such a change is urgently needed: the researchers suggest that this be attributed the kind of importance associated with the Manhattan Project and the Apollo space programme.

The United Nations Framework Convention on Climate Change[1] calls for "stabilization of greenhouse-gas concentrations in the atmosphere at a level that would prevent dangerous anthropogenic interference with the climate system ...". A standard baseline scenario[2,3] that assumes no policy intervention to limit greenhouse-gas emissions has 10 TW (10×10^{12} watts) of carbon-emission-free power being produced by the year 2050, equivalent to the power provided by all today's energy sources combined. Here we employ a carbon-cycle/energy model to estimate the carbon-emission-free power needed for various atmospheric CO₂ stabilization scenarios. We find that CO₂ stabilization with continued economic growth will require innovative, cost-effective and carbon-emission-free technologies that can provide additional tens of terawatts of primary power in the coming decades, and certainly by the middle of the twenty-first century, even with sustained improvement in the economic productivity of primary energy. At progressively lower atmospheric CO₂-stabilization targets in the 750–350 p.p.m.v. range, implementing stabilization will become even more challenging because of the increasing demand for carbon-emission-free power. The magnitude of the implied infrastructure transition suggests the need for massive investments in innovative energy research.

INTERGOVERNMENTAL Panel on Climate Change (IPCC) working groups developed six scenarios for greenhouse-gas emissions based on socioeconomic projections[2,3]. Scenario IS92a incorporated widely accepted projections and the then-current consensus on population, economic development and energy technology to generate projections of greenhouse-gas emissions for the twenty-first century assuming "no new climate change policies". This baseline IS92a scenario has been dubbed "business as usual".

未来使大气中 CO_2 含量稳定的能源要求

霍费尔特等

编者按

要在不阻碍经济增长的情况下缓解人为温室气体排放所造成的气候变化，就需要使用大量的"清洁"能源生成技术来减少或消除这些温室气体的排放。本文中，马丁·霍费尔特和他的同事们对这一挑战的规模进行了不容乐观的评估。他们估计，如果没有政府的干预，即使设置相对比较适度的稳定二氧化碳排放量的目标，也需要大量的、高于 2050 年预期目标的无碳排放能源的生产。这意味着迫切需要进行"大规模"的研究投入以实现这一改变：研究人员认为，这一研究的重要性堪比曼哈顿计划和阿波罗太空计划。

联合国气候变化框架公约[1]呼吁"把大气中温室气体浓度稳定在一定水平上，以防止人类活动对气候系统产生危险的干扰……"。在假定没有政策措施来限制温室气体排放的标准基线排放情景下[2,3]，到 2050 年可生产的无碳排放的能量将达 10 TW（10×10^{12} 瓦特），这相当于当前所有能源所提供能量的总和。在本文中，我们采用碳循环/能量模型来估计保持各种大气 CO_2 含量稳定值情景下所需的无碳排放的能源。研究发现，在接下来的几十年，也就是到二十一世纪中叶，随着经济的增长，即使一次能源的经济生产力持续增长，要使 CO_2 含量稳定，也必须寻找创新型、有成本效益的无碳排放技术来满足额外的几十太瓦的一次能源需求。在 750 ～ 350 ppmv 的范围内，随着 CO_2 稳定含量目标值的逐步降低，对无碳排放能量的需求将不断增长，这使得碳稳定化的实施变得更加严峻。其中隐含的基础设施的转型规模也表明，需要加大对创新能源的研究投入。

联合国政府间气候变化专门委员会（IPCC）工作组根据社会经济预估，提出了六种温室气体排放情景[2,3]。情景 IS92a 综合各种广受认可的预估方案以及当时的人口、经济发展状况和能源技术水平，最终形成了假定"没有关于气候变化的新政策出台"情况下二十一世纪的温室气体排放预估。该排放基线 IS92a 情景被称为"照常排放"。

In general, the rate at which carbon is emitted (as CO_2) by energy production is given by the Kaya identity[4-6];

$$\dot{M}_c \equiv \mathcal{N}(GDP/\mathcal{N})(\dot{E}/GDP)(C/E) \tag{1}$$

expressing emissions as the product of population ($\mathcal{N}$), per capita gross domestic product ($GDP/\mathcal{N}$), primary energy intensity ($\dot{E}/GDP$) and carbon intensity (C/E). Here we express the rate of primary energy consumption from all fuel sources (the "burn rate") in watts (W) and the gross domestic product in (1990 US) \$ yr^{-1} so their ratio, the energy intensity, has units of W yr \$$^{-1}$. Carbon intensity, the weighted average of the carbon-to-energy emission factors of all energy sources, has the units kg C W^{-1} yr^{-1}. For example, from equation (1) fossil-fuel CO_2 emissions in 1990 were $\dot{M}_c = 5.3 \times 10^9$ persons $\times$ 4,100 \$ per person yr$^{-1} \times$ 0.49 W yr \$$^{-1} \times$ 0.56 kg C W^{-1} yr$^{-1} \approx$ 6.0 Gt C yr^{-1} (1 Gt C $= 10^{12}$ kg C).

To illustrate the relative contributions of the factors in equation (1) historically and under IS92a, we evaluated each of them globally over the 210-year period from 1890 to 2100 (Fig. 1) from historical data[7-9] before 1990, and from documents defining IPCC scenarios[2,10-12] after 1990. Although some of this information is implicit in IPCC documents, it has not been previously presented in this way.

Although illustrating the "big picture", aggregating Kaya decomposition terms globally can mask regional developmental differences[13]. Data for individual nations indicate that $\dot{E}/GDP$ typically increases during economic development, reaching a maximum as infrastructure investments peak, and declining only after some lag as economic productivity rises and the economy shifts structurally to less-energy-intensive activities (for example, services)[14]. Apparently declining, energy intensities of India and China today are still 2 to 5 times the global mean[8]. To focus on energy supply issues we provisionally accept the IS92a projections of 1% yr^{-1} improvement in global $\dot{E}/GDP$, recognizing that achieving this will depend crucially on the technology and structural changes adopted by developing nations[15].

Another opportunity for emission reductions is continuation of the "decarbonization" of the past 100 years reflected in decreasing carbon intensity of the global energy mix[8]. Under IS92a, the global mean C/E continues to decrease monotonically over the next century (Fig. 1d). Indeed, the evolving global energy mix based on assumed declining costs of nuclear and carbon-free energy relative to fossil fuels has global C/E dropping to that of natural gas by 2030; and it declines even more thereafter. Such rapid decarbonization is possible only by the massive introduction of carbon-free power, $\sim$10 TW by 2050. Even with this much carbon-free power and sustained 1% yr^{-1} improvements in energy intensity, the net effect of the factors in equation (1) more than doubles 1990 CO_2 emissions by 2050.

通常，能源生产排放碳（以 CO_2 的形式）的速率可根据茅阳一（Kaya）碳排放公式[4-6] 得出：

$$\dot{M}_c \equiv N(GDP/N)(\dot{E}/GDP)(C/E) \tag{1}$$

以人口总数（N）、人均国内生产总值（GDP/N）、一次能源消耗强度（$\dot{E}/GDP$）和碳排放强度（C/E）的乘积来表示排放量。本文中我们用瓦特（W）来表示所有燃料能源的一次能源消耗速率（"燃速"），用（1990 年美元）$\$ \cdot yr^{-1}$ 作为国内生产总值的单位，那么两者的比值（即能源消耗强度）的单位就为 $W \cdot yr \cdot \$^{-1}$。碳排放强度是所有能源的由碳到能量的转化排放系数的加权平均值，单位为 $kg\ C \cdot W^{-1} \cdot yr^{-1}$。例如，根据公式（1），1990 年化石燃料的 CO_2 排放系数为：$\dot{M}_c = 5.3 \times 10^9$ 人 × 每人 4,100 $\$ \cdot yr^{-1} \times$ 0.49 $W \cdot yr \cdot \$^{-1} \times 0.56\ kg\ C \cdot W^{-1} \cdot yr^{-1} \approx 6.0\ Gt\ C \cdot yr^{-1}$（$1\ Gt\ C = 10^{12}\ kg\ C$）。

为了说明公式（1）中各因子在历史上以及 IS92a 情景中的相对贡献，我们研究了 1890 年至 2100 年这 210 年内每个因子在全球范围内的变化（图 1），其中 1990 年以前的数据是根据历史资料[7-9] 得到的，而 1990 年后的数据则根据定义 IPCC 情景的文献[2,10-12] 得来。尽管 IPCC 文献中隐含了上述有关信息，但本文首次清晰地展示了这些信息。

茅阳一碳排放公式虽然有利于说明整体状况，但对该公式的各项进行全球累加却有可能掩盖区域发展的不同[13]。个别国家的数据显示，经济发展过程中 $\dot{E}/GDP$ 将不断增大，在基础建设投资达峰值时 $\dot{E}/GDP$ 达到最大值，只有在经济生产力提高且经济结构向低能耗经济活动（如服务业）转型一段时间之后，$\dot{E}/GDP$ 才开始降低[14]。虽然能耗强度呈明显下降趋势，但如今印度和中国的能耗强度仍为世界平均值的 2 ~ 5 倍[8]。为突出能源供给问题，我们暂时采用 IS92a 预估值，即全球 $\dot{E}/GDP$ 每年改善 1%。必须考虑到，要实现这一目标，发展中国家要采取的技术和结构的转型至关重要[15]。

另一个减少排放的机会是过去 100 年"脱碳"的继续，这体现在全球能源结构中碳排放强度的减少[8]。根据 IS92a 情景，下个世纪全球平均 C/E 值将持续递减（图 1d）。实际上，全球能源结构的优化是基于核能与无碳能源成本相对于化石能源成本的降低这一假设而实现的，这将使 2030 年全球 C/E 值降低到天然气的碳排放强度，并且之后还会继续降低。只有大量引入无碳能源（到 2050 年约达 10 TW）才能使含碳能源的使用快速减少。即使有这样多的无碳能源，并且能耗强度每年稳定改善 1%，公式（1）中各因子的净作用仍将使 CO_2 排放量在 2050 年时达到 1990 年的两倍以上。

Fig. 1. Evolution of factors governing the rate of global fossil-fuel carbon emissions in the Kaya identity: $\dot{M}_c \equiv N(GDP/N)(\dot{E}/GDP)(C/E)$. Historical curves (1890–1990) are from archival data[7-9]; future projections (1990–2100) are computed for the IPCC IS92a scenario[2,10-12]. GDP is inflation-corrected to 1990 US dollars. **a**, Global population; **b**, Per capita GDP; **c**, primary energy intensity ($\dot{E}/GDP$: left hand scale) and economic productivity of energy (GDP/$\dot{E}$: right hand scale); **d**, carbon intensity of the energy mix; the horizontal lines are emission individual carbonaceous fuels. Global population, N, shown after 1990 is the UN mid-range projection made at the time the IS92 scenarios were developed. It reaches 11.3 billion by 2100. Per capita global mean GDP continues its monotonic rise at ~1.6% yr⁻¹ over the entire twenty-first century. The primary energy intensity incorporates both engineering energy efficiency and structural changes in the economy governing the material content of economic growth.

Figure 2 shows carbon emissions (Fig. 2a), primary power levels (Fig. 2b) and carbon-free primary power (Fig. 2c) required over the twenty-first century for IS92a and CO₂ stabilization scenarios. Even the optimistic decline of the last two factors in the Kaya identity cannot prevent emissions from increasing from 6 Gt C yr⁻¹ in 1990 to ~20 Gt C yr⁻¹ by 2100 under "business as usual" (Fig. 2a). Also shown as differently shaded zones are the relative contributions of natural gas, oil and coal to emissions. A feature of IS92a worth noting is that the share of carbon-intensive coal, relative to less-carbon-intensive natural gas and oil, rises after 2025, but the carbon intensity (C/E) of the fuel mix declines overall, a feature possible only by the massive introduction of carbon-free energy sources.

图 1. 茅阳一碳排放公式 $\dot{M}_c \equiv N(\mathrm{GDP}/N)(\dot{E}/\mathrm{GDP})(C/E)$ 中控制全球化石燃料 CO_2 排放速率的各因子的变化情况。历史曲线 (1890~1990) 是根据档案资料[7-9] 得到的，未来规划 (1990~2100) 则是根据 IPCC 的 IS92a 情景[2,10-12] 计算而来的。GDP 被修正至 1990 年美元的通胀水平。**a**，全球人口总数；**b**，人均 GDP；**c**，一次能源消耗强度 ($\dot{E}/\mathrm{GDP}$：左侧刻度) 与能源的经济生产力 (GDP/$\dot{E}$：右侧刻度)；**d**，各类含碳能源的碳排放强度，水平线为各种含碳燃料的排放因子。1990 年后的全球人口总数 N 是设计 IS92 情景时，联合国制定的人口预估的中值。到 2100 年该值将达 113 亿。整个二十一世纪，人均全球平均 GDP 以每年 1.6% 左右的速度持续递增。一次能源消耗强度综合考虑了控制经济增长物质组成的工程能源效率和经济结构的变化。

　　图 2 为 IS92a 和 CO_2 稳定情景下，二十一世纪要求的碳排放量 (图 2a)、一次能源水平 (图 2b) 和无碳一次能源 (图 2c) 情况。倘若"照常排放"，即使最乐观地估计茅阳一放碳排放公式中的后两个因子的下降速度，也无法阻止排放量由 1990 年的 6 Gt C · yr^{-1} 升至 2100 年的约 20 Gt C · yr^{-1} (图 2a)。图中还用不同的颜色带表示出了天然气、石油和煤对排放量的贡献。IS92a 中一个值得注意的特征就是，在 2025 年后，相比于含碳量较低的天然气和石油，含碳量较高的煤所占比重有所上升，而燃料结构的碳排放强度 (C/E) 总体上是下降的。这一特征只有在大量引入无碳能源的情况下才可能出现。

Fig. 2. Fossil-fuel carbon emissions and primary power in the twenty-first century for IPCC IS92a and WRE stabilization scenarios. **a**, Carbon emissions; **b**, primary power and **c**, carbon-free primary power. Coloured areas are gas, oil, coal, nuclear and renewable components of IS92a from the energy economics model of Pepper *et al.*[12]. Carbon emissions for WRE scenarios[16] are outputs of our inverse carbon-cycle model[17]. Fossil-fuel power for WRE scenarios is based on IS92a burn rates of gas, oil and coal employed sequentially in descending priority, and limited by total carbon emission caps. Carbon-free primary power is total primary power less fossil-fuel carbon power.

The curves in Fig. 2a are allowable emission levels over time which ultimate stabilize atmospheric CO₂ at 750, 650, 550, 450 and 350 p.p.m.v. computed for the Wigley, Richels and Edmonds stabilization paths[16,17]. These delayed stabilization paths, which follow IS92a emissions early on, with large reductions later (hereafter, WRE 350, 450, ..., 750 scenarios), could buy time to attain CO₂ stabilization goals. This is possible because a given atmospheric CO₂ concentration goal depends roughly on cumulative carbon emissions and can be approached by an infinite number of paths, some of which constrain emissions early, some later. However, Wigley, Richels and Edmonds did not consider whether their paths were a realistic transition from the present fossil-fuel system. They emphasized that their "results should not be interpreted as a 'do nothing' or 'wait and see' policy", calling for prompt and sustained commitment to research, development and

图 2. 在 IPCC 的 IS92a 和 WRE 稳定情景下，二十一世纪化石燃料的碳排放量与一次能源。**a**，碳排放量；**b**，一次能源；**c**，无碳一次能源。彩色部分为根据佩珀等 [12] 的能源经济模型得出的 IS92a 情景下天然气、石油、煤、核能及其他可再生能源等组分。WRE 情景的碳排放量 [16] 是根据我们的大气二氧化碳反演模式 [17] 得到的结果。WRE 情景的化石燃料能源是根据 IS92a 中天然气、石油和煤的燃速按照优先顺序得出的，并受总排放量限制。无碳一次能源是用一次能源总量减去化石燃料量得到的。

　　图 2a 中的曲线是根据威格利、里歇尔斯和埃德蒙兹的稳定路径 [16,17] 计算出的（当最终大气 CO₂ 浓度分别稳定在 750 ppmv、650 ppmv、550 ppmv、450 ppmv 和 350 ppmv 的水平上时）允许排放水平随时间的变化情况。上述延迟稳定路径是：早期依照 IS92a 的排放路径，后期大幅地降低排放（自那以后分别为 WRE 350，450，…，750 情景），来为达到 CO₂ 的稳定目标争取时间。这是可以实现的，因为一个给定的大气 CO₂ 浓度目标能否实现大致取决于累计碳排放量，可以通过部分在早期、部分在晚期进行限制排放的诸多方案来达到该目标。然而，威格利、里歇尔斯和埃德蒙兹并未考虑到，在当前的化石燃料体系下其路径能否实现。他们强调，"这一结果不应该被解释为'无所作为'或者'等等看'的策略"，而是号召人们立刻开始并不断致

demonstration to ensure that low-carbon and carbon-free energy alternatives are available when needed[16].

The black topmost curve in Fig. 2b shows the evolution of total primary power required to meet the economic goals of IS92a, with gas, oil, coal, nuclear and renewable components shown as coloured areas. Also shown are allowable primary power levels from fossil-fuel sources computed for WRE stabilization scenarios. The difference between the IS92a total primary power, $\dot{E}$, and fossil-fuel power allowable for CO_2 stabilization, $\dot{E}_f$, must be provided by carbon-free sources if the economic and "efficiency" assumptions of IPCC "business as usual" are maintained; an increasingly challenging goal as the CO_2 concentration target is lowered.

Figure 2c shows carbon-free power, $\dot{E}_{cf} = \dot{E} - \dot{E}_f$, required for IS92a and for CO_2 stabilization via WRE 350–750 paths in a world economy growing as IS92a and with the same improvement rate in $\dot{E}$/GDP. In that case stabilizing CO_2 concentrations at 1990 levels according to WRE 350 will require ~10 TW of carbon-free primary power by 2018, equal to the total 1990 primary power of the world economy. WRE 550, which leads to an approximate doubling of pre-industrial atmospheric CO_2, requires this much carbon-free power by 2035. These results imply a massive transition from the present fossil-fuel-dominated energy infrastructure to carbon-free sources in the coming decades to stabilize CO_2 at reasonable target values. Even IS92a requires ~10 TW carbon-free power by 2050.

Studies by US DOE laboratories in support of the Kyoto negotiations to reduce carbon emissions in the 1998–2010 time frame emphasize demand side reductions from improved energy efficiency in motor vehicles, buildings and electrical appliances[18]. Our analysis indicates that beyond 2010 new carbon-free primary power technologies will increasingly be needed even with significant improvements in the ability to convert primary power into GDP.

Figure 3 shows the trade-off between increases in carbon-free power and energy efficiency improvements, expressed as the annual percentage improvement in $\dot{E}$/GDP required to achieve a $2 \times$ pre-industrial CO_2 goal by the WRE 550 path. Sustained improvement of energy intensity of order $\pm 1.0\%$ yr^{-1} relative to the base case (1% yr^{-1}) creates increasingly large differences in carbon-free power required as the twenty-first century progresses (Fig. 3). For a 2% yr^{-1} compounded growth, the carbon-free power required remains modest even by the year 2100. But 2% yr^{-1} may be almost impossible to sustain over the next century, as that would imply growing the world population and economy significantly at nearly constant primary power. If there is no improvement in energy intensity, some 40 carbon-free terawatts could be needed by 2050.

力于研究、发展和论证，以保证在需要时有低碳和无碳能源替代品可用[16]。

图 2b 最上面的黑色曲线为达到 IS92a 的经济目标所需要的一次能源需求总量，其中天然气、石油、煤、核能以及其他可再生能源成分以彩色区域标注。图中还给出了根据 WRE 稳定情景计算出的、允许使用的来自于化石燃料能源的一次能源水平。倘若考虑到经济和"效率"而保留 IPCC"照常排放"的假设，IS92a 中一次能源总量 $\dot{E}$ 和 CO_2 稳定目标下允许的化石燃料能源 $\dot{E}_f$ 之差，必须由无碳能源来提供。随着 CO_2 目标浓度的降低，这是一个越来越严峻的挑战。

图 2c 所示为 IS92a 情景下和满足 WRE350～750 路径下实现 CO_2 稳定所需要的无碳能源 $\dot{E}_{cf} = \dot{E} - \dot{E}_f$，这些是建立在全球经济按照 IS92a 情景中的速率增长且 $\dot{E}$/GDP 有相同的改善效率的假设前提下的。那样的话，根据 WRE350，要想将 CO_2 浓度稳定在 1990 年的水平上，到 2018 年无碳能源就必须达到 10 TW 左右，这相当于 1990 年世界经济发展消耗的一次能源的总量。WRE550 的目标是使大气 CO_2 含量稳定在工业化以前水平的两倍左右，这要求到 2035 年时无碳能源达到 10 TW。这也意味着，未来几十年，为使 CO_2 含量稳定在合理的目标值，必然要从现今的以化石燃料为主的基本能源结构向无碳能源的大规模转变。即便是 IS92a 情景也要求，到 2050 年无碳能源需达到 10 TW 左右。

美国能源部的国家实验室为支持京都协议，对 1998～2010 年间如何减少碳排放量做了研究，研究强调可以通过提高机动车辆、建筑以及电器的能效来减少（对于能源的）需求[18]。分析结果表明，在 2010 年以后，即使一次能源转化为 GDP 的能力得到明显提高，对无碳一次能源新技术的需求仍将日益迫切。

图 3 给出了在增加无碳能源与提高能效之间的权衡，图中在 WRE550 路径将 CO_2 含量稳定在工业化以前水平的两倍的目标下，以每年 $\dot{E}$/GDP 所需要改善的百分点这一情况来表示。到二十一世纪，随着时间的推移，即使能耗强度相对于基线（1% yr^{-1}）的改善均为 ±1.0% yr^{-1} 左右，每年对无碳能源需求的差别也是逐渐增大的（图 3）。而当复合增长率为 2% yr^{-1} 时，即使到 2100 年，对无碳能源的需求将相对较少。但到下个世纪要保持 2% yr^{-1} 几乎是不可能实现的。因为，那将意味着，在一次能源近乎不变的情况下，世界人口与经济均明显增长。倘若不改善能耗强度，到 2050 年，将需要约 40 TW 的无碳能源。

Fig. 3. Twenty-first century trade-offs, between carbon-free power required and "energy efficiency", to stabilize at twice the pre-industrial CO_2 concentration. Carbon-free primary power is plotted versus the annual rate of decline in energy intensity. The latter is defined as $-[d(\dot{E}/GDP)/dt](\dot{E}/GDP)^{-1}100\%$. All cases assume WRE 550 CO_2 stabilization paths and GDP growth of 2.9% yr^{-1} to 2025, 2.3% yr^{-1} thereafter. The rate of energy intensity decline in IS92a and in our CO_2 stabilization base cases is ~1.0% yr^{-1}.

The authors of the IPCC central "business as usual" scenario (IS92a) believed that an exponential decline in $\dot{E}/GDP$ of 1% yr^{-1} would be sustainable over the next century employing only those emission-control policies internationally agreed to at the 1992 Rio climate treaty negotiations[1,2]. But either deploying 10–30 TW carbon-free power or improving $\dot{E}/GDP$ by 2% yr^{-1} will be very difficult. The need to push hard on both improving energy supply and reducing demand is demonstrated by our analysis, as well as the fact that there are real trade-offs—more of one can significantly diminish the need for the other.

Stabilizing atmospheric CO_2 at twice pre-industrial levels while meeting the economic assumptions of "business as usual" implies a massive transition to carbon-free power, particular in developing nations. There are no energy systems technologically ready at present to produce the required amounts of carbon-free power[6]. Some suggest the answer may be integrated energy systems based on fossil fuels[19] in which carbon dioxide[20] or solid carbon[21] is sequestered in reservoirs isolated from the atmosphere, or "geoengineering" compensatory climate changes[22-24]. Despite potentially serious environmental and cost problems, these approaches would allow fossil fuel, increasingly coal, to continue its historic rise as the primary energy source of the next century.

It is time now to look hard at the engineering feasibility of transformative technologies that can change the way primary energy itself is produced. It is within the range of climate change and impact projections that stabilization of atmospheric CO_2 at some level below the IS92a baseline is necessary to mitigate large adverse effects on global economies and ecosystems[3]. In that case, a massive infusion of new energy-producing technologies at the

图 3. 21 世纪，为使 CO_2 含量稳定在工业化以前水平的两倍，需在无碳能源与"能效"间做出权衡。图中纵坐标为无碳一次能源需求量，横坐标为能耗强度年降低速率。后者用 $-[d(\dot{E}/GDP)/dt](\dot{E}/GDP)^{-1}100\%$ 表示。所有情形均以 WRE550 的 CO_2 稳定路径为准，且到 2025 年 GDP 的年增长率为 2.9%，2025 年以后为 2.3%。而在 IS92a 以及我们的 CO_2 稳定基线中，能耗强度的降低速率约为 1% yr^{-1}。

制定 IPCC 最重要的"照常排放"情景 (IS92a) 的学者认为，下个世纪，只要各国的控制排放政策符合 1992 年的里约气候条约[1,2]的规定，使 $\dot{E}/GDP$ 每年指数递减 1% 是可行的。但无论是要开发 10～30 TW 的无碳能源还是使 $\dot{E}/GDP$ 每年改善 2% 都不容易。通过分析我们已经证明，需要在大力推动能源供给提高的同时减少对能源的需求，而且，实际中确实存在着这样的权衡关系——某一项的增多将大大降低对另一项的需求。

要使 CO_2 含量稳定在工业化以前水平的两倍，同时还要达到经济正常发展的目标，就意味着要大量改用无碳能源，尤其是在发展中国家。目前还没有任何技术成熟的能源系统可以生产出那么多的无碳能源[6]。有人提议，可通过整合目前以化石燃料为基础的能源体系[19]，使 CO_2[20] 或固态碳[21]保存在某个地方，与大气隔离开来；或实施"地球工程"来补偿气候的变化[22-24]。倘若不考虑一系列潜在的严峻的环境和成本问题，利用这些方法，下个世纪化石燃料(尤其是煤)将延续其在一次能源中占主要地位的历史。

现在是时候重视改造技术的工程可行性问题了，倘若改造技术实现，就可以改变一次能源本身的生产方式。在预估的气候变化与影响范围内，有必要将大气 CO_2 的稳定目标值定得比 IS92a 基线低些，以减轻给全球经济和生态系统带来的大量不利影响[3]。那样的话，就需要引入大量的新能源生产技术以防止"人类活动对气候系

required scale could be needed to prevent "dangerous anthropogenic interference with the climate system" (ref. 1).

Analyses of carbon emissions targets thus far have quite reasonably emphasized market economics theory. Some suggest that market forces alone, perhaps supplemented by carbon taxes, are sufficient to stimulate adequate levels of innovation in emission-reducing technologies. However, market inefficiencies may preclude timely development of such technologies at the required scale[25]. There are renewable[26,27], fission[28] and fusion[29] concepts incorporating innovative technological ideas at early research and development stages that could, in principle, provide the needed carbon-free power. But without policy incentives to overcome socioeconomic inertia these could take more than 50 years to penetrate to their market potential[30].

These results underscore the pitfalls of "wait-and-see". This past century, accelerated technology development from wartime and postwar research produced commercial aviation, radar, computer chips, lasers and the Internet, among other things. Researching, developing and commercializing carbon-free primary power technologies capable of 10–30 TW by the mid-twenty-first century could require efforts, perhaps international, pursued with the urgency of the Manhattan Project or the Apollo space programme. The roles of governments and market entrepreneurs in the eventual deployment of such technologies need to be considered more comprehensively than we can do here. But the potentially adverse effect of humanity on the Earth's climate could well stimulate new industries in the twenty-first century, as did the Second World War and the "cold war" in this century.

(**395**, 881-884; 1998)

Martin I. Hoffert[*], Ken Caldeira[†], Atul K. Jain[‡], Erik F. Haites[§], L. D. Danny Harvey[||], Seth D. Potter[*¶], Michael E. Schlesinger[‡], Stephen H. Schneider[#], Robert G. Watts[☆], Tom M. L. Wigley[**] & Donald J. Wuebbles[‡]

[*] Department of Physics, New York University, 4 Washington Place, New York, New York 10003-6621, USA

[†] Lawrence Livermore National Laboratory, Livermore, California 94550, USA

[‡] Department of Atmospheric Sciences, University of Illinois, Urbana, Illinois 61801, USA

[§] Margaree Consultants, Toronto, M5H 2X6, Canada

[||] Department of Geography, University of Toronto, Toronto, M5S 3G3, Canada

[#] Department of Biological Sciences, Stanford University, Stanford, California 94305, USA

[☆] Department of Mechanical Engineering, Tulane University, New Orleans, Louisiana 70118, USA

[**] National Center for Atmospheric Research, Boulder, Colorado 80307, USA

[¶] Present address: Boeing, Saal Beach, California 90740-7644, USA.

Received 10 August; accepted 8 October 1998.

References:

1. *United Nations Framework Convention on Climate Change (Text)* (UNEP/WMO, Climate Change Secretariat, Geneva, 1992).

2. Leggett, J. *et al.* in *Climatic Change 1992: the Supplementary Report to the IPCC Scientific Assessment* (eds Houghton, J. T. *et al.*) 69-95 (Cambridge Univ. Press, 1992).

3. Houghton, J. T. *et al.* (eds) *Climate Change 1995: the Science of Climate Change* (Cambridge Univ. Press, 1996).

4. Kaya, Y. Impact of carbon dioxide emission control on GNP growth: Interpretation of proposed scenarios (IPCC Response Strategies Working Group Memorandum, 1989).

统产生危险的干扰"(参考文献 1)。

　　基于迄今对碳排放目标的分析，我们完全有理由强调市场经济理论的作用。有人认为，仅凭市场力量本身，或许再辅以一定的排碳税，就足以促进减排技术的创新达到所需水平。然而，市场效率的低下可能会妨碍减排技术及时发展到所需的规模[25]。可再生的[26,27]、核裂变[28]及核聚变[29]概念结合创新技术观念正处于早期研发阶段，理论上讲，它们应该可以满足无碳能源的需求。但是，如果没有政策的激励以克服社会经济发展的惯性，要看到其市场潜能，还将需要 50 年以上的时间[30]。

　　上述结果再次强调了"等等看"策略的隐患。在过去的 100 年中，战时与战后的研究加速了技术的发展，诞生了商用飞机、雷达、计算机芯片、激光以及互联网等等科技产物。到二十一世纪中叶，要使无碳能源技术的研究、发展以及商业化达到 10～30 TW 的水平，还需要国际社会的共同努力，能源的研究发展如同曼哈顿计划或阿波罗太空计划的实施一样迫切。相比于我们文中所讨论的情况，应该更全面地考虑政府和市场中企业家在减排技术的最终部署中的作用。正如本世纪第二次世界大战和"冷战"一样，人类对地球气候的潜在危害将有效地促进二十一世纪新工业的诞生。

（齐红艳 翻译；周天军 审稿）

5. Nakićenović, N., Victor, D., Grübler, A. & Schrattenholtzer, L. Long term strategies for mitigating global warming: Introduction. *Energy* **18,** 403-409 (1993).

6. Hoffert, M. I. & Potter, S. D. in *Engineering Response to Global Climate Change* (ed. Watts, R. G.) 205-260 (Lewis, Boca Raton, FL, 1997).

7. de Vries, B. & van den Wijngaart, R. *The Targets/IMage Energy (TIME) 1.0 Model* (GLOBO Rep. Ser. No. 16, National Institute of Public Health and the Environment (RIVM), Bilthoven, Netherlands, 1995).

8. Nakićenović, N. Freeing energy from carbon. *Daedalus* **125**(3), 95-112 (1996).

9. Boden, T. A. *et al.* (eds) *Trends 93: A Compendium of Data on Global Change* 501-584 (ORNL/CDIA- 65, Carbon Dioxide Information Analysis Center, Oak Ridge National Lab., Oak Ridge, TN, 1994).

10. Alcamo, J. *et al.* in *Climate Change 1994* (eds Houghton, J. T. *et al.*) 247-304 (Cambridge Univ. Press, Cambridge, UK, 1995).

11. Alcamo, J. (ed.) *Image 2.0: Integrated Modeling of Global Climate Change* (Kluwer, Netherlands, 1994).

12. Pepper, W. J. *et al. Emission Scenarios for the IPCC—An Update* (US Environmental Protection Agency, Washington DC, 1992).

13. Yang, C. & Schneider, S. H. Global carbon dioxide scenarios: sensitivity to social and technological factors in three regions. *Mitigat. Adapt. Strat. for Global Change* **2,** 373-404 (1998).

14. Reddy, A. K. N. & Goldemberg, J. in *Energy for Planet Earth* (ed. Piel, J.) 59-71 (Freeman, New York, 1991).

15. Goldemberg, J. Energy needs in developing countries and sustainability. *Science* **269,** 1058-1059 (1995).

16. Wigley, T. M. L., Richels, R. & Edmonds, J. A. Economic and environmental choices in the stabilization of atmospheric CO_2 concentration. *Nature* **379,** 240-243 (1996).

17. Jain, A. K., Kheshgi, H. S., Hoffert, M. I. & Wuebbles, D. J. Distribution of radiocarbon as a test of global carbon cycle models. *Glob. Biogeochem. Cycles* **9,** 153-166 (1995).

18. Romm, J., Levine, M., Brown, M. & Peterson, E. A road map for U.S. carbon reductions. *Science* **279,** 669-670 (1998).

19. National Academy of Sciences *Policy Implications of Greenhouse Warming* 340-375 (National Academy Press, Washington DC, 1992).

20. Parson, E. A. & Keith, D. W. Fossil fuels without CO_2 emissions: Progress, prospects and policy implications. *Science* (in the press).

21. Steinberg, M. & Dong, Y. in *Global Climate Change: Science, Policy and Mitigation Strategies* (eds Mathai, C. V. & Stensland, C.) 858-873 (Air & Waste Management Assoc., Pittsburgh, PA, 1994).

22. Marland, G. (ed.) Special section on geoengineering. *Clim. Change* **33**(3), 275-336 (1996).

23. Flannery, B. P. *et al.* in *Engineering Response to Global Climate Change* (ed. Watts, R. G.) 379-427 (Lewis, Boca Raton, FL, 1997).

24. Fogg, M. J. *Terraforming: Engineering Planetary Environments* (SAE International, Warrendale, PA, 1995).

25. Schneider, S. H. & Goulder, L. H. Achieving low-cost emission targets. *Nature* **389,** 13-14 (1997).

26. Johansson, T. M. *et al.* (eds) *Renewable Energy* (Island, Washington DC, 1993).

27. Glaser, P. E. *et al.* (eds) *Solar Power Satellites: A Space Energy System for Earth* (Wiley-Praxis, Chichester, 1998).

28. Weinberg, A. M. in *Technologies For a Greenhouse-Constrained Society* (eds Kuliasha, M. A. *et al.*) 227-237 (Lewis, Boca Raton, FL, 1992).

29. Fowler, T. K. *The Fusion Quest* (Johns Hopkins, Baltimore, 1997).

30. Grübler, A. in *Technological Trajectories and the Human Environment* (eds Ausubel, J. H. & Langford, H. D.) 14-32 (National Academy Press, Washington DC, 1997).

Acknowledgements. We thank DOE, NASA and NSF for partial support of this work. We also thank the Aspen Global Change Institute for discussions during the 1998 summer workshop "Innovative Energy Systems and CO_2 Stabilization".

Correspondence and requests for materials should be addressed to M.I.H. (e-mail: marty.haffert@nyu. edu).

Jefferson Fathered Slave's Last Child

E. A. Foster *et al.*

Editor's Note

This paper reports one of the more dramatic examples of the ability, developed over the previous decade or so, to make genetic comparisons between individuals by looking at specific "markers" in their genomes. For many years there had been suggestions that Thomas Jefferson, one of the Founding Fathers of the United States of America and its third president, had fathered one or more children by one of his slaves, named Sally Hemings. The paper reports a genetic analysis of the male-line descendants of Hemings' youngest and eldest sons (Thomas Woodson and Eston Hemings Jefferson, each of whom will have received a Y chromosome in direct paternal succession from these two respective men), which is compared with that of male-line descendants of Jefferson's paternal uncle. The results support the view that Eston, but not Thomas Woodson, was fathered by Thomas Jefferson.

THERE is a long-standing historical controversy over the question of US President Thomas Jefferson's paternity of the children of Sally Hemings, one of his slaves[1-4]. To throw some scientific light on the dispute, we have compared Y-chromosomal DNA haplotypes from male-line descendants of Field Jefferson, a paternal uncle of Thomas Jefferson, with those of male-line descendants of Thomas Woodson, Sally Hemings' putative first son, and of Eston Hemings Jefferson, her last son. The molecular findings fail to support the belief that Thomas Jefferson was Thomas Woodson's father, but provide evidence that he was the biological father of Eston Hemings Jefferson.

In 1802, President Thomas Jefferson was accused of having fathered a child, Tom, by Sally Hemings[5]. Tom was said to have been born in 1790, soon after Jefferson and Sally Hemings returned from France where he had been minister. Present-day members of the African–American Woodson family believe that Thomas Jefferson was the father of Thomas Woodson, whose name comes from his later owner[6]. No known documents support this view.

Sally Hemings had at least four more children. Her last son, Eston (born in 1808), is said to have borne a striking resemblance to Thomas Jefferson, and entered white society in Madison, Wisconsin, as Eston Hemings Jefferson. Although Eston's descendants believe that Thomas Jefferson was Eston's father, most Jefferson scholars give more credence to the oral tradition of the descendants of Martha Jefferson Randolph, the president's daughter. They believe that Sally Hemings' later children, including Eston, were fathered by either

杰斐逊是其奴隶最小孩子的生父

福斯特等

编者按

这篇论文报道了一种非常引人注目的、在过去十年发展起来的科学手段，该手段通过在不同个体基因组中寻找特异性的"标记"来进行遗传比对。许多年以来，一直有人认为托马斯·杰斐逊——美国的开国之父之一以及第三任总统，与他的一个奴隶莎丽·海明斯，生下了一个或者多个孩子。这篇论文报道了海明斯最大的和最小的儿子（托马斯·伍德森和艾斯顿·海明斯·杰斐逊）的男性后裔（他们分别从这两个人直接遗传一条父系Y染色体）的遗传分析，并与托马斯·杰斐逊的伯父的男性后裔的基因进行比较。结果支持托马斯·杰斐逊是艾斯顿而非托马斯·伍德森的父亲这一观点。

关于美国总统托马斯·杰斐逊与其奴隶之一莎丽·海明斯的孩子之间的血缘关系，长期以来一直是历史上争论不休的一个问题[1-4]。从科学的角度来看待和分析这个争论，我们比较了不同来源的Y染色体DNA的单体型。其中一些标本来自托马斯·杰斐逊的伯父菲尔德·杰斐逊的男性后裔，另一些标本来自托马斯·伍德森的男性后裔，他被认定为莎丽·海明斯的第一个儿子，以及来自她最小的儿子艾斯顿·海明斯·杰斐逊的男性后裔的样本。分子层面的比对结果无法支持我们相信托马斯·杰斐逊是托马斯·伍德森的生父，但是提供了证据表明他是艾斯顿·海明斯·杰斐逊生物学上的生父。

1802年，总统托马斯·杰斐逊被指控与莎丽·海明斯生下了一个孩子，名叫汤姆[5]。据说汤姆生于1790年，就在杰斐逊和莎丽·海明斯从法国返回不久，杰斐逊曾经在法国做过部长。现在的非裔美籍伍德森家族成员都相信托马斯·杰斐逊是托马斯·伍德森的生父，后者的名字来自于他之后的主人[6]。但是，没有任何已知的文件支持这种观点。

莎丽·海明斯至少有四个孩子。她最小的孩子艾斯顿（生于1808年），据说与托马斯·杰斐逊惊人得相似，他以艾斯顿·海明斯·杰斐逊的身份进入威斯康星州麦迪逊城的白人社会中。尽管艾斯顿的男性后裔相信托马斯·杰斐逊是艾斯顿的生父，但是研究杰斐逊的绝大多数学者更愿意相信总统的女儿玛莎·杰斐逊·伦道夫的后裔的口口相传。他们认为莎丽·海明斯所生的孩子，包括艾斯顿在内，他们的生父

Samuel or Peter Carr, sons of Jefferson's sister, which would explain their resemblance to the president.

Because most of the Y chromosome is passed unchanged from father to son, apart from occasional mutations, DNA analysis of the Y chromosome can reveal whether or not individuals are likely to be male-line relatives. We therefore analysed DNA from the Y chromosomes of: five male-line descendants of two sons of the president's paternal uncle, Field Jefferson; five male-line descendants of two sons of Thomas Woodson; one male-line descendant of Eston Hemings Jefferson; and three male-line descendants of three sons of John Carr, grandfather of Samuel and Peter Carr (Fig. 1a). No Y-chromosome data were available from male-line descendants of President Thomas Jefferson because he had no surviving sons.

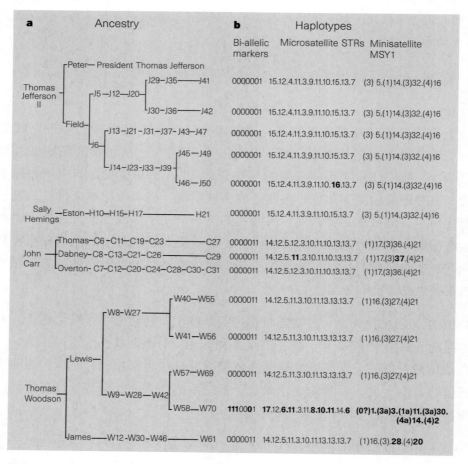

Fig. 1. Male-line ancestry and haplotypes of participants. **a**, Ancestry. Numbers correspond to reference numbers and names in more detailed genealogical charts for each family. **b**, Haplotypes. Entries in bold highlight deviations from the usual patterns for the group of descendants. **Bi-allelic markers**. Order of loci: YAP-SRYm8299-sY81-LLY22g-Tat-92R7-SRYm1532. 0, ancestral state; 1, derived state. **Microsatellite short tandem repeats (STRs)**. Order of loci: 19-388-389A-389B-389C-389D-390-391-

是塞缪尔或者彼得·卡尔——杰斐逊妹妹的儿子，这样也可以解释为什么他们的染色体会和杰斐逊总统之间有着相似之处。

绝大多数的 Y 染色体都会毫无改变地由生父传给儿子，除非偶然发生突变，因此，对 Y 染色体的 DNA 分析可以揭示不同个体之间是否具有某种亲缘关系。我们分析了来自不同人的 Y 染色体上的 DNA：总统的伯父菲尔德·杰斐逊的两个儿子的五个男性后裔；托马斯·伍德森的两个儿子的五个男性后裔；艾斯顿·海明斯·杰斐逊的男性后裔；约翰·卡尔的三个儿子的三个男性后裔，约翰·卡尔是塞缪尔和彼得·卡尔的祖父（见图 1a）。样本中没有来自于总统托马斯·杰斐逊的男性后裔的数据，因为他没有活下来的儿子。

图 1. 男性族谱以及参与者的单体型。**a**，祖先。数字对应相应的人的编码，名字则是更为具体的每个家族的宗族谱图。**b**，单体型。粗体用来标注与整个家族正常遗传情况的差异。**双等位基因标记**。位点的顺序：YAP-SRYm8299-sY81-LLY22g-Tat-92R7-SRYm 1532。0，祖先状态；1，派生状态。**微卫星短串联重复序列（STR）**。位点顺序：19-388-389A-389B-389C-389D-390-391-392-393-dxys156y。在每一个位点

392-393-dxys156y. The number of repeats at each locus is shown. **Minisatellite MSY1.** Each number in brackets represents the sequence type of the repeat unit; the number after it is the number of units with this sequence type. For example, J41 has 5 units of sequence type 3, 14 units of sequence type 1, 32 units of sequence type 3, and 16 units of sequence type 4.

Seven bi-allelic markers (refs 7–12), eleven microsatellites (ref. 13) and the minisatellite MSY1 (ref. 14) were analysed (Fig. 1b). Four of the five descendants of Field Jefferson shared the same haplotype at all loci, and the fifth differed by only a single unit at one microsatellite locus, probably a mutation. This haplotype is rare in the population, where the average frequency of a microsatellite haplotype is about 1.5 per cent. Indeed, it has never been observed outside the Jefferson family, and it has not been found in 670 European men (more than 1,200 worldwide) typed with the microsatellites or 308 European men (690 worldwide) typed with MSY1.

Four of the five male-line descendants of Thomas Woodson shared a haplotype (with one MSY1 variant) that was not similar to the Y chromosome of Field Jefferson but was characteristic of Europeans. The fifth Woodson descendant had an entirely different haplotype, most often seen in sub-Saharan Africans, which indicates illegitimacy in the line after individual W42. In contrast, the descendant of Eston Hemings Jefferson did have the Field Jefferson haplotype. The haplotypes of two of the descendants of John Carr were identical; the third differed by one step at one microsatellite locus and by one step in the MSY1 code. The Carr haplotypes differed markedly from those of the descendants of Field Jefferson.

The simplest and most probable explanations for our molecular findings are that Thomas Jefferson, rather than one of the Carr brothers, was the father of Eston Hemings Jefferson, and that Thomas Woodson was not Thomas Jefferson's son. The frequency of the Jefferson haplotype is less than 0.1 per cent, a result that is at least 100 times more likely if the president was the father of Eston Hemings Jefferson than if someone unrelated was the father.

We cannot completely rule out other explanations of our findings based on illegitimacy in various lines of descent. For example, a male-line descendant of Field Jefferson could possibly have illegitimately fathered an ancestor of the presumed maleline descendant of Eston. But in the absence of historical evidence to support such possibilities, we consider them to be unlikely.

(**396**, 27-28; 1998)

上重复的次数显示在图上。**小卫星 MSY1**。每一个括号中的数字代表重复单元的序列类型；在它之后的数目代表该序列类型单元的数目。例如，J41 个体具有 5 个单元的序列类型 3，14 个单元的序列类型 1，32 个单元的序列类型 3，以及 16 个单元的序列类型 4。

我们对七个双等位基因标记（参考文献 7～12）、十一个微卫星遗传标记（参考文献 13）以及小卫星 MSY1（参考文献 14）进行了分析研究（图 1b）。来自菲尔德·杰斐逊家族五个男性后裔中的四个人在所有位点上都具有同样的单体型，第五个人只是在其中一个微卫星遗传位点上的一个单元上略有不同，这可能是一个突变。这个单体型在人群中出现的概率是很小的，每个微卫星单体型出现的平均概率大概是百分之一点五。事实上，这种单体型从来没有在杰斐逊家族以外被发现过，在微卫星标记的 670 个欧洲男性（在全世界范围内超过 1,200 个）或者 308 个欧洲男性（全世界范围内 690 个男性）中都未曾发现过 MSY1 位点标记。

来自托马斯·伍德森五个男性后裔中有四个具有相同的单体型（有一个 MSY1 位点突变），这个单体型与来自菲尔德·杰斐逊的 Y 染色体之间并不相似，但却是欧洲人的特征。来自伍德森男性后裔的第五个后裔具有完全不同的单体型，这种单体型在亚撒哈拉非裔中最常见，这说明个体 W42 之后子嗣中存在私生情况。与之相反，艾斯顿·海明斯·杰斐逊的后代确实具有与菲尔德·杰斐逊相同的单体型。来自约翰·卡尔的两个后代的单体型是一样的；第三个后代的差别其中之一位于微卫星位点上，另一个位于 MSY1 编码上。来自卡尔男性后裔的单体型与来自菲尔德·杰斐逊男性后裔的单体型有着显著的差别。

针对我们分子研究的发现，最简单和最有可能的解释是艾斯顿·海明斯·杰斐逊的生父是托马斯·杰斐逊，而不是卡尔兄弟中的某一个。另外，托马斯·伍德森不是托马斯·杰斐逊的儿子。杰斐逊单体型出现的频率低于百分之零点一，这个结果说明，总统作为艾斯顿·海明斯·杰斐逊生父的可能性是一个毫不相干的人作为他的生父的概率的 100 倍。

基于不同谱系的异常情况，我们无法完全排除针对我们发现的其他解释。例如，菲尔德·杰斐逊的一个男性后裔有可能非法生下了一个孩子，而他是我们假定的艾斯顿后裔中的祖先。但缺少历史证据来支持这样一种假设，我们认为这是不可能发生的。

（刘振明 翻译；胡松年 审稿）

Eugene A. Foster[*], **M. A. Jobling**[†], **P. G. Taylor**[†], **P. Donnelly**[‡], **P. de Knijff**[§], **Rene Mieremet**[§], **T. Zerjal**[¶], **C. Tyler-Smith**[¶]

[*] 6 Gildersleeve Wood, Charlottesville, Virginia 22903, USA e-mail: eafoster@aol.com

[†] Department of Genetics, University of Leicester, Adrian Building, University Road, Leicester LE1 7RH, UK

[‡] Department of Statistics, University of Oxford, South Parks Road, Oxford OX1 3TG, UK

[§] MGC Department of Human Genetics, Leiden University, PO Box 9503, 2300 RA Leiden, The Netherlands

[¶] Department of Biochemistry, University of Oxford, South Parks Road, Oxford OX1 3QU, UK

References:

1. Peterson, M. D. *The Jefferson Image in the American Mind* 181-187 (Oxford Univ. Press, New York, 1960).

2. Malone, D. *Jefferson the President: First Term, 1801–1805* Appendix II, 494-498 (Little Brown, Boston, MA, 1970).

3. Brodie, F. M. *Thomas Jefferson: An Intimate History* (Norton, New York, 1974).

4. Ellis, J. J. *American Sphinx: The Character of Thomas Jefferson* (Knopf, New York, 1997).

5. Callender, J. T. *Richmond Recorder* 1 September 1802. [Cited in: Gordon-Reed, A. *Thomas Jefferson and Sally Hemings: An American Controversy* (Univ. Press of Virginia, Charlottesville, 1997)].

6. Woodson, M. S. *The Woodson Source Book* 2nd edn (Washington, 1984).

7. Hammer, M. F. *Mol. Biol. Evol.* **11**, 749-761 (1994).

8. Whitfield, L. S., Sulston, J. E. & Goodfellow, P. N. *Nature* **378**, 379-380 (1995).

9. Seielstad, M. T. *et al. Hum. Mol. Genet.* **3**, 2159-2161 (1994).

10. Zerjal, T. *et al. Am. J. Hum. Genet.* **60**, 1174-1183 (1997).

11. Mathias, N., Bayes, M. & Tyler-Smith, C. *Hum. Mol. Genet.* **3**, 115-123 (1994).

12. Kwok, C. *et al. J. Med. Genet.* **33**, 465-468 (1996).

13. Kayser, M. *et al. Int. J. Legal Med.* **110**, 125-133 (1997).

14. Jobling, M. A., Bouzekri, N. & Taylor, P. G. *Hum. Mol. Genet.* **7**, 643-653 (1998).

Light Speed Reduction to 17 Metres per Second in an Ultracold Atomic Gas

L. V. Hau *et al.*

Editor's Note

Light moves more slowly in physical media than in empty space—but generally only by a little. Yet interference effects associated with quantum physics can in principle be used to slow the speed of light dramatically in a specially designed medium. Here, Lene Vestergaard Hau and colleagues demonstrate this effect in an ultracold gas of sodium atoms. They use a laser beam travelling at right angles to a test beam to prepare the atoms such that a fraction of them are in particular excited electronic states. Light in the test beam, being repeatedly absorbed and re-emitted by these atoms, travels at a speed of only 17 metres per second, some 20 million times slower than light in a vacuum.

Techniques that use quantum interference effects are being actively investigated to manipulate the optical properties of quantum systems[1]. One such example is electromagnetically induced transparency, a quantum effect that permits the propagation of light pulses through an otherwise opaque medium[2-5]. Here we report an experimental demonstration of electromagnetically induced transparency in an ultracold gas of sodium atoms, in which the optical pulses propagate at twenty million times slower than the speed of light in a vacuum. The gas is cooled to nanokelvin temperatures by laser and evaporative cooling[6-10]. The quantum interference controlling the optical properties of the medium is set up by a "coupling" laser beam propagating at a right angle to the pulsed "probe" beam. At nanokelvin temperatures, the variation of refractive index with probe frequency can be made very steep. In conjunction with the high atomic density, this results in the exceptionally low light speeds observed. By cooling the cloud below the transition temperature for Bose–Einstein condensation[11-13] (causing a macroscopic population of alkali atoms in the quantum ground state of the confining potential), we observe even lower pulse propagation velocities (17 m s^{-1}) owing to the increased atom density. We report an inferred nonlinear refractive index of 0.18 cm^2 W^{-1} and find that the system shows exceptionally large optical nonlinearities, which are of potential fundamental and technological interest for quantum optics.

THE experiment is performed with a gas of sodium atoms cooled to nanokelvin temperatures. Our atom cooling set-up is described in some detail in ref. 14. Atoms emitted from a "candlestick" atomic beam source[15] are decelerated in a Zeeman slower and loaded into a magneto-optical trap. In a few seconds we collect a cloud of 10^{10} atoms

光速在超冷原子气中降低至 17 米每秒

光在物质媒介中的传播速度比在真空中的慢，但通常只慢一点点。然而，与量子物理相关的干涉效应原则上可以使光速在特别设计的介质中显著变慢。本文中，莱娜·韦斯特戈·豪和其同事们在超冷钠原子气体中展示了这种效应：使用与测试光束成直角传播的激光束来制备原子，使得其中的一部分处在特定的电子激发态。测试光束中的光，被这些原子反复吸收和重新发射，以每秒 17 米的速度传播，大约为真空中光速的 2,000 万分之一。

基于量子干涉效应的技术被积极研究用来操纵量子系统中的光学性质 [1]。其中的一个例子就是电磁感应透明，一种允许光脉冲在其他状况下不透明的介质中传播的量子现象 [2-5]。在此，我们报道了在超冷钠原子气中电磁感应透明的实验验证，光脉冲以在真空中光速的 2,000 万分之一的速度在该介质中传播。气体通过激光和蒸发制冷被降温至纳开 (10^{-9} K) [6-10]。控制介质光学性质的量子干涉通过与脉冲"探测"光束成直角传播的"耦合"激光束来建立。在纳开温度下，折射率随探测频率可以发生非常急剧的变化。与高原子密度相结合，就会导致所观察到的极低光速。我们将原子云冷却至玻色–爱因斯坦凝聚临界温度 [11-13] 以下（引起处于因禁势量子基态的碱金属原子的宏观布居），由于原子数密度增大，我们观测到更低的脉冲传播速度（17 m·s^{-1}）。经过测算，本文报道了该体系的非线性折射率系数为 0.18 $cm^2·W^{-1}$，发现该系统显示出非常大的光学非线性，这对于量子光学的研究而言具有潜在的基础和技术吸引力。

本实验是在降温至纳开的钠原子中进行的。文献 14 中对我们的原子冷却装置有一些细节性的描述。从"烛台"原子束源 [15] 发出的原子在塞曼减速器中被减速，然后被加载到一个磁光阱中。若干秒后我们在 1 mK 温度，6×10^{11} cm^{-3} 密度下采集到

at a temperature of 1 mK and a density of 6×10^{11} cm^{-3}. The atoms are then polarization gradient cooled for a few milliseconds to 50 μK and optically pumped into the $F = 1$ ground state with an equal population of the three magnetic sublevels. We then turn all laser beams off and confine the atoms magnetically in the "4 Dee" trap[14]. Only atoms in the $M_F = -1$ state, with magnetic dipole moments directed opposite to the magnetic field direction (picked as the quantization axis), are trapped in the asymmetric harmonic trapping potential. This magnetic filtering results in a sample of atoms that are all in a single atomic state (state $|1\rangle$ in Fig. 1b) which allows adiabatic optical preparation of the atoms, as described below, and minimal heating of the cloud.

Next we evaporatively cool the atoms for 38 s to the transition temperature for Bose–Einstein condensation, T_c. The magnetic fields are then adjusted to adiabatically soften the trap. The resulting trapping potential has a frequency of $f_z = 21$ Hz along the symmetry (z) axis of the 4 Dee trap, and transverse frequencies $f_x = f_y = 69$ Hz. The bias field, parallel to the z axis, is 11 G. When we cool well below T_c, we are left with 1–2 million atoms in the condensate. For these parameters the transition occurs at a temperature of $T_c = 435$ nK and a peak density in the cloud of 5×10^{12} cm^{-3} .

We now apply a linearly polarized laser beam, the coupling beam, tuned to the transition between the unpopulated hyperfine states $|2\rangle$ and $|3\rangle$ (Fig. 1b). This beam couples states $|2\rangle$ and $|3\rangle$ and creates a quantum interference for a weaker probe laser beam (left circularly polarized) which is tuned to the $|1\rangle \rightarrow |3\rangle$ transition. A stable eigenstate (the "dark state") of the atom in the presence of coupling and probe lasers is a coherent superposition of the two hyperfine ground states $|1\rangle$ and $|2\rangle$. The ratio of the probability amplitudes is such that the contributions to the atomic dipole moment induced by the two lasers exactly cancel. The quantum interference occurs in a narrow interval of probe frequencies, with a width determined by the coupling laser power.

一个由 10^{10} 个原子组成的原子云。这些原子随后被偏振梯度冷却若干毫秒至 50 μK，并被光泵抽运至 $F = 1$ 的基态，原子平均布居于三个磁子能级上。然后我们关闭所有的激光束，并用磁场将原子限制在"4 Dee"阱[14]中。只有处于 $M_F = -1$ 态的原子，其磁偶极矩与磁场方向（被选作量子化轴）相反，被捕获于非对称的谐振势阱中。这个磁过滤使所有的样品原子都处于同一原子态（图 1b 中的量子态 $|1\rangle$），这就使下文所述的原子绝热光学制备和对原子云最低限度的加热成为可能。

接下来我们将原子蒸发制冷 38 秒至玻色–爱因斯坦凝聚的临界转变温度 T_c。调整磁场，绝热地减小势阱的梯度。这样所获得的势阱沿 4 Dee 势阱对称轴 (z) 方向的频率 $f_z = 21$ Hz，横向频率 $f_x = f_y = 69$ Hz。偏置场平行于 z 轴，为 11 G。当温度完全低于 T_c，我们只剩下处于凝聚态的一百万到两百万个原子。在这些参数下，转变发生在 $T_c = 435$ nK，原子云峰值密度为 5×10^{12} cm^{-3}。

我们现在来加一线偏振激光束，即耦合光束，将之调谐至无粒子分布的超精细态 $|2\rangle$ 和 $|3\rangle$ 之间的跃迁（图 1b）。该光束将态 $|2\rangle$ 和 $|3\rangle$ 相耦合，从而对一更弱的调谐在态 $|1\rangle \rightarrow |3\rangle$ 跃迁的探测激光光束（左旋圆偏振）产生了量子干涉。在耦合激光和探测激光同时存在时，原子的稳定本征态（"暗"态）是两个超精细基态 $|1\rangle$ 和 $|2\rangle$ 的相干叠加。概率幅比值被设置为两激光对所激发的原子偶极矩的贡献恰好相抵消。量子干涉发生在探测频率的一狭窄的范围内，宽度由耦合激光功率决定。

Fig. 1. Experimental set-up. A "coupling" laser beam propagates along the x axis with its linear polarization along the 11-G bias field in the z direction. The "probe" laser pulse propagates along the z axis and is left-circularly polarized. With a flipper mirror in front of the camera CCD 1, we direct this probe beam either to the camera or to the photomultiplier (PMT). For pulse delay measurements, we place a pinhole in an external image plane of the imaging optics and select a small area, 15 μm in diameter, of the probe beam centred on the atom clouds (as indicated by the dashed circle in inset (i)). The pulse delays are measured with the PMT. The imaging beam propagating along the y axis is used

图 1. 实验装置图。一"耦合"激光束沿 x 轴传播，其线偏振方向 z 轴上加有 11 G 的偏置场。"探测"激光脉冲沿 z 轴传播，为左旋圆偏振。利用摄像机 CCD1 前的转向镜，我们可以引导探测光速进入摄像机或者进入光电倍增管（PMT）。对于脉冲延迟的测量，我们在成像光路中一个外部的成像平面上放置一个针孔，并选择探测光束在原子云中心直径为 15 μm 的小区域（插图（i）中虚线圆所示）。脉冲延迟通过 PMT 测量。沿 y 轴传播的成像光束被用来使原子云在 CCD2 上成像，以获得原子云在沿脉冲传播方向

to image atom clouds onto camera CCD 2 to find the length of the clouds along the pulse propagation direction (z axis) for determination of light speeds. Inset (ii) shows atoms cooled to 450 nK which is 15 nK above T_c. (Note that this imaging beam is never applied at the same time as the probe pulse and coupling laser). The position of a cloud and its diameter in the two transverse directions, x and y, are found with CCD 1. Inset (i) shows an image of a condensate.

Figure 2a shows the calculated transmission of the probe beam as a function of its detuning from resonance for parameters which are typical of this work. In the absence of dephasing of the $|1\rangle \rightarrow |2\rangle$ transition, the quantum interference would be perfect, and at line centre, the transmission would be unity. Figure 2b shows the refractive index for the probe beam as a function of detuning. Due to the very small Doppler broadening of the $|1\rangle \rightarrow |2\rangle$ transition in our nanokelvin samples, application of very low coupling intensity leads to a transparency peak with a width much smaller than the natural line width of the $|1\rangle \rightarrow |3\rangle$ transition. Correspondingly, the dispersion curve is much steeper than can be obtained by any other technique, and this results in the unprecedented low group velocities reported here. The group velocity v_g for a propagating electromagnetic pulse is[16-19]:

$$v_g = \frac{c}{n(\omega_p) + \omega_p \dfrac{dn}{d\omega_p}} \approx \frac{\hbar c \epsilon_0}{2\omega_p} \frac{|\Omega_c|^2}{|\mu_{13}|^2 N} \tag{1}$$

Here $n(\omega_p)$ is the refractive index at probe frequency ω_p (rad s^{-1}), $|\Omega_c|^2$ is the square of the Rabi frequency for the coupling laser and varies linearly with intensity, μ_{13} is the electric dipole matrix element between states $|1\rangle$ and $|3\rangle$, N is the atomic density, and ϵ_0 is the permittivity of free space. At line centre, the refractive index is unity, and the second term in the denominator of equation (1) dominates the first. An important characteristic of the refractive index profile is that on resonance the dispersion of the group velocity is zero (see ref. 16), that is, $d^2n/d\omega_p^2 = 0$, and to lowest order, the pulse maintains its shape as it propagates. The established quantum interference allows pulse transmission through our atom clouds which would otherwise have transmission coefficients of e^{-110} (below T_c), and creates a steep dispersive profile and very low group velocity for light pulses propagating through the clouds.

We note that the centres of the curves in Fig. 2 are shifted by 0.6 MHz from probe resonance. This is due to a coupling of state $|2\rangle$ to state $|4\rangle$ through the coupling laser field, which results in an a.c. Stark shift of level $|2\rangle$ and a corresponding line shift of the 2→3 transition. As the transparency peak and unity refractive index are obtained at two-photon resonance, this leads to a refractive index at the 1→3 resonance frequency which is different from unity. The difference is proportional to the a.c. Stark shift and hence to the coupling laser intensity, which is important for predicting the nonlinear refractive index as described below.

(z轴)上的长度，并以此来确定光速。插图(ii)为降温至 450 nK 的原子，即在临界温度 T_c 以上 15 nK。(注意该成像光束不能与探测光束或者耦合光束同时打开)。原子云的位置和在 x 和 y 两横向上的直径由 CCD1 测得。插图(i)为一凝聚态的成像图。

基于本文典型参数所确定的谐振频率，图 2a 为计算所得的探测光束透射率随其频率失谐的变化曲线。当 $|1\rangle \rightarrow |2\rangle$ 跃迁不存在失相时，量子干涉是完美的，在线中心，透射率应该是 1。图 2b 给出了探测光束的折射率与失谐的函数关系。由于我们的纳开温度样品中 $|1\rangle \rightarrow |2\rangle$ 跃迁时非常小的多普勒展宽，施加非常小的耦合强度都会导致一个宽度比 $|1\rangle \rightarrow |3\rangle$ 跃迁的自然线宽窄很多的透明度峰。相应地，色散曲线比通过其他任何技术所获得的都更陡，这也就导致了本文所述的前所未有的极低群速度。电磁脉冲传播的群速度 v_g 为 [16-19]：

$$v_g = \frac{c}{n(\omega_p) + \omega_p \dfrac{\mathrm{d}n}{\mathrm{d}\omega_p}} \approx \frac{\hbar c \epsilon_0}{2\omega_p} \frac{|\Omega_c|^2}{|\boldsymbol{\mu}_{13}|^2 N} \tag{1}$$

其中，$n(\omega_p)$ 为探测频率 $\omega_p (\mathrm{rad} \cdot \mathrm{s}^{-1})$ 时的折射率，$|\Omega_c|^2$ 为耦合激光的拉比频率的平方，它随光强线性变化，$\boldsymbol{\mu}_{13}$ 为态 $|1\rangle$ 和 $|3\rangle$ 间的电偶极矩矩阵元，N 为原子数密度，ϵ_0 为自由空间的介电常数。在线中央，折射率为 1，等式(1)分母中的第二项的影响超过第一项，占主导地位。折射率图谱的一个重要特性是共振时群速度色散为 0(参见文献 16)，即 $\mathrm{d}^2 n / \mathrm{d}\omega_p^2 = 0$，就最低阶来说，脉冲传播过程中保持波形不变。所建立的量子干涉允许脉冲传输通过在其他状态下透射系数仅为 $\mathrm{e}^{-110}(T_c$ 以下) 的原子云，从而产生了极陡的色散图谱和极低的群速度。

我们注意到图 2 中的曲线中心与探测共振频率偏离了 0.6 MHz。这是由于耦合激光场使态 $|2\rangle$ 和 $|4\rangle$ 发生了耦合，从而能级 $|2\rangle$ 有交流斯塔克位移和与之相应的 $2 \rightarrow 3$ 跃迁的谱线位移。由于透明度峰值和等于 1 的折射率是在两光子共振时获得的，这就导致 $1 \rightarrow 3$ 跃迁共振频率下的折射率不为 1。二者之间的差别与交流斯塔克位移成比例，也因此与耦合激光强度成比例，这点对下文所述的预估非线性折射率至关重要。

Fig. 2. Effect of probe detuning. **a**, Transmission profile. Calculated probe transmission as a function of detuning from the $|1\rangle \to |3\rangle$ resonance for an atom cloud cooled to 450 nK, with a peak density of 3.3 $\times 10^{12}$ cm^{-3} and a length of 229 μm (corresponding to the cloud in inset (ii) of Fig. 1a). The coupling laser is resonant with the $|2\rangle \to |3\rangle$ transition and has a power density of 52 mW cm^{-2}. **b**, Refractive index profile. The calculated refractive index is shown as a function of probe detuning for the same parameters as in **a**. The steepness of the slope at resonance is inversely proportional to the group velocity of transmitted light pulses and is controlled by the coupling laser intensity. Note that as a result of the a.c. Stark shift of the $|2\rangle \to |3\rangle$ transition, caused by a coupling of states $|2\rangle$ and $|4\rangle$ through the coupling laser field, the centre of the transmission and refractive index profiles is shifted by 0.6 MHz. The shift of the refractive index profile results in the nonlinear refractive index described in the text.

A diagram of the experiment is shown in Fig. 1a. The 2.5-mm-diameter coupling beam propagates along the x axis with its linear polarization parallel to the **B** field. The 0.5-mm-diameter, σ^- polarized probe beam propagates along the z axis. The size and position of the atom cloud in the transverse directions, x and y, are obtained by imaging the transmission profile of the probe beam after the cloud onto a charge-coupled-device (CCD) camera. An image of a condensate is shown as inset (i). A 55 mW cm^{-2} coupling laser beam was present during the 10-μs exposure of the atoms to a 5 mW cm^{-2} probe beam tuned close to resonance. The $f/7$ imaging optics are diffraction-limited to a resolution of 7 μm.

During the pulse delay experiments, a pinhole (placed in an external image plane of the lens system) is used to select only the part of the probe light that has passed through the central 15 μm of the atom cloud where the column density is the greatest. The outline of the pinhole is indicated with the dashed circle in inset (i).

Both coupling and probe beams are derived from the same dye laser. The frequency of the coupling beam is set by an acousto-optic modulator (AOM) to the $|2\rangle \to |3\rangle$ resonance. Here we take into account both Zeeman shifts and the a.c. Stark shift described above.

图 2. 探测光失谐的影响。**a**，透射率曲线。计算所得的探测透射率与激光频率相对原子云从 $|1\rangle \rightarrow |3\rangle$ 共振失谐的函数关系，该原子云被降温至 450 nK，峰值密度为 3.3×10^{12} cm^{-3}，长度为 229 μm（对应图 1a 中插图（ii）的原子云）。耦合激光与 $|2\rangle \rightarrow |3\rangle$ 的跃迁共振，功率密度为 52 mW · cm^{-2}。**b**，折射率曲线。计算所得的折射率与 **a** 中相同参数下探测光失谐的函数关系。达到共振时斜率的陡度与投射光脉冲的群速度成反比，并且由耦合激光强度所控制。要注意到，通过耦合激光场，态 $|2\rangle$ 和 $|4\rangle$ 产生耦合所造成的 $|2\rangle \rightarrow |3\rangle$ 跃迁的交流斯塔克位移的存在，导致透射率曲线的中心与折射率曲线的中心相差 0.6 MHz。折射率曲线的偏移引起了文中所述的非线性折射率现象。

实验图示如图 1a 所示。直径 2.5 mm 的耦合光束沿 x 轴传播，其线偏振方向平行于磁场 **B**。探测光束直径 0.5mm、σ$^-$ 偏振，沿 z 轴传播。原子云在横向 x, y 方向的尺寸和位置由探测光束通过原子云后成像在电荷耦合器件（CCD）摄像机上的透射率剖面获得。插图（i）为一凝聚态的图像。当原子在调谐至与共振频率接近的 5 mW · cm^{-2} 的探测光束中暴露 10 μs 的过程中，另一 55 mW · cm^{-2} 的耦合激光光束同时存在。$f/7$ 成像光学受衍射限制分辨率为 7 μm。

在脉冲延迟的实验中，利用一针孔（置于透镜系统的外成像面）来只选择那些通过原子云中心 15 μm 的部分探测光束，这部分原子柱的数密度最大。针孔的轮廓在插图（i）中以虚线圆标记出。

耦合光束和探测光束都源于相同的染料激光。耦合激光器的频率由一声光调制器（AOM）设定为 $|2\rangle \rightarrow |3\rangle$ 的共振频率。这里我们将塞曼位移和上文所提到的交流斯塔克位移都考虑在内。

The corresponding probe resonance is found by measuring the transmission of the probe beam as a function of its frequency. We apply a fast frequency sweep, across 32 MHz in 50 µs, and determine resonance from the transmission peak. The sweep is controlled by a separate AOM. The frequency is then fixed at resonance, and the temporal shape of the probe pulse is generated by controlling the r.f. drive power to the AOM. The resulting pulse is approximately gaussian with a full-width at half-maximum of 2.5 µs. The peak power is 1 mW cm^{-2} corresponding to a Rabi frequency of $\Omega_p = 0.20\,A$, where the Einstein A coefficient is 6.3×10^7 rad s^{-1}. To avoid distortion of the pulse, it is made of sufficient duration that its Fourier components are contained within the transparency peak.

Probe pulses are launched along the z axis 4 µs after the coupling beam is turned on (the coupling field is left on for 100 µs). Due to the magnetic filtering discussed above, all atoms are initially in state $|1\rangle$ which is a dark state in the presence of the coupling laser only. When the pulse arrives, the atoms adiabatically evolve so that the probability amplitude of state $|2\rangle$ is equal to the ratio $\Omega_p/(\Omega_p^2 + \Omega_c^2)^{1/2}$, where Ω_p is the probe Rabi frequency. To establish the coherent superposition state, energy is transferred from the front of the probe pulse to the atoms and the coupling laser field. At the end of the pulse, the atoms adiabatically return to the original state $|1\rangle$ and the energy returns to the back of the probe pulse with no net energy and momentum transfer to the atomic cloud. Because the refractive index is unity, the electric field is unchanged as the probe pulse enters the medium. As the group velocity is decreased, the total energy density must increase so as to keep constant the power per area. This increase is represented by the energy stored in the atoms and the coupling laser field during pulse propagation through the cloud.

The pulses are recorded with a photomultiplier (3-ns response time) after they penetrate the atom clouds. The output from the photomultiplier is amplified by a 150-MHz-bandwidth amplifier and the waveforms are recorded on a digital scope. With a "flipper" mirror in front of the camera we control whether the probe beam is directed to the camera or to the photomultiplier.

The result of a pulse delay measurement is shown in Fig. 3. The front pulse is a reference pulse obtained with no atoms present. The pulse delayed by 7.05 µs was slowed down in an atom cloud with a length of 229 µm (see Fig. 1a, inset (ii)). The resulting light speed is 32.5 m s^{-1}. We used a coupling laser intensity of 12 mW cm^{-2} corresponding to a Rabi frequency of $\Omega_c = 0.56\,A$. The cloud was cooled to 450 nK (which is 15 nK above T_c), the peak density was 3.3×10^{12} cm^{-3}, and the total number of atoms was 3.8×10^6. From these numbers we calculate that the pulse transmission coefficient would be e^{-63} in the absence of the coupling laser. The probe pulse was indeed observed to be totally absorbed by the atoms when the coupling beam was left off. Inhomogeneous broadening due to spatially varying Zeeman shifts is negligible ($\sim$20 kHz) for the low temperatures and correspondingly small cloud sizes used here.

相应的探测共振频率由测量探测光束的透射率与频率的函数关系得出。我们运用一快速频率扫描，在 50 μs 内扫描 32 MHz，通过透射峰值来确定共振。扫描受另一 AOM 控制。然后将频率固定在共振频率，探测脉冲的时域波形就由控制 AOM 的无线电频率驱动来产生。所得脉冲是一个近高斯分布，半高宽为 2.5 μs。拉比频率 $\Omega_p = 0.20\,A$ 时的峰值功率为 1 mW·cm^{-2}。这里取爱因斯坦自激系数 A 为 6.3×10^7 rad·s^{-1}。为避免脉冲失真，我们给予其足够的持续时间来使其傅里叶分量包含在透明度峰之中。

在耦合光束打开 4 μs 之后探测脉冲沿 z 轴发射（耦合场保持打开 100 μs）。由于上文所讨论的磁过滤，所有的原子最初都处于 |1⟩ 态，只有耦合激光存在时，这是一个暗态。当接受到光脉冲时，原子绝热演化，导致 |2⟩ 态的概率幅与 $\Omega_p/(\Omega_p^2 + \Omega_c^2)^{1/2}$ 相等，其中 Ω_p 是探测光拉比频率。为了实现相干叠加态，能量从探测光脉冲的前沿传递到原子和耦合激光场。在探测光脉冲末端，原子绝热地回到原始态 |1⟩，能量返回到探测脉冲后端，但没有净能量和动量转移到原子云。由于折射率等于 1，在探测脉冲进入介质时电场不变。随着群速度降低，总能量密度必须提高才能保证单位面积功率不变。这种提高就体现在脉冲在原子云中传播时，能量在原子以及耦合激光场的储存。

这些脉冲在穿过原子云后被一光电倍增管（响应时间为 3 ns）所记录。光电倍增管的输出信号被 150 MHz 带宽的放大器放大，波形显示在一数字示波器上。在摄像机前放置一"转向"镜，我们就可以控制探测光束是射入摄像机还是射入光电倍增管中。

探测光脉冲延迟测量的结果如图 3 所示。前面的脉冲是没有原子存在时的参考脉冲。脉冲穿过长度为 229 μm 的原子云时被减慢，延迟了 7.05 μs（见图 1a，插图 (ii)）。由此可得光速为 32.5 m·s^{-1}。实验中我们使用的耦合激光强度为 12 mW·cm^{-2}，对应拉比频率为 $\Omega_c = 0.56\,A$。原子云被冷却至 450 nK（临界温度 T_c 以上 15 nK）。峰值密度为 3.3×10^{12} cm^{-3}，原子总数为 3.8×10^6。根据这些数据我们可以计算得出在没有耦合激光时，脉冲透射系数为 e^{-63}。实验中确实观察到当耦合激光关闭时，探测脉冲完全被原子所吸收。本实验在低温下进行且原子云尺寸相对较小，由空间变化的塞曼位移引起的非均匀展宽（约 20 kHz）可以忽略。

Fig. 3. Pulse delay measurement. The front pulse (open circles) is a reference pulse with no atoms in the system. The other pulse (filled circles) is delayed by 7.05 μs in a 229-μm-long atom cloud (see inset (ii) in Fig. 1a). The corresponding light speed is 32.5 m s⁻¹. The curves represent gaussian fits to the measured pulses.

The size of the atom cloud in the z direction is obtained with another CCD camera. For this purpose, we use a separate 1 mW cm⁻² laser beam propagating along the vertical y axis and tuned 20 MHz below the $F = 2 \rightarrow 3$ transition. The atoms are pumped to the $F = 2$ ground state for 10 μs before the imaging which is performed with an exposure time of 10 μs. We image the transmission profile of the laser beam after the atom cloud with diffraction-limited $f/5$ optics. An example is shown in Fig. 1a, inset (ii), where the asymmetry of the trap is clear from the cloud's elliptical profile. We note that the imaging laser is never applied at the same time as the coupling laser and probe pulse, and for each recorded pulse or CCD picture a new cloud is loaded.

We measured a series of pulse delays and corresponding cloud sizes for atoms cooled to temperatures between 2.5 μK and 50 nK. From these pairs of numbers we obtain the corresponding propagation velocities (Fig. 4). The open circles are for a coupling power of 52 mW cm⁻² ($\Omega_c = 1.2\ A$). The light speed is inversely proportional to the atom density (equation (1)) which increases with lower temperatures, with an additional density increase when a condensate is formed. The filled circles are for a coupling power of 12 mW cm⁻². The lower coupling power is seen to cause a decrease of group velocities in agreement with equation (1). We obtain a light speed of 17 m s⁻¹ for pulse propagation in an atom cloud initially prepared as an almost pure Bose–Einstein condensate (condensate fraction is $\geqslant 90\%$). Whether the cloud remains a condensate during and after pulse propagation is an issue that is beyond the scope of this Letter.

图 3. 脉冲延迟测量。前面的脉冲（空心圆）为系统中没有原子的参考脉冲。另一个脉冲（实心圆）在 229 μm 长的原子云中被延迟 7.05 μs（见图 1a 插图（ii））。相应的光速为 32.5 m · s^{-1}。曲线为测量脉冲的高斯拟合。

沿 z 方向的原子云尺寸通过另一 CCD 摄像机捕获。为了达到这个目的，我们运用了另一独立的 1 mW · cm^{-2} 的激光束沿垂直的 y 轴传播，并调谐到比 $F = 2 \to 3$ 跃迁低 20 MHz。原子在 10 μs 的曝光成像之前，先被泵到 $F = 2$ 的基态 10 μs。我们使用衍射极限 $f/5$ 的光学器件在原子云之后对激光束的纵向透射率剖面进行成像。一个例子如图 1a 插图（ii）所示，其中由云的椭圆轮廓可清楚看见磁阱的不对称性。值得注意的是，成像激光不会与耦合激光及探测脉冲同时施加，并且对于每个记录的脉冲或 CCD 图片，都加载一新的原子云。

我们在原子冷却到温度 2.5 μK 和 50 μK 之间测量了一系列脉冲延迟和相应的云尺寸。从这些数据对中，我们获得了相应的传播速度（图 4）。空心圆对应耦合光强 52 mW · cm^{-2}（$\Omega_c = 1.2A$）。光速与原子数密度成反比（等式（1）），而原子数密度随温度降低而增大，当凝聚态形成时原子数密度进一步增加。实心圆对应耦合光强 12 mW · cm^{-2}。与等式（1）一致，可以看到耦合光强的降低引起群速度的减小。在最初制备的几乎纯净的玻色−爱因斯坦凝聚态（凝聚比率大于等于 90%）原子云中，我们获得了 17 m · s^{-1} 的光脉冲传播速度。在脉冲传播过程中和传播后原子云是否保持凝聚不在本文讨论范围之内。

Fig. 4. Light speed versus atom cloud temperature. The speed decreases with temperature due to the atom density increase. The open circles are for a coupling power of 52 mW cm^{-2} and the filled circles are for a coupling power of 12 mW cm^{-2}. The temperature T_c marks the transition temperature for Bose–Einstein condensation. The decrease in group velocity below T_c is due to a density increase of the atom cloud when the condensate is formed. From imaging measurements we obtain a maximum atom density of 8×10^{13} cm^{-3} at a temperature of 200 nK. Here, the dense condensate component constitutes 60% of all atoms, and the total atom density is 16 times larger than the density of a non-condensed cloud at T_c. The light speed measurement at 50 nK is for a cloud with a condensate fraction $\geqslant$ 90%. The finite dephasing rate due to state $|4\rangle$ does not allow pulse penetration of the most dense clouds. This problem could be overcome by tuning the laser to the D_1 line as described in the text.

Transitions from state $|2\rangle$ to state $|4\rangle$, induced by the coupling laser (detuned by 60 MHz from this transition), result in a finite decay rate of the established coherence between states $|1\rangle$ and $|2\rangle$ and limit pulse transmission. The dephasing rate is proportional to the power density of the coupling laser and we expect, and find, that probe pulses have a peak transmission that is independent of coupling intensity and a velocity which reduces linearly with this intensity. The dephasing time is determined from the slope of a semi-log plot of transmission versus pulse delay[19]. At a coupling power of 12 mW cm^{-2}, we measured a dephasing time of 9 µs for atom clouds just above T_c.

Giant Kerr nonlinearities are of interest for areas of quantum optics such as optical squeezing, quantum nondemolition, and studies of nonlocality. It was recently proposed that they may be obtained using electromagnetically induced transparency[20]. Here we report the first (to our knowledge) measurement of such a nonlinearity. The refractive index for zero probe detuning is given by $n = 1 + (n_2 I_c)$ where I_c is the coupling laser intensity, and n_2 the cross phase nonlinear refractive index. As seen from Fig. 2b, the nonlinear term $(n_2 I_c)$ equals the product of the slope of the refractive index at probe resonance and the a.c. Stark shift of the $|2\rangle \rightarrow |3\rangle$ transition caused by the coupling laser. We can then express n_2 by the formula (see equation (1));

$$n_2 = \frac{\Delta\omega_S}{I_c} \frac{dn}{d\omega_p} \approx \frac{1}{2\pi} \frac{\Delta\omega_S}{I_c} \frac{\lambda}{v_g} \tag{2}$$

where $\Delta\omega_S$ is the a.c. Stark shift, proportional to I_c, and λ the wavelength of the probe

图 4. 光速与原子云温度的关系。由于原子数密度的增大，光速随温度的降低而降低。空心圆对应耦合
光强 52 mW · cm⁻²，实心圆对应耦合光强 12 mW · cm⁻²。温度 T_c 标记出了玻色－爱因斯坦凝聚的临界转
变温度。T_c 以下的群速度减小是由形成凝聚态时原子云密度增大而引起。通过成像测量，我们得到
200 nK 时最大的原子数密度为 8×10^{13} cm⁻³。密集凝聚态成分占所有原子的 60%，并且总原子数密度是
T_c 时非凝聚态云密度的 16 倍。50 nK 时的光速测量是在凝聚分数 ⩾90% 的云中进行的。由于态 |4⟩ 造
成的有限的退相率不允许脉冲穿过最密集的云。这个问题可以通过文中所述的调谐激光至 D_1 线的方法
来解决。

由耦合激光激发的 |2⟩→|4⟩ 态的跃迁（耦合激光与该跃迁之间存在 60 MHz 失
谐），使得所建立的 |1⟩ 和 |2⟩ 态的相干具有一个有限衰变率，并限制了探测光脉冲的
透射。退相率与耦合激光的功率密度成比例，我们预期并发现，探测脉冲具有一个
透射率峰值，该值不受耦合强度以及随此强度线性减小的速度的影响。退相时间由
透射率－脉冲延迟的半对数曲线的斜率决定[19]。在耦合光强为 12 mW · cm⁻² 时，对
于温度刚刚超过 T_c 的原子云，我们测量到退相时间为 9 μs。

巨克尔非线性在量子光学领域具有很大的吸引力，例如光学压缩、量子非破坏
性以及非定域性等方面的研究。近期的研究还指出，这些现象很可能通过电磁感应
透明来获得[20]。本文报道了（据我们所知）首次对这样一种非线性的测量。零失谐探
测光的折射率表达式为 $n = 1 + (n_2 I_c)$，其中 I_c 为耦合激光强度，n_2 为交叉相位非线
性折射率。正如图 2b 所示，非线性项 $n_2 I_c$ 等于探测光在共振时的折射率曲线斜率
与耦合激光激发的 |2⟩→|3⟩ 跃迁的交流斯塔克位移之积。因此 n_2 可以用以下公式表
式（见等式（1））：

$$n_2 = \frac{\Delta \omega_S}{I_c} \frac{dn}{d\omega_p} \approx \frac{1}{2\pi} \frac{\Delta \omega_S}{I_c} \frac{\lambda}{v_g} \tag{2}$$

其中 $\Delta \omega_S$ 为交流斯塔克位移，与 I_c 成比例，λ 为探测跃迁的光波长。当耦合激光强

transition. We measured an a.c. Stark shift of 1.3×10^6 rad s^{-1} for a coupling laser intensity of 40 mW cm^{-2}. For a measured group velocity of 17 m s^{-1} (Fig. 4), we obtain a nonlinear refractive index of 0.18 cm^2 W^{-1}. This nonlinear index is $\sim 10^6$ times greater than that measured in cold Cs atoms[21].

With a system that avoids the $|1\rangle - |2\rangle$ dephasing rate described above (which can be obtained by tuning to the D_1 line in sodium), the method used here could be developed to yield the collision-induced dephasing rate of the double condensate which is generated in the process of establishing electromagnetically induced transparency (see also refs 22, 23). In that case, the square of the probability amplitude for state $|3\rangle$ could be kept below 10^{-5} during pulse propagation, with no heating of the condensate as a result. With improved frequency stability of our set-up and lower coupling intensities, even lower light speeds would be possible, perhaps of the order of centimetres per second, comparable to the speed of sound in a Bose–Einstein condensate. Under these conditions we expect phonon excitation during light pulse propagation through the condensate. By deliberately tuning another laser beam to the $|2\rangle \rightarrow |4\rangle$ transition, it should be possible to demonstrate optical switching at the single photon level[24]. Finally, we note that during propagation of the atom clouds, light pulses are compressed in the z direction by a ratio of c/v_g. For our experimental parameters, that results in pulses with a spatial extent of only 43 μm.

(**397**, 594-598; 1999)

Lene Vestergaard Hau[*†], S. E. Harris[‡], Zachary Dutton[*†] & Cyrus H. Behroozi[*§]

[*] Rowland Institute for Science, 100 Edwin H. Land Boulevard, Cambridge, Massachusetts 02142, USA

[†] Department of Physics, [§] Division of Engineering and Applied Sciences, Harvard University, Cambridge, Massachusetts 02138, USA

[‡] Edward L. Ginzton Laboratory, Stanford University, Stanford, California 94305, USA

Received 3 November; accepted 21 December 1998.

References:

1. Knight, P. L., Stoicheff, B. & Walls, D. (eds) Highlights in quantum optics. *Phil. Trans. R. Soc. Lond. A* **355**, 2215-2416 (1997).

2. Harris, S. E. Electromagnetically induced transparency. *Phys. Today* **50(7)**, 36-42 (1997).

3. Scully, M. O. & Zubairy, M. S. *Quantum Optics* (Cambridge Univ. Press, 1997).

4. Arimondo, E. in *Progress in Optics* (ed. Wolf, E.) 257-354 (Elsevier Science, Amsterdam, 1996).

5. Bergmann, K., Theuer, H. & Shore, B. W. Coherent population transfer among quantum states of atoms and molecules. *Rev. Mod. Phys.* **70**, 1003-1006 (1998).

6. Chu, S. The manipulation of neutral particles. *Rev. Mod. Phys.* **70**, 685-706 (1998).

7. Cohen-Tannoudjii, C. N. Manipulating atoms with photons. *Rev. Mod. Phys.* **70**, 707-719 (1998).

8. Phillips, W. D. Laser cooling and trapping of neutral atoms. *Rev. Mod. Phys.* **70**, 721-741 (1998).

9. Hess, H. F. Evaporative cooling of magnetically trapped and compressed spin-polarized hydrogen. *Phys. Rev. B* **34**, 3476-3479 (1986).

10. Masuhara, N. *et al.* Evaporative cooling of spin-polarized atomic hydrogen. *Phys. Rev. Lett.* **61**, 935-938 (1988).

11. Anderson, M. H., Ensher, J. R., Matthews, M. R., Wieman, C. E. & Cornell, E. A. Observation of Bose-Einstein condensation in a dilute atomic vapor. *Science* **269**, 198-201 (1995).

12. Davis, K. B. *et al.* Bose-Einstein condensation in a gas of sodium atoms. *Phys. Rev. Lett.* **75**, 3969-3973 (1995).

13. Bradley, C. C., Sackett, C. A. & Hulet, R. G. Bose-Einstein condensation of lithium: observation of limited condensate number. *Phys. Rev. Lett.* **78**, 985-989 (1997).

14. Hau, L. V. *et al.* Near-resonant spatial images of confined Bose-Einstein condensates in a 4-Dee magnetic bottle. *Phys. Rev. A* **58**, R54-R57 (1998).

15. Hau, L. V., Golovchenko, J. A. & Burns, M. M. A new atomic beam source: The "candlestick". *Rev. Sci. Instrum.* **65**, 3746-3750 (1994).

16. Harris, S. E., Field, J. E. & Kasapi, A. Dispersive properties of electromagnetically induced transparency. *Phys. Rev. A* **46**, R29-R32 (1992).

度为 40 mW · cm^{-2} 时我们测量到一 1.3×10^6 rad · s^{-1} 的交流斯塔克位移。而对于测量所得的 17 m · s^{-1} 的群速度（图 4），可得非线性折射率为 0.18 cm^2 · W^{-1}。该非线性折射率是在冷铯原子中相应值的 10^6 倍 [21]。

应用上文所述的可避免 $|1\rangle - |2\rangle$ 退相率的系统（通过调谐至钠 D_1 线而获得），可以对这里所使用的方法进一步发展以得出在建立电磁感应透明过程中发生的双凝聚态碰撞诱导失相率（参见文献 22 和 23）。在这种情况下，态 $|3\rangle$ 概率幅的平方在脉冲传播过程中可以保持在 10^{-5} 以下，因此不存在凝聚态加热。由于我们装置频率稳定性的提高以及耦合强度的减小，更低的光速也是可能实现的，可能是几厘米每秒的量级，可与玻色－爱因斯坦凝聚中的音速相比。在此条件下我们预期光脉冲传播通过凝聚体时有声子被激发。通过谨慎调谐另一激光束至 $|2\rangle \rightarrow |4\rangle$ 跃迁，应该有可能在单光子水平上演示光学开关 [24]。最后本文指出，光束在原子云传播过程中，光脉冲在 z 方向被压缩，比率为 c/v_g。对于本实验所采用的参数，这导致脉冲的空间范围仅为 43 μm。

（崔宁 翻译；石锦卫 审稿）

17. Grobe, R., Hioe, F. T. & Eberly, J. H. Formation of shape-preserving pulses in a nonlinear adiabatically integrable system. *Phys. Rev. Lett.* **73,** 3183-3186 (1994).

18. Xiao, M., Li, Y.-Q., Jin, S.-Z. & Gea-Banacloche, J. Measurement of dispersive properties of electromagnetically induced transparency in rubidium atoms. *Phys. Rev. Lett.* **74,** 666-669 (1995).

19. Kasapi, A., Jain, M., Yin, G. Y. & Harris, S. E. Electromagnetically induced transparency: propagation dynamics. *Phys. Rev. Lett.* **74,** 2447-2450 (1995).

20. Schmidt, H. & Imamoglu, A. Giant Kerr nonlinearities obtained by electromagnetically induced transparency. *Opt. Lett.* **21,** 1936-1938 (1996).

21. Lambrecht, A., Courty, J. M., Reynaud, S. & Giacobino, E. Cold atoms: A new medium for quantum optics. *Appl. Phys. B* **60,** 129-134 (1995).

22. Hall, D. S., Matthews, M. R., Wieman, C. E. & Cornell, E. A. Measurements of relative phase in two-component Bose-Einstein condensates. *Phys. Rev. Lett.* **81,** 1543-1546 (1998).

23. Ruostekoski, J. & Walls, D. F. Coherent population trapping of Bose-Einstein condensates: detection of phase diffusion. *Eur. Phys. J. D* (submitted).

24. Harris, S. E. & Yamamoto, Y. Photon switching by quantum interference. *Phys. Rev. Lett.* **81,** 3611-3614 (1998).

Acknowledgements. We thank J. A. Golovchenko for discussions and C. Liu for experimental assistance. L.V.H. acknowledges support from the Rowland Institute for Science. S.E.H. is supported by the US Air Force Office of Scientific Research, the US Army Research Office, and the US Office of Naval Research. C.H.B. is supported by an NSF fellowship.

Correspondence and requests for materials should be addressed to L.V.H. (e-mail: hau@rowland.org).

Anticipation of Moving Stimuli by the Retina

M. J. Berry II *et al.*

Editor's Note

Our senses seem to show us the world as it is. But what we see is not just the imprint of photons hitting the retina: it is produced as our neural systems filter and highlight this incoming information. Thus it takes time to generate even the simplest neural message, creating the risk that the real world has changed by the time we perceive it—a risk that crucially applies to fast-moving objects such as predators or prey. But as this paper by Michael J. Berry at Harvard University and coworkers shows, our neural systems can predict where an object in our visual field is likely to be, giving us a better chance, say, of evading or catching it.

A flash of light evokes neural activity in the brain with a delay of 30–100 milliseconds[1], much of which is due to the slow process of visual transduction in photoreceptors[2,3]. A moving object can cover a considerable distance in this time, and should therefore be seen noticeably behind its actual location. As this conflicts with everyday experience, it has been suggested that the visual cortex uses the delayed visual data from the eye to extrapolate the trajectory of a moving object, so that it is perceived at its actual location[4-7]. Here we report that such anticipation of moving stimuli begins in the retina. A moving bar elicits a moving wave of spiking activity in the population of retinal ganglion cells. Rather than lagging behind the visual image, the population activity travels near the leading edge of the moving bar. This response is observed over a wide range of speeds and apparently compensates for the visual response latency. We show how this anticipation follows from known mechanisms of retinal processing.

BECAUSE a moving object often follows a smooth trajectory, one can extrapolate from its past position and velocity to obtain an estimate of its current location. Recent experiments on motion perception[5-7] indicate that the human brain possesses just such a mechanism: Subjects were shown a moving bar sweeping at constant velocity; a second bar was flashed briefly in alignment with the moving bar. When asked what they perceived at the time of the flash, observers reliably reported seeing the flashed bar trailing behind the moving bar. This flash lag effect has been confirmed repeatedly[8-10], and various high-level processes have been invoked to explain it, such as a time delay due to the shift of visual attention. To assess whether processing in the retina contributes to this effect we analysed the "neural image" of these two stimuli at the retinal output. We recorded simultaneously the spike trains of many ganglion cells in the isolated retina of tiger salamander or rabbit. The responses to flashed and moving bars were then analysed by plotting the firing rate in the retinal ganglion-cell population as a function of space and time.

视网膜可对运动物体的刺激进行预测

贝里等

编者按

我们的感官似乎将世界原原本本地呈现给我们。其实我们所看到的世界不仅仅是投射在视网膜上的光子印记：它是输入信息经由神经系统过滤并筛选产生的。因此即使生成最简单的神经信号都需要耗费时间，这就产生以下风险，真实的世界在我们感知到它的时候就已经改变了——这对快速移动的物体诸如捕食者和猎物都是至关重要的。但是如哈佛大学迈克尔·贝里及其同事在文章中所指出的，我们的神经系统能够预测视野中物体的可能位置，从而给我们提供更好的机会去逃避追捕或者抓住猎物。

闪光所引发的脑神经活动会有一个 30~100 毫秒的延迟 [1]，而延迟的大部分原因在于光感受器中迟缓的视觉传导过程 [2,3]。在这段时间里一个运动的物体会移动相当远的距离，因此当物体被看到时，已经显著落后于其实际位置。这与我们的日常体验相矛盾，有一种解释是视觉大脑皮层利用从眼睛中获取滞后的视觉数据来推测运动物体的轨迹，从而察觉其真正的位置 [4-7]。本文报道这种对运动刺激的预测始发于视网膜。移动光柱会在一群视网膜神经节细胞诱发一个随之移动的放电。这种总体的活动紧跟着移动光柱的最前缘行进，而不是滞后于视觉的影像。这种反应在很宽的速度范围内均能观察到，很明显这是在补偿视觉反应的潜伏期。我们在本文揭示这种预测是如何遵循已知视觉处理机制的。

由于运动的物体一般沿着平滑的轨迹移动，人们可以根据其过去的位置和速度推测其目前的大体位置。最近运动知觉的实验表明 [5-7]，人类大脑拥有这样一种机制：一个移动光柱匀速从受试者前掠过；第二个光柱与这个移动光柱重合，但短暂闪烁。当询问受试者在闪烁出现时觉察到什么时，他们肯定地回答看到一个闪烁的光柱尾随在移动光柱后面。这种闪烁滞后效应已经被多次证实 [8-10]，许多高级活动被援引用来解释这种现象，例如视觉注意转换引起时间的滞后。为了确定视网膜的活动是否参与了这种效应，我们分析了这两种刺激在视网膜输出中所产生的"神经影像"。我们同时记录了从虎蝾或兔分离出来的视网膜神经节细胞所产生的放电序列。通过把群体放电频率绘制为空间和时间的函数的方法，来分析视网膜神经节细胞对闪烁和移动光柱的反应。

Figure 1 illustrates the responses of individual OFF-type ganglion cells to a dark bar flashed briefly over the receptive-field centre. In both salamander (Fig. 1a) and rabbit (Fig. 1b), the cells remained silent for a latency of ~50 ms, then fired a burst of spikes that lasted another 50 ms. When the bar was swept over the retina at constant speed (Fig. 1c, d), these same cells fired for a more extended period, beginning some time before the bar reached the position at which the flash occurred, and extending for a shorter time thereafter. When the bar was swept in the opposite direction (Fig. 1e, f), it produced a very similar response, showing that these cells had no direction-selective preference.

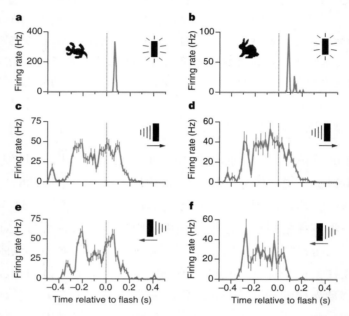

Fig. 1. Responses of two ganglion cells to flashed and moving bars. **a, c, e** Results from a "fast OFF" ganglion cell in salamander retina; **b, d, f**, results from a brisk-sustained OFF cell in rabbit retina. **a, b,** Firing rate as a function of time after a dark bar (90% contrast,133 μm width) was flashed for 15 ms on the receptive-field centre. **c, d,** Firing rate of the same two cells while the dark bar moved continuously across the retina at 0.44 mm s⁻¹. At time zero, the bar was aligned with the position of the flash in **a** and **b**. **e, f,** As in **c, d,** but with the bar moving in the opposite direction. Error bars denote standard error across repeated presentations of the stimulus.

From many single-unit measurements such as these, we compiled the neural image of the visual stimulus in the population of ganglion cells. This was done by plotting the firing rate of every cell as a function of distance from the bar stimulus and interpolating these points with a smooth line (see Methods). The neural image of the flashed bar among salamander "fast OFF" cells is shown in Fig. 2a. After a latency of 40 ms, a hump of neural activity appears that increases rapidly to a peak at 60 ms, then declines and disappears at 100 ms. As might be expected, the profile is centred on the bar. It has a width on the retina of ~200 μm at half-maximum, close to the size of the receptive-field centre for these neurons[11]. The width increases somewhat during the late phase of the response, creating the impression of an outward "splash"[12].

　　图 1 显示了单个的 OFF 型神经节细胞对暗光柱在感受域中央短暂闪现的反应。虎螈（图 1a）和兔（图 1b）的细胞均保持大约 50 ms 的静息，然后爆发一段持续 50 ms 的放电。当光柱匀速掠过视网膜时（图 1c 和 1d），同样一群细胞放电持续时间较长，开始于光柱到达闪烁位置之前的某个时刻，然后仍持续较短的一段时间。当光柱以相反的方向扫过时（图 1e 和 1f），会产生非常相似的反应，这表明这些细胞没有方向选择的偏好性。

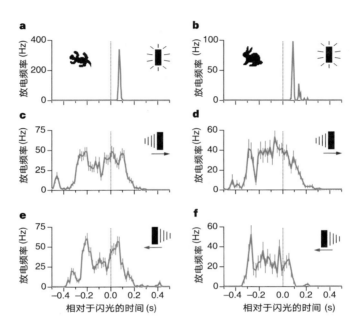

图 1. 两个神经节细胞对闪烁光柱和移动光柱的反应。a, c, e, 从虎螈视网膜"快速 OFF"神经节细胞中得来的结果；b, d, f, 从兔视网膜"持续激活 OFF"细胞得来的结果。a, b, 暗光柱（对比度 90%，宽度 133 μm）在感受域中央闪现时间为 15 ms，放电频率记为时间的函数。c, d, 当暗光柱以同样的速度 0.44 mm · s⁻¹ 持续不断地经过视网膜时，两个细胞的放电频率。在时间为 0 时，a 和 b 中移动光柱与闪烁光柱的位置相对应。e 和 f 与 c 和 d 一样，但是移动光柱向相反的方向移动。误差线表示刺激重复表现出来的标准偏差。

　　从许多像这样的单个细胞测量的结果中，我们记录到对一群神经节细胞进行视觉刺激而产生的神经影像数据。我们采用以下方法：将每个细胞的放电频率记为移动光柱距离的函数，并将这些点用平滑的曲线连接（参见实验方法）。图 2a 显示在虎螈"快速 OFF"细胞中闪烁光柱的神经影像。潜伏 40 ms 后，神经活动的高峰期开始出现，在 60 ms 时快速增长到峰值，然后减弱，在 100 ms 时消失。正如预测的那样，这些变化以移动光柱为中心。在峰值一半时，其在视网膜的宽度大约是 200 μm，这个数值接近于这些神经元感受域中央的大小 [11]。这个宽度在反应后期有所增加，给人一种向外"扩散"的感觉 [12]。

Fig. 2. Population response to flashed and moving bars. **a**, Spatial profile of firing in the population of salamander fast OFF ganglion cells in response to a flashed dark bar (90% contrast, 133 μm width, see stimulus trace in **b**) at a series of times after the flash (colour scale, 3 ms steps). **b**, Profile of the population response at four time points following a flashed bar (red, from **a**), and the same bar travelling at 0.44 mm s^{-1} rightward (blue) and leftward (green). At time 0 ms, the moving bars were aligned with the position of the flash; at 62 ms, the flash response was maximal. Curves in **a** and **b** derived from 15 cells. **c**, As in **b**, for the population of brisk-sustained OFF cells in rabbit retina. At 78 ms, the flash response was maximal. Curves derived from six cells.

The neural image of the moving bar is shown in Fig. 2b. Again, a hump of firing activity is observed, which now sweeps over the retina along with the moving bar. If this response were subject to the same time delay as the flash, one would expect the neural image to trail behind the visual image of the bar. Instead, the hump of firing activity is clearly ahead of the centre of the bar, and the peak firing rate seems to occur near the bar's leading edge. The same response occurs when the bar moves in the opposite direction. By superposing on this the response to a flash that was aligned with the moving bar (from Fig. 2a), we find that the two neural images are clearly separated—at the time when the response to the flash peaks, the response of the moving bar is displaced ~100 μm ahead in the direction of motion. A very similar displacement between the two neural images was observed among

图 2. 对闪烁光柱和移动光柱的群体响应。**a**，虎螈快速 OFF 神经节细胞群体对闪烁暗光柱（对比度 90%，宽度 133 μm，同 **b** 的刺激一样）在放电之后一系列时间点上的放电空间特性（色标，3 ms 时间间距）。**b**，闪烁光柱后四个时间点上的群体反应特性（红色曲线数据来源于 **a**），同一移动光柱以 0.44 mm·s⁻¹ 速度向右移动（蓝）和向左移动（绿）。在 0 ms 时，移动光柱与闪烁光柱的位置对齐；在 62 ms 时，对闪烁光柱的反应达到最大化。**a** 和 **b** 的曲线数据来源于 15 个细胞。**c** 和 **b** 一样，是兔视网膜持续激活 OFF 细胞群体的结果。在 78 ms 时反应最大。曲线数据采集于 6 个细胞。

    图 2b 所示为移动光柱的神经影像。我们再次观察到驼峰状的放电活动，且与移动光柱掠过视网膜的过程一致。如果这种反应与闪烁光柱滞后时间相同，人们应该会看到神经影像尾随在移动光柱的视觉影像之后。相反，放电活动的峰值明显位于移动光柱中心之前，其放电频率的最高点似乎出现在靠近移动光柱最前缘的地方。当移动光柱向相反方向移动时会发生相同的反应。通过将这种反应与一个闪烁光柱（该光柱与移动光柱对齐）所引发的反应进行重叠（图 2a），我们发现两个神经影像完全分开——在对闪烁光柱的反应达峰值时，移动光柱的反应沿着运动方向向前移动大约 100 μm。在兔视网膜持续激活 OFF 细胞中（图 2c）也观察到类似的两个神

brisk-sustained OFF cells in the rabbit retina (Fig. 2c). If subsequent stages of the visual system estimate the location of the flashed bar and the moving bar by the position of these humps of neural activity, they must conclude that the moving bar is ahead of the flashed bar.

How does this apparent anticipation of the moving bar come about? One suspects that cells ahead of the bar start firing early (Figs 1c–f, 2b, c) when the bar begins to invade their receptive-field centre. The firing profile does not extend to an equal distance behind the trailing edge of the bar, perhaps because these ganglion cells have transient responses: They fire while stimulation increases as the bar invades the receptive field, not while stimulation decreases as the bar leaves it. However, we found that spatial and temporal filtering by the ganglion cell's receptive field was by itself insufficient to explain the response profiles (see below). Instead, there is another important component, which was revealed in experiments varying the intensity of the moving bar.

Figure 3a illustrates the response of this neural population to dark bars of increasing contrast relative to the background. As expected, bars of higher contrast produced stronger modulations in firing. The peak firing rate increased in proportion to contrast at first, but then appeared to saturate (Fig. 3a, inset). In addition, the shape of the neural image changed significantly with contrast. At low contrast, the peak in firing occurred behind the bar's leading edge. At high contrast—the same condition as in Fig. 2—the peak of the profile was ahead of the leading edge, followed by a more gradual decline in firing. The saturation of the peak firing rate and the shift in the response profile can be explained if the high-contrast stimulus somehow desensitizes the response of the ganglion cell after a short time delay. In that case, a ganglion cell just ahead of the bar should be strongly excited as the edge begins to enter its receptive-field centre, but then its response gain gets reduced and the firing rate declines even before the edge is half-way across. A well-known component of retinal processing that fits this description is the "contrast-gain control"[13-15].

Following ref. 16, we incorporated this aspect into a quantitative description of a ganglion cell's light response (Fig. 4). In this scenario, the retina integrates the light stimulus over space and time, with a weighting function $k(x,t)$ given by the ganglion cell's receptive field, and the resulting signal determines the neuron's firing rate. If the stimulus provides strong excitation for an extended period of time, a negative feedback loop reduces the gain at the input and consequently the response to subsequent stimulation[17]. With just four free parameters, this model produced a satisfying account of neural responses throughout the entire contrast series (Fig. 3a). It indicates that the retinal gain is modulated as much as fourfold during passage of the high-contrast bar (Fig. 3b), which pushes the response profile towards the leading edge of the bar. Without contrast-gain control the predicted profile always lagged significantly behind (Fig. 3a).

经影像之间的位置偏差。如果视觉系统的后续阶段通过这些神经活动峰值出现的位置来估计闪烁光柱束和移动光柱的位置，他们的结论一定是移动光柱位于闪烁光柱之前。

这种对移动光柱明显的预感是如何产生的呢？有人猜测当移动光柱开始进入神经节细胞的感受域中心时，在移动光柱之前的细胞提早放电（图 1c～f、2b 和 2c）。这种放电特性在移动光柱的后缘并未进行等距离的延长，可能因为这些神经节细胞具有瞬态响应：神经节细胞在移动光柱进入感受域、刺激增加时放电；而在移动光柱离开、感受域刺激降低时不放电。但是，我们发现，通过神经节细胞感受域对空间和时间的过滤本身不足以解释反应的特性（见下文）。相反，还有另外一种重要的组分，是通过变化移动光柱的强度发现的。

图 3a 阐明了神经细胞群体对相对背景的对比度逐渐增强的暗光柱的反应。正如所料，具有较高对比度的移动光柱对放电具有更强的调节能力。起初放电的峰值频率与对比度成正比，但是随后出现饱和（图 3a，插入图）。另外，神经影像的形状随对比度的变化而显著变化。在对比度低时，放电的峰值出现在移动光柱前缘之后。当对比度高时——与图 2 条件相同——放电的峰值在移动光柱前缘之前，随后放电逐渐减弱。如果高对比度刺激在短时间之后，从某种程度上降低了神经节细胞反应的敏感性，那么放电频率峰值的饱和与放电特性之间的偏差就可以解释了。在这种情况下，当移动光柱边缘开始进入其感受域的中心时，位于移动光柱之前的神经节细胞应该非常兴奋，但是随后其反应的增益变弱，其放电频率甚至在移动光柱边缘仅通过一半时就开始衰减。符合这种描述的一个著名的视网膜信息处理过程叫做"对比度增益控制"[13-15]。

按照参考文献 16 的方法，我们把这方面纳入神经节细胞对光反应的定量描述中（图 4）。在本情形中，视网膜将空间和时间上的光刺激与神经节细胞感受域得出的权重函数 $k(x,t)$ 相结合，最终信号决定了神经元的放电频率。如果光刺激引发的强烈兴奋超过特定的时间，负反馈环在输入端减少增益，进而降低对随后刺激的响应 [17]。仅用这四个独立的参数，此模型会很好地解释贯穿整个对比系列中的神经反应（图 3a）。结果显示在高对比度移动光柱经过时视网膜增益可被调节到 4 倍（图 3b），从而将反应的曲线推向移动光柱的前缘。没有对比度增益控制，预测的曲线总是明显滞后（图 3a）。

Fig. 3. Dependence of motion extrapolation on contrast. **a**, Stimulation with moving dark bars (133 μm width, 0.44 mm s⁻¹ speed) of varying contrast: 5, 10, 20, 33, 50 and 90% (see top stimulus traces). Main panel shows the response profile derived from 15 salamander fast OFF ganglion cells (coloured dots), and the predicted response (coloured lines) from a model incorporating contrast-gain control (Fig. 4). Grey line shows the prediction without contrast-gain control. Inset, the peak firing rate of the response profile as a function of the contrast of the bar. Error bars denote standard error, derived from variation among ganglion cells. **b**, Gain variable g of the gain control model (Fig. 4). Model parameters: $\theta = 0$, $\alpha = 85$ Hz, $B = 45$ s⁻¹, $\tau = 170$ ms.

This explanation indicates that there will be clear limits to what stimuli can be anticipated. For example, if the bar moves fast enough to cross the receptive field before the contrast-gain control sets in, then the peak of the firing profile should lag behind the leading edge. Figure 5a explores these limits, and shows that up to speeds of about 1 mm s⁻¹ on the retina, the shape of the firing profile among ganglion cells remained essentially unchanged, with a peak near or ahead of the leading edge. At higher speeds, however, the response profile began to slip significantly behind the leading edge. This basic relationship was confirmed for several different populations of ganglion cells in both rabbit and salamander (Fig. 5b). The various cell types differed in the extent of anticipation at low speeds, but all began to show a lag in the neural image at speeds of 1–2 mm s⁻¹. In particular, direction selectivity does not play a special role in motion anticipation.

图 3. 运动推测对对比度的依赖性。**a**，移动暗光柱（宽度 133 μm，速度 0.44 mm · s⁻¹）在不同对比度：5%、10%、20%、33%、50% 和 90%（参见顶端的刺激轨迹）下的刺激。主图显示的是 15 个虎蝾快速 OFF 神经节细胞采集到的反应特性（彩色的点），和来自混合的对比度增益控制模型中的预测反应特性（彩色的线）（图 4）。灰色的线显示没有对比度增益控制的预测。插图显示反应曲线的放电频率峰值与移动光柱对比度之间的函数关系。误差线表示从不同的神经节细胞变异中得来的标准误差。**b**，增益控制模型的增益变异 g（图 4）。模型参数：$\theta = 0$，$\alpha = 85$ Hz，$B = 45$ s⁻¹，$\tau = 170$ ms。

这种解释表明细胞对于何种刺激可被预测有着明确的限定。例如，如果一个光柱移动得足够快，在对比度增益控制介入之前经过感受域，那么细胞放电的峰值应该滞后于光束前缘。图 5a 探索了这种限定，结果显示在视网膜上速度高达大约 1 mm · s⁻¹，神经节细胞放电特性本质上保持不变，峰值靠近前缘或在前缘之前。然而，在更高速度下，反应特性开始明显落后于前缘。这种基本关系在几种不同群体的神经节细胞（如兔和虎蝾中）中得到验证（图 5b）。在低速情况下，不同类型细胞对运动的预测程度不同，但是所有细胞在速度为 1 ~ 2 mm · s⁻¹ 时均开始出现神经影像的滞后。尤其是方向选择性在运动的预测中没有起到特殊作用。

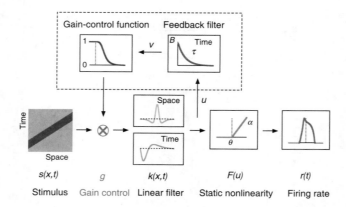

Fig. 4. Cascade model for a ganglion cell's light response. The stimulus $s(x,t)$ is multiplied by a gain factor g, convolved with a spatiotemporal filter $k(x,t)$, and rectified by a static nonlinear function $F(u)$ to produce the firing rate $r(t)$. The contrast-gain control mechanism (boxed region) takes the output of the linear filter u, averages it by exponential filtering in time, and uses the result v to set the gain factor g through a decreasing gain control function $g(v)$. Formally,

$$u(t) = g(v) \int_{-\infty}^{\infty} dx \int_{-\infty}^{t} dt'\, s(x,t')\, k(x,t-t')$$

$$v(t) = \int_{-\infty}^{t} dt'\, u(t')\, B \exp\left(-\frac{t-t'}{\tau}\right)$$

$$g(v) = \begin{cases} 1 & v < 0 \\ 1/(1+v^4) & v > 0 \end{cases}$$

$$F(u) = \begin{cases} 0 & u < 0 \\ \alpha(u-\theta^4) & u > 0 \end{cases}$$

The filter $k(x,t)$ is measured (see Methods), and $g(v)$ is taken from a previous, successful model of contrast-gain control in the salamander retina[17]. Thus, the model has four parameters: the threshold θ and slope α of the rectifier $F(u)$, and the amplitude B and time constant τ of the gain control filter.

In summary, we have shown that the extrapolation of a moving object's trajectory begins in the retina. In the neural image that the eye transmits to the brain, the moving object is clearly ahead of the corresponding flashed object (Fig. 2). According to a successful model for the ganglion cell's light response (Figs 3, 4), motion anticipation in these populations can be explained on the basis of the spatially extended receptive field, the biphasic temporal response and a nonlinear contrast-gain control. There are several indications that this retinal mechanism contributes strongly to human perception of moving stimuli. First, the requisite components of our model are well documented in many species. In the primate retina, a nonlinear contrast-gain control is found specifically in the M-type ganglion cells[15], neurons that feed the central pathways leading to motion perception[18]. Second, retinal motion extrapolation breaks down at speeds above 1 mm s⁻¹ (Fig. 5b). This corresponds well with observations on human subjects: At retinal speeds of 0.3–0.9 mm s⁻¹, perceptual motion extrapolation appeared to compensate for the entire visual delay[5], whereas at speeds of ~4 mm s⁻¹ only partial extrapolation was observed[10]. Finally, the retina anticipates high-contrast stimuli more than low-contrast stimuli (Fig. 3), a further departure from ideal extrapolation. Again, this effect has been observed in human psychophysics[9].

图 4. 一个神经节细胞光反应的级联模型。刺激 $s(x,t)$ 乘以增益因子 g，与时间空间滤子 $k(x,t)$ 卷积，经过静态的非线性函数 $F(u)$ 校正，产生放电频率 $r(t)$。增益控制机理（方框区域）接受线性滤子 u 的输出，通过时间的指数滤子求其平均值，通过减少增益控制函数 $g(v)$，用结果 v 设定增益因子 g。用公式表示为：

$$u(t) = g(v) \int_{-\infty}^{\infty} dx \int_{-\infty}^{t} dt'\, s(x,t')\, k(x,t-t')$$

$$v(t) = \int_{-\infty}^{t} dt'\, u(t')\, B \exp\left(-\frac{t-t'}{\tau}\right)$$

$$g(v) = \begin{cases} 1 & v < 0 \\ 1/(1+v^4) & v > 0 \end{cases}$$

$$F(u) = \begin{cases} 0 & u < 0 \\ \alpha(u-\theta^4) & u > 0 \end{cases}$$

滤子 $k(x,t)$ 可以测量（参见方法），$g(v)$ 从先前成功的虎螈视网膜增益控制模型中得来[17]。因此，模型有 4 个参数：整流器 $F(u)$ 的阈值 θ 和斜率 α，以及振幅 B 和增益控制滤子的时间常数 τ。

 总而言之，我们证明对运动物体轨迹的推测始于视网膜。在经眼传输至脑的神经影像中，运动物体明显先于相应的闪烁物体（图 2）。根据神经节细胞光反应的成功模型（图 3 和图 4），这些群体的运动预测可以基于如下解释：感受域空间上的延伸，时间上两阶段反应和非线性对比度增益控制。有些迹象表明这种视网膜机制极大地促成了人对运动刺激的感知。首先，我们模型中的必要组件在许多物种中得到很好的证实。在灵长类视网膜中，非线性的对比度增益控制被发现，尤其存在于 M 型神经节细胞中[15]，满足中枢通路的神经元导致对运动的感知[18]。第二，视网膜对运动的预测在速度大于 $1\ \mathrm{mm \cdot s^{-1}}$ 时失效（图 5b）。这与人体实验的观察结果很好地对应：视网膜速度为 $0.3 \sim 0.9\ \mathrm{mm \cdot s^{-1}}$，知觉运动的预测能够对整个视觉延迟产生补偿[5]，当速度约为 $4\ \mathrm{mm \cdot s^{-1}}$ 时，只观察到对运动的部分预测[10]。最后，视网膜对高对比度刺激的预测要强于对低对比度刺激的预测（图 3），这更加偏离理想推测。再一次强调，这种效应在人类精神物理学中已经观察到[9]。

Fig. 5. Dependence of motion extrapolation on speed. **a**, Stimulation with moving dark bars (90% contrast, 133 μm width) of varying speed: 0.11, 0.22, 0.44, 0.88 and 1.76 mm s⁻¹ (see top stimulus traces). Firing profiles are plotted for salamander fast OFF ganglion cells (middle panel, 19 cells) and rabbit brisk-transient OFF cells (bottom panel, 3 cells). **b**, Motion extrapolation as a function of speed for various populations of ganglion cells. The distance between the peak in the firing-rate profile and the leading edge of the moving bar is plotted as a function of speed; positive numbers indicate that the response profile peaked ahead of the leading edge. The functional types are: salamander, fast OFF (SF, 19 cells); salamander, other OFF (SO, 16 cells); rabbit, brisk-transient OFF (RT, 3 cells); rabbit, brisk-sustained OFF (RS, 6 cells); rabbit, local edge detectors (RE, 4 cells); rabbit, ON/OFF direction-selective cells (5 cells) probed in the preferred direction (RDP) and the null direction (RDN).

In general, an animal is likely to benefit from anticipating the future position of an object, for example to pounce on it or to evade it. This is particularly urgent when the primary sensory data are delayed. In principle, this delay could be compensated anywhere within the behavioural loop, even within the motor system that executes the response. However, it is advantageous to perform the correction early, before different sensory pathways merge. For example, in many animals the retina projects directly to the tectum or the superior colliculus, where a visual map of space is overlaid with an auditory map[19,20]. Auditory transduction in hair cells incurs a much shorter delay than phototransduction[21]. If the visual and auditory images of a moving object should align on the target map, the compensation for the delay in the visual pathway must occur within the retina.

It is likely that subsequent stages of the visual system continue this process, possibly by using a similar mechanism. Within the visual cortex we can certainly find the requisite

图 5. 运动推测对速度的依赖性。**a**，移动暗光柱（对比度 90%，宽度 133 μm）在不同速度下：0.11、0.22、0.44、0.88 和 1.76 mm · s⁻¹（参见顶部的刺激轨迹）的刺激。放电特性是根据虎蝾快速 OFF 神经节细胞（中间图，19 个细胞）和兔临时激活 OFF 细胞（底部图，3 个细胞）的数据绘制而来的。**b**，不同群体的神经节细胞速度函数的运动推测。细胞放电频率峰值和移动光柱前缘的距离被绘制为速度的函数；正数表明反应在光柱前缘之前出现峰值。功能类型包括：虎蝾，快速 OFF 细胞（SF，19 个）；虎蝾，其他 OFF 细胞（SO，16 个）；兔，临时激活 OFF 细胞（RT，3 个）；兔，持续激活 OFF 细胞（RS，6 个）；兔，局部边缘探测器细胞（RE，4 个）；兔，在首选方向（RDP）和无效方向（RDN）探测的 ON/OFF 方向选择性细胞（5 个）。

通常，动物可能会受益于对运动物体未来位置的预测能力，例如用来袭击或逃脱。如果初级感官数据传输滞后，这一点就显得尤其重要。从原理上来说，这种滞后在行为回路中任何地方均可以补偿，甚至在执行反应的运动系统中。然而，在不同的感觉路径合并之前，提前执行正确的决定是有利的。例如，许多动物的视网膜直接映射到上表皮层或者视上丘，在此处空间的视觉图像与听觉图像叠加[19,20]。在毛细胞中的听觉传导引发的滞后比视觉传导更短[21]。如果运动物体的视觉和听觉影像能与目标图像并列，对视觉通路的滞后补偿一定发生在视网膜。

很可能通过相似的机理，视觉系统随后的信息处理阶段会延续这个过程。在视觉皮层我们能够确切地发现图 4 模型中的必要组件：例如，兴奋输入的局部汇集，

components of the model in Fig. 4: for example, local pooling of excitatory inputs, time-delayed inhibition and mechanisms of nonlinear gain control[22,23]. More generally, there are many instances within the cortex where variables relevant to our behaviour are mapped onto two-dimensional sheets of neurons[24]. If the time course of these variables produces a smooth trajectory of neural activity on the cortical map, then a mechanism such as that described here can predict their future from past observations.

Methods

Recording. Retinae were obtained from larval tiger salamanders and Dutch belted rabbits. A piece of isolated retina was placed ganglion-cell-layer-down on a multi-electrode array, which recorded spike trains simultaneously from many ganglion cells, as described previously[11,25].

Stimulation. Visual stimuli were generated on a computer monitor and projected onto the photoreceptor layer, as described[25]. All experiments used a background of white light, with a photopic intensity of $M = 11$ mW m^{-2}. Dark bars of intensity B were presented on this background, and the contrast of a bar is defined as $C=(M-B)/M$. A screen pixel of the monitor measured 6.7 μm on the retina, and each video frame lasted 15 ms. Thus, a bar sweeping at 0.44 mm s^{-1} moved by one pixel every video frame. Flashed bars were presented for a single video frame.

Receptive fields. The spatiotemporal receptive fields of all ganglion cells were measured by reverse correlation to randomly flickering stripes[25], orientated parallel to the bars from other experiments. Each of the contiguous 13-μm wide stripes was randomly turned on or off every 30 ms. From ~60 min of recording, we computed for each ganglion cell the average stimulus sequence in the one second preceding an action potential. This reverse correlation is a measure of how the ganglion cell integrates light over space and time. Its time-reverse is the ganglion cell's linear kernel $k(x,t)$ (ref. 26), which can also be interpreted as the effect of a thin line flashed at distance x on the cell's firing rate at time t after the flash[11]. As expected, $k(x,t)$ had a "Mexican hat" spatial profile, reflecting opposite effects from centre and surround[27], and a biphasic time course (see Fig. 4 and ref. 11).

Cell types. Retinal ganglion cells appear in distinct functional types, and we took care to analyse these subpopulations separately. Salamander cells were classified based on their spatiotemporal receptive fields and on responses to uniform square-wave flashes, as described[28]. Rabbit cells were classified based on the spatiotemporal receptive field and the shape of the spike train's autocorrelation function, following the criteria of ref. 29. Direction-selective cells produced at least tenfold more spikes to one direction of the moving bar than to the opposite direction.

Population activity. The profile of population activity was evaluated along the spatial dimension perpendicular to the bars. Each cell's position was defined as the middle of its receptive field, determined by fitting a spatial gaussian to the centre lobe of the kernel $k(x,t)$. To estimate the population response to a flashed bar, the flash was repeated 75 times in each of 15 locations, separated by 33 μm. For each flash location and each ganglion cell, the firing rate following the flash

时间滞后的抑制，和非线性增益控制的机理[22,23]。通常，在皮质层有许多这样的例子，在那里与我们行为有关的可变物被映射到神经元的二维层[24]。如果这些可变物的时间进程在大脑皮层的神经活动中产生一个平稳的轨迹，那么本文描述的机制能够从过去的观察结果中预测可变物的未来。

方　法

记录　视网膜采集于幼年期的虎螈和荷兰条纹兔。将一片分离的视网膜放置在一个多电极阵列上，放置方向为神经节细胞层朝下，按照之前所述的方法[11,25]同时从许多神经节细胞记录放电信号。

刺激　视觉刺激由计算机显示器产生，然后按照文献描述的方法投射到光感受器细胞层[25]。所有实验以白光为背景，光强为 $M = 11\ \mathrm{mW \cdot m^{-2}}$。强度为 B 的暗光柱呈现在此背景中，暗光柱的对比度定义为 $C=(M-B)/M$。显示器单个屏幕像素在视网膜上的投射大小为 6.7 μm，每个视频帧持续的时间为 15 ms。因此，移动光柱以 $0.44\ \mathrm{mm \cdot s^{-1}}$ 的速度运动，每个视频帧就是一个像素。闪烁光柱在单个视频帧里出现。

感受域　所有神经节细胞的时空感受域均通过随机闪烁光柱的负相关测量[25]，方向与其他实验里的移动光柱平行。每一个连续的 13 μm 宽的条纹每隔 30 ms 随机开关一次。在大约 60 分钟的记录中，我们可以为每一个神经节细胞计算出动作电位前一秒钟之内的平均刺激序列。这种负相关是对神经节细胞如何对光进行时空整合的一种测量。其时间的逆转是神经节细胞的线性核 $k(x,t)$（文献 26），也可以解释为一条细线闪现后在 t 时间 x 距离处细胞放电频率所产生的效应[11]。正如所料，$k(x,t)$ 在空间曲线上有一个"墨西哥帽"，反映了中间和周围的相反效应[27]，以及双相的时间进程。（参见图 4 和参考文献 11）。

细胞类型　视网膜神经节细胞具有不同的功能类型，我们分别对这些亚种群进行了仔细地分析。正如前人所描述的，虎螈的细胞是根据它们的时空感受域及其对统一的矩形波闪烁光柱的反应来区分的[28]。兔的细胞是按照参考文献 29 的标准，根据时间和空间感受域以及放电序列自相关函数的形状进行区分的。方向选择性的细胞对移动光柱移动的特定方向产生的放电至少是相反方向的 10 倍。

群体活动　根据垂直于光柱的空间维度来评价种群活动的特性。每个细胞的位置定位在其感受域中央，由空间的高斯曲线拟合核 $k(x,t)$ 的中心突起形状决定。为了估计细胞群体对闪烁光柱的反应，闪烁光柱在间隔 33 μm 的 15 个位置处每处重复 75 次。对于每一个闪烁光柱的位置和每个神经节细胞，其在闪烁光柱之后的放电频率（图 1a 和 1b）用二进制 2 ms

(Fig. 1a, b) was calculated using a time bin of 2 ms. To compose the firing profile at a given time after the flash, each ganglion cell's firing rate was plotted against the cell's position relative to the flashing line. This plot was smoothed by convolution with a gaussian of standard deviation 20 μm. To estimate the population response to a moving bar, the stimulus was repeated 50 times, and each ganglion cell's firing rate computed as for flashes, but with a time bin of 15 ms. Then the firing rate was plotted against the distance from the bar, and averaged over all cells.

(**398**, 334-338; 1999)

Michael J. Berry II, Iman H. Brivanlou, Thomas A. Jordan* & Markus Meister

Department of Molecular and Cellular Biology, Harvard University, 16 Divinity Avenue, Cambridge, Massachusetts 02138, USA
* Present address: Department of Psychiatry and Behavioral Science, Stanford University School of Medicine, Stanford, California 94305, USA.

Received 11 December 1998; accepted 2 February 1999.

References:

1. Maunsell, J. H. & Gibson, J. R. Visual response latencies in striate cortex of the macaque monkey. *J. Neurophysiol.* **68**, 1332-1344 (1992).

2. Lennie, P. The physiological basis of variations in visual latency. *Vision Res.* **21**, 815-824 (1981).

3. Schnapf, J. L., Kraft, T. W. & Baylor, D. A. Spectral sensitivity of human cone photoreceptors. *Nature* **325**, 439-441 (1987).

4. De Valois, R. L. & De Valois, K. K. Vernier acuity with stationary moving Gabors. *Vision Res.* **31**, 1619-1626 (1991).

5. Nijhawan, R. Motion extrapolation in catching. *Nature* **370**, 256-257 (1994).

6. Khurana, B. & Nijhawan, R. Extrapolation or attention shift? *Nature* **378**, 566 (1995).

7. Nijhawan, R. Visual decomposition of colour through motion extrapolation. *Nature* **386**, 66-69 (1997).

8. Baldo, M. V. & Klein, S. A. Extrapolation or attention shift? *Nature* **378**, 565-566 (1995).

9. Purushothaman, G., Patel, S. S., Bedell, H. E. & Ogmen, H. Moving ahead through differential visual latency. *Nature* **396**, 424 (1998).

10. Whitney, D. & Murakami, I. Latency difference, not spatial extrapolation. *Nature Neurosci.* **1**, 656-657 (1998).

11. Smirnakis, S. M., Berry, M. J., Warland, D. K., Bialek, W. & Meister, M. Adaptation of retinal processing to image contrast and spatial scale. *Nature* **386**, 69-73 (1997).

12. Jacobs, A. L. & Werblin, F. S. Spatiotemporal patterns at the retinal output. *J. Neurophysiol.* **80**, 447-451 (1998).

13. Shapley, R. M. & Victor, J. D. The effect of contrast on the transfer properties of cat retinal ganglion cells. *J. Physiol.* **285**, 275-298 (1978).

14. Sakai, H. M., Wang, J. L. & Naka, K. Contrast gain control in the lower vertebrate retinas. *J. Gen. Physiol.* **105**, 815-835 (1995).

15. Benardete, E. A., Kaplan, E. & Knight, B. W. Contrast gain control in the primate retina: P cells are not X-like, some M cells are. *Visual Neurosci.* **8**, 483-486 (1992).

16. Victor, J. D. The dynamics of the cat retinal X cell centre. *J. Physiol.* **386**, 219-246 (1987).

17. Crevier, D. W. & Meister, M. Synchronous period-doubling in flicker vision of salamander and man. *J. Neurophysiol.* **79**, 1869-1878 (1998).

18. Merigan, W. H. & Maunsell, J. H. How parallel are the primate visual pathways? *Annu. Rev. Neurosci.* **16**, 369-402 (1993).

19. Sparks, D. L. Translation of sensory signals into commands for control of saccadic eye movements: role of primate superior colliculus. *Physiol. Rev.* **66**, 118-171 (1986).

20. Knudsen, E. I. Auditory and visual maps of space in the optic tectum of the owl. *J. Neurosci.* **2**, 1177-1194 (1982).

21. Corey, D. P. & Hudspeth, A. J. Response latency of vertebrate hair cells. *Biophys. J.* **26**, 499-506 (1979).

22. Carandini, M., Heeger, D. J. & Movshon, J. A. Linearity and normalization in simple cells of the macaque primary visual cortex. *J. Neurosci.* **17**, 8621-8644 (1997).

23. Abbott, L. F., Varela, J. A., Sen, K. & Nelson, S. B. Synaptic depression and cortical gain control. *Science* **275**, 220-224 (1997).

24. Knudsen, E. I., du Lac, S. & Esterly, S. D. Computational maps in the brain. *Annu. Rev. Neurosci.* **10**, 41-65 (1987).

25. Meister, M., Pine, J. & Baylor, D. A. Multi-neuronal signals from the retina: acquisition and analysis. *J. Neurosci. Methods* **51**, 95-106 (1994).

26. Hunter, I. W. & Korenberg, M. J. The identification of nonlinear biological systems: Wiener and Hammerstein cascade models. *Biol. Cybern.* **55**, 135-144 (1986).

27. Rodieck, R. W. Quantitative analysis of cat retinal ganglion cell response to visual stimuli. *Vision Res.* **5**, 583-601 (1965).

28. Warland, D. K., Reinagel, P. & Meister, M. Decoding visual information from a population of retinal ganglion cells. *J. Neurophysiol.* **78**, 2336-2350 (1997).

29. Devries, S. H. & Baylor, D. A. Mosaic arrangement of ganglion cell receptive fields in rabbit retina. *J. Neurophysiol.* **78**, 2048-2060 (1997).

Acknowledgements. We thank J. Keat for assistance in generating the visual stimulus, and H. Berg and T. Holy for comments on the manuscript. This work was supported by a NRSA to M.B. and a grant from the NIH and a Presidential Faculty Fellowship to M.M.

Correspondence and requests for material should be addressed to M.J.B. (e-mail: berry@biosun.harvard.edu).

的时间计算。为了描绘闪烁光柱之后给定时间的放电特性，每个神经节细胞的放电频率根据相对于闪烁光柱线的细胞位置描绘。该曲线通过与标准偏差为 20 μm 的高斯曲线卷积变得平滑。为了估计对移动光柱的群体反应，每个刺激被重复 50 次，每个神经节细胞对闪光的放电频率都以二进制 15 ms 的时间计算。然后，对神经节细胞的放电频率以及其相对于光柱的距离进行绘图，并对所有的细胞进行平均。

（董培智 翻译；巩克瑞 审稿）

Observation of Contemporaneous Optical Radiation from a γ-ray Burst

C. Akerlof *et al.*

Editor's Note

Gamma-ray bursts are brief, extremely intense flashes of gamma rays emitted by astrophysical objects and associated with high-energy explosions. Since their discovery in the late 1960s, many have been observed, but their explanation is still debated. Although numerous visible-light objects coincident with the location of gamma-ray bursts had been seen since 1997, before this paper none had been observed while the burst was still active. Carl Akerlof and colleagues used a robotic, wide-field camera to find the optical counterpart of GRB990123 while the burst was still underway, with the observations starting just 22 seconds after the burst began. The visible emission decayed more slowly than the gamma rays. Such observations help to narrow down the identity of the emitting object.

The origin of γ-ray bursts (GRBs) has been enigmatic since their discovery[1]. The situation improved dramatically in 1997, when the rapid availability of precise coordinates[2,3] for the bursts allowed the detection of faint optical and radio afterglows—optical spectra thus obtained have demonstrated conclusively that the bursts occur at cosmological distances. But, despite efforts by several groups[4-7], optical detection has not hitherto been achieved during the brief duration of a burst. Here we report the detection of bright optical emission from GRB990123 while the burst was still in progress. Our observations begin 22 seconds after the onset of the burst and show an increase in brightness by a factor of 14 during the first 25 seconds; the brightness then declines by a factor of 100, at which point (700 seconds after the burst onset) it falls below our detection threshold. The redshift of this burst, $z \approx 1.6$ (refs 8, 9), implies a peak optical luminosity of 5×10^{49} erg s^{-1}. Optical emission from γ-ray bursts has been generally thought to take place at the shock fronts generated by interaction of the primary energy source with the surrounding medium, where the γ-rays might also be produced. The lack of a significant change in the γ-ray light curve when the optical emission develops suggests that the γ-rays are not produced at the shock front, but closer to the site of the original explosion[10].

THE Robotic Optical Transient Search Experiment (ROTSE) is a programme optimized to search for optical radiation contemporaneous with the high-energy photons of a γ-ray burst. The basis for such observations is the BATSE detector on board the Compton Gamma-Ray Observatory. Via rapid processing of the telemetry data stream, the GRB Coordinates Network[11] (GCN) can supply estimated coordinates

伽马射线暴同时的光学辐射的观测

阿克洛夫等

编者按

伽马射线暴是一类由遥远天体在短时间内发出的极强伽马射线耀发，是一种高能爆发现象。自 20 世纪 60 年代末以来，人们虽已发现并观测到多个伽马射线暴，但是对于它们起源问题的解释却是众说纷纭。尽管自 1997 年以来在很多伽马射线暴的位置处人们发现了相应的发光天体，然而在本工作之前还没有人在伽马射线暴发生的过程中找到其发光对应体。卡尔·阿克洛夫和他的同事利用一个自动的宽场相机在 GRB990123 暴的过程中，即暴开始仅 22 秒之后，找到了它的光学对应体。结果发现，可见光辐射强度的衰减明显慢于伽马射线辐射。这样的观测将有助于我们证认发出辐射的天体。

自 γ 射线暴（GRB）被发现以来，它的起源问题就一直是个谜 [1]。这个状况在 1997 年有了很大的改善，因为当时 γ 射线暴快速有效的精确定位技术 [2,3] 的发展使得探测暗弱的光学和射电余辉成为可能——而由此探测到的光谱则证实 γ 射线暴是在宇宙学距离上发生的。尽管几个团队一直在不断地努力 [4-7]，然而迄今为止，人们都没能在短暂的暴持续时间内探测到 γ 射线暴的光学辐射。这里我们报道在 GRB990123 暴期间所发出的明亮的光学辐射的探测。我们的观测在暴开始 22 秒后进行，结果显示，在最初的 25 秒内其亮度增加到 14 倍；随后其亮度下降了 99%，从此（在暴开始 700 秒之后）其亮度下降到我们的探测阈值之下。这个 γ 射线暴的红移为 $z \approx 1.6$（参考文献 8 和 9），这意味着它的光学光度的峰值为 5×10^{49} erg·s^{-1}。一般认为，γ 射线暴的光学辐射产生于主要能量源和周围介质相互作用所形成的激波波前，而 γ 射线辐射也可能在这产生。由于光学辐射发展时 γ 射线的光变曲线并没有发生明显的变化，这表明 γ 射线不是在激波波前产生，而是在更接近原始爆发位置处产生 [10]。

自动光学暂现源搜寻实验（ROTSE）是个以搜寻和 γ 射线暴的高能光子同时产生的光学辐射为目标的项目。这个观测的基础来自安装在康普顿 γ 射线天文台上的 BATSE 探测仪。通过对遥测数据流的快速处理，GRB 坐标定位网 [11]（GCN）能够在

to distant observatories within a few seconds of the burst detection. The typical error of these coordinates is 5°. A successful imaging system must match this field of view to observe the true burst location with reasonable probability.

The detection reported here was performed with ROTSE-I, a two-by-two array of 35 mm camera telephoto lenses (Canon $f/1.8$, 200 mm focal length) coupled to large-format CCD (charge-coupled device) imagers (Thomson 14 μm 2,048 × 2,048 pixels). All four cameras are co-mounted on a single rapid-slewing platform capable of pointing to any part of the sky within 3 seconds. The cameras are angled with respect to each other, so that the composite field of view is 16°×16°. This entire assembly is bolted to the roof of a communications enclosure that houses the computer control system. A motor-driven flip-away cover shields the detector from precipitation and direct sunlight. Weather sensors provide the vital information to shut down observations when storms appear, augmented by additional logic to protect the instrument in case of power loss or computer failure. The apparatus is installed at Los Alamos National Laboratory in northern New Mexico.

Since March 1998, ROTSE-I has been active for ~75% of the total available nights, with most of the outage due to poor weather. During this period, ROTSE-I has responded to a total of 53 triggers. Of these, 26 are associated with GRBs and 13 are associated with soft γ-ray repeaters (SGRs). The median response time from the burst onset to start of the first exposure is 10 seconds.

During most of the night, ROTSE-I records a sequence of sky patrol images, mapping the entire visible sky with two pairs of exposures which reach a 5σ V magnitude threshold sensitivity (m_v) of 15. These data, approximately 8 gigabytes, are archived each night for later analysis. A GCN-provided trigger message interrupts any sequence in progress and initiates the slew to the estimated GRB location. A series of exposures with graduated times of 5, 75 and 200 seconds is then begun. Early in this sequence, the platform is "jogged" by ±8° on each axis to obtain coverage of a four times larger field of view.

At 1999 January 23 09:46:56.12 UTC, an energetic burst triggered the BATSE detector. This message reached Los Alamos 4 seconds later and the first exposure began 6 seconds after this. Unfortunately, a software error prevented the data from being written to disk. The first analysable image was taken 22 seconds after the onset of the burst. The γ-ray light curve for GRB990123 was marked by an initial slow rise, so the BATSE trigger was based on relatively limited statistics. Thus the original GCN position estimate was displaced by 8.9° from subsequent localization, but the large ROTSE-I field of view was sufficient to contain the transient image. At 3.8 hours after the burst, the BeppoSAX satellite provided an X-ray localization[12] in which an optical afterglow was discovered by Odewahn et al.[13] at Mt Palomar. This BeppoSAX position enabled rapid examination of a small region of the large ROTSE-I field. A bright and rapidly varying transient was found in the ROTSE images at right ascension (RA) 15 h 25 min 30.2 s, declination (dec.) 44° 46′ 0″, in excellent agreement with the afterglow found by Odewahn et al. (RA 15 h 25 min 30.53 s, dec. 44° 46′ 0.5″). Multiple absorption lines in the spectrum of the optical afterglow

探测到暴的几秒之内向远处的天文台提供估计的位置坐标。这些坐标的典型误差为5°。一个成功的成像系统必须覆盖这么大的视场，才能在适当的概率上观测到暴的真正位置。

这里我们所报道的探测是由 ROTSE-I 完成的，它是一个由 35 mm 相机摄远镜头（佳能 f/1.8，焦距 200 mm）组成的 2×2 阵，并配备大幅面 CCD（电荷耦合装置）成像仪（汤姆逊 14 μm 2,048×2,048 像素）。所有的 4 个相机都安装在一个快速回转平台上，这使得该仪器能够在 3 秒内指向天区的任何位置。相机彼此之间具有一定的倾角，这使得其仪器的综合视场为 16°×16°。整个装置固定在装有计算机控制系统的通讯围罩的顶上。有一个电机驱动的滑动盖用以保护探测仪不受降雨和日光直射的影响。当暴风雨来临前，气象传感仪将提供重要信息，关闭探测仪器，增强额外的保护措施，以避免功率损耗或者计算机关机对设备仪器带来的损坏。整个设备安装在新墨西哥州北部的洛斯阿拉莫斯国家实验室处。

自 1998 年 3 月开始，ROTSE-I 在约 75% 可观测的夜晚都在工作，而其他大多时候设备都是因为糟糕的天气而不得不停止。这段时期内，ROTSE-I 总共对 53 次触发作出了反应，其中 26 次和 GRB 成协，13 次和软 γ 重复暴成协。从暴开始到首次曝光开始之间的中值反应时间为 10 秒。

夜晚大部分时间内，ROTSE-I 记录一系列巡天图像：对整个可视天区进行两次成双的曝光，5σ V 波段极限星等 (m_v) 达到 15 星等。这样，每个晚上记录下约 8 千兆的数据有待后续分析。若 GCN 提供触发信息，将打断正在进行的巡天观测，并启动望远镜使其回转到所估计的 GRB 位置处。然后望远镜将开始对那块天区进行一系列 5 秒、75 秒和 200 秒的曝光。在这个观测序列早期，观测平台的每个轴都"慢跑"±8°以覆盖达到视场 4 倍大的天区。

在 1999 年 1 月 23 日 09:46:56.12 UTC，一个能量巨大的暴触发了 BATSE 探测仪。这个信息在 4 秒后抵达洛斯阿拉莫斯，再 6 秒后首次曝光开始。不幸的是，一个软件错误导致这次观测的数据没有被写到硬盘里。而首幅可用于分析的图像是在暴开始 22 秒后得到的。由于 GRB990123 的 γ 射线光变曲线特征为初始缓慢的增加，所以 BATSE 触发的准确度相对有限。这使得初始的 GCN 位置估计和随后的定位位置相差 8.9°，但是 ROTSE-I 的大视场已足够包含住该暂现源的像。在暴发生 3.8 小时后，BeppoSAX 卫星给出了一个 X 射线定位 [12]，而在该位置上奥德万等人 [13] 在帕洛马山发现了一个光学余辉。这个 BeppoSAX 给出的位置使得我们可以快速检验 ROTSE-I 的大视场中的一个小区域。我们在 ROTSE 图像赤经 15 h 25 min 30.2 s、赤纬 44°46′ 0″处发现了一个明亮且快速变化的暂现源，其位置和奥德万等人发现的光学余辉的位置（赤经 15 h 25 min 30.53 s、赤纬 44°46′ 0.5″）符合得很好。从光学余辉

indicate a redshift of $z > 1.6$. Dark-subtracted and flattened ROTSE-I images of the GRB field are shown in Fig. 1. Details of the light curve are shown in Table 1.

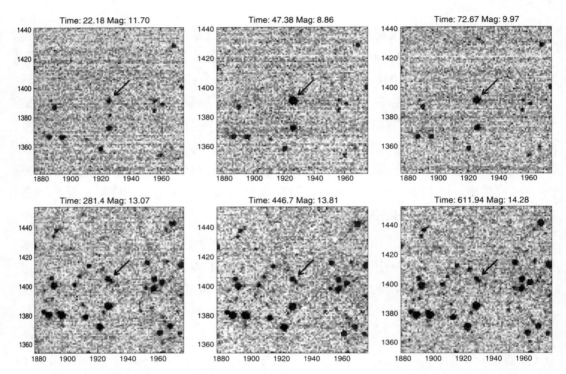

Fig. 1. Time series images of the optical burst. Each image is 24′ on a side, and represents 6×10^{-4} of the ROTSE-I field of view. The horizontal and vertical axes are the CCD pixel coordinates. The sensitivity variations are due to exposure time; the top three images are 5-s exposures, the bottom three are 75-s exposures. The optical transient (OT) is clearly detected in all images, and is indicated by the arrow. South is up, east is left. Thermal effects are removed from the images by subtracting an average dark exposure. Flat field images are generated by median averaging about 100 sky patrol (see text) images. Object catalogues are extracted from the images using SExtractor[18]. Astrometric and photometric calibrations are determined by comparison with the ~1,000 Tycho[19] stars available in each image. Residuals for stars of magnitude 8.5–9.5 are $< 1.2″$. These images are obtained with unfiltered CCDs. The optics and CCD quantum efficiency limit our sensitivity to a wavelength range between 400 and 1,100 nm. Because this wide band is non-standard, we estimate a "V equivalent" magnitude by the following calibration scheme. For each Tycho star, a "predicted ROTSE magnitude" is compared to the 2.5 pixel aperture fluxes measured for these objects to obtain a global zero point for each ROTSE-I image. For the Tycho stars, the agreement between our predicted magnitude and the measured magnitude is ± 0.15. These errors are dominated by colour variation. The zero points are determined to ± 0.02. With large pixels, we must understand the effects of crowding. (This is especially true as we follow the transient to ever fainter magnitudes.) To check the effect of such crowding, we have compared the burst location to the locations of known objects from the USNO A V2.0 catalogue[20]. The nearest object, 34″ away, is a star with R-band magnitude $R = 19.2$. More important is an $R = 14.4$ star, 42″ away. This object affects the measured magnitude of the OT only in our final detection. It can be seen in the final image to the lower right of the OT. A correction of $+0.15$ is applied to compensate for its presence. Magnitudes for the OT associated with GRB990123, measured as described, are listed in Table 1. Further information about the ROTSE-I observations is available at http://www.umich.edu/~rotse.

光谱的多条吸收线中，我们发现其红移为 $z > 1.6$。图 1 显示了扣除暗曝光并平场化的 ROTSE-I GRB 区域图像。光变曲线的细节则在表 1 中进行了展示。

图 1. 光学暴的时间序列成像图。每幅图边长 24′，代表 6×10^{-4} 的 ROTSE-I 视场。水平轴和垂直轴为 CCD 像素坐标。灵敏度会随着曝光时间的变化而发生变化；上面三幅图曝光时间为 5 秒，下面三幅曝光时间为 75 秒。所有图上都能清楚地探测到光学暂现源（OT），以箭头标示。上边是南，左边是东。热效应已通过扣掉平均暗曝光从图像中去除。平场图像则是通过对大约 100 幅巡天图进行平均得到的（见正文）。我们利用 SExtractor[18] 从图像中提取出目标源表，再通过与每幅图中存在的 1,000 颗左右的第谷恒星[19] 进行比较来进行天体测量与测光的定标。最终，星等为 8.5 ~ 9.5 的恒星的位置残差 < 1.2″。这些图像都是通过未经滤波的 CCD 得到的。光学和 CCD 量子效率限制了我们的灵敏度，使得我们的波长范围为 400 ~ 1,100 nm。因为这个宽波带是非标准的，我们通过下面的校准程序得到一个"等效 V"星等。对每颗第谷恒星而言，我们通过比较"ROTSE 预期星等"和测量到的 2.5 个像素孔径内的流量来确定每幅 ROTSE-I 图像的整体零点。这样，对第谷恒星而言，我们的预期星等和测量星等在 ±0.15 之内基本相符，这里误差主要来自色差。零点确定精确到 ±0.02 之内。对于大的像素，我们必须考虑成团效应（对更弱星等的暂现源这个效应尤其重要）。为了检查这种成团效应，我们比较了暴的位置和 USNO A V2.0 列表[20] 的已知天体的位置。其中距离最近的天体位于 34″ 开外，是一颗 R 波段星等为 19.2 的恒星。更为重要的是一颗 42″ 开外，$R = 14.4$ 的恒星，这个天体仅会在我们最后的观测中影响 OT 的测量星等。最后一张图中，可以在 OT 的右下方看到该天体。为了弥补这个影响，我们对 OT 的星等进行了 +0.15 的修正。最终我们将如上所述与 GRB990123 成协的 OT 的观测星等列于表 1。更多关于 ROTSE-I 的观测信息请参见 http://www.umich.edu/~rotse。

Table 1. ROTSE-I observations

Exposure start	Exposure duration	Magnitude	Camera
−7,922.08	75	< 14.8	C
22.18	5	11.70 ± 0.07	A
47.38	5	8.86 ± 0.02	A
72.67	5	9.97 ± 0.03	A
157.12	5	11.86 ± 0.13	C
281.40	75	13.07 ± 0.04	A
446.67	75	13.81 ± 0.07	A
611.94	75	14.28 ± 0.12	A
2,409.86	200	< 15.6	A
5,133.98	800	< 16.1	A

Exposure start times are listed in seconds, relative to the nominal BATSE trigger time (1999 January 23.407594 UT). Exposure durations are in seconds. Magnitudes are in the "V equivalent" system described in Fig. 1 legend. Errors include both statistical errors and systematic errors arising from zero-point calibration. They do not include errors due to variations in the unknown spectral slope of the emission. Magnitude limits are 5σ. The final limit results from co-adding the last four 200-s exposures and is quoted at the mean time of those exposures. Camera entries record the camera in which each observation was made.

By the time of the first exposure, the optical brightness of the transient had risen to $m_v = 11.7$ mag. The flux rose by a factor of 13.7 in the following 25 seconds and then began a rapid, apparently smooth, decline. This decline began precipitously, with a power-law slope of ~−2.5 and gradually slowed to give a slope of ~−1.5. This decline, 10 minutes after the burst, agrees well with the power-law slope found hours later in early afterglow measurements[14]. These observations cover the transition from internal burst emission to external afterglow emission. The composite light curve is shown in Fig. 2.

A number of arguments establish the association of our optical transient with the burst and the afterglow seen later. First, the statistical significance of the transient image exceeds 160σ at the peak. Second, the temporal correlation of the light curve with the GRB flux and the spatial correlations to the X-ray and afterglow positions argue strongly for a common origin. Third, the most recent previous sky patrol image was taken 130 minutes before the burst and no object is visible brighter than $m_v = 14.8$ mag. This is the most stringent limit on an optical precursor obtained to date. Searches further back in time (55 images dating to 28 September 1998) also find no signal. Finally, the "axis jogging" protocol places the transient at different pixel locations within an image and even in different cameras throughout the exposure series, eliminating the possibility of a CCD defect or internal "ghost" masquerading as a signal.

表 1. ROTSE-I 的观测

曝光开始时间	曝光持续时间	星等	照相机
−7,922.08	75	< 14.8	C
22.18	5	11.70 ± 0.07	A
47.38	5	8.86 ± 0.02	A
72.67	5	9.97 ± 0.03	A
157.12	5	11.86 ± 0.13	C
281.40	75	13.07 ± 0.04	A
446.67	75	13.81 ± 0.07	A
611.94	75	14.28 ± 0.12	A
2,409.86	200	< 15.6	A
5,133.98	800	< 16.1	A

曝光开始时间是相对于 BATSE 触发时间 (1999 年 1 月 23.407594 日 UT) 而言的，以秒为单位。曝光持续时间以秒为单位。星等系统为图 1 注中说明的"等效 V"系统。误差包括统计误差和零点校准引起的系统误差，不包括由于未知的辐射谱斜率变化所引起的误差。星等极限为 5σ。最后的极限星等是通过叠加最后 4 个 200 秒的曝光结果得到的，并按照这些曝光的平均时间给出。最后一列记录每次观测使用的照相机。

在首次曝光的时候，暂现源的光学亮度已经增加到了 $m_v = 11.7$ 星等。流量在接下来的 25 秒内增加到 13.7 倍，然后开始快速平滑的衰减。衰减开始很急剧，其幂律斜率约为 −2.5，然后逐渐变慢，幂律斜率变为约 −1.5。同时，暴 10 分钟后的衰减幂律和几个小时后的早期余辉测量获得的幂律斜率[14]一致。这些观测覆盖了从内部暴辐射到外部余辉辐射转换的整个过程。合成的光变曲线在图 2 中展示。

有多个论据表明我们观测到的光学暂现源和该暴及随后的余辉存在关联。首先，暂现源图像的统计显著性在峰值处超过 160σ。其次，其光变曲线和 GRB 流量在时间上的相关，以及其位置和 X 射线及余辉位置在空间上的相关，都强烈表明它们具有相同的起源。第三，最近观测的巡天图拍摄于暴前 130 分钟，而图中并没有亮度超过 $m_v = 14.8$ 星等的天体。这是迄今为止获得的对光学前兆最严格的限制。追溯以往的巡天图 (至 1998 年 9 月 28 日共 55 幅图像) 也没有发现信号。最后，"轴慢跑"方案使得暂现源出现在图像的不同像素位置，甚至在一系列曝光中出现在不同的照相机中，从而排除了因 CCD 缺损或内部"鬼影"产生假信号的可能性。

Fig. 2. A combined optical light curve. Afterglow data points are drawn from the GCN archive[21-33]. The early decay of the ROTSE-I light curve is not well fitted by a single power law. The final ROTSE limit is obtained by co-adding the final four 200-s images. The inset shows the first three ROTSE optical fluxes compared to the BATSE γ-ray light curve in the 100–300 keV energy band. The ROTSE-I fluxes are in arbitrary units. Horizontal error bars indicate periods of active observation. We note that there is no information about the optical light curve outside these intervals. Vertical error bars represent flux uncertainties. Further information about GCN is available at http://gcn.gsfc.nasa.gov/gcn.

The fluence of GRB990123 was exceptionally high (99.6 percentile of BATSE triggers; M. Briggs, personal communication), implying that such bright optical transients may be rare. Models of early optical emission suggest that optical intensity scales with γ-ray fluence[15-17]. If this is the case, ROTSE-I and similar instruments are sensitive to 50% of all GRBs. This translates to ~12 optically detected events per year. Our continuing analysis of less well-localized GRB data may therefore reveal similar transients. To date, this process has been hampered by the necessity of identifying and discarding typically 100,000 objects within the large field of view and optimizing a search strategy in the face of an unknown early time structure. The results we report here at least partially resolve the latter problem while increasing the incentive to complete a difficult analysis task. The ROTSE project is in the process of completing two 0.45-m telescopes capable of reaching 4 magnitudes deeper than ROTSE-I for the same duration exposures. If γ-ray emission in bursts is beamed but the optical emission is more isotropic, there may be many optical transients unassociated with detectable GRBs. These instruments will conduct sensitive searches for such events. We expect that ROTSE will be important in the exploration to come.

(**398**, 400-402; 1999)

图 2. 联合的光学光变曲线。余辉数据来自 GCN 的归档数据[21-33]。ROTSE-I 光变曲线的早期衰减无法用单个幂律来进行拟合。最后的 ROTSE 极限是通过叠加最后 4 个 200 秒曝光的图像得到的。内嵌插图显示前 3 个 ROTSE 光学流量与 100～300 keV 能段的 BATSE γ 射线光变曲线的比较。ROTSE-I 流量单位是任意选取的。水平误差棒表示有效的观测时段。注意这里没有在这些时段之外的光学光变曲线信息。垂直误差棒代表流量不确定度。更多关于 GCN 的信息请参见 http://gcn.gsfc.nasa.gov/gcn。

　　GRB990123 的能流非常大（占据 BATSE 触发事件的 99.6%；布里格斯，个人交流），这表明这样亮的光学暂现源可能很少见。早期光学辐射的模型显示光学强度和 γ 射线能流成比例[15-17]。事实如此的话，ROTSE-I 和类似设备将对 50% 的 GRB 都非常灵敏。这意味着每年我们将可以探测到约 12 例光学事件。因此我们接下来对那些定位不是很好的 GRB 数据进行分析可能可以发现类似的暂现源。迄今为止，这个方法的困难之处在于必须证认并排除大视场内约 100,000 个天体，并且在未知早期时间结构的情况下必须最大限度地优化搜寻策略。我们这里报道的结果至少部分解决了第二个问题，并激励我们去完成这些困难的分析任务。ROTSE 项目目前正在搭建两个 0.45 米望远镜使得在相同曝光时间下的星等极限比 ROTSE-I 深 4 个星等。假如暴的 γ 射线辐射是束状的，而光学辐射更加各向同性，那么就可能有很多光学暂现源并没有成协的、能探测到的 GRB。这些仪器将对这种事件做出灵敏的搜寻。我们预期 ROTSE 将在未来的研究探索中发挥非常重要的作用。

（肖莉 翻译；黎卓 审稿）

C. Akerlof*, R. Balsano[†], S. Barthelmy[‡§], J. Bloch[†], P. Butterworth[‡‖], D. Casperson[†], T. Cline[‡], S. Fletcher[†], F. Frontera[¶], G. Gisler[†], J. Heise[#], J. Hills[†], R. Kehoe*, B. Lee*, S. Marshall[✶], T. McKay*, R. Miller[†], L. Piro[**], W. Priedhorsky[†], J. Szymanski[†] & J. Wren[†]

* University of Michigan, Ann Arbor, Michigan 48109, USA
[†] Los Alamos National Laboratory, Los Alamos, New Mexico 87545, USA
[‡] NASA/Goddard Space Flight Center, Greenbelt, Maryland 20771, USA
[§] Universities Space Research Association, Seabrook, Maryland 20706, USA
[‖] Raytheon Systems, Lanham, Maryland 20706, USA
[¶] Università degli Studi di Ferrara, Ferrara, Italy
[#] Space Research Organization, Utrecht, The Netherlands
[✶] Lawrence Livermore National Laboratory, Livermore, California 94550, USA
[**] Instituto Astrofisica Spaziale, Rome, Italy

Received 5 February; accepted 19 February 1999.

References:

1. Klebesadel, R. W., Strong, I. B. & Olson, R. A. Observations of gamma-ray bursts of cosmic origin. *Astrophys. J.* **182**, L85-L88 (1973).

2. Piro, L. *et al.* The first X-ray localization of a γ-ray burst by BeppoSAX and its fast spectral evolution. *Astron. Astrophys.* **329**, 906-910 (1998).

3. Costa, E. *et al.* Discovery of an X-ray afterglow associated with the γ-ray burst of 28 February 1997. *Nature* **387**, 783-785 (1997).

4. Krimm, H. A., Vanderspek, R. K. & Ricker, G. R. Searches for optical counterparts of BATSE gamma-ray bursts with the Explosive Transient Camera. *Astron. Astrophys. Suppl.* **120**, 251-254 (1996).

5. Hudec, R. & Soldán, J. Ground-based optical CCD experiments for GRB and optical transient detection. *Astrophys. Space Sci.* **231**, 311-314 (1995).

6. Lee, B. *et al.* Results from Gamma-Ray Optical Counterpart Search Experiment: a real time search for gamma-ray burst optical counterparts. *Astrophys. J.* **482**, L125-L129 (1997).

7. Park, H. S. *et al.* New constraints on simultaneous optical emission from gamma-ray bursts measured by the Livermore Optical Transient Imaging System experiment. *Astrophys. J.* **490**, L21-L24 (1997).

8. Kelson, D. D., Illingworth, G. D., Franx, M., Magee, D. & van Dokkum, P. G. *IAU Circ.* No. 7096 (1999).

9. Hjorth, J. *et al. GCN Circ.* No. 219 (1999).

10. Fenimore, E. E., Ramirez-Ruiz, E., Wu, B. GRB990123: Evidence that the γ-rays come from a central engine. Preprint astro-ph9902007 at ⟨http://xxx.lanl.gov⟩ (1999).

11. Barthelmy, S. *et al.* in *Gamma-Ray Bursts: 4th Huntsville Symp.* (eds Meegan, C. A, Koskut, T. M. & Preece, R. D.) 99-103 (AIP Conf. Proc. 428, Am. Inst. Phys., College Park, 1997).

12. Piro, L. *et al. GCN Circ.* No. 199 (1999).

13. Odewahn, S. C. *et al. GCN Circ.* No. 201 (1999).

14. Bloom, J. S. *et al. GCN Circ.* No. 208 (1999).

15. Katz, J. I. Low-frequency spectra of gamma-ray bursts. *Astrophys. J.* **432**, L107-L109 (1994).

16. Mészáros, P. & Rees, M. J. Optical and long-wavelength afterglow from gamma-ray bursts. *Astrophys. J.* **476**, 232-237 (1997).

17. Sari, R. & Piran, T. The early afterglow. Preprint astro-ph/9901105 at ⟨http://xxx.lanl.gov⟩ (1999).

18. Bertin, E. & Arnouts, S. SExtractor: Software for source extraction. *Astron. Astrophys. Suppl.* **117**, 393-404 (1996).

19. Høg, E. *et al.* The Tycho reference catalogue. *Astron. Astrophys.* **335**, L65-L68 (1998).

20. Monet, D. *et al. A Catalog of Astrometric Standards* (US Naval Observatory, Washington DC, 1998).

21. Zhu, J. & Zhang, H. T. *GCN Circ.* No. 204 (1999).

22. Bloom, J. S. *et al. GCN Circ.* No. 206 (1999).

23. Gal, R. R. *et al. GCN Circ.* No. 207 (1999).

24. Sokolov, V. *et al. GCN Circ.* No. 209 (1999).

25. Ofek, E. & Leibowitz, E. M. *GCN Circ.* No. 210 (1999).

26. Garnavich, P., Jha, S., Stanek, K. & Garcia, M. *GCN Circ.* No. 215 (1999).

27. Zhu, J. *et al. GCN Circ.* No. 217 (1999).

28. Bloom, J. S. *et al. GCN Circ.* No. 218 (1999).

29. Maury, A., Boer, M. & Chaty, S. *GCN Circ.* No. 220 (1999).

30. Zhu, J. *et al. GCN Circ.* No. 226 (1999).

31. Sagar, R., Pandey, A. K., Yadav, R. K. R., Nilakshi & Mohan, V. *GCN Circ.* No. 227 (1999).

32. Masetti, N. *et al. GCN Circ.* No. 233 (1999).

33. Bloom, J. S. *et al. GCN Circ.* No. 240 (1999).

Acknowledgements. The ROTSE Collaboration thanks J. Fishman and the BATSE team for providing the data that enable the GCN localizations which made this experiment possible; and we thank the BeppoSAX team for rapid distribution of coordinates. This work was supported by NASA and the US DOE. The Los Alamos National Laboratory is operated by the University of California for the US Department of Energy (DOE). The work was performed in part under the auspices of the US DOE by Lawrence Livermore National Laboratory. BeppoSAX is a programme of the Italian Space Agency (ASI) with participation of the Dutch Space Agency (NIVR).

Correspondence and requests for materials should be addressed to C.A. (e-mail: akerlof@mich.physics.lsa.umich.edu).

Climate and Atmospheric History of the Past 420,000 Years from the Vostok Ice Core, Antarctica

J. R. Petit *et al.*

Editor's Note

This paper by a team of glaciologists and palaeoclimatologists reports the longest record of climate change ever to have been obtained by that time from cores of ice drilled from polar ice sheets. The composition of isotopes in the ice, and the presence of trapped gas bubbles and dust, enables changes in temperature, ice volume, and levels of atmospheric greenhouse gases and dust to be tracked over the hundreds of thousands of years during which the ice was deposited. The cores described here nearly double the previous timespan covered, allowing climate to be reconstructed over four ice-age cycles. Such records test our understanding of how climate change happened, in particular supporting the link between warming and greenhouse-gas concentrations.

The recent completion of drilling at Vostok station in East Antarctica has allowed the extension of the ice record of atmospheric composition and climate to the past four glacial–interglacial cycles. The succession of changes through each climate cycle and termination was similar, and atmospheric and climate properties oscillated between stable bounds. Interglacial periods differed in temporal evolution and duration. Atmospheric concentrations of carbon dioxide and methane correlate well with Antarctic air-temperature throughout the record. Present-day atmospheric burdens of these two important greenhouse gases seem to have been unprecedented during the past 420,000 years.

THE late Quaternary period (the past one million years) is punctuated by a series of large glacial–interglacial changes with cycles that last about 100,000 years (ref. 1). Glacial–interglacial climate changes are documented by complementary climate records[1,2] largely derived from deep sea sediments, continental deposits of flora, fauna and loess, and ice cores. These studies have documented the wide range of climate variability on Earth. They have shown that much of the variability occurs with periodicities corresponding to that of the precession, obliquity and eccentricity of the Earth's orbit[1,3]. But understanding how the climate system responds to this initial orbital forcing is still an important issue in palaeoclimatology, in particular for the generally strong ~100,000-year (100-kyr) cycle.

Ice cores give access to palaeoclimate series that includes local temperature and precipitation rate, moisture source conditions, wind strength and aerosol fluxes of marine,

南极洲东方站过去 42 万年冰芯气候和大气历史记录

珀蒂等

编者按

这篇文章由冰川学家和古气候学家组成的研究团队完成，它报道了当时从极地冰盖钻出的冰芯所能获得的最长气候变化记录。冰芯中同位素的组成以及气体包裹体和粉尘的存在，可用于捕捉过去几十万年冰沉积以来的温度、冰储量以及大气温室气体和粉尘水平的变化。这里描述的冰芯所包含的时间尺度几乎是前一次的两倍，可以在四个冰期–间冰期旋回内重建气候。这些记录检验了我们对气候变化如何发生的理解，特别是为气候变暖与温室气体浓度之间的联系提供了支持证据。

最近完成的东南极洲东方站（注：东方站也称沃斯托克站）的冰芯钻取工作，使大气成分与气候的冰芯记录延伸到了过去 4 个冰期–间冰期旋回。每一个气候旋回和冰期结束期连续变化都是相似的，而且大气和气候特性总是在稳定的范围内波动。间冰期在时间变化和持续时间方面存在差异。整个记录中，大气中二氧化碳和甲烷的浓度与南极的气温记录有很好的相关性。而现在这两种重要的温室气体在大气中的荷载量与过去 42 万年以来相比是史无前例的。

第四纪晚期（过去的 100 万年）被一系列持续时间约 10 万年的大的冰期–间冰期的周期性变化而分段（参考文献 1）。大量来自深海沉积物、大陆动植物、黄土沉积物及冰芯的记录[1,2]互为补充地说明了冰期–间冰期的气候变化。这些研究证实了地球气候变化有很大的幅度，表明许多周期性发生的变化对应于地球轨道参数岁差、地轴倾角及偏心率[1,3]的变化。但是，古气候学中，了解气候系统如何响应这些初始轨道驱动，特别对周期约 10 万年的强旋回来说，这一直是一个重要的问题。

通过冰芯记录可以了解一系列古气候变化序列，包括局地温度与降水率，水汽来源地条件，风的强度及源自海洋、火山、陆地、宇宙和人类活动的气溶胶通量。

volcanic, terrestrial, cosmogenic and anthropogenic origin. They are also unique with their entrapped air inclusions in providing direct records of past changes in atmospheric trace-gas composition. The ice-drilling project undertaken in the framework of a long-term collaboration between Russia, the United States and France at the Russian Vostok station in East Antarctica (78° S, 106° E, elevation 3,488 m, mean temperature $-55°C$) has already provided a wealth of such information for the past two glacial–interglacial cycles[4-13]. Glacial periods in Antarctica are characterized by much colder temperatures, reduced precipitation and more vigorous large-scale atmospheric circulation. There is a close correlation between Antarctic temperature and atmospheric concentrations of CO_2 and CH_4 (refs 5, 9). This discovery suggests that greenhouse gases are important as amplifiers of the initial orbital forcing and may have significantly contributed to the glacial–interglacial changes[14-16]. The Vostok ice cores were also used to infer an empirical estimate of the sensitivity of global climate to future anthropogenic increases of greenhouse-gas concentrations[15].

The recent completion of the ice-core drilling at Vostok allows us to considerably extend the ice-core record of climate properties at this site. In January 1998, the Vostok project yielded the deepest ice core ever recovered, reaching a depth of 3,623 m (ref. 17). Drilling then stopped ~120 m above the surface of the Vostok lake, a deep subglacial lake which extends below the ice sheet over a large area[18], in order to avoid any risk that drilling fluid would contaminate the lake water. Preliminary data[17] indicated that the Vostok ice-core record extended through four climate cycles, with ice slightly older than 400 kyr at a depth of 3,310 m, thus spanning a period comparable to that covered by numerous oceanic[1] and continental[2] records.

Here we present a series of detailed Vostok records covering this ~400-kyr period. We show that the main features of the more recent Vostok climate cycle resemble those observed in earlier cycles. In particular, we confirm the strong correlation between atmospheric greenhouse-gas concentrations and Antarctic temperature, as well as the strong imprint of obliquity and precession in most of the climate time series. Our records reveal both similarities and differences between the successive interglacial periods. They suggest the lead of Antarctic air temperature, and of atmospheric greenhouse-gas concentrations, with respect to global ice volume and Greenland air-temperature changes during glacial terminations.

The Ice Record

The data are shown in Figs 1, 2 and 3 (see Supplementary Information for the numerical data). They include the deuterium content of the ice (δD_{ice}, a proxy of local temperature change), the dust content (desert aerosols), the concentration of sodium (marine aerosol), and from the entrapped air the greenhouse gases CO_2 and CH_4, and the $\delta^{18}O$ of O_2 (hereafter $\delta^{18}O_{atm}$) which reflects changes in global ice volume and in the hydrological cycle[19]. (δD and $\delta^{18}O$ are defined in the legends to Figs 1 and 2, respectively.) All these measurements have been performed using methods previously described except for slight modifications (see figure legends).

394

冰芯独到之处在于其捕获的空气包裹体直接记录了过去大气中痕量气体成分的变化。这项在俄罗斯、美国、法国长期合作框架下开展的东南极洲俄罗斯东方站（78°S，106°E，海拔 3,488 米，平均气温 −55°C）冰芯钻取计划，已经为过去两个冰期−间冰期旋回[4-13]提供了大量的以上信息。冰期期间，南极地区温度更低，降水更少，大尺度大气环流更加剧烈。南极的温度与大气中 CO_2 和 CH_4 的浓度有密切的关系（参考文献 5 和 9）。这一发现表明这些温室气体是重要的原始轨道驱动作用的放大器，并可能对冰期−间冰期的变化[14-16]有显著的影响。未来人类活动导致的温室气体浓度升高会加速全球升温，东方站冰芯记录也可以被用来对这一敏感性做出经验性估算[15]。

最近东方站冰芯钻探的完成，使得我们可以大幅度地延伸在该站的冰芯关于气候属性的记录。1998 年 1 月，东方站计划到达了有史以来最长的冰芯深度，达到 3,623 米（参考文献 17）。为了避免钻孔液污染东方湖——一个存在于冰盖底部面积广大的深水冰下湖[18]，钻探停留在东方湖湖面以上约 120 米处。初步的资料[17]表明东方站冰芯记录覆盖了四个气候旋回，在 3,310 米深处冰的年龄稍老于 40 万年，因此，其覆盖的时间范围与很多海洋[1]或大陆[2]记录相当。

本文中我们展示了东方站冰芯包含这一段约 40 万年的一系列详细记录。研究表明东方站较新的气候旋回与早期的气候旋回在主要特征方面是相似的。特别是，我们证实了大气温室气体浓度与南极温度之间有强烈的相关性，而且在大多数气候时间序列里地轴倾角（即黄赤交角）和岁差也留下了强烈的印记。我们的记录揭示了相继的间冰期之间既有相似性也有差别。这些记录表明，在冰期结束期，南极温度和大气温室气体浓度的变化先于全球冰储量和格陵兰气温的变化。

冰 芯 记 录

图 1、2 和 3 展示了相关的资料（数值数据请见补充信息），包括冰中氘的含量（δD_{ice}，一个代表局地气温变化的指标），粉尘量（沙漠气溶胶），钠的浓度（海洋气溶胶），包裹气体的温室气体 CO_2 和 CH_4 以及 O_2 中的 $\delta^{18}O$ 含量（下文用 $\delta^{18}O_{atm}$ 表示）等资料，$\delta^{18}O_{atm}$ 的含量反映了全球冰储量和水循环[19]的变化。（δD 和 $\delta^{18}O$ 分别在图 1 和图 2 的图例说明中给出了定义）。所有这些测量都使用上述方法完成，只是稍有修改（参见图例说明）。

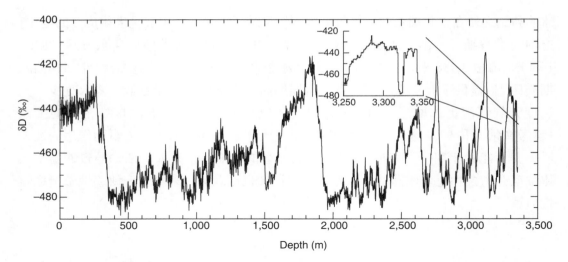

Fig. 1. The deuterium record. Deuterium content as a function of depth, expressed as δD (in ‰ with respect to Standard Mean Ocean Water, SMOW). This record combines data available down to 2,755 m (ref. 13) and new measurements performed on core 5G (continuous 1-m ice increments) from 2,755 m to 3,350 m. Measurement accuracy (1σ) is better than 1‰. Inset, the detailed deuterium profile for the lowest part of the record showing a δD excursion between 3,320 and 3,330 m. δD_{ice}(in ‰) = $[(D/H)_{sample}/(D/H)_{SMOW} - 1] \times 1,000$.

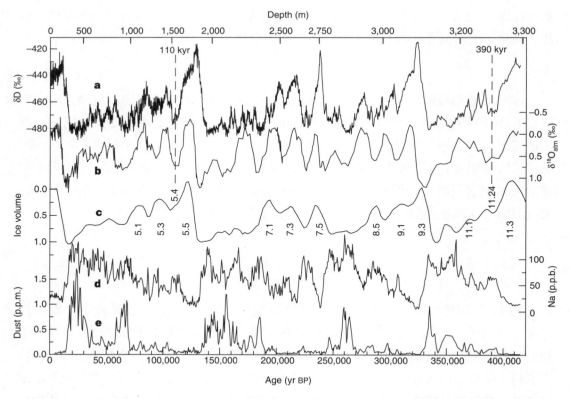

Fig. 2. Vostok time series and ice volume. Time series (GT4 timescale for ice on the lower axis, with indication of corresponding depths on the top axis and indication of the two fixed points at 110 and 390 kyr) of: **a**, deuterium profile (from Fig. 1); **b**, $\delta^{18}O_{atm}$ profile obtained combining published data[11,13,30] and

图 1. 氘的记录。氘含量随深度的变化，用 δD 表示（相对于标准平均大洋水（SMOW），用‰表示）。该记录结合了以前深达 2,755 米的资料（文献 13）以及从 5G 冰芯 2,755 米到 3,350 米段得到的新的测量结果（以 1 米间隔连续采样）。测量精度（1σ）优于 1‰。插图：记录中最低部分的详细氘剖面，展示了 δD 在 3,320 与 3,330 米之间的短期变化。$\delta D_{ice}(‰) = [(D/H)_{样本}/(D/H)_{SMOW} - 1] \times 1,000$。

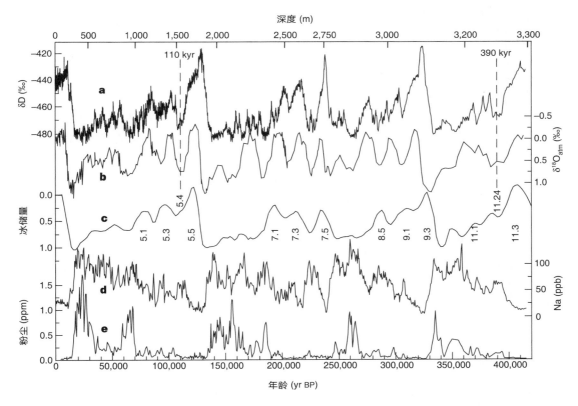

图 2. 东方站的时间序列和冰储量。各种时间序列（下面的横轴是冰的 GT4 时间标尺，上面的横轴是相应的深度，并标示出了 11 万年与 39 万年这两个固定点）：a，氘的剖面（来自图 1）；b，$\delta^{18}O_{atm}$ 剖面结

397

81 new measurements performed below 2,760 m. The age of the gas is calculated as described in ref. 20; **c**, seawater $\delta^{18}O$ (ice volume proxy) and marine isotope stages adapted from Bassinot *et al.*[26]; **d**, sodium profile obtained by combination of published and new measurements (performed both at LGGE and RSMAS) with a mean sampling interval of 3–4 m (ng g^{-1} or p.p.b); and **e**, dust profile (volume of particles measured using a Coulter counter) combining published data[10,13] and extended below 2,760 m, every 4 m on the average (concentrations are expressed in µg g^{-1} or p.p.m. assuming that Antarctic dust has a density of 2,500 kg m^{-3}). $\delta^{18}O_{atm}(in\ ‰) = [(^{18}O/^{16}O)_{sample}/(^{18}O/^{16}O)_{standard} - 1] \times 1,000$; standard is modern air composition.

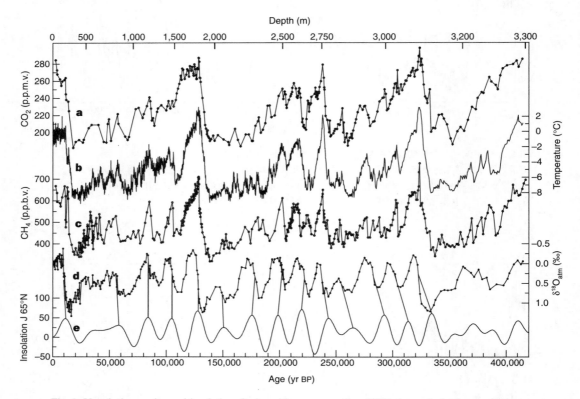

Fig. 3. Vostok time series and insolation. Series with respect to time (GT4 timescale for ice on the lower axis, with indication of corresponding depths on the top axis) of: **a**, CO_2; **b**, isotopic temperature of the atmosphere (see text); **c**, CH_4; **d**, $\delta^{18}O_{atm}$; and **e**, mid-June insolation at 65° N (in W m^{-2}) (ref. 3). CO_2 and CH_4 measurements have been performed using the methods and analytical procedures previously described[5,9]. However, the CO_2 measuring system has been slightly modified in order to increase the sensitivity of the CO_2 detection. The thermal conductivity chromatographic detector has been replaced by a flame ionization detector which measures CO_2 after its transformation into CH_4. The mean resolution of the CO_2 (CH_4) profile is about 1,500 (950) years. It goes up to about 6,000 years for CO_2 in the fractured zones and in the bottom part of the record, whereas the CH_4 time resolution ranges between a few tens of years to 4,500 years. The overall accuracy for CH_4 and CO_2 measurements are ± 20 p.p.b.v. and 2–3 p.p.m.v., respectively. No gravitational correction has been applied.

The detailed record of δD_{ice} (Fig. 1) confirms the main features of the third and fourth climate cycles previously illustrated by the coarse-resolution record[17]. However, a sudden decrease from interglacial-like to glacial-like values, rapidly followed by an abrupt return to interglacial-like values, occurs between 3,320 and 3,330 m. In addition, a transition from low to high CO_2 and CH_4 values (not shown) occurs at exactly the same depth. In undisturbed ice, the transition

合了已发表的资料[11,13,30]和 2,760 米以下的 81 个新测量值。气体的年龄根据参考文献 20 所述计算得到；**c**，海水 δ18O（代表冰储量的指标）值与海洋氧同位素阶段，来自于巴西诺等人的文章[26]；**d**，钠的剖面由已发表的测量值和平均每 3~4 米进行采样获得的新测量值（ng·g-1 或 ppb）（在法国冰川与环境地球物理学实验室（LGGE）和美国迈阿密大学罗森斯蒂尔海洋和大气科学学院（RSMAS）都进行了相关的测量）相结合得到；**e**，粉尘剖面（用库尔特粒度仪测量粒子体积），结合了已发表的资料[10,13]和 2,760 米以下的延伸数据（平均每 4 米测量一个数据点）（粉尘浓度用 μg·g-1 或 ppm 表示，假定南极粉尘的密度为 2,500 kg·m-3）。$\delta^{18}O_{atm}(‰) = [(^{18}O/^{16}O)_{样本}/(^{18}O/^{16}O)_{标准} - 1] \times 1,000$；标准是现代大气的成分。

图 3. 东方站时间序列和太阳辐射。时间序列（下面的横轴是冰的 GT4 时间标尺，上面的横轴是相应的深度）**a**，CO_2；**b**，大气的同位素温度（参见正文）；**c**，CH_4；**d**，$\delta^{18}O_{atm}$；**e**，6 月中旬在 65°N 的太阳辐射（单位 W·m-2）（文献 3）。CO_2 与 CH_4 的测量按前述方法和分析流程[5,9]进行。然而，为了增加 CO_2 检测的敏感性，对测量方法稍有修改。用火焰离子化检测器替代了热导色谱检测器，去测量转化为 CH_4 后的 CO_2。$CO_2(CH_4)$ 剖面的平均时间分辨率约为 1,500（950）年。在碎冰带和冰芯记录的底部，CO_2 的时间分辨率下降至约 6,000 年，而 CH_4 的时间分辨率范围跨度从几十年到 4,500 年。CH_4 和 CO_2 测量的总体精度分别为 ±20 ppbv 和 2~3 ppmv，这里没有经过重力校正。

详细的 δD_{ice} 记录（图 1）确认了以前用低分辨率记录[17]表示的第三和第四个气候旋回的主要特征。然而，在 3,320 米至 3,330 米之间出现了从类间冰期数值到类冰期数值的突然下降，紧接着迅速回到类间冰期数值。此外，在完全相同的深度，也发生了 CO_2 和 CH_4 从低值到高值的转变（图中未显示）。在未受扰动的冰内，出现大气

in atmospheric composition would be found a few metres lower (due to the difference between the age of the ice and the age of the gas[20]). Also, three volcanic ash layers, just a few centimetres apart but inclined in opposite directions, have been observed—10 m above this δD excursion (3,311 m). Similar inclined layers were observed in the deepest part of the GRIP and GISP2 ice cores from central Greenland, where they are believed to be associated with ice flow disturbances. Vostok climate records are thus probably disturbed below these ash layers, whereas none of the six records show any indication of disturbances above this level. We therefore limit the discussion of our new data sets to the upper 3,310 m of the ice core, that is, down to the interglacial corresponding to marine stage 11.3.

Lorius et al.[4] established a glaciological timescale for the first climate cycle of Vostok by combining an ice-flow model and an ice-accumulation model. This model was extended and modified in several studies[12,13]. The glaciological timescale provides a chronology based on physics, which makes no assumption about climate forcings or climate correlation except for one or two adopted control ages. Here, we further extend the Extended Glaciological Timescale (EGT) of Jouzel et al.[12] to derive GT4, which we adopt as our primary chronology (see Box 1). GT4 provides an age of 423 kyr at a depth of 3,310 m.

Box 1. The Vostok glaciological timescale

We use three basic assumptions[12] to derive our glaciological timescale (GT4); (1) the accumulation rate has in the past varied in proportion to the derivative of the water vapour saturation pressure with respect to temperature at the level where precipitation forms (see section on the isotope temperature record), (2) at any given time the accumulation between Vostok and Dome B (upstream of Vostok) varies linearly with distance along the line connecting those two sites, and (3) the Vostok ice at 1,534 m corresponds to marine stage 5.4 (110 kyr) and ice at 3,254 m corresponds to stage 11.2.4 (390 kyr).

Calculation of the strain-induced thinning of annual layers is now performed accounting for the existence of the subglacial Vostok lake. Indeed, running the ice-flow model[48] with no melting and no basal sliding as done for EGT[12] leads to an age > 1,000 kyr for the deepest level we consider here (3,310 m), which is much too old. Instead, we now allow for moderate melting and sliding. These processes diminish thinning for the lower part of the core and provide younger chronologies. We ran this age model[48] over a large range of values of the model parameters (present-day accumulation at Vostok, A, melting rate, M, and fraction of horizontal velocity due to base sliding, S) with this aim of matching the assumed ages at 1,534 and 3,254 m. This goal was first achieved (ages of 110 and 392 kyr) with $A = 1.96$ g cm^{-2} yr^{-1}, and M and S equal respectively to 0.4 mm yr^{-1} and 0.7 for the region 60 km around Vostok where the base is supposed to reach the melting point (we set $M = 0$ and $S = 0$ elsewhere). These values are in good agreement with observations for A (2.00 ± 0.04 g cm^{-2} yr^{-1} over the past 200 yr) and correspond to a reasonable set of parameters for M and S. We adopt this glaciological timescale (GT4), which gives an age of 423 kyr at 3,310 m, without further tuning (Fig. 2). GT4 never differs by more than 2 kyr from EGT over the last climate cycle and, in qualitative agreement with recent results[49], makes termination I slightly older (by ~700 yr). We

成分转折点的深度比同位素温度的相应转折点低几米（由于同层冰年龄和气体年龄不同[20]）。同时，在 δD 发生短期流动的上方 10 米处（3,311 米）观测到相隔只几厘米、但倾斜方向相反的三个火山灰层。在格陵兰中部 GRIP 冰芯和 GISP2 冰芯的最底部也观测到了相似的倾斜层，人们相信这些倾斜层与冰流扰动有关。因此，东方站的气候记录中，火山灰层下面的部分可能受到扰动，然而这一层位之上，这六个记录中都没有表明存在有扰动的迹象。为此，我们把对这些新的数据的讨论限定在冰芯深度 3,310 米以上的部分，即只讨论到对应海洋氧同位素 11.3 阶的间冰期。

洛里于斯等人[4]，用一个冰流模型结合积累模型建立了东方站的第一气候旋回的时间标尺。这一模式在数个研究中[12,13]得到拓展和修改。该冰川时间标尺基于物理学，除了采用一两个年龄控制点外，没有考虑任何有关气候强迫或气候相关性的假定。这里，我们进一步拓展了茹泽尔等人[12]建立的延长的冰川时标（EGT）以获得GT4，用作我们研究的基础年表（参见框 1）。按照 GT4 时标，3,310 米深处对应的年龄为 42.3 万年。

框 1. 东方站冰川的时间标尺

我们用 3 个基本假定[12]取得冰川的时间标尺（GT4）：(1) 过去的积累速率是与（在降水形成的高度处）饱和水汽压对温度的导数成比例的（参见同位素温度记录这一节）；(2) 在任何给定的时间，东方站与冰穹 B（在东方站的上游）的积累速率变化与两站连线的距离呈线性关系；(3) 在东方站，1,534 米深度处的冰对应于海洋氧同位素 5.4 阶（距今 11 万年），3,254 米深度处的冰对应于海洋氧同位素 11.2.4 阶（距今 39 万年）。

计算考虑了冰下湖（东方湖）存在的情况下，冰川应力导致的年层减薄。的确，假设没有融化和没有基底滑动的冰流模型[48]（如在 EGT[12]），运行模型得到的结果是冰川最底层（3,310 米）年龄大于 100 万年，这实在太古老了。不过，现在我们考虑有中等强度的融化和滑动。这些过程减少了深部冰芯的减薄，使冰川底部年龄更年轻。我们把模型的输入参数（东方站的现今积累量 A，融化率 M 和由于基底滑动引起的水平流速分量 S）的范围取大来运行这一模型[48]，以使得运行结果与在 1,534 米与 3,254 米的设定年龄一致。当设定在东方站周围 60 km 的区域（假定基底达到熔点）$A = 1.96$ g · cm^{-2} · yr^{-1}，M 和 S 分别等于 0.4 mm · yr^{-1} 和 0.7（设其他地方的 $M = 0$ 且 $S = 0$）时，我们得到了预期的结果（年龄为距今 11 万年和距今 39.2 万年）。这些值与 A 的观测值（在过去的 200 年为 2.00 ± 0.04 g · cm^{-2} · yr^{-1}）非常一致，并符合一组合理的参数 M 和 S 值。我们采用了这一冰川时间标尺（GT4），并未做进一步的调整，它在 3,310 米深度处给出了 42.3 万年的年龄值（图 2）。在最后一个气候旋回，GT4 从不会与 EGT 相差 2,000 年以上。与最近的研究结果[49]定性地一致，冰期结束期 I 稍微更早（提前了约 700 年）。我们注意到它对海洋

note that it provides a reasonable age for stage 7.5 (238 kyr) whereas Jouzel et al.[13] had to modify EGT for the second climate cycle by increasing the accumulation by 12% for ages older than 110 kyr. GT4 never differs by more than 4 kyr from the orbitally tuned timescale of Waelbroeck et al.[50] (defined back to 225 kyr), which is within the estimated uncertainty of this latter timescale. Overall, we have good arguments[11,50-52] to claim that the accuracy of GT4 should be better than ±5 kyr for the past 110 kyr.

The strong relationship between $\delta^{18}O_{atm}$ and mid-June 65° N insolation changes (see text and Fig. 3) enables us to further evaluate the overall quality of GT4. We can use each well-marked transition from high to low $\delta^{18}O_{atm}$ to define a "control point" giving an orbitally tuned age. The mid-point of the last $\delta^{18}O_{atm}$ transition (~10 kyr ago) has nearly the same age as the insolation maximum (11 kyr). We assume that this correspondence also holds for earlier insolation maxima. The resulting control points (Fig. 3 and Table 1) are easy to define for the period over which the precessional cycle is well imprinted in 65° N insolation (approximately between 60 and 340 kyr) but not during stages 2 and 10 where insolation changes are small. The agreement between the $\delta^{18}O_{atm}$ control points and GT4 is remarkably good given the simple assumptions of both approaches. This conclusion stands despite the fact that we do not understand controls on $\delta^{18}O_{atm}$ sufficiently well enough to know about the stability of its phase with respect to insolation. We assume that the change in phase does not exceed ±6 kyr (1/4 of a precessional period).

We conclude that accuracy of GT4 is always better than ±15 kyr, better than ±10 kyr for most of the record, and better than ±5 kyr for the last 110 kyr. This timescale is quite adequate for the discussions here which focus on the climatic information contained in the Vostok records themselves.

Climate and Atmospheric Trends

Temperature. As a result of fractionation processes, the isotopic content of snow in East Antarctica (δD or $\delta^{18}O$) is linearly related to the temperature above the inversion level, T_I, where precipitation forms, and also to the surface temperature of the precipitation site, T_S (with $\Delta T_I = 0.67\Delta T_S$, see ref. 6). We calculate temperature changes from the present temperature at the atmospheric level as $\Delta T_I = (\Delta\delta D_{ice} - 8\Delta\delta^{18}O_{sw})/9$, where $\Delta\delta^{18}O_{sw}$ is the globally averaged change from today's value of seawater $\delta^{18}O$, and 9‰ per °C is the spatial isotope/temperature gradient derived from deuterium data in this sector of East Antarctica[21]. We applied the above relationship to calculate ΔT_S. This approach underestimates ΔT_S by a factor of ~2 in Greenland[22] and, possibly, by up to 50% in Antarctica[23]. However, recent model results suggest that any underestimation of temperature changes from this equation is small for Antarctica[24,25].

To calculate ΔT_I from δD, we need to adopt a curve for the change in the isotopic composition of sea water versus time and correlate it with Vostok. We use the stacked $\delta^{18}O_{sw}$ record of Bassinot et al.[26], scaled with respect to the V19-30 marine sediment record over their common part that covers the past 340 kyr (ref. 27) (Fig. 2). To avoid distortions in the

同位素 7.5 阶（距今 23.8 万年）给出了一个合理的定年结果。而为了达到这一结果，茹泽尔等人[13]必须在 EGT 模型中调整第二气候旋回的输入参数，把 11 万年以前的积累率增加 12%。GT4 与韦尔布罗克等人[50]用轨道参数调整过的时间标尺（定义至距今 22.5 万年）相差从来没有超过 4,000 年，这一差值处在后者估计的不确定性范围之内。总之，我们有很好的论据[11,50-52]支撑，认为对过去的 11 万年，GT4 的定年精度应该优于 ±5,000 年。

从 $\delta^{18}O_{atm}$ 与 6 月中旬 65°N 的太阳辐射变化（见本文和图 3）之间的密切关系，我们可进一步评估 GT4 的总体效果。我们可以用每一个 $\delta^{18}O_{atm}$ 从高到低的显著转折点，定义一个能给出轨道修正时间的"控制点"。最后一个 $\delta^{18}O_{atm}$ 转折（约 1 万年前）的中点几乎与太阳辐射最大的年龄（距今 1.1 万年）一致。我们假定这种对应也适用于更早的太阳辐射最大值。对于 65°N 太阳辐射曲线中岁差周期显著的阶段（大约距今 6 万年至距今 34 万年之间），控制点（图 3 和表 1）是容易确定的，但 2 阶和 10 阶除外，这两个阶段太阳辐射变化很小。在给定两种方法的一些简单假设后，$\delta^{18}O_{atm}$ 控制点与 GT4 之间的一致性非常好。尽管我们对 $\delta^{18}O_{atm}$ 受到的控制还不太了解，因而不十分清楚 $\delta^{18}O_{atm}$ 与太阳辐射的相位变化的稳定性情况，但是结论仍然站得住脚。我们假定相位的变化不超过 ±6,000 年（岁差周期的 1/4）。

我们总结得出 GT4 的定年精确度总是优于 ±1.5 万年，对于大多数记录精度优于 ±1 万年，对最近的 11 万年精确度优于 ±5,000 年。这一时间序列对于这里讨论东方站记录中包含的气候信息本身来说已经足够了。

气候与大气趋势

温度　由于同位素分馏效应，东南极洲雪的同位素值（δD 或 $\delta^{18}O$）与逆温层之上（降水形成处）的温度 T_I 呈线性相关，也与降水点的地面温度 T_s 呈线性相关（$\Delta T_I = 0.67\Delta T_s$，见参考文献 6）。我们从大气层的现今温度来计算温度的变化，$\Delta T_I = (\Delta\delta D_冰 - 8\Delta\delta^{18}O_{sw})/9$，其中 $\Delta\delta^{18}O_{sw}$ 是相对于现今海水 $\delta^{18}O$ 值的全球平均变化，9‰/℃ 是从东南极洲区域内的氘数据得到的同位素与温度的空间梯度值[21]。我们应用上述关系计算 ΔT_s。这方法计算出来的格陵兰的 ΔT_s 被低估为约实际值的二分之一[22]，计算出来的在南极洲的值可能被低估了（最多）50%[23]。然而从现在的模式结果来看，从此等式得到的任何对南极洲温度变化的低估，都偏小了[24,25]。

为了通过 δD 计算 ΔT_I，我们需要采用海水同位素成分对时间的变化曲线，并将它与东方站相关联。我们将巴西诺等人[26]积累的 $\delta^{18}O_{sw}$ 记录，与 V19-30 海洋沉积物记录中的共同部分（覆盖了过去 34 万年）进行标定（文献 27）（图 2）。为避免在计

calculation of ΔT_I linked with dating uncertainties, we correlate the records by performing a peak to peak adjustment between the ice and ocean isotopic records. The $\delta^{18}O_{sw}$ correction corresponds to a maximum ΔT_I correction of ~1°C and associated uncertainties are therefore small. We do not attempt to correct ΔT_I either for the change of the altitude of the ice sheet or for the origin of the ice upstream of Vostok[13]; these terms are very poorly known and, in any case, are also small (< 1°C).

The overall amplitude of the glacial–interglacial temperature change is ~8°C for ΔT_I (inversion level) and ~12°C for ΔT_S, the temperature at the surface (Fig. 3). Broad features of this record are thought to be of large geographical significance (Antarctica and part of the Southern Hemisphere), at least qualitatively. When examined in detail, however, the Vostok record may differ from coastal[28] sites in East Antarctica and perhaps from West Antarctica as well.

Jouzel et al.[13] noted that temperature variations estimated from deuterium were similar for the last two glacial periods. The third and fourth climate cycles are of shorter duration than the first two cycles in the Vostok record. The same is true in the deep-sea record, where the third and fourth cycles span four precessional cycles rather than five as for the last two cycles (Fig. 3). Despite this difference, one observes, for all four climate cycles, the same "sawtooth" sequence of a warm interglacial (stages 11.3, 9.3, 7.5 and 5.5), followed by increasingly colder interstadial events, and ending with a rapid return towards the following interglacial. The coolest part of each glacial period occurs just before the glacial termination, except for the third cycle. This may reflect the fact that the June 65° N insolation minimum preceding this transition (255 kyr ago) has higher insolation than the previous one (280 kyr ago), unlike the three other glacial periods. Nonetheless, minimum temperatures are remarkably similar, within 1°C, for the four climate cycles. The new data confirm that the warmest temperature at stage 7.5 was slightly warmer than the Holocene[13], and show that stage 9.3 (where the highest deuterium value, −414.8‰, is found) was at least as warm as stage 5.5. That part of stage 11.3, which is present in Vostok, does not correspond to a particularly warm climate as suggested for this period by deep-sea sediment records[29]. As noted above, however, the Vostok records are probably disturbed below 3,310 m, and we may not have sampled the warmest ice of this interglacial. In general, climate cycles are more uniform at Vostok than in deep-sea core records[1]. The climate record makes it unlikely that the West Antarctic ice sheet collapsed during the past 420 kyr (or at least shows a marked insensitivity of the central part of East Antarctica and its climate to such a disintegration).

The power spectrum of ΔT_I (Fig. 4) shows a large concentration of variance (37%) in the 100-kyr band along with a significant concentration (23%) in the obliquity band (peak at 41 kyr). This strong obliquity component is roughly in phase with the annual insolation at the Vostok site[4,6,15]. The variability of annual insolation at 78° S is relatively large, 7% (ref. 3). This supports the notion that annual insolation changes in high southern latitudes influence Vostok temperature[15]. These changes may, in particular, contribute to the initiation of Antarctic warming during major terminations, which (as we show below) herald the start of deglaciation.

算 ΔT_I 时与定年不确定度有关的失真，我们通过对冰与海洋之间同位素记录作峰值对峰值的调准。$\delta^{18}O_{sw}$ 的校正引起的 ΔT_I 最大校正值不会超过约 1℃，因此导致的不确定度是很小的。我们不打算从冰盖的高度变化或是东方站上游冰流的源地[13] 对 ΔT_I 进行校正，我们对这些方面知之甚少，并且不管怎样，这些项对校正的温度影响也很小（<1℃）。

冰期–间冰期温度变化的总体幅度如下：逆温层的 ΔT_I 约为 8℃，地面的 ΔT_s 约为 12℃（图 3）。该记录具有更大地理范围（南极洲和南半球部分区域）上的意义，至少是定性的意义。然而当仔细检查时会发现，东方站的记录与南极洲东部海岸的记录存在差别[28]，也许同南极洲西部的也不同。

茹泽尔等人[13]指出从氘估计出的最后两个冰期的温度变化是相似的。在东方站的记录中，第三和第四气候旋回的持续时间比前两个周期的持续时间要短。深海记录也显示同样的特征，其中第三和第四旋回跨越的岁差周期是四个而不是像上两个气候旋回那样跨越了五个岁差周期（图 3）。尽管存在这一差异，对于这所有四个气候旋回，可以观测到相同的温度变化"锯齿形"序列温暖间冰阶（11.3 阶，9.3 阶，7.5 阶和 5.5 阶），其后紧随着逐渐转冷的间冰阶，最后以快速返回到间冰阶结束。除第三个旋回外，每个冰期最冷部分都出现在冰期结束期前。这也许反映了一个事实：出现在过渡期（25.5 万年前）之前的 65° N 6 月太阳辐射最小值比前一个（28 万年前）最小值要高，这与其他三个冰期阶段不同。无论如何，对于这四个气候旋回来说，最低温度明显相似，变化范围都在 1℃ 以内。新的资料证实 7.5 阶的最暖温度比全新世[13]还稍暖一点，9.3 阶（那里出现了氘的最高值 –414.8‰）至少和 5.5 阶一样温暖。东方站冰芯记录的 11.3 阶部分并不与深海沉积物记录的这一时期特别温暖的气候相符[29]。然而，如上所述，在 3,310 米以下东方站冰芯记录可能受到干扰，我们可能没有取到这一间冰期最温暖的冰样本。一般来说，东方站的气候旋回比深海岩芯记录[1]更均匀。此气候记录表明在过去 42 万年西南极冰盖没有可能垮塌过（或者至少表明东南极中部及其气候对这种垮塌表现不敏感）。

ΔT_I 的功率谱（图 4）在 10 万年带内出现一个很大的谱密度（37%），在地轴倾角带（峰值在 4.1 万年）还有一明显的谱密度（23%）。这个强的地轴倾角分量大致与东方站的年太阳辐射同相[4,6,15]。在 78° S，年日照量的变化相对较大，为 7%（文献 3）。这支持了南半球高纬度地区年日照量变化对东方站温度是有影响的观点[15]。特别是，这些变化促使主要冰期结束期南极变暖的开始，它也预示着冰川消退的开始（请见我们下面的说明）。

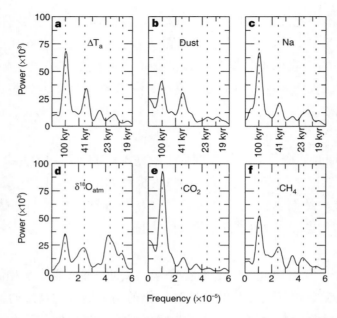

Fig. 4. Spectral properties of the Vostok time series. Frequency distribution (in cycles yr⁻¹) of the normalized variance power spectrum (arbitrary units). Spectral analysis was done using the Blackman-Tukey method (calculations were performed with the Analyseries software[47]): **a**, isotopic temperature; **b**, dust; **c**, sodium; **d**, $\delta^{18}O_{atm}$; **e**, CO_2; and **f**, CH_4. Vertical lines correspond to periodicities of 100, 41, 23 and 19 kyr.

Table 1. Comparison of the glaciological timescale and orbitally derived information

Depth (m)	Insolation maximum (kyr)	Age GT4 (kyr)	Difference (kyr)
305	11	10	1
900	58	57	1
1,213	84	83	1
1,528	105	105	0
1,863	128	128	0
2,110	151	150	1
2,350	176	179	−3
2,530	199	203	−4
2,683	220	222	−2
2,788	244	239	5
2,863	265	255	10
2,972	293	282	11
3,042	314	301	13
3,119	335	322	13

Control points were derived assuming a correspondence between maximum 65° N mid-June insolation and $\delta^{18}O_{atm}$ mid-transitions. Age GT4 refers to the age of the gas obtained after correction for the gas-age/ice-age differences[20].

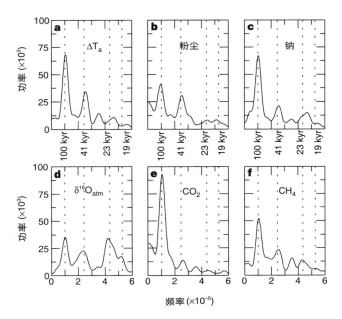

图 4. 东方站时间序列谱特征。标准方差功率谱（任意单位）的频率分布（周期：年）。用布莱克曼-图基方法（利用 Analyseries 软件[47] 计算的）完成了谱分析。a，同位素温度 ΔT_a；b，粉尘；c，钠；d，$\delta^{18}O_{atm}$；e，CO_2；f，CH_4；垂线相应于距今 10 万年，4.1 万年，2.3 万年和 1.9 万年的周期。

表 1. 冰期时间标尺和轨道推导信息的对比

深度（m）	最大太阳辐射（千年）	GT4 年龄（千年）	差值（千年）
305	11	10	1
900	58	57	1
1,213	84	83	1
1,528	105	105	0
1,863	128	128	0
2,110	151	150	1
2,350	176	179	−3
2,530	199	203	−4
2,683	220	222	−2
2,788	244	239	5
2,863	265	255	10
2,972	293	282	11
3,042	314	301	13
3,119	335	322	13

假定 65° N 的 6 月中旬太阳辐射的最大值对应 $\delta^{18}O_{atm}$ 的转折点的中点，从而可得到控制点，GT4 年龄参考经气体年龄/冰年龄差值校正后得来的气体年龄[20]。

407

There is little variance (11%) in ΔT_I around precessional periodicities (23 and 19 kyr). In this band, the position of the spectral peaks is affected by uncertainties in the timescale. To illustrate this point, we carried out, as a sensitivity test, a spectral analysis using the control points provided by the $\delta^{18}O_{atm}$ record (see Table 1). The position and strength of the 100- and 40-kyr-spectral peaks are unaffected, whereas the power spectrum is significantly modified for periodicities lower than 30 kyr.

Insolation. $\delta^{18}O_{atm}$ strongly depends on climate and related properties, which reflect the direct or indirect influence of insolation[19]. As a result, there is a striking resemblance between $\delta^{18}O_{atm}$ and mid-June insolation at 65° N for the entire Vostok record (Fig. 3). This provides information on the validity of our glaciological timescale (see Box 1). The precessional frequencies, which do not account for much variance in ΔT_I, are strongly imprinted in the $\delta^{18}O_{atm}$ record (36% of the variance in this band, Fig. 4). In addition, the remarkable agreement observed back to stage 7.5 between the amplitude of the filtered components of the mid-June insolation at 65° N and $\delta^{18}O_{atm}$ in the precessional band[13] holds true over the last four climate cycles (not shown). As suggested by the high variance of $\delta^{18}O_{atm}$ in the precessional band, this orbital frequency is also reflected in the Dole effect, the difference between $\delta^{18}O_{atm}$ and $\delta^{18}O_{sw}$, confirming results obtained on the last two climate cycles[19,30].

Aerosols. Figure 2 shows records of aerosols of different origins. The sodium record represents mainly sea-salt aerosol entrained from the ocean surface, whereas the dust record corresponds to the small size fraction (~2 μm) of the aerosol produced by the continent. The extension of the Vostok record confirms much higher fallout during cold glacial periods than during interglacials. Concentrations range up to 120 ng g^{-1}, that is, 3 to 4 times the Holocene value, for sea-salt. For dust, they rise from about 50 ng g^{-1} during interglacials to 1,000–2,000 ng g^{-1} during cold stages 2, 4, 6, 8 and 10.

The sodium concentration is closely anti-correlated with isotopic temperature ($r^2 = -0.70$ over the past 420 kyr). The power spectrum of the sodium concentration, like that of ΔT_I, shows periodicities around 100, 40 and 20 kyr (Fig. 4). Conditions prevailing during the present-day austral winter could help explain the observed glacial/interglacial changes in sodium. The seasonal increase of marine aerosol observed in the atmosphere and snow at the South Pole in September[31] corresponds to the maximum extent of sea ice; this is because the more distant source effect is compensated by the greater cyclonic activity, and by the more efficient zonal and meridional atmospheric circulation probably driven by the steeper meridional (ocean–Antarctica) temperature gradient. These modern winter conditions may be an analogue for glacial climates, supporting the apparent close anti-correlation between sodium concentration and temperature at Vostok.

The extension of the Vostok dust record confirms that continental aridity, dust mobilization and transport are more prevalent during glacial climates, as also reflected globally in many dust records (see ref. 10 and references therein). The presence of larger particles in the Vostok record, at least during the Last Glacial Maximum[10], indicates that the atmospheric circulation at high southern latitudes was more turbulent at that time. Lower atmospheric

ΔT_1 在岁差周期附近（距今 2.3 万年与距今 1.9 万年）的方差很小（11%）。在此带内，谱峰的位置受到时间标尺不确定性的影响。为了说明这一点，本文用 $\delta^{18}O_{atm}$ 记录（表 1）确定的控制点进行了谱分析，作为敏感性试验。它对距今 10 万年和 4 万年的谱峰的位置和强度没有影响，然而功率谱对低于 3 万年的周期有明显的影响。

太阳辐射　$\delta^{18}O_{atm}$ 强烈地依赖气候及其有关的特征，它们反映了太阳辐射的直接或间接影响[19]。因此，在东方站的全部记录中（图 3），$\delta^{18}O_{atm}$ 与 6 月中旬 65°N 太阳辐射之间极为相似。这为我们检验冰川时间标尺提供了信息（见框 1）。岁差频率在 ΔT_1 记录中并未占有很大的方差，但 $\delta^{18}O_{atm}$ 记录中留下了强烈的印记（在带中有 36% 的方差，图 4）。另外，65°N 的 6 月中旬的滤波分量的振幅与 $\delta^{18}O_{atm}$ 之间存在岁差带上显著的一致性，可以一直追踪到 7.5 阶[13]，这点在最后四个气候旋回中同样成立（文中未展示）。$\delta^{18}O_{atm}$ 在岁差带内大的方差，表明轨道的频率也反映在多尔效应（$\delta^{18}O_{atm}$ 与 $\delta^{18}O_{sw}$ 之间存在差异）内，证实了最后两个气候旋回中得到的结果[19,30]。

气溶胶　图 2 表示不同来源的气溶胶记录。钠的记录主要代表从海洋表面带来的海盐气溶胶，而粉尘记录则对应于陆地产生的气溶胶的细粒部分（约 2 μm）。东方站记录的延伸，证实了寒冷的冰期比间冰期沉降率要高得多。对于海盐，浓度范围可达 120 ng·g^{-1}，是全新世的 3～4 倍。对于粉尘，它们从间冰期 50 ng·g^{-1} 左右上升到寒冷海洋同位素阶段 2、4、6、8 和 10 的 1,000～2,000 ng·g^{-1}。

钠的浓度与同位素温度几乎是反相关的（在过去的 42 万年 $r^2 = -0.70$）。钠浓度的功率谱，像 ΔT_1 的功率谱一样，在 10 万年、4 万年和 2 万年左右呈周期性（图 4）。当前南方冬季的主要条件能帮助说明钠在冰期和间冰期之间的变化。在南极点 9 月观察到的大气和雪中海洋气溶胶的季节性增长[31]与海冰的最大范围对应，这是因为更远源地的影响被以下因素所补偿：更大的气旋活动，以及可能由更陡的经向（海洋–南极）温度梯度导致的更有效的纬向和经向大气环流。这些现代冬季的条件可以比拟成冰期气候，来说明东方站钠浓度与温度的显著反相关关系。

这里延长的东方站冰芯粉尘记录证实，大陆干旱和粉尘的运移与输送在冰期气候时更为活跃，这也反映在全球许多其他粉尘记录中（参考文献 10 及其中的参考文献）。东方站记录中（至少在末次冰盛期[10]）更大颗粒的出现，指示那时南半球高纬地区的大气环流更为湍急。大气含水量和水循环通量的减少可能同样是整个冰期粉

moisture content and reduced hydrological fluxes may also have contributed significantly (that is, one order of magnitude[32]) to the very large increases of dust fallout during full glacial periods because of a lower aerosol-removal efficiency.

Unlike sodium concentration, the dust record is not well correlated with temperature (see below) and shows large concentrations of variance in the 100- and 41-kyr spectral bands (Fig. 4). The Vostok dust record is, in this respect, similar to the tropical Atlantic dust record of de Menocal[33] who attributes these spectral characteristics to the progressive glaciation of the Northern Hemisphere and the greater involvement of the deep ocean circulation. We suggest that there also may be some link between the Vostok dust record and deep ocean circulation through the extension of sea ice in the South Atlantic Ocean, itself thought to be coeval with a reduced deep ocean circulation[34]. Our suggestion is based on the fact that the dust source for the East Antarctic plateau appears to be South America, most likely the Patagonian plain, during all climate states of the past 420 kyr (refs 35, 36). The extension of sea ice in the South Atlantic during glacial times greatly affects South American climate, with a more northerly position of the polar front and the belt of Westerlies pushed northward over the Andes. This should lead, in these mountainous areas, to intense glacial and fluvial erosion, and to colder and drier climate with extensive dust mobilization (as evidenced by glacial loess deposits in Patagonia). Northward extension of sea ice also leads to a steeper meridional temperature gradient and to more efficient poleward transport. Therefore, Vostok dust peaks would correspond to periods of increased sea-ice extent in the South Atlantic Ocean, probably associated with reduced deep ocean circulation (thus explaining observed similarities with the tropical ocean dust record[33]).

Greenhouse gases. The extension of the greenhouse-gas record shows that the main trends of CO_2 and CH_4 concentration changes are similar for each glacial cycle (Fig. 3). Major transitions from the lowest to the highest values are associated with glacial–interglacial transitions. At these times, the atmospheric concentrations of CO_2 rises from 180 to 280–300 p.p.m.v. and that of CH_4 rises from 320–350 to 650–770 p.p.b.v. There are significant differences between the CH_4 concentration change associated with deglaciations. Termination III shows the smallest CH_4 increase, whereas termination IV shows the largest (Fig. 5). Differences in the changes over deglaciations are less significant for CO_2. The decrease of CO_2 to the minimum values of glacial times is slower than its increase towards interglacial levels, confirming the sawtooth record of this property. CH_4 also decreases slowly to its background level, but with a series of superimposed peaks whose amplitude decreases during the course of each glaciation. Each CH_4 peak is itself characterized by rapid increases and slower decreases, but our resolution is currently inadequate to capture the detail of millennial-scale CH_4 variations. During glacial inception, Antarctic temperature and CH_4 concentrations decrease in phase. The CO_2 decrease lags the temperature decrease by several kyr and may be either steep (as at the end of interglacials 5.5 and 7.5) or more regular (at the end of interglacials 9.3 and 11.3). The differences in concentration–time profiles of CO_2 and CH_4 are reflected in the power spectra (Fig. 4). The 100-kyr component dominates both CO_2 and CH_4 records. However, the obliquity and precession components are much stronger for CH_4 than for CO_2.

尘沉降大幅增长的重要原因之一 (一个数量级[32])，因为气溶胶清除效率较低了。

与钠浓度不同，粉尘记录与温度没有很好的相关性 (参见下文)，并在 10 万年和 4.1 万年的谱带内有很大的方差变化 (图 4)。在这方面，东方站的粉尘记录与德梅诺卡尔[33]的热带大西洋粉尘记录相似，德梅诺卡尔将这些 (粉尘记录的) 谱特征归因于北半球渐进的冰川活动以及深海环流进一步参与。我们提出在东方站粉尘记录和深海环流之间，也可能通过南大西洋海冰的扩展产生一些联系，这一扩展被认为与深海环流减弱[34]是同步的。我们的设想基于以下事实：南极东部高原的粉尘在过去 42 万年的全部气候阶段 (文献 35 和 36) 都来源于南美洲，其中最有可能是巴塔哥尼亚平原。南大西洋海冰在冰期内的扩展，对南美的气候有很大影响，导致极锋位置更加靠北，西风带向北推进越过安第斯山。这将导致这些山区遭受更强烈的冰川侵蚀和河流侵蚀并使气候变得愈加干冷，粉尘运移范围增大 (如巴塔哥尼亚冰川黄土的沉积所证实的那样)。海冰向北扩张也使经向温度梯度变得更陡，并使极向输送效率更高。因此东方站的粉尘峰值对应于南大西洋海冰扩张的时期，后者可能与深海洋流的减弱有关 (因而解释了为何与观测的热带海洋粉尘记录相似[33])。

温室气体 延展的冰芯温室气体记录表明 CO_2 和 CH_4 浓度变化的主要趋势在每个冰期旋回里都相似 (图 3)。从最低到最高值的主要转变阶段与冰期到间冰期的转变密切相关。这些时期大气中 CO_2 浓度从 180 ppmv 上升到 $280 \sim 300$ ppmv，CH_4 浓度从 $320 \sim 350$ ppbv 上升到 $650 \sim 770$ ppbv。但不同的冰消期 CH_4 浓度变化之间有明显的不同。冰消期 III CH_4 增长最小，而冰消期 IV CH_4 增长最大 (图 5)。在冰消期，CO_2 变化的差异则并不明显。CO_2 减少到冰期最小值的过程比向间冰期增加的过程要慢，证实了其锯齿形的特征。在每一个冰期过程中，CH_4 也缓慢减小到背景值，但存在一系列叠加峰，并且它们的幅度逐渐减小。每一个 CH_4 峰均以快速增长和缓慢减小为特征，但是，我们的分辨率不足以捕获 CH_4 的千年尺度变化的细节。在冰期开始时，南极温度和 CH_4 浓度同步减小。CO_2 浓度下降比温度减小要滞后几千年，并且可能很陡 (如在间冰期 5.5 和 7.5 的末期) 或比较规则 (如在间冰期 9.3 和 11.3 的末期)。CO_2 和 CH_4 的浓度随时间变化的差异也反映在功率谱内 (图 4)。10 万年的分量在 CO_2 和 CH_4 记录占主要地位，然而 CH_4 地轴倾角和岁差分量强于 CO_2 的相应值。

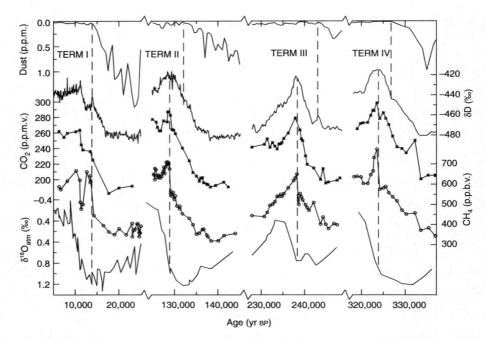

Fig 5. Vostok time series during glacial terminations. Variations with respect to time (GT4) of: **a**, dust; **b**, δD of ice (temperature proxy); **c**, CO_2; **d**, CH_4; and **e**, $δ^{18}O_{atm}$ for glacial terminations I to IV and the subsequent interglacial periods (Holocene, stage 5.5, stage 7.5 and stage 9.3).

The extension of the greenhouse-gas record shows that present-day levels of CO_2 and CH_4 (~360 p.p.m.v. and ~1,700 p.p.b.v., respectively) are unprecedented during the past 420 kyr. Pre-industrial Holocene levels (~280 p.p.m.v. and ~650 p.p.b.v., respectively) are found during all interglacials, while values higher than these are found in stages 5.5, 9.3 and 11.3 (this last stage is probably incomplete), with the highest values during stage 9.3 (300 p.p.m.v. and 780 p.p.b.v., respectively).

The overall correlation between our CO_2 and CH_4 records and the Antarctic isotopic temperature[5,9,16] is remarkable ($r^2 = 0.71$ and 0.73 for CO_2 and CH_4, respectively). This high correlation indicates that CO_2 and CH_4 may have contributed to the glacial–interglacial changes over this entire period by amplifying the orbital forcing along with albedo, and possibly other changes[15,16]. We have calculated the direct radiative forcing corresponding to the CO_2, CH_4 and N_2O changes[16]. The largest CO_2 change, which occurs between stages 10 and 9, implies a direct radiative warming of $\Delta T_{rad} = 0.75°C$. Adding the effects of CH_4 and N_2O at this termination increases the forcing to 0.95°C (here we assume that N_2O varies with climate as during termination I[37]). This initial forcing is amplified by positive feedbacks associated with water vapour, sea ice, and possibly clouds (although in a different way for a "doubled CO_2" situation than for a glacial climate[38]). The total glacial–interglacial forcing is important (~3 W m^{-2}), representing 80% of that corresponding to the difference between a "doubled CO_2" world and modern CO_2 climate. Results from various climate simulations[39,40] make it reasonable to assume that greenhouse gases have, at a

图 5. 东方站在冰消期时间序列。对应 (GT4) 时间尺度变化序列：**a**，粉尘；**b**，冰的 δD (温度指标)；**c**，CO_2；**d**，CH_4；**e**，冰消期 I 到 IV 及其后的间冰期 (全新世，5.5 阶，7.5 阶和 9.3 阶) 的 $\delta^{18}O_{atm}$。

延伸的温室气体记录显示目前的 CO_2 和 CH_4 浓度水平 (分别约为 360 ppmv 和 1,700 ppbv) 在过去 42 万年是史无前例的。工业化前的全新世浓度水平 (分别为约 280 ppmv 和约 650 ppbv) 出现于所有的间冰期，更高的数值出现在 5.5 阶，9.3 阶和 11.3 阶 (最后这一阶可能不完整)，最高值出现在 9.3 阶 (CO_2 和 CH_4 浓度水平分别为 300 ppmv 和 780 ppbv)。

总体上，CO_2 和 CH_4 记录与南极同位素温度[5,9,16]之间的相关性是显著的 (对 CO_2 和 CH_4 的相关系数分别为 $r^2 = 0.71$ 和 $r^2 = 0.73$)。这种高度相关性说明 CO_2 和 CH_4 在整个阶段都推动了冰期–间冰期的变化，这种作用是通过放大轨道强迫与反照率以及其他可能的变化[15,16]来实现的。我们计算了对应 CO_2，CH_4 和 N_2O 变化[16]的直接辐射强迫。最大的一次 CO_2 变化发生在 10 阶和 9 阶之间，其直接辐射强迫对应升温幅度为 $\Delta T_{rad} = 0.75℃$。再考虑到 CH_4 和 N_2O 的影响，在这次冰消期的辐射强迫导致升温增加到 0.95℃ (这里我们假定 N_2O 随气候变化与冰消期 I[37]的情况一样)。初始强迫被与水汽、海冰，可能还与云有关 (虽然对 "2 倍 CO_2" 情景和冰期气候情景，反馈的方式不同[38]) 的正反馈放大。整个冰期–间冰期的辐射强迫是重要的 (约 3W·m^{-2})，相当于 "2 倍 CO_2" 情景和现代 CO_2 浓度情景二者之间气候变化的 80%。从各种气候模拟的结果[39,40]可以合理推定：在全球规模上，温室气体对冰期–间冰期

global scale, contributed significantly (possibly about half, that is, 2–3°C) to the globally averaged glacial–interglacial temperature change.

Glacial Terminations and Interglacials

Our complete Vostok data set allows us to examine all glacial commencements and terminations of the past 420 kyr. We can examine the time course of the following five properties during these events: δD_{ice}, dust content, $\delta^{18}O_{atm}$, CO_2 and CH_4 (Fig. 5). We consider that, during the terminations, $\delta^{18}O_{atm}$ tracks $\delta^{18}O_{sw}$ with a lag of ~2 kyr (ref. 11), the response time of the atmosphere to changes in $\delta^{18}O_{sw}$. $\delta^{18}O_{atm}$ can thus be taken as an indicator of the large ice-volume changes associated with the deglaciations. Broecker and Henderson[41] recently supported this interpretation for the last two terminations and discussed its limitations. Our extended $\delta^{18}O_{atm}$ record indeed reinforces such an interpretation, as it shows that the amplitudes of $\delta^{18}O_{atm}$ changes parallel $\delta^{18}O_{sw}$ changes for all four terminations. $\delta^{18}O_{sw}$ changes are similar for terminations I, II and IV (1.1–1.2‰) but much smaller for termination III (~0.6‰). The same is true for $\delta^{18}O_{atm}$ (1.4–1.5‰ for I, II and IV, and 0.8‰ for III).

A striking feature of the Vostok deuterium record is that the Holocene, which has already lasted 11 kyr, is, by far, the longest stable warm period recorded in Antarctica during the past 420 kyr (Fig. 5). Interglacials 5.5 and 9.3 are different from the Holocene, but similar to each other in duration, shape and amplitude. During each of these two events, there is a warm period of ~4 kyr followed by a relatively rapid cooling and then a slower temperature decrease (Fig. 5), rather like some North Atlantic deep-sea core records[42]. Stage 7.5 is different in all respects, with a slightly colder maximum, a more spiky shape, and a much shorter duration (7 kyr at mid-transition compared with 17 and 20 kyr for stages 5.5 and 9.3, respectively). This difference between stage 7.5 and stages 5.5 or 9.3 may result from the different configuration of the Earth's orbit (in particular concerning the phase of precession with respect to obliquity[3]). Termination III is also peculiar as far as terrestrial aerosol fallout is concerned. Terminations I, II and IV are marked by a large decrease in dust; high glacial values drop to low interglacial values by the mid-point of the δD_{ice} increase. But for termination III, the dust concentration decreases much earlier, with low interglacial values obtained just before a slight cooling event, as for termination I (for which interglacial values are reached just before the "Antarctic Cold Reversal").

Unlike termination I, other terminations show, with our present resolution, no clear temperature anomalies equivalent to the Antarctic Cold Reversal[6] (except possibly at the very beginning of termination III). There are also no older counterparts to the Younger Dryas CH_4 minimum[43] during terminations II, III and IV given the present resolution of the CH_4 record (which is no better than 1,000–2,000 yr before stage 5).

The sequence of events during terminations III and IV is the same as that previously observed for terminations I and II. Vostok temperature, CO_2 and CH_4 increase in phase

的全球平均温度变化有显著贡献（可能贡献了一半的变化，即 2~3℃）。

冰期结束和间冰期

东方站的完整资料可以使我们分析过去 42 万年的全部冰期的开始期和结束期。我们能分析以下 5 个参数在这两个阶段的时间变化：δD_{ice}，粉尘量，$\delta^{18}O_{atm}$，CO_2 和 CH_4（图 5）。本文认为在结束期，$\delta^{18}O_{atm}$ 随 $\delta^{18}O_{sw}$ 而变化，但滞后约 2,000 年（文献 11），也就是大气对 $\delta^{18}O_{sw}$ 变化的响应时间。因此 $\delta^{18}O_{atm}$ 可以作为冰消期冰量大幅度变化的一个指标。最近布勒克和亨德森[41] 支持了对最后两个结束期的解释，并讨论了它的局限性。延伸了的 $\delta^{18}O_{atm}$ 记录也进一步支持了这一解释，发现在全部 4 个结束期，$\delta^{18}O_{atm}$ 与 $\delta^{18}O_{sw}$ 的变化幅度是平行的。对结束期 I、II 和 IV，$\delta^{18}O_{sw}$ 的变化是相似的（1.1‰~1.2‰）。但是，对结束期 III 来说该变化则小得多（约 0.6‰）。对 $\delta^{18}O_{atm}$ 而言也是同样的情况（I、II 和 IV 为 1.4‰~1.5‰，而 III 为 0.8‰）。

东方站氘记录的一个突出特征是，已经持续了 1.1 万年的全新世，是过去 42 万年间南极记录中最长的稳定暖期（图 5）。间冰期 5.5 和 9.3 与全新世是不同的，但他们之间彼此的持续时间、形态和幅度是相似的。这两个事件的每一个，都有约 4,000 年的暖期，随之是相对快速的变冷，接着温度较慢地降低（图 5），这很像北大西洋深海岩芯的记录[42]。7.5 阶在各方面都是不同的，有稍冷的极大值，更长而尖的形状，以及短得多的持续时间（以转折点中点计算的持续时间为 7,000 年，而 5.5 阶和 9.3 阶分别为 1.7 万年和 2 万年）。7.5 阶和 5.5 阶之间或 7.5 阶和 9.3 阶之间的差异可能是由地球轨道参数的配置不同（特别是相对于地轴倾角的岁差的相位[3]）导致的。考虑到陆地气溶胶沉降的话，结束期 III 也是特殊的。结束期 I、II 和 IV 以粉尘含量大幅度降低为标志；尘埃含量从冰期的高值向间冰期的低值降低，这种趋势一直持续到 δD_{ice} 增长阶段的中点。但对结束期 III 而言，粉尘浓度下降得更早，就在一个轻微的冷事件之前就达到了间冰期的最低值，这一点与结束期 I 有点相似（间冰期的最低值正好在"南极回冷"事件之前）。

与结束期 I 不同，在目前的分辨率下，其他结束期没有表现出与"南极回冷"事件相当的温度异常[6]（可能除了在结束期 III 的最开始阶段）。在给定的目前的 CH_4 记录的分辨率下（在 5 阶之前不会好于 1,000~2,000 年），结束期 II、III 和 IV 期间没有更老的新仙女木 CH_4 最低值[43] 对应的事件。

结束期 III 和 IV 内的事件序列与之前的结束期 I 和 II 内观测到的顺序是相似的。在各个结束期内，东方站的温度、CO_2 和 CH_4 在冰期结束期同相增长。位相的不确

during terminations. Uncertainty in the phasing comes mainly from the sampling frequency and the ubiquitous uncertainty in gas-age/ice-age differences (which are well over ± 1 kyr during glaciations and terminations). In a recent paper, Fischer *et al.*[44] present a CO_2 record, from Vostok core, spanning the past three glacial terminations. They conclude that CO_2 concentration increases lagged Antarctic warmings by 600 ± 400 years. However, considering the large gas-age/ice-age uncertainty (1,000 years, or even more if we consider the accumulation-rate uncertainty), we feel that it is premature to infer the sign of the phase relationship between CO_2 and temperature at the start of terminations. We also note that their discussion relates to early deglacial changes, not the entire transitions.

An intriguing aspect of the deglacial CH_4 curves is that the atmospheric concentration of CH_4 rises slowly, then jumps to a maximum value during the last half of the deglacial temperature rise. For termination I, the CH_4 jump corresponds to a rapid Northern Hemisphere warming (Bölling/Allerød) and an increase in the rate of Northern Hemisphere deglaciation (meltwater pulse IA)[43]. We speculate that the same is true for terminations II, III and IV. Supportive evidence comes from the $\delta^{18}O_{atm}$ curves. During each termination, $\delta^{18}O_{atm}$ begins falling rapidly, signalling intense deglaciation, within 1 kyr of the CH_4 jump. The lag of deglaciation and Northern Hemisphere warming with respect to Vostok temperature warming is apparently greater during terminations II and IV (~ 9 kyr) than during terminations I and III (~ 4–6 kyr). The changes in northern summer insolation maxima are higher during terminations II and IV, whereas the preceding southern summer insolation maxima are higher during terminations I and III. We speculate that variability in phasing from one termination to the next reflects differences in insolation curves[41] or patterns of abyssal circulation during glacial maximum. Our results suggest that the same sequence of climate forcings occurred during each termination: orbital forcing (possibly through local insolation changes, but this is speculative as we have poor absolute dating) followed by two strong amplifiers, with greenhouse gases acting first, and then deglaciation enhancement via ice-albedo feedback. The end of the deglaciation is then characterized by a clear CO_2 maximum for terminations II, III and IV, while this feature is less marked for the Holocene.

Comparison of CO_2 atmospheric concentration changes with variations of other properties illuminates oceanic processes influencing glacial–interglacial CO_2 changes. As already noted for terminations I and II[41], the sequence of climate events described above rules out the possibility that rising sea level induces the CO_2 increase at the beginning of terminations. On the other hand, the small CO_2 variations associated with Heinrich events[45] suggest that the formation of North Atlantic Deep Water does not have a large effect on CO_2 concentrations. Our record shows similar relative amplitudes of atmospheric CO_2 and Vostok temperature changes for the four terminations. Also, values of both CO_2 and temperature are significantly higher during stage 7.5 than during stages 7.1 and 7.3, whereas the deep-sea core ice volume record exhibits similar levels for these three stages. These similarities between changes in atmospheric CO_2 and Antarctic temperature suggest that the oceanic area around Antarctica plays a role in the long-term CO_2 change. An influence of high southern latitudes is also suggested by the comparison with the dust profile, which exhibits a maximum during the periods of lowest CO_2. The link between dust and CO_2

416

定性主要来自取样频率，以及气体年龄与冰年龄比值之间普遍存在的差异的不确定性（在冰期和结束期超过 ±1,000 年）。菲舍尔等人[44]在最近的一篇论文中给出了来自东方站冰芯的 CO_2 记录，跨越了过去 3 个冰期的结束期。他们推断 CO_2 浓度的增长滞后于南极变暖 600 ± 400 年。然而考虑到气体年龄与冰年龄比值之间巨大的不确定度（有 1,000 年，假如我们考虑积累率的不确定性的话则更多）。我们感觉在结束期开始时就推测 CO_2 与温度之间的位相关系的迹象还为时过早。我们还注意到，他们讨论的是冰消期的早期阶段，而不是整个转折阶段。

与冰川消退有关的 CH_4 曲线的一个有意思之处是，大气中的 CH_4 浓度上升很慢，然后在冰消期温度上升到最后一半时跳到最大值。就结束期 I 而言，CH_4 的跃升对应于北半球的快速变暖（波令/阿勒罗德）以及北半球冰川消退速率的增加（融水脉冲 IA）[43]。我们推测对结束期 II、III 和 IV 也是相同的情形。支持证据来自 $\delta^{18}O_{atm}$ 曲线。在每一个结束期，在 CH_4 跃升的 1,000 年内 $\delta^{18}O_{atm}$ 开始迅速下降，标志着强烈冰川消退。与东方站温度变暖相比，冰川消退和北半球变暖相对滞后于东方站冰芯气温转暖，而且这种滞后时间在结束期 II 和 IV（约 9,000 年）明显大于结束期 I 和 III（约 4,000 ~ 6,000 年）。在北半球夏季太阳辐射最大值阶段，CH_4 在结束期 II 和 IV 变化比较大，而在南半球夏季太阳辐射最大值阶段，CH_4 在结束期 I 和 III 阶段变化比较大。我们推测从一个结束期到下一个结束期 CH_4 相位上的变化反映了冰期最盛期太阳辐射曲线[41]或者深海环流模式的差异。我们的结果表明在每个结束期发生了同样的气候强迫序列：轨道强迫（可能是通过局地太阳辐射的变化，但是这点还没有把握，因为我们的绝对定年结果不够）之后跟随着两个放大器，首先是温室气体活动，然后是冰的反射率反馈导致的冰川消退增强。冰消期结束时，CO_2 出现一个清楚的最大值，尤其是对结束期 II、III、IV 而言；而在全新世，这一特征不明显。

大气 CO_2 浓度的变化与其他属性变化的对比阐明了海洋过程影响着冰期–间冰期 CO_2 变化。正如对结束期 I 和 II[41]已经指出的那样，上述一系列气候事件排除了在结束期一开始时海平面上升诱发 CO_2 增加的可能性。另一方面，与海因里希事件[45]对应时段 CO_2 变化非常小，说明北大西洋深水的形成对 CO_2 浓度没有太大的影响。我们的记录显示，四个结束期中的大气 CO_2 和东方站温度的相对变化幅度很相似。另外，CO_2 和温度两者的值在 7.5 阶都明显高于 7.1 阶和 7.3 阶，然而，深海岩芯的冰量记录显示在这三个阶其水平是相近的。在大气 CO_2 变化和南极温度变化之间的相似性表明南极附近的洋域对 CO_2 的长期变化是起作用的。南半球高纬的影响也可以从粉尘剖面的对比看出，在 CO_2 最低时粉尘记录是最大值。粉尘与 CO_2 变化

variations could be through the atmospheric input of iron[46]. Alternatively, we suggest a link through deep ocean circulation and sea ice extent in the Southern Ocean, both of which play a role in ocean CO_2 ventilation and, as suggested above, in the dust input over East Antarctica.

New Constraints on Past Climate Change

As judged from Vostok records, climate has almost always been in a state of change during the past 420 kyr but within stable bounds (that is, there are maximum and minimum values of climate properties between which climate oscillates). Significant features of the most recent glacial–interglacial cycle are observed in earlier cycles. Spectral analysis emphasises the dominance of the 100-kyr cycle for all six data series except $\delta^{18}O_{atm}$ and a strong imprint of 40- and/or 20-kyr periodicities despite the fact that the glaciological dating is tuned by fitting only two control points in the 100-kyr band.

Properties change in the following sequence during each of the last four glacial terminations, as recorded in Vostok. First, the temperature and atmospheric concentrations of CO_2 and CH_4 rise steadily, whereas the dust input decreases. During the last half of the temperature rise, there is a rapid increase in CH_4. This event coincides with the start of the $\delta^{18}O_{atm}$ decrease. We believe that the rapid CH_4 rise also signifies warming in Greenland, and that the deglacial $\delta^{18}O_{atm}$ decrease records rapid melting of the Northern Hemisphere ice sheets. These results suggest that the same sequence of climate forcing operated during each termination: orbital forcing (with a possible contribution of local insolation changes) followed by two strong amplifiers, greenhouse gases acting first, then deglaciation and ice-albedo feedback. Our data suggest a significant role of the Southern Ocean in regulating the long-term changes of atmospheric CO_2.

The Antarctic temperature was warmer, and atmospheric CO_2 and CH_4 concentrations were higher, during interglacials 5.5 and 9.3 than during the Holocene and interglacial 7.5. The temporal evolution and duration of stages 5.5 and 9.3 are indeed remarkably similar for all properties recorded in Vostok ice and entrapped gases. As judged from the Vostok record, the long, stable Holocene is a unique feature of climate during the past 420 kyr, with possibly profound implications for evolution and the development of civilizations. Finally, CO_2 and CH_4 concentrations are strongly correlated with Antarctic temperatures; this is because, overall, our results support the idea that greenhouse gases have contributed significantly to the glacial–interglacial change. This correlation, together with the uniquely elevated concentrations of these gases today, is of relevance with respect to the continuing debate on the future of Earth's climate.

(**399**, 429-436; 1999)

之间的关系，可以通过大气中铁[46]的输入来联系。或者，我们提出通过深海环流与南大洋海冰扩展的联系，二者对海洋 CO_2 流通以及如上所述的东南极洲粉尘输入都起着作用。

过去气候变化中的新约束

从东方站记录判断，气候在过去的 42 万年几乎总是处在变化状态中，但还在稳定的边界内（也就是说，气候特性在最大和最小值之间振荡）。最近的冰期–间冰期旋回中的重要特征在较早的旋回中就有观察到。谱分析强调了全部 6 条数据序列（除了 $\delta^{18}O_{atm}$）中 10 万年周期的主导性，以及 4 万年和/或 2 万年周期的强印记，尽管事实上冰芯 10 万年尺度上的定年是仅仅通过两个控制点进行拟合的。

在东方站冰芯记录中的 4 个冰期结束期中，一些主要的参数在每一个结束期都按以下的顺序发生变化。首先，温度与大气中的 CO_2 和 CH_4 浓度稳步上升，而粉尘的输入量却在减少。在温度上升的后半段，CH_4 浓度快速上升。这一事件与 $\delta^{18}O_{atm}$ 开始降低同步。我们相信 CH_4 迅速上升也意味着格陵兰变暖，同时冰消期 $\delta^{18}O_{atm}$ 减少记录了北半球冰盖的迅速融化。这些结果表明每一个结束期驱动气候变化的气候强迫序列是相同的：轨道强迫（也可能有局地变化的影响），之后跟随着 2 个强烈的放大器，首先是温室气体的作用，然后是冰川消退和冰反射率的反馈。我们的数据表明南大洋在调节大气 CO_2 的长期变化中起着重要的作用。

和全新世、间冰期 7.5 阶相比，间冰期 5.5 阶和 9.3 阶的南极温度更暖，大气 CO_2 和 CH_4 的浓度也更高。对东方站冰芯冰及其包裹气体中记录的所有指标，在 5.5 阶和 9.3 阶的时间演化和持续时长确实都极为相似。从东方站记录判断，持续时间长而稳定的全新世在过去 42 万年都是独一无二的，也许对人类文明的演化和发展具有深远的意义。最后，CO_2 和 CH_4 的浓度与南极温度有密切的相关性。这是因为，总的来说，我们的结果支持了温室气体对冰期–间冰期转变有重要作用的想法。考虑到关于地球未来气候变化的持续辩论，这种关系和今天这些温室气体浓度的异常升高不无联系。

（蔡则怡 翻译；田立德 审稿）

J. R. Petit[*], J. Jouzel[†], D. Raynaud[*], N. I. Barkov[‡], J.-M. Barnola[*], I. Basile[*], M. Bender[§], J. Chappellaz[*], M. Davis[‖], G. Delaygue[†], M. Delmotte[*], V. M. Kotlyakov[¶], M. Legrand[*], V. Y. Lipenkov[‡], C. Lorius[*], L. Pépin[*], C. Ritz[*], E. Saltzman[‖] & M. Stievenard[†]

[*] Laboratoire de Glaciologie et Géophysique de l'Environnement, CNRS, BP96, 38402, Saint Martin d'Hères Cedex, France

[†] Laboratoire des Sciences du Climat et de l'Environnement (UMR CEA/CNRS 1572), L'Orme des Merisiers, Bât. 709, CEA Saclay, 91191 Gif-sur-Yvette Cedex, France

[‡] Arctic and Antarctic Research Institute, Beringa Street 38, 199397, St Petersburg, Russia

[§] Department of Geosciences, Princeton University, Princeton, New Jersey 08544-1003, USA

[‖] Rosenstiel School of Marine and Atmospheric Science, University of Miami, 4600 Rickenbacker Causeway, Miami, Florida 33149, USA

[¶] Institute of Geography, Staromonetny, per 29, 109017, Moscow, Russia

Received 20 January; accepted 14 April 1999.

References:

1. Imbrie, J. *et al.* On the structure and origin of major glaciation cycles. 1. Linear responses to Milankovich forcing. *Paleoceanography* **7**, 701-738 (1992).

2. Tzedakis, P. C. *et al.* Comparison of terrestrial and marine records of changing climate of the last 500,000 years. *Earth Planet. Sci. Lett.* **150**, 171-176 (1997).

3. Berger, A. L. Long-term variations of daily insolation and Quaternary climatic change. *J. Atmos. Sci.* **35**, 2362-2367 (1978).

4. Lorius, C. *et al.* A 150,000-year climatic record from Antarctic ice. *Nature* **316**, 591-596 (1985).

5. Barnola, J. M., Raynaud, D., Korotkevich, Y. S. & Lorius, C. Vostok ice cores provides 160,000-year record of atmospheric CO_2. *Nature* **329**, 408-414 (1987).

6. Jouzel, J. *et al.* Vostok ice core: a continuous isotope temperature record over the last climatic cycle (160,000 years). *Nature* **329**, 402-408 (1987).

7. Raisbeck, G. M. *et al.* Evidence for two intervals of enhanced ^{10}Be deposition in Antarctic ice during the last glacial period. *Nature* **326**, 273-277 (1987).

8. Legrand, M., Lorius, C., Barkov, N. I. & Petrov, V. N. Vostok (Antarctic ice core): atmospheric chemistry changes over the last climatic cycle (160,000 years). *Atmos. Environ.* **22**, 317-331 (1988).

9. Chappellaz, J., Barnola, J.-M., Raynaud, D., Korotkevich, Y. S. & Lorius, C. Ice-core record of atmospheric methane over the past 160,000 years. *Nature* **345**, 127-131 (1990).

10. Petit, J. R. *et al.* Paleoclimatological implications of the Vostok core dust record. *Nature* **343**, 56-58(1990).

11. Sowers, T. *et al.* 135,000 year Vostok—SPECMAP common temporal framework. *Paleoceanography* **8**, 737-766 (1993).

12. Jouzel, J. *et al.* Extending the Vostok ice-core record of palaeoclimate to the penultimate glacial period. *Nature* **364**, 407-412 (1993).

13. Jouzel, J. *et al.* Climatic interpretation of the recently extended Vostok ice records. *Clim. Dyn.* **12**, 513- 521 (1996).

14. Genthon, C. *et al.* Vostok ice core: climatic response to CO_2 and orbital forcing changes over the last climatic cycle. *Nature* **329**, 414-418 (1987).

15. Lorius, C., Jouzel, J., Raynaud, D., Hansen, J. & Le Treut, H. Greenhouse warming, climate sensitivity and ice core data. *Nature* **347**, 139-145 (1990).

16. Raynaud, D. *et al.* The ice record of greenhouse gases. *Science* **259**, 926-934 (1993).

17. Petit, J. R. *et al.* Four climatic cycles in Vostok ice core. *Nature* **387**, 359-360 (1997).

18. Kapitza, A. P., Ridley, J. K., Robin, G. de Q., Siegert, M. J. & Zotikov, I. A. A large deep freshwater lake beneath the ice of central East Antarctica. *Nature* **381**, 684-686 (1996).

19. Bender, M., Sowers, T. & Labeyrie, L. D. The Dole effect and its variation during the last 130,000 years as measured in the Vostok core. *Glob. Biogeochem. Cycles* **8**, 363-376 (1994).

20. Barnola, J. M., Pimienta, P., Raynaud, D. & Korotkevich, Y. S. CO_2 climate relationship as deduced from the Vostok ice core: a re-examination based on new measurements and on a re-evaluation of the air dating. *Tellus B* **43**, 83-91 (1991).

21. Lorius, C. & Merlivat, L. in *Isotopes and Impurities in Snow and Ice. Proc. the Grenoble Symp. Aug./Sept. 1975* 127-137 (Publ. 118, IAHS, 1977).

22. Dahl-Jensen, D. *et al.* Past temperatures directly from the Greenland ice sheet. *Science* **282**, 268-271 (1998).

23. Salamatin, A. N. *et al.* Ice core age dating and paleothermometer calibration on the basis of isotopes and temperature profiles from deep boreholes at Vostok station (East Antarctica). *J. Geophys. Res.* **103**, 8963-8977 (1998).

24. Krinner, G., Genthon, C. & Jouzel, J. GCM analysis of local influences on ice core δ signals. *Geophys. Res. Lett.* **24**, 2825-2828 (1997).

25. Hoffmann, G., Masson, V. & Jouzel, J. Stable water isotopes in atmospheric general circulation models. *Hydrol. Processes* (in the press).

26. Bassinot, F. C. *et al.* The astronomical theory of climate and the age of the Brunhes-Matuyama magnetic reversal. *Earth Planet. Sci. Lett.* **126**, 91-108 (1994).

27. Shackleton, N. J., Imbrie, J. & Hall, M. A. Oxygen and carbon isotope record of East Pacific core V19-30: implications for the formation of deep water in the late Pleistocene North Atlantic. *Earth Planet. Sci. Lett.* **65**, 233-244 (1983).

28. Steig, E. *et al.* Synchronous climate changes in Antarctica and the North Atlantic. *Science* **282**, 92-95 (1998).

29. Howard, W. A warm future in the past. *Nature* **388**, 418-419 (1997).

30. Malaizé, B., Paillard, D., Jouzel, J. & Raynaud, D. The Dole effect over the last two glacial-interglacial cycles. *J. Geophys. Res.* (in the press).

31. Legrand, M. & Delmas, R. J. Formation of HCl in the Antarctic atmosphere. *J. Geophys. Res.* **93**, 7153- 7168 (1987).

32. Yung, Y. K., Lee, T., Chung-Ho & Shieh, Y. T. Dust: diagnostic of the hydrological cycle during the last glacial maximum. *Science* **271**, 962-963 (1996).

33. de Menocal, P. Plio-Pleistocene African climate. *Science* **270**, 53-59 (1995).

34. CLIMAP. *Seasonal Reconstructions of the Earth's Surface at the Last Glacial Maximum* (Geol. Soc. Am., Boulder, Colorado, 1981).

35. Basile, I. *et al.* Patagonian origin dust deposited in East Antarctica (Vostok and Dome C) during glacial stages 2, 4 and 6. *Earth Planet. Sci. Lett.* **146**, 573-589 (1997).

36. Basile, I. *Origine des Aérosols Volcaniques et Continentaux de la Carotte de Glace de Vostok (Antarctique).* Thesis, Univ. Joseph Fourier, Grenoble (1997).

37. Leuenberger, M. & Siegenthaler, U. Ice-age atmospheric concentration of nitrous oxide from an Antarctic ice core. *Nature* **360**, 449-451 (1992).

38. Ramstein, G., Serafini-Le Treut, Y., Le Treut, H., Forichon, M. & Joussaume, S. Cloud processes associated with past and future climate changes. *Clim. Dyn.* **14**, 233-247 (1998).

39. Berger, A., Loutre, M. F. & Gallée, H. Sensitivity of the LLN climate model to the astronomical and CO_2 forcings over the last 200 ky. *Clim. Dyn.* **14**, 615-629 (1998).

40. Weaver, A. J., Eby, M., Fanning, A. F. & Wilbe, E. C. Simulated influence of carbon dioxide, orbital forcing and ice sheets on the climate of the Last Glacial Maximum. *Nature* **394**, 847-853 (1998).

41. Broecker, W. S. & Henderson, G. M. The sequence of events surrounding termination II and their implications for the causes of glacial-interglacial CO_2 changes. *Paleoceanography* **13**, 352-364 (1998).

42. Cortijo, E. *et al.* Eemian cooling in the Norwegian Sea and North Atlantic ocean preceding ice-sheet growth. *Nature* **372**, 446-449 (1994).

43. Chappellaz, J. *et al.* Synchronous changes in atmospheric CH_4 and Greenland climate between 40 and 8 kyr BP. *Nature* **366**, 443-445 (1993).

44. Fischer, H., Wahlen, M., Smith, J., Mastroianni, D. & Deck, B. Ice core records of atmospheric CO_2 around the last three glacial terminations. *Science* **283**, 1712-1714 (1999).

45. Stauffer, B. *et al.* Atmospheric CO_2 concentration and millenial-scale climate change during the last glacial period. *Nature* **392**, 59-61 (1998).

46. Martin, J. H. Glacial-interglacial CO_2 change: The iron hypothesis. *Paleoceanography* **5**, 1-13 (1990).

47. Paillard, D., Labeyrie, L. & Yiou, P. Macintosh program performs time-series analysis. *Eos* **77**, 379 (1996).

48. Ritz, C. *Un Modele Thermo-mécanique d'évolution Pour le Bassin Glaciaire Antarctique Vostok-Glacier Byrd: Sensibilité aux Valeurs de Paramètres Mal Connus* Thesis, Univ. Grenoble (1992).

49. Blunier, T. *et al.* Timing of the Antarctic Cold Reversal and the atmospheric CO_2 increase with respect to the Younger Dryas event. *Geophys. Res. Lett.* **24**, 2683-2686 (1997).

50. Waelbroeck, C. *et al.* A comparison of the Vostok ice deuterium record and series from Southern Ocean core MD 88-770 over the last two glacial-interglacial cycles. *Clim. Dyn.* **12**, 113-123 (1995).

51. Blunier, T. *et al.* Asynchrony of Antarctic and Greenland climate change during the last glacial period. *Nature* **394**, 739-743 (1998).

52. Bender, M., Malaizé, B., Orchado, J., Sowers, T. & Jouzel, J. High precision correlations of Greenland and Antarctic ice core records over the last 100 kyr. in *The Role of High and Low Latitudes in Millennial Scale Global Change* (eds Clark, P. & Webb, R.) (AGU Monogr., Am. Geophys. Union, in the press).

Supplementary information is available on *Nature*'s World-Wide Web site (http://www.nature.com) or as paper copy from the London editorial office of *Nature*.

Acknowledgements. This work is part of a joint project between Russia, France and USA. We thank the drillers from the St Petersburg Mining Institute; the Russian, French and US participants for field work and ice sampling; and the Russian Antarctic Expeditions (RAE), the Institut Français de Recherches et Technologies Polaires (IFRTP) and the Division of Polar Programs (NSF) for the logistic support. The project is supported in Russia by the Russian Ministry of Sciences, in France by PNEDC (Programme National d'Études de la Dynamique du Climat), by Fondation de France and by the CEC (Commission of European Communities) Environment Programme, and in the US by the NSF Science Foundation.

Correspondence and requests for materials should be addressed to J.R.P. (e-mail: petit@glaciog.ujf-grenoble.fr).

Causes of Twentieth-century Temperature Change Near the Earth's Surface

S. F. B. Tett *et al.*

Editor's Note

Despite mounting evidence that human activities are causing significant and potentially catastrophic warming of the Earth's climate via the release of greenhouse gases, some sceptics—including major government leaders—continued to suggest that the observed climate changes might have predominantly natural causes, for example change in the radiation output of the Sun. Here British climatologists Simon Tett and colleagues supply an unequivocal response to that notion. Their extensive computer simulation of twentieth-century climate shows that, while natural processes might conceivably have explained warming early in the century, only a dominant anthropogenic influence can explain the temperature records since 1946. Such findings led to much stronger wording of later assessments of the human role by the Intergovernmental Panel on Climate Change.

Observations of the Earth's near-surface temperature show a global-mean temperature increase of approximately 0.6 K since 1900 (ref.1), occurring from 1910 to 1940 and from 1970 to the present. The temperature change over the past 30–50 years is unlikely to be entirely due to internal climate variability[2-4] and has been attributed to changes in the concentrations of greenhouse gases and sulphate aerosols[5] due to human activity. Attribution of the warming early in the century has proved more elusive. Here we present a quantification of the possible contributions throughout the century from the four components most likely to be responsible for the large-scale temperature changes, of which two vary naturally (solar irradiance and stratospheric volcanic aerosols) and two have changed decisively due to anthropogenic influence (greenhouse gases and sulphate aerosols). The patterns of time/space changes in near-surface temperature due to the separate forcing components are simulated with a coupled atmosphere–ocean general circulation model, and a linear combination of these is fitted to observations. Thus our analysis is insensitive to errors in the simulated amplitude of these responses. We find that solar forcing may have contributed to the temperature changes early in the century, but anthropogenic causes combined with natural variability would also present a possible explanation. For the warming from 1946 to 1996 regardless of any possible amplification of solar or volcanic influence, we exclude purely natural forcing, and attribute it largely to the anthropogenic components.

THE coupled model we use is HadCM2 (refs 6, 7), which has a horizontal resolution of 2.5° in latitude by 3.75° in longitude, 19 atmospheric and 20 oceanic levels, and a

二十世纪近地表温度变化的原因

邰蒂等

编者按

尽管越来越多的证据表明，通过排放温室气体，人类活动导致了全球气候显著而具有灾变可能的变暖，某些怀疑论者（包括一些主要的政府领导人）仍不断提出观测到的气候变化主要源于自然因素，比如太阳辐射输出的变化。本文中英国气候学家西蒙·邰蒂和他的同事们为这种说法提供了明确的回复。他们对二十世纪气候所做的大量的计算机模拟结果显示，虽然自然过程很可能可以解释二十世纪初的气候变暖，但只有把人类活动作为主要的影响因素才有可能解释自 1946 年以来的气温的变化情况。这个研究结果为未来联合国政府间气候变化专门委员会评估人类活动在气候变暖中的作用提供了更强有力的支持。

近地表温度观测结果表明，自 1900 年以来，全球平均气温大约升高了 0.6 K（参考文献 1），气温升高分别发生在 1910～1940 年和 1970 年至今这两个阶段。过去 30～50 年间的气温变化并不完全是由气候系统内部变率引起的[2-4]，而是由人类活动引起的温室气体浓度以及硫酸盐气溶胶浓度的变化[5]所致。但造成二十世纪初气候变暖的因素是比较难以确定的。本文对二十世纪以来可能引起大尺度温度变化的四种因素作了量化。其中有两个因素是自然变化（太阳辐照度和平流层火山气溶胶），而另外两个由于人类的影响发生了显著的变化（温室气体和硫酸盐气溶胶）。利用全球海洋-大气耦合环流模式对各个强迫分量引起的近地表温度的时空变化模态进行了模拟，并将这些模拟值的线性组合与实测值进行拟合。因此，本文分析结果对上述响应的模拟幅值中存在的误差并不敏感。研究发现，二十世纪初期温度的变化可能是由太阳辐射变化造成的，不过，也有可能是人为因素与自然变率相叠加的结果。关于 1946～1996 年间的气候变暖，不管太阳辐射或火山爆发对温度变化是否有放大效应，我们排除了纯粹是自然强迫的可能，并认为人类活动的影响是其主要原因。

我们所采用的耦合模式为 HadCM2（参考文献 6 和 7），水平分辨率为 2.5°×3.75°（纬度 × 经度），大气和海洋在垂直方向上分别分为 19 层和 20 层，并进行了通量校

flux correction. Its climate sensitivity to a doubling of the atmospheric concentration of CO_2 is estimated to be 3.3 K (C. A. Senior, personal communication).

The main radiative forcings of climate since 1850 are likely to be anthropogenic changes in well-mixed greenhouse gases and tropospheric aerosols (mainly sulphate), and natural changes in solar irradiance and in stratospheric aerosol due to volcanic activity[8]. We compare observations[1] of 10-year mean near-surface temperature changes over five 50-year periods (1906–56, 1916–66, ..., 1946–96) with simulations of HadCM2 forced by the following factors (see also section 1 of Supplementary Information):

"G". Changes in well-mixed greenhouse gases from 1860 to 1996[8,9,10] expressed as equivalent CO_2.

"GS". As G but also with changes in surface albedo[11] representing the effects of anthropogenic sulphate aerosols from 1860 to 1996[6,9,10] derived from an atmospheric chemistry model[12]. We assume that this albedo represents both the direct and indirect[11,13,14] effects of sulphate aerosols. When we consider both G and GS we define a further signal S, the pure sulphate signal, as GS − G (see section 9 of Supplementary Information).

"Vol". Changes in stratospheric volcanic aerosols[15] from 1850 to 1996.

"Sol". Changes in total solar irradiance from 1700 to 1996 based on proxy data[16] for 1700–1991 and extended to 1996 using satellite observations[17].

The climate response to each of the above factors was computed from the ensemble average of four simulations started from different initial conditions. Internal climate variability is estimated from a 1,700-year control simulation (Control). 50-year segments (of 10-year mean near-surface temperatures) from the responses of the four ensembles (signals), Control and observations were processed identically to allow for the effect of changing observational coverage, to filter out variability on scales less than 5,000 km (ref. 18) and to remove the 50-year time-mean (see section 2 of Supplementary Information).

We assume that the observations ($\mathbf{y}$) may be represented as the sum of simulated responses or signals ($\mathbf{x}_i$) and internal climatic variability ($\mathbf{u}$), which we assume to be normally distributed:

$$\mathbf{y} = \sum_i \beta_i \mathbf{X}_i + \mathbf{u} \tag{1}$$

This assumption of linearity has been shown to be a good approximation in at least one general circulation model[19,20]. The amplitude, β_i, represents the amount by which we have to scale the ith signal to give the best fit to the observations. We use an "optimal fingerprinting" algorithm[21-24], a form of multivariate regression, to estimate these amplitudes and uncertainty ranges (see section 3 of Supplementary Information). Here we use 5–95% uncertainty ranges and if the uncertainty range for β_i includes unity, then the amplitude of the simulated signal ($\mathbf{x}_i$) could be correct. The first millennium of Control is used to define a

正。当大气中 CO_2 的浓度增加一倍时，其气候敏感度约为 3.3 K(西尼尔，个人交流)。

1850 年以来，气候的主要辐射强迫来自两方面，一是人为因素引起的均匀混合的温室气体与对流层气溶胶(主要为硫酸盐)的变化；另一个是太阳辐照度和由火山活动引起的平流层气溶胶的自然变化[8]。我们以 50 年为一个时间段(1906~1956，1916~1966，…，1946~1996)，将近地表温度变化观测结果[1]的 10 年平均值与 HadCM2 的模拟结果作了比较，其中 HadCM2 模式受以下因素(亦可见于补充信息第 1 节)驱动：

"G"：1860~1996 年间均匀混合的温室气体的变化[8,9,10]，以 CO_2 当量表示。

"GS"：同 G，但还包含地表反照率[11]的变化，该变化代表了 1860~1996[6,9,10] 年间人类活动引起的硫酸盐气溶胶的影响，是根据大气化学模式[12]得到的。我们假定该反照率代表硫酸盐气溶胶的直接与间接[11,13,14]的效应。综合考虑 G 和 GS，我们进一步定义了信号 S，即 S = GS－G，仅代表硫酸盐的信号(见补充信息第 9 节)。

"Vol"：1850~1996 年间平流层火山气溶胶的变化[15]。

"Sol"：1700~1996 年间的太阳总辐照度，其中，1700~1991 年的数据是根据代用资料[16]得到的，之后直到 1996 年的数据为卫星观测结果[17]。

气候对上述因子的响应是通过计算不同初始条件的四组模拟结果的集合平均结果得到的。气候内部变率是利用 1,700 年的控制试验模拟得到的(控制试验)。将(十年平均近地表温度的)四组集合结果(信号)、控制试验以及观测值以 50 年为一段作分割，并保证对各资料的处理相同，以便考虑观测资料覆盖度变化的影响，同时还过滤掉尺度小于 5,000 km 的变率(参考文献 18)，并减去 50 年均值(见补充信息第 2 节)。

我们假设观测结果(y)代表模拟响应或信号(x_i)与气候内部变率(u)的总和，其中，假定它们都是正态分布的，则：

$$y = \sum_i \beta_i X_i + u \tag{1}$$

已有学者证明，至少在一个大气环流模式中，上述线性拟合是较好的近似[19,20]。为了与观测结果拟合得更好，我们对第 i 个信号进行了调整，幅值 β_i 就代表调整的比例。我们利用"最佳指纹"法[21-24](一种多元回归的形式)来估算这些幅值以及不确定区间(见补充信息第 3 节)。在这里我们取 5%~95% 作为不确定范围，并且如果 β_i 的不确定性范围包含 1 时，模拟信号(x_i)的幅值就是正确的。用控制试验的前

weighting function which minimizes the influence of patterns of high internal variability on the estimated signal amplitudes (giving "optimal fingerprints"). Observations and all simulated data are then further filtered by projection on to the leading ten modes of spatio-temporal variability from this part of Control (see section 7 of Supplementary Information). The latter seven centuries, which are statistically independent, are used to estimate the uncertainty ranges.

A minimum requirement for a signal or signal-combination to explain temperature changes over a 50-year period is that the amplitude of the estimated residual $(\Sigma_i \beta_i \mathbf{x}_i - \mathbf{y})$ should be consistent, at the 5% level, with internal climate variability[24] estimated from Control. For a signal-combination to explain change over the century we require that the estimated residual be consistent in all five 50-year periods. We test this using a F-test (see sections 4 and 6 of Supplementary Information) which rules out simulated internal variability as an explanation of temperature changes during 1906–56, 1916–66 and 1946–96 (Table 1), despite being a relatively weak test in that it makes no use of the shape of the simulated signals. Furthermore, no combination of our simulated natural signals alone can explain the warming since 1946—the period when the observational coverage is best. However, every case that includes an anthropogenic signal passes the consistency test. These results hold even if the global-mean model sensitivity or the amplitude of the forcing is wrong as we place no restriction on the amplitudes of the simulated signals.

Table 1. Consistency tests

	F-test*				
	1906–56	1916–66	1926–76	1936–86	1946–96
Int. var.†	**0.01**	**0.04**	0.69	0.76	**0.01**
G	0.18^G	0.11	0.75	0.80	0.10^G
GS	0.06^{GS}	0.23	0.76	0.85	0.30^{GS}
Sol†	0.11^{Sol}	0.06	0.75	0.87	**0.03**
Vol†	**0.03**	0.08	0.74	0.80	**0.04†**
G&S	0.21^G	0.17^G	0.68	0.83	0.31^{G,S}
G&Sol	0.23^G	0.17^{G,Sol}	0.68	0.81	0.07^G
G&Vol	0.24^G	0.09	0.67	0.73	0.08^G
GS&Sol	0.13^{Sol}	0.19^{GS}	0.68	0.82	0.25^{GS}
GS&Vol	0.05^{GS}	0.22^{GS}	0.68	0.80	0.25^{GS}
Sol&Vol†	0.08^{Sol}	0.09‡	0.67	0.82	**0.04‡**

* These columns show the probability (P) that the best-fit signal combination is consistent with observations using an F-test with 21 degrees of freedom. Values in bold are inconsistent with the observations. When a signal is detected, its name is shown as a superscript next to the P-value. Actual P-values are shown, although 0.03 is the lowest value that can be robustly estimated given the available length of Control.

† Signal combination is an inadequate explanation of twentieth-century temperature change as the F-test fails at least once.

‡ Volcanic amplitude in this signal-combination is significantly negative and thus unphysical. No other signal ever has a significant negative amplitude.

1,000 年来定义一个权重函数，以使高频内部变率模态对所估算信号幅值的影响降到最小（给出"最佳指纹图谱"）。然后通过映射到控制试验中前 10 个时空变率主要模态上，对观测结果与所有模拟数据做进一步滤波（见补充信息第 7 节）。后 700 年的模拟数据在统计意义上是独立的，用以估算不确定范围。

要解释 50 年期间发生的温度变化，对于信号或信号组合的最低要求为，所估算的残差（$\Sigma_i \beta_i \mathbf{x}_i - \mathbf{y}$）的幅值应当与根据控制试验结果估算出的气候内部变率[24]在 5% 的显著性水平上保持一致。在用信号组合来解释百年尺度上的变化时，我们要求所估算的残差与所有五个 50 年时段上的值一致。我们对此进行了 F 检验（见补充信息第 4 节和第 6 节），结果表明 1906～1956、1916～1966 和 1946～1996 年间（表 1）近地表温度的变化并非内部变率所致。不过由于未用到模拟信号的分布型，这里的检验标准相对较弱。此外，仅用我们所模拟出的自然强迫的组合并不能解释 1946 年以来的变暖现象，但在这一时间段内我们的观测资料覆盖度是最高的。而所有包含人为活动强迫的情况都通过了一致性检验。由于我们没有对模拟信号的幅值作任何限制，因此即便全球平均的模式敏感度或者强迫的幅值是错误的，上述结果依然成立。

表 1. 一致性检验

	F 检验 *				
	1906～1956	1916～1966	1926～1976	1936～1986	1946～1996
内部变率†	**0.01**	**0.04**	0.69	0.76	**0.01**
G	0.18[G]	0.11	0.75	0.80	0.10[G]
GS	0.06[GS]	0.23	0.76	0.85	0.30[GS]
Sol†	0.11[Sol]	0.06	0.75	0.87	**0.03**
Vol†	**0.03**	0.08	0.74	0.80	**0.04†**
G&S	0.21[G]	0.17[G]	0.68	0.83	0.31[G,S]
G&Sol	0.23[G]	0.17[G,Sol]	0.68	0.81	0.07[G]
G&Vol	0.24[G]	0.09	0.67	0.73	0.08[G]
GS&Sol	0.13[Sol]	0.19[GS]	0.68	0.82	0.25[GS]
GS&Vol	0.05[GS]	0.22[GS]	0.68	0.80	0.25[GS]
Sol&Vol†	0.08[Sol]	0.09‡	0.67	0.82	**0.04‡**

* 这些列中给出的是最吻合的信号组合与利用自由度为 21 的 F 检验得到的观测结果一致的概率（P）。粗体标注的值与观测结果不一致。当检测到信号时，在 P 值旁边将其名称以上标的形式标出。表中给出了实际的 P 值，不过 0.03 是控制试验可用时段下所能稳健地估算出的最小值。

† 表示信号组合至少有一次未能通过 F 检验，因此它并不足以解释二十世纪发生的温度变化。

‡ 在该信号组合中火山因素的幅值明显为负，因此没有物理意义。其他信号都没有明显的负振幅。

A risk in multivariate linear regression is signal degeneracy, which means that signals resemble linear combinations of one another. Applying tests for degeneracy (see pages 243–248 of ref. 25 and section 8 of Supplementary Information) to our signals and observations, we find that no more than two signal-amplitudes can be estimated simultaneously. While three-signal and four-signal combinations are possible explanations, results from them may be misleading. Thus we only discuss combinations of at most two signals.

A signal is formally detected in a signal-combination and period if that combination is consistent with observations and the uncertainty range for the signal is entirely positive (see sections 5 and 6 of Supplementary Information). This means that we have rejected the null hypothesis that the signal amplitude is zero (or that the simulated signal is of the wrong sign). In other words, it is highly likely that the signal is present in the observations.

All one- or two-signal combinations that include anthropogenic signals are, on the basis of the consistency test, possible explanations of twentieth-century temperature change, but we wish to focus on the "best" explanation. Ideally, this explanation would include all detectable signals and no others, provided that this combination is consistent with the observations. We find that three signals (G, S and Sol) are detected during the century (Table 1). The composite signal GS (in which the relative amplitudes of the greenhouse and sulphate signals are assumed to be as in the GS experiment, giving a single pattern of response to anthropogenic forcing) can also be detected. As signal degeneracy may make results from the three-signal combination, G&S&Sol, misleading, this leaves three two-signal combinations: G&S, GS&Sol and G&Sol. Before the most recent period, none of these three two-signal combinations are an obviously better fit to the observations than any other (Table 1). But in 1946–96, combinations including the influence of sulphate aerosols (S) fit the observations better than other explanations (Table 1), which all fail to pass the F-test at the 10% level, suggesting that some sulphate influence is required to account for recent changes. Thus we consider the two combinations containing S (G&S and GS&Sol), but we explore the sensitivity of the solar detection during 1906–56 to the size of the sulphate signal included in GS.

In G&S (unlike GS), the observations are allowed to determine the relative amplitude of the sulphate and greenhouse-gas signals. This allows for error in the prescribed sulphate forcing or modelled response which varies with each period. With these two signals we detect S in 1946–96 and G in 1906–56, 1916–66 and 1946–96 (Table 1). We find that during 1906–56 the amplitude of the sulphate aerosol signal relative to the greenhouse-gas signal is significantly less than that prescribed in GS.

Some other factor may be required to explain this discrepancy with GS rather than errors in the simulated anthropogenic signals. If the relative amplitude of the anthropogenic signals is as prescribed in the GS experiment, then Sol is detected: during 1906–56, some solar influence is required to explain the temperature changes (Table 1). If we reduce the amplitude of the sulphate signal in GS by 33% or more (making GS more like G), we detect

多元线性回归中存在一个风险，那就是信号的简并，即一个信号与其他信号的线性组合相似。通过对信号与实测值进行简并检验（见参考文献 25 中的第 243～248 页以及补充信息第 8 节），我们发现，可同时估算出的信号幅值不会多于两个。尽管三信号或四信号的组合也都是可能的解释，但依据它们得出的结论可能会存在误导。根据上述分析，我们只需讨论至多为两信号组合的情况即可。

倘若某信号组合与观测结果一致并且信号的不确定范围完全为正，那么该信号在此时间段内被以信号组合的形式检测出来（见补充信息第 5 和第 6 节）。也就是说，我们剔除了信号幅值为零（或者模拟信号符号错误）的无效假定。换句话说，信号极有可能出现于观测结果中。

根据一致性检验结果，所有包含人为因素信号的单信号或双信号组合均可能是引起二十世纪温度变化的原因，但我们希望关注的是"最佳"解释。理想的情况是，倘若该信号组合与实测值一致，则该种解释包含且只包含所有可检测信号。我们发现，二十世纪期间共检测到了三类信号（G、S 和 Sol）（表 1）。混合信号 GS 亦可检测出来（鉴于人为强迫的单一响应模态，其中假定温室气体和硫酸盐信号的相对幅值与 GS 实验中的值相同）。由于三信号的混合（G&S&Sol）导致的信号简并可能产生误导性的结论，因此这里讨论三类双信号组合：G&S、GS&Sol 以及 G&Sol。在最近一个时间段之前，上述三种双信号组合中的任一个与实测值的吻合程度并未明显优于其他两个（表 1）。而在 1946～1996 年间，包含硫酸盐气溶胶（S）因素的组合则相比其他组合与观测结果吻合得更好（表 1），其他组合均未通过 10% 显著性水平的 F 检验，说明需要考虑某些硫酸盐强迫对近期温度变化的影响。因此，我们考虑了两类含有 S 的信号组合（G&S 和 GS&Sol），但研究的是 1906～1956 年间 GS 中太阳辐射对硫酸盐信号大小的敏感度。

在 G&S（与 GS 不同）中，利用实测值可以确定出硫酸盐信号与温室气体信号的相对幅值。这就允许给定的硫酸盐强迫或模拟响应中的误差可随不同时段而变化。利用这两个信号我们检测了 1946～1996 年间的 S，以及 1906～1956、1916～1966 和 1946～1996 年间的 G（表 1）。结果发现，1906～1956 年间硫酸盐气溶胶信号与温室气体信号的相对幅值显著低于 GS 中的给定值。

上述关于 GS 的差异应该是由其他因素造成的，而非模拟人为因素信号的误差所致。倘若人为因素信号的相对幅值与 GS 实验给定的结果一致，那么应该能检测到 Sol：1906～1956 年间，温度的变化可能是由某些太阳辐射的影响引起的（表 1）。当把 GS 中硫酸盐信号的幅值降低 33% 或者更多（使 GS 更接近 G）时，我

the anthropogenic signal rather than the solar signal during 1906–56. GS is detected in 1946–96 with or without this change. The reduction of the relative amplitude of sulphate aerosols to greenhouse gases is within the possible uncertainty range[8]; thus our detection of a solar signal should be treated with some caution.

We reconstruct global-mean temperature changes by multiplying the simulated signals, x_i by the best-fit amplitudes (β_i) for 1906–56 and 1946–96. During 1906–56, in G&S, greenhouse gases warm, counterbalanced by a weaker aerosol effect than was imposed in GS (Fig. 1a). The warming peak around 1940 is accounted for by a combination of internal variability and a steadily increasing temperature due to anthropogenic forcings. In GS&Sol the observed early-century warming is explained by a combination of solar irradiance changes, internal variability and an increase in green-house gases (partly balanced by the radiative effect of sulphate aerosols), with solar activity largely responsible for the warming peak around 1940 (Fig. 1b). In both cases, from 1946 sulphate aerosols balance the effect of greenhouse gases giving little warming until the mid-1970s when the warming due to increasing greenhouse gases dominates (Fig. 1c, d).

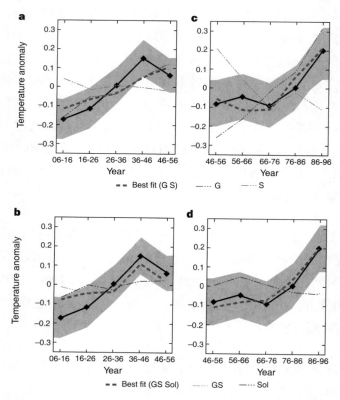

Fig. 1. Best-estimate contributions to global-mean temperature change in the twentieth century. Shown are reconstructions of temperature variations for 1906–56 (**a** and **b**) and 1946–96 (**c** and **d**) for G&S (**a** and **c**) and GS&Sol (**b** and **d**). Observed (thick black lines), best fit (dark grey dashed lines), and the uncertainty

们在 1906～1956 年间检测到的就是人为因素的信号而非太阳辐射信号了。而在 1946～1996 年间，无论是否做出上述改变都能检测到 GS。硫酸盐气溶胶与温室气体相对辐值的降低在可能的不确定范围以内[8]，因此我们所检测到的太阳辐射信号需谨慎处理。

我们将 1906～1956 年间和 1946～1996 年间的模拟信号 x_i 乘上其最佳拟合幅值 (β_i)，重建了全球平均温度的变化。1906～1956 年间，在 G&S 中温室气体的变暖效应被比 GS 中更弱的气溶胶效应所平衡（图 1a）。1940 年前后达到的变暖峰值是气候内部变率与人类活动强迫引起的温度稳步上升共同作用的结果。在 GS&Sol 中所观测到的二十世纪初的变暖现象可以解释为太阳辐照度变化、内部变率以及温室气体增加（部分被硫酸盐气溶胶的辐射效应抵消）共同作用的结果，其中太阳活动是造成 1940 年前后的变暖峰值的主要原因（图 1b）。在两种信号组合（G&S，GS&Sol）中，自 1946 年来，硫酸盐气溶胶抵消了温室气体的效应，使得升温幅度变得很小，直到 20 世纪 70 年代中期因温室气体增加导致的变暖效应逐步占据主导地位（图 1c 和 1d）。

图 1. 二十世纪全球平均温度变化贡献率值的最优估算。图中所示为利用 1906～1956 年（**a** 和 **b**）和 1946～1996 年（**c** 和 **d**）间 G&S（**a** 和 **c**）和 GS&Sol（**b** 和 **d**）的重建温度变化序列。所有图均给出了实测值（黑色粗线）、最佳拟合（深灰色虚线）以及内部变率的不确定范围（灰色阴影部分）。其中 **a** 和 **c** 给出

range due to internal variability (grey shading) are shown in all plots. Panels **a** and **c** show contributions from G (dashed red) and S (dashed green); panels **b** and **d** show the contributions from GS (dashed orange) and Sol (dashed blue). All time series were reconstructed from data in which the 50-year mean had first been removed.

In GS&Sol, solar influence is detectable during the 1906–56 period (Fig. 2), but contributes little to the linear trend in global-mean temperature (a best estimate of ~0.025 K per decade). Conversely, G&S shows that greenhouse gases could have contributed substantially to the warming during both the 1906–56 and 1916–66 periods (Fig. 2). In all other periods, the best-estimate solar contribution is negligible. For both cases the best estimate of the total anthropogenic warming is ~0.075 K per decade during 1946–96, within an approximate uncertainty range of 0.03–0.11 K per decade.

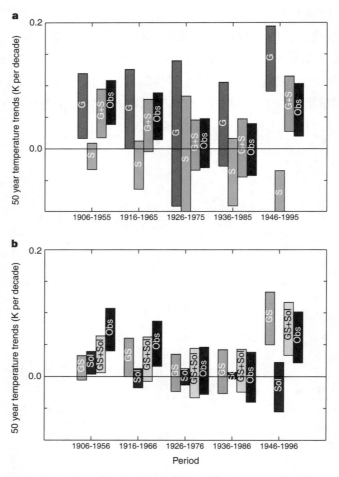

Fig. 2. 50-year temperature trends, and uncertainties, due to different causes. Black bars, observed 50-year trends (K per decade) in global-mean near-surface temperature with 5–95% range estimated from Control. **a**, Estimated contribution (and uncertainty range) to observed trends from G (red), S (green) and the sum (orange). **b**, Estimated contribution and uncertainty range from GS (orange), Sol (blue) and total (yellow). The signal name is centred at the estimated value and the bars cover the uncertainty range.

了 G(红色虚线)和 S(绿色虚线)的贡献率；**b** 和 **d** 给出了 GS(橙色虚线)和 Sol(蓝色虚线)的贡献率。
所有时间序列都是根据减去 50 年平均值后的数据重建的。

　　在 GS&Sol 中，太阳辐射的影响可在 1906～1956 年时间段上检测到(图 2)，
但对全球平均温度的线性趋势影响不大(最佳估计值约为每十年 0.025 K)。相反，
G&S 则表明温室气体对 1906～1956 年间和 1916～1966 年间温度的升高有很大的贡献
(图 2)。在所有其他的时间段内，最佳估计结果的太阳辐射的贡献率可以忽略不计。
对于(G&S 和 GS&Sol)这两种情况，1946～1996 年间，由人类活动引起的总的温度
升高值的最佳估计约为每十年 0.075 K，不确定范围大致为每十年 0.03～0.11 K。

图 2. 不同因素影响下，50 年的温度变化趋势及其不确定性区间。黑色直条表示观测得到的 50 年全球平
均近地表温度的变化趋势(单位为：K 每十年)，以及基于控制试验估算的 5%～95% 的不确定范围。**a**，
G(红)、S(绿)和两者总和(橙)对观测趋势的贡献率(及不确定范围)。**b**，GS(橙)、Sol(蓝)及总(黄)
的贡献率与不确定范围。直条中间标出了估算值的信号名称，而直条的长度则代表不确定范围。

To test the robustness of our results, we carried out six sensitivity studies in which we changed our analysis procedure (see section 10 of Supplementary Information). Detection of anthropogenic signals during 1906–56 (in G&S) and 1946–96 (in both cases) was unaltered by those changes. Detection of the 1946–96 sulphate signal is significant only at the 90% level if optimization is not used. Detection of the 1906–56 solar signal is significant at the 90% level only if greater weight is given to smaller spatial scales, but remains significant at the 95% level in all other studies. We also used a different solar irradiance reconstruction[26] from 1750, to produce an alternative Sol signal, and we reduced stratospheric ozone from 1974[4] to modify the GS signal. Our principal results are robust to both these changes. Furthermore, if we inflate the variance of Control by a factor of 4 we still detect an anthropogenic signal in the 1946–96 period in both of the two-signal cases considered.

Our simulations did not explicitly represent the effects of sulphate aerosols on cloud albedo[13] or lifetime[14] (though on the scales considered these are likely to be represented by the albedo changes imposed on the model), nor did we consider the climate effects of other aerosols, changes in the spectral distribution of the solar irradiance and possible associated changes in ozone[27,28]. Although our results are unaffected by error in the amplitude of the forcing, they could be sensitive to error in the patterns of response or other errors in the forcing, though our conclusions were unaltered by use of an alternative solar irradiance reconstruction. The test that we use to evaluate consistency between the observations and simulations could be misled by mutually compensating errors in model estimates of natural variability and the response of the model to external factors. We do not consider possible observational errors (likely to be small relative to internal climate variability) nor has our uncertainty analysis included any uncertainty due to the finite length of data used to derive the optimisation. For consistency with earlier work[21-24], we have used standard estimates of pattern amplitudes based on linear regression which are biased towards zero[25] when, as here, there is uncertainty in the signals.

Bearing in mind these caveats, we interpret our results as showing the following: first, the temperature changes over the twentieth century cannot be explained by any combination of natural internal variability and the response to natural forcings alone. Second, the recent warming, $\sim$0.25 K, can be explained by the response of the climate to anthropogenic changes in greenhouse-gas concentrations partly offset by cooling due to anthropogenic sulphate aerosols, resulting in little net temperature change from 1946 to the mid-1970s. Last, the warming early this century can also be explained by anthropogenic causes and internal variability. However, solar irradiance changes could have made a significant contribution, $\sim$0.125 K, if we assume little error in the relative amplitude of the forcing of sulphates and greenhouse gases prescribed in our model.

(399, 569-572; 1999)

为了检验结果的稳健性，我们通过调整分析步骤分别进行了六组敏感性实验（见补充信息第 10 节）。1906～1956(G&S 中) 和 1946～1996(G&S 和 GS&Sol 两种情况下) 人为因素信号的检测并没有因上述改变而发生变化。当不进行最优化处理时，1946～1996 年间硫酸盐气溶胶信号仅在 90% 的置信水平上为显著。仅当较小的空间尺度所占的权重较大时，1906～1956 年间检测到的太阳辐射信号在 90% 的置信水平上为显著，而所有其他研究显示该信号在 95% 的置信水平上仍显著。我们还通过采用不同的太阳辐照度（自 1750 年）重建序列[26]来替换 Sol 信号，并将 1974 年以来的平流层臭氧值减小[4]以改变 GS 信号。对于上述两种变化，我们的主要结果也都是稳健的。此外，即使将控制试验的方差乘以 4，在上述考虑的两种情况下，我们仍可在 1946～1996 年时段内检测到人为因素的信号。

我们的模拟研究未能显式地描述硫酸盐气溶胶对云层反照率[13]或者生命史[14]的影响（尽管在所研究的尺度范围内，它们可以由模式给定的反照率变化表示），同样，我们也不认为模拟结果能确切代表其他气溶胶的气候效应、太阳辐射光谱分布的变化以及可能伴随的臭氧层的变化[27,28]等等。尽管我们的结果并不受强迫幅值误差的影响，但该结果对于响应模态中的误差或强迫中的其他误差可能敏感。然而，当我们采用另一种太阳辐照度重建序列时，并不影响得到的结论。自然内部变率的模式估算值与模式对外部因素的响应之间的误差可相互补偿，因此我们对实测值与模拟值的一致性进行评估的检验有可能受其误导。此外，我们并未考虑可能存在的观测误差（相对于气候内部变率来说量级相对较小），在不确定分析中也未包含任何为了得到最优化组合而对数据长度进行限定所引起的不确定性。为了与早期的工作保持一致[21-24]，我们采用了基于线性回归的模态幅值的标准估算法，当信号中存在不确定性时，幅值会偏向零[25]。

考虑上述因素，我们可将得到的结果总结如下：首先，二十世纪的温度变化并不能仅用自然内部变率与对自然强迫的响应的任何组合来解释。其次，近些年的增暖，温度升高了约 0.25 K，可解释为气候对温室气体浓度变化的响应，而温室气体浓度的变化是人类活动引起的。但由于人类活动还造成了硫酸盐气溶胶的变化，进而导致气候变冷，所以这两种人类活动引起的变化部分抵消，从而使得从 1946 年到 20 世纪 70 年代中期发生的温度净变化很小。最后，二十世纪初的变暖也可用人类活动与内部变率来解释。然而，如果假设我们的模式所给定的硫酸盐强迫与温室气体强迫的相对幅值的误差很小，太阳辐射的变化应该也具有重要作用（约为 0.125 K）。

（齐红艳 翻译；周天军 审稿）

Simon F. B. Tett[*], **Peter A. Stott**[*], **Myles R. Allen**[†], **William J. Ingram**[*] & **John F. B. Mitchell**[*]

[*] Hadley Centre for Climate Prediction and Research, Meteorological Office, London Road, Bracknell, Berkshire RG12 2SY, UK

[†] Space Science Department, Rutherford Appleton Laboratory, Chilton, OX11 0QX, UK and Department of Physics, University of Oxford

Received 5 October 1998; accepted 25 March 1999.

References:

1. Parker, D. E., Jones, P. D., Folland, C. K. & Bevan, A. Interdecadal changes of surface temperature since the late nineteenth century. *J. Geophys. Res.* **99**, 14373-14399 (1994).

2. Stouffer, R. J., Manabe, S. & Vinnikov, K. Y. Model assessment of the role of natural variability in recent global warming. *Nature* **367**, 634-636 (1994).

3. Santer, B. D. *et al.* A search for human influences on the thermal structure of the atmosphere. *Nature* **382**, 39-45 (1996).

4. Tett, S. F. B., Mitchell, J. F. B., Parker, D. E. & Allen, M. R. Human influence on the atmospheric vertical temperature structure: Detection and observations. *Science* **247**, 1170-1173 (1996).

5. Hegerl, G. C. *et al.* Multi-fingerprint detection and attribution analysis of greenhouse gas, greenhouse gas-plus-aerosol and solar forced climate change. *Clim. Dyn.* **13**, 613-634 (1997).

6. Johns, T. C. *et al.* The second Hadley Centre coupled ocean-atmosphere GCM: Model description, spinup and validation. *Clim. Dyn.* **13**, 103-134 (1997).

7. Tett, S. F. B., Johns, T. C. & Mitchell, J. F. B. Global and regional variability in a coupled AOGCM. *Clim. Dyn.* **13**, 303-323 (1997).

8. Shine, K. P., Fouquart, Y., Ramaswamy, V., Solomon, S. & Srinivasan, J. in *Climate Change 1995: the Science of Climate Change* (eds Houghton, J. T. *et al.*) 108-118 (Cambridge Univ. Press, 1996).

9. Mitchell, J. F. B., Johns, T. C., Gregory, J. M. & Tett, S. F. B. Climate response to increasing levels of greenhouse gases and sulphate aerosols. *Nature* **376**, 501-504 (1995).

10. Mitchell, J. F. B. & Johns, T. C. On modification of global warming by sulfate aerosols. *J. Clim.* **10**, 245-267 (1997).

11. Mitchell, J. F. B., Davis, R. A., Ingram, W. J. & Senior, C. A. On surface temperature, greenhouse gases, and aerosols: Models and observations. *J. Clim.* **10**, 2364-2386 (1995).

12. Langner, J. & Rodhe, H. A global three-dimensional model of the tropospheric sulfur cycle. *J. Atmos. Chem.* **13**, 225-263 (1991).

13. Twomey, S. A. Pollution and the planetary albedo. *Atmos. Environ.* **8**, 1251-1256 (1974).

14. Albrecht, B. A. Aerosols, cloud microphysics and fractional cloudiness. *Science* **245**, 1227-1230 (1989).

15. Sato, M., Hansen, J. E., McCormick, M. P. & Pollack, J. B. Stratospheric aerosol optical depths (1850-1990). *J. Geophys. Res.* **98**, 22987-22994 (1993).

16. Hoyt, D. V. & Schatten, K. H. A discussion of plausible solar irradiance variations, 1700-1992. *J. Geophys. Res.* **98**, 18895-18906 (1993).

17. Willson, R. C. Total solar irradiance trend during solar cycles 21 and 22. *Science* **277**, 1963-1965 (1997).

18. Stott, P. A. & Tett, S. F. B. Scale-dependent detection of climate change. *J. Clim.* **11**, 3282-3294 (1998).

19. Haywood, J., Stouffer, R., Wetherald, R., Manabe, S. & Ramaswamy, V. Transient response of a coupled model to estimated changes in greenhouse gas and sulfate concentrations. *Geophys. Res. Lett.* **24**, 1335-1338 (1997).

20. Ramaswamy, V. & Chen, C.-T. Linear additivity of climate response for combined albedo and greenhouse perturbations. *Geophys. Res. Lett.* **24**, 567-570 (1997).

21. Hasselmann, K. Optimal fingerprints for the detection of time-dependent climate change. *J. Clim.* **6**, 1957-1971 (1993).

22. Hasselmann, K. Multi-pattern fingerprint method for detection and attribution of climate change. *Clim. Dyn.* **13**, 601-611 (1997).

23. North, G. R., Kim, K.-K., Shen, S. S. P. & Hardin, J. W. Detection of forced climate signals. Part I: filter theory. *J. Clim.* **8**, 401-408 (1995).

24. Allen, M. R. & Tett, S. F. B. Checking for model consistency in optimal fingerprinting. *Clim. Dyn.* (in the press).

25. Mardia, K. V., Kent, J. T. & Bibby, J. M. *Multivariate Analysis* (Academic, London, 1979).

26. Lean, J., Beer, J. & Bradley, R. Reconstruction of solar irradiance since 1610: implications for climate change. *Geophys. Res. Lett.* **22**, 3195-3198 (1995).

27. Haigh, J. D. Impact of solar variability on climate. *Science* **272**, 981-984 (1996).

28. Haigh, J. D. The role of stratospheric ozone in modulating the solar radiative forcing of climate. *Nature* **370**, 544-546 (1994).

Supplementary information is available on *Nature*'s World-Wide Web site (http://www.nature.com) or as paper copy from the London editorial office of *Nature*.

Acknowledgements. S.F.B.T., P.A.S. and computer time were funded by the Department of the Environment, Transport and the Regions. W.J.I. and J.F.B.M. were supported by the UK Public Meteorological Service Research and Development programme. M.R.A. was supported by a research fellowship from the UK Natural Environment Research Council. Supplementary support was provided by the European Commission.

Correspondence and requests for materials should be addressed to S.B.F.T. (e-mail: sfbtett@meto.gov.uk).

436

Design and Synthesis of an Exceptionally Stable and Highly Porous Metal-organic Framework

Hailian Li *et al.*

Editor's Note

Materials with uniformly sized pores of widths comparable to the sizes of small molecules have proved immensely valuable in industrial chemistry, for example by serving as selective catalysts and filters for separating gases. Many such materials are aluminosilicates—either natural minerals called zeolites, or synthetic analogues. But porous frameworks built by rational assembly of molecular building blocks—organic molecules linked by metal ions—could offer more control over the structure and properties of these materials. Efforts to make them are generally hindered by the fact that the frameworks collapse when not filled with solvent, especially if heated. Here Omar Yaghi and coworkers report a metal-organic porous framework that remains robust up to 300 °C even when all solvent is removed.

Open metal-organic frameworks are widely regarded as promising materials for applications[1-15] in catalysis, separation, gas storage and molecular recognition. Compared to conventionally used microporous inorganic materials such as zeolites, these organic structures have the potential for more flexible rational design, through control of the architecture and functionalization of the pores. So far, the inability of these open frameworks to support permanent porosity and to avoid collapsing in the absence of guest molecules, such as solvents, has hindered further progress in the field[14,15]. Here we report the synthesis of a metal-organic framework which remains crystalline, as evidenced by X-ray single-crystal analyses, and stable when fully desolvated and when heated up to 300 °C. This synthesis is achieved by borrowing ideas from metal carboxylate cluster chemistry, where an organic dicarboxylate linker is used in a reaction that gives supertetrahedron clusters when capped with monocarboxylates. The rigid and divergent character of the added linker allows the articulation of the clusters into a three-dimensional framework resulting in a structure with higher apparent surface area and pore volume than most porous crystalline zeolites. This simple and potentially universal design strategy is currently being pursued in the synthesis of new phases and composites, and for gas-storage applications.

THE tetranuclear supertetrahedral cluster motif shown in Fig. 1 (top) is adopted by a number of metal carboxylates (acetate, benzoate and pivalate), where combination of Zn^{2+} and the appropriate carboxylic acid yields the oxide centred cluster as a distinct and well-defined unit[16]. Working towards an extended network based on this cluster, we viewed its Zn—O—C motif as a secondary building unit capable of assembly under similar

一种异常稳定且高度多孔的金属有机骨架的设计与合成

李海连等

编者按

孔隙大小均匀且孔径与小分子尺寸相当的材料，在工业化学中具有巨大的价值，例如可以作为选择性催化剂和分离气体的过滤器。这样的材料多是铝硅酸盐类，如称作沸石的天然矿石，或者人工合成的类似物。通过分子构筑单元合理组装所构建的多孔骨架——金属离子连接的有机分子——可以为此类物质的结构和性质提供更多的调控。但这方面的努力常常受阻，因为这类骨架在没有充满溶剂时，特别是加热时会坍塌。这里，奥马尔·亚吉和其同事报告了一种金属有机多孔骨架，它甚至能在所有溶剂被去除且加热到 300 ℃时还保持稳定。

普遍认为，开放式金属有机骨架是在催化、分离、储气和分子识别等应用[1-15]中均有良好前景的材料。与沸石等常规使用的无机微孔材料相比，通过对孔的结构与功能的调控，这些有机结构具有更便于进行灵活合理设计的潜在优势。但到目前为止，这些开放式结构在支持永久孔隙结构以及避免在没有诸如溶剂等客体分子存在时发生坍塌等方面还存在明显不足，这阻碍了该领域的进一步发展[14,15]。在本文中，我们报道一种金属有机骨架的合成，它在完全去溶剂化状态和加热到 300 ℃时仍保持晶体性质（由 X 射线单晶分析表明）和稳定性。本合成的成功在于借用了金属羧酸盐簇化学的想法，在制备超四面体簇的反应中，我们使用有机二羧酸盐作为连接体，并以单羧酸盐进行封端。连接体所具有的刚性和发散性特征使簇连接成一个三维骨架，可产生出一种与大多数多孔晶体型沸石相比具有更高的表观表面积和孔隙体积的结构。目前，我们正继续利用这种简单而又具有普适性的设计策略来合成具有新相和新组成的材料，并考虑其在储气方面的应用。

图 1（上部）中显示的四核超四面体簇基元是多种金属羧酸盐（醋酸盐、苯甲酸盐和三甲基乙酸盐）所具有的，其中 Zn^{2+} 与适当的羧酸结合产生出以氧化物为中心的簇，它是一个独特且结构明确的单元[16]。在利用该簇来获得扩展网络的工作中，我们把它的 Zn—O—C 基元看作是一个次级结构单元，在相似反应条件下，它能够在有

reaction conditions but in the presence of a dicarboxylate instead of a monocarboxylate. Our earlier work[18] involving the copolymerization of 1,4-benzenedicarboxylate (BDC) with metal ions pointed to its rigid, planar, and divergent attributes, which, when coupled with the rigidity of this secondary building unit, would be ideally suited in forming the target extended three-dimensional framework shown in Fig. 1 (bottom).

Fig. 1. Construction of the MOF-5 framework. Top, the $Zn_4(O)O_{12}C_6$ cluster. Left, as a ball and stick model (Zn, blue; O, green; C, grey). Middle, the same with the $Zn_4(O)$ tetrahedron indicated in green. Right, the same but now with the ZnO_4 tetrahedra indicated in blue. Bottom, one of the cavities in the $Zn_4(O)(BDC)_3$, MOF-5, framework. Eight clusters (only seven visible) constitute a unit cell and enclose a large cavity, indicated by a yellow sphere of diameter 18.5 Å in contact with 72 C atoms (grey).

We found that diffusion of triethylamine into a solution of zinc (II) nitrate and H_2BDC in N,N'-dimethylformamide (DMF)/chlorobenzene resulted in the deprotonation of H_2BDC and its reaction with Zn^{2+} ions. A small amount of hydrogen peroxide was added to the reaction mixture in order to facilitate the formation of O^{2-} expected at the center of the secondary building unit. Elemental microanalysis of the resulting colourless cubic crystals suggested that their formula was $Zn_4O(BDC)_3\cdot(DMF)_8(C_6H_5Cl)$; here we call this material MOF-5, where MOF indicates metal organic framework. The presence of DMF and chlorobenzene guests was confirmed by solid-state ^{13}C NMR, which showed sharp characteristic peaks at the chemical shifts expected for the carbon atom resonances of these guests. Ion mass spectrometry, performed on the liberated guest vapours as the material was heated from 22 to 350 °C, showed their respective parent-ion masses.

二羧酸盐而非单羧酸盐存在时进行组装。我们在关于 1,4–苯二甲酸（BDC）与金属离子共聚的早期工作[18]中指出，BDC 的刚性、平面性和发散属性，再结合这种次级结构单元的刚性，很适用于构建我们所想要的扩展三维骨架，如图 1（下部）中所示。

图 1. MOF-5 骨架的构造。上部，$Zn_4(O)O_{12}C_6$ 原子簇。左边是其球棍模型（Zn：蓝；O：绿；C：灰）。中间同样是该原子簇，其中 $Zn_4(O)$ 四面体用绿色标出。右边也是该原子簇，但这次是用蓝色标出 ZnO_4 四面体。下部，MOF-5 骨架，$Zn_4(O)(BDC)_3$ 中的一个空腔。八个原子簇（只能看到七个）构成一个晶胞并圈起一个大的空腔，空腔用黄色球体表示，其直径为 18.5 Å，与 72 个 C 原子（灰色）接触。

我们发现，三乙胺向硝酸锌（II）和 H_2BDC 的 N,N'–二甲基甲酰胺（DMF）/氯苯溶液中扩散会导致 H_2BDC 去质子化并与 Zn^{2+} 反应。为促进次级结构单元的中心处 O^{2-} 的形成，我们向反应混合物中加入少量过氧化氢。对所得无色立方晶体进行元素微量分析，结果表明其化学式为 $Zn_4O(BDC)_3\cdot(DMF)_8(C_6H_5Cl)$；我们称该材料为 MOF-5，其中 MOF 表示金属有机骨架。通过固体 ^{13}C NMR 可确认 DMF 和氯苯客体分子的存在，核磁谱图显示出尖锐的特征峰，其化学位移与所预期的客体分子中碳原子的化学位移一致。将该物质从 22 ℃ 加热到 350 ℃ 使客体分子释放出来，由此得到的离子质谱显示出它们各自的母体离子的质量。

An X-ray single-crystal diffraction study on the as-synthesized materials reveals the expected topology (Fig. 2). The structure may be derived from a simple cubic six-connected net in two stages: first, the nodes (vertices) of the net are replaced by clusters of secondary building units; second, the links (edges) of the net are replaced by finite rods ("struts") of BDC molecules. The core of the cluster consists of a single O atom bonded to four Zn atoms, forming a regular Zn_4O tetrahedron. Each edge of each Zn tetrahedron is then capped by a $-CO_2$ group to form a $Zn_4(O)(CO_2)_6$ cluster. We note that a related zinc phosphate structure exists[17], in which the C atoms are replaced by the P atoms of PO_4 tetrahedra, which serves to link the clusters together. The important step taken in the present work is the replacement of the O_2-P-O_2 phosphate links by $O_2-C-C_6H_4-C-O_2$ (BDC) "struts", to give an extended network having a three-dimensional intersecting channel system with 12.94-Å spacing between the centres of adjacent clusters.

Fig. 2. Representation of a {100} layer of the MOF-5 framework shown along the a-axis (C, grey; O, green). The ZnO_4 tetrahedra are indicated in purple. Properties of MOF-5 are as follows. Single crystals of as-synthesized $Zn_4O(BDC)_3\cdot(DMF)_8(C_6H_5Cl)$, MOF-5, are at 213 ± 2 K cubic, space group Fm-$3m$ with $a = 25.6690(3)$ Å, $V = 16,913.2(3)$ Å^3, and $Z = 8$. Analysis for MOF-5. (1) Elemental microanalysis. Calculated (%): C, 44.21; H, 5.02; N, 7.64; Zn, 17.82%. Found (%): C, 43.25; H, 5.29; N, 7.56; Zn, 17.04%. (2) Solid-state ^{13}C NMR. First, CP MAS. Guests $(CH_3)_2NC(O)H$: $(CH_3)_2-$, δ (p.p.m.) 37.81 and 32.71; $-C(O)-$, δ 164.93. C_6H_5Cl: δ 132.04, 130.41, 128.76. Framework, $-COO$, δ 175.93; $-C(COO)$, δ 139.11; $o-C_6H_4$, δ 130.41. Second, static. Guests $(CH_3)_2NC(O)H$: $(CH_3)_2-$, δ 37.63 and 32.59; $-C(O)-$, δ 164.67. C_6H_5Cl: δ 130.22 (broad). Framework, no peaks observed. (3) Mass spectrometry, 22–350 °C. $(CH_3)_2NC(O)H$: M^+, 73 a.m.u. $(C_3H_7NO^+)$. C_6H_5Cl: M^+, 77 $(C_6H_5^+)$; M^+, 112 a.m.u. $(C_6H_5{}^{35}Cl^+)$ and 114 a.m.u. $(C_6H_5{}^{37}Cl^+)$ in 3:1 intensity ratio. Properties of single crystals of fully desolvated MOF-5, $Zn_4O(BDC)_3$, are at 169 ± 2 K cubic, space group Fm-$3m$ with $a = 25.8849(3)$ Å, $V = 17,343.6(8)$ Å^3, and $Z = 8$ (for empirical formula, $C_{24}H_{12}O_{13}Zn_4$), R, $R_w = 0.023$, 0.026. Analysis for $Zn_4O(BDC)_3$. Elemental microanalysis. Calculated (%): C, 37.45; H, 1.57; N, 0.00%. Found (%): C, 36.94; H, 1.66; N, 0.26%. Solid-state ^{13}C NMR (CP MAS and static) showed no resonances due to any guests. Mass spectrometry (22–350 °C) showed no peaks, indicative of absence of any guests in the pores. Thermogravimetric analysis showed

　　所合成材料的 X 射线单晶衍射研究说明其拓扑结构与预期相符（图 2）。从简单的立方六联网络出发经过两步即可推导出其结构：首先，用次级结构单元簇取代网络的节点（顶点）；接着，用 BDC 分子的限定棒状部分（"支柱"）取代网络中的连接（棱）。一个单独的 O 原子与四个 Zn 原子键合在一起，处于簇的核心，形成一个规则的 Zn_4O 四面体结构。随后，每个 Zn 四面体的每一条棱被包上一个 $-CO_2$ 基团，形成一个 $Zn_4(O)(CO_2)_6$ 簇。我们注意到，存在着一种相关的磷酸锌结构[17]，其中 C 原子被将簇连接起来的 PO_4 四面体中的 P 原子所取代。当前研究采取的重要步骤是用 $O_2-C-C_6H_4-C-O_2$（BDC）"支柱"取代 O_2-P-O_2 磷酸盐连接基元，它给出了一种扩展网络，这种网络具有三维交叉孔道体系，其相邻簇中心之间的间距为 12.94 Å。

图 2. MOF-5 骨架中一个 {100} 层的图式，所示为沿着 a 轴方向（C，灰；O，绿）。ZnO_4 四面体用紫色显示。MOF-5 的性质如下。所合成的 $Zn_4O(BDC)_3 \cdot (DMF)_8(C_6H_5Cl)$ 单晶，MOF-5，213 ± 2 K 下测试为立方晶系，空间群 $Fm\text{-}3m$，$a = 25.6690(3)$ Å，$V = 16,913.2(3)$ Å³，$Z = 8$。MOF-5 的分析结果如下。(1) 元素微量分析。计算值（%）：C，44.21；H，5.02；N，7.64；Zn，17.82%。测试值（%）：C，43.25；H，5.29；N，7.56；Zn，17.04%。(2) 固体 ¹³C NMR。一、CP MAS（即交叉极化魔角旋转）方法。客体分子 $(CH_3)_2NC(O)H$：$(CH_3)_2-$，δ (ppm) 37.81 和 32.71；$-C(O)-$，δ 164.93。C_6H_5Cl：δ 132.04、130.41、128.76。骨架：$-COO$，δ 175.93；$-C(COO)$，δ 139.11；$o\text{-}C_6H_4$，δ 130.41。二、静态方法。客体分子 $(CH_3)_2NC(O)H$：$(CH_3)_2-$，δ 37.63 和 32.59；$-C(O)-$，δ 164.67。C_6H_5Cl：δ 130.22（宽包）。骨架：没有观测到峰。(3) 质谱，$22 \sim 350$ ℃。$(CH_3)_2NC(O)H$：M^+，73 amu $(C_3H_7NO^+)$。C_6H_5Cl：M^+，77$(C_6H_5^+)$；M^+，112 amu $(C_6H_5{}^{35}Cl^+)$ 和 114 amu $(C_6H_5{}^{37}Cl^+)$，强度比为 3:1。完全去溶剂的 MOF-5——$Zn_4O(BDC)_3$ 的单晶性质：169 ± 2 K 下测试为立方晶系，空间群 $Fm\text{-}3m$，$a = 25.8849(3)$ Å，$V = 17,343.6(8)$ Å³，$Z = 8$（实验式 $C_{24}H_{12}O_{13}Zn_4$），R，$R_w = 0.023$，0.026。$Zn_4O(BDC)_3$ 的分析结果如下。元素微量分析。计算值（%）：C，37.45；H，1.57；N，0.00%。测试值（%）：C，36.94；H，1.66；N，0.26%。固体 ¹³C NMR（CP MAS 和静态方法）显示没有任何来自于客体分子的共振。质谱（$22 \sim 350$ ℃）显示没有峰，表明孔隙中没有任何

no weight loss up to 410 °C. Single crystals of $Zn_4O(BDC)_3$, fully desolvated and heated at 300 °C, are at 149 ± 2 K cubic, space group $Fm\text{-}3m$ with $a = 25.8496(3)$ Å.

The framework atoms in MOF-5 take up only a small fraction of the available space in the crystal. If overlapping spheres with van der Waals radii (1.5, 1.2, 1.7, 1.5 Å for Zn, H, C and O, respectively) are placed at the atomic positions, the space not so occupied is 80% of the crystal volume. The non-framework space is divided into two types of cavity lined with C and H atoms. The center of the smaller of these has 24 H atoms at 7.10 Å and 24 C atoms at 7.97 Å; the centre of the larger (Fig. 1) has 72 C atoms at 9.26 Å and 48 H atoms at 9.47 Å. The aperture joining the two cavities has 8 H at 5.10 Å and 8 C at 5.70 Å from its center. Allowing for the van der Waals radii, spheres of material with diameter 15.1 Å and 11.0 Å could fit in the large and small cavities, respectively, and the aperture would admit the passage of a sphere of diameter 8.0 Å. Assuming the same molar volume as in the respective liquids, we find that in the original material the guest molecules—$8 \times (8 \text{ DMF} + 1 \text{ } C_6H_5Cl)$—have a volume of 9,512 Å^3, which is 55% of the unit cell volume. Indeed, we show below that 55–61% of the space is accessible to guest species.

Due to their high mobility, the guests can be fully exchanged with chloroform. More significant is that all the chloroform guests can be evacuated from the pores within 3 h at room temperature and 5×10^{-5} torr without loss of framework periodicity. In fact, the desolvated single crystals were checked by elemental microanalysis, ^{13}C NMR, mass spectrometry, and thermal gravimetry to confirm the absence of any guests, while optical microscopy was used to show that they maintained their transparency, morphology and crystallinity. This has allowed us to perform another X-ray single-crystal diffraction study on the fully desolvated form of this framework—a study that revealed mono-crystallinity with cell parameters and atomic positions coincident with those of the as-synthesized material. In fact, the highest peaks and lowest valleys in the ΔF map are 0.25 and -0.17 electrons per Å^3 scattered randomly both near the framework and the void space. These contrast with the relatively large values (1.56 and -0.45 electrons per Å^3) found in the as-synthesized crystals.

Further evidence for the stability of the framework was obtained by heating the fully desolvated crystals in air at 300 °C for 24 h, which had no effect on either their morphology or crystallinity as evidence by another X-ray single-crystal diffraction study. Here again, the cell parameters obtained were unaltered relative to those found for the unheated desolvated crystals, illustrating the rigidity and stability of the framework in the absence of guest molecules. These results are interesting as the density (0.59 g cm^{-3}) of the desolvated crystals is among the lowest recorded for any crystalline material.

客体分子。热重分析显示直到 410 ℃时没有重量损失。完全去溶剂并加热到 300 ℃处理过的 $Zn_4O(BDC)_3$ 单晶，149 ± 2 K 下测试为立方晶系，空间群 *Fm-3m*，$a = 25.8496(3)$ Å。

在晶体中，MOF-5 中的骨架原子只占可用空间中很小的一部分。若将相交在一起的具有范德华半径大小（对于 Zn、H、C 和 O 分别是 1.5、1.2、1.7 和 1.5 Å）的球体置于晶格原子所在位置上，则未被占据的空间为晶体体积的 80%。非骨架空间分为沿着 C 和 H 原子排列方向的两类空腔。其中较小空腔的中心含有位于 7.10 Å 的 24 个 H 原子和位于 7.97 Å 的 24 个 C 原子；较大空腔（图 1）的中心有位于 9.26 Å 的 72 个 C 原子和位于 9.47 Å 的 48 个 H 原子。连接这两种空腔的孔隙有距离其中心 5.10 Å 的 8 个 H 和 5.70 Å 的 8 个 C。考虑到范德华半径，较大和较小空腔中分别可以纳入直径为 15.1 Å 和 11.0 Å 的球形物体，而孔隙则允许直径为 8.0 Å 的球体通行。假定与各自相应的液体具有相同的摩尔体积，我们发现在原始材料中客体分子——$8\times(8\ DMF+1\ C_6H_5Cl)$——具有 9,512 $Å^3$ 的体积，占单位晶胞体积的 55%。实际上，如下所示，有 55% ~ 61% 的空间是可容纳客体分子的。

由于客体分子的高度运动性，它们能够被氯仿完全交换出。更重要的是，所有氯仿分子可以在室温和 5×10^{-5} 托的条件下于 3 h 内完全从孔隙中挥发出来，而骨架周期性没有任何损失。实际上，对去溶剂后的单晶，元素微量分析、^{13}C NMR、质谱和热重分析可以确认其中没有任何客体分子。同时，光学显微镜观察表明，它们保持着原有的透明性、形貌和结晶度。这使得我们能够对该骨架的完全去溶剂形式进行新的 X 射线单晶衍射研究——结果表明其单晶性质具有与所合成物质一致的晶胞参数和原子位置。实际上，ΔF 图中最高的峰和最低的谷为每 $Å^3$ 中 0.25 和 −0.17 个电子，随机散落于骨架和孔隙空间附近。这与在所合成晶体中发现的相对较大的数值（每 $Å^3$ 中 1.56 和 −0.45 个电子）有所不同。

关于骨架稳定性的更多证据是通过将完全去溶剂的晶体在空气中于 300 ℃条件下加热 24 h 而获得，进一步的 X 射线单晶衍射研究证明无论是它们的形貌还是结晶度都没有受到影响。这里，所得晶胞参数相对于未加热的去溶剂晶体的晶胞参数并没有什么改变，这表明了该骨架在没有客体分子存在时的刚性和稳定性。这些结果是值得关注的，因为这种去溶剂晶体的密度（0.59 $g\cdot cm^{-3}$）在已报道的任何结晶物质密度中是属于最低的之列。

Fig. 3. Nitrogen gas sorption isotherm at 78 K for MOF-5 (filled circles, sorption; open circles, desorption). P/P_0 is the ratio of gas pressure (P) to saturation pressure (P_0), with $P_0 = 746$ torr.

Table 1. Gas and liquid vapour sorption in desolvated MOF-5

Sorbate	T (°C)	Amount sorbed (mg g^{-1})	Sorbate molecules per unit cell	Free volume (cm^3 g^{-1})	Free volume (cm^3 cm^{-3})
Ar	−194	1,492	230	1.03	0.61
N_2	−194	831	183	1.04	0.61
CH_2Cl_2	22	1,211	88	0.93	0.55
$CHCl_3$	22	1,367	71	0.94	0.55
C_6H_6	22	802	63	0.94	0.55
CCl_4	22	1,472	59	0.94	0.56
C_6H_{12}	22	703	51	0.92	0.54

To evaluate the pore volume and the apparent surface area of this framework, the gas and vapour sorption isotherms for the desolvated sample were measured using an electromicrogravimetric balance (Cahn 1000) set-up and an already published procedure[18]. The sorption of nitrogen revealed a reversible type I isotherm (Fig. 3), with concordant results obtained with large crystals (0.2 mm) and microcrystals (30 μm). The same sorption behaviour was observed for argon and organic vapours such as CH_2Cl_2, $CHCl_3$, CCl_4, C_6H_6 and C_6H_{12}. Similar to those of most zeolites, the isotherms are reversible and show no hysteresis upon desorption of gases from the pores. Using the Dubinin–Radushkevich equation, pore volumes of 0.61–0.54 cm^3 cm^{-3} were calculated and found to be nearly identical for all adsorbates shown (Table 1), which indicates the presence of uniform pores. Assuming a monolayer coverage of N_2 (which may not be strictly correct with such large cavities) the apparent Langmuir surface area was estimated at 2,900 m^2 g^{-1}. Zeolites, which generally have higher molar masses than $Zn_4O(BDC)_3$, have pore volumes that range from 0.18 cm^3 cm^{-3} for analcime to 0.47 cm^3 cm^{-3} for zeolite A[19].

(**402**, 276-279; 1999)

图 3. 78 K 时 MOF-5 的氮气吸附等温线（实心圆，吸附；空心圆，解吸附）。P/P_0 为气体压强（P）与饱和压强（P_0）的比值，且 $P_0 = 746$ 托。

表 1. 去溶剂 MOF-5 中的气体和液体蒸气吸附

吸附物	T(℃)	吸附量（mg·g⁻¹）	每单位晶胞中的吸附分子数	自由体积（cm³·g⁻¹）	自由体积（cm³·cm⁻³）
Ar	−194	1,492	230	1.03	0.61
N_2	−194	831	183	1.04	0.61
CH_2Cl_2	22	1,211	88	0.93	0.55
$CHCl_3$	22	1,367	71	0.94	0.55
C_6H_6	22	802	63	0.94	0.55
CCl_4	22	1,472	59	0.94	0.56
C_6H_{12}	22	703	51	0.92	0.54

　　为估计这种多孔骨架中的孔隙体积和表观表面积，利用电子微重分析天平（Cahn 1000）和一种已经发表的方法[18]，我们测定了去溶剂样品的气体和蒸气的吸附等温线。氮气的吸附数据揭示出这是一种可逆的 I 型等温线（图 3），无论对大晶体（0.2 mm）或微晶（30 μm）都得到了一致的结果。对于氩和诸如 CH_2Cl_2、$CHCl_3$、CCl_4、C_6H_6 和 C_6H_{12} 等有机物蒸气，也观测到了同样的吸附行为。与大多数沸石的等温线类似，该等温线是可逆的，而且没有显示出气体从孔隙中解吸附导致的滞后现象。利用 DR 方程计算出孔隙体积为 0.61 cm³·cm⁻³ ～ 0.54 cm³·cm⁻³，我们发现，对于所示的（表 1）全部吸附物而言，孔隙体积几乎都是一样的，这表明均匀孔隙的存在。假设 N_2 为单层覆盖（对于这样大的孔隙来说这可能不是严格准确的），可估算出表观朗缪尔表面积为 2,900 m²·g⁻¹。而沸石一般来说具有比 $Zn_4O(BDC)_3$ 更高的摩尔质量，其孔隙体积范围为从方沸石的 0.18 cm³·cm⁻³ 到沸石 A 的 0.47 cm³·cm⁻³[19]。

（王耀杨 翻译；陈尔强 审稿）

Design and Synthesis of an Exceptionally Stable and Highly Porous Metal-organic Framework

Hailian Li[*], **Mohamed Eddaoudi**[†], **M. O'Keeffe**[*] **and O. M. Yaghi**[†]

[*] Materials Design and Discovery Group, Department of Chemistry and Biochemistry, Arizona State University, Tempe, Arizona 85287-1604, USA

[†] Department of Chemistry, University of Michigan, 930 North University, Ann Arbor, Michigan 48109-1055, USA

Received 20 May; accepted 17 September 1999.

References:

1. Kinoshita, Y., Matsubara, I., Higuchi, T. & Saito, Y. The crystal structure of bis(adiponitrilo) copper (I) nitrate. *Bull. Chem. Soc. Jpn* **32**, 1221-1226 (1959).

2. Kitgawa, S., Munakata, M. & Tanimura, T. Tetranuclear copper(I)-based infinite one-dimensional chain complex. *Chem. Lett.* 623-626 (1991).

3. Abrahams, B. F., Hoskins, B. F. & Robson, R. Infinite polymeric frameworks consisting of three dimensionally linked rod-like segments. *J. Am. Chem. Soc.* **113**, 3606-3607 (1991).

4. Zaworotko, M. J. Cooperative bonding affords a holesome story. *Nature* **386**, 220-221 (1997).

5. Fagan, P. J. & Ward, M. D. Building molecular crystals. *Sci, Am.* **267**, 48-54 (1992).

6. Carlucci, L., Ciani, G., Proserpio, D. M. & Sironi, A. Interpenetrating diamondoid frameworks of silver (I) cations linked by N,N′-bidentate molecular rods. *J. Chem. Soc. Chem. Commun.* 2755-2756 (1994).

7. Mallouk, T. E. Crowns get organized. *Nature* **387**, 350-351 (1997).

8. Gardner, G. B., Venkataraman, D., Moore, J. S. & Lee, S. Spontaneous assembly of a hinged coordination network. *Nature* **374**, 792-795 (1995).

9. Yaghi, O. M., Li, G. & Li, H. Selective binding and removal of guests in a microporous metal-organic framework. *Nature* **378**, 703-706 (1995).

10. Lu, J. *et al.* Coordination polymers of Co(NCS)$_2$ with pyrazine and 4,4-bipyridine: syntheses and structures. *Inorg. Chem.* **36**, 923-928 (1997).

11. Vaid, T. P., Lobkovsky, E. B. & Wolczanski, P. T. Covalent 3- and 2-dimensional titanium-quinone networks. *J. Am. Chem. Soc.* **119**, 8742-8743 (1997).

12. Liu, F. Q. & Tilley, T. D. A coordination network based on d^0 transition-metal centers: synthesis and structure of the [2,4]-connected layered compound [(TiCl$_4$)$_2$Si(C$_6$H$_4$CN-p)4]·1.5C$_7$H$_8$. *J. Chem. Soc. Chem. Commun.* 103-104 (1998).

13. MacGillivray, L. R., Groeneman, R. H. & Atwood, J. L. Design and self-assembly of cavity-containing rectangular grids. *J. Am. Chem. Soc.* **120**, 2676-2677 (1998).

14. Yaghi, O. M., Li, H., Davis, C., Richardson, D. & Groy, T. L. Synthetic strategies, structure patterns, and emerging properties in the chemistry of modular porous solids. *Acc. Chem. Res.* **31**, 575-585 (1998).

15. Kepert, C. J. & Rosseinsky, M. J. Zeolite-like crystal structure of an empty microporous framework. *J. Chem. Soc. Chem. Commun.* 375-376 (1999).

16. Clegg, W. *et al.* Crystal structures of three basic zinc carboxylates together with infrared and FAB mass spectrometry studies in solution. *Inorg. Chim. Acta* **186**, 51-60 (1991).

17. Harrison, W. T. A. *et al.* Synthesis and characterization of a new family of thermally stable open framework zincophosphate/arsenate phases: M$_3$Zn$_4$O(XO$_4$)$_3$·nH$_2$O (M = Na,K,Rb,Li,..; X = P,As; n = ~3.5-6). Crystal structures of Rb$_3$Zn$_4$O(PO$_4$)$_3$·3.5H$_2$O, K$_3$Zn$_4$O(AsO$_4$)$_3$·4H$_2$O, and Na$_3$Zn$_4$O(PO$_4$)$_3$·6H$_2$O. *Chem. Mater.* **8**, 691-700 (1996).

18. Li, H., Eddaouidi, M., Groy, T. L. & Yaghi, O. M. Establishing microporosity in open metal-organic frameworks: gas sorption isotherms for Zn(BDC) (BDC = 1,4-benzenedicarboxylate). *J. Am. Chem. Soc.* **120**, 8571-8672 (1998).

19. Breck, D. W. *Zeolite Molecular Sieves* (Wiley & Sons, New York, 1974).

Supplementary information is available on *Nature's* World-Wide Web site (http://www.nature.com) or as paper copy from the London editorial office of *Nature*.

Acknowledgements. We thank F. Hollander and R. Staples for X-ray structure determinations. This work was supported by the National Science Foundation (M.O.K. and O.M.Y.), the Department of Energy (O.M.Y.) and Nalco Chemical Company.

Correspondence and requests for materials should be addressed to O.M.Y. at the University of Michigan (e-mail: oyaghi@umich.edu).

448

The DNA Sequence of Human Chromosome 22

I. Dunham et al.

Editor's Note

This paper, a key landmark in the Human Genome Project, describes the first complete sequence of a human chromosome. This sequence of chromosome 22 offered insights into the way that genes are arranged along chromosomes and into how these genes might be controlled, paving the way for developments in medical diagnostics and therapeutics. The project, led by British-based geneticist Ian Dunham, involved an international consortium of sequencing centres, and the data were made freely available. The study shows that chromosome 22 is made up of 33.5 million "letters" and includes 679 genes, over half of which were previously unknown in humans. The complete human genome sequence was published four years later.

Knowledge of the complete genomic DNA sequence of an organism allows a systematic approach to defining its genetic components. The genomic sequence provides access to the complete structures of all genes, including those without known function, their control elements, and, by inference, the proteins they encode, as well as all other biologically important sequences. Furthermore, the sequence is a rich and permanent source of information for the design of further biological studies of the organism and for the study of evolution through cross-species sequence comparison. The power of this approach has been amply demonstrated by the determination of the sequences of a number of microbial and model organisms. The next step is to obtain the complete sequence of the entire human genome. Here we report the sequence of the euchromatic part of human chromosome 22. The sequence obtained consists of 12 contiguous segments spanning 33.4 megabases, contains at least 545 genes and 134 pseudogenes, and provides the first view of the complex chromosomal landscapes that will be found in the rest of the genome.

TWO alternative approaches have been proposed to determine the human genome sequence. In the clone by clone approach, a map of the genome is constructed using clones of a suitable size (for example, 100–200 kilobases (kb)), and then the sequence is determined for each of a representative set of clones that completely covers the map[1]. Alternatively, a whole genome shotgun[2] requires the sequencing of unmapped genomic clones, typically in a size range of 2–10 kb, followed by a monolithic assembly to produce the entire sequence. Although the merits of these two strategies continue to be debated[3], the public domain human genome sequencing project is following the clone by clone approach[4] because it is modular, allows efficient organization of distributed resources and sequencing capacities, avoids problems arising from distant repeats and results in early completion of significant units of the genome. Here we report the first sequencing

人类 22 号染色体的 DNA 序列

邓纳姆等

编者按

本文是人类基因组计划的一个关键里程碑，介绍了单条人类染色体的第一个完整序列。22 号染色体的序列帮助我们了解基因在染色体上的编排方式以及这些基因是如何被调控的，并为医学诊断和治疗的发展奠定了基础。本项目由英国遗传学家伊恩·邓纳姆领衔，多个测序中心组成的国际联盟共同完成，数据可免费获取。本研究表明，22 号染色体是由 3,350 万个"字母"组成，包含 679 个基因，其中半数以上之前在人类中是未知的。完整的人类基因组序列发表于 4 年后。

关于一种生物的完整基因组 DNA 序列的知识使我们可以用系统的方法确定其遗传组分。基因组序列可以提供所有基因的完整结构，包括功能未知的基因及其控制元件，通过推理还可得到它们编码的蛋白质，以及所有其他生物学上的重要序列。此外，对于针对生物体设计进一步的生物学研究和通过跨物种序列比对来进行演化研究而言，该物种的序列都是丰富且永久的信息来源。一系列微生物和模式生物序列的测定已经充分证明了这种方法的强大能力。下一步是获得整个人类基因组的完整序列。在本文中我们报道了人类 22 号染色体常染色质部分的序列。该序列由跨越 33.4 Mb 的 12 个连续片段组成，包含至少 545 个基因和 134 个假基因，并首次展示了在基因组其他部分将会发现的复杂的染色体概况。

目前有两种测定人类基因组序列的方法可供选择。连续克隆法用适当大小（如 100 ~ 200 千碱基（kb））的多个克隆构建基因组图谱，然后测定完全覆盖图谱的一套代表性克隆中每个克隆的序列[1]。另一种是全基因组鸟枪法[2]，需要对未作图的基因组克隆进行测序，大小通常在 2 ~ 10 kb，然后通过整体组装得到整个序列。虽然这两种策略的优点仍然存在争议[3]，但公开的人类基因组测序项目已经采取连续克隆法[4]，因为这种方法是模块化的，可以有效地组织分散的资源及测序能力，避免远距离重复引起的问题，而且能够迅速完成基因组重要单元的测定。在本文中，我们报道了人类基因组计划的第一个测序里程碑：第一条人类染色体常染色质部分的

landmark of the human genome project, the operationally complete sequence of the euchromatic portion of a human chromosome.

Chromosome 22 is the second smallest of the human autosomes, comprising 1.6–1.8% of the genomic DNA[5]. It is one of five human acrocentric chromosomes, each of which shares substantial sequence similarity in the short arm, which encodes the tandemly repeated ribosomal RNA genes and a series of other tandem repeat sequence arrays. There is no evidence to indicate the presence of any protein coding genes on the short arm of chromosome 22 (22p). In contrast, direct[6] and indirect[7,8] mapping methods suggest that the long arm of the chromosome (22q) is rich in genes compared with other chromosomes. The relatively small size and the existence of a high-resolution framework map of the chromosome[9] suggested to us that sequencing human chromosome 22 would provide an excellent opportunity to show the feasibility of completing the sequence of a substantial unit of the human genome. In addition, alteration of gene dosage on part of 22q is responsible for the aetiology of a number of human congenital anomaly disorders including cat eye syndrome (CES, Mendelian Inheritance in Man (MIM) 115470, http://www.ncbi.nlm.nih.gov/omim/) and velocardiofacial/DiGeorge syndrome (VCFS, MIM 192430; DGS, MIM 188400). Other regions associated with human disease are the schizophrenia susceptibility locus[10,11], and the sequences involved in spinocerebellar ataxia 10 (SCA10)[12]. Making the sequence of human chromosome 22 freely available to the community early in the data collection phase has benefited studies of disease-related and other genes associated with this human chromosome[13-19].

Genomic Sequencing

To identify genomic clones as the substrate for sequencing chromosome 22, extensive clone maps of the chromosome were constructed using cosmids, fosmids, bacterial artificial chromosomes (BACs) and P1-derived artificial chromosomes (PACs). Clones representing parts of chromosome 22 were identified by screening BAC and PAC libraries representing more than 20 genome equivalents using sequence tagged site (STS) markers known to be derived from the chromosome, or by using cosmid and fosmid libraries derived from flow-sorted DNA from chromosome 22. Overlapping clone contigs were assembled on the basis of restriction enzyme fingerprints and STS-content data, and ordered relative to each other using the established framework map of the chromosome[9]. The resulting nascent contigs were extended and joined by iterative cycles of chromosome walking using sequences from the end of each contig. In two places, yeast artificial chromosome (YAC) clones were used to join or extend contigs (AL049708, AL049760). The sequence-ready map covers 22q in 11 clone contigs with 10 gaps and stretches from sequences containing known chromosome 22 centromeric tandem repeats to the 22q telomere[20].

In the final sequence, one additional gap that was intractable to sequencing is found 234 kb from the centromere (see below). The gaps between the clone contigs are located at the two ends of the map, in the 4.3 Mb adjacent to the centromere and in 7.3 Mb at the telomeric

可使用的完整序列。

22 号染色体是人类第二小的常染色体,占基因组 DNA 的 1.6% ~ 1.8%[5]。它是人类 5 条近端着丝粒染色体之一,这 5 条染色体具有序列高度相似的短臂,这些短臂编码串联重复的核糖体 RNA 基因和一系列其他串联重复序列阵列。目前没有证据表明 22 号染色体短臂(22p)上存在任何蛋白质编码基因。相反,直接[6]和间接[7,8]作图方法都表明该染色体的长臂(22q)与其他染色体相比拥有丰富的基因。人类 22 号染色体相对较小,并具有高分辨率框架图[9],这表明对其进行测序是展示人类基因组大型单元的序列测定可行性的绝佳机会。此外,部分 22q 上基因数量的改变是引起很多人类先天性异常疾病的病因,这些疾病包括猫眼综合征(CES,人类孟德尔遗传数据库(MIM)115470,http://www.ncbi.nlm.nih.gov/omim/)和腭心面/迪格奥尔格综合征(VCFS,MIM 192430;DGS,MIM 188400)。其他与人类疾病相关的区域包括精神分裂症易感性位点[10,11]和涉及脊髓小脑性共济失调 10(SCA10)的序列[12]。我们早在数据收集阶段就将人类 22 号染色体的序列免费对社会开放,这使得一些与该染色体相关的疾病和其他基因的研究因此受益[13-19]。

基因组测序

为了识别作为 22 号染色体测序底物的基因组克隆,科研人员用黏粒、F 黏粒、细菌人工染色体(BAC)和 P1 衍生人工染色体(PAC)构建了大量的该染色体的克隆图谱。使用已知的来自该染色体的序列标签位点(STS)标记的序列,对覆盖超过 20 倍基因组的 BAC 和 PAC 克隆文库进行筛选,或使用 22 号染色体流式分选的 DNA 的黏粒和 F 黏粒文库进行筛选,识别来自部分 22 号染色体的克隆。在限制性内切酶指纹和 STS 含量数据的基础上组装重叠的克隆重叠群,并用已建立的该染色体框架图对其进行相应排列[9]。通过用每个重叠群末端的序列进行染色体步移迭代循环,将上述生成的新重叠群延长并连接。其中两处重叠群(AL049708 和 AL049760)的连接或延长使用了酵母人工染色体(YAC)来进行。已知序列图以存在 10 个缺口的 11 个克隆重叠群覆盖 22q,从包含已知的 22 号染色体着丝粒串联重复的序列延伸至 22q 端粒[20]。

在最终序列中,距着丝粒 234 kb 处发现另一个缺口(见下文),这个缺口很难进行测序。克隆重叠群之间的各个缺口分布于图的两端,在与着丝粒邻近的 4.3 Mb 处及端粒末端的 7.3 Mb 处。这些区域被一个 23 Mb 的中央重叠群分开。我们使用与重

end. These regions are separated by a central contig of 23 Mb. We have concluded that the gaps contain sequences that are unclonable with the available host-vector systems, as we were unable to detect clones containing the sequences in these gaps by screening more than 20 genome equivalents of bacterial clones using sequences adjacent to the contig ends.

The size of the seven gaps in the telomeric region has been estimated by DNA fibre fluorescence *in situ* hybridization (FISH). No gap in this region is judged to be larger than ~150 kb. For three of these gaps, a number of BAC and PAC clones that contain STSs on either side of the gap were shown to be deleted for at least a minimal core region by DNA fibre FISH. As these clones come from multiple donor DNA sources, these results are unlikely to be due to deletion in the DNA used to make the libraries. Furthermore, the same result was observed for the gap at 32,600 kb from the centromeric end of the sequence, when the DNA fibre FISH experiments were performed on DNA from two different lymphoblastoid cell lines. One possible explanation for this observation is that DNA fragments containing the gap sequences are initially cloned in the BAC library but clones that delete these sequences have a significant selective advantage as the library is propagated. As the observed size range of the cloned inserts in the BAC libraries ranges from 100 kb to more than 230 kb (http://bacpac.med.buffalo.edu/), such deletion events are not distinguishable on the basis of size from undeleted BACs. Additional analysis of the distribution of BAC end sequences from dbGSS (http://www.ncbi.nlm. nih.gov/dbGSS/index.html) suggests that the BAC coverage is sparser closer to the gaps and that this analysis did not identify any BACs spanning the gaps. The three remaining clone-map gaps in the proximal region of the long arm are in regions that may contain segments of previously characterized low-copy repeats[21]. These gaps could not be sized by DNA fibre FISH because of the extensive intra- and interchromosomal repeat sequences (see below) but were amenable to long-range restriction mapping. The gap between AP000529 and AP000530 was estimated to be shorter than 150 kb by comparison with a previously established long-range restriction map[22]. The gap closest to the centromere, which is less than 2 kb in size, could not be sequenced despite BAC clone coverage as it was unrepresented in plasmid or M13 libraries, and was intractable to all sequencing strategies applied. Detailed descriptions of several of the clone contigs have been published[21,23,24] or will be published elsewhere.

Each sequencing group took responsibility for completion of adjacent areas of the sequence as illustrated in Fig. 1. (Editorial note: this figure was original included as a fold-out insert. For details, see http://www.nature.com/articles/990031/figures/1) A set of minimally overlapping clones (the "tile path") was chosen from the physical map and sequenced using a combination of a random shotgun assembly, followed by directed sequencing to close gaps and resolve ambiguities ("finishing"). The major problems encountered during completion of the sequence in the directed sequencing phase were CpG islands, tandem repeats and apparent cloning biases. Directed sequencing using oligonucleotide primers, very short insert plasmid libraries, or identification of bridging clones by screening high complexity plasmid or M13 libraries solved these problems.

叠群末端相邻的序列对覆盖超过 20 倍基因组的细菌克隆进行筛选，仍无法检测到含有这些缺口序列的克隆，因此我们认为这些缺口包含用现有宿主–载体系统无法克隆的序列。

通过 DNA 纤维荧光原位杂交（FISH）估算端粒区域七个缺口的大小。经判断，这一区域的缺口均不超过 150 kb 左右。据 DNA 纤维荧光原位杂交显示，对其中三个缺口而言，一些在缺口的任意一侧包含 STS 的 BAC 和 PAC 克隆被删去了至少一处最小核心区。由于这些克隆有多个 DNA 供体来源，因此这些结果不可能是由于用于构建文库的 DNA 存在缺失。此外，当在两种不同成淋巴母细胞细胞系 DNA 上进行 DNA 纤维荧光原位杂交实验时，在序列中距着丝粒末端 32,600 kb 的缺口处也观察到同样的结果。这个现象的一种可能解释是，包含缺口序列的 DNA 片段最初在 BAC 文库中进行了克隆，但当文库扩增时，删除这些序列的克隆有显著的选择性优势。观察到的插入 BAC 文库的克隆片段的大小从 100 kb 到 230 kb 以上不等（http://bacpac.med.buffalo.edu/），因此这些缺失状况无法根据未缺失的 BAC 大小进行区分。对来自 dbGSS（http://www.ncbi.nlm.nih.gov/dbGSS/index.html）的 BAC 末端序列的分布进一步分析表明，接近缺口处 BAC 覆盖稀疏，这一分析也没有发现任何跨过缺口的 BAC。剩下的三个在长臂近端区域的克隆图谱缺口位于可能包含早先表征过的低拷贝重复片段的区域[21]。由于大量染色体内和染色体间重复序列（见下文）的存在，这些缺口的大小无法通过 DNA 纤维荧光原位杂交测定，但可以通过长距离限制性作图得到。通过与先前建立的长距离限制图比较可知，AP000529 和 AP000530 之间的缺口估计小于 150 kb[22]。与着丝粒最近的缺口不到 2 kb，但由于在质粒和 M13 文库中没有表达，因此尽管被 BAC 克隆覆盖却仍无法测序，而且在所有测序策略中均无法处理。几个克隆重叠群的详细介绍已经发表[21,23,24]，或将另行发表。

序列相邻区域的测序由每个测序小组负责完成，如图 1 所示。（编者注：这张图在原文中是一个折叠插入图，细节请见 http://www.nature.com/articles/990031/figures/1）从物理图中选出一套最小重叠克隆（"覆瓦式"）并采用随机鸟枪法组件的组合进行测序，继而为封闭缺口和消除模糊（"精加工"）进行直接测序。在直接测序阶段的序列完成期间遇到的主要问题是 CpG 岛、串联重复序列和明显的克隆偏好。这些问题通过以下方法进行解决：使用寡核苷酸引物进行直接测序、使用极短的插入质粒文库，或通过筛选高复杂性质粒或 M13 文库识别桥接克隆。

Fig. 1. The sequence of human chromosome 22. Coloured boxes depict the annotated features of the sequence of human chromosome 22, with the centromere to the left and the telomere to the right. Coordinates are in kilobases. Vertical yellow blocks indicate the positions of the gaps in the sequence and are proportional in size to the estimated size of each gap. From bottom to top the following features are displayed: positions of interspersed repetitive sequences including tandem repeats categorized by nucleotide repeat unit length (at this resolution *Alu* repeats are not visibly separated in some regions); the positions of the microsatellite markers in the genetic map of Dib *et al*[36]; the tiling path of genomic clones used to determine the sequence labelled by their GenBank/EMBL/DDBJ accession number and coloured according to the source of the sequence; and the annotated gene, pseudogene and CpG island content of the sequence. Transcripts and pseudogenes oriented 5′ to 3′ on the DNA strand from centromere to telomere are designated "+", those on the opposite strand "−". In the transcript rows, the annotated genes are subdivided by colour according to the criteria in the text. Annotated genes with approved gene symbols from the HUGO nomenclature committee are labelled. For details of all the genes with their positions in the reference sequence, see Supplementary Information, Table 1. In the case of the immunoglobulin variable region, the entire locus has been drawn as a single block; in reality, this is a complex of variable chain genes (see ref. 27). At the top is a graphical plot of the repeat density for the common interspersed repeats *Alu* and Line1, and the C+G base frequency across the sequence. Each is calculated as a percentage of the sequence using a sliding 100-kb window moved in 50-kb iterations. Since the production of Fig. 1, six accession codes have been updated. The new codes are AL050347 (for Z73987), AL096754 (for Z68686), AL049749 (for Z82197), Z75892 (for Z75891), AL078611 (for Z79997) and AL023733 (for AL023593).

The completed sequence covers 33.4 Mb of 22q with 11 gaps and has been estimated to be accurate to less than 1 error in 50,000 bases, by internal and external checking exercises[25]. The order and size of each of the contiguous pieces of sequence is detailed in Table 1. The largest contiguous segment stretches over 23 Mb. From our gap-size estimates, we calculate that we have completed 33,464 kb of a total region spanning 34,491 kb and that therefore the sequence is complete to 97% coverage of 22q. The complete sequence and analysis is available on the internet (http://www.sanger.ac.uk/HGP/Chr22 and http://www. genome.ou.edu/Chr22.html).

Table 1. Sequence contigs on chromosome 22

Contig*	Size (kb)	
AP000522–AP000529	234	
gap		**1.9**
AP000530–AP000542	406	
gap		**~150**
AP000543–AC006285	1,394	
gap		**~150**
AC008101–AC007663	1,790	
gap		**~100**
AC007731–AL049708	23,006	
gap		**~50**
AL118498–AL022339	767	
gap†		**~50-100**

图 1. 人类 22 号染色体的序列。彩色方块指示人类 22 号染色体序列的注释特征，其着丝粒在左侧，端粒在右侧。坐标单位为千碱基。垂直黄色区域指示序列中缺口的位置，其大小与每个缺口的估算大小成比例。自下而上显示的特征是：散布重复序列的位置，包括根据核苷酸重复单位长度分类的串联重复（在此分辨率下 Alu 重复在某些区域无法通过视觉区分）；迪卜等人的遗传图中微卫星标记物的位置[36]；基因组克隆覆瓦式路径用来决定 GenBank/EMBL/DDBJ 检索编号标记的序列，并根据序列来源用不同颜色显示；以及序列中注释的基因、假基因和 CpG 岛含量。在 DNA 链上，从着丝粒到端粒按 5′ 到 3′ 走向的转录本和假基因被命名为"+"，相应在反义链上的为"−"。在转录物各行中，注释基因根据文中的标准用颜色进行了细分。来自 HUGO 命名委员会核准的基因符号的注释基因进行了标记。所有基因及其在参考序列中的位置的详细情况见补充信息表 1。对于免疫球蛋白可变区，整个基因座已绘制为单一区域；实际上这是可变链基因的复合体（见参考文献 27）。顶部是常见散布重复 Alu 和 Line1 的重复密度，以及序列中 C+G 碱基频率的图表。二者都是使用 100 kb 的滑动窗口及 50 kb 的迭代进行计算得到的，并表示为序列的百分比。图 1 制成之后有 6 个检索号发生了更新。新编号为：AL050347（原 Z73987）、AL096754（原 Z68686）、AL049749（原 Z82197）、Z75892（原 Z75891）、AL078611（原 Z79997）和 AL023733（原 AL023593）。

　　全部的序列覆盖 22q 33.4 Mb，有 11 个缺口，通过内部和外部检查，序列准确度预计达到每 50,000 碱基中错误数小于 1[25]。每一个连续的序列片段的顺序和大小详见表 1。最大的连续片段延伸超过 23 Mb。根据对缺口大小的估算，我们已经完成了总长 34,491 kb 区域中的 33,464 kb，因此，序列对 22q 的覆盖率达到 97%。完整的序列及分析可以在网上获得（http://www.sanger.ac.uk/HGP/Chr22 和 http://www.genome.ou.edu/Chr22.html）。

表 1. 22 号染色体的序列重叠群

重叠群 *	大小 (kb)
AP000522–AP000529	234
缺口	1.9
AP000530–AP000542	406
缺口	约 150
AP000543–AC006285	1,394
缺口	约 150
AC008101–AC007663	1,790
缺口	约 100
AC007731–AL049708	23,006
缺口	约 50
AL118498–AL022339	767
缺口 †	约 50～100

Continued

Contig*	Size (kb)	
Z85994–AL049811	1,528	
gap		**~150**
AL049853–AL096853	2,485	
gap‡		**~50**
AL096843–AL078607	190	
gap†		**~100**
AL078613–AL117328	993	
gap		**~100**
AL080240–AL022328	291	
gap†		**~100**
AL096767–AC002055	380	
Total sequence length	33,464	
Total length of 22q	34,491	

* Contigs are indicated by the first and last sequence in the orientation centromere to telomere, and are named by their GenBank/EMBL/DDBJ accession numbers.

† These gaps are spanned by BAC and/or PAC clones with deletions.

‡ This gap shows a complex duplication of AL096853 in DNA fibre FISH.

Sequence Analysis and Gene Content

Analysis of the genomic sequence of the model organisms has made extensive use of predictive computational analysis to identify genes[26-28]. In human DNA, identification of genes by these methods is more difficult because of extensive splicing, lower density of exons and the high proportion of interspersed repetitive sequences. The accuracy of *ab initio* gene prediction on vertebrate genomic sequence has been difficult to determine because of the lack of sequence that has been completely annotated by experiment. To determine the degree of overprediction made by such algorithms, all genes within a region need to be experimentally identified and annotated, however it is virtually impossible to know when this job is complete. A 1.4-Mb region of human genomic sequence around the BRCA2 locus has been subjected to extensive experimental investigation, and it is believed that the 170 exons identified is close to the total number expressed in the region.

The most recent calibration of *ab initio* methods against this region (R.B.S.K. and T.H., manuscript in preparation) shows that with the best methods[29,30] more than 30% of exon predictions do not overlap any experimental exons, in other words, they are overpredictions. Furthermore, having now applied this analysis to larger amounts of data (more than 15 Mb from the Sanger Annotated Genome Sequence Repository which can

续表

重叠群 *	大小（kb）	
Z85994–AL049811	1,528	
缺口		约 150
AL049853–AL096853	2,485	
缺口 ‡		约 50
AL096843–AL078607	190	
缺口 †		约 100
AL078613–AL117328	993	
缺口		约 100
AL080240–AL022328	291	
缺口 †		约 100
AL096767–AC002055	380	
序列总长度	33,464	
22q 总长度	34,491	

* 重叠群按照从着丝粒到端粒方向的第一个和最后一个序列进行标记，并用其在 GenBank/EMBL/DDBJ 检索编号命名。
† 被删除的 BAC 和/或 PAC 克隆横跨这些缺口。
‡ 该缺口在 DNA 纤维荧光原位杂交中显示出复杂的 AL096853 重复。

序列分析和基因含量

模式生物的基因组序列分析已经广泛用于确定基因的预测计算分析中[26-28]。人类 DNA 中存在剪接多、外显子密度低和散在重复序列比例高的问题，因此通过这些方法鉴定基因更为困难。由于缺乏完全通过实验注释的序列，脊椎动物基因组中从头预测基因的准确性一直难以确定。为确定这些算法产生的过度预测的程度，一个区域内所有的基因都需要用实验方法鉴定并注释，但是这项任务何时能完成又是几乎不可知的。针对 BRCA2 基因座周围 1.4 Mb 的人类基因组序列区域的深入实验研究认为，鉴定出的 170 个外显子接近该区域中表达的总数。

针对这个区域的从头算法的最新校准（布鲁斯克耶维奇和哈伯德，稿件准备中）表明，使用最佳方法[29,30]时，超过 30% 的外显子预测未与任何实验证实的外显子重合，换句话说，它们的预测是过度的。此外，将这一分析应用于更大规模的数据（超过 15 Mb，来自桑格注释基因组序列存储库，可作为 Genesafe 集合（http://www.hgmp.mrc.ac.uk/Genesafe/）的一部分而获得）之后证实，在序列不同区域基因模型预

be obtained as part of the Genesafe collection (http://www.hgmp.mrc.ac.uk/Genesafe/)), it is confirmed that prediction accuracy also varies considerably between different regions of sequence. It was hoped that these calibration efforts would lead to rules for reliable gene prediction based on *ab initio* methods alone, perhaps on the basis of combining several different methods, GC content and so on. However, so far this has not been possible. The same analysis also shows that although ~95% of genes are at least partially predicted by *ab initio* methods, few gene structures are completely correct (none in BRCA2) and more than 20% of experimental exons are not predicted at all. The comparison of *ab initio* predictions and the annotated gene structures (see below) in the chromosome 22 sequence is consistent with this, with 94% of annotated genes at least partially detected by a Genscan gene prediction, but only 20% of annotated genes having all exons predicted exactly. Sixteen per cent of all the exons in annotated genes were not predicted at all, although this is only 10% for internal exons (that is, not 5' and 3' ends). As a result, we do not consider that *ab initio* gene prediction software can currently be used directly to reliably annotate genes in human sequence, although it is useful when combined with other evidence (see below), for example, to define splice-site boundaries, and as a starting point for experimental studies.

Fortunately, a vast resource of experimental data on human genes in the form of complementary DNA and protein sequences and expressed sequence tags (ESTs) is available which can be used to identify genes within genomic DNA. Furthermore about 60% of human genes have distinctive CpG island sequences at their 5' ends[31] which can also be used to identify potential genes. Thus, the approach we have taken to annotating genes in the chromosome 22 sequence relies on a combination of similarity searches against all available DNA and protein databases, as well as a series of *ab initio* predictions. Upon completion of the sequence of each clone in the tile path, the sequence was subjected to extensive computational analysis using a suite of similarity searches and prediction tools. Briefly, the sequences were analysed for repetitive sequence content, and the repeats were masked using RepeatMasker (http://ftp.genome.washington.edu/RM/RepeatMasker. html). Masked sequence was compared to public domain DNA and protein databases by similarity searches using the blast family of programs[32]. Unmasked sequence was analysed for C+G content and used to predict the presence of CpG islands, tandem repeat sequences, tRNA genes and exons. The completed analysis was assembled into contigs and visualized using implementations of ACEDB (http://www.sanger. ac.uk/Software/Acedb/). In addition, the contiguous masked sequence was analysed using gene prediction software[29,30].

Gene features were identified by a combination of human inspection and software procedures. Figure 1 shows the 679 gene sequences annotated across 22q. They were grouped according to the evidence that was used to identify them as follows: genes identical to known human gene or protein sequences, referred to as "known genes" (247); genes homologous, or containing a region of similarity, to gene or protein sequences from human or other species, referred to as "related genes" (150); sequences homologous to only ESTs, referred to as "predicted genes" (148); and sequences homologous to a known gene or protein, but with a disrupted open reading frame, referred to "pseudogenes" (134). (See

测的准确度有很大的差别。人们希望这些校准工作可以形成单纯基于从头算法或基于几种不同方法和 GC 含量等相结合的可靠的基因预测标准。然而迄今为止这还从未实现。同样的分析还表明，虽然大约 95% 的基因通过从头算法得到了至少部分的预测，但只有很少数基因的预测结构是完全正确的（在 BRCA2 中完全没有），而且 20% 以上实验验证的外显子根本无法被预测到。22 号染色体序列的从头算法预测和已注释的基因结构的对比（见下文）与此相符，通过 Genscan 基因预测，94% 的注释基因至少能部分检测到，但只有 20% 注释基因的所有外显子能准确预测。注释基因中所有外显子的 16% 完全未被预测，然而这只占内部外显子（即不是 5′ 和 3′ 端）的 10%。因此我们认为，目前基因从头预测软件还不能直接用于对人类序列基因进行可靠的注释，但它在结合其他证据时还是有用的（见下文），例如确定剪接位点边界和作为实验研究的起点。

幸运的是，大量关于人类基因的互补 DNA 和蛋白质序列及表达序列标签（EST）的实验数据资源可以用于确定基因组 DNA 中的基因。另外，约 60% 的人类基因在其 5′ 端有独特的 CpG 岛序列[31]，也可以用来确定可能存在的基因。因此，我们采取的用于注释 22 号染色体序列中基因的方法依赖于综合运用所有类似的可用的 DNA 和蛋白质数据库以及一系列从头预测。一旦完成覆瓦式分析中每个克隆的序列，该序列会用一套相似性的搜索和预测工具进行大量计算分析。简言之，分析序列的重复序列含量，并且用 RepeatMasker 对重复序列进行标记（http://ftp.genome.washington.edu/RM/RepeatMasker.html）。使用 blast 系列程序进行相似性搜索，将标记的序列与公共领域的 DNA 和蛋白质数据库进行比对[32]。分析未标记序列 C+G 的含量，并且用于预测 CpG 岛、串联重复序列、tRNA 基因和外显子的存在。将已完成的分析组装为重叠群，并通过 ACEDB 进行查询实现可视化（http://www.sanger.ac.uk/Software/Acedb/）。此外，用基因预测软件对连续标记的序列进行分析[29,30]。

基因特征通过人为识别检查和软件程序相结合确定。图 1 给出了 22q 中已注释的 679 个基因序列。根据识别它们的证据将其分组如下：与已知的人类基因或蛋白质序列一致的基因命名为"已知基因"（247 个）；与来自人类或其他物种的基因或蛋白质序列同源或含有相似区域的基因命名为"相关基因"（150 个）；只与 EST 同源的序列命名为"预测基因"（148 个）；与已知基因或蛋白质序列同源，但其可读框被中断的序列命名为"假基因"（134 个）。（关于这些基因的详细情况见补充信息表 1。）

Supplementary Information, Table 1, for details of these genes.) The *ab initio* gene prediction program, Genscan, predicted 817 genes (6,684 exons) in the contiguous sequence, of which 325 do not form part of the annotated genes categorized above. Given the calibration of *ab initio* prediction methods discussed above, we estimate that of the order of 100 of these will represent parts of "real" genes for which there is currently no supporting evidence in any sequence database, and that the remainder are likely to be false positives.

The total length of the sequence occupied by the annotated genes, including their introns, is 13.0 Mb (39% of the total sequence). Of this, only 204 kb contain pseudogenes. About 3% of the total sequence is occupied by the exons of these annotated genes. This contrasts sharply with the 41.9% of the sequence that represents tandem and interspersed repeat sequences. There is no significant bias towards genes encoded on one strand at the 5% level ($\chi^2 = 3.83$).

A striking feature of the genes detected is their variety in terms of both identity and structure. There are several gene families that appear to have arisen by tandem duplication. The immunoglobulin λ locus is a well-known example, but there also are other immunoglobulin-related genes on the chromosome outside the immunoglobulin λ region. These include the three genes of the immunoglobulin λ-like (IGLL) family plus a fourth possible member of the family (AC007050.7). There are five clustered immunoglobulin κ variable region pseudogenes in AC006548, and an immunoglobulin variable-related sequence (VpreB3) in AP000348. Much further away from the λ genes is a variable region pseudogene, ~123 kb telomeric of IGLL3 in sequence AL008721 (coordinates ~9,420–9,530 kb from the centromeric end of the sequence), and a cluster of two λ constant region pseudogenes and a variable region pseudogene in sequences AL008723/AL021937 (coordinates ~16,060–16,390 kb from the centromeric end).

Human chromosome 22 also contains other duplicated gene families that encode glutathione *S*-transferases, Ret-finger-like proteins[19], phorbolins or APOBECs, apolipoproteins and β-crystallins. In addition, there are families of genes that are interspersed among other genes and distributed over large chromosomal regions. The γ-glutamyl transferase genes represent a family that appears to have been duplicated in tandem along with other gene families, for instance the BCR-like genes, that span the 22q11 region and together form the well-known LCR22 (low-copy repeat 22) repeats (see below).

The size of individual genes encoded on this chromosome varies over a wide range. The analysis is incomplete as not all 5′ ends have been defined. However, the smallest complete genes are only of the order of 1 kb in length (for example, HMG1L10 is 1.13 kb), whereas the largest single gene (LARGE[15]) stretches over 583 kb. The mean genomic size of the genes is 19.2 kb (median 3.7 kb). Some complete gene structures appear to contain only single exons, whereas the largest number of exons in a gene (PIK4CA) is 54. The mean exon number is 5.4 (median 3). The mean exon size is 266 bp (median 135 bp). The smallest complete exon we have identified is 8 bp in the PITPNB gene. The largest single exon is 7.6 kb in the PKDREJ, which is an intron-less gene with a 6.7-kb open reading frame. In addition,

基因从头预测程序 Genscan 在连续序列中预测了 817 个基因（6,684 个外显子），其中 325 个不属于上面分类的注释基因。鉴于上文讨论的从头预测方法的校准，我们估计其中 100 个将代表部分目前在任何序列数据库中还没有支持性证据的"真正"基因，而其余则可能是假阳性。

这些注释基因包括其内含子所占的序列总长度为 13.0 Mb（占总序列的 39%），其中只有 204 kb 含有假基因。这些注释基因的外显子约占总序列的 3%，这与代表串联和散布重复序列的序列所占的比例（41.9%）形成鲜明对比。对于一条链上的编码基因，在 5% 的水平上不存在显著性偏差（$\chi^2 = 3.83$）。

检测到的基因的一个显着特点是它们在一致性和结构上的多样性。有几个基因家族可能是通过串联重复产生的。免疫球蛋白 λ 位点是众所周知的例子，但在免疫球蛋白 λ 区域外的染色体上也有其他免疫球蛋白相关基因。其中包括免疫球蛋白 λ 样（IGLL）家族的 3 个基因以及该家族的第 4 个可能成员（AC007050.7）。AC006548 有五个成簇的免疫球蛋白 κ 可变区假基因，AP000348 有一个免疫球蛋白可变相关序列（VpreB3）。距离 λ 基因更远的地方，在序列 AL008721 中，IGLL3 端粒侧约 123 kb 处（距序列着丝粒端约 9,420 ~ 9,530 kb 处）有一个可变区假基因，在序列 AL008723/AL021937 中（距着丝粒端约 16,060 ~ 16,390 kb 处）有一个由两个 λ 恒定区假基因和一个可变区假基因形成的簇。

人类 22 号染色体还包含其他重复基因家族，这些基因家族编码谷胱甘肽 S-转移酶、Ret-指样蛋白[19]、phorbolin 或 APOBEC、载脂蛋白和 β-晶状体蛋白。此外，有些基因家族散布在其他基因中并分散在大的染色体区域内。γ-谷氨酰转移酶基因代表一个可能与其他基因家族串联重复的家族，如 BCR 样基因，该家族跨越 22q11 区域并共同组成了著名的 LCR22（低拷贝重复 22）重复（见下文）。

这条染色体编码的单个基因大小差别很大。并非所有编码基因的 5′ 端都已确定，所以该分析是不完整的。然而，最小的完整基因长度仅为 1 kb 量级（例如，HMG1L10 是 1.13 kb），而最大的单基因（LARGE[15]）超过 583 kb。基因的平均大小是 19.2 kb（中位数为 3.7 kb）。一些完整的基因结构似乎只包含单一的外显子，而单个基因中外显子数量最多达 54 个（PIK4CA）。平均外显子数目是 5.4 个（中位数为 3 个）。外显子的平均大小为 266 bp（中位数为 135 bp）。我们已鉴定的最小的完整外显子为 8 bp，位于 PITPNB 基因中。最大的单一外显子为 7.6 kb，位于 PKDREJ 中，

two genes occur within the introns of other expressed genes. The 61-kb TIMP3 gene, which is involved in Sorsby fundus macular degeneration, lies within a 268-kb intron of the large SYN3 gene, and the 8.5-kb HCF2 gene lies within a 27.5-b intron of the PIK4CA gene. In each case, the genes within genes are oriented in the opposite transcriptional orientation to the outer gene. We also observe pseudogenes frequently lying within the introns of other functional genes.

Peptide sequences for the 482 annotated full-length and partial genes with an open reading frame of greater than or equal to 50 amino acids were analysed against the protein family (PFAM)[33], Prosite[34] and SWISS-PROT[35] databases. These data were processed and displayed in an implementation of ACEDB. Overall, 240 (50%) predicted proteins had matching domains in the PFAM database encompassing a total of 164 different PFAM domains. Of the residues making up these 482 proteins, 25% were part of a PFAM domain. This compares with PFAM's residue coverage of SWISS-PROT/TrEMBL, which is more than 45% and indicates that the human genome is enriched in new protein sequences. Sixty-two PFAM domains were found to match more than one protein, including ten predicted proteins containing the eukaryotic protein kinase domain (PF00069), nine matching the Src homology domain 3 (PF00018) and eight matching the RhoGAP domain (PF00620). Fourteen predicted proteins contain zinc-finger domains (See Supplementary Information, Table 2, for details of the PFAM domains identified in the predicted proteins).

Nineteen per cent of the coding sequences identified were designated as pseudogenes because they had significant similarity to known genes or proteins but had disrupted protein coding reading frames. Because 82% of the pseudogenes contained single blocks of homology and lacked the characteristic intron-exon structure of the putative parent gene, they probably are processed pseudogenes. Of the remaining spliced pseudogenes, most represent segments of duplicated gene families such as the immunoglobulin κ variable genes, the β-crystallins, CYP2D7 and CYP2D8, and the GGT and BCR genes. The pseudogenes are distributed over the entire sequence, interspersed with and sometimes occurring within the introns of annotated expressed genes. However, there also is a dense cluster of 26 pseudogenes in the 1.5-Mb region immediately adjacent to the centromere; the significance of this cluster is currently unclear.

Given that the sequence of 33.4 Mb of chromosome 22q represents 1.1% of the genome and encodes 679 genes, then, if the distribution of genes on the other chromosomes is similar, the minimum number of genes in the entire human genome would be at least 61,000. Previous work has suggested that chromosome 22 is gene rich[6] by a factor of 1.38 (http://www.ncbi.nlm.nih.gov/genemap/page.cgi?F = GeneDistrib.html), which would reduce this estimate to ~45,000 genes. It is important, however, to recognize that the analysis described here only provides a minimum estimate for the gene content of chromosome 22q, and that further studies will probably reveal additional coding sequences that could not be identified with the current approaches.

该基因是一个有 6.7 kb 可读框的无内含子的基因。此外，有两个基因出现在其他表达基因的内含子中。与索斯比眼底黄斑变性有关的 61 kb 的 TIMP3 基因位于较大的 SYN3 基因的一个 268 kb 的内含子中，而 8.5 kb 的 HCF2 基因位于 PIK4CA 基因的 27.5 b 的内含子中。在这两种情况中，内部基因的转录方向与外部基因相反。我们还观察到，假基因经常位于其他功能性基因的内含子中。

使用蛋白质家族 (PFAM)[33]、Prosite[34] 和 SWISS-PROT[35] 数据库，对可读框大于等于 50 个氨基酸的 482 个已注释的全长和部分基因的多肽序列进行了分析。这些数据在执行 ACEDB 任务查询中被处理和显示。总体而言，240 个 (50%) 预测蛋白质在总数为 164 个不同 PFAM 域的 PFAM 数据库中有匹配结构域。在组成这 482 个蛋白质的残基中，有 25% 属于一个 PFAM 结构域。与此相比，PFAM 的残基覆盖 SWISS-PROT/TrEMBL 超过 45%，表明人类基因组在新的蛋白质序列中被富集。有 62 个 PFAM 结构域可匹配一个以上的蛋白质，包括 10 个含有真核蛋白质激酶结构域 (PF00069) 的测预蛋白质，9 个匹配 Src 同源结构域 3 (PF00018) 的测预蛋白质和 8 个匹配 RhoGAP 域 (PF00620) 的测预蛋白质。14 个预测蛋白质含有锌指结构域（在预测蛋白中鉴定 PFAM 域的详细信息见补充信息表 2）。

已鉴定的编码序列中有 19% 被认为是假基因，其原因是它们与已知基因或蛋白有显著相似性，但蛋白质编码可读框被破坏。由于 82% 的假基因含单一区域同源性，而且缺乏假定的亲本基因特征性的内含子-外显子结构，因此它们可能是被加工过的假基因。在其余的剪接假基因中，大多数代表重复的基因家族片段，如免疫球蛋白 κ 可变基因、β-晶状体蛋白、CYP2D7 和 CYP2D8，以及 GGT 和 BCR 基因。假基因分布在整个序列中，分散存在于已注释的表达基因的内含子之间，有时存在于其内部。然而，还有一簇密集的 26 个假基因位于毗邻着丝粒的 1.5 Mb 区域内；这个基因簇的意义目前还不清楚。

考虑到染色体 22q 上 33.4 Mb 的序列代表人类基因组的 1.1%，并编码 679 个基因，因此，如果基因在其他染色体上的分布与此相似，那么整个人类基因组的最小基因总数可能至少为 61,000 个。之前的工作已经显示，22 号染色体基因丰度较高[6]，系数为 1.38 (http://www.ncbi.nlm.nih.gov/genemap/page.cgi?F = GeneDistrib.html)，据此，该估值将降为约 45,000 个基因。尽管认识到此处描述的分析只提供 22q 染色体最低基因含量的估值很重要，进一步研究可能会揭示更多不能用现有方法鉴定的编码序列。

Two lines of evidence point to the existence of additional genes that are not detected in this analysis. First, the 553 predicted CpG islands, which typically lie at the true 5′ ends of about 60% of human genes[31], are in excess of 60% of the number of genes identified (60% = 327, excluding pseudogenes); 282 of the genes identified have CpG islands at or close to the 5′ end (within 5-kb upstream of the first exon, or 1-kb downstream). Thus, there could be up to 271 additional genes associated with CpG islands undetected in the sequence. Second, there are 325 putative genes predicted by the *ab initio* gene prediction program, Genscan, that are not in regions already containing annotated transcripts. We estimate (see above) that roughly 100 of these will represent parts of real genes. Identifying additional genes will require further computational and experimental studies. These studies are continuing and entail testing candidate sequences for possible messenger RNA expression, implementing new gene prediction software able to detect the regions around or near CpG islands that currently have no identified transcript, and further analysis of sequences that are conserved between human and mouse. Furthermore, full-length cDNA sequences that accumulate in the sequence databases of human and other species will be used to refine the gene structures.

The Long-range Chromosome Landscape

Critical to the utility of the genomic sequence to genetic studies is the integration of established genetic maps. The positions of the commonly used microsatellite markers from the Genethon genetic map[36] are given in Fig. 1. The correlation of the order of markers between the genetic map and the sequence is good, within the limitations of genetic mapping. Only a single marker (D22S1175) is discrepant between the two data sets, and this lies in a sequence that is repeated twice on the chromosome (AL021937, see below). In the telomeric region, four of the Genethon markers must lie in our sequence gaps, and we were unable to identify clones from all libraries tested for these. Comparison of genetic distance against physical distance for all the microsatellites whose order is maintained between the datasets shows a mean value of 1.87 cM Mb^{-1}. However, the relationship between genetic and physical distance across the chromosome partitions into two types of region, areas of high and low recombination (Fig. 2). The areas of high recombination may represent recombinational hot spots, although we have not yet been able to identify any specific sequence characteristics common to these areas.

The mean G+C content of the sequence is 47.8%. This is significantly higher than the G+C content calculated for the sum of all human genomic sequence determined so far (42%). Although this result was expected from previous indirect measurements of the G+C content of chromosome 22[7,8,37], the distribution is not uniform, but regionally segmented as illustrated in Fig. 1. There are clear fluctuations in the base content, resulting in areas that are relatively G+C rich and others that are relatively G+C poor. On chromosome 22 these regions stretch over several megabases. For example, the 2 Mb of sequence closest to the centromeric end of the sequence is relatively G+C poor, with the G+C content dropping below 40%. Similarly, the area between 16,000 and 18,800 kb from the

466

有两个系列的证据指出存在着更多在这一分析中没有检测到的基因。首先，CpG 岛通常位于约 60% 的人类基因的真正 5' 端[31]，而 553 个预测 CpG 岛超过已鉴定基因数量的 60%（不包括假基因，则 60% = 327 个）；有 282 个基因被发现在 5' 端或接近 5' 端处（第一外显子上游 5 kb 或下游 1 kb 内）有 CpG 岛。因此，在序列中可能还有与 CpG 岛有关的多达 271 个额外基因未检测到。其次，有 325 个由基因从头预测程序 Genscan 预测的假定基因未包含在已注释转录物的区域内。我们估计（见上文），其中大约 100 个代表部分真正的基因。要鉴定更多的基因需要进一步的计算与实验研究。这些研究仍在继续，并需要检测候选序列，寻找可能存在的信使 RNA 表达，应用新的基因预测软件，以检测目前没有鉴定到转录物的 CpG 岛的周围或附近区域，并进一步分析人类与小鼠之间的保守序列。此外，在人类和其他物种序列数据库中积累的全长 cDNA 序列将用于完善基因结构。

长距离染色体概况

用基因组序列进行遗传研究的关键是整合已有的遗传图谱。Genethon 遗传图谱常用的微卫星标记的位置[36] 如图 1。遗传图谱和序列之间标记顺序的相关性良好，并在遗传作图的要求限制之内。只有一个标记（D22S1175）在两个数据集之间有差异，它位于一个在染色体中重复两次的序列内（AL021937，见下文）。在端粒区域，一定有四个 Genethon 标志位于我们的序列缺口中，我们无法从为这些缺口而测试的所有文库中识别出克隆。将在这些数据集之间保持顺序的所有微卫星的遗传距离与物理距离进行对比显示其平均值为 1.87 cM · Mb^{-1}。然而，整个染色体中遗传距离和物理距离之间的关系分成两个区域类型：高重组区和低重组区（见图 2）。高重组区可能代表重组热点，不过我们还未能确定任何这些区域常见的特定序列特征。

序列的平均 G+C 含量为 47.8%。显著高于目前确定的所有人类基因组序列计算得到的 G+C 含量（42%）。虽然从先前间接测量的 22 号染色体的 G+C 含量[7,8,37] 可以预测这一结果，但分布并不一致，其区域分割如图 1 所示。碱基含量存在明显波动，导致某些区域的 G+C 含量相对较高，而其他区域的 G+C 含量相对较低。在 22 号染色体上，这些区域可延伸达几 Mb。例如，最接近序列着丝粒末端的 2 Mb 序列的 G+C 含量相对较低，降至 40% 以下。同样，距序列着丝粒末端 16,000 到 18,800 kb 的区域 G+C 含量也始终低于 45%。G+C 丰富的区域（如距序列着丝粒

centromeric end of the sequence is consistently below 45% G+C. The G+C rich regions often reach more than 55% G+C (for example, at 20,100–23,400 kb from the centromeric end of the sequence). This fluctuation appears to be consistent with previous observations that vertebrate genomes are segmented into "isochores" of distinct G+C content[38] and is similar to the structure seen in the human major histocompatibility complex (MHC) sequence[39]. Isochores correlate with both genes and chromosome structure. The G+C rich isochores are rich in genes and *Alu* repeats, and are located in the G+C rich chromosomal R-bands, whereas the G+C poor isochores are relatively depleted in genes and *Alu* repeats, and are located in the G-bands[8,37,40]. The G+C poor regions of chromosome 22 are depleted in genes and relatively poor in *Alu* sequences. For example, the region between 16,000 and 18,800 kb from the centromeric end contains just three genes, two of which are greater than 400 kb in length. The G+C poor regions also are depleted in CpG islands, which are clustered in the gene-rich, G+C rich regions. Although it is tempting to correlate the sequence features that we see with the chromosome banding patterns, we believe that high-resolution mapping of the chromosome band boundaries will be required to assign definitively these to genomic sequence.

Fig. 2. The relationship between physical and genetic distance. The sex-averaged genetic distances of Dib *et al.*[36] were obtained from ftp://ftp.genethon.fr/pub/Gmap/Nature-1995/ and the cumulative intermarker distances for unambiguously ordered markers (in cM) were plotted against the positions of the microsatellite markers in the genomic sequence. It should be stressed that the y axis does not represent the true genetic distance between distant markers but the sum of the local intermarker distances. The positions of selected genetic markers are labelled. Grey regions are indicative of areas of relatively increased recombination per unit physical distance.

Over 41.9% of the chromosome 22 sequence comprises interspersed and tandem repeat family sequences (Table 2). The density of repeats across the sequence is plotted in Fig. 1. There is variation in the density of *Alu* repeats and some of the regions with low *Alu* density correlate with the G+C poor regions, for example, in the region 16,000–18,800 kb from the centromeric end, and these data support the relationship of isochores with *Alu* distribution. However, in other areas the relationship is less clear. We provide a World-Wide Web interface to the long-range analyses presented here and to further analysis of the

末端 20,100 ～ 23,400 kb 的区域）中，其含量往往超过 55%。这种波动似乎与以前的结果一致，即脊椎动物基因组分割为不同 G+C 含量的"等容线"[38]，与人类主要组织相容性复合物（MHC）序列中的结构相似[39]。等容线与基因和染色体结构有关。G+C 丰富的等容线富含基因和 *Alu* 重复，位于 G+C 丰富的染色体 R 带，而 G+C 稀少的等容线所含的基因和 *Alu* 重复相对较少，且位于 G 带[8,37,40]。22 号染色体 G+C 稀少的区域不含基因且 *Alu* 序列也相对较少。例如，距着丝粒端 16,000 和 18,800 之间的区域只包含三个基因，其中两个基因长度大于 400 kb。G+C 稀少的区域也缺少 CpG 岛，后者集中在基因和 G+C 丰富的区域。虽然将我们看到的序列特征与染色体带型相结合是很吸引人的，但我们认为，要将这些序列特征明确地分配到基因组序列中，需要对染色体带的界限进行高分辨率作图。

图 2. 物理和遗传距离之间的关系。迪卜等人研究的性别平均遗传距离[36] 来自 ftp://ftp.genethon.fr/pub/Gmap/Nature-1995/，将顺序明确的累积的标记间距离（以 cM 为单位）相对基因组序列中微卫星标记的位置进行作图。应当指出，y 轴并不代表远距离标记物间的真正遗传距离，但代表局部标记间的距离总和。选定的遗传标记物的位置已标出。灰色区域指示每单位物理距离相对增加的重组区域。

22 号染色体上超过 41.9% 的序列包含散在和串联重复家族序列（见表 2）。序列中的重复密度绘制在图 1 中。*Alu* 重复的密度存在差异，一些低 *Alu* 密度的区域与 G+C 稀少区域（如距着丝粒末端 16,000 ～ 18,800 kb 的区域）有关，这些数据支持等容线与 *Alu* 分布的关系。但是，这种关系在其他区域不太明显。我们为本文进行的长距离分析以及对序列的许多其他重复类型和特征的进一步分析提供一个万维网界

many other repeat types and features of the sequence at http://www.sanger.ac.uk/cgi-bin/cwa/22cwa.pl. The 1-Mb region closest to the centromere contains several interesting repeat sequence features that may be typical of other pericentromeric regions. In addition to the density of pseudogenes described above, there is a large 120-kb block of tandemly repeated satellite sequence (D22Z3) centred 500 kb from the centromeric sequence start (not shown in Fig. 1, but evident from the absence of *Alu* and LINE1 sequences at this point). There is also a cluster of satellite II repeats 80-kb telomeric of the D22Z3 sequences. Isolated alphoid satellite repeats are found closer to the centromeric end of the sequence. Furthermore, this pericentromeric 1 Mb closest to the centromere contains many sequences that are shared with a number of different chromosomes, particularly chromosomes 2 and 14. During map construction, 33 out of 37 STSs designed from sequence that was free of high-copy repeats amplified from more than one chromosome in somatic cell hybrid panel analysis.

Table 2. The interspersed repeat content of human chromosome 22

Repeat type	Total number	Coverage (bp)	Coverage (%)
Alu	20,188	5,621,998	16.80
HERV	255	160,697	0.48
Line1	8,043	3,256,913	9.73
Line2	6,381	1,273,571	3.81
LTR	848	256,412	0.77
MER	3,757	763,390	2.28
MIR	8,426	1,063,419	3.18
MLT	2,483	605,813	1.81
THE	304	93,159	0.28
Other	2,313	625,562	1.87
Dinucleotide	1,775	133,765	0.40
Trinucleotide	166	18,410	0.06
Quadranucleotide	404	47,691	0.14
Pentanucleotide	16	1,612	0.0048
Other tandem	305	102,245	0.31
Total	55,664	14,024,657	41.91

Low-copy Repeats on Chromosome 22

To detect intra- and interchromosomal repeats, we compared the entire sequence of chromosome 22 to itself, and also to all other existing human genomic DNA sequence using Blastn[32] after masking high and medium frequency repeats. The results of the

面：http://www.sanger.ac.uk/cgi-bin/cwa/22cwa.pl。最接近着丝粒的 1 Mb 区域包含几个有趣的可能代表其他着丝粒周边区域的重复序列特征。除了上述假基因密度，有一个大的 120 kb 的串联重复卫星序列（D22Z3）集中在距着丝粒序列起始位置的 500 kb 处（图 1 中未显示，但根据这一位置缺乏 *Alu* 及 LINE1 序列可明显看出）。还有一组卫星 II 重复位于 D22Z3 序列的端粒 80 kb 处。孤立的 alphoid 卫星重复接近序列的着丝粒末端。此外，最接近着丝粒周边的 1 Mb 区域含有许多不同染色体（特别是染色体 2 和 14）共有的序列。在染色体图谱构建过程中，通过无高拷贝重复的序列设计的 37 个 STS 中，有 33 个在体细胞杂交分析中从不止一处染色体发生了扩增。

表 2. 人类 22 号染色体散布的重复情况

重复类型	总数目	覆盖范围（bp）	覆盖范围（%）
Alu	20,188	5,621,998	16.80
HERV	255	160,697	0.48
Line1	8,043	3,256,913	9.73
Line2	6,381	1,273,571	3.81
LTR	848	256,412	0.77
MER	3,757	763,390	2.28
MIR	8,426	1,063,419	3.18
MLT	2,483	605,813	1.81
THE	304	93,159	0.28
其他	2,313	625,562	1.87
二核苷酸	1,775	133,765	0.40
三核苷酸	166	18,410	0.06
四核苷酸	404	47,691	0.14
五核苷酸	16	1,612	0.0048
其他串联	305	102,245	0.31
总数	55,664	14,024,657	41.91

22 号染色体上的低拷贝重复

为检测染色体内和染色体间重复，在标记高、中频重复之后，我们用 Blastn 将 22 号染色体的整个序列与其本身进行比对，也与所有其他现有的人类基因组 DNA intrachromosomal sequence analysis were plotted as a dot matrix (Fig. 3) and reveal a series of interesting features. Locally duplicated gene families lie close to the diagonal axis of the plot. The most striking is the immunoglobulin λ locus that comprises a cluster of 36 potentially functional V-λ gene segments, 56 V-λ pseudogenes, and 27 partial V-λ pseudogenes ("relics"), together with 7 each of the J and C λ segments[24]. Other duplicated gene families that are visible from the dot matrix plot include the clustered genes for glutathione S-transferases, β-crystallins, apolipoproteins, phorbolins or APOBECs, the lectins LGALS1 and LGALS2 and the CYP2Ds. A partial inverted duplication of CSF2RB is also observed.

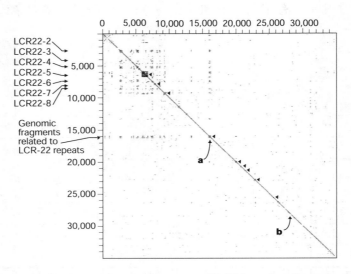

Fig. 3. Intrachromosomal repeats on human chromosome 22. High- and medium-copy repeats and low complexity sequence were masked using RepeatMasker and Dust, and masked sequences were compared using Blastn. The results were filtered to identify regions of more than 50% identity to the query sequence, and were plotted in a 2D matrix with a line proportional to the size of the region of identity. Localized gene family repeats are indicated by arrowheads along the diagonal. From the top, these are the immunoglobulin λ locus, the glutathione S-transferase genes, the β-crystallin genes, the Ret-finger-protein-like genes, the apolipoprotein genes, the colony-stimulating factor receptor (CSF2RB) inverted partial duplication, the lectins LGALS1 and LGALS2, the APOBEC genes and the CYP2D genes. Two 60-kb regions of more than 90% homology are labelled "a" (AL008723/AL021937) and "b" (AL031595/AL022339). Seven low-copy repeat regions (LCR22) and a region containing related genomic fragments are indicated at the left margin.

Much more striking are the long-range duplications, which are visible away from the diagonal axis. For example, a 60-kb segment of more than 90% similarity is seen between sequences AL008723/AL021937(at ~16,060–16,390 kb from the centromeric end) and AL031595/AL022339 (at ~27,970–28,110 kb from the centromeric end) separated by almost 12 Mb. The 22q11 region is particularly rich in repeated clusters[41]. Previous work described a low-copy repeat family in 22q11 that might mediate recombination events leading to the chromosomal rearrangements seen in cat eye, velocardiofacial and DiGeorge syndromes[21,42]. The availability of the entire DNA sequence allows detailed dissection of the molecular structure of these low-copy repeats (LCR22s). Edelmann et al. described eight

序列进行比对[32]。染色体内序列分析的结果绘制为点阵图（图 3），并显示出一系列有趣的特征。局部重复基因家族位于接近图对角线轴处。最引人注目的是免疫球蛋白 λ 位点，它包含由 36 个潜在功能 V-λ 基因片段、56 个 V-λ 假基因和 27 个部分 V-λ 假基因（"残迹"）形成的一个簇，以及 J 和 C λ 片段形成的 7 个簇[24]。其他重复基因家族在点阵图上都可以看到，包括以下成簇基因：谷胱甘肽 S-转移酶、β-晶状体蛋白、载脂蛋白、phorbolin 或 APOBEC、凝集素 LGALS1 和 LGALS2，以及 CYP2D。此外还观察到 CSF2RB 的部分反向重复。

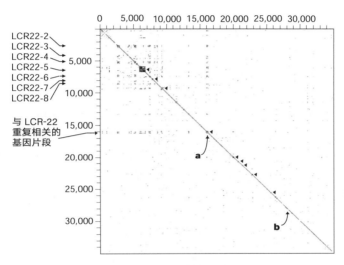

图 3. 人类 22 号染色体上的染色体内重复。用 RepeatMasker 和 Dust 标记高拷贝和中拷贝重复以及低复杂性序列，用 Blastn 比较被标记的序列。结果进行过滤以确定与所查询序列同一性多于 50% 的区域，并用与同一性区域大小成比例的直线绘制在二维矩阵中。沿对角线的箭头指示局部基因家族重复。从上方开始依次是免疫球蛋白 λ 位点、谷胱甘肽 S-转移酶基因、β-晶状体蛋白基因、Ret 指蛋白样基因、载脂蛋白基因、集落刺激因子受体（CSF2RB）倒置部分重复、凝集素 LGALS1 和 LGALS2、APOBEC 基因和 CYP2D 基因。同源性大于 90% 的两个 60 kb 区域标记为 "a"（AL008723/AL021937）和 "b"（AL031595/AL022339）。7 个低拷贝重复区域（LCR22）和一个包含相关基因组片段的区域显示在左边空白处。

更引人注目的是远离对角线轴的长距离重复。例如，在相距接近 12 Mb 的 AL008723/AL021937 序列（距着丝粒末端约 16,060 ~ 16,390 kb）和 AL031595/AL022339 序列（距着丝粒末端约 27,970 ~ 28,110 kb）之间可见一个相似性 90% 以上的 60 kb 的片段。22q11 区域尤其富含重复簇[41]。以往的工作介绍了 22q11 中有可能介导重组事件的一个低拷贝重复家族，这些重组事件导致猫眼、腭心面和迪格奥尔格综合征中观察到的染色体重排[21,42]。整个 DNA 序列的获得使我们可以详细分析这些低拷贝重复序列（LCR22）的分子结构。埃德尔曼等描述了 8 个 LCR22 区域[21,42]。我们无法

LCR22 regions[21,42]. We were unable to find the LCR22 repeat closest to the centromere, but it may lie in the gap at 700 kb from the centromeric end of the sequence. The other LCR22 regions are distributed over 6.5 Mb of 22q11. Analysis of the sequence shows that each LCR22 contains a set of genes or pseudogenes (Fig. 4). For example, five of the LCR22s contain copies of the γ-glutamyl transferase genes and γ-glutamy-transferase-related genes. There is also evidence that a more distant sequence at ~16,000 kb from the centromeric start of the genomic sequence shares certain sequences with the LCR22 repeats. This similarity involves related genomic fragments including parts of the Ret-finger-protein-like genes, and the IGLC and IGLV genes.

Fig. 4. Sequence composition of the LCR22 repeats. Illustration of the sequence composition of seven LCR22 repeats. The span of each LCR22 region is shown in megabases from the centromere. Coloured arrows indicate the extent of one of the thirteen genomic repeat regions and the orientation of the repeat. The known gene and marker content of these genomic repeat regions is indicated in the key. The black oval indicates the position of the gap in the sequence in LCR22-3.

Regions of Conserved Synteny with the Mouse

The genomic organization of different mammalian species is well known to be conserved[43]. Comparison of genetic and physical maps across species can aid in predicting gene locations in other species, identifying candidate disease genes[13], and revealing various other features relevant to the study of genome organization and evolution. For all the cross-species relationships, that between man and mouse has been most studied. We have examined the relationship of the human chromosome 22 genes to their mouse orthologues.

Of the 160 genes we identified in the human chromosome 22 sequence that have orthologues in mouse, 113 of the murine orthologues have known mouse chromosomal

发现最接近着丝粒的 LCR22 重复，但它可能位于距序列着丝粒末端 700 kb 的缺口中。其他 LCR22 区域分布在 22q11 上超过 6.5 Mb 的范围内。序列分析显示，每个 LCR22 包含一组基因或假基因（图 4）。例如，5 个 LCR22 包含 γ–谷氨酰转移酶基因和 γ–谷氨酰转移酶相关基因的拷贝。还有证据表明，一处更远的，距基因组序列着丝粒起点约 16,000 kb 的序列与 LCR22 重复存在某些共有序列。这种相似性涉及相关的基因组片段，包括部分 Ret 指蛋白样基因以及 IGLC 和 IGLV 基因。

图 4. LCR22 重复的序列组成。7 个 LCR22 重复的序列组成图示。每个 LCR22 区域的跨度从着丝粒开始计算，以 Mb 为单位。彩色箭头表示 13 个基因重复区域中一个的长度和重复方向。这些基因组重复区域的已知基因和标记物含量在图例中注明。黑色椭圆表示序列 LCR22-3 中缺口的位置。

与小鼠具有保守共线性的区域

目前已经清楚地知道，不同哺乳动物物种的基因组的组成是保守的[43]。比较物种间的遗传图谱和物理图谱有助于预测其他物种的基因位置，确定可能的疾病基因[13]，并揭示与基因组的组成和演化等研究相关的各种其他特征。在所有跨物种关系中，人与小鼠之间的关系研究得最多。我们之前已研究过人类 22 号染色体基因与小鼠直系同源基因之间的关系。

我们在人类 22 号染色体序列中鉴定出 160 个基因在小鼠中有直系同源基因，其中 113 个小鼠直系同源基因在小鼠染色体上的位置是已知的（数据可在以下网址获

locations (data available at http://www.sanger.ac.uk/HGP/Chr22/Mouse/). Examination of these mouse chromosomal locations mapped onto the human chromosome 22 sequence confirms the conserved linkage groups corresponding to human chromosome 22 on mouse chromosomes 6, 16, 10, 5, 11, 8 and 15[18,44-46] (Fig. 5). Furthermore, these studies allow placement of the sites of evolutionary rearrangements that have disrupted the conservation of synteny more accurately at the DNA sequence scale. For example, the breakdown of synteny between the mouse 8C1 block and the mouse 15E block occurs between the equivalents of the human HMOX1 and MB genes, which are separated by less than 160 kb that also contains a conspicuous 41-copy 18-nucleotide tandem repeat. A clear prediction from these data is that, for the most part, the unmapped murine orthologues of the human genes lie within these established linkage groups, along with the orthologues of the human genes that currently lack mouse counterparts. Exploitation of the chromosome 22 sequence may hasten the determination of the mouse genomic sequence in these regions.

Fig. 5. Regions of conserved synteny between human chromosome 22 and the mouse genome. Regions of mouse chromosomes with conserved synteny to human chromosome 22 are shown as adjacent coloured blocks, determined by the mouse map position of mouse orthologues to human chromosome 22 genes. The size of human chromosome 22 corresponding to each mouse chromosomal region is indicated in kb, as well as the size of the gap between the last orthologue in each conserved block. These data are available at http://www.sanger.ac.uk/Chr22/Mouse.

得：http://www.sanger.ac.uk/HGP/Chr22/Mouse/）。将小鼠染色体中的位置绘制到人类 22 号染色体序列上的检查，确认了小鼠 6、16、10、5、11、8 和 15 号染色体上的与人类 22 号染色体相对应的保守连锁群[18,44-46]（图 5）。此外，这些研究使我们能够在 DNA 序列的尺度上更准确地定位这些已经破坏了共线性的保守序列的演化重排。例如，小鼠 8C1 模块和 15E 模块之间共线性的破坏发生在相应的人 HMOX1 和 MB 基因之间的位置，这两个基因之间的距离不到 160 kb，其中包含一个明显的 41 拷贝的 18 个核苷酸串联重复。根据这些数据可以做出明确的预测：在大多数情况下，未作图的人类基因的小鼠直系同源基因与目前尚无小鼠对应物的人类基因的直系同源基因共同位于这些既定连锁群内。对 22 号染色体序列的开发利用有望加快确定这些区域的小鼠基因组序列。

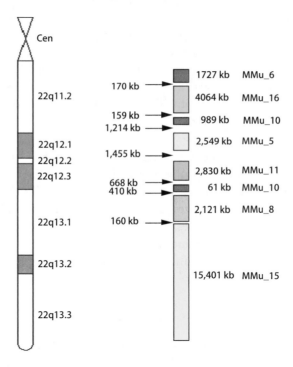

图 5. 人类 22 号染色体与小鼠基因组间具有保守共线性的区域。小鼠染色体上与人类 22 号染色体具有保守共线性的区域用相邻的彩色方块标出，通过小鼠与人类 22 号染色体基因的直系同源基因在小鼠图谱中的位置测得。对应于每个小鼠染色体区域的人类 22 号染色体的大小，以及每个保守模块中最后一个直系同源基因之间的缺口的大小，均以 kb 为单位。这些数据可在以下网站获得：http://www.sanger.ac.uk/Chr22/Mouse。

Conclusions

We have shown that the clone by clone strategy is capable of generating long-range continuity sufficient to establish the operationally complete genomic sequence of a chromosome. In doing so, we have generated the largest contiguous segment of DNA sequence to our knowledge to date. The analysis of the sequence gives a foretaste of the information that will be revealed from the remaining chromosomes.

We were unable to obtain sequence over 11 small gaps using the available cloning systems. It may be possible that additional approaches such as using combinations of cloning systems with small insert sizes and low-copy number could reduce the size of these gaps. Direct cloning of restriction fragments that cross these gaps into small insert plasmid or M13 libraries, or direct sequencing approaches might eventually provide access to all the sequence in the gaps. However, closing these gaps is certain to require considerable time and effort, and might be considered as a specialist activity outside the core genome-sequencing efforts. It also is probable that the sequence features responsible for several of these gaps are unlikely to be specific to chromosome 22. In the best case, similar unclonable sequences might be restricted to the centromeric and telomeric regions of the other chromosomes and areas with large tandem repeats, and it will be possible to obtain large contiguous segments for the bulk of the euchromatic genome.

Over the course of the project, the emerging sequence of chromosome 22 has been made available in advance of its final completion through the internet sites of the consortium groups and the public sequence databases[47]. The benefits of this policy can be seen in both the regular requests received from investigators for materials and information that arise as the result of sequence homology searches, and the publications that have used the data[14-19]. The genome project will continue to pursue this data release policy as we move closer to the anticipated completed sequence of humans, mice and other complex genomes[47,48].

Methods

The methods for construction of clone maps have been previously described[24,49,50] and can also be found at http://www.sanger.ac.uk/HGP/methods/. Details of sequencing methods and software are available at http://www.sanger.ac.uk/HGP/methods/, http://www.genome.ou.edu/proto.html, http://www-alis.tokyo.jst.go.jp/HGS/team_KU/team.html and in the literature[1,24].

(**402**, 489-495; 1999)

I. Dunham, N. Shimizu, B. A. Roe, S. Chissoe et al.[†]
[†] A full list of authors and affiliations is given in the original paper.

Received 5 November; accepted 11 November 1999.

结 论

我们已经证实，连续克隆这一方法产生的长距离连续性足以建立一条可操作的完整的染色体基因组序列。在此过程中，我们已经生成了迄今所知最大的连续 DNA 序列片段。对序列的分析预示了其他染色体将要揭示的信息。

使用现有的克隆系统，我们无法获取横跨 11 个小缺口的序列。其他方法，例如将具有小插入尺寸和低拷贝数目的克隆系统结合使用，有望缩减这些缺口的大小。将跨越这些缺口的限制性片段直接克隆到小插入片段质粒或 M13 文库中或直接进行测序，可能最终能够得到缺口中所有的序列。然而，弥合这些缺口必然需要大量的时间和精力，并且可能会被视为核心的基因组测序工作以外的专项活动。也有可能其中一些缺口的序列特征不是 22 号染色体特有的。最理想的情况是，类似的不能克隆的序列会局限于其他染色体的着丝粒和端粒区域，以及存在大串联重复的区域，这样我们就有可能获得大量基因组常染色质大的连续片段。

在项目执行过程中，22 号染色体的序列在最终完成前已通过合作单位的网站和公共序列数据库对外公布[47]。研究者在检索序列同源性后通常要求获取相应的材料和信息，也有一些出版物使用了我们的数据，由此可见该政策确实具有一定的益处[14-19]。在我们获取期望的完整的人类、小鼠和其他复杂基因组的序列的过程中，基因组计划将继续奉行这一数据发布政策[47,48]。

方 法

用于构建克隆图谱的方法此前已描述过[24,49,50]，也可以在 http://www.sanger.ac.uk/HGP/methods/ 找到。测序方法和软件的详细信息可在 http://www.sanger.ac.uk/HGP/methods/，http://www.genome.ou.edu/proto.html 和 http://www-alis.tokyo.jst.go.jp/HGS/team_KU/team.html 以及文献中找到[1,24]。

（李梅 翻译；肖景发 审稿）

References:

1. The Sanger Centre & The Genome Sequencing Centre. Toward a complete human genome sequence. *Genome Res.* **8**, 1097-1108 (1998).

2. Weber, J. L. & Myers, E. W. Human whole-genome shotgun sequencing. *Genome Res.* **7**, 401-409 (1997).

3. Green, P. Against a whole-genome shotgun. *Genome Res.* **7**, 410-417 (1997).

4. Collins, F. S. *et al.* New goals for the U.S. human genome project: 1998-2003. *Science* **282**, 682-689 (1998).

5. Morton, N. E. Parameters of the human genome. *Proc. Natl Acad. Sci. USA* **88**, 7474-7476 (1991).

6. Deloukas, P. *et al.* A physical map of 30,000 human genes. *Science* **282**, 744-746 (1998).

7. Craig, J. M. & Bickmore, W. A. The distribution of CpG islands in mammalian chromosomes. *Nature Genet.* **7**, 376-382 (1994).

8. Saccone, S., Caccio, S., Kusuda, J., Andreozzi, L. & Bernardi, G. Identification of the gene-richest bands in human chromosomes. *Gene* **174**, 85-94 (1996).

9. Collins, J. E. *et al.* A high-density YAC contig map of human chromosome 22. *Nature* **377**, 367-379 (1995).

10. Pulver, A. E. *et al.* Psychotic illness in patients diagnosed with velo-cardio-facial syndrome and their relatives. *J. Nerv. Ment. Dis.* **182**, 476-478 (1994).

11. Gill, M. *et al.* A combined analysis of D22S278 marker alleles in affected sib-pairs: support for a susceptibility locus for schizophrenia at chromosome 22q12. Schizophrenia Collaborative Linkage Group (Chromosome 22). *Am. J. Med. Genet.* **67**, 40-45 (1996).

12. Zu, L., Figueroa, K. P., Grewal, R. & Pulst, S. M. Mapping of a new autosomal dominant spinocerebellar ataxia to chromosome 22. *Am. J. Hum. Genet.* **64**, 594-599 (1999).

13. Southard-Smith, E. M. *et al.* Comparative analyses of the dominant megacolon-SOX10 genomic interval in mouse and human. *Mamm. Genome* **10**, 744-749 (1999).

14. Nishino, I., Spinazzola, A. & Hirano, M. Thymidine phosphorylase gene mutations in MNGIE, a human mitochondrial disorder. *Science* **283**, 689-692 (1999).

15. Peyrard, M. *et al.* The human LARGE gene from 22q12.3-q13.1 is a new, distinct member of the glycosyltransferase gene family. *Proc. natl Acad. Sci. USA* **96**, 598-603 (1999).

16. Kao, H. T. *et al.* A third member of the synapsin gene family. *Proc. Natl Acad. Sci. USA* **95**, 4667-4672 (1998).

17. Mittman, S., Guo, J., Emerick, M. C. & Agnew, W. S. Structure and alternative splicing of the gene encoding alpha1I, a human brain T calcium channel alpha1 subunit. *Neurosci. Lett.* **269**, 121-124 (1999).

18. Seroussi, E. *et al.* TOM1 genes map to human chromosome 22q13.1 and mouse chromosome 8C1 and encode proteins similar to the endosomal proteins HGS and STAM. *Genomics* **57**, 380-388 (1999).

19. Seroussi, E. *et al.* Duplications on human chromosome 22 reveal a novel ret finger protein-like gene family with sense and endogenous antisense transcripts. *Genome Res.* **9**, 803-814 (1999).

20. Ning, Y., Rosenberg, M., Biesecker, L. G. & Ledbetter, D. H. Isolation of the human chromosome 22q telomere and its application to detection of cryptic chromosomal abnormalities. *Hum. Genet.* **97**, 765-769 (1996).

21. Edelmann, L., Pandita, R. K. & Morrow, B. E. Low-copy repeats mediate the common 3-Mb deletion in patients with velo-cardio-facial syndrome. *Am. J. Hum. Genet.* **64**, 1076-1086 (1999).

22. McDermid, H. E. *et al.* Long-range mapping and construction of a YAC contig within the cat eye syndrome critical region. *Genome Res.* **6**, 1149-1159 (1996).

23. Johnson, A. *et al.* A 1.5-Mb contig within the cat eye syndrome critical region at human chromosome 22q11.2. *Genomics* **57**, 306-309 (1999).

24. Kawasaki, K. *et al.* One-megabase sequence analysis of the human immunoglobulin lambda gene locus. *Genome Res.* **7**, 250-261 (1997).

25. Felsenfeld, A., Peterson, J., Schloss, J. & Guyer, M. Assessing the quality of the DNA sequence from the Human Genome Project. *Genome Res.* **9**, 1-4 (1999).

26. Mewes, H. W. *et al.* Overview of the yeast genome. *Nature* **387**, 7-65 (1997).

27. Blattner, F. R. *et al.* The complete genome sequence of Escherichia coli K-12. *Science* **277**, 1453-1474 (1997).

28. The C. elegans Sequencing Consortium. Genome sequence of the nematode C. elegans: a platform for investigating biology. *Science* **282**, 2012-2018 (1998).

29. Solovyev, V. & Salamov, A. The Gene-Finder computer tools for analysis of human and model organisms genome sequences. *Ismb* **5**, 294-302 (1997).

30. Burge, C. & Karlin, S. Prediction of complete gene structures in human genomic DNA. *J. Mol. Biol.* **268**, 78-94 (1997).

31. Cross, S. H. & Bird, A. P. CpG islands and genes. *Curr. Opin. Genet. Dev.* **5**, 309-314 (1995).

32. Altschul, S. F., Gish, W., Miller, W., Myers, E. W. & Lipman, D. J. Basic local alignment search tool. *J. Mol. Biol.* **215**, 403-410 (1990).

33. Bateman, A. *et al.* Pfam 3.1: 1313 multiple alignments and profile HMMs match the majority of proteins. *Nucleic Acids Res.* **27**, 260-262 (1999).

34. Hofmann, K., Bucher, P., Falquet, L. & Bairoch, A. The PROSITE database, its status in 1999. *Nucleic Acis Res.* **27**, 215-219 (1999).

35. Bairoch, A. & Apweiler, R. The SWISS-PROT protein sequence data bank and its supplement TrEMBL in 1999. *Nucleic Acids Res.* **27**, 49-54 (1999).

36. Dib, C. *et al.* A comprehensive genetic map of the human genome based on 5,264 microsatellites. *Nature* **380**, 152-154 (1996).

37. Holmquist, G. P. Chromosome bands, their chromatin flavors, and their functional features. *Am. J. Hum. Genet.* **51**, 17-37 (1992).

38. Bernardi, G. *et al.* The mosaic genome of warm-blooded vertebrates. *Science* **228**, 953-958 (1985).

39. The MHC sequencing consortium. Complete sequence and gene map of a human major histocompatibility complex. *Nature* **401**, 921-923 (1999).

40. Bernardi, G. The isochore organization of the human genome. *Annu. Rev. Genet.* **23**, 637-661 (1989).

41. Collins, J. E., Mungall, A. J., Badcock, K. L., Fay, J. M. & Dunham, I. The organization of the gamma-glutamyl transferase genes and other low copy repeats in human chromosome 22q11. *Genome Res.* **7**, 522-531 (1997).

42. Edelmann, L. *et al.* A common molecular basis for rearrangement disorders on chromosome 22q11. *Hum. Mol. Genet.* **8**, 1157-1167 (1999).

43. Eppig, J. T. & Nadeau, J. H. Comparative maps: the mammalian jigsaw puzzle. *Curr. Opin. Genet. Dev.* **5**, 709-716 (1995).

44. Bucan, M. *et al.* Comparative mapping of 9 human chromosome 22q loci in the laboratory mouse. *Hum. Mol. Genet.* **2**, 1245-1252 (1993).

45. Carver, E. A. & Stubbs, L. Zooming in on the human-mouse comparative map: genome conservation re-examined on a high-resolution scale. *Genome Res.* **7**, 1123-1137 (1997).

46. Puech, A. *et al.* Comparative mapping of the human 22q11 chromosomal region and the orthologous region in mice reveals complex changes in gene organization. *Proc. Natl Acad. Sci.* USA **94**, 14608-14613 (1997).

47. Bentley, D. R. Genomic sequence information should be released immediately and freely in the public domain. *Science* **274**, 533-534 (1996).

48. Guyer, M. Statement on the rapid release of genomic DNA sequence. *Genome Res.* **8**, 413 (1998).

49. Dunham, I., Dewar, K., Kim, U.-J. & Ross, M. T. in *Genome Analysis: A Laboratory Manual Series, Volume 3: Cloning Systems* (eds Birren, B. *et al.*) 1-86 (Cold Spring Harbor Laboratory Press, Cold Spring Harbor, New York, 1999).

50. Asakawa, S. *et al.* Human BAC library: construction and rapid screening. *Gene* **191**, 69-79 (1997).

Supplementary information is available on *Nature*'s World-Wide Web site (http://www.nature.com) or as paper copy from the London editorial office of *Nature*.

Correspondence and requests for materials should be addressed to I.D. (e-mail: id1@sanger.ac.uk).

Molecular Analysis of Neanderthal DNA from the Northern Caucasus

I.V. Ovchinnikov *et al.*

Editor's Note

The only thing better than having a sequence of DNA from an extinct species is having a second one, for comparative purposes. Mitochondrial DNA extracted from the original bones of type specimen Neanderthal 1 in 1997 showed that Neanderthals were not closely related to modern humans. But how secure was this single set of data? Here Igor Ovchinnikov and colleagues describe mitochondrial DNA extracted from 29,000-year-old Neanderthal remains from the northern Caucasus. Although far removed in space and time from the other Neanderthal sequence, the results still showed that the Caucasus DNA grouped more closely with the original Neanderthal finds, further ruling out admixture with modern humans.

The expansion of premodern humans into western and eastern Europe ~40,000 years before the present led to the eventual replacement of the Neanderthals by modern humans ~28,000 years ago[1]. Here we report the second mitochondrial DNA (mtDNA) analysis of a Neanderthal, and the first such analysis on clearly dated Neanderthal remains. The specimen is from one of the eastern-most Neanderthal populations, recovered from Mezmaiskaya Cave in the northern Caucasus[2]. Radiocarbon dating estimated the specimen to be ~29,000 years old and therefore from one of the latest living Neanderthals[3]. The sequence shows 3.48% divergence from the Feldhofer Neanderthal[4]. Phylogenetic analysis places the two Neanderthals from the Caucasus and western Germany together in a clade that is distinct from modern humans, suggesting that their mtDNA types have not contributed to the modern human mtDNA pool. Comparison with modern populations provides no evidence for the multiregional hypothesis of modern human evolution.

THE first successful extraction and sequencing of the mtDNA hypervariable regions (I and II (HVRI & HVRII)) was performed on the Neanderthal type specimen from Feldhofer Cave, the Neander valley, Germany[4,5]. Phylogenetic analysis of the sequence placed the Neanderthal mtDNA outside the mtDNA pool of modern humans. This was regarded as a breakthrough in the study of modern human evolution, providing molecular evidence that Neanderthals did not contribute mtDNA to modern humans. From this sequence the divergence of Neanderthals and modern humans was estimated to have occurred between 317,000 and 741,000 years ago[4,5]. However, these estimates were based on the molecular analysis of a single specimen. The shortage of potentially well preserved Neanderthal material[6] and limited access to Neanderthal remains for destructive analysis have hindered the analysis of additional specimens, but genetic

高加索北部尼安德特人 DNA 的分子分析

奥夫钦尼科夫等

编者按

比从已灭绝的物种得到一个 DNA 序列更好的事情只有一件，那就是获得第二个序列，以便进行对比。1997 年从尼安德特人 1 的原始骨骼标本中提取的线粒体 DNA 显示，尼安德特人与现代人的关系并不密切。但这仅有的一组数据的可信度怎样呢？在本文中，伊戈尔·奥夫钦尼科夫及其同事描述了从高加索北部绝对年龄为 29,000 年的尼安德特人遗骸中提取的线粒体 DNA。尽管在时空上与另一个尼安德特人序列相距甚远，但是结果仍表明在高加索发现的该 DNA 与最初发现的尼安德特人关系更近，并进一步排除了与现代人有基因交流的可能性。

距今约 40,000 年前，古老型智人扩散至西欧和东欧，并最终导致尼安德特人在约 28,000 年前被现代人取代[1]。在本文中我们报道了第二例对尼安德特人线粒体 DNA（mtDNA）的分子分析，这也是首例对有清晰年代尼安德特人遗骸进行的此类分析。标本来自尼安德特人最东部的种群之一，发现于高加索北部的梅兹迈斯卡亚洞[2]。根据放射性碳同位素年代测定，该标本绝对年龄约为 29,000 年，因此是生存最晚的尼安德特人之一[3]。该序列显示其与费尔德霍费尔原始的尼安德特人之间存在 3.48% 的差异[4]。系统发育分析将高加索和德国西部的这两个尼安德特人置于有别于现代人的同一分支，表明他们的 mtDNA 类型对现代人的 mtDNA 库没有贡献。与现代人种群进行的比较没有为现代人演化的多地起源说提供证据。

第一次对 mtDNA 高变区（I 和 II，即 HVRI 和 HVRII）的成功提取和测序是用德国尼安德谷费尔德霍费尔洞出土的尼安德特人模式标本完成的[4,5]。该序列的系统发育分析将此尼安德特人的 mtDNA 置于现代人的 mtDNA 库之外。这曾被认为是现代人类演化研究的一项突破，为证明尼安德特人对现代人的 mtDNA 没有贡献提供了分子证据。根据这一序列推测尼安德特人和现代人的分化发生在 741,000 年至 317,000 年前[4,5]。然而，这些推测是以单一标本的分子分析为基础的。保存完好的尼安德特人原材料的缺乏[6]以及对尼安德特人遗骸进行破坏性分析的局限性阻碍了对更多样本的分析。然而，为了理解尼安德特人的分子多样性及不同尼安德特人种

characterization of additional Neanderthals is essential to understand their molecular diversity and the relationship between different Neanderthal populations, and to assess their relationship to modern humans further.

The Caucasus, which is located on the southeastern boundary between Europe and Asia, is one of the areas through which pre-modern humans and anatomically modern *Homo sapiens* may have entered Europe from the Near East and Africa. Neanderthals invaded the region at an unknown point in time[7,8] and may have occupied the region alongside modern humans from ~40,000 years before the present (B.P.). During the excavation of the Mezmaiskaya Cave[2], which is located in the northern Caucasus (Fig. 1), a fragmentary skeleton of an infant was found that contained a set of morphological characteristics which indicated clear affinities to the Neanderthals of western and central Europe[2]. Mitochondrial DNA analysis was undertaken using one of this Neanderthal's ribs.

Fig. 1. The area within which Neanderthal remains have been found (dotted line). The Mezmaiskaya Cave is situated 1,310 m above sea level within the northern Caucasus at 44° 10′ N 40° 00′ E on the bank of the Sukhoy Kurdzhips river. The location of the Feldhofer Cave in Germany is also shown.

The preservation of collagen-type debris was used as an indicator of macromolecule preservation in the bone. The amount of collagen-type debris extracted[9] from 130 mg of the Mezmaiskaya Neanderthal rib fragment was 22% of the average level extracted from modern bones, and the extracted collagen contained 41.6% carbon and 14.7% nitrogen. This is within the values recovered from prehistoric samples displaying good preservation[10]. These data suggested that there were low levels of diagenetic modification. The high collagen yield made it possible to date the Neanderthal infant to $29,195 \pm 965$ (Ua-14512) years B.P. by using a radio-carbon accelerator. This date does not agree with the previously published dates of more than 45,000 (Le-3841) and $40,660 \pm 1,600$ (Le-3599) years for the Mousterian layers in the Mezmaiskaya Cave[2] with which the skeleton was associated. The most likely reason for this discrepancy is the incorrect identification of the poorly defined layers in this area of the cave. The value obtained from the bone itself rather than from associated material gives the most reliable date for this individual.

Two sections of one rib (90 mg and 123 mg) were used for DNA extraction in two

群之间的关系，并进一步评估他们与现代人的关系，了解更多尼安德特人的遗传特征是至关重要的。

高加索位于欧洲和亚洲的东南交界处，可能是古老型智人和早期现代人从近东和非洲进入欧洲途经的地区之一。尼安德特人在某个未知的时间侵入了这一地区[7,8]，并且在距今（BP）约 40,000 年与现代人共同占据这一地区。梅兹迈斯卡亚洞[2]位于高加索北部（图 1），在挖掘该洞期间发现了一具破碎的幼儿骨架，其蕴含的一组形态学特征展现了与西欧和中欧尼安德特人明确的亲缘关系[2]。线粒体 DNA 分析正是使用这个尼安德特人的一根肋骨进行的。

图 1. 发现尼安德特人遗骸的区域（虚线所示）。梅兹迈斯卡亚洞海拔 1,310 米，位于高加索北部苏霍伊库尔吉普斯河畔，北纬 44°10′，东经 40°00′。德国费尔德霍费尔洞的位置也在图中标明。

骨骼中胶原蛋白型片断的保存状况被用作大分子保存状况的指标。从 130 mg 梅兹迈斯卡亚尼安德特人肋骨碎片提取的胶原蛋白型片断[9]为现代骨骼平均提取水平的 22%，提取出的胶原蛋白含碳量为 41.6%，含氮量为 14.7%。这一数值处于保存良好的史前样本的数值范围内[10]。这些数据表明成岩改造作用水平较低。该肋骨碎片的高胶原含量使得我们可以利用放射性碳加速器测定该尼安德特幼儿的年龄为距今 29,195±965(Ua-14512) 年。这一年代与之前发表的梅兹迈斯卡亚洞[2]此骨架出土的莫斯特文化层年代为距今 45,000(Le-3841) 年和 40,660±1,600(Le-3599) 年是不一致的。导致这一差异最可能的原因是对该洞穴中这一区域不明确的骨架出土层位的错误鉴定。从骨骼本身而非间接关联材料得到的数值才能给出该个体最可信的年代信息。

两个独立的实验室分别选取了一段肋骨的两个切片（90 mg 和 123 mg）来提取

independent laboratories. In the Glasgow laboratory, a total of 345 base pairs (bp) of HVRI was determined from two overlapping polymerase chain reaction (PCR) fragments with lengths of 232 and 256 bp. Forty PCR amplification cycles produced sufficient product to enable direct sequencing. Products from independent PCR amplifications were also cloned into a TA vector and sequenced (Fig. 2).

Position header (read vertically):

```
1 1 1 1 1 1 1 1 1 1 1 1 1 1 1 1 1 1 1 1 1 1 1 1 1 1 1 1 1 1 1 1 1 1 1 1 1 1 1 1
6 6 6 6 6 6 6 6 6 6 6 6 6 6 6 6 6 6 6 6 6 6 6 6 6 6 6 6 6 6 6 6 6 6 6 6 6 6 6 6
0 0 0 0 1 1 1 1 1 1 1 1 1 1 1 1 1 1 1 1 2 2 2 2 2 2 2 2 2 2 2 2 2 2 2 3 3 3 3 3
3 7 8 9 0 0 1 1 1 2 3 4 5 5 6 8 8 8 0 2 3 4 4 5 5 6 6 7 9   1 2 4 6 9
7 8 6 3 7 8 1 2 8 9 9 8 4 6 9 2 3 9 9 3 0 4 3 4 0 6 8 1 2 3.1 8 9 1 0 4 2 5 3
```

Label	Sequence
Reference	A A T T C C C C G G A C T G C A A T T C A C T G C C A C C - C A T C C T C C
Direct 1	. C . . . . . . A T T . A T C C C C T G T . A . A .
P1	. C . . . . . . A T T . A T C C C C T G T . A . A . . T A T
P2	. C . . . . . . A T T . A T C C C C T G T . A . A . . T A T
P3	. C . . . . . A A T T . A T C C C C T G T . A . A . . T A T
Direct 2	T G T . A . A . . T A T G C T T C . .
577.1	T G T . A . A . T T A T G C T T C . T
557.2	T G T . A T A . . T A T G C T T C . .
581.2	T G T . A . A . . T A T G C T T C . .
581.3	T G T C A . A . . T A T G C T T C T .
Mezmaiskaya	. C . . . . . . A T T . A T C C C C **T G T . A . A . . T A T G C T** T C . .
Feldhofer	G G . C T T T T . A T T C . T . C C C T G T . A . A G . T A T G C T . C . .

Fig. 2. Variable sites in the DNA sequences of the PCR fragments obtained by direct sequencing (Direct 1 and 2) and cloned PCR products derived from the Neanderthal from Mezmaiskaya Cave. The human reference sequence[11] and the sequence of the Neanderthal from Feldhofer Cave[4] are included for comparison. A full stop indicates that the sequence is the same as the reference. The sequence that could be duplicated in the Stockholm laboratory is shown in bold within the compiled Mezmaiskaya sequence.

The authenticity of the DNA sequence obtained in the Glasgow laboratory is supported by a number of factors. First, a section of the mtDNA was isolated and sequenced with congruent results in the Stockholm laboratory. Second, the PCR products were generated using Neanderthal-specific primer pairs that, under the amplification conditions, failed to amplify any fragments using modern DNA controls from individuals of different ethnic origins. Third, the retrieval of the sequence was not dependent on the primers used. Fourth, the low level of diagenetic modification indicated that the sample could theoretically contain amplifiable DNA. Last, and most convincingly, the sequence is similar to, and after phylogenetic analysis clusters strongly with, the previously analysed Neanderthal sequence[4].

Comparison of the 345-bp fragment of HVRI with the Anderson reference sequence[11] and the Neanderthal from Feldhofer Cave[4] revealed 22 differences (17 transitions, 4 transversions and 1 insertion) and 12 differences (11 transitions and 1 transversion), respectively. The Feldhofer Neanderthal HVRI contained 27 differences to Anderson reference sequence[11] (over the equivalent 345 bp[4]). The two Neanderthals share 19 substitutions relative to the reference sequence. The cloned PCR products contained all the substitutions that were detected by direct sequencing; six other non-reproducible substitutions occurred in seven different clones. No

DNA。格拉斯哥实验室通过长度分别为 232 bp 和 256 bp 的两个重叠的聚合酶链式反应(PCR)测定了片段总长度为 345 个碱基对(bp)的 HVRI。通过 40 个 PCR 扩增循环产生了足够的产物，可以进行直接测序。同时也将独立 PCR 扩增的产物克隆到 TA 载体中并进行了测序(图 2)。

```
                1 1 1 1 1 1 1 1 1 1 1 1 1 1 1 1 1 1 1 1 1 1 1 1 1 1 1 1 1 1 1 1 1 1 1 1 1 1
                6 6 6 6 6 6 6 6 6 6 6 6 6 6 6 6 6 6 6 6 6 6 6 6 6 6 6 6 6 6 6 6 6 6 6 6 6 6
                0 0 0 0 1 1 1 1 1 1 1 1 1 1 1 1 1 1 2 2 2 2 2 2 2 2 2 2 2 2 3 3 3 3 3 3
                3 7 8 9 0 0 1 1 1 2 3 4 5 5 6 8 8 8 0 2 3 4 5 5 6 6 7 9 1 2 4 6 6 9
                7 8 6 3 7 8 1 2 8 9 9 8 4 6 9 2 3.1 8 9 1 0 4 0 6 8 1 2 3.1 8 9 1 0 4 2 5 3

参考序列        A A T T C C C C G G A C T G C A A T T C A C T G C C A C C - C A T C C T C C
Direct 1        . C . . . . A T T . A T C C C C T G T . A . A .
P1              . C . . . . A T T . A T C C C C T G T . A . A . . T A T
P2              . . . . . . A T T . A T C C C C T G T . A . A . . T A T
P3              . . A A T T . A T C C C C T G T . A . A . . T A T
Direct 2                            T G T . A . . T A T G C T T C
577.1                               T G T . A . T A T G C T T C . T
557.2                               T G T . A . T A T G C T T C
581.2                               T G T . A . T A T G C T T C
581.3                               T G T C A . T A T G C T T C
梅兹迈斯卡亚    . C . . . . A T T . A T C C C C T G T . A . A . . T A T G C T T C
费尔德霍费尔  G G . C T T T T . A T T C . T . C C C T G T . A . A G . T A T G C T T C .
```

图 2. 通过直接测序(Direct 1 和 2) PCR 片段及梅兹迈斯卡亚洞尼安德特人的克隆 PCR 产物，得到 DNA 序列上的可变位点。现代人参考序列[11]及费尔德霍费尔洞的尼安德特人序列[4]都包含在内，进行比对。圆点表示序列与参考序列相同。在斯德哥尔摩实验室中可被复制的序列在梅兹迈斯卡亚合成序列中用黑体表示。

有多个因素支持格拉斯哥实验室得到的 DNA 序列的可靠性。首先，一段线粒体 DNA 被分离并测序，取得了与斯德哥尔摩实验室一致的结果。第二，PCR 产物是使用针对尼安德特人的特异性引物对生成的，在扩增条件下，这些引物无法扩增来自不同种族个体的现代 DNA 对照片段。第三，序列的获取不取决于所使用的引物。第四，低水平的成岩改造作用表明这一样本理论上含有可扩增的 DNA。最后且最有说服力的是，该序列与以前分析过的尼安德特人序列[4]相似，且系统发育分析显示它们强烈类聚。

该 345 bp 的 HVRI 片段与安德森参考序列[11]和费尔德霍费尔洞的尼安德特人[4]序列的分别对比显示出 22 处碱基差异(17 处转换，4 处颠换及 1 处插入)和 12 处碱基差异(11 处转换及 1 处颠换)。费尔德霍费尔尼安德特人的 HVRI 与安德森参考序列[11]相比有 27 处碱基差异(在相应的 345 bp 中[4])。与参考序列相比，这两个尼安德特人共同拥有 19 处碱基替换。克隆的 PCR 产物包含了直接测序检测到的所有碱基替换；六处其他不可重复的替换出现于七个不同的克隆中。在格拉斯哥实验室中，

modern sequences were found in the Glasgow laboratory either by direct sequencing or by sequencing cloned PCR products. The Stockholm laboratory experienced problems with contamination: most of the cloned PCR products that they analysed contained sequences that are found in the modern human mtDNA pool, with two haplotypes predominant. However, three clones contained DNA that was the same as the sequence determined in Glasgow (two of these contained non-reproducible substitutions).

The preservation of 256-bp DNA fragments in bone that is ~29,000 years old, that has not been preserved in permafrost and that contained sufficient DNA to enable direct DNA sequencing after amplification is unprecedented and may be attributed to specific features of the microenvironment of the limestone cavern[2]. The retrieval of mtDNA showed a positive correlation to the preservation of collagen content and the skeletal morphology.

Phylogenetic analysis using both distance and parsimony optimizations places the two Neanderthal sequences together, in a distinct clade, basal to modern humans. Neighbour-joining analysis supports this separation (Fig. 3a). Parsimony analysis, which makes minimal assumptions about the model of evolution and optimizes the fit between the tree and data, produced similar results (Fig. 3b).

Fig. 3. Phylogenetic relationship of the two Neanderthals and modern humans. **a**, A neighbour-joining

直接测序和克隆 PCR 产物测序都没有发现现代序列。斯德哥尔摩实验室则遇到了污染问题：他们分析的大部分克隆 PCR 产物都含有现代人线粒体 DNA 库中存在的序列，主要为两个单倍型。不过，有三个克隆含有的 DNA 与格拉斯哥实验室确定的序列相同（其中两个含有不可重复的替换）。

年龄约 29,000 年的骨骼中保存了 256 bp 的 DNA 片段，没有保存在永久冻土中却含有足够的 DNA 可供扩增后直接 DNA 测序，这种史无前例的情况或许可以归因于这一石灰岩洞穴中特殊的微环境[2]。线粒体 DNA 的获得表明胶原蛋白成分的保存状况与骨骼形态是正相关的。

使用距离和简约性优化法则进行的系统发育分析将这两个尼安德特人的序列归并到一起，构成一个独立的分支，并位于现代人基底位置。邻接分析支持这一分化（图 3a）。简约性分析得到了类似的结果，该分析对演化模式的假设最少，并会优化系统树与数据之间的拟合（图 3b）。

图 3. 两个尼安德特人与现代人的系统发育关系。a，使用来自 5,846 个现代人的共 1,897 个单倍型计算

tree computed using a total of 1,897 haplotypes derived from 5,846 modern humans[19]. **b**, A maximum parsimony branch and bound search with the two Neanderthal sequences along with the sequences of one !Kung, three other Africans, three Asians and three Europeans, all randomly selected[19]. This result is congruent with four additional data sets that were analysed. In both analyses, three chimpanzee sequences[13] were used as an outgroup. The numbers in both diagrams refer to the bootstrap frequencies (%) obtained from 1,000 replicates.

The level of pairwise difference found between the two Neanderthals was higher than the average values found in random samples of 300 Caucasoids (5.28 ± 2.24) and Mongoloids (6.27 ± 2.29)—less than 1% of Caucasoid and Mongoloid pairs differ at 12 or more positions—but comparable to a random sample of 300 Africans (8.36 ± 3.2), where 37% of pairs differed at 12 or more positions. When analysing ancient DNA there is the possibility of misincorporating nucleotides in the early stages of PCR, especially when the target DNA is possibly damaged and present in low copy number[12]. As both Neanderthals were analysed in replicate and the results were consistent, however, errors of this type can be discounted.

The Feldhofer and Mezmaiskaya Neanderthals were separated geographically by over 2,500 km. Given that these two individuals contained closely related mtDNA, which is phylogenetically distinct from modern humans, and displays only a moderate level of sequence diversity compared with some primates[13], these data provide further support for the hypothesis of a very low gene flow between the Neanderthals and modern humans. In particular, these data reduce the likelihood that Neanderthals contained enough mtDNA sequence diversity to encompass modern human diversity.

The "out-of-Africa" hypothesis for the origin of modern humans predicts equal distances between the Neanderthal sequences and all modern sequences. We observed this in our analysis—the average pairwise differences between the Neanderthals and 300 randomly selected Africans, Mongoloids and Caucasoids were calculated to be 23.09 ± 2.86, 23.27 ± 4.06 and 25.45 ± 3.27, respectively.

We estimated the age of the most recent common ancestor (MRCA) of the mtDNA of the eastern and western Neanderthals to be 151,000–352,000 years. This coincides with the time of emergence of the Neanderthal lineage in the palaeontological records[14]. The divergence of modern human and Neanderthal mtDNA was estimated to be between 365,000 and 853,000 years. Using the same model, we estimated the age of the earliest modern human divergences in mtDNA to be between 106,000 and 246,000 B.P.

The results obtained from this specimen suggest that some other Neanderthal samples may be amenable to molecular analysis. To obtain a more complete picture of the relationship of Neanderthals to modern humans, additional Neanderthals and early modern humans must be analysed, especially from the regions where they may have co-existed. The excellent preservation of this specimen leads to the potential of analysing the entire Neanderthal mitochondrial genome.

出的邻接树[19]。**b**，两个尼安德特人序列与随机选择的一个 !Kung 人、三个其他非洲人、三个亚洲人和三个欧洲人的序列采用分支限界法搜索到的最简约系统树[19]。这一结果与另外四组数据的分析结果一致。以上两个分析使用三只黑猩猩的序列[13]作为外群。两个图中的数字代表 1,000 次重复得到的自举频率（%）。

两个尼安德特人的配对差异水平高于随机选择的 300 个高加索人种（5.28±2.24）和蒙古人种（6.27±2.29）样本的平均值——不到 1% 的高加索人种和蒙古人种配对组合有 12 个或更多位点存在差异——但是与一个 300 个非洲人（8.36±3.2）的随机样本相当，该非洲样本在 12 个及更多位点有 37% 的配对组合存在差异。在分析古 DNA 时，PCR 初始阶段可能会发生核苷酸被错误插入的情况，特别是当标靶 DNA 可能损坏且拷贝数较低时[12]。因为这两个尼安德特人都进行了重复分析而且结果是一致的，所以该类失误可以被忽略。

费尔德霍费尔尼安德特人和梅兹迈斯卡亚尼安德特人在地理上相距 2,500 多千米。考虑到这两个个体拥有密切相关的线粒体 DNA，且在系统发育上不同于现代人，与某些灵长类相比[13]仅显示出中等水平的序列多样性，这些证据为尼安德特人和现代人之间基因交流很少这一假说提供了进一步的支持。需要特别指出的是，这些证据同时反驳了尼安德特人拥有足够的线粒体 DNA 序列多样性且足以覆盖现代人类多样性这一说法。

关于现代人类起源的"走出非洲"的假说认为尼安德特人序列与所有现代序列间的差异距离相等。在我们的分析中也观察到了这一点——经计算，尼安德特人与 300 个随机选择的非洲人、蒙古人和高加索人间的平均配对差异分别为 23.09±2.86、23.27±4.06 和 25.45±3.27。

我们推测东西方尼安德特人线粒体 DNA 的最近共同祖先（MRCA）的年龄约为距今 151,000 至 352,000 年。这与古生物学记录中尼安德特人谱系出现的时间是一致的[14]。据推测现代人和尼安德特人线粒体 DNA 的分化是在距今 365,000 至 853,000 年。使用同一模型，我们推测最早的现代人类线粒体 DNA 分化发生在距今 106,000 至 246,000 年。

从该标本得到的结果表明，一些其他尼安德特人标本也可以用来进行分子分析。为了得到尼安德特人与现代人类关系更完整的图谱，必须分析其他尼安德特人和早期现代人类，特别是来自他们共同生存地区的标本。该标本极佳的保存状况使得对尼安德特人整个线粒体基因组进行分析成为可能。

Methods

DNA extraction, PCR, cloning and sequencing

The DNA extraction methods used in Glasgow[4] and Stockholm[15] have been described. We took precautions to prevent contamination from modern DNA[4]. The Neanderthal-specific primer pairs, NL16,055 and NH16,262, and NL16,209 and NH16,400 (5'-TGATTTCACGGAGGATGGTGA-3') were used in Glasgow and the primers L16,212 (5'-ATGCTTACAAGCAAGCACA-3') and H16,332 (5'-TTGACTGTAATGTGCTATG-3') were used in Stockholm. The annealing temperatures for the primer pairs NL16,055–NH16,262, NL16,209–NH16,400 and L16,212–H16,332 were 50°C, 60°C and 50°C respectively; 40 cycles were used for the first two pairs, 55 cycles for the third. AmpliTaq Gold (Perkin Elmer Cetus) was used in all PCRs. PCR products were purified using the QIAquick Gel Extraction kit (Qiagen) before direct sequencing using the Dye Terminator sequencing kit (Perkin Elmer) or cloning into the TA vector (Invitrogen) before sequencing with the same kit using the M13 and T7 primers.

Sequence analyses

The neighbour-joining and the maximum parsimony branch and bound trees were both constructed using PAUP* 4.0 (ref. 16). For the neighbour-joining analysis, the Tamura-Nei DNA substitution model[17] was used with a gamma distribution of 0.4 (ref. 18), for all other parameters the defaults provided by PAUP* 4.0 were used. The MRCA was calculated using the described methods and assumptions[5]. PAUP* 4.0 was used to calculate pairwise differences between sequences: the data sets used for this were constructed by randomly selecting appropriate samples from a published data set[19].

(**404**, 490-493; 2000)

Igor V. Ovchinnikov[*†‡], Anders Götherström[§], Galina P. Romanova[∥], Vitaliy M. Kharitonov[¶], Kerstin Lidén[§] & William Goodwin[*]

[*] Human Identification Centre, University of Glasgow, Glasgow G12 8QQ, Scotland, UK

[†] Institute of Gerontology, Moscow 129226, Russia

[§] Archaeological Research Laboratory, Stockholm University, 106 91 Stockholm, Sweden

[∥] Institute of Archaeology, Moscow 117036, Russia

[¶] Institute and Museum of Anthropology, Moscow State University, Moscow 103009, Russia

[‡] Present address: Department of Medicine, Columbia University, New York, New York 10032 USA

Received 15 November 1999; accepted 31 January 2000.

References:

1. Stringer, C. B. & Mackie, R. *African Exodus: the Origin of Modern Humanity* (Cape, London, 1996).

2. Golovanova, L. V., Hoffecker, J. F., Kharitonov, V. M. & Romanova, G. P. Mezmaiskaya Cave: A Neanderthal occupation in the Northern Caucasus. *Curr. Anthropol.* **40**, 77-86 (1999).

3. Smith, F. H., Trinkaus, E., Pettitt, P. B., Karavanic, I. & Paunovic, M. Direct radiocarbon dates for Vindija G1 and Velika Pecina Late Pleistocene hominid remains.

方　法

DNA 提取、PCR、克隆及测序

格拉斯哥[4]和斯德哥尔摩[15]实验室使用的 DNA 提取方法已经介绍过。我们采取了一些预防措施以防止来自现代 DNA 的污染[4]。格拉斯哥实验室使用的尼安德特人特异性引物对包括 NL16,055 和 NH16,262，以及 NL16,209 和 NH16,400(5′-TGATTTCACGGAGGATGGTGA-3′)；斯德哥尔摩实验室使用的引物对为 L16,212(5′-ATGCTTACAAGCAAGCACA-3′)和 H16,332(5′-TTGACTGTAATGTGCTATG-3′)。引物对 NL16,055–NH16,262、NL16,209–NH16,400 和 L16,212–H16,332 的退火温度分别为 50℃、60℃ 和 50℃；前两对引物扩增了 40 个循环，第三对扩增了 55 个循环。所有 PCR 均使用 AmpliTaq Gold(Perkin Elmer Cetus)试剂。用 QIAquick 凝胶回收试剂盒(Qiagen)对 PCR 产物进行纯化，然后使用 Dye Terminator 测序试剂盒(Perkin Elmer)进行直接测序，或者使用 M13 和 T7 引物，用相同的试剂盒在测序之前克隆到 TA 载体(Invitrogen)上。

序列分析

使用 PAUP* 4.0 构建邻接分析和最简约分支界限树(参考文献 16)。邻接分析中使用 Tamura-Nei DNA 替换模型[17]，γ 分布取 0.4(参考文献 18)，其他所有参数使用 PAUP* 4.0 提供的默认值。使用文献中描述的方法和假设计算 MRCA[5]。使用 PAUP* 4.0 计算序列之间的成对差异；进行该计算的数据集是通过从已发表的数据集中随机选择适当样本而构建的[19]。

（刘皓芳 翻译；张颖奇 审稿）

Proc. Natl Acad. Sci. USA **96**, 12281-12286 (1999).

4. Krings, M. *et al.* Neandertal DNA sequence and the origin of modern humans. *Cell* **90**, 19-30 (1997).

5. Krings, M., Geisert, H., Schmitz, R. W., Krainitzki, H. & Pääbo, S. DNA sequence of the mitochondrial hypervariable region II from the Neandertal type specimen. *Proc. Natl Acad. Sci.* USA **96**, 5581-5585 (1999).

6. Cooper, A. *et al.* Neandertal genetics. *Science* **277**, 1021-1023 (1997).

7. Gabunia, L. & Vekua, A. A Plio-Pleistocene hominid from Dmanisi, East Georgia, Caucasus. *Nature* **373**, 509-512 (1995).

8. Kozlowski, J. K. in *Neandertals and Modern Humans in Western Asia* 461-482 (Plenum, New York-London, 1998).

9. Brown, T. A., Nelson, D. E., Vogel, J. S. & Southon, J. R. Improved collagen extraction by modified Longin method. *Radiocarbon* **30**, 171-177 (1988).

10. DeNiro, M. J. Postmortem preservation and alteration of *in vivo* bone collagen isotope ratios in relation to palaeodietary reconstruction. *Nature* **317**, 806-809 (1985).

11. Anderson, S. *et al.* Sequence and organisation of the human mitochondrial genome. *Nature* **290**, 457-474 (1981).

12. Höss, M. *et al.* DNA damage and DNA sequence retrieval from ancient tissue. *Nucleic Acids Res.* **24**, 1304-1307 (1996).

13. Gagneux, P. *et al.* Mitochondrial sequences show diverse evolutionary histories of African hominoids. *Proc. Natl Acad. Sci.* USA **96**, 5077-5082 (1999).

14. Gamble, C. in *Prehistoric Europe* 5-41 (Oxford Univ. Press, Oxford, 1998).

15. Lidén, K., Götherström, A. & Eriksson, E. Diet, gender and rank. *ISKOS* **11**, 158-164 (1997).

16. Swofford, D. L. *PAUP*: Phylogenetic Analysis Using Parsimony (* and Other Methods)* Version 4. (Sinauer Associates, Sunderland, Massachusetts, 1998).

17. Tamura, K. & Nei, M. Estimation of the number of nucleotide substitutions in the control region of mitochondrial DNA in humans and chimpanzees. *J. Mol. Evol.* **10**, 512-526 (1993).

18. Excoffier, L. & Yang, Z. Substitution rate variation among sites in mitochondrial hypervariable region I of humans and chimpanzees. *Mol. Biol. Evol.* **16**, 1357-1368 (1999).

19. Burckhardt, F., von Haeseler, A. & Meyer, S. HvrBase: compilation of mtDNA control region sequences from primates. *Nucleic Acids Res.* **27**, 138-142 (1999).

Acknowledgements. We are indebted to L. V. Golovanova for the excavations in Mezmaiskaya Cave that provided materials for analysis. We thank V. P. Ljubin and P. Vanezis for encouragement and support; B. L. Cohen for numerous discussions; J. L. Harley, O. I. Ovtchinnikova, E. B. Druzina and J. Wakefield for technical help and assistance; R. Page for help with the phylogenetic analysis; and P. Beerli, A. Cooper, M. Cusack, M. Nordborg and M. Ruvolo for useful comments. I.V.O. thanks his host G. Curry. I.V.O. was supported by a Royal Society/NATO Fellowship. We thank the Swedish Royal Academy of Sciences and the Swedish Research Council for Natural Sciences for partial financial support.

Correspondence and requests for material should be addressed to W.G. (e-mail: w.goodwin@formed.gla.ac.uk).

A Refugium for Relicts?

M. Manabe *et al.*

Editor's Note

The Yixian Formation of Liaoning Province in north-east China has yielded one of the finest assemblages of fossils, including feathered dinosaurs and early flowering plants. Estimates of the age of the Yixian varied over a 25-million-year timespan, from the Late Jurassic to Early Cretaceous. Evidence placing the age at 124 million years—the younger, Cretaceous end of the spectrum—made the Yixian look like a refuge for ancient relics: a real-life Jurassic Park. This view was put forward in a News and Views article in *Nature* by Zhexi Luo of the Carnegie Museum of Natural History. But it is countered in this paper by palaeontologist Makoto Manabe and colleagues, who show that Cretaceous forms from Japan also have a Jurassic cast, making the picture more complex than Luo had indicated.

LUO[1] suggests that the vertebrate fauna from the Yixian Formation (Liaoning Province, China) shows that this region of eastern Asia was a refugium, in which several typically Late Jurassic lineages (compsognathid theropod dinosaurs, "rhamphorhynchoid" pterosaurs, primitive mammals) survived into the Early Cretaceous[1] (Fig. 1). Data from slightly older sediments in the Japanese Early Cretaceous, however, suggest that the faunal composition of this region can only be partly explained by the concept of a refugium.

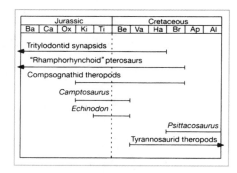

Fig. 1. Stratigraphic ranges of clades that include taxa recovered from the Yixian Formation, China, and the Kuwajima and Itsuki Formations, Japan[1,4,9]. Data on *Camptosaurus* and *Echinodon* are from ref. 13. Arrows, lineage extends beyond the time range shown here; solid bars, first and last occurrences. Al, Albian; Ap, Aptian; Ba, Bathonian; Be, Berriasian; Br, Barremian; Ca, Callovian; Ha, Hauterivian; Ki, Kimmeridgian; Ox, Oxfordian; Ti, Tithonian; Va, Valanginian.

The Kuwajima Formation of Ishikawa Prefecture, central Japan, is yielding an important Early Cretaceous vertebrate fauna. This unit is a lateral equivalent of the Okurodani

残遗种庇护所？

真锅真等

编者按

中国东北部的辽宁省义县组已经产出了最完美的化石群之一，这些化石包括带羽毛的恐龙和早期的被子植物。对义县组的年代估测有着超过 2,500 万年的差异，从晚侏罗世到早白垩世。有证据表明该地层年龄为 1 亿 2,400 万年，对应于更年轻的白垩纪，这使得义县看起来似乎是古代孑遗的避难所：一个真实的侏罗纪公园。这个观点由美国卡内基自然历史博物馆的罗哲西博士发表于《自然》的"新闻与观点"栏目中。但是在本文中，它被古生物学家真锅真和他的同事们反驳了，他们指出日本的白垩纪形成时也有一个"侏罗纪公园"，使得情况远比罗哲西提出的要复杂得多。

罗哲西[1]认为义县组（中国辽宁省）的脊椎动物群说明该亚洲东部地区是一个残遗种庇护所。在这个区域内，晚侏罗世的几个典型谱系（兽脚亚目的美颌龙类、翼龙目的"喙嘴翼龙类"、原始的哺乳类）存活到早白垩世[1]（图 1）。但是，日本早白垩世的一些更古老沉积物的数据显示，这个区域的动物群组成不能仅通过残遗种庇护所的概念进行解释。

图 1. 包括中国义县组和日本桑岛组、五木村组恢复的分类单元在内的分支的地层分布图[1,4,9]。弯龙属和棘齿龙属的数据来自参考文献 13。箭头：谱系延伸的时间范围超过图示；实心棒：最先和最后出现。Al：阿尔必阶；Ap：阿普特阶；Ba：巴通阶；Be：贝里阿斯阶；Br：巴列姆阶；Ca：卡洛维阶；Ha：欧特里沃阶；Ki：基默里奇阶；Ox：牛津阶；Ti：提塘阶；Va 代表凡兰吟阶。

日本中部石川县桑岛组正在出产一个重要的早白垩世脊椎动物群。桑岛组与邻近的岐阜县大黑谷组层位相同[2]。地层学、生物地层学和放射性测量的数据表明大

Formation that outcrops in neighbouring Gifu Prefecture[2]. Stratigraphic, biostratigraphic and radiometric data show that the Okurodani Formation is basal Cretaceous (Valanginian or Hauterivian) in age[3]. The Kuwajima Formation has yielded more than one hundred isolated teeth of a new genus of tritylodontid synapsid[4]. Before these discoveries, tritylodontids were thought to have become extinct sometime in the Middle or early Late Jurassic, as the youngest-known tritylodontid (*Bienotheroides*) was recovered from late Middle Jurassic deposits. This discovery supports the concept of an East Asian refugium, but other evidence suggests that different factors may have had an equally strong influence on faunal composition.

A theropod dinosaur referable to the unnamed clade Oviraptorosauria + Therizinosauroidea[5] has also been found in the tritylodontid locality. This clade is best known from the Late Cretaceous of mainland Asia, although several taxa referable to this clade are known from the late Early Cretaceous of Liaoning (*Beipiaosaurus*[6] and *Caudipteryx*[7]), and possibly from the Early Jurassic of Yunnan Province, China[8]. The Japanese material, consisting of a single manual ungual (Fig. 2) with a pronounced posterodorsal lip (a feature synapomorphic of this group of theropods[5]), is one of the earliest representatives of this group. The Itsuki Formation of Fukui Prefecture, a lateral equivalent of the Okurodani and Kuwajima Formations[2], has produced an isolated tyrannosaurid tooth, identifiable by its D-shaped cross-section—a synapomorphy of tyrannosaurids[9].

Fig. 2. Manual ungual of a theropod dinosaur from the Kuwajima Formation (Valanginian or Hauterivian) of Shiramine, Ishikawa Prefecture, Japan. Note the prominent lip posterodorsal to the articular surface of the ungual, a synapomorphy of the clade Oviraptorosauria + Therizinosauroidea[5]. Scale bar, 5 mm.

These Japanese discoveries, combined with the presence of late Early Cretaceous taxa in the Yixian Formation (such as the ornithischian dinosaur *Psittacosaurus*[10]), suggest that several dinosaur clades (such as tyrannosaurids and psittacosaurids) may have originated and diversified in eastern Asia while a number of other lineages (tritylodontid synapsids, compsognathid dinosaurs and "rhamphorhynchoid" pterosaurs) persisted in this region. Moreover, the presence of hypsilophodontid and iguanodontid ornithopod dinosaurs in the Japanese Early Cretaceous[11] suggests faunal connections with western Asia and Europe. The historical biogeography of this region appears to be much more complex than was thought previously.

Alternatively, the so-called relict taxa in eastern Asia may indicate that faunal turnover at the Jurassic–Cretaceous boundary was not as marked as has been suggested[12]. The presence of camptosaurid (*Camptosaurus*) and heterodontosaurid (*Echinodon*) ornithopods

黑谷组在白垩系基部（凡兰吟阶或者欧特里沃阶）[3]。桑岛组发现了一个下孔类的三列齿兽新属[4]的一百多颗独立的牙齿。在这些发现之前，由于最晚的三列齿兽（似卞氏兽）在中侏罗世晚期沉积物中发现，因此人们认为三列齿兽在中侏罗世或晚侏罗世早期的某个时间早已灭绝。尽管桑岛组这个发现支持亚洲东部残遗种庇护所的观点，但是其他证据表明不同的因素可能同样强烈地影响了动物群的组成。

一种未命名的兽脚亚目恐龙也在三列齿兽的产地发现，可能属于窃蛋龙类和镰刀龙类共同组成的一个未命名分支[5]。这个分支大部分属种主要发现自晚白垩世的亚洲大陆，只有少数几个分类单元在中国辽宁省的早白垩世晚期地层（北票龙[6]和尾羽龙[7]）以及可能在中国云南省的早侏罗世地层[8]被发现。日本发现的材料包括一个带有明显后背向的唇突（该兽脚类类群的共同衍征[5]）的单一手爪尖（图2），这是该类群最早的代表之一。在福井县五木村组（与大黑谷组和桑岛组层位相同[2]）发现了一颗单独的恐龙牙齿。通过 D 形横断面——暴龙的共同衍征[9]可以将其鉴定为暴龙牙齿。

图 2. 日本石川县白峰村桑岛组（凡兰吟阶或欧特里沃阶）发现的兽脚亚目恐龙的手爪尖。注意爪尖关节面后背向的明显的唇突，此为窃蛋龙类 + 镰刀龙类分支[5]的共同衍征。比例尺为 5 毫米。

日本的这些发现，结合义县组早白垩世晚期存在的分类单元（如鸟臀目的鹦鹉嘴龙[10]），表明一些恐龙分支（例如暴龙科和鹦鹉嘴龙科）可能从亚洲东部起源并且发生分化，而许多其他谱系（下孔类的三列齿兽、美颌龙类恐龙和翼龙目"喙嘴翼龙类"）在该地区一直存在。此外，日本早白垩世的棱齿龙类和鸟脚亚目的禽龙类的发现[11]揭示在亚洲西部和欧洲之间存在动物群的联系。该地区的历史生物地理学似乎比之前预想的要复杂得多。

或者说，亚洲东部所谓的残遗分类单元可能表明侏罗纪–白垩纪边界的动物群转化不像人们猜测的那么明显[12]。在欧洲早白垩世动物群中存在的鸟脚亚目恐龙——弯龙类（弯龙属）和异齿龙类（棘齿龙属）[13]表现出与北美洲晚侏罗世莫里森组

in European Early Cretaceous faunas[13] indicates faunal similarities to the Late Jurassic Morrison Formation of North America. The presence of "Late Jurassic" taxa in eastern Asia may simply represent another example of this more gradual Jurassic–Cretaceous faunal transition (Fig. 1), although more evidence is needed to distinguish between these alternatives.

(**404**, 953; 2000)

Makoto Manabe[*], **Paul M. Barrett**[†], **Shinji Isaji**[‡]

[*] Department of Geology, National Science Museum, 3-23-1 Hyakunin-cho, Shinjuku-ku, Tokyo 169-0073, Japan

[†] Department of Zoology, University of Oxford, South Parks Road, Oxford OX1 3PS, UK e-mail: paul.barrett@zoo.ox.ac.uk

[‡] Chiba Prefectural Museum of Natural History, Chiba 260-0682, Japan

References:

1. Luo, Z. *Nature* **400**, 23-25 (1999).

2. Maeda, S. *J. Collect. Arts Sci. Chiba Univ.* **3**, 369-426 (1961).

3. Evans, S. E. *et al.* *New Mexico Mus. Nat. Hist. Sci. Bull.* **14**, 183-186 (1998).

4. Setoguchi, T., Matsuoka, H. & Matsuda, M. in *Proc. 7th Annu. Meet. Chinese Soc. Vert. Paleontol.* (eds Wang, Y.-Q. & Deng, T.) 117-124 (China Ocean, Beijing, 1999).

5. Makovicky, P. J. & Sues, H.-D. *Am. Mus. Novitates* **3240**, 1-27 (1998).

6. Xu, X., Tang, Z.-L. & Wang, X.-L. *Nature* **399**, 350-354 (1999).

7. Sereno, P. C. *Science* **284**, 2137-2147 (1999).

8. Zhao, X.-J. & Xu, X. *Nature* **394**, 234-235 (1998).

9. Manabe, M. *J. Paleontol.* **73**, 1176-1178 (1999).

10. Xu, X. & Wang, X.-L. *Vertebrata PalAsiatica* **36**, 147-158 (1998).

11. Manabe, M. & Hasegawa, Y. in *6th Symp. Mesozoic Terrest. Ecosyst. Biotas* (eds Sun, A.-L. & Wang, Y.-Q.) 179 (China Ocean, 1995).

12. Bakker, R. T. *Nature* **274**, 661-663 (1978).

13. Norman, D. B. & Barrett, P. M. *Spec. Pap. Palaeontol.* (in the press).

的动物群的相似性。尽管我们需要更多的证据去区分这两种可能性，但是亚洲东部"晚侏罗世"分类单元的存在可能仅仅代表侏罗纪向白垩纪的动物群逐渐演变的另外一个例证（图1）。

（吕静 张茜楠 翻译；汪筱林 审稿）

A Flat Universe from High-resolution Maps of the Cosmic Microwave Background Radiation

P. de Bernardis *et al.*

Editor's Note

In the early Universe, before subatomic particles united into atoms, photons, electrons and atomic nuclei were sloshing around in a kind of primordial soup. As with sloshing water in a bathtub, there were certain naturally resonant frequencies. Radiation from this time carries echoes of those resonances, preserved as characteristic ripples in the cosmic microwave background radiation. Paolo de Bernardis and his colleagues launched a high-altitude balloon in the Antarctic to measure these ripples. Here they report their findings: the ripples are best explained by a "flat" Universe, in which the sum of standard matter, dark matter and dark energy is equal to a "critical density", poised between positive (closed) and negative (open) curvature. Subsequently the WMAP satellite confirmed this conclusion.

The blackbody radiation left over from the Big Bang has been transformed by the expansion of the Universe into the nearly isotropic 2.73 K cosmic microwave background. Tiny inhomogeneities in the early Universe left their imprint on the microwave background in the form of small anisotropies in its temperature. These anisotropies contain information about basic cosmological parameters, particularly the total energy density and curvature of the Universe. Here we report the first images of resolved structure in the microwave background anisotropies over a significant part of the sky. Maps at four frequencies clearly distinguish the microwave background from foreground emission. We compute the angular power spectrum of the microwave background, and find a peak at Legendre multipole $l_{peak} = (197 \pm 6)$, with an amplitude $\Delta T_{200} = (69 \pm 8)$ μK. This is consistent with that expected for cold dark matter models in a flat (euclidean) Universe, as favoured by standard inflationary models.

PHOTONS in the early Universe were tightly coupled to ionized matter through Thomson scattering. This coupling ceased about 300,000 years after the Big Bang, when the Universe cooled sufficiently to form neutral hydrogen. Since then, the primordial photons have travelled freely through the Universe, redshifting to microwave frequencies as the Universe expanded. We observe those photons today as the cosmic microwave background (CMB). An image of the early Universe remains imprinted in the temperature anisotropy of the CMB. Anisotropies on angular scales larger than ~2° are dominated by the gravitational redshift the photons undergo as they leave the density fluctuations present at decoupling[1,2]. Anisotropies on smaller angular scales are enhanced

高分辨率的宇宙微波背景辐射观测揭示
我们的宇宙是平直的

贝尔纳迪斯等

编者按

在宇宙早期，亚原子粒子结合成原子之前，光子、电子以及原子核在某种原始汤中游荡。类似于浴缸中受到扰动的水，其中自然而然存在一些共振的频率。这个时期的辐射携带了这些共振的回音，以典型涟漪的形式保留在宇宙微波背景辐射上。保罗·德·贝尔纳迪斯和他的合作者们在南极洲发射了一个高海拔的气球来探测这些涟漪。这里报道了他们的结果：涟漪能够通过"平直"宇宙模型得到最好的解释。在这个模型中，标准物质、暗物质以及暗能量的总密度等于"临界密度"，介于正的（封闭的）以及负的（开的）曲率之间。随后，WMAP 卫星证实了这个结论。

随着宇宙的膨胀，大爆炸遗留下来的黑体辐射逐步演化成为几乎各向同性、温度为 2.73 K 的宇宙微波背景。早期宇宙的不均匀性在微波背景上留下了微小的各向异性的痕迹。这些各向异性蕴含着宇宙学基本参数的信息，尤其是宇宙整体能量密度与曲率。在本工作中，我们首次展示了一块足够大的天区上微波背景各向异性结构的高分辨率图像。四个波段下的图像可以清楚地将微波背景辐射与前景辐射区分开。我们计算了微波背景的角功率谱，并在勒让德阶数 $l_{peak} = (197 \pm 6)$ 处发现了一个峰，其幅度为 $\Delta T_{200} = (69 \pm 8)$ μK。该结果同平直（欧几里得）宇宙下冷暗物质模型的理论预期相吻合，也被标准的暴胀模型所支持。

在宇宙早期，光子通过汤姆孙散射与电离物质紧密耦合在一起。这种耦合状态一直持续到大爆炸之后 300,000 年，这个时候宇宙冷却到足以形成中性氢。自那时候开始，原初光子就在宇宙中自由地传播，随着宇宙膨胀而红移到微波波段。这就是我们今天所观测到的宇宙微波背景（CMB）。而 CMB 中的温度各向异性则保留了早期宇宙的基本图像。角尺度大于约 2° 的各向异性信息由退耦时离开密度扰动的光子经历的引力红移所主导[1,2]。而更小角尺度上各向异性的程度因退耦前光子–重子

by oscillations of the photon–baryon fluid before decoupling[3]. These oscillations are driven by the primordial density fluctuations, and their nature depends on the matter content of the Universe.

In a spherical harmonic expansion of the CMB temperature field, the angular power spectrum specifies the contributions to the fluctuations on the sky coming from different multipoles l, each corresponding to the angular scale $\theta = \pi/l$. Density fluctuations over spatial scales comparable to the acoustic horizon at decoupling produce a peak in the angular power spectrum of the CMB, occurring at multipole l_{peak}. The exact value of l_{peak} depends on both the linear size of the acoustic horizon and on the angular diameter distance from the observer to decoupling. Both these quantities are sensitive to a number of cosmological parameters (see, for example, ref. 4), but l_{peak} primarily depends on the total density of the Universe, Ω_0. In models with a density Ω_0 near 1, $l_{peak} \approx 200/\Omega_0^{1/2}$. A precise measurement of l_{peak} can efficiently constrain the density and thus the curvature of the Universe.

Observations of CMB anisotropies require extremely sensitive and stable instruments. The DMR[5] instrument on the COBE satellite mapped the sky with an angular resolution of $\sim 7°$, yielding measurements of the angular power spectrum at multipoles $l < 20$. Since then, experiments with finer angular resolution[6-16] have detected CMB fluctuations on smaller scales and have produced evidence for the presence of a peak in the angular power spectrum at $l_{peak} \approx 200$.

Here we present high-resolution, high signal-to-noise maps of the CMB over a significant fraction of the sky, and derive the angular power spectrum of the CMB from $l = 50$ to 600. This power spectrum is dominated by a peak at multipole $l_{peak} = (197 \pm 6)$ (1σ error). The existence of this peak strongly supports inflationary models for the early Universe, and is consistent with a flat, euclidean Universe.

The Instrument

The Boomerang (balloon observations of millimetric extragalactic radiation and geomagnetics) experiment is a microwave telescope that is carried to an altitude of ~ 38 km by a balloon. Boomerang combines the high sensitivity and broad frequency coverage pioneered by an earlier generation of balloon-borne experiments with the long (~ 10 days) integration time available in a long-duration balloon flight over Antarctica. The data described here were obtained with a focal plane array of 16 bolometric detectors cooled to 0.3 K. Single-mode feedhorns provide two 18′ full-width at half-maximum (FWHM) beams at 90 GHz and two 10′ FWHM beams at 150 GHz. Four multi-band photometers each provide a 10.5′, 14′ and 13′ FWHM beam at 150, 240 and 400 GHz respectively. The average in-flight sensitivity to CMB anisotropies was 140, 170, 210 and 2,700 $\mu K\ s^{1/2}$ at 90, 150, 240 and 400 GHz, respectively. The entire optical system is heavily baffled against terrestrial radiation. Large sunshields improve rejection of radiation from $> 60°$ in azimuth from the telescope boresight. The rejection has been measured to be greater than

流体振荡而加剧[3]。这些振荡由原初密度扰动驱动，而它们的本质依赖于宇宙中的物质成分。

对 CMB 温度场进行球谐展开，其角功率谱表征了全天不同阶数 l（对应角尺度 $\theta = \pi/l$）处扰动的强度。与退耦时声学视界相比拟的空间尺度上的密度扰动在 CMB 的角功率谱上产生一个峰，对应阶数为 l_{peak}。l_{peak} 的精确取值依赖于声学视界的线性尺度以及观测者（现在）到退耦时期的角直径距离。虽然这些量与一系列宇宙学参数密切相关（比如参考文献 4），但是 l_{peak} 主要取决于宇宙整体密度 Ω_0。对于密度 Ω_0 接近 1 的宇宙学模型，$l_{peak} \approx 200/\Omega_0^{1/2}$。因此，对 l_{peak} 进行精确测量可有效地限制宇宙整体的密度，从而可以限制宇宙的曲率。

对 CMB 各向异性的观测需要极高分辨率和稳定性的观测仪器。COBE 卫星上的 DMR[5] 设备的巡天角分辨率约为 7°，这使得对 $l < 20$ 的角功率谱的测量成为可能。自此之后，具有更高角分辨率的实验[6-16]探测到更小尺度上的 CMB 扰动，并且得到的证据表明在角功率谱上 l_{peak} 约 200 处存在一个峰。

这里我们展示了一块足够大天区的 CMB 高分辨率高信噪比的图像，得到了 $l = 50$ 到 600 的 CMB 角功率谱。在这个范围内，功率谱在 $l_{peak} = 197 \pm 6$（1σ 误差范围）处存在一个峰。这个峰的存在极大地支持了早期宇宙的暴胀模型，与一个平直的欧几里得宇宙的理论预言相吻合。

观 测 设 备

Boomerang（毫米波段河外辐射和地磁场球载观测）实验利用球载微波望远镜在海拔约 38 千米的高空进行观测。Boomerang 在上一代球载实验开创的高分辨率和宽波段覆盖特性的基础上，更具在南极上空长时间的飞行中可用积分时间长（约 10 天）的能力。本工作所采用的数据来源于由 16 个冷却到 0.3 K 的热辐射探测器所组成的焦平面阵列。通过单模喇叭馈源，我们在 90 GHz 处得到了两个半峰全宽为 18 角分的波束，并在 150 GHz 处得到了两个半峰全宽为 10 角分的波束。而四个多波段光度计均在 150、240 以及 400 GHz 处得到了半峰全宽分别为 10.5、14 以及 13 角分的波束。CMB 各向异性在 90、150、240 以及 400 GHz 处运行中的平均灵敏度分别为 140、170、210 以及 2,700 $\mu K \cdot s^{1/2}$。整个光学系统可以很好地抵御地球辐射的影响。大型遮阳板有助于遮挡来自望远镜视轴方向且方位角大于 60° 的辐射。我们测

80 dB at all angles occupied by the Sun during the CMB observations. Further details on the instrument can be found in refs 17–21.

Observations

Boomerang was launched from McMurdo Station (Antarctica) on 29 December 1998, at 3:30 GMT. Observations began 3 hours later, and continued uninterrupted during the 259-hour flight. The payload approximately followed the 79° S parallel at an altitude that varied daily between 37 and 38.5 km, returning within 50 km of the launch site.

We concentrated our observations on a target region, centred at roughly right ascension (RA) 5 h, declination (dec.) −45°, that is uniquely free of contamination by thermal emission from interstellar dust[22] and that is approximately opposite the Sun during the austral summer. We mapped this region by repeatedly scanning the telescope through 60° at fixed elevation and at constant speed. Two scan speeds (1° s^{-1} and 2° s^{-1} in azimuth) were used to facilitate tests for systematic effects. As the telescope scanned, degree-scale variations in the CMB generated sub-audio frequency signals in the output of the detector[23]. The stability of the detector system was sufficient to allow sensitive measurements on angular scales up to tens of degrees on the sky. The scan speed was sufficiently rapid with respect to sky rotation that identical structures were observed by detectors in the same row in each scan. Detectors in different rows observed the same structures delayed in time by a few minutes.

At intervals of several hours, the telescope elevation was interchanged between 40°, 45° and 50° in order to increase the sky coverage and to provide further systematic tests. Sky rotation caused the scan centre to move and the scan direction to rotate on the celestial sphere. A map from a single day at a single elevation covered roughly 22° in declination and contained scans rotated by ±11° on the sky, providing a cross-linked scan pattern. Over most of the region mapped, each sky pixel was observed many times on different days, both at 1° s^{-1} and 2° s^{-1} scan speed, with different topography, solar elongation and atmospheric conditions, allowing strong tests for any contaminating signal not fixed on the celestial sphere.

The pointing of the telescope has been reconstructed with an accuracy of 2′ r.m.s. using data from a Sun sensor and rate gyros. This precision has been confirmed by analysing the observed positions of bright compact H II regions in the Galactic plane (RCW38[24], RCW57, IRAS08576 and IRAS1022) and of radio-bright point sources visible in the target region (the QSO 0483–436, the BL Lac object 0521–365 and the blazar 0537–441).

量发现，在整个 CMB 观测中各角度的太阳光均被遮挡了 80 dB 以上。更多关于设备的细节请参看参考文献 17～21。

观　　测

格林尼治标准时间 1998 年 12 月 29 日 3 时 30 分，Boomerang 从南极洲麦克默多站发射。观测始于 3 小时后，并在 259 小时的飞行过程中保持不间断。探测器每天大致在离发射场 50 千米范围内沿着南纬 79°飞行，海拔高度在 37～38.5 千米范围内。

我们将观测集中在以赤经 5 h、赤纬 −45°为中心的目标区域内。这块区域非常独特，不仅可以免受星际尘埃热辐射的污染[22]，且在整个南半球夏季都会背对着太阳。我们利用望远镜以 60°倾角和恒定的速度进行重复扫描来对该区域成图。为帮助测试其中的系统误差，我们使用了两种扫描速度（每秒方位角 1°和 2°）。随着望远镜对天区进行扫描，CMB 的度尺度上的变化在探测器输出中产生了亚音频信号[23]。整个探测器系统的稳定性很好，使得对天区进行大到数十度角尺度的高灵敏度的测量成为可能。所采用的扫描速度相对于天空旋转而言是足够快的，这样在每次扫描过程中同一行的探测器观测到的是相同的结构。而不同行的探测器则会在延迟几分钟之后也观测到这些相同的结构。

为了增加天区覆盖并且进行更多系统误差的测试，望远镜的倾角每隔几小时会在 40°、45°以及 50°之间交替变化。而天空的旋转不仅会使扫描中心发生移动，同时还会使扫描方向在天球上发生旋转。同一天同一倾角的图像大致覆盖赤纬 22°的范围，包含天空中旋转了 ±11°的扫描模式，这就形成了交联的扫描模式。对于大部分成图的区域而言，每个天空格点都会在不同时间里以两种扫描速度（每秒 1°和 2°）在不同地形、太阳距角以及大气条件下被观测多次，这就使得我们可以对天球上各种可能的污染信号进行强有力的测试。

利用太阳传感器和速率陀螺的数据，望远镜的指向已进行重构，其均方根精度为 2 角分。通过对银道面上明亮的致密 H II 区（RCW38[24]、RCW57、IRAS08576 以及 IRAS1022）以及目标天区可见的射电明亮点源（类星体 QSO 0483–436、BL Lac 天体 0521–365 以及耀变体 0537–441）观测位置的分析，我们进一步确认了望远镜的指向精度。

Calibrations

The beam pattern for each detector was mapped before flight using a thermal source. The main lobe at 90, 150 and 400 GHz is accurately modelled by a gaussian function. The 240 GHz beams are well modelled by a combination of two gaussians. The beams have small shoulders (less than 1% of the total solid angle), due to aberrations in the optical system. The beam-widths were confirmed in flight via observations of compact sources. By fitting radial profiles to these sources we determine the effective angular resolution, which includes the physical beamwidth and the effects of the 2' r.m.s. pointing jitter. The effective FWHM angular resolution of the 150 GHz data that we use here to calculate the CMB power spectrum is $(10 \pm 1)'$, where the error is dominated by uncertainty in the pointing jitter.

We calibrated the 90, 150 and 240 GHz channels from their measured response to the CMB dipole. The dipole anisotropy has been accurately (0.7%) measured by COBE-DMR[25], fills the beam and has the same spectrum as the CMB anisotropies at smaller angular scales, making it the ideal calibrator for CMB experiments. The dipole signal is typically ~3 mK peak-to-peak in each 60° scan, much larger than the detector noise, and appears in the output of the detectors at $f = 0.008$ Hz and $f = 0.016$ Hz in the $1°\,\mathrm{s}^{-1}$ and $2°\,\mathrm{s}^{-1}$ scan speeds, respectively. The accuracy of the calibration is dominated by two systematic effects: uncertainties in the low-frequency transfer function of the electronics, and low-frequency, scan-synchronous signals. Each of these is significantly different at the two scan speeds. We found that the dipole-fitted amplitudes derived from separate analysis of the $1°\,\mathrm{s}^{-1}$ and $2°\,\mathrm{s}^{-1}$ data agree to within $\pm 10\%$ for every channel, and thus we assign a 10% uncertainty in the absolute calibration.

From Detector Signals to CMB Maps

The time-ordered data comprises 5.4×10^7 16-bit samples for each channel. These data are flagged for cosmic-ray events, elevation changes, focal-plane temperature instabilities, and electromagnetic interference events. In general, about 5% of the data for each channel are flagged and not used in the subsequent analysis. The gaps resulting from this editing are filled with a constrained realization of noise in order to minimize their effect in the subsequent filtering of the data. The data are deconvolved by the bolometer and electronics transfer functions to recover uniform gain at all frequencies.

The noise power spectrum of the data and the maximum-likelihood maps[26-28] were calculated using an iterative technique[29] that separates the sky signal from the noise in the time-ordered data. In this process, the statistical weights of frequencies corresponding to angular scales larger than 10° on the sky are set to zero to filter out the largest-scale modes of the map. The maps were pixelized according to the HEALPix pixelization scheme[30].

校　准

在进行飞行试验前我们利用一个热源对每一个探测器的波束模式进行了成像。在 90、150 以及 400 GHz 的主瓣可以精确地用高斯函数进行拟合，而在 240 GHz 的波束则可以用两个高斯函数进行叠加。因为光学系统存在光行差，波束存在小的肩状分布（小于整个立体角的 1%）。在整个飞行过程中通过对致密源进行观测进一步确认了波束宽度。通过对这些源的径向轮廓进行拟合，我们得到了有效的角分辨率，这其中不仅包含其本身波束宽度的贡献，还包含 2 角分均方根指向抖动带来的影响。本工作中我们计算 CMB 功率谱所采用的 150 GHz 数据的有效半峰全宽角分辨率为 (10 ± 1) 角分，其误差主要来源于指向抖动的不确定性。

我们通过测量 90、150 以及 240 GHz 波段对 CMB 偶极子的响应对相应波段的观测进行校准。偶极子各向异性充满整个波束，并且在更小的角尺度上与 CMB 各向异性拥有相同的谱结构，而之前 COBE-DMR 已经对偶极子的各向异性进行了准确的测量（0.7%）[25]，因此偶极子各向异性是校准 CMB 实验观测的理想工具。每次 60° 扫描的典型偶极子信号总幅度大约为 3 mK，比探测器噪声大很多，且在每秒 1° 以及 2° 的扫描速度下分别在探测器输出的 $f = 0.008$ Hz 以及 $f = 0.016$ Hz 处出现。校准的准确性主要受到两个系统误差的影响：电子设备低频转移函数的不确定性以及低频扫描同步信号的不确定性。我们发现，对不同波段以及不同扫描速度（每秒 1° 以及每秒 2°）下的数据单独分析得到的偶极子拟合幅度在 $\pm10\%$ 范围内相互吻合。因此我们绝对校准的不确定度定为 10%。

从探测器信号到 CMB 图像

每个通道的时间序列数据包含 5.4×10^7 个 16 位样本。我们将受到宇宙线事件、倾角变化、焦平面温度不稳定性和电磁干扰事件影响的数据进行了标记。整体来说，每个通道大约有 5% 的数据被标记，这些数据不用于后续分析。为了降低后续数据平滑过滤过程中上述操作所带来的影响，我们利用一个约束噪声来填补这个过程所造成的数据缺失。随后，通过测辐射热计和电子设备转移函数对数据进行解卷积，我们重新得到了在所有频段具有均匀增益的数据样本。

通过一个可以在时间序列数据中将天空信号和噪声分离的迭代技术[29]，我们计算得到了数据的噪声功率谱以及最大似然图像[26-28]。在这个过程中，我们将对应天空角尺度大于 10° 的频率的统计权重设为 0，以此来滤除图像中的最大尺度模式。整个图像根据 HEALPix 像素化方法进行像素化[30]。

Figure 1 shows the maps obtained in this way at each of the four frequencies. The 400 GHz map is dominated by emission from interstellar dust that is well correlated with that observed by the IRAS and COBE/DIRBE satellites. The 90, 150 and 240 GHz maps are dominated by degree-scale structures that are resolved with high signal-to-noise ratio. A qualitative but powerful test of the hypothesis that these structures are CMB anisotropy is provided by subtracting one map from another. The structures evident in all three maps disappear in both the $90 - 150$ GHz difference and in the $240 - 150$ GHz difference, as expected for emission that has the same spectrum as the CMB dipole anisotropy used to calibrate the maps.

Fig. 1. Boomerang sky maps (equatorial coordinates). The sky maps at 90, 150 and 240 GHz (left panels) are shown with a common colour scale, using a thermodynamic temperature scale chosen such that CMB anisotropies will have the same amplitude in the three maps. Only the colour scale of the 400 GHz map

510

图 1 中显示了利用上述方法得到的四个频段的图像。400 GHz 的图像由星际尘埃的辐射主导，与 IRAS 和 COBE/DIRBE 卫星的观测结果存在很好的相关性。而 90、150 以及 240 GHz 的图像则由高信噪比的度尺度结构所主导。假设这些结构是 CMB 各向异性的，一个定性但有效检验这一假设的方法是将这些图像相互去减。那些在三个图像中均明显存在的结构在 90－150 GHz 的残差图以及 240－150 GHz 的残差图中都消失了，这从辐射中可以预见出，这些辐射与用来校准图像的 CMB 偶极子各向异性具有相同谱结构。

图 1. Boomerang 天图（赤道坐标）。左图中 90、150 以及 240 GHz 的天图具有相同的颜色显示标度，均采用相同的热力学温标，这样在三幅天图中 CMB 各向异性具有相同的幅度。只有右下角的 400 GHz 天

(bottom right) is 14 times larger than the others: this has been done to facilitate comparison of emission from interstellar dust (ISD), which dominates this map, with ISD emission present in the lower-frequency maps. The maps at 90 and 400 GHz are each from a single detector, while maps at 150 and 240 GHz have each been obtained by co-adding data from three detectors. For purposes of presentation, the maps have been smoothed with gaussian filters to obtain FWHM effective resolution of 22.5′ (small circle in the bottom right side of each panel). Structures along the scan direction larger than 10° are not present in the maps. Several features are immediately evident. Most strikingly, the maps at 90, 150 and 240 GHz are dominated by degree-scale structures that fill the map, have well-correlated morphology and are identical in amplitude in all three maps. These structures are not visible at 400 GHz. The 400 GHz map is dominated by diffuse emission which is correlated with the ISD emission mapped by IRAS/DIRBE[22]. This emission is strongly concentrated towards the right-hand edge of the maps, near the plane of the Galaxy. The same structures are evident in the 90, 150 and 240 GHz maps at Galactic latitude $b > -15°$, albeit with an amplitude that decreases steeply with decreasing frequency. The large-scale gradient evident especially near the right edge of the 240 GHz map is a result of high-pass-filtering the very large signals near the Galactic plane (not shown). This effect is negligible in the rest of the map. The two top right panels show maps constructed by differencing the 150 and 90 GHz maps and the 240 and 150 GHz maps. The difference maps contain none of the structures that dominate the maps at 90, 150 and 240 GHz, indicating that these structures do indeed have the ratios of brightness that are unique to the CMB. The morphology of the residual structures in the $240 - 150$ GHz map is well-correlated with the 400 GHz map, as is expected if the residuals are due to the ISD emission. Three compact sources of emission are visible in the lower-frequency maps, as indicated by the circles. These are known radio-bright quasars from the SEST pointing catalogue at 230 GHz. The boxed area has been used for computing the angular power spectrum shown in Fig. 2.

Fig. 2. Angular power spectrum measured by Boomerang at 150 GHz. Each point is the power averaged over $\Delta l = 50$ and has negligible correlations with the adjacent points. The error bars indicate the uncertainty due to noise and cosmic/sampling variance. The errors are dominated by cosmic/sampling variance at $l < 350$; they grow at large l due to the signal attenuation caused by the combined effects[39] of the 10′ beam and the 14′ pixelization (0.87 at $l = 200$ and 0.33 at $l = 600$). The current $\pm 10\%$ uncertainty in the calibration corresponds to an overall re-scaling of the y-axis by $\pm 20\%$, and is not shown. The current 1′ uncertainty in the angular resolution of the measurement creates an additional uncertainty—indicated by the distance between the ends of the red error bars and the blue horizontal lines—that is completely correlated and is largest (11%) at $l = 600$. The green points show the power spectrum of a difference map obtained as follows. We divided the data into two parts corresponding to the first and second halves of the timestream. We made two maps (A and B) from these halves, and the green points show the power spectrum computed from the difference map, $(A-B)/2$. Signals originating from the sky should disappear in this map, so this is a test for contamination in the data (see text). The solid curve has parameters $(\Omega_b, \Omega_m, \Omega_\Lambda, n_s, h) = (0.05, 0.31, 0.75, 0.95, 0.70)$. It is the best-fit model for the Boomerang test flight data[15,16], and is shown for comparison only. The model that best fits the new data reported here will be presented elsewhere.

图的颜色标度是其他图像的 14 倍，这么做的原因是为了方便将此天图与其他更低频段天图的星际尘埃辐射进行对比。对 400 GHz 天图而言，星际尘埃的辐射占主导。90 和 400 GHz 的天图的数据各由单独探测器获得，而 150 和 240 GHz 的天图则是将三个探测器的数据进行叠加之后所得。为了便于展示，所有天图均经过高斯滤波平滑处理，使得有效半峰全宽分辨率为 22.5 角分（每幅图右下角的小圆圈的大小）。沿扫描方向大于 10° 的结构没有显示在天图中。图中有几个特征非常明显。其中最为显著的是，90、150 以及 240 GHz 的天图由充满天图的度尺度结构主导，在三幅天图中它们的形态存在很好的相关性，且幅度完全相同。然而在 400 GHz 的天图中却看不到这些结构。400 GHz 天图由弥散的辐射所主导，与 IRAS/DIRBE[22] 观测得到的星际尘埃辐射存在很好的相关性。该辐射主要集中在天图的右边缘，靠近银道面的区域。在 90、150 以及 240 GHz 的天图对应银纬 $b > -15°$ 的区域中，这些结构同样显著，尽管随着频率的下降其幅度急剧减小。在 240 GHz 的天图中，特别是右边缘附近存在较为明显的大尺度梯度，这是由对银道面（未显示）附近非常高的信号进行高通滤波所造成的结果。这个效应对天图其他的区域所造成的影响可以忽略不计。右上的两幅图分别显示了 150 GHz 天图同 90 GHz 天图相减以及 240 GHz 同 150 GHz 天图相减所得的残差图。这些残差图中并不存在那些在 90、150 以及 240 GHz 天图中占主导的结构，这意味着这些结构确实具有 CMB 所特有的亮度比例。而 240 - 150 GHz 残差图中剩余结构的形态分布同 400 GHz 天图存在很好的相关性，这与我们假设残差主要源自星际尘埃辐射所得到的理论预期相符。在低频段的天图中，三个致密的辐射源清晰可见，具体位置已用圆圈标记。它们均为 230 GHz 的 SEST 星表中已知的射电明亮类星体。方框内的区域被用来计算图 2 中显示的角功率谱。

图 2. 150 GHz 处 Boomerang 测量得到的角功率谱。每个点为对应区间内功率的平均值，区间宽度 $\Delta l = 50$，相邻两点间的相关性可以忽略不计。误差棒反映了因噪声以及宇宙/样本方差所造成的不确定性。对于 $l < 350$ 的数据点而言，其误差主要来自宇宙/样本方差的不确定性；由于将 10 角分的波束同 14 角分的格点相结合导致的信号衰减[39]（$l = 200$ 时为 0.87，而 $l = 600$ 时为 0.33），误差会随着 l 的增加而变大。目前校准过程带来的 ±10% 的不确定性对应 y 轴整体改变 ±20%，这在本图中并未显示。而目前测量中角分辨率中存在的 1 角分的不确定性还会导致一个额外的不确定因素（表现在红色误差棒端与蓝色水平线之间的距离），这些不确定因素完全相关，且在 $l = 600$ 处最大（可达 11%）。绿色的点显示了用下面方法得到的残差图的功率谱。我们将数据按时间流分为两半，分别独立成图（A 和 B），而绿色的点显示了残差图（A - B）/2 的功率谱。在这幅残差图中所有来自天空的信号都将消失，因此这是检验数据中污染源的一个测试。实线对应的宇宙学参数（Ω_b, Ω_m, Ω_Λ, n_s, h）=（0.05, 0.31, 0.75, 0.95, 0.70）。这是与 Boomerang 测试飞行数据[15,16] 最相符的拟合参数，在此显示只作比较之用。与本工作新数据最相符的宇宙学模型将在别处讨论。

To quantify this conclusion, we performed a "colour index" analysis of our data. We selected the ~18,000 14′ pixels at Galactic latitude $b < -15°$, and made scatter plots of 90 GHz versus 150 GHz and 240 GHz versus 150 GHz. A linear fit to these scatter plots gives slopes of 1.00 ± 0.15 and 1.10 ± 0.16, respectively (including our present 10% calibration error), consistent with a CMB spectrum. For comparison, free–free emission with spectral index -2.35 would produce slopes of 2.3 and 0.85, and was therefore rejected with > 99% confidence; emission from interstellar dust with temperature $T_d = 15$ K and spectral index of emissivity $\alpha = 1$ would produce slopes of 0.40 and 2.9. For any combination of $T_d > 7$ K and $1 < \alpha < 2$, the dust hypothesis is rejected with > 99% confidence. We conclude that the dominant source of structure that we detect at 90, 150 and 240 GHz is CMB anisotropy.

We further argue that the 150 GHz map at $b < -15°$ is free of significant contamination by any known astrophysical foreground. Galactic synchrotron and free–free emission is negligible at this frequency[31]. Contamination from extragalactic point sources is also small[32]; extrapolation of fluxes from the PMN survey[33] limits the contribution by point sources (including the three above-mentioned radio-bright sources) to the angular power spectrum derived below to < 0.7% at $l = 200$ and < 20% at $l = 600$. The astrophysical foreground that is expected to dominate at 150 GHz is thermal emission from interstellar dust. We placed a quantitative limit on this source of contamination as follows. We assumed that dust properties are similar at high ($b < -20°$) and moderate ($-20° < b < -5°$) Galactic latitudes. We selected the pixels at moderate Galactic latitudes and correlated the structure observed in each of our four bands with the IRAS/DIRBE map, which is dominated by dust in cirrus clouds. The best-fit slope of each of the scatter plots measures the ratios of the dust signal in the Boomerang channels to the dust signal in the IRAS/DIRBE map. We found that the 400 GHz map is very well correlated to the IRAS/DIRBE map, and that dust at $b < -20°$ can account for at most 10% of the signal variance at 240 GHz, 3% at 150 GHz and 0.5% at 90 GHz.

Angular Power Spectra

We compared the angular power spectrum of the structures evident in Fig. 1 with theoretical predictions. In doing so, we separated and removed the power due to statistical noise and systematic artefacts from the power due to the CMB anisotropies in the maps. The maximum-likelihood angular power spectrum of the maps was computed using the MADCAP[34] software package, whose algorithms fully take into account receiver noise and filtering.

Full analysis of our entire data set is under way. Because of the computational intensity of this process, we report here the results of a complete analysis of a limited portion of the data chosen as follows. We analysed the most sensitive of the 150 GHz detectors. We restricted the sky coverage to an area with RA > 70°, $b < -20°$ and $-55° < $ dec. $< -35°$, and we used only the ~50% of the data from this detector that was obtained at a scan speed of $1° \, s^{-1}$. We used a relatively coarse pixelization of 8,000 14-arcmin pixels as a compromise

为了将这个结论定量化，我们对数据进行了"色指数"分析。我们挑选了银纬 $b < -15°$ 的大约 18,000 个 14 角分的格点，并对其作 90 GHz 相对于 150 GHz 以及 240 GHz 相对于 150 GHz 的散点图。对这些散点图进行线性拟合，其斜率分别为 1.00 ± 0.15 以及 1.10 ± 0.16(其中包含我们之前提及的 10% 的校准误差)，与 CMB 谱结果相吻合。作为比较，谱指数为 −2.35 的自由−自由辐射产生的斜率分别为 2.3 和 0.85，因此以 >99% 的置信度被排除；温度为 $T_d = 15$ K、发射率谱指数为 $α = 1$ 的星际尘埃辐射产生的斜率分别为 0.40 和 2.9。满足 $T_d > 7$ K 以及 $1 < α < 2$ 范围中的尘埃辐射都会以 >99% 的置信度被排除。因此我们得出结论：我们在 90、150 以及 240 GHz 图像上探测到的结构，其主要来源为 CMB 各向异性。

进一步，我们认为银纬 $b < -15°$ 的 150 GHz 图像几乎免受任何已知前景天体的严重污染。银河系同步辐射以及自由−自由辐射在这个频段可以忽略不计[31]。河外点源的污染也很小[32]；对 PMN 巡天[33] 的光通量进行外推，可以限制点源(包括三个上面提及的射电明亮天体)对角功率谱的贡献：$l = 200$ 处低至 < 0.7%，而 $l = 600$ 处低至 < 20%。在 150 GHz 频段，我们预测最主要的前景天体应该是星际尘埃的热辐射。我们采用如下方法对这一污染源进行定量化限制。首先我们假设中($-20° < b < -5°$)、高($b < -20°$)银纬的尘埃性质类似。我们选取中等银纬的天区图像格点，将我们四个波段所观测到的由卷云尘埃主导的结构同 IRAS/DIRBE 图像进行相关分析。这几个散点图的最佳拟合斜率表征了 Boomerang 各通道测量得到的尘埃信号与 IRAS/DIRBE 图像中的尘埃信号的比值。我们发现 400 GHz 图像同 IRAS/DIRBE 图像存在很好的相关性，同时银纬 $b < -20°$ 的尘埃分别至多可以贡献 240 GHz、150 GHz 以及 90 GHz 图像中 10%、3% 以及 0.5% 的信号变化。

角 功 率 谱

我们将图 1 中明显结构的角功率谱同理论预言进行比较。在这个过程中，我们从图像中将统计噪声以及系统误差的贡献和 CMB 各向异性的信号分离并去除。利用 MADCAP[34] 软件包计算了这些图像的最大似然角功率谱，该软件的算法充分考虑了接收器噪声以及滤波过程所带来的影响。

我们正在对整个数据进行详尽的分析。由于整个过程的计算量很大，这里我们只展示如下所选的有限的一部分数据的完整分析结果。我们选择分析最为敏感的 150 GHz 探测器所得到的数据。我们将天区范围限制在赤经 > 70°，$b < -20°$ 以及 $-55° < 赤纬 < -35°$ 的区域内，并只分析该探测器扫描速度为每秒 1° 所得到的近一半的数据。作为计算速度与高的多级覆盖的折中选择，我们使用一套相对粗糙且包含 8,000 个 14 角分的格点。最后，我们将分析限制在 $l \leqslant 600$ 的范围内，因为在该

between computation speed and coverage of high multipoles. Finally, we limited our analysis to $l \lesssim 600$ for which the effects of pixel shape and size and our present uncertainty in the beam size (1′) are small and can be accurately modelled.

The angular power spectrum determined in this way is shown in Fig. 2 and reported in Table 1. The power spectrum is dominated by a peak at $l_{peak} \approx 200$, as predicted by inflationary cold dark matter models. These models additionally predict the presence of secondary peaks. The data at high l limit the amplitude, but do not exclude the presence of a secondary peak. The errors in the angular power spectrum are dominated at low multipoles ($l \lesssim 350$) by the cosmic/sampling variance, and at higher multipoles by detector noise.

Table 1. Angular power spectrum of CMB anisotropy

l range	150 GHz ([1st half] + [2nd half])/2	150 GHz ([1st half] − [2nd half])/2
26–75	$1,140 \pm 280$	63 ± 32
76–125	$3,110 \pm 490$	16 ± 20
126–175	$4,160 \pm 540$	17 ± 28
176–225	$4,700 \pm 540$	59 ± 44
226–275	$4,300 \pm 460$	68 ± 59
276–325	$2,640 \pm 310$	130 ± 82
326–375	$1,550 \pm 220$	-7 ± 92
376–425	$1,310 \pm 220$	-60 ± 120
426–475	$1,360 \pm 250$	0 ± 160
476–525	$1,440 \pm 290$	220 ± 230
526–575	$1,750 \pm 370$	130 ± 300
576–625	$1,540 \pm 430$	-430 ± 360

Shown are measurements of the angular power spectrum of the cosmic microwave background at 150 GHz, and tests for systematic effects. The values listed are for $\Delta T_l^2 = l(l+1)c_l/2\pi$, in μK^2. Here $c_l = \langle a_{lm}^2 \rangle$, and a_{lm} are the coefficients of the spherical harmonic decomposition of the CMB temperature field: $\Delta T(\theta, \phi) = \Sigma a_{lm} Y_{lm}(\theta, \phi)$. The stated 1σ errors include statistical and cosmic/sample variance, and do not include a 10% calibration uncertainty.

The CMB angular power spectrum shown in Fig. 2 was derive from 4.1 days of observation. As a test of the stability of the result, we made independent maps from the first and second halves of these data. The payload travels several hundred kilometres, and the Sun moves 2° on the sky, between these maps. Comparing them provides a stringent test for contamination from sidelobe pickup and thermal effects. The angular power spectrum calculated for the difference map is shown in Fig. 2. The reduced χ^2 of this power spectrum with respect to zero signal is 1.11 (12 degrees of freedom), indicating that the difference map is consistent with zero contamination.

范围内格点形状、大小以及目前波束尺寸（1 角分）的不确定性所带来的影响很小而且能够利用模型准确进行描述。

  图 2 及表 1 中展示了用这种方法得到的角功率谱结果。该功率谱在 $l_{peak} \approx 200$ 处存在一个主峰，这与冷暗物质暴胀模型的预言相符。这些模型还预言了次峰的存在。高 l 的数据的幅度受到了限制，但并不排除次峰存在的可能性。角功率谱中低的多级区域（$l \leqslant 350$）的误差主要来自宇宙/样本方差，而高的多级区域的误差则主要来自探测器噪声。

表 1. CMB 各向异性的角功率谱

l 范围	150 GHz （[前一半]+[后一半]）/2	150 GHz （[前一半]−[后一半]）/2
26~75	1,140 ± 280	63 ± 32
76~125	3,110 ± 490	16 ± 20
126~175	4,160 ± 540	17 ± 28
176~225	4,700 ± 540	59 ± 44
226~275	4,300 ± 460	68 ± 59
276~325	2,640 ± 310	130 ± 82
326~375	1,550 ± 220	−7 ± 92
376~425	1,310 ± 220	−60 ± 120
426~475	1,360 ± 250	0 ± 160
476~525	1,440 ± 290	220 ± 230
526~575	1,750 ± 370	130 ± 300
576~625	1,540 ± 430	−430 ± 360

这里显示的是 150 GHz 处测量得到的宇宙微波背景的角功率谱以及系统误差的测试结果。这里显示的值对应 $\Delta T_l^2 = l(l+1) c_l/2\pi$，单位为 μK^2。这里 $c_l = \langle a_{lm}^2 \rangle$，$a_{lm}$ 为 CMB 温度场的球谐分解系数：$\Delta T(\theta, \phi) = \Sigma a_{lm} Y_{lm}(\theta, \phi)$。所展示的 1σ 误差包含统计误差以及宇宙/样本方差，但没有包含 10% 的校准不确定性。

  图 2 中显示的 CMB 角功率谱是基于 4.1 天的观测数据分析所得。为了测试结果的稳定性，我们将所有数据按时间分为两半，分别独立成图。在这两套图像之间，观测设备移动了数百千米，而太阳在天空中移动了 2°。通过比较这些图像可以对旁瓣污染以及热效应等污染因素进行严格的测试。图 2 还展示了两套图像残差结果的功率谱。该功率谱相对于零信号的约化 χ^2 为 1.11（12 个自由度），这个结果表明残差结果与零污染结果相吻合。

A Peak at $l \approx 200$ Implies a Flat Universe

The location of the first peak in the angular power spectrum of the CMB is well measured by the Boomerang data set. From a parabolic fit to the data at $l = 50$ to 300 in the angular power spectrum, we find $l_{peak} = (197 \pm 6)$ (1σ error). The parabolic fit does not bias the determination of the peak multipole: applying this method to Monte Carlo realizations of theoretical power spectra we recover the correct peak location for a variety of cosmological models. Finally, the peak location is independent of the details of the data calibration, which obviously affect only the height of the peak and not its location. The height of the peak is $\Delta T_{200} = (69 \pm 4) \pm 7$ μK (1σ statistical and calibration errors, respectively).

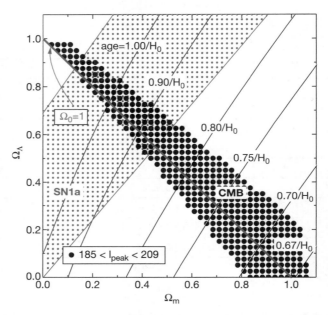

Fig. 3. Observational constraints on Ω_m and Ω_Λ. All the cosmological models (from our data base) consistent with the position of the peak in the angular power spectrum measured by Boomerang (95% confidence intervals) define an "allowed" region in the Ω_m–Ω_Λ plane (marked by large black dots). Such a region is elongated around the $\Omega_0 = 1$ line identifying a flat geometry, euclidean Universe. The blue lines define the age of the Universe for the considered models. The green-dotted region is consistent (95% confidence contour) with the recent results of the high-redshift supernovae surveys[40,41].

The data are inconsistent with current models based on topological defects (see, for example, ref. 35) but are consistent with a subset of cold dark matter models. We generated a database of cold dark matter models[36,37], varying six cosmological parameters (the range of variation is given in parentheses): the non-relativistic matter density, Ω_m (0.05–2); the cosmological constant, Ω_Λ (0–1); the Hubble constant, h (0.5–0.8); the baryon density, $h^2\Omega_b$ (0.013–0.025); the primordial scalar spectral index, n_s (0.8–1.3); and the overall normalization A (free parameter) of the primordial density fluctuation power spectrum. We compared these models with the power spectrum we report here to place constraints

$l \approx 200$ 的峰意味着一个平直宇宙

通过 Boomerang 数据，我们很好地测量到 CMB 角功率谱第一个峰的位置。通过对角功率谱 $l = 50 \sim 300$ 范围内的数据进行抛物线拟合，我们发现 $l_{peak} = (197 \pm 6)$（1σ 误差范围）。这种抛物线拟合不会对多级峰值的测量带来偏差：将这种方法应用于理论功率谱的蒙特卡洛实现，我们恢复出一系列宇宙学模型正确的峰值位置。最后可知，峰值位置不受数据校准细节的影响，因为数据校准细节仅仅影响峰的高度而并不影响它的位置。峰的高度为 $\Delta T_{200} = (69 \pm 4) \pm 7\ \mu K$（分别对应 1σ 的统计误差和校准误差）。

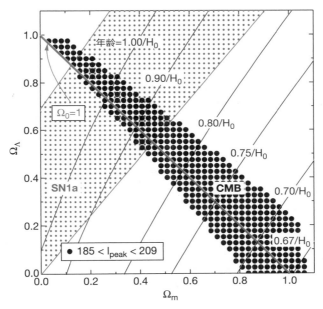

图 3. 对 Ω_m 和 Ω_Λ 的观测限制。所有与 Boomerang 测量得到的角功率谱的峰位置一致（95% 置信区间）的宇宙学模型（来自我们模型库）在 Ω_m–Ω_Λ 平面定义了一个"允许"区域（用大的黑色点进行标记）。这样的一个区域沿 $\Omega_0 = 1$ 的线进行延伸，这意味着宇宙是平直的，符合欧几里得几何。蓝色的线表征了所考虑的模型的宇宙年龄。绿色点的区域在 95% 置信度上符合最近高红移超新星巡天观测结果[40,41]。

这些数据与目前基于拓扑缺陷所建立的模型（比如参考文献 35）预言不吻合，但同冷暗物质模型的一个子集的理论预言相吻合。我们通过改变六个宇宙学参数构建了冷暗物质模型的模型库[36,37]（括号中显示参数的变化范围）：非相对论性的物质密度 $\Omega_m(0.05 \sim 2)$、宇宙学常数 $\Omega_\Lambda(0 \sim 1)$、哈勃常数 $h(0.5 \sim 0.8)$、重子密度 $h^2\Omega_b$（$0.013 \sim 0.025$）、原初标量谱指数 $n_s(0.8 \sim 1.3)$ 以及原初密度扰动功率谱的归一化因子 A（自由参数）。通过将这些模型同我们得到的功率谱进行比较，我们可以在这个 6 参数空间中对所允许的区域进行限制。图 3 中我们用大的黑色圆点标记了 Ω_m–Ω_Λ

on allowed regions in this 6-parameter space. In Figure 3 we mark with large black dots the region of the Ω_m–Ω_Λ plane where some combination of the remaining four parameters within the ranges defined by our model space gives a power spectrum consistent with our 95% confidence interval for l_{peak}. This region is quite narrow, and elongated along the "flat Universe" line $\Omega_m + \Omega_\Lambda = 1$. The width of this region is determined by degeneracy in the models, which produce closely similar spectra for different values of the parameters[38]. We further evaluated the likelihood of the models given the Boomerang measurement and the same priors (constraints on the values of the cosmological parameters) as in ref. 16. Marginalizing over all the other parameters, we found the following 95% confidence interval for $\Omega_0 = \Omega_m + \Omega_\Lambda$: $0.88 < \Omega_0 < 1.12$. This provides evidence for a euclidean geometry of the Universe. Our data clearly show the presence of power beyond the peak at $l = 197$, corresponding to smaller-scale structures. The consequences of this fact will be fully analysed elsewhere.

(**404**, 955-959; 2000)

P. de Bernardis[1], P. A. R. Ade[2], J. J. Bock[3], J. R. Bond[4], J. Borrill[5,12], A. Boscaleri[6], K. Coble[7], B. P. Crill[8], G. De Gasperis[9], P. C. Farese[7], P. G. Ferreira[10], K. Ganga[8,11], M. Giacometti[1], E. Hivon[8], V. V. Hristov[8], A. Iacoangeli[1], A. H. Jaffe[12], A. E. Lange[8], L. Martinis[13], S. Masi[1], P. V. Mason[8], P. D. Mauskopf[14,15], A. Melchiorri[1], L. Miglio[16], T. Montroy[7], C. B. Netterfield[16], E. Pascale[6], F. Piacentini[1], D. Pogosyan[4], S. Prunet[4], S. Rao[17], G. Romeo[17], J. E. Ruhl[7], F. Scaramuzzi[13], D. Sforna[1] & N. Vittorio[9]

[1] Dipartimento di Fisica, Universita' di Roma "La Sapienza", P.le A. Moro 2, 00185 Roma, Italy

[2] Department of Physics, Queen Mary and Westfield College, Mile End Road, London E1 4NS, UK

[3] Jet Propulsion Laboratory, Pasadena, California 91109, USA

[4] CITA University of Toronto, Toronto M5S 3H8, Canada

[5] NERSC-LBNL, Berkeley, California 94720, USA

[6] IROE–CNR, Via Panciatichi 64, 50127 Firenze, Italy

[7] Department of Physics, University of California at Santa Barbara, Santa Barbara, California 93106, USA

[8] California Institute of Technology, Mail Code 59-33, Pasadena, California 91125, USA

[9] Dipartimento di Fisica, Universita' di Roma Tor Vergata, Via della Ricerca Scientifica 1, 00133 Roma, Italy

[10] Astrophysics, University of Oxford, Keble Road, OX1 3RH, UK

[11] PCC, College de France, 11 pl. Marcelin Berthelot, 75231 Paris Cedex 05, France

[12] Center for Particle Astrophysics, University of California at Berkeley, 301 Le Conte Hall, Berkeley, California 94720, USA

[13] ENEA Centro Ricerche di Frascati, Via E. Fermi 45, 00044 Frascati, Italy

[14] Physics and Astronomy Department, Cardiff University, Cardiff CF2 3YB, UK

[15] Department of Physics and Astronomy, University of Massachusetts, Amherst, Massachusetts 01003, USA

[16] Department of Physics and Astronomy, University of Toronto, Toronto M5S 3H8, Canada

[17] Istituto Nazionale di Geofisica, Via di Vigna Murata 605, 00143, Roma, Italy

Received 24 March; accepted 3 April 2000.

References:

1. Sachs, R. K. & Wolfe, A. M. Perturbations of a cosmological model and angular variations of the microwave background. *Astrophys. J.* **147**, 73-90 (1967).

2. Weinberg S., *Gravitation and Cosmology* (Wiley & Sons, New York, 1972).

3. Hu, W., Sugiyama, N. & Silk, J. The physics of cosmic microwave background anisotropies. *Nature* **386**, 37-43 (1997).

4. Bond, J. R., Efstathiou, G. & Tegmark, M. Forecasting cosmic parameter errors from microwave background anisotropy experiments. *Mon. Not. R. Astron. Soc.* **291**, L33-L41 (1997).

5. Hinshaw, G. *et al.* Band power spectra in the COBE-DMR four-year anisotropy map. *Astrophys. J.* **464**, L17-L20 (1996).

6. Scott, P. F. *et al.* Measurement of structure in the cosmic background radiation with the Cambridge cosmic anisotropy telescope. *Astrophys. J.* **461**, L1-L4 (1996).

平面上"允许"的区域；该区域中，在我们参数空间定义的范围内，通过对剩余四个参数进行组合，所得的功率谱在 95% 的置信区间内与得到的 l_{peak} 结果相吻合。这个区域相当窄，而且沿着"平直宇宙"线 $\Omega_m + \Omega_\Lambda = 1$ 进行延伸。这个区域的宽度由模型的简并性决定，当这些参数取不同的数值时可以得到非常相似的光谱[38]。我们进一步基于 Boomerang 的测量结果以及同参考文献 16 中相同的先验信息（对宇宙学参数值的限制）评估了不同模型的似然性。通过对所有其他参数进行边缘化分析，我们得到了对 $\Omega_0 = \Omega_m + \Omega_\Lambda$ 的欧几里得几何学在 95% 置信区间内的限制结果：$0.88 < \Omega_0 < 1.12$。这为宇宙模型的欧几里得几何学提供了依据。我们的结果也清楚地显示出在峰值 $l = 197$ 位置之外存在功率，这对应着更小尺度的结构。我们将在别处对这一现象展开详细的分析。

（刘项琨 翻译；李然 审稿）

7. Netterfield, C. B. *et al.* A measurement of the angular power spectrum of the anisotropy in the cosmic microwave background. *Astrophys. J.* **474**, 47-66 (1997).

8. Leitch, E. M. *et al.* A measurement of anisotropy in the cosmic microwave background on 7-22 arcminute scales. *Astrophys. J.* (submitted); also as preprint astro-ph/9807312 at ⟨http://xxx.lanl.gov⟩ (1998).

9. Wilson, G. W. *et al.* New CMB power spectrum constraints from MSAMI. *Astrophys. J.* (submitted); also as preprint astro-ph/9902047 at ⟨http://xxx.lanl.gov⟩ (1999).

10. Baker, J. C. *et al.* Detection of cosmic microwave background structure in a second field with the cosmic anisotropy telescope. *Mon. Not. R. Astron. Soc.* (submitted); also as preprint astro-ph/9904415 at ⟨http://xxx.lanl.gov⟩ (1999).

11. Peterson, J. B. *et al.* First results from Viper: detection of small-scale anisotropy at 40 GHZ. Preprint astro-ph/9910503 at ⟨http://xxx.lanl.gov⟩ (1999).

12. Coble, K. *et al.* Anisotropy in the cosmic microwave background at degree angular scales: Python V results. *Astrophys. J.* **519**, L5-L8 (1999).

13. Torbet, E. *et al.* A measurement of the angular power spectrum of the microwave background made from the high Chilean Andes. *Astrophys. J.* **521**, 79-82 (1999).

14. Miller, A. D. *et al.* A measurement of the angular power spectrum of the CMB from $l = 100$ to 400. *Astrophys. J.* (submitted); also as preprint astro-ph/9906421 at ⟨http://xxx.lanl.gov⟩ (1999).

15. Mauskopf, P. *et al.* Measurement of a peak in the CMB power spectrum from the test flight of BOOMERanG. *Astrophys. J.* (submitted); also as preprint astro-ph/9911444 at ⟨http://xxx.lanl. gov⟩ (1999).

16. Melchiorri, A. *et al.* A measurement of Ω from the North American test flight of BOOMERanG. *Astrophys. J.* (submitted); also as preprint astro-ph/9911445 at ⟨http://xxx.lanl.gov⟩ (1999).

17. de Bernardis, P. *et al.* Mapping the CMB sky: the BOOMERanG experiment. *New Astron. Rev.* **43**, 289-296 (1999).

18. Mauskopf, P. *et al.* Composite infrared bolometers with Si_3N_4 micromesh absorbers. *Appl. Opt.* **36**, 765-771 (1997).

19. Bock, J. *et al.* Silicon nitride micromesh bolometer arrays for SPIRE. *Proc. SPIE* **3357**; 297-304 (1998).

20. Masi, S. *et al.* A self contained ^{3}He refrigerator suitable for long duration balloon experiments. *Cryogenics* **38**, 319-324 (1998).

21. Masi, S. *et al.* A long duration cryostat suitable for balloon borne photometry. *Cryogenics* **39**, 217-224 (1999).

22. Schlegel, D. J., Finkbeiner, D. P. & Davis, M. Maps of dust IR emission for use in estimation of reddening and CMBR foregrounds. *Astrophys. J.* **500**, 525-553 (1998).

23. Delabrouille, J., Gorski, K. M. & Hivon, E. Circular scans for CMB anisotropy observation and analysis. *Mon. Not. R. Astron. Soc.* **298**, 445-450 (1998).

24. Cheung, L. H. *et al.* 1.0 millimeter maps and radial density distributions of southern HII/molecular cloud complexes. *Astrophys. J.* **240**, 74-83 (1980).

25. Kogut, A. *et al.* Dipole anisotropy in the COBE DMR first-year sky maps. *Astrophys. J.* **419**, 1-6 (1993).

26. Tegmark, M. CMB mapping experiments: a designer's guide. *Phys. Rev. D* **56**, 4514-4529 (1997).

27. Bond, J. R., Crittenden, R., Jaffe, A. H. & Knox, L. E. Computing challenges of the cosmic microwave background. *Comput. Sci. Eng.* **21**, 1-21 (1999).

28. Borrill, J. in *Proc. 3K Cosmology EC-TMR Conf.* (eds Langlois, D., Ansari, R. & Vittorio, N.) 277 (American Institute of Physics Conf. Proc. Vol. 476, Woodbury, New York, 1999).

29. Prunet, S. *et al.* in *Proc. Conf. Energy Density in the Universe* (eds Langlois, D., Ansari, R. & Bartlett, J.) (Editiones Frontieres, Paris, 2000).

30. Gorski, K. M., Hivon, E. & Wandelt, B. D. in *Proc. MPA/ESO Conf.* (eds Banday, A. J., Sheth, R. K. & Da Costa, L.) (European Southern Observatory, Garching); see also ⟨http://www.tac.dk/~healpix/⟩.

31. Kogut, A. in *Microwave Foregrounds* (eds de Oliveira Costa, A. & Tegmark, M.) 91-99 (Astron. Soc. Pacif. Conf. Series. Vol 181, San Francisco, 1999).

32. Toffolatti, L. *et al.* Extragalactic source counts and contributions to the anisotropies of the CMB. *Mon. Not. R. Astron. Soc.* **297**, 117-127 (1998).

33. Wright, A. E. *et al.* The Parkes-MIT-NRAO (PMN) surveys II. Source catalog for the southern survey. *Astrophys. J. Supp. Ser.* **91**, 111-308 (1994); see also ⟨http://astron.berkeley.edu/wombat/foregrounds/radio.html⟩.

34. Borrill, J. in *Proc. 5th European SGI/Cray MPP Workshop* (CINECA, Bologna, 1999); Preprint astro-ph/9911389 at ⟨xxx.lanl.gov⟩ (1999); see also ⟨http://cfpa.berkeley.edu/~borrill/cmb/madcap.html⟩.

35. Durrer, R., Kunz, M. & Melchiorri, A. *Phys. Rev. D* **59**, 1-26 (1999).

36. Seljak, U. & Zaldarriaga, M. A line of sight approach to cosmic microwave background anisotropies. *Astrophys. J.* **437**, 469-477 (1996).

37. Lewis, A., Challinor, A. & Lasenby, A. Efficient computation of CMB anisotropies in closed FRW models. Preprint astro-ph/9911177 at ⟨http://xxx.lanl.gov⟩ (1999).

38. Efstathiou, G. & Bond, R. Cosmic confusion: degeneracies among cosmological parameters derived from measurements of microwave background anisotropies. *Mon. Not. R. Astron. Soc.* **304**, 75-97 (1998).

39. Wright, E. *et al.* Comments on the statistical analysis of excess variance in the COBE-DMR maps. *Astrophys. J.* **420**, 1-8 (1994).

40. Perlmutter, S. *et al.* Measurements of and Λ from 42 high-redshift supernovae. *Astrophys. J.* **517**, 565-586 (1999).

41. Schmidt, B. P. *et al.* The high-Z supernova search: measuring cosmic deceleration and global curvature of the Universe using type Ia supernovae. *Astrophys. J.* **507**, 46-63 (1998).

Acknowledgements. The Boomerang experiment was supported by Programma Nazionale di Ricerche in Antartide, Universita' di Roma "La Sapienza", and Agenzia Spaziale Italiana in Italy, by the NSF and NASA in the USA, and by PPARC in the UK. We thank the staff of the National Scientific Ballooning Facility, and the United States Antarctic Program personnel in McMurdo for their preflight support and an effective LDB flight. DOE/NERSC provided the supercomputing facilities.

Correspondence and requests for materials should be addressed to P. d. B. (e-mail: debernardis@roma1.infn.it). Details of the experiment and numerical data sets are available at the web sites ⟨http://oberon.roma1.infn.it/boomerang⟩ and ⟨http://www.physics.ucsb.edu/~boomerang⟩.

The Accelerations of Stars Orbiting the Milky Way's Central Black Hole

A. M. Ghez *et al.*

Editor's Note

It had been widely believed for several years that black holes with masses of a million or more solar masses reside at the centres of most galaxies. But proving that notion was challenging. Here Andrea Ghez and colleagues track the motions of stars very close to the centre of the Milky Way, seeing them move in their orbits. Subsequent work has tracked these stars through their entire orbits; one travels around the Galactic Centre at the tremendous speed of over 5,000 km/s. These studies strongly suggest that the stars are gravitationally influenced by an object such as a supermassive black hole; the only (increasingly unlikely) alternative is a massive star made of some kind of exotic matter.

Recent measurements[1-4] of the velocities of stars near the centre of the Milky Way have provided the strongest evidence for the presence of a supermassive black hole in a galaxy[5], but the observational uncertainties poorly constrain many of the black hole's properties. Determining the accelerations of stars in their orbits around the centre provides much more precise information about the position and mass of the black hole. Here we report measurements of the accelerations of three stars located ~0.005 pc (projected on the sky) from the central radio source Sagittarius A* (Sgr A*); these accelerations are comparable to those experienced by the Earth as it orbits the Sun. These data increase the inferred minimum mass density in the central region of the Galaxy by an order of magnitude relative to previous results, and localize the dark mass to within 0.05 ± 0.04 arcsec of the nominal position of Sgr A*. In addition, the orbital period of one of the observed stars could be as short as 15 years, allowing us the opportunity in the near future to observe an entire period.

IN 1995, we initiated a programme of high-resolution 2.2-μm (K band) imaging of the inner 5 arcsec × 5 arcsec of the Galaxy's central stellar cluster with the W. M. Keck 10-m telescope on Mauna Kea, Hawaii (1 arcsec = 0.04 pc at the distance to the Galactic Centre, 8 kpc, ref. 6). From each observation, several thousand short exposure ($t_{exp} = 0.137$ s) frames were collected, using the facility near-infrared camera, NIRC[7,8], and combined to produce a final diffraction-limited image having an angular resolution of 0.05 arcsec. Between 1995 and 1997, images were obtained once a year with the aim of detecting the stars' velocities in the plane of the sky. The results from these measurements are detailed in ref. 4; in summary, two-dimensional velocities were measured for 90 stars with simple

环绕银河系中心黑洞运动的恒星的加速度

盖兹等

编者按

近年来，人们普遍相信在大部分的星系中心都存在质量超过百万太阳质量的黑洞。然而要想证明这一观点却是极具挑战性的。在本文中，安德烈娅·盖兹和她的同事们追踪了那些非常接近银河系中心的恒星的运动，以观测这些恒星的运动轨迹。其中有一颗围绕银河系中心运动的恒星，其速度竟可高达 5,000 km/s。这些研究结果表明银河系中心很有可能存在一个超大质量的黑洞，而这些恒星正是在这个超大质量黑洞的引力影响下围绕银河系中心运动。除此之外，唯一的可能性（越来越不可能）就是银河系中心存在一个由某种奇异物质组成的大质量恒星。

近年来对银河系中心附近恒星速度的测量[1-4]为星系中心存在超大质量黑洞提供了最有力的证据[5]，但是观测误差使得我们很难对黑洞的许多性质给出强有力的限制。确定恒星环绕中心轨道的加速度，将向我们提供更精确的黑洞位置和质量信息。在本文中，我们报道了距离中心射电源人马座 A*（简称 Sgr A*）约 0.005 秒差距（pc）（投影到天球上）处三颗恒星加速度的测量结果；这些加速度和地球环绕太阳经历的加速度相似。相对以前的结果，从这些数据推导出的银河系中心的最小质量密度增加了一个量级，并将暗质量区域限定在 Sgr A* 标定位置的 0.05 ± 0.04 角秒以内。此外，其中一颗恒星的轨道周期可能只有短短的 15 年，这让我们在未来有机会观测它的整个运动轨道周期。

我们在 1995 年启动了一个项目，利用夏威夷冒纳凯阿山的 10 米凯克望远镜在 2.2 μm 波段（K 波段）对银河系中心星团内部 5 角秒 × 5 角秒的区域做高分辨率的成图观测（距离银河系中心 8 kpc 处，1 角秒 = 0.04 pc，参考文献 6）。对于每次观测，我们使用近红外照相机设备 NIRC[7,8]收集了几千幅短曝光（t_{exp} = 0.137 s）图像，并将这些图像合在一起最终得到一幅角分辨率为 0.05 角秒的衍射极限图像。为了测量恒星在天球切面上的速度，我们从 1995 年到 1997 年每年成图一次。这些测量的具体结果罗列在参考文献 4 中；总的来说，我们对 90 颗恒星的位置与时间关系进行简单的线性拟合得到它们的二维速度。这些速度，有的可以高达 1,400 km · s⁻¹， linear fits to the positions as a function of time. These velocities, which reach up to 1,400 km s^{-1}, implied the existence of a 2.6×10^6 $M_\odot$ black hole coincident (± 0.1 arcsec) with the nominal location of Sgr A* (ref. 9), the unusual radio source[10-12] long believed to be the counterpart of the putative black hole.

The new observations presented here were obtained several times a year from 1997 to 1999 to improve the sensitivity to accelerations. With nine independent measurements, we now fit the positions of stars as a function of time with second order polynomials (see Fig. 1). The resulting velocity uncertainties are reduced by a factor of 3 compared to our earlier work, primarily as a result of the increased time baseline, and, in the central square arcsecond, by a factor of 6 compared to that presented in ref. 3, owing to our higher angular resolution. Among the 90 stars in our original proper motion sample[4], we have now detected significant accelerations for three stars, S0-1, S0-2 and S0-4 (see Table 1); specifically, these are the sources for which the reduced chi-squared value for a quadratic fit is smaller than that for the linear model of their motions by more than 1. These three stars are independently distinguished in our sample, being among the fastest moving stars ($v = 570$ to $1,350$ km s^{-1}) and among the closest to the nominal position of Sgr A* ($r_{1995} = 0.004$–0.013 pc). With accelerations of 2–5 milliarcsec yr^{-2}, or equivalently $(3$–$6) \times 10^{-6}$ km s^{-2}, they are experiencing accelerations similar to the Earth in its orbit about the Sun.

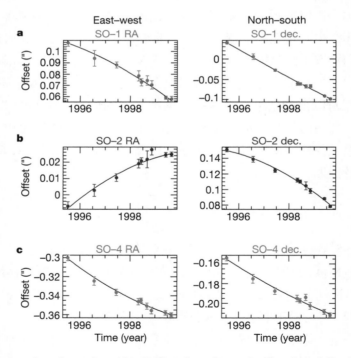

Fig. 1. East–west and north–south positional offsets from the nominal location of Sgr A* versus time for (**a**) S0-1, (**b**) S0-2, and (**c**) S0-4. The offset range shown is scaled to the points in each plot and therefore varies from ~$-0.4''$ to ~$0.15''$. Each of these stars is located with a precision of about 1–5 mas in the individual maps and the alignment of these positions, which is carried out by minimizing

意味着在 Sgr A* 的标定位置（参考文献 9）处（±0.1 角秒）很可能存在一个质量为 $2.6 \times 10^6 \, M_\odot$ 的黑洞。而 Sgr A* 这个不寻常的射电源[10-12]一直以来被认为是假定黑洞的对应体。

　　这里所采用的新数据是从 1997 年到 1999 年每年观测好几次得到的，为的是提高测量加速度的灵敏度。利用 9 次独立的测量结果，我们现在用二阶多项式来拟合恒星的位置–时间关系（见图 1）。主要因为时间基线变长，得到的速度误差减少为我们早期工作的 1/3；又因为角分辨率的提高，在图像中央的平方角秒区域内，速度误差减少为参考文献 3 的 1/6。在原初样本中有自行信息的 90 颗恒星中[4]，我们现在已经探测到 S0-1、S0-2 和 S0-4 这三颗恒星的显著加速度（见表 1）；特别是，用二次多项式拟合这些源的运动所得的约化 χ^2 值比线性拟合的约化 χ^2 值要少 1 以上。这三颗星作为运动最快（$v = 570 \sim 1{,}350 \, \mathrm{km \cdot s^{-1}}$）且最接近 Sgr A* 标定位置的恒星（$r_{1995} = 0.004 \sim 0.013 \, \mathrm{pc}$），在我们的样本中被单独区分出来。它们的加速度为 $2 \sim 5$ $\mathrm{milliarcsec \cdot yr^{-2}}$，或等效于 $(3 \sim 6) \times 10^{-6} \, \mathrm{km \cdot s^{-2}}$，正在经历与地球环绕太阳类似的加速运动过程。

图 1. 恒星（**a**）S0-1、（**b**）S0-2 和（**c**）S0-4 相对于 Sgr A* 标定位置在东–西、北–南方向上的偏移随时间的变化。每幅图中偏移范围都拟合在数据点上，其变化范围约在 $-0.4''$ 到 $0.15''$ 之间。这三颗恒星在各自图中的位置精度为 $1 \sim 5$ 毫角秒，按参考文献 4 描述的方法，我们通过将所有恒星的净位移最小化来将位置对准，半抽样自举重采样方法[22]带来大约 3 毫角秒的对准误差（对准误差在图中间最小，随着半径

the net displacement of all stars as described in ref. 4, has an uncertainty of about 3 mas based on the half sample bootstrap resampling method[22] (the alignment uncertainty is at a minimum at the centre of the map and grows linearly with radius). These two uncertainty terms are added in quadrature; the results are used in the fitting process and depicted as errorbars here. In each plot, the solid line shows the second order polynomial used to derive the acceleration term. These plots demonstrate that we are able to measure, for the first time, accelerations of 2 to 5 mas yr^{-2} (0.3–0.6 cm s^{-2}) for stars orbiting a supermassive black hole.

Table 1. Measurements for stars with significant accelerations

	S0-1 (S1)	S0-2 (S2)	S0-4 (S8)
Radius from Sgr A*-magnitude (milliparsecs)	4.42 ± 0.05	5.83 ± 0.04	13.15 ± 0.04
Radius from Sgr A*-position angle (degrees)	290.1 ± 0.7	3.1 ± 0.4	117.3 ± 0.2
Velocity-magnitude (km s^{-1})	$1{,}350 \pm 40$	570 ± 20	990 ± 30
Velocity-position angle (degrees)	168 ± 2	241 ± 2	129 ± 2
Acceleration-magnitude (milliarcsec yr^{-2})	2.4 ± 0.7	5.4 ± 0.3	3.2 ± 0.5
Acceleration-position angle (degrees)	80 ± 15	154 ± 4	294 ± 7

The primary nomenclature adopted here and in the text is from ref. 4; in parentheses star names from ref. 1 are also given. All quantities listed are derived from the second-order polynomial fit to the data and are given for epoch 1995.53. All position angles are measured east of north. All uncertainties are 1σ and are determined by the jackknife resampling method[22]. The radius uncertainties listed include only the relative positional uncertainties and not the uncertainty in the origin used (the nominal position of Sgr A*; see text for offset to measured dynamical centre).

Acceleration vectors, in principle, are more precise tools than the velocity vectors for studying the central mass distribution. Even projected onto the plane of the sky, each acceleration vector should be oriented in the direction of the central mass, assuming a spherically symmetric potential. Thus, the intersection of multiple acceleration vectors is the location of the dark mass. Figure 2 shows the acceleration vector's direction for the three stars. With in 1σ, these vectors do indeed overlap, and furthermore, the intersection point lies a mere 0.05 ± 0.03 arcsec east and 0.02 ± 0.03 arcsec south of the nominal position of Sgr A*, consistent with the identification of Sgr A* as the carrier of the mass. Previously, with statistical treatments of velocities only, the dynamical centre was located to within ± 0.1 arcsec (1σ) of Sgr A*'s position[4]. This velocity-based measurement is unaffected by the increased time baseline, as its uncertainty is dominated by the limited number of stars at a given radius. The accelerations thus improve the localization of our Galaxy's dynamical centre by a factor of 3, which is essential for reliably associating any near-infrared source with the black hole given the complexity of the region.

的增加而线性增大）。对这两个误差项取平方和开根号；得到拟合时所用的总误差，并在图中用误差棒描述。每幅图中，实线表示用二阶多项式拟合的最佳结果，用来推导恒星的加速度。这些结果显示，对环绕超大质量黑洞运动的恒星，我们首次能够测得它们量级在 $2\sim5$ mas $\cdot$ yr^{-2}（$0.3\sim0.6$ cm $\cdot$ s^{-2}）的运动加速度。

表 1. 有明显加速度的恒星的测量结果

	S0-1(S1)	S0-2(S2)	S0-4(S8)
相对 Sgr A* 的位置-大小 (milliparsec)	4.42±0.05	5.83±0.04	13.15±0.04
相对 Sgr A* 的位置-位置角 (度)	290.1±0.7	3.1±0.4	117.3±0.2
速度-大小 (km·s⁻¹)	1,350±40	570±20	990±30
速度-位置角 (度)	168±2	241±2	129±2
加速度-大小 (milliarcsec·yr⁻²)	2.4±0.7	5.4±0.3	3.2±0.5
加速度-位置角 (度)	80±15	154±4	294±7

这里和正文中采用的主要命名方式来自参考文献 4；参考文献 1 所给出的恒星名字也在圆括号里给出。所有列出量均来源于二阶多项式拟合所得数据，对应历元为 1995.53。所有方位角由北向东起量。误差都是 1σ，由刀切法确定[22]。列出的半径误差仅包括相对位置误差，没有包括中心的位置误差（Sgr A* 的标定位置；关于测量到的动力学中心与标定位置的偏移的具体细节请见正文）。

原则上来说，比起速度矢量，利用加速度矢量可以更精确地研究中心质量分布。假设一个球对称的引力势，就算投影到天球切面上，每个加速度矢量还将指向中心质量的方向。因此，多个加速度矢量的交叉点就是暗质量所在的位置。图 2 显示了这三颗恒星的加速度矢量方向。这些矢量在 1σ 误差范围内确实发生重叠，而且交叉点正好位于 Sgr A* 标定位置往东 0.05±0.03 角秒、往南 0.02±0.03 角秒处，与暗质量位于 Sgr A* 的结论一致。之前，在仅有对速度的相关统计分析的情况下，人们大致将动力学中心确定在位于 Sgr A* 位置 ±0.1 角秒（1σ）的范围内[4]。这种基于速度的测量并不依赖时间基线的长短，因为它的误差主要来自给定半径内恒星数目的限制。因此，对恒星进行加速度矢量分析将银河系动力学中心位置的定位精度提高为原来的 3 倍。考虑到这个区域的复杂度，这点对于研究近红外源和黑洞的可靠成协关系来说很重要。

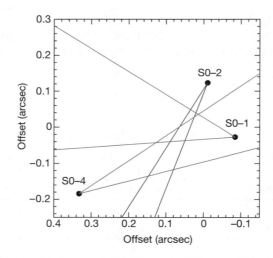

Fig. 2. The acceleration uncertainty cones and their intersections. The cones' edges represent the directions for which the accelerations deviate by 1σ from their best-fit values and their vertices are the time-averaged positions, measured relative to the nominal position of Sgr A*, rather than the positions listed in Table 1. If the accelerations are caused by a single supermassive black hole, or even a spherically symmetric mass distribution, these vectors should intersect at a common location, the centre of the mass. The 1σ intersection point lies 0.05 ± 0.03 arcsec east and 0.02 ± 0.03 arcsec south of the nominal position of Sgr A*. The existence of an intersection point suggests that there is indeed a common origin for the acceleration and pinpoints the location of the black hole to within 0.03 arcsec.

Like the directions, the magnitudes of the acceleration vectors also constrain the central black hole's properties. In three dimensions, the acceleration and radius vectors (a_{3D} and r_{3D}, respectively) provide a direct measure of the enclosed mass simply by $a_{3D} = G \times M/r_{3D}^2$. For a central potential, the acceleration and radius vectors are co-aligned and, with a projection angle to the plane of the sky θ, the two-dimensional projections place the following lower limit on the central mass: $M \cos^3(\theta) = a_{2D} \times r_{2D}^2/G$. This analysis is independent of the star's orbital parameters, although θ is in fact a lower limit for the orbital inclination angle. Figure 3 shows the minimum mass implied by each star's two-dimensional acceleration as a function of projected radius, with dashed curves displaying how the implied mass and radius grow with projection angle. For each point, the uncertainty in the position of the dynamical centre dominates the minimum mass uncertainties. Also plotted are the results from the statistical analysis of the velocity vectors measured in the plane of the sky, which imply a dark mass of $(2.3–3.3) \times 10^6 \, M_\odot$ inside a radius of 0.015 pc[3,4]. If, as has been assumed, this dark mass is in the form of a single supermassive black hole, the enclosed mass should remain level at smaller radii. Projection angles of 51–56° and 25–37° for S0-1 and S0-2, respectively, would yield the mass inferred from velocities and place these stars at a mere ~0.008 pc (solid line portions of the limiting mass curves in Fig. 3), thus increasing the dark mass density implied by velocities by an order of magnitude to $8 \times 10^{12} \, M_\odot \, pc^{-3}$. With smaller projection angles, these two stars also allow for the enclosed mass to decrease at smaller radii, as would occur in the presence of an extended distribution of dark matter surrounding a less massive black hole[13-17]. In contrast to the agreement between the mass distribution inferred from

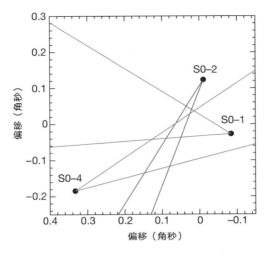

图 2. 加速度误差锥以及它们的交叠区域。锥的边缘代表加速度偏离它们的最佳拟合值 1σ 的方向，顶点则是它们相对 Sgr A* 标定位置的时间平均位置，而不是表 1 中所列举的位置。假如加速运动是由单个超大质量黑洞或者甚至是一个球形对称质量分布所引起的，这些矢量应该会在质量中心处相交。1σ 交叉点位于 Sgr A* 标定位置东边 0.05±0.03 角秒和南边 0.02±0.03 角秒处。交叉点的存在表明加速度确实来自一个共同的来源，并将黑洞位置精确定位在 0.03 角秒内。

和方向一样，加速度矢量的大小也能够用来限制中心黑洞的性质。在三维空间中，利用加速度和径向矢量（分别是 a_{3D} 和 r_{3D}），仅通过 $a_{3D} = G \times M/r_{3D}^2$，我们就可以直接测量所考虑半径范围内的质量。在中心引力势作用下，加速度和径向矢量的方向一致，若它们在天球切面上的投影角为 θ，那么两维投影将给出中心质量的下限为：$M\cos^3(\theta) = a_{2D} \times r_{2D}^2/G$。这个分析与恒星的轨道参数无关，尽管 θ 实际上就是轨道倾角的下限。图 3 显示由每颗恒星的二维加速度所推导的中心黑洞的最小质量随恒星与中心的投影距离的变化，其中虚线显示了导出的质量和距离随投影角的变化规律。对图中每个点，这个质量下限的误差主要来自动力学中心的位置误差。同时图中还画上了对投影在天球切面上的速度矢量的统计分析结果，表明在半径 0.015 pc 内存在 $(2.3 \sim 3.3) \times 10^6\, M_\odot$ 的暗质量[3,4]。如果和假设的一样，暗质量是一个超大质量黑洞，那么这些暗质量应该被限制在一个更小半径之内。S0-1 和 S0-2 的投影角分别为 51°~56° 和 25°~37°，这些投影角使得我们可以从速度推导得质量并且将这些恒星的位置限定在距离中心仅仅约 0.008 pc 以内的区域（图 3 中质量下限曲线的实线部分），因此由速度推导得出的暗质量密度将增加一个量级，达到 $8 \times 10^{12}\, M_\odot \cdot pc^{-3}$。假如这两颗恒星具有更小的投影角，那么这两颗恒星的观测结果也同样允许出现所考虑半径范围内暗质量随着半径减小而减少的可能性，就和在一个质量较小的黑洞周围存在一个延展暗物质分布所造成的情形一样[13-17]。虽然从 S0-1 和 S0-2 的速度和加速度推断得到的质量分布相互吻合，可是从 S0-4 加速度

the velocities and the accelerations for S0-1 and S0-2, the minimum mass implied by S0-4's acceleration is inconsistent at least at the 1σ level. We note, in support of the validity of S0-4's acceleration vector, that its orientation is consistent with the intersection of the S0-1 and S0-2 acceleration vectors (see Fig. 2). Nonetheless, continued monitoring of S0-4 will be important for assessing this possible discrepancy. Overall, the individual magnitudes of the three acceleration vectors support the existence of a central black hole with a mass of approximately $3 \times 10^6 \, M_\odot$.

Fig. 3. The minimum enclosed mass implied by each star's acceleration measurement versus projected distance from the newly determined dynamical centre position. If the projection between the plane of the sky and both the radius and the acceleration vectors is θ, then the true mass increases as $1/\cos^3(\theta)$ and the true acceleration and radius vectors increase as $1/\cos(\theta)$. Also plotted is the mass range implied from a statistical analysis of the approximately 100 velocity vectors that have been measured in the plane of the sky[3,4].

Using acceleration measurements, it is now possible to constrain the individual orbits. We checked the conclusions of the previous studies[3,4] by assuming that the stars are bound to a central mass of $(2.2-3.3) \times 10^6 \, M_\odot$ located within 0.03 arcsec of the nominal position of Sgr A*. Excellent orbital fits were found for S0-1 and S0-2 for the entire range of masses and for true foci within 0.01 arcsec of the nominal position of Sgr A*, suggesting that we now have comparable accuracy in determining the infrared location of Sgr A* (ref. 9) and the dynamical centre of our Galaxy (see Fig. 4). The orbital solutions for these stars have eccentricities ranging from 0 (circular) to 0.9 for S0-1 and 0.5 to 0.9 for S0-2 and periods in the range 35–1,200 and 15–550 years, respectively, raising the possibility of seeing a star make a complete journey around the centre of the Galaxy within the foreseeable future. Although the fits are not yet unique, they impose a maximum orbital distance from the black hole, or apoapse, of 0.1 pc. This suggests that S0-1 and S0-2 might have formed locally. If these stars are indeed young[2], then their small apoapse distance presents a challenge to classical star formation theories in light of the strong tidal forces created by the central black hole and might require a collisional or compressional star formation scenario[18,19]. However, dynamical friction may be able to act on a short enough timescale to bring these stars in from a much larger distance[20]. More accurate orbital

推出的暗质量下限在 1σ 水平内，和其他两颗星得出的结果不一致。值得注意的是，S0-4 的加速度矢量方向在 S0-1 和 S0-2 的加速度矢量的交叠范围内（见图 2），这表明 S0-4 的加速度矢量是正确的。虽然如此，继续监测 S0-4 对判断这个差异是否存在非常重要。总体来看，三个加速度矢量的大小都支持银河系中心存在一个质量约为 $3 \times 10^6\ M_\odot$ 的超大质量黑洞。

图 3. 根据每颗恒星的加速度测量值推导出的所考虑半径范围内的质量下限同新确定的动力学中心位置的投影距离的关系图。假如径向矢量和加速度矢量在天球切面的投影角均为 θ，那么真实的质量随着 $1/\cos^3(\theta)$ 增加，真实的加速度和径向矢量随着 $1/\cos(\theta)$ 增加。对在天球切面上测量到的接近 100 个速度矢量进行统计分析所得到的质量范围也画在图中 [3,4]。

通过测量加速度，我们现在能够分别限制这三颗恒星各自的轨道。通过假设恒星束缚在位于 Sgr A* 标定位置 0.03 角秒内且质量为 $(2.3 \sim 3.3) \times 10^6\ M_\odot$ 的中心质量周围，我们检查了前人的研究结论 [3,4]。假定轨道实焦点在 Sgr A* 标定位置 0.01 角秒以内，对于整个可能的中心质量范围，我们都可以对 S0-1 和 S0-2 的轨道给出很好的拟合结果，这表明我们现在确定的 Sgr A* 红外位置（参考文献 9）和银河系动力学中心的精确度都相当好（见图 4）。在得到的轨道解当中，S0-1 解出的轨道偏心率分布在 0（圆）到 0.9 之间，S0-2 的轨道偏心率分布在 0.5 到 0.9 之间，周期分别分布在 35～1,200 年和 15～550 年的范围之内。这意味着在可预见的将来，也许我们能够完整地看到某颗恒星环绕银河系中心的运动轨迹。虽然所得到的拟合结果并不是唯一的，但是它们给出了离黑洞的最大轨道距离（或远质心点）为 0.1 pc。这表明 S0-1 和 S0-2 可能是在中心附近形成。如果这些恒星实际上很年轻 [2]，那么这些恒星拥有这么小的远质心点距离将对经典恒星形成理论提出挑战。考虑到中心黑洞产生的强潮汐力，我们可能需要一个在碰撞或压缩条件下的恒星形成理论 [18,19]。不过，

parameters are needed to fully address these problems and others such as the distance to the Galactic Centre[21]. The determinations of these parameters will be considerably improved when radial velocities are measured for these stars using adaptive optics techniques, as the current solutions based on the proper motion data alone predict radial velocities ranging from 200 and 2,000 km s^{-1}.

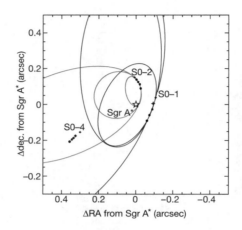

Fig. 4. The measured motion of S0-1, S0-2 and S0-4 and several allowed orbital solutions. Only the measurements obtained in June of each of the 5 years are shown. S0-1 and S0-2 are moving clockwise about Sgr A* and S0-4 is travelling radially outward. In the orbital analysis, two constraints are applied, a central mass of $2.6 \times 10^6 M_\odot$ and a true focus located at the position of Sgr A*. Displayed are orbital solutions with periods of 17, 80 and 505 years for S0-2 and 63, 200 and 966 years for S0-1.

(**407**, 349-351; 2000)

A. M. Ghez, M. Morris, E. E. Becklin, A. Tanner & T. Kremenek
Department of Physics and Astronomy, UCLA, Los Angeles, California 90095-1562, USA

Received 24 May; accepted 19 July 2000.

References:

1. Eckart, A. & Genzel, R. Stellar proper motions in the central 0.1 pc of the Galaxy. *Mon. Not. R. Astron. Soc.* **284**, 576-598 (1997).

2. Genzel, R., Eckart, A., Ott, T. & Eisenhauer, F. On the nature of the dark mass in the centre of the Milky Way. *Mon. Not. R. Astron. Soc.* **291-234**, 219 (1997).

3. Genzel, R., Pichon, C., Eckart, A., Gerhard, O. E. & Ott, T. Stellar dynamics in the galactic centre: Proper motions and anisotropy. *Mon. Not. R. Astron. Soc.* (in the press).

4. Ghez, A. M., Klein, B. L., Morris, M. & Becklin, E. E. High proper-motion stars in the vicinity of Sagittarius A*: Evidence for a supermassive black hole at the center of our galaxy. *Astrophys. J.* **509**, 678-686 (1998).

5. Maoz, E. Dynamical constraints on alternatives to supermassive black holes in galactic nuclei. *Astrophys. J.* **494**, L181-L184 (1998).

6. Reid, M. J. The distance to the center of the Galaxy. *Annu. Rev. Astron. Astrophys.* **31**, 345-372 (1993).

7. Matthews, K. & Soifer, B. T. in *Astronomy with Infrared Arrays: The Next Generation* (ed. McLean, I.) Vol. 190, 239-246 (Astrophysics and Space Sciences Library, Kluwer Academic, Dordrecht, 1994).

8. Matthews, K., Ghez, A. M., Weinberger, A. J. & Neugebauer, G. The diffraction-limited images from the W. M. Keck Telescope. *Proc. Astron. Soc. Pacif.* **108**, 615-619 (1996).

9. Menten, K. M., Reid, M. J., Eckart, A. & Genzel, R. The position of Sgr A*: Accurate alignment of the radio and infrared reference frames at the galactic center. *Astrophys. J.* **475**, L111-L114 (1997).

动力学摩擦也可能在足够短的时标内将这些恒星从更远距离处拉进来[20]。要解决这些问题，以及对其他诸如距银河系中心的距离[21]等问题有更加准确的理解，我们还需要更精确的轨道参数的测量。应用自适应光学技术测量这些恒星的视向速度，将极大地提高这些恒星轨道参数的测量精度，因为目前仅依赖自行数据得到的恒星视向速度只能限制在 200 到 2,000 km · s^{-1} 的广阔范围内。

图 4. 测量到的 S0-1、S0-2 和 S0-4 的运动轨迹和几个可能的轨道解。图中只显示 5 年中每年 6 月份的观测。S0-1 和 S0-2 围着 Sgr A* 顺时针运动，S0-4 沿径向向外运动。在轨道分析中我们应用了中心质量为 $2.6 \times 10^6\ M_\odot$ 和实焦点位于 Sgr A* 处这两个限制条件。图中显示了 S0-2 的周期分别为 17、80 和 505 年的轨道解，以及 S0-1 的周期分别为 63、200 和 966 年的轨道解。

（肖莉 翻译；周礼勇 审稿）

10. Lo, K. Y., Shen, Z.-Q., Zhao, J.-H. & Ho, P. T. Intrinsic size of SGR A*: 72 Schwarzschild radii. *Astrophys. J.* **508**, L61-L64 (1998).

11. Reid, M. J., Readhead, A. C. S., Vermeulen, R. C. & Treuhaft, R. N. The proper motion of Sagittarius A*. I. First VLBA results. *Astrophys. J.* **524**, 816-823 (1999).

12. Backer, D. C. & Sramek, R. A. Proper motion of the compact, nonthermal radio source in the galactic center, Sagittarius A*. *Astrophys. J.* **524**, 805-815 (1999).

13. Salati, P. & Silk, J. A stellar probe of dark matter annihilation in galactic nuclei. *Astrophys. J.* **338**, 24-31 (1989).

14. Tsiklauri, D. & Viollier, R. D. Dark matter concentration in the galactic center. *Astrophys. J.* **500**, 591-595 (1998).

15. Gondolo, P. & Silk, J. Dark matter annihilation at the galactic center. *Phys. Rev. Lett.* **83**, 1719-1722 (1999).

16. Torres, D. F., Capozziello, S. & Lambiase, G. A supermassive boson star at the galactic center? *Astrophys. J.* (in the press).

17. Romanowsky, A. & Kochanek, C. in *Proceedings of Dynamics of Star Clusters and the Milky Way* (ASP Conference Series, Astronomical Society of the Pacific, San Francisco, in the press).

18. Sanders, R. H. The case against a massive black hole at the Galactic Centre. *Nature* **359**, 131-132 (1992).

19. Morris, M., Ghez, A. M. & Becklin, E. E. The galactic center black hole: clues for the evolution of black holes in galactic nuclei. *Adv. Space Res.* **23**, 959-968 (1999).

20. Gerhard, O. The galactic center He I stars: remains of a dissolved young cluster? *Astrophys. J.* (submitted).

21. Salim, S. & Gould, A. Sagittarius A* "Visual Binaries": A direct measurement of the galactocentric distance. *Astrophys. J.* **523**, 633-641 (1999).

22. Babu, G. J. & Feigelson, E. D. *Astrostatistics* (Chapman & Hall, London, 1996).

Acknowledgements. This work was supported by the National Science Foundation and the Packard Foundation. We are grateful to J. Larkin for exchanging telescope time; O. Gerhard, M. Jura, and A. Weinberger for useful input; telescope observing assistants J. Aycock, T. Chelminiak, G. Puniwai, C. Sorenson, W. Wack, M. Whittle and software/instrument specialists A. Conrad and B. Goodrich for their help during the observations. The data presented here were obtained at the W. M. Keck Observatory, which is operated as a scientific partnership among the California Institute of Technology, the University of California and the National Aeronautics and Space Administration. The Observatory was made possible by the financial support of the W. M. Keck Foundation.

Correspondence and requests for materials should be addressed to A.G. (e-mail: ghez@astro.ucla.edu).

Evidence from Detrital Zircons for the Existence of Continental Crust and Oceans on the Earth 4.4 Gyr Ago

S. A. Wilde *et al.*

Editor's Note

The Earth is thought to have formed about 4.56 Gyr ago. Initially it was entirely molten, but as it cooled, the chemical components of the planet differentiated and its surface solidified. Although tectonic movements have recycled the earliest crust, some remnants do remain, offering evidence for when it was first formed. Here geologist Simon Wilde and coworkers report the oldest crustal material so far known, showing that it was formed at about 4.4 Gyr ago. It comprises a mineral called zircon, which can be dated from radioactive decay in the uranium-thorium-lead series. The zircon seems to have formed from material in the crust interacting with surface water, suggesting that oceans may have existed by that time.

No crustal rocks are known to have survived since the time of the intense meteor bombardment that affected Earth[1] between its formation about 4,550 Myr ago and 4,030 Myr, the age of the oldest known components in the Acasta Gneiss of northwestern Canada[2]. But evidence of an even older crust is provided by detrital zircons in metamorphosed sediments at Mt Narryer[3] and Jack Hills[4-8] in the Narryer Gneiss Terrane[9], Yilgarn Craton, Western Australia, where grains as old as ~4,276 Myr have been found[4]. Here we report, based on a detailed micro-analytical study of Jack Hills zircons[10], the discovery of a detrital zircon with an age as old as $4,404 \pm 8$ Myr—about 130 million years older than any previously identified on Earth. We found that the zircon is zoned with respect to rare earth elements and oxygen isotope ratios ($\delta^{18}O$ values from 7.4 to 5.0‰), indicating that it formed from an evolving magmatic source. The evolved chemistry, high $\delta^{18}O$ value and micro-inclusions of SiO_2 are consistent with growth from a granitic melt[11,2] with a $\delta^{18}O$ value from 8.5 to 9.5‰. Magmatic oxygen isotope ratios in this range point toward the involvement of supracrustal material that has undergone low-temperature interaction with a liquid hydrosphere. This zircon thus represents the earliest evidence for continental crust and oceans on the Earth.

WE extracted a new aliquot of zircon from the original heavy mineral concentrate of the Jack Hills conglomerate from which the oldest documented crystal (~4,276 Myr; ref. 4) was obtained, and identified several grains with ages in excess of 4 Gyr. One of these is a deep purple zircon (W74/2-36), measuring 220 by 160 μm, that is a broken fragment of a larger crystal (Fig. 1). It shows few internal complexities or inclusions, a

44 亿年前地球上存在大陆壳与海洋：
来自碎屑锆石的证据

怀尔德等

编者按

地球被认为形成于 45.6 亿年前。在地球形成之初，熔浆遍布，当它冷却之后，这个星球发生了化学组成的分离和表层的固化。尽管之后的多期构造运动已使最早期陆壳遭受再循环作用，但仍有部分残留物质保存了下来，为其何时形成提供了证据。本文中，地质学家西蒙·怀尔德及其合作者报道了迄今所知的最古老陆壳物质，并揭示其形成于 44 亿年前。它含有一种被称为锆石的矿物，这种矿物可以通过铀钍铅体系的放射性衰变来定年。锆石似乎由地壳与水面交汇处的物质形成，这表明当时可能已经出现了海洋。

地球自约 45.5 亿年前诞生直到 40.3 亿年前这一期间遭受了强烈的陨石撞击，这期间的地壳岩石没有保留下来 [1]。目前已知的最古老岩石年龄为 40.3 亿年，仅见于加拿大西北部的阿卡斯塔片麻岩 [2]。但是，在西澳大利亚伊尔岗克拉通纳里耶片麻岩地体 [9] 的纳里耶山 [3] 和杰克山 [4-8] 变质沉积物中，42.76 亿年碎屑锆石的发现提供了更古老地壳物质存在的证据 [4]。基于对杰克山锆石 [10] 详细微区分析研究，本文报道了年龄为 (4,404 ± 8) Myr（编者注：Myr 为百万年）的碎屑锆石——比之前在地球上识别出的最古老年龄纪录还要早约 1.3 亿年。锆石具有与稀土元素和氧同位素比值（$\delta^{18}O$ 值：7.4‰ ~ 5.0‰）有关的环带结构，表明其生长过程中，岩浆源处于演化过程中。演化的化学特征、高的 $\delta^{18}O$ 值以及 SiO_2 包体的存在都表明锆石形成于 $\delta^{18}O$ 值为 8.5‰ ~ 9.5‰ 的花岗质熔体 [11,2]。这一范围的岩浆氧同位素比值表明，花岗质岩浆形成过程中有与液态水圈存在过低温相互作用的地表物质的参与。因此，该锆石提供了地球上存在最古老陆壳和海洋的证据。

杰克山砾岩中曾发现的最古老锆石的年龄约为 42.76 亿年 [4]。我们从原重矿物样中重新取了部分碎屑锆石进行研究，识别出数粒年龄超过 40 亿年的锆石颗粒。其中一粒（W74/2-36）呈深紫色，尺寸为 220 μm × 160 μm，是一粒原本更大锆石晶体的碎片（图 1）。锆石内部结构简单，含少量包体，这些特征同样存在于杰克山砾岩

feature previously noted in zircons older than 4 Gyr from the Jack Hills conglomerate[4,13].

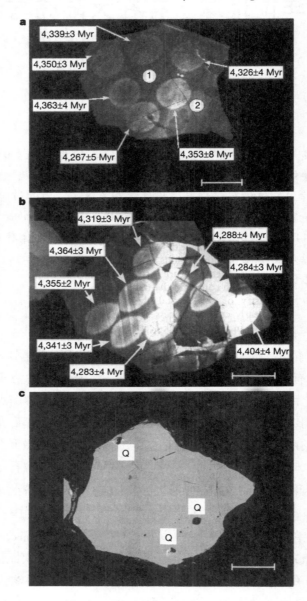

Fig.1. Cathodoluminescence and back-scattered electron images of zircon crystal W74/2-36. Scale bars are 50 μm. **a**, Image taken subsequent to first SHRIMP analysis. We note that lighter circular areas are the SHRIMP analytical sites and the values record the $^{207}Pb/^{206}Pb$ age (1σ) of each site. The two white areas represent the approximate location of the oxygen analytical spots, with $\delta^{18}O$ of 5‰ at point 1 and 7.4‰ at point 2. **b**, Cathodoluminescence image taken after the second SHRIMP analytical session showing the sites of analysis (as in **a**) and the $^{207}Pb/^{206}Pb$ ages (1σ) for each spot. We note the larger area showing light luminescence, the well defined cracks and the oscillatory zoning in both the light and dull portions of the crystal. We note the circular outline of the SHRIMP analytical sites and the lighter rectangular area, near the pointed termination, which corresponds to the dark area in the cathodoluminescence image. **c**, Back-scattered electron image obtained after the second SHRIMP analytical session. The black areas (marked Q) are SiO_2 inclusions.

老于 40 亿年的锆石中 [4,13]。

图 1. 锆石晶体 W74/2-36 的阴极发光图像和背散射电子图像（比例尺为 50 μm）。**a**，第一次 SHRIMP 分析后的阴极发光图像。较亮的圆形区域为分析点，旁边数字为 $^{207}Pb/^{206}Pb$ 年龄（1σ）。两个小圆圈为氧同位素分析的大致位置，分析点 1 的 $\delta^{18}O$ 值为 5‰，分析点 2 的 $\delta^{18}O$ 值为 7.4‰。**b**，第二次 SHRIMP 分析后的阴极发光图像，同图 a 一样，显示了分析点位置，并标出了 $^{207}Pb/^{206}Pb$ 年龄（1σ）。与第一次分析相比，阴极发光高亮度区域的范围更大，在阴极发光的亮部和暗部都存在清晰的裂隙和振荡环带。注意靠近锆石右侧突出部位的 SHRIMP 分析点圆形轮廓和更亮的矩形区域，后者与阴极发光图像中的暗色区域相对应。**c**，第二次 SHRIMP 分析后的背散射电子图像。黑色区域（以 Q 标识）为 SiO_2 包裹体。

We performed U-Th-Pb zircon analyses on the Perth Consortium **SHRIMP II** ion microprobe at Curtin University of Technology in Western Australia, following standard operating techniques[14-16]. Six analyses of grain W74/2-36 were initially made and five of these gave $^{207}Pb/^{206}Pb$ ages in excess of 4.3 Gyr (Table 1); the oldest and most concordant (97% concordance, Table 1) had an age of $4{,}363 \pm 8$ Myr (2σ), approximately 90 Myr older than the oldest known terrestrial material[4]. Other sites yielded more discordant ages and fell on a discordia line that passed through zero, indicative of recent lead loss (Fig. 2). A detailed cathodoluminescence (CL) image made after analysis indicated that all but the oldest site overlapped cracks within the crystal (Fig. 1a). However, crack-free domains greater than 50 μm in diameter were present and, after oxygen isotope and rare earth element (REE) analysis, approximately 20 μm was ground off the surface of the zircon to remove all previous analytical pits; the grain was then re-analysed on **SHRIMP II** in an attempt to obtain more concordant data. Care was taken to locate new analytical sites away from identifiable cracks and this proved partially successful, with four analyses obtained from such areas (Fig. 1b). Three of these sites yielded data that are 100, 98 and 95% concordant (Table 1), and confirm the initial estimate of the age, giving $^{207}Pb/^{206}Pb$ ages of $4{,}355 \pm 4$ Myr, $4{,}341 \pm 6$ Myr and $4{,}364 \pm 6$ Myr (2σ), respectively (Table 1 and Fig. 2). Importantly, the fourth site, located near the pointed, broken termination of the crystal (right corner of Fig. 1b), was also nearly concordant (99%) and this gave a $^{207}Pb/^{206}Pb$ age of $4{,}404 \pm 8$ Myr (2σ) (Fig. 2), about 40 Myr older than the other results and only about 150 Myr younger than the oldest high-temperature inclusions known in meteorites[17]($\sim$4,560 Myr), which constrain the maximum age for the Earth.

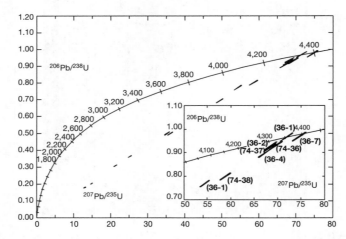

Fig. 2. Combined concordia plot for grain W74/2-36, showing the U-Pb results obtained during the two analytical sessions. The inset shows the most concordant data points together with their analysis number (as in Table 1). Error boxes are shown at 1σ.

The chemistry of this crystal therefore provides important insights into early crustal processes. Because the internal cracks that are evident in CL and back-scattered electron (BSE) images (Fig. 1) may affect the chemistry, they were investigated using a high-resolution scanning electron microscope (SEM) and electron microprobe. Unlike the cracks in the

利用西澳大利亚科廷技术大学珀斯联盟的 SHRIMP II 离子探针，我们遵循标准操作技术[14-16]对锆石进行了 U-Th-Pb 同位素分析。第一次分析中，在锆石 W74/2-36 上选取了 6 个点，其中 5 个分析点的 $^{207}Pb/^{206}Pb$ 年龄超过 43 亿年（表 1）；最古老且最谐和（谐和度 97%，表 1）的年龄为 $(4,363 \pm 8)\,Myr\,(2\sigma)$，比已知的最古老陆壳物质大约早 9,000 万年[4]。其他分析点的年龄更不谐和，落在一条过原点的不一致线上，反映了近代铅丢失（图 2）。根据分析后重照的高清阴极发光（CL）图像，除最古老年龄分析点外，其他所有分析点均位于晶体内部的裂隙之上（图 1a）。不过，锆石中也存在直径大于 50 μm 的无裂隙区域。在完成氧同位素和稀土元素（REE）分析后，磨除锆石表面大约 20 μm 的厚度以去掉之前测试造成的凹坑，然后再次进行 SHRIMP 分析以获得更谐和的年龄数据。谨慎选择的新分析点远离可见裂隙，这一尝试是部分成功的，有 4 个分析点落在了无裂隙的区域（图 1b）。其中 3 个 $^{207}Pb/^{206}Pb$ 年龄分别为 $(4,355 \pm 4)\,Myr$、$(4,341 \pm 6)\,Myr$ 和 $(4,364 \pm 6)\,Myr\,(2\sigma)$（表 1 和图 2），谐和度分别为 100%、98% 和 95%（表 1），与第一次分析获得的年龄结果一致。重要的是，在右侧突出的晶体碎片末端（图 1b），即第 4 个分析点的年龄几乎完全谐和（谐和度为 99%），并给出了 $(4,404 \pm 8)\,Myr\,(2\sigma)$ 的 $^{207}Pb/^{206}Pb$ 年龄（图 2）。比其他年龄大约老 4,000 万年，后者比已知的陨石[17]中最古老高温包裹体（约 45.60 亿年）仅年轻约 1.5 亿年，这限定了地球年龄的最大值。

图 2. 锆石 W74/2-36 的 U-Pb 谐和图，给出了两次分析的 U-Pb 结果。插图给出了最谐和的分析点及编号（与表 1 的一致）。误差框为 1σ。

这粒锆石的化学特征可为研究早期地壳过程提供重要信息。在阴极发光图像和背散射电子（BSE）图像中，内部裂隙清楚可见（图 1），由于它们可能会影响元素分布特征，因此用高分辨率扫描电镜（SEM）和电子探针进行了研究。锆石 W74/2-36

Table 1. Shrimp U-Pb-Th isotopic analytical data

Spot	U (p.p.m.)	Th (p.p.m.)	Th/U ratio	Pb (p.p.m.)	f206%	$^{204}Pb/^{206}Pb$	$^{207}Pb*/^{206}Pb*$	$^{208}Pb*/^{232}Th$	$^{208}Pb*/^{206}Pb*$	$^{206}Pb*/^{238}U$	$^{207}Pb*/^{235}U$	Conc. (%)	$^{206}Pb*/^{238}U$ age (Myr)	$^{207}Pb*/^{235}U$ age (Myr)	$^{208}Pb*/^{232}Th$ age (Myr)	$^{207}Pb*/^{206}Pb$ age (Myr)
Session 1																
74-36	258	178	0.69	355	0.22	0.00014	0.5432±1	0.222±5	0.1645±12	0.928±18	69.5±1.4	97	4,233±61	4,321±20	4,058±80	4,363±4
74-37	449	347	0.77	615	0.048	0.00003	0.5386±1	0.225±5	0.1895±8	0.919±18	68.2±1.3	97	4,201±59	4,303±20	4,109±75	4,350±3
74-38	450	1,224	2.72	544	0.098	0.00006	0.5345±1	0.065±1	0.2227±9	0.797±15	58.8±1.2	87	3,780±55	4,153±20	1,277±25	4,339±3
74-58	487	1,731	3.56	217	1.142	0.00071	0.5088±2	0.012±0	0.1419±2	0.304±6	21.4±0.4	40	1,713±29	3,155±19	244±6	4,267±5
74-59	454	765	1.68	335	0.781	0.00049	0.5297±1	0.048±1	0.1637±17	0.496±10	36.2±0.7	60	2,595±41	3,672±20	952±21	4,326±4
74-60	390	1,336	3.43	120	1.9	0.00119	0.5394±3	0.010±0	0.1641±41	0.200±4	14.9±0.3	27	1,177±21	2,808±20	193±6	4,353±8
Session 2																
36-1	361	262	0.73	515	0.002	0.00001	0.5401±8	0.232±5	0.1743±6	0.965±18	71.9±1.4	100	4,356±60	4,355±19	4,211±74	4,355±2
36-2	258	174	0.67	351	0.01	0.00006	0.5353±10	0.226±5	0.1641±7	0.929±18	68.6±1.3	98	4,235±59	4,307±19	4,125±75	4,341±3
36-3	184	117	0.64	204	0	0	0.5143±12	0.194±4	0.1612±10	0.768±15	54.5±1.1	86	3,674±53	4,078±20	3,588±68	4,283±4
36-4	250	188	0.75	333	0	0	0.5436±10	0.218±4	0.1831±7	0.897±17	67.2±1.3	95	4,126±58	4,287±19	3,986±72	4,364±3
36-5	208	304	1.46	153	0	0	0.5163±13	0.067±1	0.1959±10	0.498±9	35.4±0.7	61	2,604±40	3,651±19	1,306±25	4,288±4
36-6	346	940	2.71	182	0.001	0	0.5147±11	0.026±1	0.2005±9	0.356±7	25.2±0.5	46	1,961±32	3,317±19	524±10	4,284±3
36-7	127	75	0.59	180	0	0	0.5587±14	0.237±5	0.1437±9	0.968±19	74.6±1.5	99	4,364±61	4,392±20	4,291±83	4,404±4
36-8	329	339	1.03	337	0.013	0.00001	0.5272±9	0.141±3	0.2134±8	0.683±13	49.6±0.9	78	3,355±49	3,985±19	2,672±49	4,319±3

* Common lead corrected using ^{204}Pb.

Data for zircon grain W74/2-36. f206% is (common ^{206}Pb/total ^{206}Pb) × 100. Conc. (%) is percentage concordance defined as [($^{206}Pb/^{238}U$ age)/($^{207}Pb/^{206}Pb$ age)] × 100. All errors are quoted at 1σ level. Errors given for Pb/Pb and Pb/Th ratios are based on counting statistics. Errors in Pb/U ratios also include an estimate of the Pb/U reproducibility error based on multiple analyses of the standard zircon CZ3 during the analytical sessions. During the first analytical session, all spots were given a unique number. In the second session, the grain was identified as W74-36 and each site was numbered consecutively, 36-1 to 36-8.

表 1. Shrimp U-Pb-Th 同位素分析数据

数据点	U (ppm)	Th (ppm)	Th/U ratio	Pb (ppm)	f206%	$^{204}Pb/^{206}Pb$	$^{207}Pb*/^{206}Pb*$	$^{208}Pb*/^{232}Th$	$^{208}Pb*/^{206}Pb*$	$^{206}Pb*/^{238}U$	$^{207}Pb*/^{235}U$	Conc. (%)	$^{206}Pb*/^{238}U$ age (Myr)	$^{207}Pb*/^{235}U$ age (Myr)	$^{208}Pb*/^{232}Th$ age (Myr)	$^{207}Pb*/^{206}Pb*$ age (Myr)
第一次分析																
74-36	258	178	0.69	355	0.22	0.00014	0.5432±1	0.222±5	0.1645±12	0.928±18	69.5±1.4	97	4,233±61	4,321±20	4,058±80	4,363±4
74-37	449	347	0.77	615	0.048	0.00003	0.5386±1	0.225±5	0.1895±8	0.919±18	68.2±1.3	97	4,201±59	4,303±20	4,109±75	4,350±3
74-38	450	1,224	2.72	544	0.098	0.00006	0.5345±1	0.065±1	0.2227±9	0.797±15	58.8±1.2	87	3,780±55	4,153±20	1,277±25	4,339±3
74-58	487	1,731	3.56	217	1.142	0.00071	0.5088±2	0.012±0	0.1419±2	0.304±6	21.4±0.4	40	1,713±29	3,155±19	244±6	4,267±5
74-59	454	765	1.68	335	0.781	0.00049	0.5297±1	0.048±1	0.1637±17	0.496±10	36.2±0.7	60	2,595±41	3,672±20	952±21	4,326±4
74-60	390	1,336	3.43	120	1.9	0.00119	0.5394±3	0.010±0	0.1641±41	0.200±4	14.9±0.3	27	1,177±21	2,808±20	193±6	4,353±8
第二次分析																
36-1	361	262	0.73	515	0.002	0.00001	0.5401±8	0.232±5	0.1743±6	0.965±18	71.9±1.4	100	4,356±60	4,355±19	4,211±74	4,355±2
36-2	258	174	0.67	351	0.01	0.00006	0.5353±10	0.226±5	0.1641±7	0.929±18	68.6±1.3	98	4,235±59	4,307±19	4,125±75	4,341±3
36-3	184	117	0.64	204	0	0	0.5143±12	0.194±4	0.1612±10	0.768±15	54.5±1.1	86	3,674±53	4,078±20	3,588±68	4,283±4
36-4	250	188	0.75	333	0	0	0.5436±10	0.218±4	0.1831±7	0.897±17	67.2±1.3	95	4,126±58	4,287±19	3,986±72	4,364±3
36-5	208	304	1.46	153	0	0	0.5163±13	0.067±1	0.1959±10	0.498±9	35.4±0.7	61	2,604±40	3,651±19	1,306±25	4,288±4
36-6	346	940	2.71	182	0.001	0	0.5147±11	0.026±1	0.2005±9	0.356±7	25.2±0.5	46	1,961±32	3,317±19	524±10	4,284±3
36-7	127	75	0.59	180	0	0	0.5587±14	0.237±5	0.1437±9	0.968±19	74.6±1.5	99	4,364±61	4,392±20	4,291±83	4,404±4
36-8	329	339	1.03	337	0.013	0.00001	0.5272±9	0.141±3	0.2134±8	0.683±13	49.6±0.9	78	3,355±49	3,985±19	2,672±49	4,319±3

* 由 ^{204}Pb 作普通铅校正。

锆石颗粒 W74/2-36 的数据。f206% = (普通 ^{206}Pb/ 总 ^{206}Pb) × 100。Conc.(%) 是百分比协和度，定义为 [($^{206}Pb/^{238}U$ 年龄) / ($^{207}Pb/^{206}Pb$ 年龄)] × 100。所有误差为 1σ。Pb/Pb 和 Pb/Th 比值的误差基于计数统计。Pb/U 比值的误差也包括了分析过程中基于标准锆石 CZ3 的多次分析对 Pb/U 再现性误差的估计。第一次分析中，每个分析点对应一个特定的编号。第二次分析中，锆石颗粒被标记为 W74/2-36，每个分析点从 36-1 至 36-8 连续编号。

xenocrysts older than 4 Gyr that were recently discovered in granitoids from the Narryer and Murchison Terranes of Western Australia[18], which are infilled with recrystallized zircon, the cracks in W74/2-36 are open. They contain thin (generally less than 300 nm thick), discontinuous films of phosphates, resulting in slightly elevated values of Fe, Al, P and Y. These are, however, too small to have a significant effect on the oxygen budget of 25-μm analytical sites; thus they do not compromise our interpretation of the oxygen data.

Grain W74/2-36 has U and Th values ranging from 127–487 and 75–1,731 p.p.m., respectively (Table 1), reaching values considerably higher than those recorded from the ~4,276-Myr-old crystal[4]. There is no correlation between the ^{207}Pb/^{206}Pb age of the various analytical sites and the U, Th and Pb contents, or the Th/U ratio (Table 1), although the oldest site has the lowest values for all of these except Pb. These results suggest complex micrometre to sub-micrometre variations in composition, as indicated by several detailed studies[18-20], and also preclude any estimate of the composition of the host rock based on isotopic characteristics. The Th/U ratio varies from 0.59 to 3.56, with those sites in the range 0.59 to 0.77 having ^{208}Pb/^{232}Th ages greater than 3,588 Myr and being the least discordant (Table 1). The large differences in Pb/U for similar ^{207}Pb/^{206}Pb ages (Table 1) indicate recent lead loss. This is especially evident within the combined light and dark rectangular area visible in the CL image, which may have formed part of the central region of the original zircon (Fig. 1b). The three spots from the second analytical run (36-3, 36-5 and 36-6), which partially overlap this zone, define a weighted ^{207}Pb/^{206}Pb age of 4,289 ± 7 Myr (2σ) that is younger than the ^{207}Pb/^{206}Pb age of all other sites (Table 1). A similar feature was noted in the core of a xenocrystic zircon older than 4.0 Gyr in granitic gneiss from Churla Well in the Narryer Terrane[18] and was interpreted as reflecting an ancient episode of lead loss resulting from an event at high temperature. Unlike Churla Well, our data show no evidence of subsequent lead loss during Precambrian time, suggesting that the zircon was not affected by later igneous or metamorphic processes before its deposition in the conglomerate.

We interpret the concordant ^{207}Pb/^{206}Pb age of 4,404 ± 8 Myr (2σ) as recording the time of crystallization of zircon W74/2-36. Although this is represented by only one analysis, it is concordant (99%), is not affected by cracks, and there is no evidence from the analytical data that this site, rather than any other measured, may be anomalous. The crystal was subsequently affected by one or more episodes of ancient lead loss, but the timing of these is unresolved. The concordant and near-concordant ages of 4,364 ± 6 Myr, 4,355 ± 4 Myr and 4,341 ± 6 Myr (2σ) may represent actual geological events, possibly triggered by meteor bombardment[18], or they may indicate slight changes in ^{207}Pb/^{206}Pb without generating much discordance[2], because of their position on the concordia curve (Fig. 2). The ^{207}Pb/^{206}Pb age of 4,289 ± 7 Myr (2σ) for the three more discordant points from the light and dark area in the CL image (Fig. 1b) were most probably reset at this time by a high-temperature event, and subsequently underwent recent lead loss.

546

的裂隙是开放的，这不同于最近发现于西澳大利亚纳里耶和默奇森地体的花岗质岩石中老于 40 亿年的捕虏锆石，后者的裂隙都被重结晶锆石充填[18]。锆石 W74/2-36 的裂隙中存在不连续的磷酸盐薄膜（通常小于 300 nm），导致 Fe、Al、P 和 Y 含量轻微升高。然而这些裂隙太小，完全不足以对大小为 25 μm 的分析点的氧同位素分析产生影响，因此也不会影响我们对氧同位素数据的解释。

锆石 W74/2-36 的 U 和 Th 含量分别为 127～487 ppm 和 75～1,731 ppm（表 1），明显高于早期发现的年龄约 42.76 亿年的锆石[4]。不同分析点的 $^{207}Pb/^{206}Pb$ 年龄与 U、Th、Pb 含量或 Th/U 比值之间不具有相关性（表 1），尽管除了 Pb 以外，最古老年龄分析点的其他元素含量都最低。与其他一些详细研究[18-20]一样，这些结果暗示了锆石内部的化学组成在微米到亚微米尺度上存在复杂的变化，也排除了基于锆石同位素特征对母岩做出组成判断的可能。Th/U 比值范围为 0.59～3.56，其中 Th/U 比值为 0.59～0.77 的分析点 $^{208}Pb/^{232}Th$ 年龄大于 35.88 亿年，并具有最高的谐和度（表 1）。锆石 $^{207}Pb/^{206}Pb$ 年龄相似而 Pb/U 比值存在巨大差异（表 1），表明近代铅丢失的存在。这一现象在阴极发光图像中亮暗结合的矩形区域内尤为明显，这些矩形区域可能构成了原始锆石中央区域的一部分（图 1b）。第二次分析的 3 个点（36-3，36-5 和 36-6）与该区域部分重合，给出了 $(4,289 \pm 7)$ Myr (2σ) 的 $^{207}Pb/^{206}Pb$ 加权平均年龄，比其他所有分析点的 $^{207}Pb/^{206}Pb$ 年龄都要年轻（表 1）。类似特征也存在于纳里耶地体 Churla Well 花岗质片麻岩的老于 40 亿年锆石捕虏晶的核部[18]，年龄被解释为一次高温事件所导致的古铅丢失的时代。与 Churla Well 花岗质片麻岩不同的是，我们的数据显示，在前寒武纪时期不存在后继的铅丢失，表明该锆石在沉积进入砾石之前并未再次受到岩浆或变质过程的影响。

我们将 $(4,404 \pm 8)$ Myr 这一谐和的 $^{207}Pb/^{206}Pb$ 年龄解释为锆石 W74/2-36 的结晶时间。尽管只有一个分析点，但没受裂隙的影响，谐和度很高（99%），而且从分析数据看，没有证据表明该分析点存在异常情况，而其他分析点没有异常。锆石在后来受到了一次或多次古铅丢失事件的影响，但其时间仍未确定。谐和或近于谐和的 3 个年龄值 $(4,364 \pm 6)$ Myr、$(4,355 \pm 4)$ Myr 和 $(4,341 \pm 6)$ Myr (2σ) 也许代表了可能由陨石轰击所触发的真实地质事件，或者可能指示了 $^{207}Pb/^{206}Pb$ 比值的轻微变化，但没有导致明显的不谐和[2]，因为分析点仍位于谐和线上（图 2）。位于阴极发光图像（图 1b）中明暗结合区域而谐和度更差的 3 个分析点，其 $(4,289 \pm 7)$ Myr (2σ) 的 $^{207}Pb/^{206}Pb$ 年龄很可能代表了一次高温事件的重置时间，并随后经历了近代铅丢失。

Most of the crystal exhibits weak banding in the CL images (Fig. 1a and b), indicating elemental variation marked by differences in luminescence which usually extend fully across the crystal, suggesting that the zircon was originally much larger. The development of banding parallel to the two sharp crystal boundaries in the top left-hand corner of the image and also within the bright area (Fig. 1b) suggests that it reflects oscillatory zoning of magmatic origin. The bright area almost entirely encloses the dark central region, which is devoid of any CL pattern.

Variation in the CL image is confirmed by the REE data (Fig. 3), which were obtained from the floors of five of the initial SHRIMP analytical pits. The analyses yielded prominent positive Ce anomalies, negative Eu anomalies, and heavy (H)REE-enrichment relative to light (L)REE contents; these are features typical of zircons analysed by ion microprobe[11] and from other Jack Hills detrital zircons[13]. The crystal is zoned with respect to LREE (La by about 10-fold), with greater LREE enrichment within and around the bright portion of the crystal. Calculated partition coefficients[11] yield magma compositions with marked LREE-enrichment for this part of the crystal (Lu/La_n (magma) is 238 to 616) and negative Eu anomalies, features indicative of evolved granitic melts. The crystal's growth in a silica-saturated environment is further supported by the identification of three areas, up to 20-μm in diameter, with SiO_2 inclusions (Fig. 1c).

Fig. 3. Rare earth element data for Jack Hills zircon W74-2/36 measured by ion microprobe. We note that spacing of elements along the x-axis is based on radii of 3^+ cations (in Å).

Four analyses of oxygen isotope ratio were made on the Edinburgh Cameca ion microprobe on two spots close to two of the initial SHRIMP sites. One spot was located near the $4,339 \pm 3$ Myr site in the low LREE region that is dull and banded in CL (Fig. 1a). This has a $\delta^{18}O$ of $5.0 \pm 0.7‰$ (1σ), which is indistinguishable from the $\delta^{18}O$ values of mantle-derived zircon[21] and zircon from juvenile, 3.0 to 2.7 Gyr tonalite-trondhjemite-granodiorite plutonic rocks of the Superior Province[22]. The second spot was located in the high LREE region of the grain, which is brighter in the CL image (Fig. 1a), close to the site yielding a $^{207}Pb/^{206}Pb$ age of $4,353 \pm 8$ Myr (2σ). This has a $\delta^{18}O$ value of $7.4 \pm 0.7‰$ (1σ), consistent with equilibrium with a magma of about 8.5 to 9.5‰. Magmatic oxygen isotope ratios in

548

在阴极发光图中，锆石晶体的大部分显示出微弱的环带 (图 1a 和 1b)，指示了由阴极发光亮度变化所标记的元素组成变化。这种变化通常贯穿整个晶体，表明锆石的原始粒度要大得多。在图像的左上角及明亮区域，带状结构发育，并与两条锆石平直边界相平行 (图 1b)，它们为岩浆成因的振荡环带。明亮区域几乎完全包围了没有任何阴极发光结构的暗色中央区域。

在 5 个原 SHRIMP 分析点位置进行了稀土元素元素分析，结果印证了阴极发光图像所显示的锆石结构变化。锆石具有明显的正 Ce 异常和负 Eu 异常，重稀土元素 (HREE) 相对于轻稀土元素 (LREE) 更为富集。这些是以往离子探针分析已揭示出的锆石的典型特征 [11]，也是其他来自杰克山的碎屑锆石的典型特征 [13]。锆石的轻稀土元素组成显示环带结构 (La 的丰度相差 10 倍)，阴极发光高亮度区域及其附近轻稀土元素更为富集。计算出的分配系数 [11] 表明，锆石晶体的这些部位 (Lu/La_n (岩浆) 的范围为 238 ~ 616) 显示与之平衡的岩浆具有轻稀土元素明显富集的组成特征，同时存在负 Eu 异常，表明锆石结晶于已具有一定演化的花岗质熔体。在锆石晶体中识别出 3 个直径达 20 μm 的 SiO_2 包体 (图 1c)，也支持了其生长于 Si 饱和环境的认识。

图 3. 杰克山锆石 W74-2/36 的稀土元素数据，由离子探针方法测定。各元素在 x 轴上的间距基于 3^+ 价阳离子的半径，以 Å 为单位。

在两个 SHRIMP 分析点的附近选取了两个点，在爱丁堡 Cameca 离子探针上进行了 4 次氧同位素分析。其中一个位于年龄为 (4,339±3) Myr 的分析点附近轻稀土元素含量低的位置，在阴极发光图像中颜色灰暗，呈环带结构 (图 1a)。这一点的 $\delta^{18}O$ 值为 5.0‰ ± 0.7‰ (1σ)，氧同位素组成与地幔来源的岩浆锆石 [21] 难以区别，也与苏必利尔省 30 亿到 27 亿年新生英云闪长岩–奥长花岗岩–花岗闪长岩侵入体的岩浆锆石 [22] 难以区别。第二个点位于阴极发光图像中更明亮 (图 1a) 轻稀土元素含量高的区域，紧挨着 $^{207}Pb/^{206}Pb$ 年龄为 (4,353±8) Myr (2σ) 的分析点位置。该点的 $\delta^{18}O$ 值为

this range are indicative of involvement of supracrustal material which has undergone low-temperature interaction with a liquid hydrosphere; there is no known primitive or mantle reservoir of this composition.

REE and oxygen isotope compositions in grain W74/2-36 provide unique insights into the Earth's crust at 4.4 Gyr ago. They indicate formation in a granitic melt derived by partial melting of pre-existing crust. Calculated magma compositions show characteristics distinctive of evolved melts (such as LREE enrichment, prominent negative Eu anomalies, silica saturation), and are not consistent with the REEs of primitive, mafic rocks[10]. The variation from relatively high to low LREEs, coupled with a 2.4‰ decrease in the oxygen isotope ratio, is consistent with igneous zoning associated with melting and assimilation and subsequent equilibration with a mantle-derived melt. The initially high-δ^{18}O magma (~9‰) could result from melting of ocean crust that was hydrothermally altered at low temperatures[23], altered or evolved continental crust, or sediments. The high δ^{18}O value cannot result from closed-system fractional crystallization by a normal mantle melt. In the case of simple melting without assimilation, zircons in the melt would have a similar δ^{18}O value to zircons in its protolith. An alternative hypothesis, involving assimilation coupled with fractional crystallization (AFC) by a normal basalt of high δ^{18}O wallrock, is unlikely, as it would require either energetically unrealistic amounts of assimilation (> 50%) or wallrocks with average δ^{18}O values above 12‰ which are uncommon even in the late Archaean[22]. The correlation of high δ^{18}O values and enriched LREEs is most consistent with the melting of continental crust or sediments, but whichever of these processes dominated, a large reservoir of liquid water is required on the surface of the Earth.

The zoning of zircon W74/2-36 provides further insights into magmatic processes at 4.4 Gyr ago. Such zones could form during AFC, but we suggest that the zircon first crystallized in a magma derived from the melting of existing continental crust at $4,404 \pm 8$ Myr ago, which subsequently formed a magmatic over-growth when mixed with, or remelted by, a more primitive magma between $4,364 \pm 6$ Myr ago and $4,289 \pm 7$ Myr ago. This indicates that at 4.4 Gyr ago there were already intermediate to granitic, high-δ^{18}O continental rocks to contaminate the magma in which grain W74/2-36 grew.

The existence of liquid water at 4.4 Gyr ago could have important implications for the evolution of life. Microfossils as old as 3.5 Gyr are known[24]. Metasediments and carbonaceous materials with biogenic carbon isotope ratios as low as δ^{13}C = -28‰ are known at 3.8 Gyr ago[25]. Zircon crystal W74/2-36 is over 500 Myr older than this organic matter and if liquid water was available to cause the evolved geochemistry that we have measured, then such water was also available for possible biological processes. High-energy asteroid bombardment before 3.9 Gyr ago is consistent with periodic formation and destruction of early oceans and the possibility that primitive life, if it evolved in the oceans, was globally extinguished more than once.

7.4‰±0.7‰（1σ），大致与 δ¹⁸O 值约为 8.5‰～9.5‰ 的岩浆平衡。这一氧同位素比值表明，岩浆过程中有与液态水圈发生过低温反应的地表物质参与。已知的原始储库或地幔储库都不具有这种氧同位素组成特征。

锆石 W74/2-36 的稀土元素和氧同位素组成使人们对 44 亿年前的地壳有了独特的认识，刻画了先存地壳发生部分熔融进而形成花岗岩熔体的过程。计算所得的岩浆成分显示了一定程度的演化特征，例如轻稀土元素富集、明显的负 Eu 异常以及 Si 饱和等，与原始基性岩的稀土元素特征[10]存在明显区别。轻稀土元素相对含量从高到低的变化，以及氧同位素比值 2.4‰ 的下跌，表明火成岩浆作用具有分带性，这与熔融作用、同化作用以及其后与幔源熔体的平衡作用有关。高 δ¹⁸O 值的初始岩浆（～9‰）可由遭受过低温热液蚀变的洋壳发生熔融而形成[23]，也可由蚀变或演化的陆壳或沉积物发生熔融而形成，但不可能由正常地幔熔体在封闭系统内通过结晶分异而形成。在缺乏同化作用的简单熔融情况下，熔体中的锆石与其母岩中的锆石应有相似的 δ¹⁸O 值。另一种假设，即存在高 δ¹⁸O 围岩的正常玄武质岩浆同时经历同化作用和结晶分异作用（AFC 过程），也是不可能的，因为这需要极高的同化量（＞50%，从能量角度讲这并不现实），或者围岩的平均 δ¹⁸O 值要高于 12‰，而这即使在晚太古代也是不常见的[22]。高 δ¹⁸O 值和轻稀土元素富集之间的相关性与大陆地壳或沉积物的熔融最吻合，无论哪个过程占主导地位，都需要地球表面存在大规模的液态水。

锆石 W74/2-36 的环带结构为 44 亿年前的岩浆活动提供了新的相关信息。这些环带可能形成于结晶分异过程，但我们认为，锆石首先是在（4,404±8）Myr 前从已存在的陆壳熔融而来的岩浆中结晶而出。随后在（4,364±6）Myr 前和（4,289±7）Myr 前这一期间，由于与更为原始的岩浆进行混合或由其引发再次熔融，形成了岩浆锆石增生边。这表明，在 44 亿年前就已存在中性至花岗质的、具有高 δ¹⁸O 值的大陆岩石，正是这些大陆岩石与原始岩浆发生混染，生长出了锆石 W74/2-36 的岩浆锆石增生边。

44 亿年前液态水的存在可能对生命演化有重要启示。目前已经发现 35 亿年前的微体化石[24]。38 亿年前便存在具有生物成因碳同位素比值（δ¹³C 低至 −28‰）的变质沉积物和碳质物质[25]。锆石 W74/2-36 比这些有机物还要早 5 亿年以上。如果液态水能影响地球演化过程的化学特征（如本文确定的那样），那么也同样有助于可能的生物演化进程。39 亿年以前的高能小行星撞击与早期海洋的周期性消长相吻合，如果原始生命的进化发生在海洋中，那它们曾不止一次地发生过全球性灭绝。

Table 2. Rare earth element and oxygen isotope data

Trace element data (p.p.m.)												
Spot number	La	Ce	Pt	Nd	Sm	Eu	Gd	Tb	Dy	Ho	Yb	Lu
m2-13	5.5	134	9.4	55	41.4	6.3	100	34	338	106	666	135
m2-14	9.2	122	9.5	59	42.6	5.6	155	47	518	173	1065	225
m2-17	0.6	61	1.1	9	12.3	1.0	85	28	347	124	768	159
m2-30	13.6	226	21.8	119	78.4	12.7	170	49	424	119	672	130
m2-31	0.3	69	0.6	9	18.4	1.4	108	36	438	149	877	182

Oxygen isotope data			
Spot number	Analysis number	Measured $^{18}O/^{16}O$ ($\times 10^{-3}$)	$\delta^{18}O$ (VSMOW)
m2-1	2(15)	1.9378	4.8
m2-2d	2(16)	1.9388	5.3
			Avg. 5.0
m2-3	2(21)	1.9414	6.8
m2-4d	2(22)	1.9436	8
			Avg. 7.4

Data were measured by ion microprobe for crystal W74-2/36.

Methods

Zircon data collection

Approximately 100 zircon grains were hand picked from a previously prepared +135-µm concentrate and mounted onto double-sided adhesive tape, along with pieces of the Curtin University Sri Lankan gem zircon standard (CZ3) with a conventionally-measured U-Pb age of 564 Myr (ref. 26). They were enclosed in epoxy resin disks, ground and polished so as to effectively cut all zircon grains in half, and then gold coated. Samples were imaged by cathodoluminescence (CL), resulting in a map that allowed us to identify grains, as well as providing information on internal structure that could be tested during analysis. During the first analytical session, a mass resolution of 5,400 was obtained and the error associated with the measurement of Pb/U isotopic ratios for the standard, at 1 standard deviation, was 1.96% for seven standards. After discovery of a grain with an age in excess of 4.3 Gyr, and following the collection of oxygen isotope and trace element data, the sample was reground, repolished and gold coated and, on the basis of a new CL image, the grain was reanalysed on SHRIMP II, with a total of eight new sites selected so that most were away from cracks in the crystal. During this session, the mass resolution was 4,885 and the error on the standard, at 1 standard deviation, was 1.86% for six standards. The relationship between measured Pb/U and UO/U ratios on SHRIMP follows a power-law equation with the exponent equal to two (ref. 27). The Pb/U ratios on the unknowns were normalized to those measured on the standard zircon (CZ3 $-$ ($^{206}Pb/^{238}U = 0.0914$)). Both data sets were reduced following the methods of Nelson[16], using the single-stage model Broken Hill common Pb correction for mass ^{204}Pb, since this

表 2. 稀土元素和氧同位素数据

稀土元素数据（ppm）												
数据点编号	La	Ce	Pt	Nd	Sm	Eu	Gd	Tb	Dy	Ho	Yb	Lu
m2-13	5.5	134	9.4	55	41.4	6.3	100	34	338	106	666	135
m2-14	9.2	122	9.5	59	42.6	5.6	155	47	518	173	1065	225
m2-17	0.6	61	1.1	9	12.3	1.0	85	28	347	124	768	159
m2-30	13.6	226	21.8	119	78.4	12.7	170	49	424	119	672	130
m2-31	0.3	69	0.6	9	18.4	1.4	108	36	438	149	877	182

氧同位素数据			
数据点编号	分析编号	测量过的 $^{18}O/^{16}O(\times 10^{-3})$	$\delta^{18}O$(VSMOW)
m2-1	2(15)	1.9378	4.8
m2-2d	2(16)	1.9388	5.3
			平均 5.0
m2-3	2(21)	1.9414	6.8
m2-4d	2(22)	1.9436	8
			平均 7.4

数据通过离子探针测定锆石 W74-2/36 得到。

方　　法

锆石数据收集

从已有的 +135-μm 精矿中手工挑选出大约 100 粒锆石，连同科廷大学的斯里兰卡宝石级标准锆石（CZ3，用传统方法测得的 U-Pb 年龄为 5.64 亿年）碎片[26] 一起放在双面胶带上，封装在环氧树脂盘内，经研磨和抛光，露出所有锆石颗粒的中部，然后镀金。再照阴极发光图像，以便识别颗粒并提供有助于分析测试的颗粒内部结构信息。在第一次分析中，质量分辨率为 5,400，七个标准样品 Pb/U 同位素比值的分析误差为 1.96%（标准差为 1）。在发现年龄超过 43 亿年的一粒锆石并测定其氧同位素和微量元素数据后，锆石样品靶被重新研磨、抛光和镀金，在新的阴极发光图像基础上，避开晶体中的裂隙，选择八个新的位置，在 SHRIMP II 上对该粒锆石进行了重新分析。在这一分析过程中，质量分辨率为 4,885，六个标准样品的分析误差为 1.86%（标准差为 1）。SHRIMP 测得的 Pb/U 和 UO/U 比值之间的关系遵循指数为 2 的幂律方程[27]。未知分析点的 Pb/U 比值通过标准锆石的测量值（CZ3 − ($^{206}Pb/^{238}U = 0.0914$)）进行标准化。两组数据均按照纳尔逊的方法[16] 进行处理，使用单阶段模型布罗肯山普通铅作 ^{204}Pb 校正，因为普通铅主要是在镀金过程中带入的[16]。每一次分析中，分析点的平均直径为 30 μm，每一个点在分析前，对分析位置作扫描清洗，清洗范围为

is considered to be introduced chiefly through the gold coating[16]. The analytical spot size averaged 30 µm during each analytical run and each spot was rastered over 100 µm for five minutes before analysis to remove common Pb on the surface or contamination from the gold coating. All stated uncertainties and data listed in Table 1, and the error bars shown in Fig. 2, are at 1σ; ages discussed in the text are all 2σ.

Oxygen isotope analysis

Four analyses were made by Cameca ims 4f ion microprobe on two spots on grain W74/2- 36 using an energy offset of 350 eV. These were analysed for a total of 2×10^6 counts of ^{18}O for each analysis, yielding precision close to 0.7‰ (1σ), based on gaussian counting statistics[28]. Internal precision for each analysis was ± 0.3 and ± 0.6‰ (1σ), comparing 80-cycle analysis halves on each full analysis, in agreement with theoretical counting statistics. The two point-analyses of the zircon crystal were interspersed with 11 analyses of Kim-5, a homogeneous zircon standard $(\delta^{18}O = 5.04 \pm 0.07$‰ VSMOW by laser fluorination) mounted in a separate standard block. Five standard zircons with 1.06 to 1.52 wt% HfO_2 were also analysed by ion microprobe and laser fluorination[10], and no statistically significant dependence of instrumental mass fractionation on HfO_2 content was found[29] for the narrow range of Hf in these samples.

Rare earth element analysis

In situ determination of REEs was performed by Cameca ims 4f ion microprobe[11]. Five ion microprobe REE analyses of the zircon crystal were made using a 14.5-keV primary beam of O⁻ defocused to an approximately 20 to 30 µm spot. Positive secondary ions were collected using an energy offset of 125 eV. Analyses were standardized to the SRM-610 glass standard. Energy filtering and strategies to avoid and correct for isobaric interferences were used[11].

(**409**, 175-178; 2001)

Simon A. Wilde[*], **John W. Valley**[†], **William H. Peck**[†‡] **& Colin M. Graham**[§]

[*] School of Applied Geology, Curtin University of Technology, GPO Box U1987, Perth, Australia

[†] Department of Geology & Geophysics, University of Wisconsin, Madison, Wisconsin 53706, USA

[§] Department of Geology & Geophysics, University of Edinburgh, Edinburgh, EH9 3JW, UK

[‡] Present address: Department of Geology, Colgate University, Hamilton, New York 13346, USA

Received 1 August; accepted 24 November 2000.

References:

1. Ryder, G. Chronology of early bombardment in the inner solar system. *Geol. Soc. Am. Abstr. Progm* **21** A299 (1992).

2. Bowring, S. A. & Williams, I. S. Priscoan (4.00-4.03) orthogneisses from northwestern Canada. *Contrib. Mineral. Petrol.* **134**, 3-16 (1999).

3. Froude, D. O. *et al.* Ion microprobe identification of 4,100-4,200 Myr-old terrestrial zircons. *Nature* **304**, 616-618 (1983).

4. Compston, W. & Pidgeon, R. T. Jack Hills, evidence of more very old detrital zircons in Western Australia. *Nature* **321**, 766-769 (1986).

5. Wilde, S. A. & Pidgeon, R. T. in *3rd International Archaean Symposium (Perth), Excursion Guidebook* (eds Ho, S. E., Glover, J. E., Myers, J. S. & Muhling, J. R.) 82-95 (University of Western Australia Extension Publication, Vol. 21, Perth, 1990).

6. Kober, B., Pidgeon, R. T. & Lippolt, H. J. Single-zircon dating by step-wise Pb-evaporation constrains the Archean history of detrital zircons from the Jack Hills, Western Australia. *Earth Planet. Sci. Lett.* **91**, 286-296 (1989).

100 μm，持续时间为 5 分钟，以除去样品靶表面的普通铅或镀金带来的污染。表 1 中提到的不确定性和列出的数据以及图 2 中的误差棒都为 1 个标准差，而文中讨论的所有年龄的误差都为 2 个标准差。

氧同位素分析

利用 Cameca ims 4f 离子探针，对锆石 W74/2-36 上的两个点进行了 4 次氧同位素分析，所用的能量补偿为 350 eV。每次分析 ^{18}O 的总计数为 2×10^6，基于高斯计数统计 [28]，分析精确度接近 0.7‰（1σ）。每次分析的内部精度为 ±0.3‰ 和 ±0.6‰（1σ），分别对应于全分析和数量减半的 80 组分析，其精度与理论计数统计一致。在对锆石 W74/2-36 两个点进行分析的过程中，插入了 11 次标准锆石 Kim-5 的分析，该标准锆石的氧同位素组成均一（$\delta^{18}O = 5.04$‰ ±0.07‰ VSMOW，激光氟化分析），被固定于一个独立放置标样的位置。同时也利用离子探针和激光氟化法对五个 HfO_2 含量为 1.06 wt% ~ 1.52 wt% 的标准锆石进行了分析 [10]。在这样 Hf 含量变化不大的情况下，未发现仪器质量分馏效应与 HfO_2 含量之间存在具有统计意义上的相关性 [29]。

稀土元素分析

稀土元素的原位测定由 Cameca ims 4f 离子探针 [11] 完成。使用 14.5 keV 的 O^- 一次粒子束，散焦至大约 20 ~ 30 μm 的束斑范围。对锆石 W74/2-36 进行了 5 次离子探针稀土元素分析。能量补偿为 125 eV，对正二次离子进行收集。利用 SRM-610 玻璃标准样品对分析结果进行标准化。此外还使用了能量过滤及其他方法来避免并校正同质异位素的干扰 [11]。

（卢皓 翻译；万渝生 刘守偈 审稿）

7. Amelin, Y. V. Geochronology of the Jack Hills detrital zircons by precise U-Pb isotope dilution analysis of crystal fragments. *Chem. Geol.* **146**, 25-38 (1998).

8. Amelin, Y., Lee, D.-C., Halliday, A. N. & Pidgeon, R. T. Nature of the Earth's earliest crust from hafnium isotopes in single detrital zircons. *Nature* **399**, 252-255 (1999).

9. Myers, J. S. in *Early Precambrian Processes* (eds Coward, M. P. & Ries, A. C.) 143-154 (Geological Society of London Special Publication No. 95, 1995).

10. Peck, W. H., Valley, J. W., Wilde, S. A. & Graham, C. M. Oxygen isotope ratios and rare earth elements in 3.3 to > 4.0 Ga zircons: ion microprobe evidence for Early Archaean high δ^{18}O continental crust. *Geochim. Cosmochim. Acta* (submitted).

11. Hinton, R. W. & Upton, B. G. J. The chemistry of zircon; variations within and between large crystals from syenite and alkali basalt xenoliths. *Geochim. Cosmochim. Acta* **55**, 3287-3302 (1991).

12. Valley, J. W., Chiarenzelli, J. R. & McLelland, J. M. Oxygen isotope geochemistry of zircon. *Earth Planet. Sci. Lett.* **126**, 187-206 (1994).

13. Maas, R., Kinny, P. D., Williams, I. S., Froude, D. O. & Compston, W. The earth's oldest known crust: a geochronological and geochemical study of 3900-4200 Ma old detrital zircons from Mt. Narryer and Jack Hills, Western Australia. *Geochim. Cosmochim. Acta* **56**, 1281-1300 (1992).

14. Compston, W., Williams, I. S., Kirschvink, J. L., Zhang, Z. & Ma, G. Zircon U-Pb ages for the Early Cambrian time-scale. *J. Geol. Soc. Lond.* **149**, 171-184 (1992).

15. Williams, I. S. in *Applications of Microanalytical Techniques to Understanding Mineralizing Processes* (eds McKibben, M. A., Shanks III, W. C. & Ridley, W. I.) 1-95 (Reviews in Economic Geology, Vol. 7, Society of Economic Geologists, Littleton, Colorado, 1998).

16. Nelson, D. R. Compilation of SHRIMP U-Pb geochronology data, 1996. *Geol. Surv. Western Australia Rec.* **1997/2**, 1-11 (1997).

17. Taylor, S. R. *Solar System Evolution: A New Perspective* 289 (Cambridge Univ. Press, Cambridge, 1992).

18. Nelson, D. R., Robinson, B. W. & Myers, J. S. Complex geological histories extending from > 4.0 Ga deciphered from xenocryst zircon microstructures. *Earth Planet. Sci. Lett.* **181**, 89-102 (2000).

19. Williams, I. S., Compston, W., Black, L. P., Ireland, T. R. & Foster, J. J. Unsupported radiogenic Pb in zircon: a cause of anomalously high Pb-Pb, U-Pb and Th-Pb ages. *Contrib. Mineral. Petrol.* **88**, 322-327 (1984).

20. Mattinson, J. M. A study of complex discordance in zircons using step-wise dissolution techniques. *Contrib. Mineral. Petrol.* **16**, 117-129 (1994).

21. Valley, J. W., Kinny, P. D., Schulze, D. J. & Spicuzza, M. J. Zircon megacrysts from kimberlite: oxygen isotope variability among mantle melts. *Contrib. Mineral. Petrol.* **133**, 1-11 (1998).

22. King, E. M., Valley, J. W., Davis, D. W. & Edwards, G. R. Oxygen isotope ratios of Archean plutonic zircons from granite-greenstone belts of the Superior province: indicator of magmatic source. *Precamb. Res.* **92**, 365-387 (1998).

23. Muehlenbachs, K. in *Stable Isotopes* (eds Valley, J. W. *et al.*) *MSA Rev. Min.* **16**, 425-444 (1986).

24. Schopf, J. W. Microfossils in the early Archean Apex Chert: New evidence for the antiquity of life. *Science* **260**, 640-646 (1993).

25. Hayes, J. M., Kaplan, I. R. & Wedeking, K. W. in *Earth's Earliest Biosphere; its Origin and evolution* 93-134 (Princeton Univ. Press, Princeton, NJ, 1983).

26. Pidgeon, R. T. *et al.* in *Eighth Int. Conf. Geochron., Cosmochron. Isotope Geol.* (eds Lanphere, M. A., Dalrymple, G. B. & Turrin, B. D.) 251 (US Geological Survey Circular 1107, Denver, Colorado, 1994).

27. Claoué-Long, J. C., Compston, W., Roberts, J. & Fanning, C. M. in *Geochronology, Time Scales and Global Stratigraphic Correlation* (eds Berggren, W. A., Kent, D. V., Aubry, M.-P. & Hardenbol, J.) 3-21 (Soc. of Sedimentary Geology, SEPM Sp. Publ. 4, 1995).

28. Valley, J. W., Graham, C. M., Harte, B., Eiler, J. M. & Kinny, P. D. in *Applications of Microanalysis to Understanding Mineralizing Processes* (eds McKibben, M. A., Shanks III, W. C. & Ridley, W. I.) 73-98 (xReviews in Economic Geology, Vol. 7, Society of Economic Geologists, Littleton, Colorado, 1998).

29. Eiler, J. M., Graham, C. M. & Valley, J. W. SIMS analysis of oxygen isotopes: matrix effects in complex minerals and glasses. *Chem. Geol.* **138**, 221-244 (1997).

Acknowledgements. We thank A. Nemchin for assistance with the cathodoluminescence imaging, J. Craven for assistance in stable isotope analysis by ion microprobe and J. Fournelle for assistance with electron microprobe analysis. Initial fieldwork was supported by the Australian Research Council and analytical work by NERC, NSF and the US Department of Energy. D. Nelson and K. McNamara kindly commented on the manuscript.

Correspondence and requests for materials should be addressed to S.A.W. (e-mail: wildes@lithos.curtin.edu.au).

Observation of Coherent Optical Information Storage in an Atomic Medium Using Halted Light Pulses

C. Liu *et al.*

Editor's Note

Laser light shining on an opaque medium can sometimes make it transparent to other light, a phenomenon known as electromagnetically induced transparency. The optical properties of the medium change so dramatically that light pulses can be slowed and compressed by many orders of magnitude. Here Chien Liu and colleagues report on experiments in which they used the effect to bring laser pulses to a complete standstill in a cold gas of sodium atoms held in a magnetic trap. They also show that information may be frozen into the atomic medium for as long as 1 microsecond, and then recovered. Liu and colleagues suggest that this technique could be useful in the development of quantum computers and other quantum information systems.

Electromagnetically induced transparency[1-3] is a quantum interference effect that permits the propagation of light through an otherwise opaque atomic medium; a "coupling" laser is used to create the interference necessary to allow the transmission of resonant pulses from a "probe" laser. This technique has been used[4-6] to slow and spatially compress light pulses by seven orders of magnitude, resulting in their complete localization and containment within an atomic cloud[4]. Here we use electromagnetically induced transparency to bring laser pulses to a complete stop in a magnetically trapped, cold cloud of sodium atoms. Within the spatially localized pulse region, the atoms are in a superposition state determined by the amplitudes and phases of the coupling and probe laser fields. Upon sudden turn-off of the coupling laser, the compressed probe pulse is effectively stopped; coherent information initially contained in the laser fields is "frozen" in the atomic medium for up to 1 ms. The coupling laser is turned back on at a later time and the probe pulse is regenerated: the stored coherence is read out and transferred back into the radiation field. We present a theoretical model that reveals that the system is self-adjusting to minimize dissipative loss during the "read" and "write" operations. We anticipate applications of this phenomenon for quantum information processing.

WITH the coupling and probe lasers used in the experiment, the atoms are accurately modelled as three-level atoms interacting with the two laser fields (Fig. 1a). Under perfect electromagnetically-induced transparency (EIT) conditions (two-photon resonance), a stationary eigenstate exists for the system of a three-level atom and resonant laser fields, where the atom is in a "dark", coherent superposition of states $|1\rangle$ and $|2\rangle$:

运用停止光脉冲来观测原子介质中的相干光学信息存储

刘谦（音译）等

编者按

照射在不透明介质上的激光有时会使介质对其他光线透明，这种现象称为电磁感应透明。介质的光学性质变化非常显著，以至于光脉冲可以被放慢和压缩许多个数量级。本文中，刘谦（音译）与其同事们报道了使用这种效应的实验，在这些实验中，他们使激光脉冲完全停滞在磁阱中的冷钠原子气团中。他们还展示了信息可冻结在原子介质中长达1微秒，然后恢复。刘谦与其同事们认为这种技术可以用于量子计算机和其他量子信息系统的开发。

电磁感应透明[1-3]是一种量子干涉效应，它允许光在其他状态下非透明的原子介质中传播；"耦合"激光被用来产生必要的干涉，以实现从"探测"激光发出的共振脉冲的传输。这种技术[4-6]已经被用于减缓及空间压缩光脉冲达七个数量级之多，从而导致其在原子云内的完全局域化和容纳[4]。本文运用电磁感应透明来使激光脉冲在磁阱捕获的冷钠原子云中完全停止。在空间局域化脉冲区域内，原子处于由耦合激光场和探测激光场的振幅和相位所决定的叠加态。当突然关闭耦合激光时，压缩的探测光束会有效地停止；最初存储在激光场中的相干信息就被"冷冻"在原子介质中，最长可达1 ms。随后耦合激光被重新开启，探测脉冲便再次产生：所存储的相干信息被读取出来并转移回辐射场。本文提出了一个理论模型，揭示了该系统的自调节特征使得"读"和"写"操作过程中耗散损失最小。我们预期这种现象可以被应用于量子信息处理。

通过实验中所使用的耦合和探测激光，原子被精确地建模为与两激光场相互作用的三能级原子（图1a）。在完全电磁感应透明（EIT）条件下（双光子共振），对于三能级原子和共振激光场组成的系统存在一稳定的本征态，其中原子处于态 $|1\rangle$ 和 $|2\rangle$ 的相干叠加"暗"状态：

$$|D\rangle = \frac{\Omega_c|1\rangle - \Omega_p|2\rangle \exp[i(\mathbf{k}_p - \mathbf{k}_c)\cdot\mathbf{r} - i(\omega_p - \omega_c)t]}{\sqrt{\Omega_c^2 + \Omega_p^2}} \qquad (1)$$

Here Ω_p and Ω_c are the Rabi frequencies, $\mathbf{k}_p$ and $\mathbf{k}_c$ the wavevectors, and ω_p and ω_c the optical angular frequencies of the probe and coupling lasers, respectively. The Rabi frequencies are defined as $\Omega_{p,c} \equiv e\,\mathbf{E}_{p,c}\cdot\mathbf{r}_{13,23}/\hbar$, where e is the electron charge, $\mathbf{E}_{p,c}$ are the slowly varying envelopes of probe and coupling field amplitudes, and $e\,\mathbf{r}_{13,23}$ are the electric dipole moments of the atomic transitions. The dark state does not couple to the radiatively decaying state $|3\rangle$, which eliminates absorption of the laser fields[1-3].

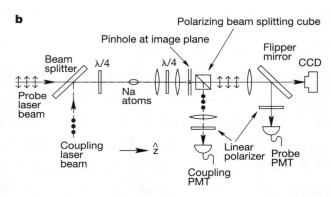

Fig. 1. Experimental set-up and procedure. **a**, States $|1\rangle$, $|2\rangle$ and $|3\rangle$ form the three-level EIT system. The cooled atoms are initially magnetically trapped in state $|1\rangle = |3S, F = 1, M_F = -1\rangle$. Stimulated photon exchanges between the probe and coupling laser fields create a "dark" superposition of states $|1\rangle$ and $|2\rangle$, which renders the medium transparent for the resonant probe pulses. **b**, We apply a 2.2-mm diameter, σ^--polarized coupling laser, resonant with the $|3S, F = 2, M_F = +1\rangle \rightarrow |3P, F = 2, M_F = 0\rangle$ transition, and a co-propagating, 1.2-mm diameter σ^+-polarized probe pulse tuned to the $|3S, F = 1, M_F = -1\rangle \rightarrow |3P, F = 2, M_F = 0\rangle$ transition. The two laser beams start out with orthogonal linear polarizations (two-headed arrows and filled circles show the directions of linear polarization of the probe and coupling lasers, respectively). They are combined with a beam splitter, circularly polarized with a quarter-wave plate ($\lambda/4$), and then injected into the atom cloud. After leaving the cloud, the laser beams pass a second quarter-wave plate and regain their original linear polarizations before being separated with a polarizing beam-splitting cube. The atom cloud is imaged first onto an external image plane and then onto a CCD (charge-coupled device) camera. A pinhole is placed in the external image plane and positioned at the centre of the cloud image. With the pinhole and flipper mirror in place, only those portions of the probe and coupling laser beams that have passed through the central region of the cloud are selected and monitored simultaneously by two photomultiplier tubes (PMTs). States $|1\rangle$ and $|2\rangle$ have identical first-order Zeeman shifts so the two-photon resonance is maintained across the trapped atom clouds. Cold atoms and co-propagating lasers eliminate Doppler effects. However, off-resonance transitions to state $|4\rangle$ prevent perfect transmission of the light pulses in this case.

$$|D\rangle = \frac{\Omega_c|1\rangle - \Omega_p|2\rangle \exp[i(\mathbf{k}_p - \mathbf{k}_c)\cdot\mathbf{r} - i(\omega_p - \omega_c)t]}{\sqrt{\Omega_c^2 + \Omega_p^2}} \tag{1}$$

这里 Ω_p 和 Ω_c 分别为探测和耦合激光的拉比频率，$\mathbf{k}_p$ 和 $\mathbf{k}_c$ 为波矢，ω_p 和 ω_c 为光学角频率。拉比频率定义为 $\Omega_{p,c} \equiv e\mathbf{E}_{p,c}\cdot\mathbf{r}_{13,23}/\hbar,$，其中 e 为电子电荷，$\mathbf{E}_{p,c}$ 为探测和耦合场振幅的缓慢变化包络，$e\mathbf{r}_{13,23}$ 为原子跃迁的电偶极矩。暗态不会与辐射衰减态 $|3\rangle$ 耦合，从而抵消了激光场的吸收[1-3]。

图 1. 实验装置和实验过程。**a**，量子态 $|1\rangle$，$|2\rangle$，$|3\rangle$ 构成一个三能级 EIT 系统。被降温的原子最初被磁阱捕获于态 $|1\rangle = |3S,\ F=1,\ M_F=-1\rangle$。探测和耦合激光场之间的受激光子交换产生了态 $|1\rangle$ 和 $|2\rangle$ 的"暗"叠加态，这使得介质对共振探测脉冲是透明的。**b**，我们施加一个直径 2.2 mm 的 σ⁻ 偏振耦合激光，频率与 $|3S,\ F=2,\ M_F=+1\rangle\rightarrow|3P,\ F=2,\ M_F=0\rangle$ 态的跃迁共振，还施加一个同向传播的，1.2 mm 直径，频率调谐至 $|3S,\ F=1,\ M_F=-1\rangle\rightarrow|3P,\ F=2,\ M_F=0\rangle$ 跃迁的 σ⁺ 偏振探测激光。两激光束以正交的线性偏振方向发出（双箭头和实心圆分别代表探测和耦合光束的偏振方向）。它们通过分束器合成，经四分之一 (λ/4) 波片形成圆偏振，然后射入原子云。从原子云中射出后，激光束又经过四分之一 (λ/4) 波片，在被偏振分束立方体分离之前重获原来各自的线偏振态。原子云首先成像在一外置的成像平面，然后成像在 CCD（电荷耦合器件）摄像机上。一针孔被置于外置的成像平面上，位于云图像的中心。通过针孔和翻转镜的适当摆放，只有通过云中心区域的探测和耦合激光束被采集并且同时由两个光电倍增管（PMT）监测。量子态 $|1\rangle$ 和 $|2\rangle$ 有相同的一阶塞曼位移，所以双光子共振在被捕获的原子云中保持下来。冷原子和同向传播的激光消除了多普勒效应。但是，在这种情况下，由于存在到量子态 $|4\rangle$ 的非共振跃迁，光脉冲无法获得理想的透射率。

Atoms are prepared (magnetically trapped) in a particular internal quantum state $|1\rangle$ (Fig. 1a). The atom cloud is first illuminated by a coupling laser, resonant with the $|2\rangle$–$|3\rangle$ transition. With only the coupling laser on and all atoms in $|1\rangle$, the system is in a dark state (equation (1) with $\Omega_p = 0$). A probe laser pulse, tuned to the $|1\rangle$–$|3\rangle$ transition and co-propagating with the coupling laser, is subsequently sent through the atomic medium. Atoms within the pulse region are driven into the dark-state superposition of states $|1\rangle$ and $|2\rangle$, determined by the ratio of the instantaneous Rabi frequencies of the laser fields (equation (1)).

The presence of the coupling laser field creates transparency, a very steep refractive index profile, and low group velocity, V_g, for the probe pulse[1-10]. As the pulse enters the atomic medium, it is spatially compressed by a factor c/V_g whereas its peak electric amplitude remains constant during the slow-down[4,7].

The experiment is performed with the apparatus described in refs 4 and 11. Figure 1 shows the new optical set-up and atomic energy levels involved. A typical cloud of 11 million sodium atoms is cooled to 0.9 μK, which is just above the critical temperature for Bose–Einstein condensation. The cloud has a length of 339 μm in the z direction, a width of 55 μm in the transverse directions, and a peak density of 11 μm^{-3}. Those portions of the co-propagating probe and coupling laser beams that have passed through the 15-μm-diameter centre region of the cloud are selected and monitored simultaneously by two photomultiplier tubes (PMTs).

Figure 2a shows typical signals detected by the PMTs. The dashed curve is the measured intensity of the coupling laser, which is turned on a few microseconds before the probe pulse. The open circles indicate a gaussian-shaped reference probe pulse recorded in the absence of atoms (1/e full width is 5.70 μs). The filled circles show a probe pulse measured after it has passed through a cold atom cloud, and the solid curve is a gaussian fit to the data. The delay of this probe pulse, relative to the reference pulse, is 11.8 μs corresponding to a group velocity of 28 m s^{-1}, a reduction by a factor of 10^7 from its vacuum value. The measured delay agrees with the theoretical prediction of 12.2 μs based on a measured coupling Rabi frequency Ω_c of 2.57 MHz $\times$ 2π and an observed atomic column density of 3,670 μm^{-2}.

原子制备（磁阱捕获）时处于一特定的内量子态 $|1\rangle$（图1a）。原子云最初受一耦合激光辐射，与 $|2\rangle$–$|3\rangle$ 跃迁共振。只有耦合激光开启，并且所有的原子都处于 $|1\rangle$ 态时，系统处于暗态中（等式（1）中 $\Omega_p = 0$）。一探测激光脉冲，被调谐至 $|1\rangle$–$|3\rangle$ 跃迁，与耦合激光同向传播，随后被发送穿过原子介质。在脉冲区域的原子被驱动至 $|1\rangle$ 和 $|2\rangle$ 的暗叠加态，该叠加态由激光场的瞬时拉比频率的比率决定（等式（1））。

耦合激光场的存在产生了透明现象，并导致探测脉冲的折射率图谱变得非常陡峭，群速度 V_g 变得很低[1-10]。当脉冲进入原子介质时，其空间尺寸被压缩了 c/V_g 倍，而在减速期间其峰值电子振幅保持恒定[4,7]。

实验装置如参考文献4和11所述。图1给出了新的光学装置以及所涉及的原子能级。一典型的原子云包含1,100万钠原子，它被冷却至 $0.9\ \mu K$，刚好在玻色–爱因斯坦凝聚临界温度以上。原子云在 z 方向长 $339\ \mu m$，横向宽度 $55\ \mu m$，峰值密度为 $11\ \mu m^{-3}$。选择同向传播的探测和耦合激光光束中通过原子云中心直径 $15\ \mu m$ 区域的部分，并用两个光电倍增管（PMT）同时监测。

图2a给出了PMT探测到的典型信号。虚线表示耦合激光的测量强度，比探测脉冲早几微秒打开。空心圆为没有原子存在时（1/e 全宽为 $5.70\ \mu s$）所记录的高斯型参考探测脉冲。实心圆为探测脉冲通过一冷原子云后所测得的信号，实线为数据的高斯拟合。这个探测脉冲与参考脉冲相比的延迟为 $11.8\ \mu s$，对应群速度为 $28\ m \cdot s^{-1}$，相当于真空中速度的 $1/10^7$。实验测得的延迟与理论预测值 $12.2\ \mu s$ 相符合。该理论预测值是基于测量所得的耦合拉比频率 Ω_c（$2.57\ MHz \times 2\pi$）以及观测所得的原子柱密度（$3,670\ \mu m^{-2}$）获得的。

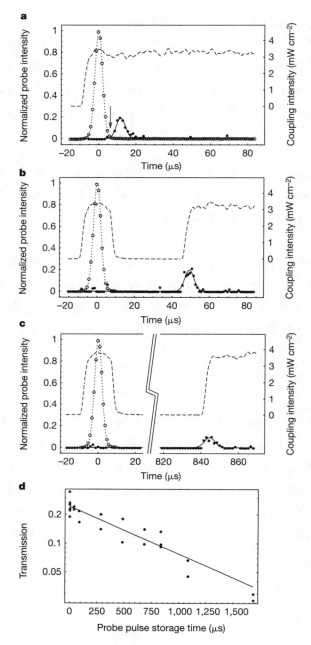

Fig. 2. Measurements of delayed and revived probe pulses. Open circles (fitted to the dotted gaussian curves) show reference pulses obtained as the average of 100 probe pulses recorded in the absence of atoms. Dashed curves and filled circles (fitted to the solid gaussian curves) show simultaneously measured intensities of coupling and probe pulses that have propagated under EIT conditions through a 339-μm-long atom cloud cooled to 0.9 μK. The measured probe intensities are normalized to the peak intensity of the reference pulses (typically, $\Omega_p/\Omega_c = 0.3$ at the peak). **a**, Probe pulse delayed by 11.8 μs. The arrow at 6.3 μs indicates the time when the probe pulse is spatially compressed and contained completely within the atomic cloud. (The intersection of the back edge of the reference pulse and the front edge of the delayed pulse defines a moment when the tail of the probe pulse has just entered the cloud and the leading

图 2. 探测脉冲延迟和再生的测量。空心圆（高斯拟合用点线表示）对应参考脉冲，为没有原子时所记录的 100 个探测脉冲的平均值。虚线和实心圆（高斯拟合用实线表示）对应在 EIT 条件下同时测量耦合和探测脉冲经由 339 μm 长、降温至 0.9 μK 的原子云传播所得到的强度。测量所得的探测强度相对参考脉冲的峰值强度进行了归一化（一般地，峰值处的 $\Omega_{p}/\Omega_{c} = 0.3$）。**a**，探测脉冲延迟 11.8 μs。6.3 μs 处的箭头表示探测脉冲空间上被压缩并被完全包含在原子云中的时刻（参考脉冲的后沿与延迟脉冲的前沿之间的交叉点决定了脉冲尾部刚刚进入云而前沿又恰好要离开的时刻）。**b**，**c**，耦合场在 $t = 6.3$ μs 关闭，

565

edge is just about to exit.) **b**, **c**, Revival of a probe pulse after the coupling field is turned off at $t = 6.3$ µs and turned back on at $t = 44.3$ µs and $t = 839.3$ µs, respectively. During the time interval when the coupling laser is off, coherent information imprinted by the probe pulse, is stored in the atomic medium. Upon subsequent turn-on of the coupling field, the probe pulse is regenerated through coherent stimulation. The time constants for the probe and coupling PMT amplifiers are 0.3 µs and 3 µs, respectively. The actual turn on/off time for the coupling field is 1 µs, as measured with a fast photodiode. **d**, Measured transmission of the probe pulse energy versus storage time. The solid line is a fit to the data, which gives a 1/e decay time of 0.9 ms for the atomic coherence.

At time $t = 6.3$ µs, indicated by the arrow in Fig. 2a, the probe pulse is spatially compressed and contained completely within the atomic cloud. The probe pulse in free space is 3.4 km long and contains 27,000 photons within a 15-µm diameter at its centre. It is compressed in the atomic medium to match the size of the cloud (339 µm), and the remaining optical energy in the probe field is only 1/400 of a free-space photon. Essentially all of the probe energy has been transferred through stimulated emission into the coupling laser field and the atomic medium, and coherent optical information has been imprinted on the atoms (equation (1)).

To store this coherent information, we turn off the coupling field abruptly when the probe pulse is contained within the cloud. The stored information is read out at a later time by turning the coupling laser back on. A result is shown in Fig. 2b. The dashed curve shows the coupling laser's turn-off at $t = 6.3$ µs and its subsequent turn-on at 44.3 µs. The filled circles represent the measured probe intensity. As seen from the data, when the coupling laser is turned back on the probe pulse is regenerated: we can stop and controllably regenerate the probe pulse. Similar effects have been predicted in a recent theoretical paper[12].

When the probe pulse is contained within the medium, the coherence of the laser fields is already imprinted on the atoms. As the coupling laser is turned off, the probe field is depleted to maintain the dark state (equation (1)) and (negligible) atomic amplitude is transferred from state $|1\rangle$ to state $|2\rangle$ through stimulated photon exchange between the two light fields. Because of the extremely low energy remaining in the compressed probe pulse, as noted above, it is completely depleted before the atomic population amplitudes have changed by an appreciable amount. When the coupling laser is turned back on, the process reverses and the probe pulse is regenerated through stimulated emission into the probe field. It propagates subsequently under EIT conditions as if the coupling beam had never been turned off.

During the storage time, information about the amplitude of the probe field is contained in the population amplitudes defining the atomic dark states. Information about the mode vector of the probe field is contained in the relative phase between different atoms in the macroscopic sample. The use of cold atoms minimizes thermal motion and the associated smearing of the relative phase during the storage time. (We obtain storage times that are up to 50 times larger than the time it takes an atom to travel one laser wavelength. As seen from equation (1), the difference between the wavevectors of the two laser fields determines the wavelength of the periodic phase pattern imprinted on the medium, which is 10^5 times larger than the individual laser wavelengths.)

又分别在 $t = 44.3\ \mu s$ 和 $t = 839.3\ \mu s$ 重新开启之后探测脉冲的再生。在耦合激光关闭的时间间隔期间内，探测脉冲所携带的相干信息就存储在原子介质中。随着耦合场再次开启，探测脉冲通过相干激励再次产生。探测和耦合 PMT 放大器的时间常数分别为 $0.3\ \mu s$ 和 $3\ \mu s$。根据快速光电二极管的测量，耦合场的实际开启/关闭时间为 $1\ \mu s$。**d**，测量所得的探测脉冲能量透射率与存储时间的关系。实线是对数据进行的拟合结果，给出了对于原子相干的 $1/e$ 衰减时间 $0.9\ ms$。

当时间 $t = 6.3\ \mu s$ 时，如图 2a 中的箭头所示，探测脉冲空间上被压缩并被完全包含在原子云中。这个探测脉冲在自由空间中长 3.4 km，在其中心 15 μm 直径范围内含有 27,000 个光子。为了与云尺寸（339 μm）相匹配，它在原子介质中被压缩，且探测场所剩余的光能仅为自由空间光子的 1/400。实质上来讲几乎所有的探测能量都通过受激辐射被转移至耦合激光场和原子介质，而相干光学信息也被印记于原子之上（等式（1））。

为了存储这些相干信息，当探测脉冲刚好被原子云包含时我们突然关闭耦合场。所存储的信息在随后耦合激光开启时被读取出来。图 2b 给出了一结果图。虚线显示耦合激光在 $t = 6.3\ \mu s$ 时关闭，随后在 44.3 μs 时开启。实心圆表示测得的探测强度。从这些数据中可以看出，当耦合激光再一次被开启时探测脉冲也再次产生，也就是说我们可以停止并控制探测脉冲的再生。类似的现象已经被近期的理论文章所预测[12]。

当探测脉冲被包含在介质中，激光场的相干信息已经被印记在原子上。当耦合激光关闭时，探测场被耗尽以保持暗态（等式（1）），而（可忽略的）原子振幅通过两光场间的受激光子交换从 $|1\rangle$ 态转移到 $|2\rangle$ 态。如上所述，由于被压缩的探测脉冲剩余的能量相当低，在原子布居振幅发生可观的改变之前，能量已经完全被耗尽。当耦合激光被重新开启时，逆过程发生，探测脉冲通过受激辐射到探测场而再生。随后探测脉冲在 EIT 条件下传播，就像耦合光束从未被关闭一样。

在存储时间内，探测场的振幅信息包含在定义原子暗态的布居振幅之中。探测场的模式矢量信息包含在宏观样本中不同原子间的相对相位之中。冷原子的运用使热运动降至最低，也就使存储过程中相应的相对相位拖尾效应达到最小。（我们获得存储时间最长达到一个原子通过一个激光波长所需时间的 50 倍。通过等式（1）可以得出，两激光场波矢的差决定了印记在介质中的周期性相位图样的波长，该波长是单个激光波长的 10^5 倍。）

The regenerated probe pulse in Fig. 2b has the same shape as the "normal" EIT pulse shown in Fig. 2a. Figure 2c shows a case where the optical coherence is stored in the atomic medium for more than 800 µs before it is read out by the coupling laser. Here the amplitude of the revived probe pulse is reduced compared to that of the pulse in Fig. 2b. Figure 2d shows the measured transmission for a series of pulses as a function of their storage time in the atom cloud. The data are consistent with an exponential decay with a $1/e$ decay time of 0.9 ms, comparable to the calculated mean free time of 0.5 ms between elastic collisions in the atom cloud with a density of $11 \ \mu m^{-3}$. Further studies of the decoherence mechanisms are planned but are beyond the scope of this Letter.

We have verified experimentally that the probe pulse is regenerated through stimulated rather than spontaneous emission. To do this, we prepared all atoms in state $|2\rangle$ and subsequently turned on the coupling laser alone. The coupling laser was completely absorbed for tens of microseconds without generating any signal in the probe PMT.

In Fig. 3a–c, we show three PMT signal traces recorded under similar conditions except that we vary the intensity, I_{c2}, of the coupling laser when it is turned back on. When I_{c2} is larger than the original coupling intensity, I_{c1}, the amplitude of the revived probe pulse increases and its temporal width decreases (Fig. 3a). For $I_{c2} < I_{c1}$, the opposite occurs (Fig. 3c). These results support our physical picture of the process. The stored atomic coherence dictates the ratio of the Rabi frequencies of the coupling and revived probe fields, as well as the spatial width of the regenerated pulse. In Fig. 3d we show that with a large I_{c2}, the peak intensity of the revived probe pulse exceeds that of the original input pulse by 40%.

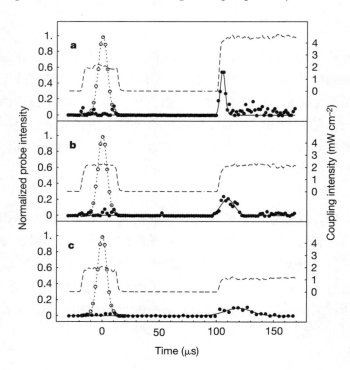

图 2b 中的再生探测脉冲与图 2a 中所示的"正常"EIT 脉冲波形相同。图 2c 显示了光学相干信息在被耦合激光读取前，存储在原子介质中超过 800 μs 的情况。这里的再生探测脉冲振幅与图 2b 相比有所降低。图 2d 为测量所得的一系列脉冲在原子云中的透射率与存储时间的函数关系图。这些数据给出了 0.9 ms 的 1/e 衰减时间，与计算所得的在密度为 11 μm⁻³ 的原子云中弹性碰撞的平均自由时间 0.5 ms 相当。关于退相干机制的进一步研究正在计划中，但不在本文讨论范围之内。

我们已经在实验上验证了探测脉冲的再生是由于受激辐射而非自发辐射。为了实现这个目的，我们准备了所有原子处于 $|2\rangle$ 的态，随后单独开启耦合激光。耦合激光在几十个毫秒内被完全吸收，但没有在 PMT 上产生任何信号。

图 3a ~ 3c 显示了在相似条件下记录的三种 PMT 信号轨迹，不同之处在于我们改变了当耦合激光再次开启时的强度 I_{c2}。当 I_{c2} 比最初的耦合强度 I_{c1} 大时，再生的探测脉冲振幅增大，其时间宽度减小（图 3a）。对于 $I_{c2} < I_{c1}$，情况相反（图 3c）。这些结果支持我们为整个过程建立的物理图像。存储的原子相干信息限定了耦合与再生探测场的拉比频率比率，以及再生脉冲的空间宽度。在图 3d 中，当 I_{c2} 很大时，再生的探测脉冲峰值强度超过初始输入脉冲的 40%。

Fig. 3. Measurements of revived probe pulses for varying intensities (I_{c2}) of the second coupling pulse. The intensity (I_{c1}) of the first coupling pulse is held constant. **a–c**, The figures are recorded for I_{c2}/I_{c1} ratios of 2, 1, and 0.5, respectively. A series of data show that the height and the inverse temporal width of the revived pulses are each proportional to I_{c2}. These observations are consistent with our physical picture. Because the atomic coherence dictates the ratio of the Rabi frequencies for the coupling and revived probe fields (equation (1)), the intensity of the regenerated probe pulse is proportional to the intensity of the coupling laser when it is turned back on. Furthermore, the spatial width of the revived pulse is determined by the distribution of the atomic coherence and is thus the same as the spatial extent of the original compressed pulse. The group velocity of the probe pulse under EIT conditions is proportional to the coupling intensity[4,7]. With a larger (smaller) I_{c2}, the revived probe pulse acquires a proportionally larger (smaller) group velocity, which causes its temporal width to be inversely proportional to I_{c2}. Panel **d** shows that the intensity of the revived probe pulse can exceed that of the original input pulse, in this instance by 40%. (The observed peak-to-peak fluctuation of laser intensity is less than 10%.) The energy in the revived probe pulses is the same in all panels **a–d**, owing to the fact that the total stored amplitude of state $|2\rangle$ atoms (available to stimulate photons into the probe field) is the same in all cases. Meanings of lines and symbols as in Fig. 2.

Dissipationless pulse storage and revival processes are only possible if the ratio between the rates of dissipative and coherence-preserving events is small. When the coupling field is increased or decreased quickly compared to the duration of the probe pulse (τ) but slowly compared to $1/\Gamma$, this ratio is equal to (Z.D. and L.V.H., manuscript in preparation)

$$\frac{2\Gamma}{\Omega_c^2 + \Omega_p^2}\left(\frac{\dot{\Omega}_p}{\Omega_p} - \frac{\dot{\Omega}_c}{\Omega_c}\right) \qquad (2)$$

where Γ is the spontaneous decay rate from state $|3\rangle$. Our numerical simulations show that the probe field is constantly adjusting to match the changes in the coupling field in such a way that the terms in brackets in equation (2) nearly cancel[13,14]. Even for turn-off times faster than $1/\Gamma$, we can show that there is no decay of the coherence between states $|1\rangle$ and $|2\rangle$ as long as $\tau \gg \Gamma/(\Omega_{c_0}^2 + \Omega_{p_0}^2)$; here Ω_{c_0} and Ω_{p_0} are the Rabi frequencies before the coupling turn-off. (The adiabatic requirement introduced in ref. 12 as necessary for non-dissipative behaviour is much too strict. That requirement would inevitably break down for low coupling laser powers during turn-on or turn-off.)

We have demonstrated experimentally that coherent optical information can be stored in

图 3. 不同的第二耦合脉冲强度 (I_{c2}) 下再生探测脉冲的测量。第一耦合脉冲强度 (I_{c1}) 保持恒定。**a ~ c**，记录的是分别对应 I_{c2}/I_{c1} 之比为 2，1 以及 0.5 的图形。一系列数据表明，再生脉冲的高度、时间宽度的倒数均与 I_{c2} 成正比。观察到的现象与我们的物理图像相一致。由于原子相干限定了耦合和再生探测场的拉比频率之比（等式（1）），再生探测脉冲的强度与耦合激光再次开启时的强度成正比。另外，再生脉冲的空间宽度由原子相干的分布决定，因此与最初被压缩的脉冲的空间范围相同。EIT 条件下探测脉冲的群速度与耦合强度成正比[4,7]。对于更大（或更小）的 I_{c2}，再生探测脉冲获得了按比例更大（或更小）的群速度，从而导致其时间宽度与 I_{c2} 成反比。图 **d** 显示再生的探测脉冲强度可以超过初始输入脉冲的强度，图中所示情况超过了 40%。（观察到的激光强度的峰—峰波动在 10% 以内。）再生探测脉冲的能量在所有 **a ~ d** 图中相同，这是由于在所有四种情况下，处于量子态 $|2\rangle$ 的原子（可用于将光子激发到探测场中）的总存储振幅相等。线和符号所对应的含义与图 2 一致。

无耗散的脉冲存储和再生过程只有在耗散率和相干保持事件率之比很小时才可能实现。当耦合场的增大或减小与探测脉冲的持续时间 (τ) 相比很迅速，而与 $1/\Gamma$ 相比变化缓慢时，这个比值等于（扎卡里·达顿和莱娜·韦斯特戈·豪，稿件准备中）

$$\frac{2\Gamma}{\Omega_c^2 + \Omega_p^2}\left(\frac{\dot{\Omega}_p}{\Omega_p} - \frac{\dot{\Omega}_c}{\Omega_c}\right) \tag{2}$$

这里 Γ 为态 $|3\rangle$ 的自发衰减率。我们的数值模拟显示，探测场一直通过使等式（2）的括号内项几乎相消的方式不断调节至与耦合场变化相匹配[13,14]。甚至对于关闭时间小于 $1/\Gamma$ 的情况，我们也可以证明，只要 $\tau \gg \Gamma/(\Omega_{c0}^2 + \Omega_{p0}^2)$，态 $|1\rangle$ 和 $|2\rangle$ 的相干就不存在衰减；这里 Ω_{c0} 和 Ω_{p0} 为在耦合激光关闭前的拉比频率。（文献 12 中提到的对于非耗散行为所必需的绝热要求太过严格。这个条件在低耦合激光电源开启和关闭时就不可避免地被破坏。）

本文实验论证了相干光学信息可以被存储在原子介质中，并随后在磁阱捕获的

an atomic medium and subsequently read out by using the effect of EIT in a magnetically trapped, cooled atom cloud. We have experimentally verified that the storage and read-out processes are controlled by stimulated photon transfers between two laser fields. Multiple read-outs can be achieved using a series of short coupling laser pulses. In Fig. 4a and b we show measurements of double and triple read-outs spaced by up to hundreds of microseconds. Each of the regenerated probe pulses contains part of the contents of the "atomic memory", and for the parameters chosen, the memory is depleted after the second pulse and after the third pulse.

Fig. 4. Measurements of double and triple read-out of the atomic memory. To deplete the atomic memory in these cases, we use two (**a**) and three (**b**) short coupling pulses. The total energy in the two (three) revived probe pulses is measured to be the same as the energy in the single revived probe pulse obtained with a single, long coupling laser pulse (as used in Figs 2 and 3). Meanings of lines and symbols as in Fig. 2.

We believe that this system could be used for quantum information transfer; for example, to inter-convert stationary and flying qubits[15]. By injection of multiple probe pulses into a Bose–Einstein condensate—where we expect that most atomic collisions are coherence-preserving—and with use of controlled atom–atom interactions, quantum information processing may be possible during the storage time.

(**409**, 490-493; 2001)

冷原子云中利用 EIT 效应读取出来。本文通过实验验证了存储和读取过程是由两激光场之间的受激光子转移来控制的。应用一系列短耦合激光脉冲可以实现多重读取。图 4a 和 4b 显示了间隔高达几百个毫秒的二重和三重读取的测量结果。每个再生的探测脉冲包含"原子内存"的部分内容，而对于本实验所选择的参数，内存在第二和第三个脉冲之后被耗尽。

图 4. 原子内存的二重和三重读取测量。为了耗尽这些情况下的原子内存，我们使用了二重（**a**）和三重（**b**）短耦合脉冲。二（三）重再生探测脉冲的总能量与具有单一长耦合激光脉冲的单再生探测脉冲（图 2 和 3 中使用的脉冲）的能量相等。线和符号所对应的含义与图 2 一致。

我们相信该系统可以应用于量子信息传递；例如，用于定态量子比特和飞行量子比特的互相转换[15]。通过注入多重探测脉冲至玻色–爱因斯坦凝聚体（我们预计此条件下多数原子碰撞是可以相干保留的）并运用受控制的原子–原子之间的相互作用，量子信息处理在存储时间之内或许是可能的。

（崔宁 翻译；石锦卫 审稿）

Chien Liu[*†], **Zachary Dutton**[*‡], **Cyrus H. Behroozi**[*†] **& Lene Vestergaard Hau**[*†‡]

[*] Rowland Institute for Science, 100 Edwin H. Land Boulevard, Cambridge, Massachusetts 02142, USA

[†] Division of Engineering and Applied Sciences, [‡] Department of Physics, Harvard University, Cambridge, Massachusetts 02138, USA

Received 13 October; accepted 17 November 2000.

References:

1. Harris, S. E. Electromagnetically induced transparency. *Phys. Today* **50**, 36-42 (1997).

2. Scully, M. O. & Zubairy, M. S. *Quantum Optics* (Cambridge Univ. Press, Cambridge, 1997).

3. Arimondo, E. in *Progress in Optics* (ed. Wolf, E.) 257-354 (Elsevier Science, Amsterdam, 1996).

4. Hau, L. V., Harris, S. E., Dutton, Z. & Behroozi, C. H. Light speed reduction to 17 metres per second in an ultracold atomic gas. *Nature* **397**, 594-598 (1999).

5. Kash, M. M. *et al.* Ultraslow group velocity and enhanced nonlinear optical effects in a coherently driven hot atomic gas. *Phys. Rev. Lett.* **82**, 5229-5232 (1999).

6. Budker, D., Kimball, D. F., Rochester, S. M. & Yashchuk, V. V. Nonlinear magneto-optics and reduced group velocity of light in atomic vapor with slow ground state relaxation. *Phys. Rev. Lett.* **83**, 1767-1770 (1999).

7. Harris, S. E., Field, J. E. & Kasapi, A. Dispersive properties of electromagnetically induced transparency. *Phys. Rev. A* **46**, R29-R32 (1992).

8. Grobe, R., Hioe, F. T. & Eberly, J. H. Formation of shape-preserving pulses in a nonlinear adiabatically integrable system. *Phys. Rev. Lett.* **73**, 3183-3186 (1994).

9. Xiao, M., Li, Y.-Q., Jin, S.-Z. & Gea-Banacloche, J. Measurement of dispersive properties of electromagnetically induced transparency in rubidium atoms. *Phys. Rev. Lett.* **74**, 666-669 (1995).

10. Kasapi, A., Jain, M., Yin, G. Y. & Harris, S. E. Electromagnetically induced transparency: propagation dynamics. *Phys. Rev. Lett.* **74**, 2447-2450 (1995).

11. Hau, L. V. *et al.* Near-resonant spatial images of confined Bose-Einstein condensates in a 4-Dee magnetic bottle. *Phys. Rev. A* **58**, R54-R57 (1998).

12. Fleischhauer, M. & Lukin, M. D. Dark-state polaritons in electromagnetically induced transparency. *Phys. Rev. Lett.* **84**, 5094-5097 (2000).

13. Harris, S. E. Normal modes for electromagnetically induced transparency. *Phys. Rev. Lett.* **72**, 52-55 (1994).

14. Fleischhauer, M. & Manak, A. S. Propagation of laser pulses and coherent population transfer in dissipative three-level systems: An adiabatic dressed-state picture. *Phys. Rev. A* **54**, 794-803 (1996).

15. DiVincenzo, D. P. The physical implementation of quantum computation. Preprint quant-ph/0002077 at ⟨http://xxx.lanl.gov⟩ (2000).

Acknowledgements. We thank J. Golovchenko for discussions during which the idea of the rapid turn off and on of the coupling laser first emerged. We also thank M. Burns for critical reading of the manuscript. This work was supported by the Rowland Institute for Science, the Defense Advanced Research Projects Agency, the US Airforce Office of Scientific Research, and the US Army Research Office OSD Multidisciplinary University Research Initiative Program.

Correspondence and requests for materials should be addressed to C.L. (e-mail: chien@deas.harvard.edu).

Experimental Violation of a Bell's Inequality with Efficient Detection

M. A. Rowe *et al.*

Editor's Note

By the new millennium, careful tests of John Bell's celebrated "inequalities" had indicated that quantum physics seems to be inconsistent with any local realistic interpretation—that is, with a view in which systems have definite properties independent of other parts of the universe, and no influence can travel faster than light. But argument persisted due to various "loopholes" linked to experimental imperfections, including the limited efficiency of particle detectors. Here Mary Rowe and colleagues report violation of Bell's inequalities in experiments using heavy beryllium ions, for which they were able to detect all particles and thus close one loophole. Nonetheless, not all possible local realistic interpretations of quantum theory have been excluded even now.

Local realism is the idea that objects have definite properties whether or not they are measured, and that measurements of these properties are not affected by events taking place sufficiently far away[1]. Einstein, Podolsky and Rosen[2] used these reasonable assumptions to conclude that quantum mechanics is incomplete. Starting in 1965, Bell and others constructed mathematical inequalities whereby experimental tests could distinguish between quantum mechanics and local realistic theories[1,3-5]. Many experiments[1,6-15] have since been done that are consistent with quantum mechanics and inconsistent with local realism. But these conclusions remain the subject of considerable interest and debate, and experiments are still being refined to overcome "loopholes" that might allow a local realistic interpretation. Here we have measured correlations in the classical properties of massive entangled particles ($^9Be^+$ ions): these correlations violate a form of Bell's inequality. Our measured value of the appropriate Bell's "signal" is 2.25 ± 0.03, whereas a value of 2 is the maximum allowed by local realistic theories of nature. In contrast to previous measurements with massive particles, this violation of Bell's inequality was obtained by use of a complete set of measurements. Moreover, the high detection efficiency of our apparatus eliminates the so-called "detection" loophole.

EARLY experiments to test Bell's inequalities were subject to two primary, although seemingly implausible, loopholes. The first might be termed the locality or "lightcone" loophole, in which the correlations of apparently separate events could result from unknown subluminal signals propagating between different regions of the apparatus. Aspect[16] has given a brief history of this issue, starting with the experiments of ref. 8 and highlighting the strict relativistic separation between measurements reported by the

利用高效检测来实验验证贝尔不等式的违背

罗等

编者按

新的千年到来之前，对约翰·贝尔著名的"不等式"进行的种种仔细的验证表明量子物理学似乎与任何定域实在论的解释都不相吻合，定域实在论认为系统有确定的性质，与世界的其他事物无关，且任何影响都不能超光速传播。但由于存在与实验不完美有关的各种各样的、包括粒子探测器的有效探测效率在内的"漏洞"，争论一直持续存在。本文中，玛丽·罗和其同事们报道了利用重铍离子所做的实验中贝尔不等式的违背。由于他们在实验中可以探测到所有的粒子，从而堵上了一个漏洞。然而，即使是现在，仍不能排除对量子理论的所有可能的定域实在论的解释。

定域实在论的观点认为，无论是否被测量，物体都具有确定的性质，对这些性质的测量并不受足够远发生的事件的影响[1]。爱因斯坦–波多尔斯基–罗森[2]用这些合理的假设，得出量子力学是不完备的结论。从 1965 年开始，贝尔和其他人构建了一个数学不等式，依靠实验验证能区分量子力学与定域实在论的理论[1,3-5]。已进行的很多实验[1,6-15]与量子力学理论相符，而与定域实在论不符。但这些结论仍然是大家相当感兴趣和有争议的问题，一些实验仍在不断完善以克服那些允许定域实在论解释的"漏洞"。我们现已测量了大质量的纠缠粒子($^9Be^+$ 离子)在经典性质下的关联：这些关联违反了贝尔不等式的形式。我们得到的贝尔"信号"测量值是 2.25 ± 0.03，然而 2 是自然界定域实在论所允许的最大值。与过去的重粒子测量相比，这次背离贝尔不等式的结果是使用一组完备测量得出的。此外，我们装置的高检测效率消除了所谓的"检测"漏洞。

验证贝尔不等式的早期实验受限于两个似乎令人难以置信的初级漏洞。第一个漏洞可称为定域性的，或"光锥"漏洞，这个漏洞指的是两个明显分离的事件之间的关联有可能是某些未知的亚光速信号在装置的不同区域之间传播造成的。阿斯佩[16]给出了这个问题的简明综述，综述从文献 8 的实验开始，并着重介绍了由因斯布鲁克小组[15]报道的测量之间严格的相对论性分离。日内瓦实验[14,17]也报道了类似的结果。

Innsbruck group[15]. Similar results have also been reported for the Geneva experiment[14,17]. The second loophole is usually referred to as the detection loophole. All experiments up to now have had detection efficiencies low enough to allow the possibility that the subensemble of detected events agrees with quantum mechanics even though the entire ensemble satisfies Bell's inequalities. Therefore it must be assumed that the detected events represent the entire ensemble; a fair-sampling hypothesis. Several proposals for closing this loophole have been made[18-24]; we believe the experiment that we report here is the first to do so. Another feature of our experiment is that it uses massive particles. A previous test of Bell's inequality was carried out on protons[25], but the interpretation of the detected events relied on quantum mechanics, as symmetries valid given quantum mechanics were used to extrapolate the data to a complete set of Bell's angles. Here we do not make such assumptions.

A Bell measurement of the type suggested by Clauser, Horne, Shimony and Holt[5] (CHSH) consists of three basic ingredients (Fig. 1a). First is the preparation of a pair of particles in a repeatable starting configuration (the output of the "magic" box in Fig. 1a). Second, a variable classical manipulation is applied independently to each particle; these manipulations are labelled ϕ_1 and ϕ_2. Finally, in the detection phase, a classical property with two possible outcomes is measured for each of the particles. The correlation of these outcomes

$$q(\phi_1, \phi_2) = \frac{\mathcal{N}_{same}(\phi_1, \phi_2) - \mathcal{N}_{different}(\phi_1, \phi_2)}{\mathcal{N}_{same} + \mathcal{N}_{different}} \tag{1}$$

is measured by repeating the experiment many times. Here $\mathcal{N}_{same}$ and $\mathcal{N}_{different}$ are the number of measurements where the two results were the same and different, respectively. The CHSH form of Bell's inequalities states that the correlations resulting from local realistic theories must obey:

$$B(\alpha_1, \delta_1, \beta_2, \gamma_2) = |q(\delta_1, \gamma_2) - q(\alpha_1, \gamma_2)| + |q(\delta_1, \beta_2) + q(\alpha_1, \beta_2)| \leq 2 \tag{2}$$

where α_1 and δ_1 (β_2 and γ_2) are specific values of ϕ_1 (ϕ_2). For example, in a photon experiment[15], parametric down-conversion prepares a pair of photons in a singlet Einstein–Podolsky–Rosen (EPR) pair. After this, a variable rotation of the photon polarization is applied to each photon. Finally, the photons' polarization states, vertical or horizontal, are determined.

第二个漏洞通常被认为是检测漏洞。至今的所有实验检测的效率很低，以至于允许存在即使整个系综满足贝尔不等式，而检测事件的子系综与量子力学符合的可能性。因此，必须假设检测的事件代表整个系综；这是一个合理的取样假设。现已提出了堵上这个漏洞的数个建议[18-24]；我们相信，本文所述乃是首次针对堵上此漏洞所进行的实验。我们实验的另一个特点是采用大质量粒子。之前的贝尔不等式验证是利用质子进行的[25]，但检测事件的解释依据是量子力学，如量子力学中给出的对称性被用于将数据外推到贝尔角的完备集。此处我们并未采用这些假设。

由克劳塞、霍恩、希莫尼和霍尔特[5]（CHSH）提出的这类贝尔测量包括三个基本部分（图 1a）。第一部分是制备在可重复的起始组态中的一对粒子（图 1 a 中"魔盒"的输出）。第二部分是对每个粒子独立地用一个可变的经典操控，这些操控标记为 ϕ_1 和 ϕ_2；最后在检测阶段，对每个粒子的经典性质进行测量，皆有两个可能的结果。这些结果的关联函数为

$$q(\phi_1, \phi_2) = \frac{N_{\text{same}}(\phi_1, \phi_2) - N_{\text{different}}(\phi_1, \phi_2)}{N_{\text{same}} + N_{\text{different}}} \tag{1}$$

式（1）是多次重复实验的测量结果。式中 N_{same} 和 $N_{\text{different}}$ 分别是两个结果相同和不同时的测量数目。贝尔不等式的 CHSH 形式表述为，由定域实在论得出的相关性必须遵从下式：

$$B(\alpha_1, \delta_1, \beta_2, \gamma_2) = |q(\delta_1, \gamma_2) - q(\alpha_1, \gamma_2)| + |q(\delta_1, \beta_2) + q(\alpha_1, \beta_2)| \leqslant 2 \tag{2}$$

式中 α_1 和 δ_1（β_2 和 γ_2）是 ϕ_1（ϕ_2）的特定值。例如，在光子实验中[15]，利用参数下转换技术把一对光子制备在爱因斯坦–波多尔斯基–罗森（EPR）单重态上，然后让每个光子通过一个角度可变的偏振片。最后确定光子的偏振状态：垂直或水平。

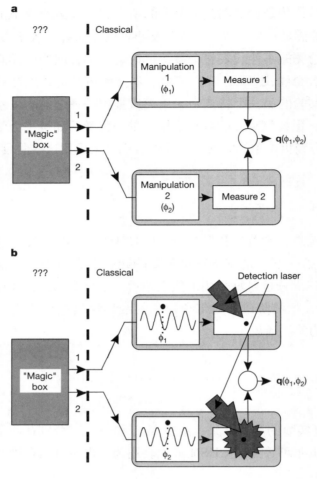

Fig. 1. Illustration of how Bell's inequality experiments work. The idea is that a "magic box" emits a pair of particles. We attempt to determine the joint properties of these particles by applying various classical manipulations to them and observing the correlations of the measurement outputs. **a**, A general CHSH type of Bell's inequality experiment. **b**, Our experiment. The manipulation is a laser wave applied with phases ϕ_1 and ϕ_2 to ion 1 and ion 2 respectively. The measurement is the detection of photons emanating from the ions upon application of a detection laser. Two possible measurement outcomes are possible, detection of few photons (as depicted for ion 1 in the figure) or the detection of many photons (as depicted for ion 2 in the figure).

Our experiment prepares a pair of two-level atomic ions in a repeatable configuration (entangled state). Next, a laser field is applied to the particles; the classical manipulation variables are the phases of this field at each ion's position. Finally, upon application of a detection laser beam, the classical property measured is the number of scattered photons emanating from the particles (which effectively measures their atomic states). Figure 1b shows how our experiment maps onto the general case. Entangled atoms produced in the context of cavity-quantum-electrodynamics[26] could similarly be used to measure Bell's inequalities.

图 1. 贝尔不等式验证实验如何开展的示意图。实验思想是一个"魔盒"发射一对粒子。通过应用各种经典的操控方法，我们试图测定这些粒子的联合性质，并观测其测量输出的关联。**a**，一般的 CHSH 型贝尔不等式实验；**b**，我们的实验。操控是用相位为 ϕ_1 和 ϕ_2 的激光波分别加到离子 1 和 2 上。测量是对离子施加探测激光后，检测从离子发射出来的光子。有两个可能的测量结果，几乎检测不到光子（如图中对离子 1 的描绘）或检测到许多光子（如图中对离子 2 的描绘）。

实验中我们把一对二能级原子离子制备在可重复组态（纠缠态）上。其次，在粒子上加一激光场；经典操控的变量是每个离子所在处这个场的相位。最后，应用检测激光束之后，被测的经典性质是从粒子发射出的散射光子的数量（通过它可有效地测量粒子的原子态）。图 1b 展示了我们的实验与一般实验的对应。在腔量子电动力学意义下产生的纠缠的原子[26]能类似地用于测量贝尔不等式。

The experimental apparatus is as described in ref. 27. Two $^9\text{Be}^+$ ions are confined along the axis of a linear Paul trap with an axial centre-of-mass frequency of 5 MHz. We select two resolved levels of the $2S_{1/2}$ ground state, $|\downarrow\rangle \equiv |F=2, m_F=-2\rangle$ and $|\uparrow\rangle \equiv |F=1, m_F=-1\rangle$, where F and m_F are the quantum numbers of the total angular momentum. These states are coupled by a coherent stimulated Raman transition. The two laser beams used to drive the transition have a wavelength of 313 nm and a difference frequency near the hyperfine splitting of the states, $\omega_0 \cong 2\pi \times 1.25$ GHz. The beams are aligned perpendicular to each other, with their difference wavevector $\Delta\mathbf{k}$ along the trap axis. As described in ref. 27, it is possible in this configuration to produce the entangled state

$$|\psi_2\rangle = \frac{1}{\sqrt{2}} \left(|\uparrow\uparrow\rangle - |\downarrow\downarrow\rangle \right) \tag{3}$$

The fidelity $F = \langle\psi_2|\rho|\psi_2\rangle$, where ρ is the density matrix for the state we make, was about 88% for the data runs. In the discussion below we assume $|\psi_2\rangle$ as the starting condition for the experiment.

After making the state $|\psi_2\rangle$, we again apply Raman beams for a pulse of short duration ($\sim$400 ns) so that the state of each ion j is transformed in the interaction picture as

$$|\uparrow_j\rangle \rightarrow \frac{1}{\sqrt{2}} \left(|\uparrow_j\rangle - ie^{-i\phi}|\downarrow_j\rangle \right); |\downarrow_j\rangle \rightarrow \frac{1}{\sqrt{2}} \left(|\downarrow_j\rangle - ie^{i\phi}|\uparrow_j\rangle \right) \tag{4}$$

The phase, ϕ_j, is the phase of the field driving the Raman transitions (more specifically, the phase difference between the two Raman beams) at the position of ion j and corresponds to the inputs ϕ_1 and ϕ_2 in Fig. 1. We set this phase in two ways in the experiment. First, as an ion is moved along the trap axis this phase changes by $\Delta\mathbf{k} \cdot \Delta\mathbf{x}_j$. For example, a translation of $\lambda/\sqrt{2}$ along the trap axis corresponds to a phase shift of 2π. In addition, the laser phase on both ions is changed by a common amount by varying the phase, ϕ_s, of the radio-frequency synthesizer that determines the Raman difference frequency. The phase on ion j is therefore

$$\phi_j = \phi_s + \Delta\mathbf{k} \cdot \mathbf{x}_j \tag{5}$$

In the experiment, the axial trap strength is changed so that the ions move about the centre of the trap symmetrically, giving $\Delta\mathbf{x}_1 = -\Delta\mathbf{x}_2$. Therefore the trap strength controls the differential phase, $\Delta\phi \equiv \phi_1 - \phi_2 = \Delta\mathbf{k} \cdot (\mathbf{x}_1 - \mathbf{x}_2)$, and the synthesizer controls the total phase, $\phi_{\text{tot}} \equiv \phi_1 + \phi_2 = 2\phi_s$. The calibration of these relations is discussed in the Methods.

The state of an ion, $|\downarrow\rangle$ or $|\uparrow\rangle$, is determined by probing the ion with circularly polarized light from a "detection" laser beam[27]. During this detection pulse, ions in the $|\downarrow\rangle$ or bright state scatter many photons, and on average about 64 of these are detected with a photomultiplier tube, while ions in the $|\uparrow\rangle$ or dark state scatter very few photons. For two ions, three cases can occur: zero ions bright, one ion bright, or two ions bright. In the one-ion-bright case it is not necessary to know which ion is bright because the Bell's

实验装置如文献 27 中所描述。两个 $^9Be^+$ 离子以 5 MHz 的轴向质心频率约束在沿着线性保罗阱的轴上。我们选择 $2S_{1/2}$ 基态的两个可分辨的能级，$|\downarrow\rangle \equiv |F=2$，$m_F = -2\rangle$ 和 $|\uparrow\rangle \equiv |F=1$，$m_F = -1\rangle$，式中 F 和 m_F 是总角动量的量子数。这些态经由相干受激拉曼跃迁耦合。用于驱动跃迁的两束激光波长为 313 nm，两者的差频接近态的超精细分裂 $\omega_0 \cong 2\pi \times 1.25$ GHz 的跃迁。两束激光彼此相互垂直，其波矢差 $\Delta\mathbf{k}$ 沿着阱的轴。如文献 27 中所述，在这种组态中可能产生纠缠态

$$|\psi_2\rangle = \frac{1}{\sqrt{2}} (|\uparrow\uparrow\rangle - |\downarrow\downarrow\rangle) \tag{3}$$

对于运行数据，保真度 $F = \langle\psi_2|\rho|\psi_2\rangle$ 约为 88%，式中 ρ 是我们所产生的态的密度矩阵。在以下讨论中，我们假定 $|\psi_2\rangle$ 是实验的起始条件。

在产生了态 $|\psi_2\rangle$ 后，我们再应用拉曼光束作为一个短脉冲（约 400 ns），因此每个离子 j 的态在相互作用绘景中转变为

$$|\uparrow_j\rangle \rightarrow \frac{1}{\sqrt{2}} (|\uparrow_j\rangle - ie^{-i\phi}|\downarrow_j\rangle); \quad |\downarrow_j\rangle \rightarrow \frac{1}{\sqrt{2}} (|\downarrow_j\rangle - ie^{i\phi}|\uparrow_j\rangle) \tag{4}$$

相位 ϕ_j 是在离子 j 的位置上驱动拉曼跃迁的场的相位（更明确地说，是两束拉曼光束之间的相位差），对应于图 1 中的输入 ϕ_1 和 ϕ_2。我们在实验中按两种方式设定其相位。首先，在离子沿着阱轴运动时，相位变化为 $\Delta\mathbf{k} \cdot \Delta\mathbf{x}_j$。例如，沿着阱轴的平移 $\lambda/\sqrt{2}$，相当于 2π 的相移。此外，改变决定拉曼差频的射频合成器的相位 ϕ_s，使加在两个离子上的激光相位发生同量的变化。从而离子 j 的相位是

$$\phi_j = \phi_s + \Delta\mathbf{k} \cdot \mathbf{x}_j \tag{5}$$

在实验中，轴向阱的强度改变，因此离子绕阱的中心对称地运动，给出 $\Delta\mathbf{x}_1 = -\Delta\mathbf{x}_2$。因此阱的强度控制了相位差值，$\Delta\phi \equiv \phi_1 - \phi_2 = \Delta\mathbf{k} \cdot (\mathbf{x}_1 - \mathbf{x}_2)$，合成器控制了总相位 $\phi_{tot} \equiv \phi_1 + \phi_2 = 2\phi_s$。这些关系的标定在方法一节中进行讨论。

一个离子的态，$|\downarrow\rangle$ 或 $|\uparrow\rangle$，用"检测"激光束中的圆偏振光探测离子来确定[27]。在检测脉冲持续时间内，处于 $|\downarrow\rangle$ 态或明态的离子散射许多光子，用光电倍增管检测到平均约 64 个，处于 $|\uparrow\rangle$ 态或暗态的离子散射很少的光子。对两个离子而言可能出现三种情况：无离子处于明态，一个离子处于明态，两个离子处于明态。在一个

measurement requires only knowledge of whether or not the ions' states are different. Figure 2 shows histograms, each with 20,000 detection measurements. The three cases are distinguished from each other with simple discriminator levels in the number of photons collected with the phototube.

Fig. 2. Typical data histograms comprising the detection measurements of 20,000 experiments taking a total time of about 20 s. In each experiment the population in the $|\uparrow\rangle$ state is first coherently transferred to the $|F = 1, M_F = +1\rangle$ to make it even less likely to fluoresce upon application of the detection laser. The detection laser is turned on and the number of fluorescence photons detected by the phototube in 1 ms is recorded. The cut between the one bright and two bright cases is made so that the fractions of two equal distributions which extend past the cut points are equal. The vertical arrows indicate the location of the cut between the 0 (1) bright and 1 (2) bright peaks at 25 (86) counts. **a**, Data histogram with a negative correlation using $\phi_1 = 3\pi/8$ and $\phi_2 = 3\pi/8$. For these data $\mathcal{N}_0 \cong 2,200$, $\mathcal{N}_1 \cong 15,500$ and $\mathcal{N}_2 \cong 2,300$. **b**, Data histogram with a positive correlation using $\phi_1 = 3\pi/8$ and $\phi_2 = -\pi/8$. For these data $\mathcal{N}_0 \cong 7,700$, $\mathcal{N}_1 \cong 4,400$ and $\mathcal{N}_2 \cong 7,900$. The zero bright peak extends vertically to 2,551.

An alternative description of our experiment can be made in the language of spin-one-half magnetic moments in a magnetic field (directed in the $\hat{z}$ direction). The dynamics of the spin system are the same as for our two-level system[28]. Combining the manipulation (equation (4)) and measurement steps, we effectively measure the spin projection of each ion j in the $\hat{r}_j$ direction, where the vector $\hat{r}_j$ is in the $\hat{x}$–$\hat{y}$ plane at an angle ϕ_j to the $\hat{y}$ axis. Although we have used quantum-mechanical language to describe the manipulation and measurement steps, we emphasize that both are procedures completely analogous to the classical rotations of wave-plates and measurements of polarization in an optical apparatus.

离子处于明态的情况下，不必知道是哪一个离子，因为贝尔的测量仅要求知道离子态是否不同。图 2 示出了直方图，每个实验重复测量 20,000 次。用光电管收集到的光子进行计数即可区分这三种情况。

图 2. 包含 20,000 次实验的检测结果的典型数据直方图，所用的总时间约为 20 s。在每次实验中，在 $|\uparrow\rangle$ 态的粒子数，首先相干转移到 $|F=1，M_F=+1\rangle$，使得它在检测激光作用下也不发出荧光。打开检测激光，光电管在 1 ms 内记录检测到的荧光光子数。在一个离子处于明态和两个离子处于明态的情况之间进行截断，使两个相等分布扩展到截断点以外的部分所占的比例相等。垂直的箭头表示在 25(86) 计数时，在 0(1) 个离子处于明态与 1(2) 个离子处于明态峰值之间的截断。**a**. 用 $\phi_1=3\pi/8$ 和 $\phi_2=3\pi/8$ 的负相关数据直方图。对于这些数据，$N_0 \cong 2,200$，$N_1 \cong 15,500$ 和 $N_2 \cong 2,300$。**b**. 用 $\phi_1=3\pi/8$ 和 $\phi_2=-\pi/8$ 的正相关数据直方图。对于这些数据，$N_0 \cong 7,700$，$N_1 \cong 4,400$ 和 $N_2 \cong 7,900$。无离子处于明态的峰值将垂直扩展到 2,551。

我们的实验还能用磁场中（在 $\hat{z}$ 方向上）1/2 自旋磁矩的语言这另一种方式进行描述。自旋系统的动力学与我们的二能级系统是相同的[28]。结合操控（式（4））和测量步骤，我们有效地测量了每个离子 j 在 $\hat{r}_j$ 方向上的自旋投影，其中矢量 $\hat{r}_j$ 在 $\hat{x}-\hat{y}$ 平面上与 $\hat{y}$ 呈角度 ϕ_j。虽然，我们已经使用量子力学的语言来描述操控和测量步骤，我们强调两者是与光学装置中波片的经典旋转和偏振的测量完全类似的步骤。

Here we calculate the quantum-mechanical prediction for the correlation function. Our manipulation step transforms the starting state, $|\psi_2\rangle$, to

$$|\psi_2'\rangle = \frac{1}{2\sqrt{2}} \left\{ \left(1+e^{i(\phi_1+\phi_2)}\right)\left(|\uparrow\uparrow\rangle - e^{-i(\phi_1+\phi_2)}|\downarrow\downarrow\rangle\right) - i\left(1-e^{i(\phi_1+\phi_2)}\right)\left(e^{-i\phi_2}|\uparrow\downarrow\rangle + e^{-i\phi_1}|\downarrow\uparrow\rangle\right) \right\} \tag{6}$$

Using the measurement operators $\hat{N}_{\text{same}} = N_{\text{tot}}[|\uparrow\uparrow\rangle\langle\uparrow\uparrow| + |\downarrow\downarrow\rangle\langle\downarrow\downarrow|]$ and $\hat{N}_{\text{different}} = N_{\text{tot}}[|\uparrow\downarrow\rangle\langle\uparrow\downarrow| + |\downarrow\uparrow\rangle\langle\downarrow\uparrow|]$, the correlation function is calculated to be

$$q(\phi_1, \phi_2) = \frac{1}{8}\left[2\left|1+e^{i(\phi_1+\phi_2)}\right|^2 - 2\left|1-e^{i(\phi_1+\phi_2)}\right|^2\right] = \cos(\phi_1+\phi_2) \tag{7}$$

The CHSH inequality (equation (2)) is maximally violated by quantum mechanics at certain sets of phase angles. One such set is $\alpha_1 = -(\pi/8)$, $\delta_1 = 3\pi/8$, $\beta_2 = -(\pi/8)$ and $\gamma_2 = 3\pi/8$. With these phase angles quantum mechanics predicts

$$B\left(-\frac{\pi}{8}, \frac{3\pi}{8}, -\frac{\pi}{8}, \frac{3\pi}{8}\right) = 2\sqrt{2} \tag{8}$$

This violates the local realism condition, which requires that $B \leq 2$.

The correlation function is measured experimentally at four sets of phase angles, listed in Table 1. The experiment is repeated $N_{\text{tot}} = 20{,}000$ times at each of the four sets of phases. For each set of phases the correlation function is calculated using

$$q = \frac{(N_0 + N_2) - N_1}{N_{\text{tot}}} \tag{9}$$

Here N_0, N_1 and N_2 are the number of events with zero, one and two ions bright, respectively. The correlation values from the four sets of phase angles are combined into the Bell's signal, $B(\alpha_1, \delta_1, \beta_2, \gamma_2)$, using equation (2). The correlation values and resulting Bell's signals from five data runs are given in Table 2.

Table 1. The four sets of phase angles used for the Bell's experiment

Experiment input	ϕ_1	ϕ_2	$\Delta\phi$	ϕ_{tot}
$\alpha_1 \beta_2$	$-\pi/8$	$-\pi/8$	0	$-\pi/4$
$\alpha_1 \gamma_2$	$-\pi/8$	$3\pi/8$	$-\pi/2$	$+\pi/4$
$\delta_1 \beta_2$	$3\pi/8$	$-\pi/8$	$+\pi/2$	$+\pi/4$
$\delta_1 \gamma_2$	$3\pi/8$	$3\pi/8$	0	$+3\pi/4$

这里，我们计算了关联函数的量子力学预测结果。我们的操控步骤将起始态 $|\psi_2\rangle$ 变换为

$$|\psi_2'\rangle = \frac{1}{2\sqrt{2}}\left\{\left(1+e^{i(\phi_1+\phi_2)}\right)\left(|\uparrow\uparrow\rangle-e^{-i(\phi_1+\phi_2)}|\downarrow\downarrow\rangle\right)-i\left(1-e^{i(\phi_1+\phi_2)}\right)\left(e^{-i\phi_2}|\uparrow\downarrow\rangle+e^{-i\phi_1}|\downarrow\uparrow\rangle\right)\right\} \tag{6}$$

应用测量算符 $\hat{N}_{\text{same}} = N_{\text{tot}}[|\uparrow\uparrow\rangle\langle\uparrow\uparrow|+|\downarrow\downarrow\rangle\langle\downarrow\downarrow|]$ 和 $\hat{N}_{\text{different}} = N_{\text{tot}}[|\uparrow\downarrow\rangle\langle\uparrow\downarrow|+|\downarrow\uparrow\rangle\langle\downarrow\uparrow|]$，计算的关联函数为

$$q(\phi_1, \phi_2) = \frac{1}{8}\left[2|1+e^{i(\phi_1+\phi_2)}|^2 - 2|1-e^{i(\phi_1+\phi_2)}|^2\right] = \cos(\phi_1+\phi_2) \tag{7}$$

根据量子力学，CHSH 不等式（式（2））在特定相角组合处达到了最大的背离。一组这样的组合为 $\alpha_1 = -(\pi/8)$，$\delta_1 = 3\pi/8$，$\beta_2 = -(\pi/8)$ 及 $\gamma_2 = 3\pi/8$。用这些相角，量子力学预测

$$B\left(-\frac{\pi}{8}, \frac{3\pi}{8}, -\frac{\pi}{8}, \frac{3\pi}{8}\right) = 2\sqrt{2} \tag{8}$$

这背离了要求 $B \leqslant 2$ 的定域实在论条件。

实验上用列于表 1 的四组相角测量关联函数。四组相角的每一组，实验都重复 $N_{\text{tot}} = 20{,}000$ 次。对每组相位，用下式计算关联函数

$$q = \frac{(N_0+N_2)-N_1}{N_{\text{tot}}} \tag{9}$$

式中 N_0，N_1，N_2 分别是以 0，1 和 2 个离子处于明态的事件数目。四组相角的相关值已用式（2）代入贝尔信号 $B(\alpha_1, \delta_1, \beta_2, \gamma_2)$ 中。表 2 给出了五次数据运行的相关值和得出的贝尔信号。

表 1. 用于贝尔实验的四组相角

实验输入	ϕ_1	ϕ_2	$\Delta\phi$	ϕ_{tot}
$\alpha_1\,\beta_2$	$-\pi/8$	$-\pi/8$	0	$-\pi/4$
$\alpha_1\,\gamma_2$	$-\pi/8$	$3\pi/8$	$-\pi/2$	$+\pi/4$
$\delta_1\,\beta_2$	$3\pi/8$	$-\pi/8$	$+\pi/2$	$+\pi/4$
$\delta_1\,\gamma_2$	$3\pi/8$	$3\pi/8$	0	$+3\pi/4$

Table 2. Correlation values and resulting Bell's signals for five experimental runs

Run number	$q(\alpha_1, \beta_2)$	$q(\alpha_1, \gamma_2)$	$q(\delta_1, \beta_2)$	$q(\delta_1, \gamma_2)$	$B(\alpha_1, \delta_1, \beta_2, \gamma_2)$
1	0.541	0.539	0.569	−0.573	2.222
2	0.575	0.570	0.530	−0.600	2.275
3	0.551	0.634	0.590	−0.487	2.262
4	0.575	0.561	0.559	−0.551	2.246
5	0.541	0.596	0.537	−0.571	2.245

The experimental angle values were $\alpha_1 = -(\pi/8)$, $\delta_1 = 3\pi/8$, $\beta_2 = -(\pi/8)$, and $\gamma_2 = 3\pi/8$. The statistical errors are 0.006 and 0.012 for the q and B values respectively. The systematic errors (see text) are 0.03 and 0.06 for the q and B values respectively.

So far we have described the experiment in terms of perfect implementation of the phase angles. In the actual experiment, however, α_1, δ_1, β_2 and γ_2 are not quite the same angles both times they occur in the Bell's inequality. In our experiment the dominant reason for this error results from the phase instability of the synthesizer, which can cause the angles to drift appreciably during four minutes, the time required to take a complete set of measurements. This random drift causes a root-mean-squared error for the correlation function of ±0.03 on this timescale, which propagates to an error of ±0.06 for the Bell's signal. The error for the Bell's signal from the five combined data sets is then ±0.03, consistent with the run-to-run variation observed. Averaging the five Bell's signals from Table 2, we arrive at our experimental result, which is

$$B\left(-\frac{\pi}{8}, \frac{3\pi}{8}, -\frac{\pi}{8}, \frac{3\pi}{8}\right) = 2.25 \pm 0.03 \tag{10}$$

If we take into account the imperfections of our experiment (imperfect state fidelity, manipulations, and detection), this value agrees with the prediction of quantum mechanics.

The result above was obtained using the outcomes of every experiment, so that no fair-sampling hypothesis is required. In this case, the issue of detection efficiency is replaced by detection accuracy. The dominant cause of inaccuracy in our state detection comes from the bright state becoming dark because of optical pumping effects. For example, imperfect circular polarization of the detection light allows an ion in the $|\downarrow\rangle$ state to be pumped to $|\uparrow\rangle$, resulting in fewer collected photons from a bright ion. Because of such errors, a bright ion is misidentified 2% of the time as being dark. This imperfect detection accuracy decreases the magnitude of the measured correlations. We estimate that our Bell's signal would be 2.37 with perfect detection accuracy.

We have thus presented experimental results of a Bell's inequality measurement where a measurement outcome was recorded for every experiment. Our detection efficiency was high enough for a Bell's inequality to be violated without requiring the assumption of fair sampling, thereby closing the detection loophole in this experiment. The ions were

表 2 五次实验运行的相关值和得出的贝尔信号

运行序号	$q(\alpha_1, \beta_2)$	$q(\alpha_1, \gamma_2)$	$q(\delta_1, \beta_2)$	$q(\delta_1, \gamma_2)$	$B(\alpha_1, \delta_1, \beta_2, \gamma_2)$
1	0.541	0.539	0.569	−0.573	2.222
2	0.575	0.570	0.530	−0.600	2.275
3	0.551	0.634	0.590	−0.487	2.262
4	0.575	0.561	0.559	−0.551	2.246
5	0.541	0.596	0.537	−0.571	2.245

实验的角度数值是 $\alpha_1 = -(\pi/8)$，$\delta_1 = 3\pi/8$，$\beta_2 = -(\pi/8)$ 及 $\gamma_2 = 3\pi/8$。对 q 和 B 的统计误差分别为 0.006 和 0.012。对 q 和 B 的系统误差（见正文）分别为 0.03 和 0.06。

在此为止，我们已用理想的相角设定描述了实验。然而，在实际实验中，两次代入贝尔不等式的角 α_1、δ_1、β_2 和 γ_2 并不是完全相同的。在我们的实验中，这个误差主要来自合成器的相位不稳定度，使相角在四分钟内产生了明显的漂移，这正是一整套测量所需要的时间。这项随机漂移对于关联函数来说，在这一时标上产生了 ± 0.03 的方均根误差，它传递到贝尔信号的误差为 ± 0.06。来自五个数据组的贝尔信号的误差则为 ± 0.03，与观测到的每次运行变化是相符的。对表 2 中五个贝尔信号求平均，我们得到的实验结果为

$$B\left(-\frac{\pi}{8}, \frac{3\pi}{8}, -\frac{\pi}{8}, \frac{3\pi}{8} \right) = 2.25 \pm 0.03 \tag{10}$$

如果考虑到我们实验中的不完美的方面（不完美的态保真度、操控和检测），这个结果与量子力学的预测值是一致的。

上述结果是利用每个实验的输出量得出的，因此不要求有合理取样的前提。在这种情况下，检测效率的问题由检测准确度代替。在我们实验中，态检测的不准确的主要原因来自于光抽运效应引起的明态变为暗态。例如，检测光不完美的圆偏振允许离子由 $|\downarrow\rangle$ 态抽运到 $|\uparrow\rangle$，从而处于明态的离子收集到较少的光子。由于这类误差的存在，一个离子处于明态而被错判为处于暗态的概率是 2%。这类不完美的检测准确度降低了测量相关性的量级。我们估计本文贝尔信号在完美检测准确度下将是 2.37。

我们已经给出了每次实验记录的贝尔不等式测量的实验结果。我们的检测效率高到足以不要求有合理取样的前提也可以给出贝尔不等式背离的结论，从而在这个实验中堵上了检测漏洞这个问题。离子之间相距很远，远到没有已知的相互作用可

separated by a distance large enough that no known interaction could affect the results; however, the lightcone loophole remains open here. Further details of this experiment will be published elsewhere.

Methods

Phase calibration

The experiment was run with specific phase differences of the Raman laser beam fields at each ion. In order to implement a complete set of laser phases, a calibration of the phase on each ion as a function of axial trap strength was made. We emphasize that the calibration method is classical in nature. Although quantum mechanics guided the choice of calibration method, no quantum mechanics was used to interpret the signal. General arguments are used to describe the signal resulting from a sequence of laser pulses and its dependence on the classical physical parameters of the system, the laser phase at the ion, and the ion's position.

In the calibration procedure, a Ramsey experiment was performed on two ions. The first $\pi/2$ Rabi rotation was performed identically each time. The laser phases at the ions' positions for the second $\pi/2$ Rabi rotation were varied, ϕ_1 for ion 1 and ϕ_2 for ion 2. The detection signal is the total number of photons counted during detection. With an auxiliary one-ion experiment we first established empirically that the individual signal depends only on the laser phase at an individual ion and is $C+A\cos\phi_j$. Here C and A are the offset and amplitude of the one-ion signal. We measure the detector to be linear, so that the detection signal is the sum of the two ions' individual signals. The two-ion signal is therefore

$$C+A\cos\phi_1+C+A\cos\phi_2 = 2C+2A\cos\left[\frac{1}{2}(\phi_1+\phi_2)\right]\cos\left[\frac{1}{2}(\phi_1-\phi_2)\right] \tag{11}$$

By measuring the fringe amplitude and phase as $\phi_s = (\phi_1+\phi_2)/2$ is swept, we calibrate $\phi_1-\phi_2$ as a function of trap strength and ensure that $\phi_1+\phi_2$ is independent of trap strength.

We use the phase convention that at the ion separation used for the entanglement preparation pulse the maximum of the correlation function is at $\phi_1 = \phi_2 = 0$ (or $\Delta\phi = \phi_{tot} = 0$). Our measurement procedure begins by experimentally finding this condition of $\phi_1 = \phi_2 = 0$ by keeping $\Delta\phi = 0$ and scanning the synthesizer phase to find the maximum correlation. The experiment is then adjusted to the phase angles specified above by switching the axial trap strength to set $\Delta\phi$ and incrementing the synthesizer phase to set ϕ_{tot}.

Locality issues

The ions are separated by a distance of approximately 3 μm, which is greater than 100 times the size of the wavepacket of each ion. Although the Coulomb interaction strongly couples the ions' motion, it does not affect the ions' internal states. At this distance, all known relevant interactions are expected to be small. For example, dipole–dipole interactions between the ions slightly modify the light-

以影响实验结果；但是，本文还没有解决光锥漏洞的问题。这个实验的更多细节将发表在其他地方。

方　　法

相位标定

实验是在每个离子的拉曼激光光束场的特定相位差下运行的。为了实现激光相位的完备集，每个离子上的激光相位被标定为轴向阱强度的函数。我们强调标定方法本质上是经典的。虽然，量子力学影响了标定方法的选择，但并没有使用量子力学来解释信号。一般的理论用于描述从一系列激光脉冲得出的信号，以及它与系统的经典物理参量的相关关系，经典的物理参量包括离子上的激光相位和离子的位置。

在标定过程中，对两个离子进行了拉姆齐实验。每次实验中第一个 $\pi/2$ 的拉比旋转都相同。对于第二个 $\pi/2$ 拉比旋转，离子处的激光相位发生了改变，离子 1 处为 ϕ_1，离子 2 处为 ϕ_2。检测信号是在检测期间记录的总光子数。用一个辅助的单离子实验，我们首先在实践经验上确立了单个信号仅与单个离子处的激光相位有关，信号记为 $C+A\cos\phi_j$。此处的 C 和 A 是单离子信号的偏置和振幅。我们测得检测器是线性的，因此检测信号是两个离子的单独信号之和。从而两个离子的信号为

$$C+A\cos\phi_1+C+A\cos\phi_2 = 2C+2A\cos\left[\frac{1}{2}(\phi_1+\phi_2)\right]\cos\left[\frac{1}{2}(\phi_1-\phi_2)\right] \tag{11}$$

当扫描 $\phi_s=(\phi_1+\phi_2)/2$ 时，通过测量条纹振幅和相位，我们标定了 $\phi_1-\phi_2$ 作为阱强度的函数，并确保 $\phi_1+\phi_2$ 与阱强度无关。

我们按照惯例，在用于纠缠制备脉冲的离子分离处，关联函数在 $\phi_1=\phi_2=0$（或 $\Delta\phi=\phi_{tot}=0$）处取得最大值。在测量的开始，我们通过保持 $\Delta\phi=0$，进而用实验方法找到 $\phi_1=\phi_2=0$ 的条件，并扫描合成器的相位来找到关联函数最大值。然后在实验中通过调整轴阱强度来设置 $\Delta\phi$，通过增加合成器相位来设置 ϕ_{tot}，把相角调整到上文给出的相应值。

定域性的争论

离子间相隔的距离约为 3 μm，这是每个离子的波包尺寸的 100 倍。虽然，库仑相互作用与离子的运动发生强烈的耦合，但它并不影响离子的内部状态。在这个距离上，所有已知的相互作用的预期都是很小的。例如，在离子之间的偶极−偶极

scattering intensity, but this effect is negligible for the ion–ion separations used[29]. Also, the detection solid angle is large enough that Young's interference fringes, if present, are averaged out[30]. Even though all known interactions would cause negligible correlations in the measurement outcomes, the ion separation is not large enough to eliminate the lightcone loophole.

We note that the experiment would be conceptually simpler if, after creating the entangled state, we separated the ions so that the input manipulations and measurements were done individually. However, unless we separated the ions by a distance large enough to overcome the lightcone loophole, this is only a matter of convenience of description and does not change the conclusions that can be drawn from the results.

(**409**, 791-794; 2001)

M. A. Rowe*, D. Kielpinski*, V. Meyer*, C. A. Sackett*, W. M. Itano*, C. Monroe† & D. J. Wineland*

* Time and Frequency Division, National Institute of Standards and Technology, Boulder, Colorado 80305, USA
† Department of Physics, University of Michigan, Ann Arbor, Michigan 48109, USA

Received 25 October; accepted 30 November 2000.

References:

1. Clauser, J. F. & Shimony, A. Bell's theorem: experimental tests and implications. *Rep. Prog. Phys.* **41**, 1883-1927 (1978).

2. Einstein, A., Podolsky, B. & Rosen, N. Can quantum-mechanical description of reality be considered complete? *Phys. Rev.* **47**, 777-780 (1935).

3. Bell, J. S. On the Einstein-Podolsky-Rosen paradox. *Physics* **1**, 195-200 (1965).

4. Bell, J. S. in *Foundations of Quantum Mechanics* (ed. d'Espagnat, B.) 171-181 (Academic, New York, 1971).

5. Clauser, J. F., Horne, M. A., Shimony, A. & Holt, R. A. Proposed experiment to test local hidden-variable theories. *Phys. Rev. Lett.* **23**, 880-884 (1969).

6. Freedman, S. J. & Clauser, J. F. Experimental test of local hidden-variable theories. *Phys. Rev. Lett.* **28**, 938-941 (1972).

7. Fry, E. S. & Thompson, R. C. Experimental test of local hidden-variable theories. *Phys. Rev. Lett.* **37**, 465-468 (1976).

8. Aspect, A., Grangier, P. & Roger, G. Experimental realization of Einstein-Podolsky-Rosen-Bohm *Gedankenexperiment*: a new violation of Bell's inequalities. *Phys. Rev. Lett.* **49**, 91-94 (1982).

9. Aspect, A., Dalibard, J. & Roger, G. Experimental test of Bell's inequalities using time-varying analyzers. *Phys. Rev. Lett.* **49**, 1804-1807 (1982).

10. Ou, Z. Y. & Mandel, L. Violation of Bell's inequality and classical probability in a two-photon correlation experiment. *Phys. Rev. Lett.* **61**, 50-53 (1988).

11. Shih, Y. H. & Alley, C. O. New type of Einstein-Podolsky-Rosen-Bohm experiment using pairs of light quanta produced by optical parametric down conversion. *Phys. Rev. Lett.* **61**, 2921-2924 (1988).

12. Tapster, P. R., Rarity, J. G. & Owens, P. C. M. Violation of Bell's inequality over 4 km of optical fiber. *Phys. Rev. Lett.* **73**, 1923-1926 (1994).

13. Kwiat, P. G., Mattle, K., Weinfurter, H. & Zeilinger, A. New high-intensity source of polarization-entangled photon pairs. *Phys. Rev. Lett.* **75**, 4337-4341 (1995).

14. Tittel, W., Brendel, J., Zbinden, H. & Gisin, N. Violation of Bell inequalities by photons more than 10 km apart. *Phys. Rev. Lett.* **81**, 3563-3566 (1998).

15. Weihs, G. *et al.* Violation of Bell's inequality under strict Einstein locality conditions. *Phys. Rev. Lett.* **81**, 5039-5043 (1998).

16. Aspect, A. Bell's inequality test: more ideal than ever. *Nature* **398**, 189-190 (1999).

17. Gisin, N. & Zbinden, H. Bell inequality and the locality loophole: active versus passive switches. *Phys. Lett. A* **264**, 103-107 (1999).

18. Lo, T. K. & Shimony, A. Proposed molecular test of local hidden-variable theories. *Phys. Rev. A* **23**, 3003-3012 (1981).

19. Kwiat, P. G., Eberhard, P. H., Steinberg, A. M. & Chiao, R. Y. Proposal for a loophole-free Bell inequality experiment. *Phys. Rev. A* **49**, 3209-3220 (1994).

20. Huelga, S. F., Ferrero, M. & Santos, E. Loophole-free test of the Bell inequality. *Phys. Rev. A* **51**, 5008-5011 (1995).

21. Fry, E. S., Walther, T. & Li, S. Proposal for a loophole free test of the Bell inequalities. *Phys. Rev. A* **52**, 4381-4395 (1995).

22. Freyberger, M., Aravind, P. K., Horne, M. A. & Shimony, A. Proposed test of Bell's inequality without a detection loophole by using entangled Rydberg atoms. *Phys. Rev. A* **53**, 1232-1244 (1996).

23. Brif, C. & Mann, A. Testing Bell's inequality with two-level atoms via population spectroscopy. *Europhys. Lett.* **49**, 1-7 (2000).

24. Beige, A., Munro, W. J. & Knight, P. L. A Bell's inequality test with entangled atoms. *Phys. Rev. A* **62**, 052102-1–052102-9 (2000).

25. Lamehi–Rachti, M. & Mittig, W. Quantum mechanics and hidden variables: a test of Bell's inequality by the measurement of the spin correlation in low-energy proton-proton scattering. *Phys. Rev. D* **14**, 2543-2555 (1976).

26. Hagley, E. *et al.* Generation of Einstein-Podolsky-Rosen pairs of atoms. *Phys. Rev. Lett.* **79**, 1-5 (1997).

相互作用稍微改变了光散射强度，但这种影响对于所用的离子之间的距离来说是可以忽略不计的 [29]。同时，检测立体角大到足以使杨氏干涉条纹（如存在）被平均掉 [30]。即使所有已知的相互作用在测量结果中的相关性可以忽略不计，但离子之间的距离仍不会大到足以消除光锥漏洞。

我们注意到，如果在建立纠缠态后分开离子，使输入操控和测量分别进行，实验将在概念上更为简单。然而，除非我们把离子之间的距离扩大到足以克服光锥漏洞，否则，这只是描述方便与否的问题，而并不会改变从实验结果所得出的结论。

（沈乃澂 翻译；李军刚 审稿）

27. Sackett, C. A. *et al.* Experimental entanglement of four particles. *Nature* **404**, 256-259 (2000).

28. Feynman, R. P., Vernon, F. L. & Hellwarth, R. W. Geometrical representation of the Schrödinger equation for solving maser problems. *J. Appl. Phys.* **28**, 49-52 (1957).

29. Richter, T. Cooperative resonance fluorescence from two atoms experiencing different driving fields. *Optica Acta* **30**, 1769-1780 (1983).

30. Eichmann, U. *et al.* Young's interference experiment with light scattered from two atoms. *Phys. Rev. Lett.* **70**, 2359-2362 (1993).

Acknowledgements. We thank A. Ben-Kish, J. Bollinger, J. Britton, N. Gisin, P. Knight, P. Kwiat and I. Percival for useful discussions and comments on the manuscript. This work was supported by the US National Security Agency (NSA) and the Advanced Research and Development Activity (ARDA), the US Office of Naval Research, and the US Army Research Office. This paper is a contribution of the National Institute of Standards and Technology and is not subject to US copyright.

Correspondence and requests for materials should be addressed to D.J.W. (e-mail: david.wineland@boulder.nist.gov).

Guide to the Draft Human Genome

T. G. Wolfsberg *et al.*

Editor's Note

The release of the first draft of the human genome—the genetic sequence of all human chromosomes—presented the scientific community with a data set that was almost overwhelming in its implications, questions, complications and repercussions. To accompany the paper reporting the results obtained by the International Human Genome Sequencing Consortium, *Nature* here presented an analysis of how the data might be used. As the authors point out, the sequence data joined a considerable existing body of information about the structure and evolution of the human genome, ranging from detailed studies of individual genes and their protein products to linkages between particular inherited phenotypes. The paper provides some pointers for how these disparate types of data might be integrated.

There are a number of ways to investigate the structure, function and evolution of the human genome. These include examining the morphology of normal and abnormal chromosomes, constructing maps of genomic landmarks, following the genetic transmission of phenotypes and DNA sequence variations, and characterizing thousands of individual genes. To this list we can now add the elucidation of the genomic DNA sequence, albeit at "working draft" accuracy. The current challenge is to weave together these disparate types of data to produce the information infrastructure needed to support the next generation of biomedical research. Here we provide an overview of the different sources of information about the human genome and how modern information technology, in particular the internet, allows us to link them together.

THE ultimate goal of the Human Genome Project is to produce a single continuous sequence for each of the 24 human chromosomes and to delineate the positions of all genes. The working draft sequence described by the International Human Genome Sequencing Consortium was constructed by melding together sequence segments derived from over 20,000 large-insert clones[1]. All of the results of this analysis are available on a web site maintained by the University of California at Santa Cruz (http://genome.ucsc.edu). Over the next few years, draft quality sequence will be steadily replaced by more accurate data. The National Center for Biotechnology Information (NCBI) has developed a system for rapidly regenerating the genomic sequence and gene annotation as sequences of the underlying clones are revised (http://www.ncbi.nlm.nih.gov/genome/guide). Undoubtedly, others will apply a variety of approaches to large-scale annotation of genes and other features. One such project is Ensembl, a joint project of the European Bioinformatics Institute (EBI) and the Sanger Centre (http://www.ensembl.org).

人类基因组草图导读

沃尔夫斯伯格等

编者按

人类基因组——全人类染色体遗传序列第一份草图的发布向科学界提供了一个数据集，这个数据集所带来的启发和疑问，以及所具有的复杂性和影响力都是空前的。随着国际人类基因组测序联盟发表文章公布其成果，《自然》杂志在这里刊出了一篇关于如何使用这些数据的分析文章。正如作者所指出的，这些序列数据将大量已知的关于人类基因组结构和进化的信息连接起来，范围从单个基因及其蛋白产物的详细研究到与特定遗传表型之间的关联。本文为如何整合这些不同类型的数据提供了一些指南。

已经有大量的方法被用于研究人类基因组的结构、功能和进化。这些方法包括检测正常和异常染色体的形态，构建基因组标记图谱，追踪表型和 DNA 序列变异的遗传传递，以及描述数千个单基因的特征。虽然这还处于"工作草图"的准确度阶段，但我们已经可以在此列表中加上基因组 DNA 序列的解析。我们目前面临的挑战是将这些类型各异的数据编织在一起，进而形成能够支持下一代生物医学研究的信息学基础框架。在这里，我们将会概述这些与人类基因组相关的不同来源的信息，以及如何利用现代信息技术，特别是互联网，将它们联系在一起。

人类基因组计划的最终目标是为人类 24 条染色体中的每一条都构建一个单独的连续序列，并描述所有基因的位置。国际人类基因组测序联盟所绘制的工作草图序列，是通过把超过 20,000 个大片断插入克隆的序列合并在一起而构建得到的[1]。所有的分析结果均可在加利福尼亚大学圣克鲁兹分校维护的网站（http://genome.ucsc.edu）上获取。在未来几年间，草图质量序列会不断地被更精确的数据替代。美国国家生物技术信息中心（NCBI）已经开发了一个系统，它能在相应的克隆序列被修订后，迅速更新对应的基因组序列和基因注释（http://www.ncbi.nlm.nih.gov/genome/guide）。毋庸置疑的是其他研究小组将会采用各种各样的方法对基因以及其他一些特征进行大规模注释。其中一个项目是 Ensembl，它是由欧洲生物信息研究所（EBI）和桑格中心（http://www.ensembl.org）联合建立的一个合作项目。

Pinpointing New Genes

Recent estimates have placed the number of human genes at 25,000–35,000 (refs 2, 3). More than 10,000 human genes have been catalogued in the Online *Mendelian Inheritance in Man*[4] (OMIM), which documents all inherited human diseases and their causal gene mutations. Integration of the information contained in OMIM with the working draft is facilitated by the fact that it has already been tied to reference messenger RNA sequences through a collaborative effort between OMIM, the Human Gene Nomenclature Committee and the NCBI[5,6]. As a result, the positions of many known genes have been determined by alignment of mRNAs with genomic sequences. For the remaining genes, we must currently resort to computational gene-finding methods (reviewed in refs 7, 8).

When mRNA species align differently to a genomic sequence, this indicates that alternative splicing has taken place. In the current set of full-length reference mRNAs, 11,174 transcripts have been sequenced from 10,742 distinct genes (2.4% of the genes have multiple splicing variants). Alignments of expressed sequence tag (EST) sequences to the working draft sequence, however, suggest that about 60% of human genes have multiple splicing variants, which has important implications for the complexity of human gene expression[1]. By their sheer numbers (currently over 2.5 million) we might expect ESTs to sample a larger fraction of splicing variants than would be the case for more traditional targeted approaches. For example, alignment of the mRNA of the membrane-bound metalloprotease-disintegrin ADAM23 (ref. 9) to the draft genome reveals that the gene consists of at least 23 exons. Of the many ESTs that also align to the *ADAM23* locus, one lacks the exon that encodes the transmembrane domain, which suggests an alternatively spliced, soluble protein. Although this is a biologically plausible conclusion, one should exercise caution when interpreting such results: ESTs are partial single-pass sequences that have been associated with a variety of artefacts, including sequencing errors and improper splicing[10,11].

Finding Relatives

Genes can be found through an implied relationship to something else—for example, being a putative orthologue (related to a gene in another species). To do this, it is useful to search the genomic sequence or, preferably, its mRNA sequences and protein products, using BLAST[12]. As an example, we use the mouse *Lmx1b* gene, which encodes a LIM homeobox protein that is important in pattern development[13]. When we used the protein sequence encoded by *Lmx1b* as a query in a BLAST search against the working draft human genome sequence, the best match was to a region of 9q34, and the positions of the alignments line up with the exons of the human *LMX1B* gene (Fig. 1a).

查明新基因

最近的估计结果认定人类基因的数目大概是介于 25,000 ~ 35,000 之间（参考文献 2 和 3）。已经有超过 10,000 个基因被编入在线"人类孟德尔遗传"（OMIM）数据库[4]中，这个系统记录了所有的人类遗传性疾病以及导致疾病发生的基因突变。通过 OMIM、人类基因命名委员会和 NCBI 的协作，OMIM 中包含的信息已经关联到相关的信使 RNA(mRNA) 序列上，这促进了 OMIM 中的信息与工作草图的整合[5,6]。因此，很多已知基因的位置都已经通过 mRNA 与基因组序列的比对确定下来。对于剩下的基因，目前我们必须要求助于各种基于计算的基因寻找方法（参考文献 7 和 8 中的相关综述）。

当 mRNA 种类与基因组序列的比对结果不同时，意味着发生了选择性剪接。在目前的一整套全长参考 mRNA 中，有 11,174 个转录产物从 10,742 个特定基因中（2.4% 的基因有多剪接变异体的情况）测序得到。然而，将表达序列标签（EST）序列与基因组草图序列进行比对，结果却发现大概有 60% 的人类基因具有多剪接变异体，这对于解释人类基因表达的复杂性具有重要意义[1]。仅考虑其数目的话（目前超过了 250 万），我们可以期望 EST 的样本数相对于传统靶向方法具有更多的剪接变异体。举例来讲，将细胞膜结合金属蛋白酶—解整联蛋白 ADAM23(参考文献 9) 所对应的 mRNA 与基因组草图进行对比发现该基因至少包含 23 个外显子。在与 ADAM23 位点比对的 EST 中，其中一个 EST 缺少编码跨膜区的外显子，这意味着 mRNA 发生了选择性剪接，得到的是可溶性蛋白。尽管这是生物学上合理的结论，但当解释这一类结果时我们仍然需要保持谨慎：EST 是部分单向的序列，可能会与各种各样的人为修饰相关联，包括测序错误以及不适当的剪接[10,11]。

寻找亲缘关系

通过基因与其他一些事物之间暗含的关系寻找基因——例如，推定直系同源基因（与其他物种某个基因相关）。这可以利用 BLAST[12] 搜索基因组序列，或者最好使用 mRNA 序列或者蛋白质产物来寻找基因。以小鼠的 *Lmx1b* 基因为例，这个基因编码的是一个 LIM 同源异形框蛋白，该蛋白在模式发育方面具有重要作用[13]。当我们用 *Lmx1b* 编码的蛋白质序列作为查询序列，通过 BLAST 在人类基因组草图序列数据库中进行检索时，最匹配的区域位于基因组 9p34 区域，其对应序列的位置是人类 *LMX1B* 基因外显子的区域（图 1a）。

Fig. 1. *Lmx1b* encodes a transcription factor that helps to control the trajectory of motor axons during mammalian limb development. **a**, The results of a search of the six-frame translation of the draft genome sequence on the NCBI site using mouse *Lmx1b* protein NP_034855.1 as a query and using TBLASTN with standard search parameters. The best match was to a region of chromosome 9 that contains the human *LMX1B* gene. **b**, The mouse *Lmx1b* and the human *LMX1B* genes lie within a conserved syntenic block of genes, in mouse on chromosome 2 and in human on chromosome 9. This conservation of gene order supports the theory that *Lmx1b* and *LMX1B* are orthologous.

Additional support for two genes being orthologous comes from the mouse-human homology map. Despite being separated by 200 million years of evolution, mouse and human genes often fall into homologous chromosomal regions that share a conserved gene order (synteny). In fact, the working draft sequence has helped to refine the homology map and provides inferred map positions for many mouse genes[1]. The two homeobox genes fall within a conserved syntenic block between mouse chromosome 2 and human

600

图 1. *Lmx1b* 编码一个转录因子，该转录因子在哺乳动物肢体发育过程中，帮助控制运动神经元轴突的轨迹方向。**a**，在 NCBI 网站上，以小鼠的 Lmx1b 蛋白 NP_034855.1 作为查询序列，使用 TBLASTN 及标准搜索参数，在人类基因组草图序列的六种读码框翻译中进行检索的结果。最佳匹配是 9 号染色体上的一段包含有人类 *LMX1B* 基因的区域。**b**，小鼠的 *Lmx1b* 基因和人类的 *LMX1B* 基因都位于一个保守的线性基因区域中，小鼠的这个基因在 2 号染色体上，而人类的在 9 号染色体上。这种保守的基因排布支持 *Lmx1b* 和 *LMX1B* 是直系同源基因的推测。

　　进一步支持两个基因是直系同源的证据来自小鼠–人类同源基因图谱。尽管各自独立地进化了 2 亿年，小鼠和人类的基因常常位于具有保守基因序列（共线性）的同源染色体区域内。事实上，人类基因组草图已经帮助修正了小鼠和人类之间的同源基因图谱，为许多小鼠基因的定位提供了推测的图谱位置[1]。这两个同源异形框基因定位于小鼠的 2 号染色体和人类的 9 号染色体上的一个共同的保守线性区域中（图 1b）。除

chromosome 9 (Fig. 1b). Furthermore, the human *LMX1B* gene has been implicated in nail patella syndrome (NPS), an autosomal recessive disorder characterized by limb and kidney defects. A mouse in which *Lmx1b* has been inactivated shows a phenotype that is strikingly similar to NPS[13]. Besides providing additional support for the conclusion of orthology, this connection may provide a useful mouse model for the human disorder. In this way, information from OMIM and mouse mutants can further define human genes.

Another way to find a gene is by looking for paralogues—family members derived by gene duplication. As an example, we used human *ADAM23*, which maps to 2q33 (ref. 14). In a BLAST search against a set of proteins predicted from the draft sequence, aside from matching itself, the best match was to a peptide from chromosome 20. No ADAM family member has previously been mapped to this chromosome. The predicted protein encoded by this gene does not begin with a methionine and appears to be incomplete at its amino terminus when aligned with other family members: this could be due to an erroneous protein prediction or a gap in the draft sequence. Computational analysis can reveal protein family domains and their relationships to three-dimensional protein structures. In this case, the putative ADAM paralogue contains both the zinc metalloprotease and disintegrin motifs characteristic of the ADAM family. Critical amino acids of the metalloprotease domain are conserved in the putative paralogue (Fig. 2b), including a trio of histidine residues in the active site (shaded yellow), which are important in complexing the zinc ion (Fig. 2a). The finding that the sequence of the new predicted ADAM member has an intact active site suggests that the predicted gene is functional, rather than being a pseudogene.

Fig. 2. The ADAM23 protein sequence NP_003803.1 was used in a BLASTP search of the Ensembl confirmed peptides produced from the 5 Sep 2000 version of the working draft sequence. As of October 2000, the best match was to the peptide ENSP00000025626 derived from chromosome 2, the predicted peptide for ADAM23. The second match was to peptide ENSP00000072108, derived from chromosome 20 and falling within GenBank Acc. No. AC055771.2. We used this predicted peptide to search a database of Pfam[24] and SMART[25] protein domains that are aligned with protein structures. This Conserved Domain Database (CDD) search at NCBI resulted in hits to reprolysin and disintegrin domains. **a**, Pfam family 01421, Reprolysin, has a structure associated with it: the zinc-dependent metalloprotease Atrolysin C (PDB: 1ATL). **b**, The query ENSP00000072108 aligns with the 1ATL protein sequence and eight other ADAMs from the Pfam Reprolysin entry. In the structure and alignment, red indicates conserved residues; grey indicates non-aligned sequences. The three histidines of the metalloprotease active site, which complex with the zinc ion, are highlighted in yellow. The structure and alignment were created using the structure viewing program Cn3D.

此之外，人类的 *LMX1B* 基因被认为与指甲髌骨综合征(NPS)的发生相关，它是一种常染色体隐性疾病，其特征是肢体和肾脏的缺陷。*Lmx1b* 基因失活的小鼠会表现出与 NPS 极为相似的症状[13]。除了可以为同源基因的结论提供更多的支持以外，这种关联性也可以为研究人类疾病提供一种有用的小鼠模型。通过这样一种方式，来自 OMIM 和小鼠的突变体的信息可以进一步定义人类的基因。

另外一种寻找基因的方法是寻找旁系同源序列——由基因复制得到的家族成员。以人类的 *ADAM23* 基因为例，它在基因组草图上对应的是 2q33(参考文献 14)。通过 BLAST 检索人类基因组草图预测的所有蛋白质发现，除了与其自身蛋白匹配外，最佳的匹配结果为 20 号染色体上的一个多肽。在此之前还没有任何一个 ADAM 蛋白质家族的成员被定位到这条染色体上。通过与其他家族成员的比对发现，推测的这个基因所编码的蛋白质并不是以甲硫氨酸起始的，它的氨基末端似乎是不完整的：这可能是由于蛋白质预测错误或者是由于在人类基因草图序列上存在缺口所引起的。通过计算分析可以揭示蛋白家族结构域以及它们与蛋白质三维结构之间的关系。在这个例子中，预测得到的 ADAM 旁系同源蛋白同时具有 ADAM 家族特征性的锌金属蛋白酶和解整联蛋白基序。金属蛋白酶结构域的关键氨基酸在推定的旁系同源蛋白中是保守的(图 2b)，这其中包括位于活性部位的组氨酸残基三联体(黄色阴影表示)，它对于络合锌离子至关重要(图 2a)。新预测的 ADAM 家族成员的序列具有一个完整的活性位点，说明这个预测的基因是有功能的，并不是一个假基因。

图 2. 在 Ensembl 中用 BLASTP 检索 ADAM23 蛋白序列 NP_003803.1，确认了 2000 年 9 月 5 日版本中人类基因草图序列得到的多肽产物。截至 2000 年 10 月，最好的匹配结果是来自 2 号染色体的多肽 ENSP00000025626，也就是预测的 ADAM23 多肽。匹配结果排在第二位的多肽是 ENSP00000072108，来自 20 号染色体，其在 GenBank 中的编号是 AC055771.2。我们将这个预测的多肽在一个数据库中检索，该数据库包含了与蛋白结构相匹配的 Pfam[24] 和 SMART[25] 蛋白结构域。在 NCBI 上搜索的保守结构域数据库(CDD)，对应的是锌金属蛋白酶和解整联蛋白结构域。**a**，Pfam 家族 01421——锌金属蛋白酶具有一个和它相关的结构：锌依赖的金属蛋白酶 Atrolysin C(PDB 代码：1ATL)。**b**，ENSP00000072108 作为查询序列，与 1ATL 蛋白序列以及 Pfam 锌金属蛋白酶条目下的另外八个 ADAMs 进行比对。在结构图和比对图中，红色代表保守性残基；灰色代表没有比对上的序列。金属蛋白酶活性位点上的三个组氨酸残基，采用黄色突出显示，它们可以与锌离子络合。图中的结构和比对结果采用结构可视化程序 Cn3D 生成。

Searching by Position

It is sometimes desirable to find genes by their position in the genome, rather than by sequence similarity. For example, when genetic or cytogenetic analysis has implicated a particular region in the aetiology of a disease, it is of interest to see what genes lie in the region. A natural way to describe positions in a sequence would be by base coordinates, but this is impractical for the working draft sequence, as the sequence is still being revised. Cytogenetic band nomenclature is more commonly used to describe positions in the genome, and many human diseases are linked to chromosomal deletions, amplifications and translocations[15]. However, to be useful in conjunction with the working draft, these designations must be related to the sequence. Towards this end, a consortium has integrated this information using fluorescence *in situ* hybridization (FISH) to localize BAC clones that also bear sequence tags that can be found in the draft sequence[16]. In addition to providing cytogenetic coordinates as entry points into the genome, they also provide mapped clone reagents that may be useful in further experimental work.

Another way to describe positions in the genome is relative to mapped sequence tagged site (STS) markers. This is particularly useful in positional cloning projects, where candidate regions are usually defined by polymorphic STSs used in genetic linkage analysis. For example, the breast cancer susceptibility locus *BRCA2* was originally localized by fine genetic mapping to a 600-kilobase (kb) interval on chromosome 13 centred around the STS marker D13S171 (ref. 17). STS markers from several genetic and physical maps have been localized in the working draft sequence using a procedure known as electronic PCR[18]. Thus, by simply looking up the position of D13S171, we can see the region around what is now known to be *BRCA2*, together with other features such as adjacent genes and markers, translocation breakpoints, and genetic variations.

Variations on a Theme

A map of DNA sequence variations will aid our understanding of complex diseases and human population dynamics. The most common class of variation is the single nucleotide polymorphism (SNP) and the total number of SNPs in the public database (dbSNP)[19] now exceeds 2.5 million, representing 1.5 million unique SNP loci. Because database entries include flanking sequence surrounding the polymorphic base(s), it is possible to localize variations within the working draft by simple sequence alignment[20].

Histone deacetylase 3 (HDAC3) is a nucleosome-remodelling enzyme that deacetylates the lysine residues of histones, affecting transcriptional repression[21]. Its genomic region contains seven mapped SNPs near the locus, one of which falls within the coding region—a G-to-C substitution that results in the nonsynonymous substitution Arg265Pro in the protein product. The three-dimensional structure of an *Aquifex aeolicus* homologue shows that this residue is at the lip of the active-site pocket[22]. Of the two classes of eukaryotic histone

604

基于位置的检索

有时候，通过基因在基因组上的位置来寻找基因比通过序列相似性来寻找基因更能获得令人满意的结果。举例来讲，当遗传学或者细胞遗传学分析已经暗示了某一个染色体特定区域和疾病发生密切相关时，搞清楚有什么基因位于这个区域内就显得非常有意义。描述序列位置最自然的一种方法就是采用碱基坐标，但是这种方法用于描述基因组草图序列是行不通的，因为序列还在不断的修正过程中。细胞遗传学条带系统命名法是一种更为普遍的用于描述基因组序列位置的方法，许多人类疾病都与染色体缺失、扩增以及易位相关[15]。然而，为了更好地与草图衔接使用，这些名称必须与序列相关联。为了达到这个目的，某个联盟利用荧光原位杂交技术（FISH）定位了在人类基因组草图序列中可以找到的含有序列标签的 BAC 克隆，从而整合了这些信息[16]。他们不仅可以为细胞遗传学切入基因组提供相匹配的坐标，还能提供已经比对好的克隆用于后续的实验工作。

另外一种描述基因组序列位置的方法为序列标签位点（STS）标记物定位法。这种方法特别适用于定位克隆的项目，这些候选区域通常采用遗传连锁分析中使用的多态性 STS 来定义。举例来讲，乳腺癌易感位点 *BRCA2* 最初就采用精细遗传图谱定位在 13 号染色体上以 STS 标记 D13S171 为中心的大约 600 kb 区域内（参考文献 17）。现在，来自多个遗传和物理图谱上的 STS 标记已经通过一种叫电子 PCR 的方法被定位在基因组草图序列上[18]。因而，简单地查询 D13S171 的位置，我们就可以看到这个区域位于 *BRCA2* 附近，并且还可以看到其他特征，如临近基因和标记物、易位断点以及遗传变异等。

基因组序列上的变异

DNA 序列变异图谱将帮助我们理解复杂疾病和人类种群的动态变化。最常见的一类变异是单核苷酸多态性（SNP），在公共数据库（dbSNP）[19]中存储的 SNP 总数目前已经超过了 250 万个，代表了 150 万个唯一 SNP 位点。由于数据库条目包含了多态性碱基的侧翼序列，因此采用简单的序列比对方法就可以确定这些变异在基因组草图上的位置[20]。

组蛋白脱乙酰酶 3（HDAC3）是一个核小体重构酶，可以催化组蛋白中的赖氨酸残基去乙酰化，从而影响转录抑制[21]。它所在的基因组区域包含七个确定位置的 SNP，其中一个就位于其编码区域内——一个 G 碱基到 C 碱基的替换，这会导致蛋白质产物发生非同义突变，即 265 位的精氨酸突变为脯氨酸。来自超嗜热菌的同源物的三维结构显示，这个残基位于活性位点口袋的边缘[22]。真核细胞组蛋白脱乙酰

deacetylase, one most often has Arg at this position and the other most often has Pro[23], a trait shared with the bacterial members of the histone deacetylase superfamily. This SNP might therefore occur at a functionally interesting site, and also gives pause for speculation: as bacterial members of the superfamily predominantly have a Pro in this position, perhaps Pro is the ancient residue at this site, and not Arg. Note that several high-throughput SNP discovery methods have been used to generate these data and not all SNPs have been rigorously validated.

Conclusions

The draft sequence provides us with the first comprehensive integration of diverse genomic resources. The mapping of ESTs, gene predictions, STSs and SNPs onto the draft sequence can enable identification of alternative splicing, orthologues, paralogues, map positions and coding sequence variations. Users should remember, though, that these genomic resources represent a work-in-progress, and will evolve as the genome is finished and computation methods further refined.

(**409**, 824-826; 2001)

Tyra G. Wolfsberg[*], Johanna McEntyre[†] & Gregory D. Schuler[†]

[*] Genome Technology Branch, National Human Genome Research Institute, National Institutes of Health, Bethesda, Maryland 20892, USA

[†] National Center for Biotechnology Information, National Library of Medicine, National Institutes of Health, Bethesda, Maryland 20894, USA

References:

1. International Human Genome Sequencing Consortium. Initial sequencing and analysis of the human genome. *Nature* **409**, 860-921 (2001).

2. Ewing, B. & Green, P. Analysis of expressed sequence tags indicates 35,000 human genes. *Nature Genet.* **25**, 232-234 (2000).

3. Roest Crollius, H. *et al.* Estimate of human gene number provided by genome-wide analysis using *Tetraodon nigroviridis* DNA sequence. *Nature Genet.* **25**, 235-238 (2000).

4. McKusick, V. A. *Mendelian Inheritance in Man. Catalogs of Human Genes and Genetic Disorders* (Johns Hopkins Univ. Press, Baltimore, 1998).

5. Maglott, D. R., Katz, K. S., Sicotte, H. & Pruitt, K. D. NCBI's LocusLink and RefSeq. *Nucleic Acids Res.* **28**, 126-128 (2000).

6. Pruitt, K. D., Katz, K. S., Sicotte, H. & Maglott, D. R. Introducing RefSeq and LocusLink: curated human genome resources at the NCBI. *Trends Genet.* **16**, 44-47 (2000).

7. Guigo, R., Agarwal, P., Abril, J. F., Burset, M. & Fickett, J. W. An assessment of gene prediction accuracy in large DNA sequences. *Genome Res.* **10**, 1631-1642 (2000).

8. Stormo, G. D. Gene-finding approaches for eukaryotes. *Genome Res.* **10**, 394-397 (2000).

9. Sagane, K., Ohya, Y., Hasegawa, Y. & Tanaka, I. Metalloproteinase-like, disintegrin-like, cysteine-rich proteins MDC2 and MDC3: novel human cellular disintegrins highly expressed in the brain. *Biochem. J.* **334**, 93-98 (1998).

10. Wolfsberg, T. G. & Landsman, D. A comparison of expressed sequence tags (ESTs) to human genomic sequences. *Nucleic Acids Res.* **25**, 1626-1632 (1997).

11. Wolfsberg, T. G. & Landsman, D. in *Bioinformatics: A Practical Guide to the Analysis of Genes and Proteins* (eds Baxevanis, A. D. & Ouellette, B. F. F.) (Wiley-Liss, Inc., New York, 2001).

12. Altschul, S. F. *et al.* Gapped BLAST and PSI-BLAST: a new generation of protein database search programs. *Nucleic Acids Res.* **25**, 3389-3402 (1997).

13. Chen, H. *et al.* Limb and kidney defects in Lmx1b mutant mice suggest an involvement of LMX1B in human nail patella syndrome. *Nature Genet.* **19**, 51-55 (1998).

14. Poindexter, K., Nelson, N., DuBose, R. F., Black, R. A. & Cerretti, D. P. The identification of seven metalloproteinase-disintegrin (ADAM) genes from genomic libraries. *Gene* **237**, 61-70 (1999).

15. Mitelman, F., Mertens, F. & Johansson, B. A breakpoint map of recurrent chromosomal rearrangements in human neoplasia. *Nature Genet.* **15**, 417-474 (1997).

16. The BAC Resource Consortium. Integration of cytogenetic landmarks into the draft sequence of the human genome. *Nature* **409**, 953-958 (2001).

酶分为两类，一类在这个位置上通常是精氨酸，而另一类则与细菌组蛋白脱乙酰酶超家族一样，在这个位置上通常是脯氨酸。因此这个 SNP 位点可能出现在一个有趣的功能性位点上，同时我们可以推测：鉴于细菌组蛋白脱乙酰酶超家族在这个位置上主要是脯氨酸，或许脯氨酸才是这个位置上的古老残基，而非精氨酸。需要注意的是，已经有几种高通量 SNP 发现方法被用来产生这些数据，并且不是所有的 SNP 位点都能被严格验证。

结　　论

基因组草图序列使我们得以首次全面整合不同的基因组资源。将 EST、基因预测、STS 和 SNP 定位到草图序列上，可以帮助我们确认可变剪接、直系同源序列、旁系同源序列、比对位置以及编码序列的变异。但是，使用者也要注意，这些基因组资源尚在"加工"之中，会随着基因组测序的最终完成和计算方法的进一步优化而不断地修改。

（刘振明 翻译；陈捷胤 审稿）

17. Wooster, R. *et al.* Localization of a breast cancer susceptibility gene, BRCA2, to chromosome 13q12-13. *Science* **265**, 2088-2090 (1994).

18. Schuler, G. D. Sequence mapping by electronic PCR. *Genome Res.* **7**, 541-550 (1997).

19. Smigielski, E. M., Sirotkin, K., Ward, M. & Sherry, S. T. dbSNP: a database of single nucleotide polymorphisms. *Nucleic Acids Res.* **28**, 352-355 (2000).

20. The International SNP Map Working Group. A map of human genome sequence variation containing 1.42 million single nucleotide polymorphisms. *Nature* **409**, 928-933 (2001).

21. Struhl, K. Histone acetylation and transcriptional regulatory mechanisms. *Genes Dev.* **12**, 599-606 (1998).

22. Finnin, M. S. *et al.* Structures of a histone deacetylase homologue bound to the TSA and SAHA inhibitors. *Nature* **401**, 188-193 (1999).

23. Leipe, D. D. & Landsman, D. Histone deacetylases, acetoin utilization proteins and acetylpolyamine amidohydrolases are members of an ancient protein superfamily. *Nucleic Acids Res.* **25**, 3693-3697 (1997).

24. Bateman, A. *et al.* The Pfam protein families database. *Nucleic Acids Res.* **28**, 263-266 (2000).

25. Schultz, J., Copley, R. R., Doerks, T., Ponting, C. P. & Bork, P. SMART: a web-based tool for the study of genetically mobile domains. *Nucleic Acids Res.* **28**, 231-234 (2000).

Acknowledgements. We thank G. Marth, S. Sherry, D. Landsman, D. Church and D. Lipman for suggestions and review of the manuscript.

Correspondence should be addressed to G.D.S. (e-mail: schuler@ncbi.nlm.nih.gov).

Mining the Draft Human Genome

E. Birney *et al.*

Editor's Note

The first draft of the human genome provided a wealth of information of potential interest to researchers in many fields, ranging from medicine to palaeontology. The sequence was made publicly available, but making productive use of it required some knowledge both of the nature of the information it contained and the tools provided for navigating these data. Here some researchers from the team involved in the genome project supply a quick guide to the possibilities of such data mining.

Now that the draft human genome sequence is available, everyone wants to be able to use it. However, we have perhaps become complacent about our ability to turn new genomes into lists of genes. The higher volume of data associated with a larger genome is accompanied by a much greater increase in complexity. We need to appreciate both the scale of the challenge of vertebrate genome analysis and the limitations of current gene prediction methods and understanding.

IN this issue, accompanying the description of the sequence[1], there are nine data-mining papers that interrogate the genome from distinct biological perspectives. These range from broad topics—cancer[2], addiction[3], gene expression[4], immunology[5] and evolutionary genomics[6]—to the more focused: membrane trafficking[7], cytoskeleton[8], cell cycle[9] and circadian clock[10]. The findings reported by these authors are likely to be indicative of many people's experiences with the draft human genome: frustrating and rewarding in equal measures.

The Current Data Set

The human genome—the first vertebrate genome sequence to be determined—seems likely to be quite representative of what we will find in other vertebrate genomes. It is around 30 times larger than the recently sequenced worm and fly genomes, and 250 times larger than that of yeast, the first eukaryotic genome to be sequenced[11]. Despite its size, it seems likely to have only two or three times as many genes as the fly and worm genomes, with the coding regions of genes accounting for only 3% of the DNA. Repeat sequences form a large proportion of the remaining DNA, around 46%. These repeats may or may not have a function, but they are certainly characteristic of large vertebrate genomes. The rest of the sequence contains promoters, transcriptional regulatory sequences and other

挖掘人类基因组草图

伯尼等

编者按

人类基因组的第一份草图为从医学到古生物学等众多领域的研究者提供了大量有用的信息。序列已经可以公开获取，但是要高效利用这些序列既需要了解这些序列所包含信息的本质，也需要了解浏览这些数据的工具。在这里，一些参与该基因组项目的研究者为挖掘这些数据的可能性提供了快速指南。

既然已经有了人类基因组草图序列，每个人都希望能够使用它。然而，我们可能已经为我们拥有将新基因组变成一个个基因列表的能力而沾沾自喜。基因组越大，包含的数据越多，同时还伴随着复杂程度大大增加。我们需要意识到对脊椎动物基因组进行分析所面临挑战的规模，以及目前在基因预测方法上和认识上的局限性。

在这一期中，除了对序列的描述[1]，还有九篇数据挖掘方面的研究论文从截然不同的生物学视角对基因组进行审视。这些研究的范围从宽泛的主题——癌症[2]、成瘾性[3]、基因表达[4]、免疫学[5]和进化基因组学[6]，到更具体的主题——膜转运[7]、细胞骨架[8]、细胞周期[9]和生物钟[10]。这些作者报道的发现可能代表了许多人类基因组草图研究者的经验：挫折和收获一样多。

目前的数据集

人类基因组——作为第一个被测序的脊椎动物基因组——在我们将要发现的其他脊椎动物基因组中，似乎很具有代表性。它大约是目前已经测序的蠕虫和苍蝇基因组的 30 倍，是第一个测序的真核生物——酵母的基因组的 250 倍[11]。尽管很大，但是它所包含的基因数目看起来只有蠕虫和苍蝇基因组的两到三倍，因为它的基因编码区仅占整个 DNA 长度的 3%。重复序列构成了其余 DNA 的一大部分，大概占到 46%。这些重复序列可能有功能，也可能没有功能，但是它们确实是大型脊椎动物基因组的典型特征。剩下的序列包含启动子、转录调控序列和其他一些尚未知晓

features, as yet unknown.

The International Human Genome Sequencing Consortium has been sequencing the genome in fragments of about 100–200 kilobases (kb). These fragments exist as bacterial artificial chromosome (BAC) clones, which are derived from sequences whose chromosomal location is known. Each newly generated sequence is deposited in the high-throughput genome sequence (HTGS) division of the International Nucleotide Database (GenBank/EMBL/DDBJ) within 24 hours of being assembled and is assigned a unique identifier (its accession number). For the working draft, about 75% of clones are "unfinished": each still consists of about 10–20 unassembled sequence fragments. Sequencing centres are continuously reading new sequence data from these clones until all the gaps are eliminated, at which point the sequence is declared "finished". As the HTGS entries are updated they retain the same accession numbers, but their version numbers increase.

There is a great deal of overlap between BAC clones, so it is typically more convenient to view a cleaned up version of the raw data, in which the sequences of the clones are correctly ordered and overlapped to remove redundancy and create a contiguous DNA sequence for each chromosome. These virtual chromosome sequences change continuously as gaps are closed and fragment ordering is refined.

Finding Genes

With over 30 genomes sequenced, the casual observer could be forgiven for thinking that gene prediction, or annotation, was a problem filed neatly under "solved". Unfortunately this is far from true. The large size of the genome makes finding the genes much more difficult. The protein-coding parts of human genes, called exons, are split into pieces in the genome and these pieces are separated by non-coding sequence called introns. Nearly all of the increase in gene size in human compared with fly or worm is due to the introns becoming much longer (about 50 kb versus 5 kb). The protein-encoding exons, on the other hand, are roughly the same size. This decrease in signal (exon) to noise (intron) ratio in the human genome leads to misprediction by computational gene-finding strategies.

Many methods for predicting genes are based on compositional signals that are found in the DNA sequence. These methods detect characteristics that are expected to be associated with genes, such as splice sites and coding regions, and then piece this information together to determine the complete or partial sequence of a gene. Unfortunately, these *ab initio* methods tend to produce false positives, leading to overestimates of gene numbers, which means that we cannot confidently use them for annotation. They also do not work well with unfinished sequence that has gaps and errors, which may give rise to frameshifts, when the reading frame of the gene is disrupted by the addition or removal of bases.

Thankfully, there is a wealth of data that we can use to produce more reliable gene predictions. Information on expressed sequences (expressed sequence tags (ESTs) and

612

的特征性序列。

国际人类基因组测序联盟一直在对长约 100～200 kb 的基因组片段进行测序。这些片段以细菌人工染色体(BAC)克隆的形式存在，这些克隆来自于那些染色体位置已知的序列。每一条新测序的序列都会在组装完成后的 24 小时内存入国际核酸序列数据库(GenBank/EMBL/DDBJ)中的高通量测序基因组序列(HTGS)子库，并且被分配一个唯一的标识符(它的编号)。对于整个工作草图而言，还有大概 75% 的克隆处于"未完成"的状态：它们中的每一个大约包含 10～20 个没有完成组装的序列片段。测序中心正在不断地从这些克隆中读取新的序列数据，直到序列上所有的空缺都被消除为止，直到此时，整个序列的测序工作才能宣告"完成"。在 HTGS 条目更新的过程中，原有编号会保留下来，但是它们的版本号会增加。

细菌人工染色体克隆之间会有大量重叠，因此通常查看原始数据处理后的版本会比较方便，在整洁版中，这些克隆的序列按照正确的顺序进行排列、相互重叠时移除冗余部分，为每一条染色体构造一个连续的 DNA 序列。伴随着序列内空缺的闭合和片段排列顺序的修正，这些实际的染色体序列会不断地改变。

寻 找 基 因

面对 30 多个已经测序的基因组，对旁观者而言，认为"基因的预测或注释领域的问题已经解决"也情有可原。但不幸的是，事实远非如此。庞大的基因组让寻找基因的工作变得更加困难。人类基因中蛋白编码的部分称为外显子，在基因组中被非编码序列的内含子分隔成为片段。与苍蝇和蠕虫基因相比，几乎所有人类基因大小的增加都是由内含子变长造成的(约为 50 kb 比 5 kb)。而另一方面，编码蛋白的外显子，长度则大致相同。人类基因组中的这种信(外显子)噪(内含子)比降低的情况，会导致通过计算寻找基因的策略给出错误的预测。

许多预测基因的方法都是基于在 DNA 序列中找到的组成信号。这些方法首先探测某些期望与基因相关的特征，例如剪接位点和编码区，然后把这些信息拼接在一起，从而确定基因的完整序列或部分序列。然而不幸的是，这些从头预测的方法倾向于给出假阳性的结果，导致基因数目的高估，这就意味着我们不能自信地应用它们来进行基因注释。此外，这些方法也不能很好地处理含有缺口和错误的未完成序列，因为如果增加或者移除的碱基破坏了基因的阅读框，就可能会产生移码。

万幸的是，已经有丰富的数据可以用来进行更为可靠的基因预测。来自人和其他生物的表达序列(表达序列标签(EST)和互补 DNA)和蛋白质信息，为从浩瀚的

complementary DNAs) and proteins from humans and other organisms provide a more accurate resource for resolving gene structures against the vast genomic background. The most effective algorithms integrate gene-prediction methods with similarity comparisons. Such algorithms are integral to software programs such as GeneWise[12], Genomescan[13] and Genie[14], which provide accurate, automatic predictions, whereas BLAST or FASTA programs typically require considerable manual effort to determine the complete structure of a single gene.

The most powerful tool for finding genes may be other vertebrate genomes. Comparing conserved sequence regions between two closely related organisms will enable us to find genes and other important regions in both genomes with no previous knowledge of the gene content of either. The next couple of years should see the sequencing of the mouse, zebrafish and *Tetraodon* genomes. The preliminary sequence of *Tetraodon* has already proved useful in estimating gene numbers[15], and shows much promise for the use of comparative genomics in gene prediction.

Resources Available to the User

There are a number of resources currently available for perusing the human genome. "Human Genome Central"[16] attempts to gather together the most useful web sites (see http://www.ensembl.org/genome/central/ or http://www.ncbi.nlm.nih.gov/genome/central). The best starting point for the uninitiated will be a site such as those of NCBI, Ensembl or the University of California Santa Cruz (UCSC). These sites offer a mixture of genomic viewers and web-searchable datasets, and allow analysis of the human genome sequence without the need to run complex software locally.

For more involved analysis, it might be necessary to download some of the data locally. Useful downloadable sequence-oriented datasets include protein datasets (available from Ensembl and NCBI) and the assembled DNA sequence for regions of the genome, available at UCSC. Other genomic datasets are also available, such as the global physical map from The Genome Sequencing Center in St Louis and the single nucleotide polymorphism (SNP) database from NCBI. Raw sequence data is available from the International Nucleotide Database (GenBank/EMBL/DDBJ), but this data is generally more difficult to handle because it is very fragmentary, can contain contaminating non-human DNA and may include misleading information such as incorrect map assignment.

This loose network of sites will probably coalesce into a more coordinated network of sites offering informative web pages and resources. NCBI, Ensembl and UCSC are developing new, more accessible resources that will become available within the next year.

614

基因组背景中解析出基因结构提供了更为精确的数据源。最有效的算法是把基因预测方法和相似性比较整合在一起。这类算法已经被整合进一系列的软件程序中，例如 GeneWise[12]、Genomescan[13]以及 Genie[14]，它们可以提供准确的自动化预测。与之相比，使用 BLAST 和 FASTA 程序通常需要相当多的人工工作来确定一个基因的完整结构。

寻找基因最为有效的工具也许就是其他脊椎动物的基因组。比较两个近缘生物的序列保守区可以使我们不必知道两个基因组中任何一个基因的内容就能发现这两个基因组中的基因和其他重要区域。未来几年应该会看到对小鼠、斑马鱼和河鲀鱼基因组的测序。河鲀鱼基因组的初步测序结果在预测基因数目方面的作用已经得到证实[15]，同时显示出比较基因组学在基因预测方面的应用很有前景。

用户可以利用的资源

目前，已经有了一些可用于详尽分析人类基因组的资源。"人类基因组中心"[16]正试图将最有用的网站（参见 http://www.ensembl.org/genome/central/ 或者 http://www.ncbi.nlm.nih.gov/genome/central）集合在一起。对于缺少经验的人而言，最好的起点就是类似于 NCBI、Ensembl 或者加州大学圣克鲁兹分校（UCSC）这样的一些站点。这些站点都提供了基因组浏览器以及可通过网络搜索的数据库，这样可以允许使用者对人类基因组序列进行分析，而无需在本地运行复杂的软件。

对于更进一步的分析，可能就需要将一些数据下载到本地了。有用的可供下载的定位于序列的数据库，包括蛋白质数据库（可以在 Ensembl 和 NCBI 上获得）以及基因组区域组装好的 DNA 序列，可以在 UCSC 上获得。其他一些基因组数据库也是可以利用的，比如来自圣路易斯的基因组测序中心的完整物理图谱，以及 NCBI 提供的单核苷酸多态性（SNP）数据库。原始的序列数据可以从国际核酸数据库（GenBank/EMBL/DDBJ）获得，但是这类数据通常更难处理，因为它们的片段化非常严重，可能包含受污染的非人类 DNA 序列，还可能包含误导性信息，比如错误的图谱排列。

这些松散的网络站点有可能合并成为一个更为协同的网络，可以提供信息丰富的网页以及资源。NCBI、Ensembl 以及 UCSC 等正在开发新的、更容易使用的资源，这些资源在接下来的一年内将可以供人使用。

How to Use the Resources

There are two main ways to use the human genome sequence. First, we can look for a homologue of a protein that is known from another organism. For example, Clayton *et al.*[10] looked for relatives of the *Drosophila* period clock protein and found the three known relatives and a possible fourth cousin on chromosome 7. Or we can try and find all of the proteins belonging to a particular family—in ref. 4, Tupler *et al.* catalogue all homeobox domains[4]. The easiest way to approach these problems is to use a protein set. This sidesteps the frustration of predicting genes, but makes the researcher reliant on the quality of the predictions being provided. For most of the accompanying reports, a single protein set was the most useful resource provided. For example, Nestler *et al.* searched for G-protein receptor kinases[3] using PSI-BLAST, which searches only protein datasets.

What are the potential pitfalls of the data? Human genes are hard to predict and are often fragmented. If each end of a query protein matches to a different predicted protein, we should suspect that the query sequence may in fact be two parts of a fragmented gene. The two matched human genes should be in the same or adjacent genomic locations. Pollard[8] discovered that fragmentation complicated the analysis of myosin genes. In addition, the unfinished human genomic DNA may contain contamination, particularly from bacteria but also from other sources. Contaminating DNA is routinely removed from finished sequence, but some is still present in unfinished sequence. If the predicted gene matches a bacterial gene more closely than any vertebrate gene then it will almost always be a contaminant. Futreal *et al.*[2] were led up a blind alley for a week before they discovered that cDNA contamination in draft genomic sequences was giving the false impression of multiple p53 proteins in the genome.

During the assembly of unfinished human genomic data it is possible to create artificial duplications, which can result in artefacts in the subsequent analysis. Very similar gene sequences found within the same clone may represent duplicate genes, but could also be the result of an assembly error. This also means that predicted protein sets may contain artificial duplications, leading to overestimation of the number of members in a family.

What does this analysis tell us? For Bock *et al.*[7], the draft genome revealed a list of the molecular players involved in membrane trafficking, providing a platform for experiments that may complete our understanding of this area of biology. In contrast, Murray and Marks[9] found no new cyclin-dependent kinases, indicating that they were all found by traditional experimental techniques. Futreal *et al.* had a similar experience for known cancer genes, but suggest that with new techniques the genome will provide new avenues of cancer research[2].

The interpretation of unfinished draft genomic data may seem like hard work. But it is something to become accustomed to, because we expect future vertebrate genomes to be

如何使用这些资源

使用人类基因组序列有两种主要方式。首先，我们可以寻找与其他生物中已知蛋白质同源的蛋白质。例如，克莱顿等人[10]在人类基因组序列中寻找与果蝇周期性时钟蛋白具有亲缘关系的蛋白，结果在 7 号染色体上发现了三个已知的同源蛋白以及可能的第四个远亲蛋白。或者，我们可以尝试寻找属于一个特定家族的所有蛋白质——在参考文献 4 中，图普勒等人整理了所有的同源异型框结构域[4]。解决这些问题最简单的途径是使用一个蛋白质数据库。这样就规避了预测基因的困难，但这使研究者要依赖提供的数据质量。对于大多数研究产生的报告，单一的蛋白质数据库是所提供的最为有效的数据源。举例来讲，内斯特勒等人使用 PSI-BLAST 程序搜索 G 蛋白受体激酶[3]，这个过程只搜索了蛋白质数据库。

这些数据潜在的缺陷是什么？人类基因难以预测，并且通常是片段化的。如果所查询蛋白的每一端匹配上了不同的预测蛋白，我们应该怀疑查询序列实际上可能是一个片段化基因的两个部分。两个匹配上的人类基因应当在基因组上处于相同或者邻近的位置。波拉德[8]发现基因的片段化使得对肌球蛋白基因的分析变得复杂。除此之外，没有完成的人类基因组 DNA 可能会含有污染，特别是来自细菌的污染，当然，也有可能是其他来源的污染。按照规程，污染 DNA 会从完成的序列中移除，但是仍然会有一些留存在尚未完成的序列中。如果预测的基因与细菌基因的相似性超过了任何脊椎动物的基因，那么几乎可以肯定就是污染物。富特雷亚尔等人[2]被带进了死胡同里，他们花了将近一个星期的时间，才发现基因组草图序列中的 cDNA 污染造成了人类基因组中含有多个 p53 蛋白这一错误印象。

在对未完成的人类基因组数据进行组装的过程中，有可能会造成人为的重复，从而导致后续序列分析中的假象。在同一个克隆中找到的非常相似的基因序列可能代表基因复制，但也可能是组装错误的结果。这也意味着预测得到的蛋白质数据库中可能包含人为引入的重复，从而导致高估某个家族中所包含成员的数目。

这个分析能告诉我们什么？对于博克等人而言[7]，人类基因组草图揭示了一系列参与细胞膜转运过程的分子成员，为实验提供了一个平台，可能完善我们对生物学该领域的理解。与之相反，默里和马克斯[9]没有找到新的周期蛋白依赖性激酶，说明它们都已经被传统的实验技术发现了。弗特利尔等人对已知的癌症基因也有相似的经验，但他们的研究说明，随着新技术的使用，基因组将会为癌症的研究提供新的途径[2]。

对尚未完成的基因组草图数据的解析看起来是一项困难的工作。但是它会成为一件平常的事情，因为我们预计未来脊椎动物基因组最先会以草图的形式发布出来。

released initially in draft form. The database providers must develop better ways of viewing the data; and researchers need to be educated in how to use them. That said, there are many undiscovered treasures in the current data set waiting to be found by intuition, hard work and experimental verification. Good luck, and happy hunting!

(**409**, 827-828; 2001)

Ewan Birney[*], Alex Bateman[†], Michele E. Clamp[†] & Tim J. Hubbard[†]
[*] The European Bioinformatics Institute, Wellcome Trust Genome Campus, Hinxton, Cambridge, CB10 1SA, UK
[†] The Sanger Centre, Wellcome Trust Genome Campus, Hinxton, Cambridge CB10 1SA, UK

References:

1. International Human Genome Sequencing Consortium. Initial sequencing and analysis of the human genome. *Nature* **409**, 860-921 (2001).

2. Futreal, A., Wooster, R., Kasprzyk, A., Birney, E. & Stratton, S. Cancer and genomics. *Nature* **409**, 850- 852 (2001).

3. Nestler, E. J. & Landsman, E. Learning about addiction from the genome. *Nature* **409**, 834-835 (2001).

4. Tupler, R., Perini, G. & Green, M. R. Expressing the human genome. *Nature* **409**, 832-833 (2001).

5. Fahrer, A. M., Bazan, J. F., Papathanasiou, P., Nelms, K. A. & Goodnow, C. C. A genomic view of immunology. *Nature* **409**, 836-838 (2001).

6. Li, W-H., Gu, Z., Wang, H. & Nekrutenko, A. Evolutionary analyses of the human genome. *Nature* **409**, 847-849 (2001).

7. Bock, J. B., Matern, H. T., Peden, A. A. & Scheller, R. H. A genomic perspective on membrane compartment organization. *Nature* **409**, 839-841 (2001).

8. Pollard, T. D. Genomics, the cytoskeleton and motility. *Nature* **409**, 842-843 (2001).

9. Murray, A. W. & Marks, D. Can sequencing shed light on cell cycling? *Nature* **409**, 844-846 (2001).

10. Clayton, J. D., Kyriacou, C. P. & Reppert, S. M. Keeping time with the human genome. *Nature* **409**, 829-831 (2001).

11. Goffeau, A. *et al.* The Yeast Genome Directory. *Nature* **387** (suppl.), 1-105 (1997).

12. Birney, E. & Durbin, R. Using GeneWise in the *Drosophila* annotation experiment. *Genome Res.* **10**, 547-548 (2000).

13. Burge *et al. Nature Genet.* (submitted).

14. Reese, M. G., Kulp, D., Tammana, H., Haussler, D. Genie—gene finding in *Drosophila melanogaster*. *Genome Res.* **10**, 529-538 (2000).

15. Crollius, H. R. *et al.* Characterization and repeat analysis of the compact genome of the freshwater pufferfish *Tetraodon nigroviridis*. *Genome Res.* **10**, 939-949 (2000).

16. Genome website set up to help with sequence analysis. *Nature* **406**, 929 (2000).

Correspondence should be addressed to E.B. (e-mail: birney@ebi.ac.uk).

数据库的提供者必须开发更好的方式来查看数据；研究者则需要接受培训以运用这些方法。也就是说，在现有的数据库中，还有许多未知的宝藏等待我们通过感知、努力工作以及实验验证去发现。祝大家好运，并开始快乐的探索旅程！

（刘振明 翻译；解彬彬 审稿）

Initial Sequencing and Analysis
of the Human Genome*

International Human Genome Sequencing Consortium

Editor's Note

This paper details the first draft sequence of the human genome. The data, which were published at the same time as Celera Genomics' privately-funded human genome sequence, were the results of an international collaboration between 20 sequencing centres in 6 different countries. This draft sequence, which covers about 94% of the human genome, suggests a presence of some 30,000 to 40,000 protein-coding genes. The final count, revealed with the publication of the complete genome sequence two years later, was down-graded to around 25,000. But the paper remains important because it was the largest extensively sequenced genome of its time, the first vertebrate genome to be extensively sequenced, and uniquely, a first glimpse at the genome of our own species, holding clues to human development, physiology, medicine and evolution.

The human genome holds an extraordinary trove of information about human development, physiology, medicine and evolution. Here we report the results of an international collaboration to produce and make freely available a draft sequence of the human genome. We also present an initial analysis of the data, describing some of the insights that can be gleaned from the sequence.

THE rediscovery of Mendel's laws of heredity in the opening weeks of the 20th century[1-3] sparked a scientific quest to understand the nature and content of genetic information that has propelled biology for the last hundred years. The scientific progress made falls naturally into four main phases, corresponding roughly to the four quarters of the century. The first established the cellular basis of heredity: the chromosomes. The second defined the molecular basis of heredity: the DNA double helix. The third unlocked the informational basis of heredity, with the discovery of the biological mechanism by which cells read the information contained in genes and with the invention of the recombinant DNA technologies of cloning and sequencing by which scientists can do the same.

---

* This is a shortened version of the original paper. Some, but by no means all, of the omissions have been indicated in the text. Lists of authors and affiliations are given in the original paper. Citations are numbered herein as they are in the original paper; only those references that are cited in this version are listed in the "References" section.

620

人类基因组的初步测序与分析*

国际人类基因组测序联盟

编者按

本文详细解析了人类基因组的第一个草图序列。本文的数据是 6 个国家的 20 个测序中心的国际合作的结果，与塞莱拉基因组公司资助的人类基因组序列同时发表。草图序列覆盖了约 94% 的人类基因组，提示可能存在 30,000～40,000 个蛋白质编码基因。随着两年后完整基因组序列的发表，最终蛋白质编码基因计数结果降至 25,000 个。但是，本文仍旧占据重要地位，因为它是其所处时代最大规模的测序基因组，也是第一个经大规模测序的脊椎动物的基因组，而且非常独特的是，这也是对我们自身物种基因组的第一次探索，获得了关于人类发育、生理学、医药和进化的诸多研究线索。

人类基因组蕴含着与人类发育、生理学、医药和进化相关的海量信息。本文报道了国际合作组织的测序结果，该组织完成了人类基因组草图序列，该信息可以免费获取。我们也对这些数据进行了初步分析，描述了从序列中获得的启示。

20 世纪初，孟德尔遗传定律的重新发现[1-3]激发了人们对遗传信息的本质与内涵的探索，推动了生物学近一百年多年的发展。这些科学进展自然地分成了四个主要的阶段，大体上对应了 20 世纪的四个二十五年。第一个阶段建立了遗传的细胞学基础：染色体。第二个阶段定义了遗传的分子基础：DNA 双螺旋。第三个阶段解密了遗传的信息学基础，发现了细胞读取包含在基因中的遗传信息的生物学机制，并发明了克隆和测序的 DNA 重组技术，使得科学家可以进行 DNA 重组。

---

* 这是原文的缩略版。有一些删减在文本中标示出来了，但并非所有的删减都进行了标注。作者及单位名单请参见原文。本文中引用参考文献处的编号与原文一致；文末 "References" 部分仅保留了本文中有所引用的文献。

The last quarter of a century has been marked by a relentless drive to decipher first genes and then entire genomes, spawning the field of genomics. The fruits of this work already include the genome sequences of 599 viruses and viroids, 205 naturally occurring plasmids, 185 organelles, 31 eubacteria, seven archaea, one fungus, two animals and one plant.

Here we report the results of a collaboration involving 20 groups from the United States, the United Kingdom, Japan, France, Germany and China to produce a draft sequence of the human genome. The draft genome sequence was generated from a physical map covering more than 96% of the euchromatic part of the human genome and, together with additional sequence in public databases, it covers about 94% of the human genome. The sequence was produced over a relatively short period, with coverage rising from about 10% to more than 90% over roughly fifteen months. The sequence data have been made available without restriction and updated daily throughout the project. The task ahead is to produce a finished sequence, by closing all gaps and resolving all ambiguities. Already about one billion bases are in final form and the task of bringing the vast majority of the sequence to this standard is now straightforward and should proceed rapidly.

The sequence of the human genome is of interest in several respects. It is the largest genome to be extensively sequenced so far, being 25 times as large as any previously sequenced genome and eight times as large as the sum of all such genomes. It is the first vertebrate genome to be extensively sequenced. And, uniquely, it is the genome of our own species.

Much work remains to be done to produce a complete finished sequence, but the vast trove of information that has become available through this collaborative effort allows a global perspective on the human genome. Although the details will change as the sequence is finished, many points are already clear.

- The genomic landscape shows marked variation in the distribution of a number of features, including genes, transposable elements, GC content, CpG islands and recombination rate. This gives us important clues about function. For example, the developmentally important HOX gene clusters are the most repeat-poor regions of the human genome, probably reflecting the very complex coordinate regulation of the genes in the clusters.

- There appear to be about 30,000–40,000 protein-coding genes in the human genome— only about twice as many as in worm or fly. However, the genes are more complex, with more alternative splicing generating a larger number of protein products.

- The full set of proteins (the "proteome") encoded by the human genome is more complex than those of invertebrates. This is due in part to the presence of vertebrate-specific protein domains and motifs (an estimated 7% of the total), but more to the fact that vertebrates appear to have arranged pre-existing components into a richer collection of domain architectures.

20 世纪的最后二十五年，科学家们通过不懈努力破译了第一组基因，随后进一步破译了完整的基因组，从而开创了新的研究领域——基因组学。这项工作的研究成果包括了 599 个病毒和类病毒、205 个天然质粒、185 个细胞器、31 株真细菌、7 株古菌、1 株真菌、2 种动物和 1 种植物的基因组序列。

本文报道了来自美国、英国、日本、法国、德国和中国的 20 多个团队的合作研究成果，他们合作完成了人类基因组草图的构建。基因组草图序列由物理图谱产生，该图谱覆盖了基因组常染色质 96% 的序列，加上公共数据库中的其他序列，大约覆盖了人类基因组 94% 的序列。序列的构建所耗费的时间相对较短，序列覆盖度从大约 10% 达到 90% 以上只用了大约 15 个月。序列数据可开放获取，没有任何限制，且在项目进行过程中每天更新。项目下一步的任务是构建基因组完成图，修补所有序列缺口，并解决所有序列歧义。人类基因组中已经有 10 亿个碱基得到了确认，将大部分序列按上述标准落实是项目的首要任务，需要迅速完成。

人类基因组序列从多个方面来看都十分有趣。它是目前被大规模测序的基因组中最大的一个，是之前测序的任意一个基因组的 25 倍，也是之前测序的基因组总和的 8 倍。它是第一个被大规模测序的脊椎动物的基因组。而且，特别的是，它还是我们人类自己的基因组。

为了构建基因组完成图，仍有大量工作需要做，但是在合作者的共同努力下，我们已经获得了海量有价值的信息，可以从全球视角认识人类基因组。尽管当序列全部完成时一些细节会改变，但是很多要点已经理清。

- 基因组全景显示，基因组的大量特征在分布上存在显著差异，包括基因、转座元件、GC 含量、CpG 岛和重组率，这为我们提供了重要的功能线索。例如，对发育非常重要的 HOX 基因簇是基因组上重复序列最贫瘠的区域，这可能反映了基因簇中复杂的基因间协同调控。

- 人类基因组上约有 30,000 ~ 40,000 个蛋白质编码基因，仅约为线虫或果蝇的两倍。然而，人类基因更为复杂，具有更多的可变剪接，可产生更多的蛋白质产物。

- 人类基因组所编码的全部蛋白质（"蛋白质组"）比无脊椎动物更为复杂。这一现象部分是由于脊椎动物特异性蛋白质结构域和基序的出现（约占总量的 7%），但更重要的是，脊椎动物似乎已经将先前存在的组分组装为更丰富的结构域集合体系。

- Hundreds of human genes appear likely to have resulted from horizontal transfer from bacteria at some point in the vertebrate lineage. Dozens of genes appear to have been derived from transposable elements.

- Although about half of the human genome derives from transposable elements, there has been a marked decline in the overall activity of such elements in the hominid lineage. DNA transposons appear to have become completely inactive and long-terminal repeat (LTR) retroposons may also have done so.

- The pericentromeric and subtelomeric regions of chromosomes are filled with large recent segmental duplications of sequence from elsewhere in the genome. Segmental duplication is much more frequent in humans than in yeast, fly or worm.

- Analysis of the organization of Alu elements explains the longstanding mystery of their surprising genomic distribution, and suggests that there may be strong selection in favour of preferential retention of Alu elements in GC-rich regions and that these "selfish" elements may benefit their human hosts.

- The mutation rate is about twice as high in male as in female meiosis, showing that most mutation occurs in males.

- Cytogenetic analysis of the sequenced clones confirms suggestions that large GC-poor regions are strongly correlated with "dark G-bands" in karyotypes.

- Recombination rates tend to be much higher in distal regions (around 20 megabases (Mb)) of chromosomes and on shorter chromosome arms in general, in a pattern that promotes the occurrence of at least one crossover per chromosome arm in each meiosis.

- More than 1.4 million single nucleotide polymorphisms (SNPs) in the human genome have been identified. This collection should allow the initiation of genome-wide linkage disequilibrium mapping of the genes in the human population.

In this paper, we start by presenting background information on the project and describing the generation, assembly and evaluation of the draft genome sequence. We then focus on an initial analysis of the sequence itself: the broad chromosomal landscape; the repeat elements and the rich palaeontological record of evolutionary and biological processes that they provide; the human genes and proteins and their differences and similarities with those of other organisms; and the history of genomic segments. (Comparisons are drawn throughout with the genomes of the budding yeast *Saccharomyces cerevisiae*, the nematode worm *Caenorhabditis elegans*, the fruitfly *Drosophila melanogaster* and the mustard weed *Arabidopsis thaliana*; we refer to these for convenience simply as yeast, worm, fly and mustard weed.) Finally, we discuss applications of the sequence to biology and medicine and describe next steps in the project. A full description of the methods is provided as Supplementary Information on *Nature*'s web site (http://www. nature.com).

- 几百个人类基因似乎来自细菌的横向转移，这可能发生在脊椎动物世系的某个点。很多基因似乎起源于转座元件。

- 尽管人类基因组约半数起源于转座元件，类人猿世系中的这一类元件的整体活性出现了显著的降低。DNA 转座子似乎已完全失活，长末端重复序列（LTR）反转录转座子可能也已失活。

- 染色体的近着丝粒和亚端粒区域被近期发生的大片段的重复序列所填补，这些序列来自基因组的其他区域。在人类基因组中，片段重复的发生概率远高于酵母、果蝇或线虫。

- 对 Alu 元件结构组织的分析解释了长期困扰我们的谜团，即它们惊人的全基因组范围的分布，提示了可能存在强烈的选择，使 Alu 元件偏好性地保留在 GC 富集区。这些"自私"元件可能使其人类宿主收益。

- 男性减数分裂的突变率约为女性的两倍，显示多数突变发生在男性中。

- 对已测序的克隆的细胞遗传学分析确认了一种假设，即大片段的 GC 匮乏区与染色体核型中的"暗 G 带"存在强烈关联。

- 染色体远端（约 20 兆碱基（Mb））的重组率显著升高，在染色体短臂上则为平均值，这种模式促使每条染色体臂在每次减数分裂时至少发生一次交换。

- 在人类基因组中识别出了超过 140 万个单核苷酸多态性（SNP），这使我们可以在人类种群中建立基因组范围的连锁不平衡图谱。

在本文中，我们从展示人类基因组计划的背景信息开始，描述了基因组草图序列的产生、组装和评估。随后，我们聚焦于序列本身的初步分析：宽泛的染色体全景；重复序列元件，以及丰富的关于进化的古生物学证据以及它们提供的生物学过程；人类基因和蛋白质与其他生物的基因和蛋白质的差异和相似性；基因组片段的历史。（这些比较是通过出芽生殖的酿酒酵母、线虫类的秀丽隐杆线虫、黑腹果蝇、芥草拟南芥的基因组提取的；方便起见，我们将这四种生物简称为酵母、线虫、果蝇和芥草。）最后，我们讨论了这些序列在生物学和医药方面的应用，并描述了人类基因组计划的下一步工作。《自然》杂志网站（http://www.nature.com）上的补充信息提供了关于研究方法的完整描述。

We recognize that it is impossible to provide a comprehensive analysis of this vast dataset, and thus our goal is to illustrate the range of insights that can be gleaned from the human genome and thereby to sketch a research agenda for the future.

Background to the Human Genome Project

The Human Genome Project arose from two key insights that emerged in the early 1980s: that the ability to take global views of genomes could greatly accelerate biomedical research, by allowing researchers to attack problems in a comprehensive and unbiased fashion; and that the creation of such global views would require a communal effort in infrastructure building, unlike anything previously attempted in biomedical research.

The idea of sequencing the entire human genome was first proposed in discussions at scientific meetings organized by the US Department of Energy and others from 1984 to 1986 (refs 21, 22). A committee appointed by the US National Research Council endorsed the concept in its 1988 report[23], but recommended a broader programme, to include: the creation of genetic, physical and sequence maps of the human genome; parallel efforts in key model organisms such as bacteria, yeast, worms, flies and mice; the development of technology in support of these objectives; and research into the ethical, legal and social issues raised by human genome research. The programme was launched in the US as a joint effort of the Department of Energy and the National Institutes of Health. In other countries, the UK Medical Research Council and the Wellcome Trust supported genomic research in Britain; the Centre d'Etude du Polymorphisme Humain and the French Muscular Dystrophy Association launched mapping efforts in France; government agencies, including the Science and Technology Agency and the Ministry of Education, Science, Sports and Culture supported genomic research efforts in Japan; and the European Community helped to launch several international efforts, notably the programme to sequence the yeast genome. By late 1990, the Human Genome Project had been launched, with the creation of genome centres in these countries. Additional participants subsequently joined the effort, notably in Germany and China. In addition, the Human Genome Organization (HUGO) was founded to provide a forum for international coordination of genomic research. Several books[24-26] provide a more comprehensive discussion of the genesis of the Human Genome Project.

Through 1995, work progressed rapidly on two fronts. The first was construction of genetic and physical maps of the human and mouse genomes[27-31], providing key tools for identification of disease genes and anchoring points for genomic sequence. The second was sequencing of the yeast[32] and worm[33] genomes, as well as targeted regions of mammalian genomes[34-37]. These projects showed that large-scale sequencing was feasible and developed the two-phase paradigm for genome sequencing. In the first, "shotgun", phase, the genome is divided into appropriately sized segments and each segment is covered to a high degree of redundancy (typically, eight- to tenfold) through the sequencing of randomly selected subfragments. The second is a "finishing" phase, in which sequence gaps are closed and

我们认识到本文无法提供关于这些海量数据的全面分析，因此我们的目标是，举例说明从人类基因组中所得到的具有普遍意义的新发现，从而建立起未来的研究框架。

人类基因组计划的背景

人类基因组计划起源于20世纪80年代初期的两个重要的远见：通过让研究者以深刻而无偏见的方式挑战难题，全面把握基因组的能力可以极大地促进生物医药的研究；这一全局视野的产生需要全世界在科研的基础设施建设方面共同努力，而不像之前试图进行的任何生物医药研究。

对人类全基因组进行测序的想法是在一次学术会议的讨论中产生的，该会议由美国能源部和其他机构在1984~1986年组织（参考文献21和22）。美国国家研究委员会在其1988年的报告中签署同意了这一概念[23]，但是他们建议将项目的目标拓宽，包括：建立人类基因组的遗传图谱、物理图谱和序列图谱；同时建立关键模式生物如细菌、酵母、线虫、果蝇和小鼠的上述三种图谱；发展支持上述目标的技术；研究因人类基因组研究而产生的伦理、法律和社会议题。该项目由美国能源部和美国国立卫生研究院联合启动。在其他国家，英国医学研究理事会和维康信托基金会支持了英国的基因组研究；法国人类多态性研究中心和肌肉萎缩症协会落实了法国的测序工作；政府机构，包括日本科学振兴机构、文部科学省支持了日本的基因组研究；欧洲共同体发起了若干国际项目，尤其是酵母基因组测序项目。至1990年末，人类基因组计划已经展开，并在这些国家建立了基因组研究中心。随后有更多的国家加入到这一项目，主要是德国和中国。而且还成立了国际人类基因组组织（HUGO），为基因组研究的国际协作提供论坛。一些著作[24-26]提供了关于人类基因组计划产生的更加深入的讨论。

1995年，研究工作在以下两个前沿快速进展。第一，建立了人类和小鼠基因组的遗传和物理图谱[27-31]，提供了识别疾病基因和基因组序列锚定位点的关键工具。第二，测定了酵母[32]和线虫[33]的基因组以及哺乳动物基因组的靶区域[34-37]。这些项目表明了大规模测序是灵活可变的，并建立了基因组测序的两步法范例。在第一步即"鸟枪"阶段，基因组被打断成合适大小的片段，通过随机挑取亚片段测序，每个片段都被覆盖且高度冗余（通常来说，8~10倍）。第二步是"完成"阶段，在这一阶段，通过直接分析，填补序列的缺口，纠正序列歧义。上述结果也显示，完整

remaining ambiguities are resolved through directed analysis. The results also showed that complete genomic sequence provided information about genes, regulatory regions and chromosome structure that was not readily obtainable from cDNA studies alone.

The human genome sequencing effort moved into full-scale production in March 1999. The idea of first producing a draft genome sequence was revived at this time, both because the ability to finish such a sequence was no longer in doubt and because there was great hunger in the scientific community for human sequence data. In addition, some scientists favoured prioritizing the production of a draft genome sequence over regional finished sequence because of concerns about commercial plans to generate proprietary databases of human sequence that might be subject to undesirable restrictions on use[42-44].

The consortium focused on an initial goal of producing, in a first production phase lasting until June 2000, a draft genome sequence covering most of the genome. Such a draft genome sequence, although not completely finished, would rapidly allow investigators to begin to extract most of the information in the human sequence. Experiments showed that sequencing clones covering about 90% of the human genome to a redundancy of about four- to fivefold ("half-shotgun" coverage) would accomplish this[45,46]. The draft genome sequence goal has been achieved, as described below.

The second sequence production phase is now under way. Its aims are to achieve full-shotgun coverage of the existing clones during 2001, to obtain clones to fill the remaining gaps in the physical map, and to produce a finished sequence (apart from regions that cannot be cloned or sequenced with currently available techniques) no later than 2003.

Strategic Issues

Hierarchical shotgun sequencing

Soon after the invention of DNA sequencing methods[47,48], the shotgun sequencing strategy was introduced[49-51]; it has remained the fundamental method for large-scale genome sequencing[52-54] for the past 20 years. The approach has been refined and extended to make it more efficient. For example, improved protocols for fragmenting and cloning DNA allowed construction of shotgun libraries with more uniform representation. The practice of sequencing from both ends of double-stranded clones ("double-barrelled" shotgun sequencing) was introduced by Ansorge and others[37] in 1990, allowing the use of "linking information" between sequence fragments.

Practical difficulties arise because of repeated sequences and cloning bias. The human genome is filled (> 50%) with repeated sequences, including interspersed repeats derived from transposable elements, and long genomic regions that have been duplicated in tandem, palindromic or dispersed fashion. Such features complicate the assembly of a correct and finished genome sequence.

628

的基因组序列提供了关于基因、调控区和染色体结构的信息，这些信息是无法仅从cDNA研究中获得的。

1999年3月，人类基因组测序经过努力，进入了全序列产生阶段。首先生成一个基因组草图序列的想法在这一时期重新流行起来，这一方面是因为完成这样的序列的能力已经不再是问题，另一方面也是因为科学共同体对人类序列数据有着强大的需求。而且，一些科学家支持优先产生基因组草图序列，而不是局部完成序列。因为一些商业计划企图对人类基因组序列数据库申请专利，这可能会对数据的使用造成不良限制[42-44]。

科学共同体聚焦于产生数据这一首要目标，即第一阶段持续到2000年6月，在此之前使基因组草图序列覆盖基因组的大部分区域。这一基因组草图序列尽管没有彻底完成，但也使得研究者们能够尽快地提取到人类基因组中的大部分信息。实验显示，测序克隆覆盖约90%的人类基因组，约4～5倍冗余（"半鸟枪"覆盖率）[45,46]。如下所示，人类基因组草图序列目标已完成。

第二阶段正在进行中，旨在于2001年获得目前所有克隆的全鸟枪覆盖，并获得能够填补物理图谱缺口的克隆，以便在2003年之前生成基因组序列完成图（除了现有技术无法克隆和测序的基因组区域之外）。

策 略 问 题

层次鸟枪法测序

DNA测序方法[47,48]发明以后，很快就出现了鸟枪法测序[49-51]的策略；在过去的二十多年里，鸟枪法仍然是大规模基因组测序[52-54]的基础方法。鸟枪法也在不断地补充和改进，以便更加高效。例如，DNA片段化和克隆的方法改进后，鸟枪法构建的文库更加均一。1990年，安佐格等人[37]提出了双链克隆的两端测序法（"双管"鸟枪法测序），使测序片段之间"连接信息"的使用成为可能。

由于重复序列和克隆偏好性的存在，实际操作存在不少困难。人类基因组含有大量（＞50%）重复序列，包括起源于转座元件的散在重复序列，以及以串联、回文或散在等重复形式存在的长基因组区域。这些情况使一个正确完整的基因序列的组装工作更加复杂。

There are two approaches for sequencing large repeat-rich genomes. The first is a whole-genome shotgun sequencing approach, as has been used for the repeat-poor genomes of viruses, bacteria and flies, using linking information and computational analysis to attempt to avoid misassemblies. The second is the "hierarchical shotgun sequencing" approach (Fig. 2), also referred to as "map-based", "BAC-based" or "clone-by-clone". This approach involves generating and organizing a set of large-insert clones (typically 100–200 kb each) covering the genome and separately performing shotgun sequencing on appropriately chosen clones. Because the sequence information is local, the issue of long-range misassembly is eliminated and the risk of short-range misassembly is reduced.

Fig 2. Idealized representation of the hierarchical shotgun sequencing strategy. A library is constructed by fragmenting the target genome and cloning it into a large-fragment cloning vector; here, BAC vectors are shown. The genomic DNA fragments represented in the library are then organized into a physical map and individual BAC clones are selected and sequenced by the random shotgun strategy. Finally, the clone sequences are assembled to reconstruct the sequence of the genome.

A biotechnology company, Celera Genomics, has chosen to incorporate the whole-genome shotgun approach into its own efforts to sequence the human genome. Their plan[60,61] uses a mixed strategy, involving combining some coverage with whole-genome shotgun data generated by the company together with the publicly available hierarchical shotgun data generated by the International Human Genome Sequencing Consortium. If the raw sequence reads from the whole-genome shotgun component are made available, it may be possible to evaluate the extent to which the sequence of the human genome can be assembled without the need for clone-based information. Such analysis may help to refine sequencing strategies for other large genomes.

对富含重复序列的大型基因组进行测序，目前有两种途径。一种是全基因组鸟枪测序法，这种方法用于完成病毒、细菌、果蝇等重复较少的基因组测序，使用片段链接的信息和电脑分析来避免错误组装。第二种是"层次鸟枪法测序"（图2），也称为"基于图谱""基于 BAC"或"连续克隆"法。这种方法包括生成并组装一组能覆盖整个基因组的大片段克隆（通常每个 100～200 kb），选择其中合适的克隆进行鸟枪法测序。由于所得的序列信息都是局部的，这样就不存在长程错误组装的问题，也降低了短程错误组装的风险。

图 2. 理想的层次鸟枪法测序策略。通过目的基因组片段化并克隆到大片段载体上构建文库；此处显示的是 BAC 文库。库中的基因组 DNA 片段组建成物理图谱，挑选出单个的 BAC 克隆利用随机鸟枪法测序。最后，对克隆序列进行组装并重建基因组序列。

一家生物技术公司——塞莱拉基因选择在他们的方法中融入全基因组鸟枪法来完成人类基因组测序。他们计划[60,61]使用混合式策略，将公司全基因组鸟枪法测序得到的数据与国际人类基因组测序联盟公布的层次鸟枪法数据联合。如果可获得全基因组鸟枪法组分的原始数据，就有可能估算出在不依赖克隆信息的前提下，多大程度上可对人类基因组进行组装。这样的分析会帮助修正今后其他大型基因组测序的策略。

Coordination and public data sharing

The Human Genome Project adopted two important principles with regard to human sequencing. The first was that the collaboration would be open to centres from any nation. Although potentially less efficient, in a narrow economic sense, than a centralized approach involving a few large factories, the inclusive approach was strongly favoured because we felt that the human genome sequence is the common heritage of all humanity and the work should transcend national boundaries, and we believed that scientific progress was best assured by a diversity of approaches. The collaboration was coordinated through periodic international meetings (referred to as "Bermuda meetings" after the venue of the first three gatherings) and regular telephone conferences. Work was shared flexibly among the centres, with some groups focusing on particular chromosomes and others contributing in a genome-wide fashion.

The second principle was rapid and unrestricted data release. The centres adopted a policy that all genomic sequence data should be made publicly available without restriction within 24 hours of assembly[79,80]. Pre-publication data releases had been pioneered in mapping projects in the worm[11] and mouse genomes[30,81] and were prominently adopted in the sequencing of the worm, providing a direct model for the human sequencing efforts. We believed that scientific progress would be most rapidly advanced by immediate and free availability of the human genome sequence. The explosion of scientific work based on the publicly available sequence data in both academia and industry has confirmed this judgement.

Generating the Draft Genome Sequence

Generating a draft sequence of the human genome involved three steps: selecting the BAC clones to be sequenced, sequencing them and assembling the individual sequenced clones into an overall draft genome sequence.

The draft genome sequence is a dynamic product, which is regularly updated as additional data accumulate en route to the ultimate goal of a completely finished sequence. The results below are based on the map and sequence data available on 7 October 2000, except as otherwise noted. At the end of this section, we provide a brief update of key data.

Clone selection

The hierarchical shotgun method involves the sequencing of overlapping large-insert clones spanning the genome. For the Human Genome Project, clones were largely chosen from eight large-insert libraries containing BAC or P1-derived artificial chromosome (PAC) clones (refs 82–88). The libraries were made by partial digestion of genomic DNA with restriction

632

项目协调与公共数据共享

关于人类基因组全序列，人类基因组计划采用了两项重要的原则。一是此项计划的合作面向全世界所有国家的研究中心。尽管从狭隘的经济学角度看，集中于几个大的中心的工作效率会更高，但我们强烈赞成更具包容性的合作，因为我们认为，人类基因组序列是全人类共同的财富，此项工作应跨越国家的界限，而且我们相信，多样化的途径是获得科学进展的最好保证。合作中的协调工作是通过定期的国际会议（百慕大会议，由前三次的会议地点命名）和日常电话会议完成。某些小组集中于特定的染色体，而另一些则着眼于全基因组的范围，各中心间的进展分享非常灵活。

第二点原则是快速的不受限的数据发布。所有的测序中心都遵循一个政策：在基因组序列完成组装的 24 小时内，要将其不受限地公布于众[79,80]。在线虫[11]和小鼠[30,81]基因组的图谱工作中，公开发表前的数据发布已经为人类基因组测序做了很好的榜样。我们确信，伴随人类基因组数据的及时和无偿使用，科学研究将获得迅速的进展。在学术界和产业界，基于公共可获取序列的科学研究成果的激增充分肯定了我们的判断。

生成基因组草图序列

生成人类基因组草图序列包括三步：选择要测序的 BAC 克隆，测序，将测序完成的单个克隆组装为整个基因组草图序列。

基因组草图序列是动态产物，草图序列会因数据的不断积累而经常更新，最终目标是完整的完成序列。除非特别注明，下文的结论都是基于 2000 年 10 月 7 日的图谱与序列数据。在本节的末尾，我们会提供关键数据的简要更新。

克隆选择

层次鸟枪法的测序包括遍布整个基因组的相互重叠的大片段插入克隆。对人类基因组计划来说，克隆大部分选自 8 个大片段插入文库，包括 BAC 或 P1 人工染色体（PAC）克隆（参考文献 82～88）。文库是由限制性内切酶部分消化基因组 DNA 后

enzymes. Together, they represent around 65-fold coverage (redundant sampling) of the genome. Libraries based on other vectors, such as cosmids, were also used in early stages of the project.

The libraries were prepared from DNA obtained from anonymous human donors in accordance with US Federal Regulations for the Protection of Human Subjects in Research (45CFR46) and following full review by an Institutional Review Board. Briefly the opportunity to donate DNA for this purpose was broadly advertised near the two laboratories engaged in library construction. Volunteers of diverse backgrounds were accepted on a first-come, first-taken basis. Samples were obtained after discussion with a genetic counsellor and written informed consent. The samples were made anonymous as follows: the sampling laboratory stripped all identifiers from the samples, applied random numeric labels, and transferred them to the processing laboratory, which then removed all labels and relabelled the samples. All records of the labelling were destroyed. The processing laboratory chose samples at random from which to prepare DNA and immortalized cell lines.

Because the sequencing project was shared among twenty centres in six countries, it was important to coordinate selection of clones across the centres. Most centres focused on particular chromosomes or, in some cases, larger regions of the genome. We also maintained a clone registry to track selected clones and their progress. In later phases, the global map provided an integrated view of the data from all centres, facilitating the distribution of effort to maximize coverage of the genome. Before performing extensive sequencing on a clone, several centres routinely examined an initial sample of 96 raw sequence reads from each subclone library to evaluate possible overlap with previously sequenced clones.

Sequencing

The selected clones were subjected to shotgun sequencing. Detailed protocols are available on the web sites of many of the individual centres.

The overall sequencing output rose sharply during production (Fig. 4). Following installation of new sequence detectors beginning in June 1999, sequencing capacity and output rose approximately eightfold in eight months to nearly 7 million samples processed per month, with little or no drop in success rate (ratio of useable reads to attempted reads). By June 2000, the centres were producing raw sequence at a rate equivalent to onefold coverage of the entire human genome in less than six weeks. This corresponded to a continuous throughput exceeding 1,000 nucleotides per second, 24 hours per day, seven days per week. This scale-up resulted in a concomitant increase in the sequence available in the public databases (Fig. 4).

构建的。总的来说，样品覆盖 65 倍的基因组（样品冗余）。在计划早期，我们也应用了其他的一些载体，比如黏粒等。

制备文库所使用的 DNA 来自匿名的捐献者，符合美国联邦法律对于保护研究中的人类受试对象的规定（45CFR46），并且接受机构审查委员会的监督。简单地说就是构建文库的两个实验室在其附近广泛宣传了此次捐献 DNA 的机会。不同背景的志愿者的接收采取先到先取的方式。在与遗传顾问讨论并签署知情同意书后，样品被采集。样品的匿名程序如下：采样实验室去掉所有样品的标签，用随机数字进行编号，将样品移交给处理实验室，后者再次去掉标签并重新标记。所有的标记记录都被销毁。处理实验室会随机选取制备 DNA 的样品，并且将细胞系永生化。

由于测序计划是在 6 个国家的 20 个中心共同完成的，协调各中心的克隆选择是非常重要的。大部分中心的测序集中于特定染色体，另一些则着眼于全基因组范围。我们维护了一个克隆注册表，用以跟踪选出的克隆及后续进展。在后期，全局图谱提供了来自所有研究中心的数据整合视图，这样有助于在各中心间分配工作从而获得基因组的最大覆盖度。在对某个克隆进行详细测序以前，几个中心通常会对最初样品的每一个亚克隆文库的 96 个原始读序进行检验，评估其与已完成测序的克隆出现重叠的可能性。

测序

选出的克隆随后被送去做鸟枪法测序。具体的操作方法可在各中心的网站上获得。

在计划完成过程中，测序结果的输出量在急剧增加（图 4）。1999 年 6 月开始安装新的测序仪后，测序能力和输出量在 8 个月内增长至原来的 8 倍，每月可处理近 700 万样品，而成功率（可用读序与尝试读序的比率）几乎没有下降。到 2000 年 6 月，所有中心获得原始序列的速度相当于在不到 6 周时间内将整个人类基因组覆盖一遍。这相当于每周七天、每天工作 24 小时、每秒测出的核苷酸超过 1,000 个的连续通量。这种扩容也同步增加了公共数据库中的可用序列（图 4）。

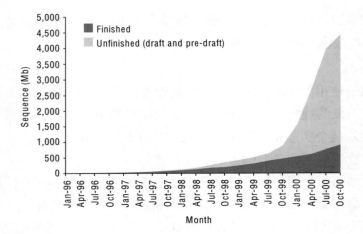

Fig 4. Total amount of human sequence in the High Throughput Genome Sequence (HTGS) division of GenBank. The total is the sum of finished sequence (red) and unfinished (draft plus predraft) sequence (yellow).

Although the main emphasis was on producing a draft genome sequence, the centres also maintained sequence finishing activities during this period, leading to a twofold increase in finished sequence from June 1999 to June 2000 (Fig. 4). The total amount of human sequence in this final form stood at more than 835 Mb on 7 October 2000, or more than 25% of the human genome. This includes the finished sequences of chromosomes 21 and 22 (refs 93, 94). As centres have begun to shift from draft to finished sequencing in the last quarter of 2000, the production of finished sequence has increased to an annualized rate of 1 Gb per year and is continuing to rise.

Assembly of the draft genome sequence

We then set out to assemble the sequences from the individual large-insert clones into an integrated draft sequence of the human genome. The assembly process had to resolve problems arising from the draft nature of much of the sequence, from the variety of clone sources, and from the high fraction of repeated sequences in the human genome. (Editorial note: several details of the assembly procedure have been omitted in this shortened version.)

The result of the assembly process is an integrated draft sequence of the human genome. (Editorial note: details of sequence quality assessment have been omitted.)

The contiguity of the draft genome sequence at each level is an important feature.

Genome coverage

We assessed the nature of the gaps within the draft genome sequence, and attempted to

图 4. GenBank 中经高通量基因组测序 (HTGS) 的人类基因组序列总量。总数为完成序列 (红色) 和未完成 (草图和前草图) 序列 (黄色) 的总量。

尽管工作重点在于生成基因组草图序列，但各中心在此期间也一直在做最终序列的整理，使 1999 年 6 月到 2000 年 6 月之间完成序列的数量增加了一倍 (图 4)。2000 年 10 月 7 日，最终形式的人类基因组序列总量超过 835 Mb，大于人类基因组的 25%。这其中包含了测序完成的第 21 和 22 号染色体 (参考文献 93 和 94)。2000 年最后一个季度开始，各中心的工作从草图测序转向完成序列，完成序列的产量每年增加 1 Gb，并持续上升。

基因组草图序列的组装

随后，我们着手将单独的大片段插入克隆的序列组装成人类基因组草图序列。装配过程必须解决大部分序列以草图形式存在产生的问题、不同克隆来源产生的问题和人类基因组中高比例的重复序列产生的问题。(编者注：在这篇删减版中组装过程的细节被删减了。)

组装过程的结果是产生一个整合的人类基因组草图序列。(编者注：序列质量的测试细节被删减了。)

基因组草图序列在各层次上的连续性是一个重要特征。

基因组覆盖度

我们对基因组草图序列中间隙的性质进行了评估，并尝试估计人类基因组未表

estimate the fraction of the human genome not represented within the current version.

Our results indicate that about 88% of the human genome is represented in the draft genome sequence and about 94% in the combined publicly available sequence databases. The figure of 88% agrees well with our independent estimates above that about 3%, 5% and 4% of the genome reside in the three types of gap in the draft genome sequence.

We arrived at a total human genome size estimate of around 3,200 Mb, which compares favourably with previous estimates based on DNA content.

We also independently estimated the size of the euchromatic portion of the genome by determining the fraction of the 5,615 random raw sequences that matched the finished portion of the human genome (whose total length is known with greater precision). Twenty-nine per cent of these raw sequences found a match among 835 Mb of nonredundant finished sequence. This leads to an estimate of the euchromatic genome size of 2.9 Gb. This agrees reasonably with a prediction based on the length of the draft genome sequence.

Broad Genomic Landscape

What biological insights can be gleaned from the draft sequence? In this section, we consider very large-scale features of the draft genome sequence: the distribution of GC content, CpG islands and recombination rates, and the repeat content and gene content of the human genome. The draft genome sequence makes it possible to integrate these features and others at scales ranging from individual nucleotides to collections of chromosomes. Unless noted, all analyses were conducted on the assembled draft genome sequence described above.

Figure 9 (Editorial note: since the Figure is oversized and cannot fit here, it is provided on *Nature*'s web site) provides a high-level view of the contents of the draft genome sequence, at a scale of about 3.8 Mb per centimetre. Of course, navigating information spanning nearly ten orders of magnitude requires computational tools to extract the full value. We have created and made freely available various "Genome Browsers". These web-based computer tools allow users to view an annotated display of the draft genome sequence, with the ability to scroll along the chromosomes and zoom in or out to different scales.

Fig. 9. Overview of features of draft human genome. The Figure shows the occurrences of twelve important types of feature across the human genome. Large grey blocks represent centromeres and centromeric heterochromatin (size not precisely to scale). Each of the feature types is depicted in a track, from top to bottom as follows. (1) Chromosome position in Mb. (2) The approximate positions of Giemsa-stained chromosome bands at the 800 band resolution. (3) Level of coverage in the draft genome sequence. Red, areas covered by finished clones; yellow, areas covered by predraft sequence. Regions covered by draft sequenced clones are in orange, with darker shades reflecting increasing shotgun sequence coverage. (4) GC content. Percentage of bases in a 20,000 base window that are C or G. (5) Repeat density. Red line, density of SINE class repeats in a 100,000-base window; blue

示在当前版本中的部分。

我们的结果显示，约 88% 的人类基因组存在于草图序列中，94% 在公开数据库中可获取。我们在前文的独立评估显示，约 3%、5% 和 4% 的基因组存在于基因组草图序列的三种间隙中，88% 的数字与这一结果良好吻合。

我们估计人类基因组约 3,200 Mb，与先前基于 DNA 含量的估计值接近。

我们还通过测算 5,615 个随机原始序列与人类基因组完成序列（精度更高的整体长度）的匹配度，独立估算了基因组中常染色质部分的体量。这些原始序列中的 29% 在 835 Mb 的无冗余完成序列中找到了匹配，由此估计常染色质体量为 2.9 Gb，这与依据基因组草图序列长度所做的预测结果相当。

宏观基因组蓝图

从草图序列中我们可以获得哪些生物学启示呢？在这一部分，我们将考虑那些基因组草图序列体现出的非常大范围上的特征：GC 含量分布，CpG 岛和重组率，人类基因组的重复含量和基因含量。基因组草图序列使得从单核苷酸到染色体集合等各个尺度范围上的特征的整合成为可能。除特殊说明外，以下所有分析都是基于前面所描述的组装后的基因组草图序列。

图 9（编者注：图片过大，此处无法呈现，请在《自然》杂志网站获取）提供了基因组草图序列的高级视图，每厘米约对应 3.8 Mb。当然，浏览的内容跨越近 10 个数量级，需要计算工具来提取出完整的信息。我们已经创建并免费提供各种"基因组浏览器"。这些基于网页的电脑工具使使用者能看到基因组草图序列的注释，也能沿着染色体滚动并放大或缩小到不同的比例。

图 9. 人类基因组草图特征概览。本图展示了人类基因组上 12 种重要的特征序列。大灰色方块代表着丝粒和着丝粒异染色质（大小与实际并非准确相关）。每一种特征类型都标注在基因组上，从上到下依次如下文所述。(1) 染色体位置，单位为 Mb。(2) 吉姆萨染色法染出的染色体条带位置，分辨率为 800 个条带。(3) 基因组草图序列的覆盖程度。红色，该区域被最终克隆覆盖；黄色，该区域被预组装序列覆盖。被草图序列覆盖的区域用橙色表示，深色阴影表示不断增长的鸟枪测序覆盖率。(4) GC 含量。在 20,000 碱基窗口中碱基 C 或 G 的百分比。(5) 重复序列密度。红线，SINE 类重复序列在 100,000 碱基窗口的密度；蓝线，LINE 类重复序列在 100,000 碱基窗口的密度。(6) SNP 在 50,000 碱基窗口的密

line, density of LINE class repeats in a 100,000-base window. (6) Density of SNPs in a 50,000-base window. The SNPs were detected by sequencing and alignments of random genomic reads. Some of the heterogeneity in SNP density reflects the methods used for SNP discovery. Rigorous analysis of SNP density requires comparing the number of SNPs identified to the precise number of bases surveyed. (7) Non-coding RNA genes. Brown, functional RNA genes such as tRNAs, snoRNAs and rRNAs; light orange, RNA pseudogenes. (8) CpG islands. Green ticks represent regions of ~200 bases with CpG levels significantly higher than in the genome as a whole, and GC ratios of at least 50%. (9) Exofish ecores. Regions of homology with the pufferfish *T. nigroviridis*[292] are blue. (10) ESTs with at least one intron when aligned against genomic DNA are shown as black tick marks. (11) The starts of genes predicted by Genie or Ensembl are shown as red ticks. The starts of known genes from the RefSeq database[110] are shown in blue. (12) The names of genes that have been uniquely located in the draft genome sequence, characterized and named by the HGM Nomenclature Committee. Known disease genes from the OMIM database are red, other genes blue. This Figure is based on an earlier version of the draft genome sequence than analysed in the text, owing to production constraints. We are aware of various errors in the Figure, including omissions of some known genes and misplacements of others. Some genes are mapped to more than one location, owing to errors in assembly, close paralogues or pseudogenes. Manual review was performed to select the most likely location in these cases and to correct other regions. For updated information, see http://genome.ucsc.edu/ and http://www.ensembl.org/.

In addition to using the Genome Browsers, one can download from these sites the entire draft genome sequence together with the annotations in a computer-readable format. The sequences of the underlying sequenced clones are all available through the public sequence databases. URLs for these and other genome websites are listed in Box 2.

Box 2. Sources of publicly available sequence data and other relevant genomic information

http://genome.ucsc.edu/

University of California at Santa Cruz

Contains the assembly of the draft genome sequence used in this paper and updates

http://genome.wustl.edu/gsc/human/Mapping/

Washington University

Contains links to clone and accession maps of the human genome

http://www.ensembl.org

EBI/Sanger Centre

Allows access to DNA and protein sequences with automatic baseline annotation

http://www.ncbi.nlm.nih.gov/genome/guide/

NCBI

Views of chromosomes and maps and loci with links to other NCBI resources

http://www.ncbi.nlm.nih.gov/genemap99/

Gene map 99: contains data and viewers for radiation hybrid maps of EST-based STSs

度。SNP 是通过读取随机基因组测序和比对检测到的。SNP 密度的异质性反映了 SNP 检测方法的不同。SNP 密度的精确分析需要将识别出的 SNP 数量与所研究的精确的碱基数量作比较。(7)非编码 RNA 基因。棕色，功能 RNA 基因如 tRNA、snoRNA 和 rRNA；浅橙色，RNA 假基因。(8)CpG 岛。绿色钩代表约 200 个碱基的区域，该区域的 CpG 水平显著高于全基因组，且 GC 含量至少为 50%。(9)鱼类外显子。与河豚序列[292]同源的区域为蓝色。(10)与基因组序列比对，带有至少一个内含子的 EST 用黑色钩表示。(11)通过 Genie 或 Ensembl 预测的基因起始位点用红色钩表示。从 RefSeq 数据库[110]中得到的已知基因的起始位点用蓝色表示。(12)每一个基因特有的名字已经定位在基因组草图序列中，经 HGM 命名委员会表征并命名。来自 OMIM 数据库的已知疾病基因用红色表示，其他基因用蓝色表示。限于输出限制，本图是基于基因组草图序列的早期版本而不是本文分析的内容绘制的。我们意识到图中有几处错误，包括遗漏了一些已知基因以及搞错了其他一些基因的位置。由于组装、相近的同源序列或假基因方面的错误，一些基因被标注在多个位点。通过人工检查我们挑出了上述情况中最有可能的位置，并将其更正。关于更新的信息，请见 http://genome.ucsc.edu/ 和 http://ensembl.org/。

除了使用基因组浏览器之外，使用者还可以从这些网站下载计算机可读的基因组草图序列和相应的注释。那些基础测序的克隆的序列都可以从公共序列数据库获得。上述网站和其他基因组网站的 URL 列表在框 2 中。

框 2. 可公开获取的序列数据及其他相关基因组信息的来源

http://genome.ucsc.edu/
加州大学圣克鲁兹分校
包含本文及后续更新中使用的基因组草图序列的组装

http://genome.wustl.edu/gsc/human/Mapping/
华盛顿大学
包含人类基因组的克隆和接入图谱的链接

http://www.ensembl.org
EBI/桑格中心
可以访问带有自动基线注释的 DNA 和蛋白质序列

http://www.ncbi.nlm.nih.gov/genome/guide/
NCBI
可浏览染色体、图谱和基因座，并带有其他 NCBI 资源的链接

http://www.ncbi.nlm.nih.gov/genemap99/
Gene map 99：包含基于 EST 的 STS 辐射杂交图谱的数据和阅读器

http://compbio.ornl.gov/channel/index.html

Oak Ridge National Laboratory

Java viewers for human genome data

http://hgrep.ims.u-tokyo.ac.jp/

RIKEN and the University of Tokyo

Gives an overview of the entire human genome structure

http://snp.cshl.org/

The SNP Consortium

Includes a variety of ways to query for SNPs in the human genome

http://www.ncbi.nlm.nih.gov/Omim/

Online *Mendelian Inheritance in Man*

Contain information about human genes and disease

http://www.nhgri.nih.gov/ELSI/ and http://www.ornl.gov/hgmis/elsi/elsi.html

NHGRI and DOE

Contains information, links and articles on a wide range of social, ethical and legal issues

Long-range variation in GC content

The existence of GC-rich and GC-poor regions in the human genome was first revealed by experimental studies involving density gradient separation, which indicated substantial variation in average GC content among large fragments. Subsequent studies have indicated that these GC-rich and GC-poor regions may have different biological properties, such as gene density, composition of repeat sequences, correspondence with cytogenetic bands and recombination rate[112-117]. Many of these studies were indirect, owing to the lack of sufficient sequence data.

The draft genome sequence makes it possible to explore the variation in GC content in a direct and global manner. Visual inspection (Fig. 9) confirms that local GC content undergoes substantial long-range excursions from its genome-wide average of 41%.

There are huge regions (> 10 Mb) with GC content far from the average.

Long-range variation in GC content is evident not just from extreme outliers, but throughout the genome.

The correlation between GC content domains and various biological properties is of great interest, and this is likely to be the most fruitful route to understanding the basis of variation http://compbio.ornl.gov/channel/index.html

橡树岭国家实验室

用于人类基因组数据的 Java 阅读器

http://hgrep.ims.u-tokyo.ac.jp/

RIKEN 及东京大学

给出整个人类基因组结构的总览

http://snp.cshl.org/

SNP 联盟

包含查询人类基因组中 SNP 的多种方式

http://www.ncbi.nlm.nih.gov/Omim/

在线人类孟德尔遗传数据库

包含关于人类基因和疾病的信息

http://www.nhgri.nih.gov/ELSI/and http://www.ornl.gov/hgmis/elsi/elsi.html

NHGRI 及 DOE

包含大量与社会、伦理和法律问题相关的信息、链接及文章

GC 含量的远距离变化

人类基因组中存在 GC 富集区和 GC 匮乏区，这一特征最初是通过密度梯度离心的实验发现的，揭示了大片段之间平均 GC 含量存在显著变化。随后的研究表明，GC 富集区和 GC 匮乏区可能具有不同的生物学特性，如基因密度、重复序列组成以及细胞遗传学带和重组率的对应关系[112-117]。由于缺乏足够的序列数据，许多研究是间接的。

基因组草图序列的完成使直接而全面地研究 GC 含量变化成为可能。直接观察（图 9）证实，全基因组范围内的平均 GC 含量是 41%，而局部 GC 含量与之相比则有大量的远程偏移。

有很大的区域（> 10 Mb）的 GC 含量远高于平均值。

GC 含量的远程变化是很明显的，不仅来自极端的异常点，而是存在于整个基因组。

区域的 GC 含量与各种生物学性质之间的相关性引起了人们极大的兴趣，这可

in GC content. We confirm the existence of strong correlations with both repeat content and gene density.

CpG islands

A related topic is the distribution of so-called CpG islands across the genome. The dinucleotide CpG is notable because it is greatly under-represented in human DNA, occurring at only about one-fifth of the roughly 4% frequency that would be expected by simply multiplying the typical fraction of Cs and Gs (0.21×0.21). The deficit occurs because most CpG dinucleotides are methylated on the cytosine base, and spontaneous deamination of methyl-C residues gives rise to T residues. (Spontaneous deamination of ordinary cytosine residues gives rise to uracil residues that are readily recognized and repaired by the cell.) As a result, methyl-CpG dinucleotides steadily mutate to TpG dinucleotides. However, the genome contains many "CpG islands" in which CpG dinucleotides are not methylated and occur at a frequency closer to that predicted by the local GC content. CpG islands are of particular interest because many are associated with the 5′ ends of genes[122-127].

We searched the draft genome sequence for CpG islands.

The density of CpG islands varies substantially among some of the chromosomes. Most chromosomes have 5–15 islands per Mb, with a mean of 10.5 islands per Mb. However, chromosome Y has an unusually low 2.9 islands per Mb, and chromosomes 16, 17 and 22 have 19–22 islands per Mb. The extreme outlier is chromosome 19, with 43 islands per Mb. Similar trends are seen when considering the percentage of bases contained in CpG islands. The relative density of CpG islands correlates reasonably well with estimates of relative gene density on these chromosomes, based both on previous mapping studies involving ESTs and on the distribution of gene predictions discussed below.

Comparison of genetic and physical distance

The draft genome sequence makes it possible to compare genetic and physical distances and thereby to explore variation in the rate of recombination across the human chromosomes. We focus here on large-scale variation. Finer variation is examined in an accompanying paper[131].

Two striking features emerge from analysis of these data. First, the average recombination rate increases as the length of the chromosome arm decreases. A similar trend has been seen in the yeast genome[132,133], despite the fact that the physical scale is nearly 200 times as small.

The second observation is that the recombination rate tends to be suppressed near the centromeres and higher in the distal portions of most chromosomes, with the increase largely in the terminal 20–35 Mb. The increase is most pronounced in the male meiotic map.

能是了解 GC 含量变化本质的最有效途径。我们确定重复序列与基因密度存在强相关性。

CpG 岛

一个相关的话题是所谓的 CpG 岛在基因组内的分布。CpG 二核苷酸引人注意是因为它在人类 DNA 中所占比例非常少，如果按 CpG 出现的理论概率计算，简单将 C 和 G 的占比相乘（0.21×0.21）即大约 4%，而 CpG 的出现率仅为 4% 的五分之一。发生缺失的原因是大多数 CpG 二核苷酸的胞嘧啶发生甲基化，甲基化的 C 残基自发脱氨基而使 T 残基增加（普通胞嘧啶的自发脱氨基使尿嘧啶残基增加，尿嘧啶很容易被细胞识别和修复）。结果，甲基化 CpG 二核苷酸稳步突变为 TpG 二核苷酸。然而，基因组含有许多"CpG 岛"，岛内 CpG 二核苷酸没有被甲基化，发生频率与局部 GC 含量预测频率接近。CpG 岛非常有趣，因为许多 CpG 岛与基因的 5′ 端相关[122-127]。

我们在基因组草图序列中搜寻 CpG 岛。

CpG 岛的密度在不同染色体之间差异很大。大多数染色体每 Mb 有 5 ~ 15 个岛，平均每 Mb 有 10.5 个岛。不过，Y 染色体的 CpG 岛密度异常低，每 Mb 仅有 2.9 个，而 16 号、17 号和 22 号染色体每 Mb 则有 19 ~ 22 个岛。最为异常的是 19 号染色体，每 Mb 约有 43 个 CpG 岛。考虑 CpG 岛所含碱基的百分比时能看到类似的趋势。基于之前包含 EST 的图谱研究和下面讨论的基因预测的分布，CpG 岛的相对密度与这些染色体上估算的相对基因密度之间相关性良好。

遗传距离与物理距离的比较

基因组草图序列的完成，使遗传距离和物理距离的比较成为可能，进而可以探索人类染色体间重组率的变化。此处，我们将重点放在大范围内的变化上，更细微的变化在附带的论文中讨论[131]。

数据分析显示出两个明显特征：一是平均重组率随着染色体臂长的减少而增加。尽管酵母基因组的物理大小约为人类的 200 分之一，但相似的趋势仍然存在[132,133]。

第二个观察结果是，在大多数染色体上，接近着丝粒的重组率倾向于被抑制，而重组率在远端部分更高，在末端 20 ~ 35 Mb 更是大幅增加。这种重组率的增长在男性减数分裂图谱中更加显著。

Why is recombination higher on smaller chromosome arms? A higher rate would increase the likelihood of at least one crossover during meiosis on each chromosome arm, as is generally observed in human chiasmata counts[135]. Crossovers are believed to be necessary for normal meiotic disjunction of homologous chromosome pairs in eukaryotes.

Mechanistically, the increased rate of recombination on shorter chromosome arms could be explained if, once an initial recombination event occurs, additional nearby events are blocked by positive crossover interference on each arm. Evidence from yeast mutants in which interference is abolished shows that interference plays a key role in distributing a limited number of crossovers among the various chromosome arms in yeast[136]. An alternative possibility is that a checkpoint mechanism scans for and enforces the presence of at least one crossover on each chromosome arm.

Variation in recombination rates along chromosomes and between the sexes is likely to reflect variation in the initiation of meiosis-induced double-strand breaks (DSBs) that initiate recombination. DSBs in yeast have been associated with open chromatin[137,138], rather than with specific DNA sequence motifs. With the availability of the draft genome sequence, it should be possible to explore in an analogous manner whether variation in human recombination rates reflects systematic differences in chromosome accessibility during meiosis.

Repeat Content of the Human Genome

A puzzling observation in the early days of molecular biology was that genome size does not correlate well with organismal complexity. For example, *Homo sapiens* has a genome that is 200 times as large as that of the yeast *S. cerevisiae*, but 200 times as small as that of *Amoeba dubia*[139,140]. This mystery (the C-value paradox) was largely resolved with the recognition that genomes can contain a large quantity of repetitive sequence, far in excess of that devoted to protein-coding genes (reviewed in refs 140, 141).

In the human, coding sequences comprise less than 5% of the genome (see below), whereas repeat sequences account for at least 50% and probably much more. Broadly, the repeats fall into five classes: (1) transposon-derived repeats, often referred to as interspersed repeats; (2) inactive (partially) retroposed copies of cellular genes (including protein-coding genes and small structural RNAs), usually referred to as processed pseudogenes; (3) simple sequence repeats, consisting of direct repetitions of relatively short k-mers such as $(A)_n$, $(CA)_n$ or $(CGG)_n$; (4) segmental duplications, consisting of blocks of around 10–300 kb that have been copied from one region of the genome into another region; and (5) blocks of tandemly repeated sequences, such as at centromeres, telomeres, the short arms of acrocentric chromosomes and ribosomal gene clusters. (These regions are intentionally under-represented in the draft genome sequence and are not discussed here.)

Repeats are often described as "junk" and dismissed as uninteresting. However, they actually represent an extraordinary trove of information about biological processes. The repeats

为什么在较小的染色体臂上重组率较高？通常在人类交叉计数中观察到，更高的重组率会增加每条染色体臂在减数分裂过程中至少进行一次交换的可能性[135]。交换被认为是真核生物中同源染色体配对正常减数分裂分离所必需的。

从机制上来看，较短染色体臂上重组率的增加可以这样解释：一旦发生第一次重组事件，每条染色体臂上的交换都会被干扰，进而阻止附近区域重组事件的发生。对干扰作用被破坏的酵母突变体的研究表明，在酵母各染色体臂之间分配有限的交换次数时，干扰作用发挥了关键作用[136]。另一种可能性是检查点机制扫描基因组并促成每个染色体臂上至少存在一个交换。

染色体上以及性别之间的重组率的差异可能反映了减数分裂导致的双链DNA断裂(DSB)起始过程的差异，该过程是重组的起始阶段。酵母中的DSB与开放的染色质而不是特定的DNA序列基序有关[137,138]。如果得到了基因组草图序列，就能用相似的方法探索人类重组率的差异是否反映了减数分裂过程中染色体可接近性的系统性差异。

人类基因组重复序列含量

早期分子生物学领域令人困惑的一个观察结果是基因组大小与生物复杂性的相关性不强。例如，智人的基因组大小是酿酒酵母的200倍，但也是变形虫的两百分之一[139,140]。这个谜团(C值悖论)在很大程度上得到了解决，是由于认识到基因组可以包含大量的重复序列，远远超过了蛋白质编码基因的序列(参考文献140和141中有综述)。

人类的编码序列在基因组占比小于5%(见下文)，而重复序列至少占50%，甚至更多。概括地说，重复序列分为五类：(1)转座子起源的重复，通常称为散在重复；(2)基因(包括蛋白质编码基因和小的结构RNA)的退化失活(或部分失活)拷贝，通常称为加工过的假基因；(3)简单重复序列，由相对比较短的核苷酸如$(A)_n$、$(CA)_n$或$(CGG)_n$正向重复组成；(4)片段重复，由$10\sim300$ kb的大片段组成，这些片段是从基因组的一个区域复制到另一区域形成；(5)串联重复序列，如着丝粒、端粒、近端着丝粒染色体的短臂和核糖体基因簇等区域。(这些区域在基因组草图序列中代表性不足，本文不讨论。)

重复序列通常被描述为"垃圾"，并且被认为是没有意义的。但实际上它们代表了一个关于生物学过程的特殊信息库。这些重复构成了丰富的古生物学记录，包含

constitute a rich palaeontological record, holding crucial clues about evolutionary events and forces. As passive markers, they provide assays for studying processes of mutation and selection. It is possible to recognize cohorts of repeats "born" at the same time and to follow their fates in different regions of the genome or in different species. As active agents, repeats have reshaped the genome by causing ectopic rearrangements, creating entirely new genes, modifying and reshuffling existing genes, and modulating overall GC content. They also shed light on chromosome structure and dynamics, and provide tools for medical genetic and population genetic studies.

The human is the first repeat-rich genome to be sequenced, and so we investigated what information could be gleaned from this majority component of the human genome. Although some of the general observations about repeats were suggested by previous studies, the draft genome sequence provides the first comprehensive view, allowing some questions to be resolved and new mysteries to emerge.

Transposon-derived repeats

Most human repeat sequence is derived from transposable elements[142,143]. We can currently recognize about 45% of the genome as belonging to this class. Much of the remaining "unique" DNA must also be derived from ancient transposable element copies that have diverged too far to be recognized as such.

In mammals, almost all transposable elements fall into one of four types, of which three transpose through RNA intermediates and one transposes directly as DNA. These are long interspersed elements (LINEs, an ancient and common innovation in eukaryotes), short interspersed elements (SINEs, which are freeloaders on LINEs), LTR retrotransposons and DNA transposons.

Transposable elements employ different strategies to ensure their evolutionary survival. LINEs and SINEs rely almost exclusively on vertical transmission within the host genome[154] (but see refs 148, 155). DNA transposons are more promiscuous, requiring relatively frequent horizontal transfer. LTR retroposons use both strategies, with some being long-term active residents of the human genome (such as members of the ERVL family) and others having only short residence times.

Currently recognized SINEs, LINEs, LTR retroposons and DNA transposon copies comprise 13%, 20%, 8% and 3% of the sequence, respectively. We expect these densities to grow as more repeat families are recognized, among which will be lower copy number LTR elements and DNA transposons, and possibly high copy number ancient (highly diverged) repeats.

Age distribution. The age distribution of the repeats in the human genome provides a rich "fossil record" stretching over several hundred million years. The ancestry and

关于进化事件和进化驱动力的重要线索。作为一种被动标记，它们提供了用于研究突变过程和选择过程的材料。我们可以识别在同一时间"出生"的一群重复序列，追踪它们在基因组的不同区域或不同物种中的命运。作为活跃分子，重复序列通过引起异位重排、创建全新基因、修饰和重组现有基因及调整总体 GC 含量等重塑了基因组。它们还揭示了染色体结构和动力学，并为医学遗传学和群体遗传学研究提供了工具。

人类是第一个经过测序的富含重复序列的基因组，因此我们研究了从人类基因组大多数组分中可以收集到哪些信息。虽然以前的研究也提出了一些关于重复的普遍观察结果，但基因组草图序列第一次提供了序列的全貌，在解决某些问题的同时产生了新的谜团。

转座子起源的重复

大多数人类重复序列来源于转座元件[142,143]。目前，我们可以认定约 45% 的基因组属于这一类。剩下的"独特"DNA 中，许多应该也来自远古转座元件的拷贝，这些拷贝已经因分化得太远而无法识别。

在哺乳动物中，几乎所有的转座元件都可归入四个大类，其中三类是由 RNA 介导，一类是 DNA 直接转座完成。这四类分别是：长散在重复序列（LINE，在真核生物中古老而常见的创新序列）、短散在重复序列（SINE，LINE 中的自由插入序列）、LTR 逆转座子和 DNA 转座子。

转座元件采用不同的策略来确保它们的进化生存。LINE 和 SINE 几乎完全依赖宿主基因组内的垂直传递[154]（请参见参考文献 148 和 155）。DNA 转座子更加杂乱，需要相对频繁的水平转移。LTR 逆转座子则使用上述两种策略，一些在人类基因组长期活跃驻扎（例如 ERVL 家族的成员），其他则是短暂停留。

目前公认的 SINE、LINE、LTR 逆转座子和 DNA 转座子的拷贝数分别占序列的 13%、20%、8% 和 3%。我们预计上述数字会随着更多重复家族的识别而增加，其中包括较低拷贝数的 LTR 元件和 DNA 转座子，可能还有高拷贝数的远古（高度分化）重复。

年代分布　人类基因组中重复序列的年龄分布提供了绵延数亿年的丰富的"化

approximate age of each fossil can be inferred by exploiting the fact that each copy is derived from, and therefore initially carried the sequence of, a then-active transposon and, being generally under no functional constraint, has accumulated mutations randomly and independently of other copies. We can infer the sequence of the ancestral active elements by clustering the modern derivatives into phylogenetic trees and building a consensus based on the multiple sequence alignment of a cluster of copies. Using available consensus sequences for known repeat subfamilies, we calculated the per cent divergence from the inferred ancestral active transposon for each of three million interspersed repeats in the draft genome sequence.

The percentage of sequence divergence can be converted into an approximate age in millions of years (Myr) on the basis of evolutionary information.

Several facts are apparent from analysis.

First, most interspersed repeats in the human genome predate the eutherian radiation. This is a testament to the extremely slow rate with which nonfunctional sequences are cleared from vertebrate genomes.

Second, LINE and SINE elements have extremely long lives. The monophyletic LINE1 and Alu lineages are at least 150 and 80 Myr old, respectively. In earlier times, the reigning transposons were LINE2 and MIR[148,158]. The SINE MIR was perfectly adapted for reverse transcription by LINE2, as it carried the same 50-base sequence at its 3′ end. When LINE2 became extinct 80–100 Myr ago, it spelled the doom of MIR.

Third, there were two major peaks of DNA transposon activity. The first involved Charlie elements and occurred long before the eutherian radiation; the second involved Tigger elements and occurred after this radiation. Because DNA transposons can produce large-scale chromosome rearrangements[159-162], it is possible that widespread activity could be involved in speciation events.

Fourth, there is no evidence for DNA transposon activity in the past 50 Myr in the human genome. The youngest two DNA transposon families that we can identify in the draft genome sequence (MER75 and MER85) show 6–7% divergence from their respective consensus sequences representing the ancestral element, indicating that they were active before the divergence of humans and new world monkeys. Moreover, these elements were relatively unsuccessful, together contributing just 125 kb to the draft genome sequence.

Finally, LTR retroposons appear to be teetering on the brink of extinction, if they have not already succumbed. For example, the most prolific elements (ERVL and MaLRs) flourished for more than 100 Myr but appear to have died out about 40 Myr ago[163,164].

More generally, the overall activity of all transposons has declined markedly over the past

石记录"。每个"化石"的祖先和大致年龄可以通过探究以下事实来推断：每个拷贝来源于一个当时活跃的转座子并因此在最初携带其序列，同时在没有功能选择压力的情况下独立于其他拷贝之外随机累积突变。我们可以通过将现代衍生物聚类为系统发生树并基于拷贝簇的多重序列比对建立共识，来推断祖先活性元件的序列。根据已知的重复亚家族的共有序列，我们计算了基因组草图序列中三百万个散在重复序列各自与推测的祖先活跃转座子的百分比差异。

依据进化的信息，序列差异的百分比可近似转化为以百万年计 (Myr) 的时间。

分析后有几点明显的特征：

首先，人类基因组中大多数散在重复序列早于真兽亚纲的扩张，这证明了非功能性序列从脊椎动物基因组中被清除的速率非常缓慢。

其次，LINE 元件和 SINE 元件具有很长的寿命。单源 LINE1 和 Alu 谱系至少有 1.5 亿年和 8,000 万年的历史。早期，居于统治地位的转座子是 LINE2 和 MIR[148,158]。SINE MIR 的 3′ 端携带与 LINE2 相同的 50 个碱基序列，因而完全适用于 LINE2 的逆转录。当 LINE2 在 8,000 万～1 亿年前灭绝时，MIR 也难逃厄运。

第三，DNA 转座子的活性曾有两次峰值。第一次涉及 Charlie 元件，发生在真兽亚纲扩张之前很久；第二次涉及 Tigger 元件，发生在扩张后。因为 DNA 转座子可以产生大规模的染色体重排[159-162]，所以转座子的广泛活动可能涉及形成物种的事件。

第四，在人类基因组中，过去 5,000 万年里没有 DNA 转座子活性的证据。我们在基因组草图序列中鉴定出的最年轻的两个 DNA 转座子家族 (MER75 和 MER85) 显示出与各自的代表祖先元件的共有序列有 6%～7% 的差异，这表明它们在人类与新世界猴分化之前是有活性的。而且，这些元件没那么成功，合在一起仅占基因组草图序列 125 kb 的长度。

最后，即使 LTR 逆转座子还没有屈服，但似乎已在灭绝的边缘了。例如，最丰富的元件 (ERVL 和 MaLRs) 兴盛了 1 亿年，但它们已经在 4,000 万年前消失了[163,164]。

更普遍的是，在过去的 3,500 万～5,000 万年间，所有转座子的整体活性显著下

35–50 Myr, with the possible exception of LINE1. Indeed, apart from an exceptional burst of activity of Alus peaking around 40 Myr ago, there would appear to have been a fairly steady decline in activity in the hominid lineage since the mammalian radiation. The extent of the decline must be even greater than it appears because old repeats are gradually removed by random deletion and because old repeat families are harder to recognize and likely to be under-represented in the repeat databases.

What explains the decline in transposon activity in the lineage leading to humans? There is no similar decline in the mouse genome.

Comparison with other organisms.   In contrast to their possible extinction in humans, LTR retroposons are alive and well in the mouse. These evolutionary findings are consistent with the empirical observations that new spontaneous mutations are 30 times more likely to be caused by LINE insertions in mouse than in human (~3% versus 0.1%)[170] and 60 times more likely to be caused by transposable elements in general. It is estimated that around 1 in 600 mutations in human are due to transpositions, whereas 10% of mutations in mouse are due to transpositions (mostly IAP insertions).

The contrast between human and mouse suggests that the explanation for the decline of transposon activity in humans may lie in some fundamental difference between hominids and rodents. Population structure and dynamics would seem to be likely suspects. Rodents tend to have large populations, whereas hominid populations tend to be small and may undergo frequent bottlenecks. Evolutionary forces affected by such factors include inbreeding and genetic drift, which might affect the persistence of active transposable elements[171]. Studies in additional mammalian lineages may shed light on the forces responsible for the differences in the activity of transposable elements[172]. (Editorial note: a detailed discussion of inter-species comparisons has been omitted.)

Distribution by GC content.   We next focused on the correlation between the nature of the transposons in a region and its GC content. We calculated the density of each repeat type as a function of the GC content in 50-kb windows. As has been reported[142,173-176], LINE sequences occur at much higher density in AT-rich regions (roughly fourfold enriched), whereas SINEs (MIR, Alu) show the opposite trend (for Alu, up to fivefold lower in AT-rich DNA). LTR retroposons and DNA transposons show a more uniform distribution, dipping only in the most GC-rich regions.

The preference of LINEs for AT-rich DNA seems like a reasonable way for a genomic parasite to accommodate its host, by targeting gene-poor AT-rich DNA and thereby imposing a lower mutational burden.

The contrary behaviour of SINEs, however, is baffling. How do SINEs accumulate in GC-rich DNA, particularly if they depend on the LINE transposition machinery[178]?

降，也许只有 LINE1 是个例外。事实上，除了 4,000 万年前 Alu 的活性爆发并达到顶峰之外，自哺乳动物扩张以来，类人猿世系的转座子活性似乎已经相当稳定地下降了。由于古老的重复序列逐渐地随机删除，同时古老重复序列家族难以识别且可能在数据库中代表不足，实际下降幅度应该更大。

什么能够解释人类谱系中的转座子活性下降呢？在小鼠的基因组中并未观察到同样的现象。

与其他生物的比较　与在人类中可能灭绝的情况相反，LTR 逆转座子在小鼠中存活得很好。这些进化上的发现与经验观察值相吻合，在小鼠中，由 LINE 插入产生新的自发突变的可能性是人类中的 30 倍（约 3% 相对于 0.1%）[170]，由转座元件插入产生的可能性是人类的 60 倍。据估计，人类突变中约六百分之一由转座引起，在小鼠中由转座引起的突变占到 10%（大多数为 IAP 插入）。

人类与小鼠的对比表明，人类转座子活性的下降可能基于类人猿世系和啮齿类动物的某些根本差异。种群结构和种群动态似乎是个疑点。啮齿动物往往拥有大种群，而人类种群倾向于变小，并经常遇到瓶颈。进化动力受近亲繁殖和遗传漂变等因素的影响，可能会影响活跃转座元件的持续[171]。其他哺乳动物谱系的研究也许能揭示转座元件活性差异的原因[172]。（编者注：关于种群间比较的详细讨论被删减了。）

GC 含量的分布　下面我们将重点关注区域内转座子的性质和 GC 含量之间的关系。以 50 kb 为窗口，我们将每类重复序列的密度与 GC 含量关联起来。正如已报道的[142,173-176]，LINE 序列分布在 AT 富集区（大约 4 倍富集），而 SINE（MIR、Alu）呈现相反的趋势（Alu 在富含 AT 的 DNA 区域密度低至五分之一）。逆转录子 LTR 和 DNA 转座子呈现更均匀的分布，仅处于 GC 富集区。

LINE 序列对 AT 富集 DNA 的偏好似乎是适应基因组寄生生活的合理途径，AT 富集 DNA 通常基因分布较少，插入后引起的突变负担更小。

然而，SINE 的相反行为令人困惑。SINE 如何在 GC 富集 DNA 中积累，特别是如果它们依赖于 LINE 转座机制[178]？

We used the draft genome sequence to investigate this mystery by comparing the proclivities of young, adolescent, middle-aged and old Alus. Strikingly, recent Alus show a preference for AT-rich DNA resembling that of LINEs, whereas progressively older Alus show a progressively stronger bias towards GC-rich DNA. These results indicate that the GC bias must result from strong pressure: there is a 13-fold enrichment of Alus in GC-rich DNA within the last 30 Myr, and possibly more recently.

These observations indicate that there may be some force acting particularly on Alus. This could be a higher rate of random loss of Alus in AT-rich DNA, negative selection against Alus in AT-rich DNA or positive selection in favour of Alus in GC-rich DNA. The first two possibilities seem unlikely because AT-rich DNA is gene-poor and tolerates the accumulation of other transposable elements. The third seems more feasible, in that it involves selecting in favour of the minority of Alus in GC-rich regions rather than against the majority that lie in AT-rich regions. But positive selection for Alus in GC-rich regions would imply that they benefit the organism.

Our results may support the controversial idea that SINEs actually earn their keep in the genome. Clearly, much additional work will be needed to prove or disprove the hypothesis that SINEs are genomic symbionts.

Fast living on chromosome Y. The pattern of interspersed repeats can be used to shed light on the unusual evolutionary history of chromosome Y. Our analysis shows that the genetic material on chromosome Y is unusually young, probably owing to a high tolerance for gain of new material by insertion and loss of old material by deletion. Overall, chromosome Y seems to maintain a youthful appearance by rapid turnover.

Interspersed repeats on chromosome Y can also be used to estimate the relative mutation rates, α_m and α_f, in the male and female germlines. Chromosome Y always resides in males, whereas chromosome X resides in females twice as often as in males. The substitution rates, μ_Y and μ_X, on these two chromosomes should thus be in the ratio $\mu_Y:\mu_X = (\alpha_m):(\alpha_m + 2\alpha_f)/3$, provided that one considers equivalent neutral sequences. Page and colleagues[192] obtained an estimate of $\mu_Y:\mu_X = 1.36$, corresponding to $\alpha_m:\alpha_f = 1.7$.

Our estimate is in reasonable agreement with that of Page *et al.*, although it is based on much more total sequence (360 kb on Y, 1.6 Mb on X) and a much longer time period. Various theories have been proposed for the higher mutation rate in the male germline, including the greater number of cell divisions in the formation of sperm than eggs and different repair mechanisms in sperm and eggs. (Editorial note: a detailed discussion of transposon dynamics and simple sequence repeats has been omitted.)

Segmental duplications

A remarkable feature of the human genome is the segmental duplication of portions of

我们使用基因组草图序列，通过比较"青年"、"青少年"、"中年"和"老年"Alu 序列的倾向性来调查这个谜团。引人注目的是，较年轻的 Alu 展示了一种类似于 LINE 对 AT 富集 DNA 优先选择的倾向性，而逐渐变老的 Alu 对富含 GC 的 DNA 的偏好逐渐增强。这些结果表明，GC 偏好性应该是强大的压力造成的。Alu 序列在 GC 富集 DNA 中约 13 倍富集，这发生在距今 3,000 万年内或更近。

这些观察结果表明，可能会有一些力量在 Alu 上发挥独特的作用。这可能是富含 AT 的 DNA 随机丢失 Alu 的概率较高，AT 富集 DNA 对 Alu 的负选择或者 GC 富集 DNA 对 Alu 的正选择。前两种似乎可能性不大，因为 AT 富集 DNA 缺乏基因，并且容忍其他转座元件的积累。第三种看起来更可行，因为它意味着在 GC 富集区选择偏好少数 Alu，而不是在 AT 富集区排斥多数 Alu。但是 GC 富集区正向选择 Alu 意味着生物体将因此获益。

我们的研究结果也许支持了这样一个有争议的观点，那就是 SINE 在基因组中争得了一席之地。显然，若想证实或否定 SINE 是基因组共生体的假设，需要做更多的工作。

在 Y 染色体上快速生存 散在重复的模式可用于阐明 Y 染色体不寻常的进化历史。我们的分析表明，Y 染色体上的遗传物质异常年轻，可能对于是对插入新物质和删除旧物质具有较高耐受性。总的来说，Y 染色体似乎通过快速更新而保持年轻的外貌。

Y 染色体上的散布重复也可用于估算男性和女性生殖系中的相对突变率 α_m 和 α_f。染色体 Y 总是存在于雄性中，而染色体 X 存在于女性中的频率是男性的两倍。这两种染色体上的替代率 μ_Y 和 μ_X 应符合比值 $\mu_Y : \mu_X = (\alpha_m) : (\alpha_m + 2\alpha_f)/3$，前提是考虑相等的中性序列。佩奇及其同事[192]估算 $\mu_Y : \mu_X = 1.36$，相应的 $\alpha_m : \alpha_f = 1.7$。

尽管我们的估计基于更多的全序列（Y 染色体 360 kb，X 染色体 1.6 Mb）和更长的时间周期，但是与佩奇等人的估计相当吻合。对于男性生殖系中的较高突变率，目前已经提出了不同理论，包括精子形成中细胞分裂的数量多于卵子以及精子和卵子中修复机制不同。（编者注：关于转座子动力学和简单序列重复的详细讨论被删除了。）

片段重复

人类基因组的一个显著特征是基因组序列的部分片段重复[215-217]。这种片段重复

genomic sequence[215-217]. Such duplications involve the transfer of 1–200-kb blocks of genomic sequence to one or more locations in the genome. The locations of both donor and recipient regions of the genome are often not tandemly arranged, suggesting mechanisms other than unequal crossing-over for their origin. They are relatively recent, inasmuch as strong sequence identity is seen in both exons and introns (in contrast to regions that are considered to show evidence of ancient duplications, characterized by similarities only in coding regions). Indeed, many such duplications appear to have arisen in very recent evolutionary time, as judged by high sequence identity and by their absence in closely related species.

Segmental duplications can be divided into two categories. First, interchromosomal duplications are defined as segments that are duplicated among nonhomologous chromosomes.

The second category is intrachromosomal duplications, which occur within a particular chromosome or chromosomal arm.

Until now, the identification and characterization of segmental duplications have been based on anecdotal reports. The availability of the entire genomic sequence will make it possible to explore the nature of segmental duplications more systematically.

We performed a global genome-wide analysis to characterize the amount of segmental duplication in the genome.

The finished sequence consists of at least 3.3% segmental duplication. Interchromosomal duplication accounts for about 1.5% and intrachromosomal duplication for about 2%, with some overlap (0.2%) between these categories. We analysed the lengths and divergence of the segmental duplications. The duplications tend to be large (10–50 kb) and highly homologous, especially for the interchromosomal segments. The sequence divergence for the interchromosomal duplications appears to peak between 96.5% and 97.5%. This may indicate that interchromosomal duplications occurred in a punctuated manner. It will be intriguing to investigate whether such genomic upheaval has a role in speciation events.

We compared the entire human draft genome sequence (finished and unfinished) with itself to identify duplications with 90–98% sequence identity. The draft genome sequence contains at least 3.6% segmental duplication. The actual proportion will be significantly higher, because we excluded many true matches with more than 98% sequence identity (at least 1.1% of the finished sequence). Although exact measurement must await a finished sequence, the human genome seems likely to contain about 5% segmental duplication, with most of this sequence in large blocks (> 10 kb). Such a high proportion of large duplications clearly distinguishes the human genome from other sequenced genomes, such as the fly and worm.

涉及 1~200 kb 的序列转移至基因组一个或多个位置。基因组的供体和受体区域的位置通常不是串联排列的,这提示可能存在与其起源的不等交换不同的其他机制。这类重复是相对较晚出现的,因为不管是外显子还是内含子都能观察到较强的序列一致性(与此相反,那些被认为古老的重复序列仅在编码区域中具有相似性)。事实上,许多这样的重复似乎是在最近的进化年代中出现的,它们不仅序列一致性高,而且不会出现在关系很近的物种之间。

片段重复可以分为两类。第一类,染色体间的重复被定义为非同源染色体间的重复片段。

第二类是染色体内重复,发生在特定的染色体或染色体臂内。

到目前为止,对片段重复的确定和描述基本来自坊间的报道。全基因组序列的可用性使得人们可以更系统地探索片段重复的性质。

我们在全基因组范围内进行分析,识别片段重复的数量。

完成序列包含至少 3.3% 的片段重复。染色体间重复约占 1.5%,染色体内重复约占 2%,两类之间有部分重叠(0.2%)。我们分析了片段重复的长度和差异性。重复的片段往往很大(10~50 kb)并且高度同源,尤其是染色体间重复。染色体间重复的序列差异的峰值似乎在 96.5% 和 97.5% 之间。这可能表明染色体间重复以间断的形式发生。调查此类基因组的巨变在物种形成中是否发挥作用将是非常有趣的。

我们将人类全基因组草图序列(完成和未完成)与其自身进行比较,用以鉴定具有 90%~98% 序列一致性的重复序列。基因组草图序列至少包含 3.6% 的片段重复,我们排除了许多序列一致性在 98% 以上(至少 1.1% 的完成序列)的真实匹配,因此实际比例将更高。精确值必须等到基因组序列完成后才可测量,但人类基因组很可能含有约 5% 的片段重复,其中大部分重复序列是大片段的(>10 kb)。人类基因组内大段重复的比例如此之高是其与其他已测序基因组(如果蝇和线虫)的明显区别。

Gene Content of the Human Genome

Genes (or at least their coding regions) comprise only a tiny fraction of human DNA, but they represent the major biological function of the genome and the main focus of interest by biologists. They are also the most challenging feature to identify in the human genome sequence.

The ultimate goal is to compile a complete list of all human genes and their encoded proteins, to serve as a "periodic table" for biomedical research[243]. But this is a difficult task. In organisms with small genomes, it is straightforward to identify most genes by the presence of long open reading frames (ORFs). In contrast, human genes tend to have small exons (encoding an average of only 50 codons) separated by long introns (some exceeding 10 kb). This creates a signal-to-noise problem, with the result that computer programs for direct gene prediction have only limited accuracy. Instead, computational prediction of human genes must rely largely on the availability of cDNA sequences or on sequence conservation with genes and proteins from other organisms. This approach is adequate for strongly conserved genes (such as histones or ubiquitin), but may be less sensitive to rapidly evolving genes (including many crucial to speciation, sex determination and fertilization).

Noncoding RNAs

Although biologists often speak of a tight coupling between "genes and their encoded protein products", it is important to remember that thousands of human genes produce noncoding RNAs (ncRNAs) as their ultimate product[244]. There are several major classes of ncRNA. (1) Transfer RNAs (tRNAs) are the adapters that translate the triplet nucleic acid code of RNA into the amino-acid sequence of proteins; (2) ribosomal RNAs (rRNAs) are also central to the translational machinery, and recent X-ray crystallography results strongly indicate that peptide bond formation is catalysed by rRNA, not protein[245,246]; (3) small nucleolar RNAs (snoRNAs) are required for rRNA processing and base modification in the nucleolus[247,248]; and (4) small nuclear RNAs (snRNAs) are critical components of spliceosomes, the large ribonucleoprotein (RNP) complexes that splice introns out of pre-mRNAs in the nucleus.

We can identify genomic sequences that are homologous to known ncRNA genes, using BLASTN or, in some cases, more specialized methods.

It is sometimes difficult to tell whether such homologous genes are orthologues, paralogues or closely related pseudogenes (because inactivating mutations are much less obvious than for protein-coding genes). For tRNA, there is sufficiently detailed information about the cloverleaf secondary structure to allow true genes and pseudogenes to be distinguished with high sensitivity. For many other ncRNAs, there is much less structural information and so we employ an operational criterion of high sequence similarity (> 95% sequence identity

人类基因组的基因含量

基因（至少是它们的编码区）只占人类 DNA 的很小一部分，但体现了基因组的主要生物学功能，是生物学家研究的焦点。它们也是人类基因组序列中识别起来最富挑战性的一项特征。

我们的终极目标是编制一张用于生物医学研究的"元素周期表"，罗列所有人类基因及其编码的蛋白质[243]。但是这是一项很困难的工作。对于基因组较小的物种来说，通过长的开放阅读框（ORF）可以直接确定大部分基因。与此相反，人类基因倾向于含有被大的内含子（有些超过 10 kb）分隔开的小的外显子（仅平均编码 50 个密码子）。这就产生了信噪比问题，因此利用电脑程序直接预测基因的准确性很有限。因此，人类基因的电脑预测要极大地依赖于 cDNA 序列或来自其他物种的基因和蛋白质的保守序列。这个方法对高度保守的基因（如组蛋白或泛素）足以胜任，但是对于快速进化的基因（包括很多对物种形成、性别决定和受精非常重要的基因）就没那么敏感了。

非编码 RNA

虽然生物学家经常说"基因与其编码的蛋白质产物"连接紧密，但请务必记得还有数以千计的人类基因产生非编码 RNA（ncRNA）作为其最终产物[244]。ncRNA 主要分以下几大类：（1）转运 RNA（tRNA），负责将 RNA 的三联体密码翻译为蛋白质的氨基酸序列；（2）核糖体 RNA（rRNA），是转录机器的核心，最近的 X 射线晶体学结果显示肽键的形成是由 rRNA 而非蛋白质催化[245,246]；（3）小核仁 RNA（snoRNA），参与核仁中的 rRNA 编辑和碱基修饰[247,248]；（4）小核 RNA（snRNA），剪切体的关键组分，剪切体是大型核糖核蛋白（RNP）复合物，负责在细胞核中将前 mRNA 的内含子切除。

我们可以利用 BLASTN 或其他更专业的方法识别与已知的 ncRNA 基因同源的基因组序列。

有时，很难讲清这些同源关系是直系同源、旁系同源还是密切相关的假基因（因为与编码蛋白质的基因相比，ncRNA 基因的失活突变更不明显）。对 tRNA 来说，三叶草的二级结构提供了足够多的信息，用来判定基因和假基因的灵敏度很高。但是对于其他 ncRNA 来说，结构信息要少得多，因此我们引入了一条序列高度相似（大于 95% 的一致性和大于 95% 的全长）的操作标准来区别基因和假基因。这些工

and > 95% full length) to distinguish true genes from pseudogenes. These assignments will eventually need to be reconciled with experimental data.

Transfer RNA genes. In the draft genome sequence, we find only 497 human tRNA genes. This appears to include most of the known human tRNA species. The draft genome sequence contains 37 of 38 human tRNA species listed in a tRNA database[253], allowing for up to one mismatch.

The results indicate that the human has fewer tRNA genes than the worm, but more than the fly. This may seem surprising, but tRNA gene number in metazoans is thought to be related not to organismal complexity, but more to idiosyncrasies of the demand for tRNA abundance in certain tissues or stages of embryonic development. For example, the frog *Xenopus laevis*, which must load each oocyte with a remarkable 40 ng of tRNA, has thousands of tRNA genes[254].

The tRNA genes are dispersed throughout the human genome. However, this dispersal is nonrandom. tRNA genes have sometimes been seen in clusters at small scales[262,263] but we can now see striking clustering on a genome-wide scale. More than 25% of the tRNA genes (140) are found in a region of only about 4 Mb on chromosome 6. This small region, only about 0.1% of the genome, contains an almost sufficient set of tRNA genes all by itself. The 140 tRNA genes contain a representative for 36 of the 49 anticodons found in the complete set; and of the 21 isoacceptor types, only tRNAs to decode Asn, Cys, Glu and selenocysteine are missing. Many of these tRNA genes, meanwhile, are clustered elsewhere; 18 of the 30 Cys tRNAs are found in a 0.5-Mb stretch of chromosome 7 and many of the Asn and Glu tRNA genes are loosely clustered on chromosome 1. More than half of the tRNA genes (280 out of 497) reside on either chromosome 1 or chromosome 6. Chromosomes 3, 4, 8, 9, 10, 12, 18, 20, 21 and X appear to have fewer than 10 tRNA genes each; and chromosomes 22 and Y have none at all (each has a single pseudogene). (Editorial note: much of the discussion of RNA genes has been omitted.)

Our observations confirm the striking proliferation of ncRNA-derived pseudogenes. There are hundreds or thousands of sequences in the draft genome sequence related to some of the ncRNA genes. The most prolific pseudogene counts generally come from RNA genes transcribed by RNA polymerase III promoters, including U6, the hY RNAs and SRP-RNA. These ncRNA pseudogenes presumably arise through reverse transcription. The frequency of such events gives insight into how ncRNA genes can evolve into SINE retroposons, such as the tRNA-derived SINEs found in many vertebrates and the SRP-RNA-derived Alu elements found in humans.

Protein-coding genes

(Editorial note: this section has been significantly shortened.) Identifying the protein-coding genes in the human genome is one of the most important applications of the

作最终需要实验数据来协调。

转运 RNA 基因　在基因组草图序列中，我们仅找到了 497 个人类 tRNA 基因。这包含了目前已知的大多数 tRNA 种类。在 tRNA 数据库[253]列举的 38 种人类 tRNA 中，基因组草图中出现了 37 种，允许最多出现一次错配。

研究结果显示，人类的 tRNA 基因少于线虫，但多于果蝇。虽然出人意料，但在多细胞生物中，tRNA 基因的数量被认为与生物体的复杂程度无关，而是与某些组织的对 tRNA 需求或胚胎发育的阶段等特征有关。如非洲爪蟾，它的卵母细胞会携带多达 40 ng 的 tRNA，而它的 tRNA 基因也多达上千种[254]。

tRNA 基因分散在整个人类基因组中。但并非随机分布。曾经也发现过 tRNA 基因小规模聚集成簇[262,263]，但是我们现在看到，tRNA 基因在基因组范围内有非常显著的基因簇。超过 25% 的 tRNA(140 个)位于 6 号染色体的长约 4 Mb 的一个区域内。这个小区域仅约占人类基因组总长的 0.1%，但却包含了几乎一整套必需的 tRNA 基因。这 140 个 tRNA 基因包含 49 个反密码子中典型的 36 个；而 21 个同工型中只缺少天冬酰胺、半胱氨酸、谷氨酸和硒代半胱氨酸的解码 tRNA。这些 tRNA 基因大多成簇存在于其他位置，30 个半胱氨酸 tRNA 中的 18 个在 7 号染色体的 0.5 Mb 区域内，很多天冬酰胺和谷氨酸 tRNA 基因则松散地成簇出现在 1 号染色体上。超过一半的 tRNA 基因(497 个中的 280 个)位于 1 号或 6 号染色体上，第 3、4、8、9、10、12、18、20、21 号染色体和 X 染色体上各自分布不到 10 个 tRNA 基因，22 号和 Y 染色体则完全没有 tRNA 基因(各自含有一个假基因)。(编者注：关于 RNA 基因的大部分讨论被删减了。)

我们的观察证实了起源于 ncRNA 的假基因的显著增殖过程。基因组草图中，成千上万的序列与某些 ncRNA 基因有关。大量的假基因一般来自 RNA 聚合酶 III 启动子转录的 RNA 基因，包括 U6、hY RNA 和 SRP-RNA。这些 ncRNA 假基因很可能起源于逆转录。这种事件发生的频率也让我们有机会了解，ncRNA 基因是怎样进化为 SINE 逆转座子的，就像 tRNA 起源的 SINE 存在于很多脊椎动物基因组中，SRP-RNA 起源的 Alu 元件存在于人类基因组中。

蛋白质编码基因

(编者注：这部分有大量的删减。)在人类基因组中识别出蛋白质编码基因，是

sequence data, but also one of the most difficult challenges.

Towards a complete index of human genes. We focused on creating an initial index of human genes and proteins. This index is quite incomplete, owing to the difficulty of gene identification in human DNA and the imperfect state of the draft genome sequence. Nonetheless, it is valuable for experimental studies and provides important insights into the nature of human genes and proteins.

Gene identification is difficult in human DNA. The signal-to-noise ratio is low: coding sequences comprise only a few per cent of the genome and an average of about 5% of each gene; internal exons are smaller than in worms; and genes appear to have more alternative splicing. The challenge is underscored by the work on human chromosomes 21 and 22. Even with the availability of finished sequence and intensive experimental work, the gene content remains uncertain, with upper and lower estimates differing by as much as 30%. The initial report of the finished sequence of chromosome 22 (ref. 94) identified 247 previously known genes, 298 predicted genes confirmed by sequence homology or ESTs and 325 *ab initio* predictions without additional support. Many of the confirmed predictions represented partial genes. In the past year, 440 additional exons (10%) have been added to existing gene annotations by the chromosome 22 annotation group, although the number of confirmed genes has increased by only 17 and some previously identified gene predictions have been merged[286].

Creating an initial gene index. We set out to create an initial integrated gene index (IGI) and an associated integrated protein index (IPI) for the human genome.

Evaluation of IGI/IPI. We used several approaches to evaluate the sensitivity, specificity and fragmentation of the IGI/IPI set.

Comparison with "new" known genes. One approach was to examine newly discovered genes arising from independent work that were not used in our gene prediction effort. We identified 31 such genes: 22 recent entries to RefSeq and 9 from the Sanger Centre's gene identification program on chromosome X. Of these, 28 were contained in the draft genome sequence and 19 were represented in the IGI/IPI. This suggests that the gene prediction process has a sensitivity of about 68% (19/28) for the detection of novel genes in the draft genome sequence and that the current IGI contains about 61% (19/31) of novel genes in the human genome.

Comparison with RIKEN mouse cDNAs. In a less direct but larger-scale approach, we compared the IGI gene set to a set of mouse cDNAs sequenced by the Genome Exploration Group of the RIKEN Genomic Sciences Center[309]. Around 81% of the genes in the RIKEN mouse set showed sequence similarity to the human genome sequence, whereas 69% showed sequence similarity to the IGI/IPI. This suggests a sensitivity of 85% (69/81).

序列数据最重要的应用之一，也是最艰巨的挑战之一。

生成人类基因的完整索引　我们聚焦于产生一个人类基因与蛋白质的初始索引。由于在人类 DNA 中识别基因的困难，以及基因组草图序列的未完成状态，该索引离完成之日尚早。尽管如此，它对实验性研究仍有价值，并可从中洞察人类基因与蛋白质的本质。

在人类 DNA 中识别基因是很困难的。有信噪比很低的问题：编码序列只构成了基因组很小的一部分，平均只占每个基因的 5%；基因内部的外显子比线虫的还小；基因可能存在更多的可变剪接。对人类 21 和 22 号染色体进行测序所面临的挑战被低估了。即使能够得到最终序列和深入的实验研究，基因含量仍旧是不确定的，估计值上限和下限的差异可达 30%。22 号染色体完成序列的初始报告（参考文献 94）确认了 247 个已知基因、298 个根据序列同源性或表达序列标签 EST 预测的基因以及 325 个没有其他证据支持的从头预测的基因。许多预测基因不完整。在过去的一年里，在 22 号染色体的注释数据组中，尽管已确定基因的数量只增长了 17 个，一些之前识别出来的基因也有所重叠，我们在现有基因注释的基础上又发现了 440 个外显子（10%）[286]。

生成初始基因索引　我们着手对人类基因组生成一个初始的整合基因索引（IGI），和一个相关的整合蛋白质索引（IPI）。

IGI/IPI 的评估　我们用几种方法评估 IPI/IGI 数据组的灵敏性、特异性和片段化。

与"新的"已知基因的比较　一种方法是检查那些新发现的基因，它们来自我们的基因预测中尚未使用的独立工作。我们发现了 31 个这样的基因：有 22 个最近刚加入 RefSeq 数据库，有 9 个来自桑格中心的 X 染色体基因识别项目。在这些基因中，有 28 个包含在基因组草图序列中，有 19 个出现在 IGI/IPI 数据组中。这提示，基因预测过程中，从基因组草图序列中预测新基因的灵敏性约为 68%（19/28），而目前的 IGI 数据组包含了人类基因组中 61%（19/31）的新基因。

与 RIKEN 小鼠 cDNA 比较　通过一个较为间接而规模较大的方法，我们将 IGI 基因数据组与小鼠的 cDNA 数据组进行比较，该小鼠的 cDNA 序列是由日本理化研究所（RIKEN）基因组科学中心的基因组探索团队测序的[309]。在 RIKEN 小鼠数据组中，有 81% 的基因与人类基因组存在序列相似性，而有 69% 的基因与 IGI/IPI 数据组存在序列相似性。这提示了 85%（69/81）的灵敏度。

Chromosomal distribution. Finally, we examined the chromosomal distribution of the IGI gene set. The average density of gene predictions is 11.1 per Mb across the genome, with the extremes being chromosome 19 at 26.8 per Mb and chromosome Y at 6.4 per Mb. It is likely that a significant number of the predictions on chromosome Y are pseudogenes (this chromosome is known to be rich in pseudogenes) and thus that the density for chromosome Y is an overestimate.

Summary. We are clearly still some way from having a complete set of human genes. The current IGI contains significant numbers of partial genes, fragmented and fused genes, pseudogenes and spurious predictions, and it also lacks significant numbers of true genes. This reflects the current state of gene prediction methods in vertebrates even in finished sequence, as well as the additional challenges related to the current state of the draft genome sequence. Nonetheless, the gene predictions provide a valuable starting point for a wide range of biological studies and will be rapidly refined in the coming year.

The analysis above allows us to estimate the number of distinct genes in the IGI, as well as the number of genes in the human genome. The IGI set contains about 15,000 known genes and about 17,000 gene predictions. Assuming that the gene predictions are subject to a rate of overprediction (spurious predictions and pseudogenes) of 20% and a rate of fragmentation of 1.4, the IGI would be estimated to contain about 24,500 actual human genes. Assuming that the gene predictions contain about 60% of previously unknown human genes, the total number of genes in the human genome would be estimated to be about 31,000. This is consistent with most recent estimates based on sampling, which suggest a gene number of 30,000–35,000.

Comparative proteome analysis

Knowledge of the human proteome will provide unprecedented opportunities for studies of human gene function. Often clues will be provided by sequence similarity with proteins of known function in model organisms. Such initial observations must then be followed up by detailed studies to establish the actual function of these molecules in humans.

For example, 35 proteins are known to be involved in the vacuolar protein-sorting machinery in yeast. Human genes encoding homologues can be found in the draft human sequence for 34 of these yeast proteins, but precise relationships are not always clear. In nine cases there appears to be a single clear human orthologue (a gene that arose as a consequence of speciation); in 12 cases there are matches to a family of human paralogues (genes that arose owing to intra-genome duplication); and in 13 cases there are matches to specific protein domains[311-314]. Hundreds of similar stories emerge from the draft sequence, but each merits a detailed interpretation in context. To treat these subjects properly, there will be many following studies, the first of which appear in accompanying papers[315-323].

Genes shared with fly, worm and yeast. IPI.1 contains apparent homologues of 61%

染色体分布　　最后，我们检验了 IGI 数据组的染色体分布。基因预测在全基因组范围内的平均密度是每 Mb 分布 11.1 个基因，极限是 19 号染色体上每 Mb 分布 26.8 个基因，Y 染色体上每 Mb 分布 6.4 个基因。可能 Y 染色体上大量预测出来的是假基因（已知这条染色体富含假基因），因此 Y 染色体的密度被高估了。

小结　　我们显然还未得到完整的人类基因数据组。目前的 IGI 包含了大量的不完整基因、片段化和融合基因、假基因以及错误的预测；它也同样缺少相当数量的真基因。这反映了在脊椎动物完成序列中基因预测方法的当前状态，以及与基因组草图序列当前状态相关的更多挑战。尽管如此，基因预测还是为大范围的生物学研究提供了宝贵的起点，并将在未来快速优化。

上述分析使我们能够估计 IGI 中不同基因的数量以及人类基因组中的基因数量。IGI 数据组中包含约 15,000 个已知基因和约 17,000 个预测基因。假设赋予基因预测 20% 的高估率（错误预测和假基因）以及 1.4 倍的片段化率，则 IGI 数据组估计应含 24,500 个实际人类基因。假设基因预测包含 60% 未知人类基因，则人类基因组中的基因总数估算为约 31,000 个。这与最近基于采样的估计结果一致，该结果为 30,000 至 35,000 个。

比较蛋白质组学分析

人类蛋白质组学的知识将为研究人类基因功能提供前所未有的重大机遇。这些线索常常由模式生物中已知功能的蛋白质的序列相似性所提供。必须进行详细的研究跟进这些初始的观察，从而发现这些分子在人类中的实际功能。

例如，已知酵母的液泡蛋白分选机制涉及 35 个蛋白质。在人类基因组草图序列中，可以找到 34 个酵母此类蛋白质的人类基因编码的同源物，但它们之间精细的关系还不清楚。有 9 个可能是人类的直系同源物（由于物种形成产生的基因）；有 12 个可能与人类旁系同源物（基因组内的序列倍增产生的基因）家族匹配；有 13 个与特异性的蛋白质结构域匹配[311-314]。在草图序列中产生了几百个相似的例子，但每一个都值得在文中详细解析。为妥善处理这些研究对象，我们需要许多后续研究，最先开始的工作就出现在附随的文章中[315-323]。

与果蝇、线虫和酵母共有的基因　　IPI.1 包含了果蝇蛋白质组中 61% 的显著同源

of the fly proteome, 43% of the worm proteome and 46% of the yeast proteome. We next considered the groups of proteins containing likely orthologues and paralogues (genes that arose from intragenome duplication) in human, fly, worm and yeast.

We identified 1,308 groups of proteins, each containing at least one predicted orthologue in each species and many containing additional paralogues. The 1,308 groups contained 3,129 human proteins, 1,445 fly proteins, 1,503 worm proteins and 1,441 yeast proteins. These 1,308 groups represent a conserved core of proteins that are mostly responsible for the basic "housekeeping" functions of the cell, including metabolism, DNA replication and repair, and translation.

Most proteins do not show simple 1-1-1 orthologous relationships across the three animals.

New architectures from old domains. Whereas there appears to be only modest invention at the level of new vertebrate protein domains, there appears to be substantial innovation in the creation of new vertebrate proteins. This innovation is evident at the level of domain architecture, defined as the linear arrangement of domains within a polypeptide. New architectures can be created by shuffling, adding or deleting domains, resulting in new proteins from old parts.

We quantified the number of distinct protein architectures found in yeast, worm, fly and human by using the SMART annotation resource[339]. The human proteome set contained 1.8 times as many protein architectures as worm or fly and 5.8 times as many as yeast. This difference is most prominent in the recent evolution of novel extracellular and transmembrane architectures in the human lineage. Human extracellular proteins show the greatest innovation: the human has 2.3 times as many extracellular architectures as fly and 2.0 times as many as worm.

Conclusion. Five lines of evidence point to an increase in the complexity of the proteome from the single-celled yeast to the multicellular invertebrates and to vertebrates such as the human. Specifically, the human contains greater numbers of genes, domain and protein families, paralogues, multidomain proteins with multiple functions, and domain architectures. According to these measures, the relatively greater complexity of the human proteome is a consequence not simply of its larger size, but also of large-scale protein innovation.

An important question is the extent to which the greater phenotypic complexity of vertebrates can be explained simply by two- or threefold increases in proteome complexity. The real explanation may lie in combinatorial amplification of these modest differences, by mechanisms that include alternative splicing, post-translational modification and cellular regulatory networks. The potential numbers of different proteins and protein–protein interactions are vast, and their actual numbers cannot readily be discerned from the genome sequence. Elucidating such system-level properties presents one of the great challenges for modern biology. (Editorial note: a discussion of genome segmental history and comparison of conserved segments between human and mouse genomes has been omitted.)

物、线虫蛋白质组中 43% 的显著同源物及酵母蛋白质组中 46% 的显著同源物。我们接下来考虑的蛋白质类群包括人类、果蝇、线虫和酵母中可能的直系同源物和旁系同源物（来自基因组内的基因加倍）。

我们识别出 1,308 个蛋白质类群，每个类群至少包含每个物种中一个预测的直系同源物，有许多类群包含更多的旁系同源物。1,308 个类群中包含了 3,129 个人类蛋白质、1,445 个果蝇蛋白质、1,503 个线虫蛋白质和 1,441 个酵母蛋白质。这 1,308 个类群代表了一组保守的核心蛋白质，它们大多数主要负责细胞中最基本的"管家"功能，包括代谢、DNA 复制和修复以及翻译。

在这三种动物中，大多数蛋白质未显示出 1-1-1 的直系同源关系。

来自旧结构域的新型组织结构 尽管看起来在脊椎动物新的蛋白质结构域水平只有少量发现，但在产生脊椎动物新的蛋白质方面有实质性新发现。这一发现在结构域组织结构水平十分显著，即在多肽中结构域的线性排列。新的组织结构可通过变换结构域位置、添加或删除结构域来实现，使旧的组件中产生新的蛋白质。

通过 SMART 注释资源[339]，我们对酵母、线虫、果蝇和人类中找到的不同蛋白质组织结构进行计数。人类蛋白质组包含的蛋白质组织结构数量是线虫或果蝇的 1.8 倍，是酵母的 5.8 倍。在人类谱系新的细胞外和跨膜组织结构的近期演化中，这些差异最为显著。人类细胞外蛋白质中的新发现是最多的：人类细胞外组织结构数量是果蝇的 2.3 倍、线虫的 2.0 倍。

结论 从单细胞的酵母到多细胞的无脊椎动物再到脊椎动物，例如人类，蛋白质组的复杂性逐渐升高，有 5 条证据均指向这一点。具体地说，人类包含更多的基因、结构域和蛋白质家族、旁系同源物、具有多功能的多结构域蛋白质以及结构域组织结构。通过这些衡量可以发现，人类蛋白质组相对高的复杂性不仅仅是由于它的基因组有更大的尺寸，也是由于大规模的蛋白质新组合。

一个重要的问题是，脊椎动物表型的复杂程度可简单地用蛋白质组复杂性的两倍或者三倍的增长来解释。真正的解释可能存在于这些基本差异的组合扩增，可通过包括可变剪接、翻译后修饰和细胞调控网络在内的机制实现。不同的蛋白质和蛋白质–蛋白质相互作用的潜在数量是巨大的，也无法从基因组序列中可靠地辨明实际数量。对这些系统水平的性质的阐释，代表了现代生物学面临的巨大挑战之一。（编者注：对基因组片段历史以及人类和小鼠基因组保守片段的比较被删除了。）

Applications to Medicine and Biology

In most research papers, the authors can only speculate about future applications of the work. Because the genome sequence has been released on a daily basis over the past four years, however, we can already cite many direct applications. We focus on a handful of applications chosen primarily from medical research.

Disease genes

A key application of human genome research has been the ability to find disease genes of unknown biochemical function by positional cloning[388]. This method involves mapping the chromosomal region containing the gene by linkage analysis in affected families and then scouring the region to find the gene itself. Positional cloning is powerful, but it has also been extremely tedious. When the approach was first proposed in the early 1980s[9], a researcher wishing to perform positional cloning had to generate genetic markers to trace inheritance; perform chromosomal walking to obtain genomic DNA covering the region; and analyse a region of around 1 Mb by either direct sequencing or indirect gene identification methods. The first two barriers were eliminated with the development in the mid-1990s of comprehensive genetic and physical maps of the human chromosomes, under the auspices of the Human Genome Project. The remaining barrier, however, has continued to be formidable.

All that is changing with the availability of the human draft genome sequence. The human genomic sequence in public databases allows rapid identification *in silico* of candidate genes, followed by mutation screening of relevant candidates, aided by information on gene structure. For a mendelian disorder, a gene search can now often be carried out in a matter of months with only a modestly sized team.

At least 30 disease genes[55,389-422] have been positionally cloned in research efforts that depended directly on the publicly available genome sequence. As most of the human sequence has only arrived in the past twelve months, it is likely that many similar discoveries are not yet published. In addition, there are many cases in which the genome sequence played a supporting role, such as providing candidate microsatellite markers for finer genetic linkage analysis.

The genome sequence has also helped to reveal the mechanisms leading to some common chromosomal deletion syndromes. In several instances, recurrent deletions have been found to result from homologous recombination and unequal crossing over between large, nearly identical intrachromosomal duplications. Examples include the DiGeorge/velocardiofacial syndrome region on chromosome 22 (ref. 238) and the Williams-Beuren syndrome recurrent deletion on chromosome 7 (ref. 239).

在医学与生物学上的应用

对基因组序列在未来的应用，大多数研究性论文的作者仅能做出预测。然而，由于基因组序列的数据在过去的四年中每天都在增加，现在我们已经可以引用很多直接的应用实例了。我们在这里精选了几个医学上的研究应用。

疾病基因

目前，人类基因组研究一项最关键的应用是通过定位克隆来找到生化功能未知的致病基因[388]。这种方法涉及通过家系的连锁分析将包括该基因的染色体进行定位，再从该区域搜寻基因。定位克隆是有效的，但也极度冗余。当此方法在 20 世纪 80 年代早期被首次提出时[9]，研究者要做定位克隆首先要生成一个遗传标记跟踪该基因；然后通过染色体步移获得覆盖整个区域的基因组 DNA；再通过直接测序或间接鉴定基因的方法来分析 1 Mb 左右的区域。在 20 世纪 90 年代中期，在人类基因组计划的助力下，人类染色体遗传图谱和物理图谱的广泛绘制使前两步障碍已经扫除。即便如此，逾越剩下的障碍仍然非常困难。

当人类基因组草图完成后，一切都为之改观。我们可以利用储存在公共数据库中的人类基因组序列，通过生物信息学方法对目标基因进行快速鉴定，随后还可根据基因结构信息对目标基因的突变进行筛选。对某种孟德尔遗传疾病来说，一个中等规模的团队现在大约只需数月就能完成寻找特定基因的工作。

直接基于已发表的基因组序列，至少 30 个致病基因[55,389-422]已经完成定位克隆。由于大多数的人类基因组序列是在过去 12 个月内进入数据库的，可能还有很多此类研究尚未发表。此外，基因组序列还在很多研究中起到辅助作用，比如为精细的遗传连锁分析提供可用的微卫星标记。

基因组序列还帮助揭示了某些常见染色体缺失综合征的致病机制。在一些疾病中，我们发现频发性缺失是由大段的、几乎完全相同的染色体内部重复序列的同源重组和不等交换导致的。比如 22 号染色体上区域缺失引起的迪格奥尔格 /腭心面综合征（参考文献 238）和 7 号染色体上频发性缺失引起的威廉姆斯综合征（参考文献 239）。

Drug targets

Over the past century, the pharmaceutical industry has largely depended upon a limited set of drug targets to develop new therapies. A recent compendium[426,427] lists 483 drug targets as accounting for virtually all drugs on the market. Knowing the complete set of human genes and proteins will greatly expand the search for suitable drug targets. Although only a minority of human genes may be drug targets, it has been predicted that the number will exceed several thousand, and this prospect has led to a massive expansion of genomic research in pharmaceutical research and development. (Editorial note: the original text includes discussion of some specific applications of this new genomic information to drug development.)

Basic biology

Response to certain bitter tastes.   Recently, investigators mapped this trait in both humans and mice and then searched the relevant region of the human draft genome sequence for G-protein coupled receptors. These studies led, in quick succession, to the discovery of a new family of such proteins, the demonstration that they are expressed almost exclusively in taste buds, and the experimental confirmation that the receptors in cultured cells respond to specific bitter substances[433-435].

The Next Steps

Considerable progress has been made in human sequencing, but much remains to be done to produce a finished sequence. Even more work will be required to extract the full information contained in the sequence. Many of the key next steps are already underway.

Developing the IGI and IPI

A high priority will be to refine the IGI and IPI to the point where they accurately reflect every gene and every alternatively spliced form. Several steps are needed to reach this ambitious goal.

Finishing the human sequence will assist in this effort, but the experiences gained on chromosomes 21 and 22 show that sequence alone is not enough to allow complete gene identification. One powerful approach is cross-species sequence comparison with related organisms at suitable evolutionary distances. The sequence coverage from the pufferfish *T. nigroviridis* has already proven valuable in identifying potential exons[292]; this work is expected to continue from its current state of onefold coverage to reach at least fivefold coverage later this year. The genome sequence of the laboratory mouse will provide a

药物靶点

在过去的一个世纪里，制药产业极大地依赖有限的药物靶点来寻找新的治疗方法。最近发布的一项纲要总结了目前市场上所有药物的 483 个靶点[426,427]。而对人类的所有基因和蛋白质的揭示将极大地扩展对适当药物靶点的寻找。尽管目前只有少数人类基因可作为药物靶点，但可预见的是，这个数量将超过几千种，而此预期已经带来了药物研发领域中基因组研究的大发展。（编者注：原文包括新的基因信息在药物研发中的特定应用的讨论。）

基础生物学

对某些苦味的反应　最近，研究者们将这一特征定位在人类和小鼠的基因组上，并在人类基因组草图序列的相关区域中寻找 G 蛋白偶联受体。这些连贯的研究导致了这类蛋白质新家族的发现，证明了这些基因只在味蕾中表达，并实验验证了在体外培养的细胞中这些受体对苦味底物有信号反应[433-435]。

后　　续

尽管人类基因组序列已经取得了相当的进展，但要获得完整的最终序列，还有很多工作要做。而挖掘序列中包含的所有信息需要更多的工作。后续计划中的很多关键步骤已在进行中。

发展 IGI 和 IPI

高度优先的任务是将 IGI 和 IPI 精细到点，以精确地反映每一个基因和每一个可变剪接形式。这个宏伟的目标还需要几个步骤。

人类基因组序列的完成对这项工作有很大的帮助，但是从 21 号和 22 号染色体上获取的经验表明，仅有序列信息还不足以完成全部基因的识别。与演化距离适当的物种进行跨物种序列比对是一个有力的工具。河豚鱼基因组序列的覆盖率对识别潜在的外显子很有价值[292]，这项工作有望在今年从一倍覆盖率达到至少五倍覆盖率。实验室小鼠的基因组序列将为外显子识别提供相当有力的工具，序列相似性有

particularly powerful tool for exon identification, as sequence similarity is expected to identify 95–97% of the exons, as well as a significant number of regulatory domains[436-438].

Another important step is to obtain a comprehensive collection of full-length human cDNAs, both as sequences and as actual clones. The Mammalian Gene Collection project has been underway for a year[18] and expects to produce 10,000–15,000 human full-length cDNAs over the coming year, which will be available without restrictions on use. The Genome Exploration Group of the RIKEN Genomic Sciences Center is similarly developing a collection of cDNA clones from mouse[309], which is a valuable complement because of the availability of tissues from all developmental time points.

Large-scale identification of regulatory regions

The one-dimensional script of the human genome, shared by essentially all cells in all tissues, contains sufficient information to provide for differentiation of hundreds of different cell types, and the ability to respond to a vast array of internal and external influences. Much of this plasticity results from the carefully orchestrated symphony of transcriptional regulation. Although much has been learned about the *cis*-acting regulatory motifs of some specific genes, the regulatory signals for most genes remain uncharacterized. It will also be of considerable interest to study epigenetic modifications such as cytosine methylation on a genome-wide scale, and to determine their biological consequences[446,447]. Towards this end, a pilot Human Epigenome Project has been launched[448,449].

Sequencing of additional large genomes

More generally, comparative genomics allows biologists to peruse evolution's laboratory notebook—to identify conserved functional features and recognize new innovations in specific lineages. Determination of the genome sequence of many organisms is very desirable. Already, projects are underway to sequence the genomes of the mouse, rat, zebrafish and the pufferfishes *T. nigroviridis* and *Takifugu rubripes*. Plans are also under consideration for sequencing additional primates and other organisms that will help define key developments along the vertebrate and nonvertebrate lineages.

To realize the full promise of comparative genomics, however, it needs to become simple and inexpensive to sequence the genome of any organism. Sequencing costs have dropped 100-fold over the last 10 years, corresponding to a roughly twofold decrease every 18 months. This rate is similar to "Moore's law" concerning improvements in semiconductor manufacture.

望识别 95% ~ 97% 的外显子以及大量的调控结构域[436-438]。

另一个重要的工作是获得人类基因组的全长 cDNA 库，既有序列信息，又有实际使用的克隆。哺乳动物基因库计划已经执行了一年[18]，预计将在明年产生 10,000 ~ 15,000 个人类全长 cDNA，并向公众开放使用。同样，日本理化研究所基因组科学中心的基因组探索团队也用小鼠建立了 cDNA 克隆库[309]，该库是极有价值的补充，因为它含有所有发育时间点的组织。

调控区域的大规模识别

人类基因组的一维文本信息在所有组织中为所有细胞共享，为几百种不同细胞类型的分化提供充足的信息，并对大量内部和外部的影响做出反应。这种可塑性多数来自精细安排的转录调控。尽管已经对一些特定基因的顺式作用调控模体做了很多研究，大多数基因的调控信号仍然未知。人们对研究表观遗传学修饰，例如基因组范围内的胞嘧啶甲基化，以及确定它们的生物学效果也有很大的兴趣[446,447]。一个领航性的人类表观基因组计划已经为实现此目标而发起[448,449]。

更多的大基因组测序

通常来说，比较基因组学使得生物学家能够利用演化的实验室数据识别保守的功能特征以及特定谱系中的新序列。我们需要确定大量物种的基因组序列。已经有一些项目在测定小鼠、大鼠、斑马鱼、河豚鱼和红旗东方鲀的基因组。人们也在酝酿测定更多灵长类动物和其他生物的基因组，这将帮助解释脊椎动物与非脊椎动物的关键发育过程。

要建立完善的比较基因组学，就需要简单而廉价地测定生物体的基因组。在过去的 10 年中，测序费用已经下降为最初的 100 分之一，大约每 18 个月下降一半。这一速率与半导体制造业发展的"摩尔定律"相符。

Completing the catalogue of human variation

The human draft genome sequence has already allowed the identification of more than 1.4 million SNPs, comprising a substantial proportion of all common human variation. This program should be extended to obtain a nearly complete catalogue of common variants and to identify the common ancestral haplotypes present in the population. In principle, these genetic tools should make it possible to perform association studies and linkage disequilibrium studies[376] to identify the genes that confer even relatively modest risk for common diseases. Launching such an intense era of human molecular epidemiology will also require major advances in the cost efficiency of genotyping technology, in the collection of carefully phenotyped patient cohorts and in statistical methods for relating large-scale SNP data to disease phenotype.

From sequence to function

The scientific program outlined above focuses on how the genome sequence can be mined for biological information. In addition, the sequence will serve as a foundation for a broad range of functional genomic tools to help biologists to probe function in a more systematic manner. These will need to include improved techniques and databases for the global analysis of: RNA and protein expression, protein localization, protein–protein interactions and chemical inhibition of pathways.

Concluding Thoughts

The Human Genome Project is but the latest increment in a remarkable scientific program whose origins stretch back a hundred years to the rediscovery of Mendel's laws and whose end is nowhere in sight. In a sense, it provides a capstone for efforts in the past century to discover genetic information and a foundation for efforts in the coming century to understand it.

We find it humbling to gaze upon the human sequence now coming into focus. In principle, the string of genetic bits holds long-sought secrets of human development, physiology and medicine. In practice, our ability to transform such information into understanding remains woefully inadequate.

The scientific work will have profound long-term consequences for medicine, leading to the elucidation of the underlying molecular mechanisms of disease and thereby facilitating the design in many cases of rational diagnostics and therapeutics targeted at those mechanisms. But the science is only part of the challenge. We must also involve society at large in the work ahead. We must set realistic expectations that the most important benefits will not be reaped overnight. Moreover, understanding and wisdom will be required to ensure that

完成人类变异目录

在人类基因组草图中已经识别出超过 1,400,000 个 SNP，它们构成了人类基因组序列变异的大部分。这一项目应扩展以建立基本包括所有常见变异的目录，并识别出种群中常见的祖先单倍型。原则上，这些遗传学工具应当使我们能够开展相关性研究和连锁不平衡研究[376]以辨别出即便是仅有中度风险的常见疾病基因。要开启这样一个人类分子流行病学的时代，也需要基因分型技术的成本效率、精细分型的患者群体的收集以及将大规模 SNP 数据与疾病分型关联起来的统计学方法等方面的重大进展。

从序列到功能

科学项目勾勒出了以上研究热点，关注如何从基因组数据中挖掘生物学信息。而且，序列数据还是大规模功能基因组学工具的基础，能帮助生物学家以更加系统化的方式验证功能。这些都需要优化技术和数据库，用于如下全局性分析：RNA 和蛋白质表达、蛋白质定位、蛋白质–蛋白质相互作用和通路的化学抑制。

结　语

人类基因组计划只是一个举世瞩目的科学研究计划中的最新增长点，它的起源可回溯至一百年前孟德尔遗传定律的重新发现，而它的终点则延伸至未知的未来。从某种意义上讲，它是过去一个世纪以来发现遗传学信息科学研究的顶峰，并为下一个世纪解析这些数据提供了基础。

只关注目前聚焦的人类基因组序列令人感到惭愧。理论上，这些遗传信息蕴含着关于人类发育、生理和医学中我们长期探求的秘密。而实际上，我们将这些信息转化理解的能力严重不足。

科学研究工作蕴含着深刻而长远的医学成果，能够阐释疾病的分子机制，也因此方便根据这些机制设计合理的诊断学和治疗学手段。但是，科学只是挑战的一部分。在开展工作之前，我们也必须关注到全社会。我们必须正确面对现实的期待，不能急于求成。而且，我们需要理解和智慧来确保这些好处能够公平合理地普惠大

these benefits are implemented broadly and equitably. To that end, serious attention must be paid to the many ethical, legal and social implications (ELSI) raised by the accelerated pace of genetic discovery. This paper has focused on the scientific achievements of the human genome sequencing efforts. This is not the place to engage in a lengthy discussion of the ELSI issues, which have also been a major research focus of the Human Genome Project, but these issues are of comparable importance and could appropriately fill a paper of equal length.

Finally, it is has not escaped our notice that the more we learn about the human genome, the more there is to explore.

"We shall not cease from exploration. And the end of all our exploring will be to arrive where we started, and know the place for the first time. "—T. S. Eliot[450]

(**409**, 860-921; 2001)

Received 7 December 2000; accepted 9 January 2001.

References:

1. Correns, C. Untersuchungen u ber die Xenien bei Zea mays. *Berichte der Deutsche Botanische Gesellschaft*, **17**, 410-418 (1899).

2. De Vries, H. Sur la loi de disjonction des hybrides. *Comptes Rendue Hebdemodaires*, *Acad. Sci. Paris* **130**, 845-847 (1900).

3. von Tschermack, E. Uber Künstliche Kreuzung bei Pisum sativum. *Berichte der Deutsche Botanische Gesellschaft*, **18**, 232-239 (1900).

9. Botstein, D., White, R. L., Skolnick, M. & Davis, R. W. Construction of a genetic linkage map in man using restriction fragment length polymorphisms. *Am. J. Hum. Genet.* **32**, 314-331 (1980).

11. Coulson, A., Sulston, J., Brenner, S. & Karn, J. Toward a physical map of the genome of the nematode *Caenorhabditis elegans*. *Proc. Natl Acad. Sci. USA* **83**, 7821-7825 (1986).

18. Strausberg, R. L., Feingold, E. A., Klausner, R. D. & Collins, F. S. The mammalian gene collection. *Science* **286**, 455-457 (1999).

21. Sinsheimer, R. L. The Santa Cruz Workshop-May 1985. *Genomics* **5**, 954-956 (1989).

22. Palca, J. Human genome-Department of Energy on the map. *Nature* **321**, 371 (1986).

23. National Research Council *Mapping and Sequencing the Human Genome* (National Academy Press, Washington DC, 1988).

24. Bishop, J. E. & Waldholz, M. *Genome* (Simon and Schuster, New York, 1990).

25. Kevles, D. J. & Hood, L. (eds) *The Code of Codes: Scientific and Social Issues in the Human Genome Project* (Harvard Univ. Press, Cambridge, Massachusetts, 1992).

26. Cook-Deegan, R. *The Gene Wars: Science, Politics, and the Human Genome* (W. W. Norton & Co., New York, London, 1994).

27. Donis-Keller, H. *et al.* A genetic linkage map of the human genome. *Cell* **51**, 319-337 (1987).

28. Gyapay, G. *et al.* The 1993-94 Genethon human genetic linkage map. *Nature Genet.* **7**, 246-339 (1994).

29. Hudson, T. J. *et al.* An STS-based map of the human genome. *Science* **270**, 1945-1954 (1995).

30. Dietrich, W. F. *et al.* A comprehensive genetic map of the mouse genome. *Nature* **380**, 149-152 (1996).

31. Nusbaum, C. *et al.* A YAC-based physical map of the mouse genome. *Nature Genet.* **22**, 388-393 (1999).

32. Oliver, S. G. *et al.* The complete DNA sequence of yeast chromosome III. *Nature* **357**, 38-46 (1992).

33. Wilson, R. *et al.* 2.2 Mb of contiguous nucleotide sequence from chromosome III of C. elegans. *Nature* **368**, 32-38 (1994).

34. Chen, E. Y. *et al.* The human growth hormone locus: nucleotide sequence, biology, and evolution. *Genomics* **4**, 479-497 (1989).

35. McCombie, W. R. *et al.* Expressed genes, Alu repeats and polymorphisms in cosmids sequenced from chromosome 4p16.3. *Nature Genet.* **1**, 348-353 (1992).

36. Martin-Gallardo, A. *et al.* Automated DNA sequencing and analysis of 106 kilobases from human chromosome 19q13.3. *Nature Genet.* **1**, 34-39 (1992).

37. Edwards, A. *et al.* Automated DNA sequencing of the human HPRT locus. *Genomics* **6**, 593-608 (1990).

42. Marshall, E. A second private genome project. *Science* **281**, 1121 (1998).

43. Marshall, E. NIH to produce a `working draft' of the genome by 2001. *Science* **281**, 1774-1775 (1998).

44. Pennisi, E. Academic sequencers challenge Celera in a sprint to the finish. *Science* **283**, 1822-1823 (1999).

45. Bouck, J., Miller, W., Gorrell, J. H., Muzny, D. & Gibbs, R. A. Analysis of the quality and utility of random shotgun sequencing at low redundancies. *Genome Res.* **8**, 1074-1084 (1998).

46. Collins, F. S. *et al.* New goals for the U. S. Human Genome Project: 1998-2003. *Science* **282**, 682-689 (1998).

众。为此，我们应当严肃地关注加速发展的遗传学发现导致的伦理、法律和社会问题（ELSI）。本文聚焦于人类基因组测序产生的科学成就。这里并未就 ELSI 问题进行长篇大论，但这些问题已经成为人类基因组研究的主要热点之一，这些问题也同等重要，可以写一篇同样长的论文。

最终我们意识到，对人类基因组了解得越多，就有越多未知需要去探索。

"我们不会停止求索，万般求索终将抵达最初的起点，此时才把这个地方看个透彻。"——艾略特[450]

（王海纳 任奕 翻译；于军 审稿）

47. Sanger, F. & Coulson, A. R. A rapid method for determining sequences in DNA by primed synthesis with DNA polymerase. *J. Mol. Biol.* **94**, 441-448 (1975).

48. Maxam, A. M. & Gilbert, W. A new method for sequencing DNA. *Proc. Natl Acad. Sci. USA* **74**, 560- 564 (1977).

49. Anderson, S. Shotgun DNA sequencing using cloned DNase I-generated fragments. *Nucleic Acids Res.* **9**, 3015-3027 (1981).

50. Gardner, R. C. *et al.* The complete nucleotide sequence of an infectious clone of cauliflower mosaic virus by M13mp7 shotgun sequencing. *Nucleic Acids Res.* **9**, 2871-2888 (1981).

51. Deininger, P. L. Random subcloning of sonicated DNA: application to shotgun DNA sequence analysis. *Anal. Biochem.* **129**, 216-223 (1983).

52. Chissoe, S. L. *et al.* Sequence and analysis of the human ABL gene, the BCR gene, and regions involved in the Philadelphia chromosomal translocation. *Genomics* **27**, 67-82 (1995).

53. Rowen, L., Koop, B. F. & Hood, L. The complete 685-kilobase DNA sequence of the human beta T cell receptor locus. *Science* **272**, 1755-1762 (1996).

54. Koop, B. F. *et al.* Organization, structure, and function of 95 kb of DNA spanning the murine T-cell receptor C alpha/C delta region. *Genomics* **13**, 1209-1230 (1992).

55. Wooster, R. *et al.* Identification of the breast cancer susceptibility gene BRCA2. *Nature* **378**, 789-792 (1995).

60. Venter, J. C. *et al.* Shotgun sequencing of the human genome. *Science* **280**, 1540-1542 (1998).

61. Venter, J. C. *et al.* The sequence of the human genome. *Science* **291**, 1304-1351 (2001).

79. Bentley, D. R. Genomic sequence information should be released immediately and freely in the public domain. *Science* **274**, 533-534 (1996).

80. Guyer, M. Statement on the rapid release of genomic DNA sequence. *Genome Res.* **8**, 413 (1998).

81. Dietrich, W. *et al.* A genetic map of the mouse suitable for typing intraspecific crosses. *Genetics* **131**, 423-447 (1992).

82. Kim, U. J. *et al.* Construction and characterization of a human bacterial artificial chromosome library. *Genomics* **34**, 213-218 (1996).

83. Osoegawa, K. *et al.* Bacterial artificial chromosome libraries for mouse sequencing and functional analysis. *Genome Res.* **10**, 116-128 (2000).

84. Marra, M. A. *et al.* High throughput fingerprint analysis of large-insert clones. *Genome Res.* **7**, 1072- 1084 (1997).

85. Marra, M. *et al.* A map for sequence analysis of the *Arabidopsis thaliana* genome. *Nature Genet.* **22**, 265-270 (1999).

86. The International Human Genome Mapping Consortium. A physical map of the human genome. *Nature* **409**, 934-941 (2001).

87. Zhao, S. *et al.* Human BAC ends quality assessment and sequence analyses. *Genomics* **63**, 321-332 (2000).

88. Mahairas, G. G. *et al.* Sequence-tagged connectors: A sequence approach to mapping and scanning the human genome. *Proc. Natl Acad. Sci. USA* **96**, 9739-9744 (1999).

93. Hattori, M. *et al.* The DNA sequence of human chromosome 21. *Nature* **405**, 311-319 (2000).

94. Dunham, I. *et al.* The DNA sequence of human chromosome 22. *Nature* **402**, 489-495 (1999).

110. Pruit, K. D. & Maglott, D. R. RefSeq and LocusLink: NCBI gene-centered resources. *Nucleic Acids Res.* **29**, 137-140 (2001).

112. Hurst, L. D. & Eyre-Walker, A. Evolutionary genomics: reading the bands. *Bioessays* **22**, 105-107 (2000).

113. Saccone, S. *et al.* Correlations between isochores and chromosomal bands in the human genome. *Proc. Natl Acad. Sci. USA* **90**, 11929-11933 (1993).

114. Zoubak, S., Clay, O. & Bernardi, G. The gene distribution of the human genome. *Gene* **174**, 95-102 (1996).

115. Gardiner, K. Base composition and gene distribution: critical patterns in mammalian genome organization. *Trends Genet.* **12**, 519-524 (1996).

116. Duret, L., Mouchiroud, D. & Gautier, C. Statistical analysis of vertebrate sequences reveals that long genes are scarce in GC-rich isochores. *J. Mol. Evol.* **40**, 308- 317 (1995).

117. Saccone, S., De Sario, A., Della Valle, G. & Bernardi, G. The highest gene concentrations in the human genome are in telomeric bands of metaphase chromosomes. *Proc. Natl Acad. Sci. USA* **89**, 4913-4917 (1992).

122. Bird, A., Taggart, M., Frommer, M., Miller, O. J. & Macleod, D. A fraction of the mouse genome that is derived from islands of nonmethylated, CpG-rich DNA. *Cell* **40**, 91-99 (1985).

123. Bird, A. P. CpG islands as gene markers in the vertebrate nucleus. *Trends Genet.* **3**, 342-347 (1987).

124. Chan, M. F., Liang, G. & Jones, P. A. Relationship between transcription and DNA methylation. *Curr. Top. Microbiol. Immunol.* **249**, 75-86 (2000).

125. Holliday, R. & Pugh, J. E. DNA modification mechanisms and gene activity during development. *Science* **187**, 226-232 (1975).

126. Larsen, F., Gundersen, G., Lopez, R. & Prydz, H. CpG islands as gene markers in the human genome. *Genomics* **13**, 1095-1107 (1992).

127. Tazi, J. & Bird, A. Alternative chromatin structure at CpG islands. *Cell* **60**, 909-920 (1990).

131. Yu, A. Comparison of human genetic and sequence-based physical maps. *Nature* **409**, 951-953 (2001).

132. Kaback, D. B., Guacci, V., Barber, D. & Mahon, J. W. Chromosome size-dependent control of meiotic recombination. *Science* **256**, 228-232 (1992).

133. Riles, L. *et al.* Physical maps of the 6 smallest chromosomes of *Saccharomyces cerevisiae* at a resolution of 2.6-kilobase pairs. *Genetics* **134**, 81-150 (1993).

135. Laurie, D. A. & Hulten, M. A. Further studies on bivalent chiasma frequency in human males with normal karyotypes. *Ann. Hum. Genet.* **49**, 189-201 (1985).

136. Roeder, G. S. Meiotic chromosomes: it takes two to tango. *Genes Dev.* **11**, 2600-2621 (1997).

137. Wu, T.-C. & Lichten, M. Meiosis-induced double-strand break sites determined by yeast chromatin structure. *Science* **263**, 515-518 (1994).

138. Gerton, J. L. *et al.* Global mapping of meiotic recombination hotspots and coldspots in the yeast *Saccharomyces cerevisiae*. *Proc. Natl Acad. Sci. USA* **97**, 11383-11390 (2000).

139. Li, W. -H. *Molecular Evolution* (Sinauer, Sunderland, Massachusetts, 1997).

140. Gregory, T. R. & Hebert, P. D. The modulation of DNA content: proximate causes and ultimate consequences. *Genome Res.* **9**, 317-324 (1999).

141. Hartl, D. L. Molecular melodies in high and low C. *Nature Rev. Genet.* **1**, 145-149 (2000).

142. Smit, A. F. Interspersed repeats and other mementos of transposable elements in mammalian genomes. *Curr. Opin. Genet. Dev.* **9**, 657-663 (1999).

143. Prak, E. L. & Haig, H. K. Jr Mobile elements and the human genome. *Nature Rev. Genet.* **1**, 134-144 (2000).

148. Smit, A. F. The origin of interspersed repeats in the human genome. *Curr. Opin. Genet. Dev.* **6**, 743- 748 (1996).

154. Malik, H. S., Burke, W. D. & Eickbush, T. H. The age and evolution of non-LTR retrotransposable elements. *Mol. Biol. Evol.* **16**, 793-805 (1999).

155. Kordis, D. & Gubensek, F. Bov-B long interspersed repeated DNA (LINE) sequences are present in *Vipera ammodytes* phospholipase A2 genes and in genomes of Viperidae snakes. *Eur. J. Biochem.* **246**, 772-779 (1997).

158. Smit, A. F., Toth, G., Riggs, A. D., & Jurka, J. Ancestral, mammalian-wide subfamilies of LINE-1 repetitive sequences. *J. Mol. Biol.* **246**, 401-417 (1995).

159. Lim, J. K. & Simmons, M. J. Gross chromosome rearrangements mediated by transposable elements in *Drosophila melanogaster*. *Bioessays* **16**, 269-275 (1994).

160. Caceres, M., Ranz, J. M., Barbadilla, A., Long, M. & Ruiz, A. Generation of a widespread Drosophila inversion by a transposable element. *Science* **285**, 415-418 (1999).

161. Gray, Y. H. It takes two transposons to tango: transposable-element-mediated chromosomal rearrangements. *Trends Genet.* **16**, 461-468 (2000).

162. Zhang, J. & Peterson, T. Genome rearrangements by nonlinear transposons in maize. *Genetics* **153**, 1403-1410 (1999).

163. Smit, A. F. Identification of a new, abundant superfamily of mammalian LTR-transposons. *Nucleic Acids Res.* **21**, 1863-1872 (1993).

164. Cordonnier, A., Casella, J. F. & Heidmann, T. Isolation of novel human endogenous retrovirus-like elements with foamy virus-related pol sequence. *J. Virol.* **69**, 5890-5897 (1995).

170. Kazazian, H. H. Jr & Moran, J. V. The impact of L1 retrotransposons on the human genome. *Nature Genet.* **19**, 19-24 (1998).

171. Malik, H. S. & Eickbush, T. H. NeSL-1, an ancient lineage of site-specific non-LTR retrotransposons from *Caenorhabditis elegans*. *Genetics* **154**, 193-203 (2000).

172. Casavant, N. C. *et al.* The end of the LINE?: lack of recent L1 activity in a group of South American rodents. *Genetics* **154**, 1809-1817 (2000).

173. Meunier-Rotival, M., Soriano, P., Cuny, G., Strauss, F. & Bernardi, G. Sequence organization and genomic distribution of the major family of interspersed repeats of mouse DNA. *Proc. Natl Acad. Sci. USA* **79**, 355-359 (1982).

174. Soriano, P., Meunier-Rotival, M. & Bernardi, G. The distribution of interspersed repeats is nonuniform and conserved in the mouse and human genomes. *Proc. Natl Acad. Sci. USA* **80**, 1816- 1820 (1983).

175. Goldman, M. A., Holmquist, G. P., Gray, M. C., Caston, L. A. & Nag, A. Replication timing of genes and middle repetitive sequences. *Science* **224**, 686-692 (1984).

176. Manuelidis, L. & Ward, D. C. Chromosomal and nuclear distribution of the *Hind*III 1.9-kb human DNA repeat segment. *Chromosoma* **91**, 28-38 (1984).

178. Jurka, J. Sequence patterns indicate an enzymatic involvement in integration of mammalian retroposons. *Proc. Natl Acad. Sci. USA* **94**, 1872-1877 (1997).

192. Bohossian, H. B., Skaletsky, H. & Page, D. C. Unexpectedly similar rates of nucleotide substitution found in male and female hominids. *Nature* **406**, 622-625 (2000).

215. Ji, Y., Eichler, E. E., Schwartz, S. & Nicholls, R. D. Structure of chromosomal duplicons and their role in mediating human genomic disorders. *Genome Res.* **10**, 597-610 (2000).

216. Eichler, E. E. Masquerading repeats: paralogous pitfalls of the human genome. *Genome Res.* **8**, 758- 762 (1998).

217. Mazzarella, R. & D. Schlessinger, D. Pathological consequences of sequence duplications in the human genome. *Genome Res.* **8**, 1007-1021 (1998).

238. Shaikh, T. H. *et al.* Chromosome 22-specific low copy repeats and the 22q11.2 deletion syndrome: genomic organization and deletion endpoint analysis. *Hum. Mol. Genet.* **9**, 489-501 (2000).

239. Francke, U. Williams-Beuren syndrome: genes and mechanisms. *Hum. Mol. Genet.* **8**, 1947-1954 (1999).

243. Lander, E. S. The new genomics: Global views of biology. *Science* **274**, 536-539 (1996).

244. Eddy, S. R. Noncoding RNA genes. *Curr. Op. Genet. Dev.* **9**, 695-699 (1999).

245. Ban, N., Nissen, P., Hansen, J., Moore, P. B. & Steitz, T. A. The complete atomic structure of the large ribosomal subunit at 2.4 angstrom resolution. *Science* **289**, 905-920 (2000).

246. Nissen, P., Hansen, J., Ban, N., Moore, P. B. & Steitz, T. A. The structural basis of ribosome activity in peptide bond synthesis. *Science* **289**, 920-930 (2000).

247. Weinstein, L. B. & Steitz, J. A. Guided tours: from precursor snoRNA to functional snoRNP. *Curr. Opin. Cell Biol.* **11**, 378-384 (1999).

248. Bachellerie, J.-P. & Cavaille, J. in *Modification and Editing of RNA* (ed. Benne, H. g. a. R.) 255-272 (ASM, Washington DC, 1998).

253. Sprinzl, M., Horn, C., Brown, M., Ioudovitch, A. & Steinberg, S. Compilation of tRNA sequences and sequences of tRNA genes. *Nucleic Acids Res.* **26**, 148-153 (1998).

254. Long, E. O. & Dawid, I. B. Repeated genes in eukaryotes. *Annu. Rev. Biochem.* **49**, 727-764 (1980).

262. Buckland, R. A. A primate transfer-RNA gene cluster and the evolution of human chromosome 1. *Cytogenet. Cell Genet.* **61**, 1-4 (1992).

263. Gonos, E. S. & Goddard, J. P. Human tRNA-Glu genes: their copy number and organization. *FEBS Lett.* **276**, 138-142 (1990).

286. Dunham, I. The gene guessing game. *Yeast* **17**, 218-224 (2000).

292. Roest Crollius, H. *et al.* Estimate of human gene number provided by genome-wide analysis using *Tetraodon nigroviridis* DNA sequence. *Nature Genet.* **25**, 235-238 (2000).

309. The RIKEN Genome Exploration Research Group Phase II Team and the FANTOM Consortium. Functional annotation of a full-length mouse cDNA collection. *Nature* **409**, 685-690 (2001).

311. Janin, J. & Chothia, C. Domains in proteins: definitions, location, and structural principles. *Methods Enzymol.* **115**, 420-430 (1985).

312. Ponting, C. P., Schultz, J., Copley, R. R., Andrade, M. A. & Bork, P. Evolution of domain families. *Adv. Protein Chem.* **54**, 185-244 (2000).

313. Doolittle, R. F. The multiplicity of domains in proteins. *Annu. Rev. Biochem.* **64**, 287-314 (1995).

314. Bateman, A. & Birney, E. Searching databases to find protein domain organization. *Adv. Protein Chem.* **54**, 137-157 (2000).

315. Futreal, P. A. *et al.* Cancer and genomics. *Nature* **409**, 850-852 (2001).

316. Nestler, E. J. & Landsman, D. Learning about addiction from the human draft genome. *Nature* **409**, 834-835 (2001).

317. Tupler, R., Perini, G. & Green, M. R. Expressing the human genome. *Nature* **409**, 832-835 (2001).

318. Fahrer, A. M., Bazan, J. F., Papathanasiou, P., Nelms, K. A. & Goodnow, C. C. A genomic view of immunology. *Nature* **409**, 836-838 (2001).

319. Li, W. -H., Gu, Z., Wang, H. & Nekrutenko, A. Evolutionary analyses of the human genome. *Nature* **409**, 847-849 (2001).

320. Bock, J. B., Matern, H. T., Peden, A. A. & Scheller, R. H. A genomic perspective on membrane compartment organization. *Nature* **409**, 839-841 (2001).

321. Pollard, T. D. Genomics, the cytoskeleton and motility. *Nature* **409**, 842-843 (2001).

322. Murray, A. W. & Marks, D. Can sequencing shed light on cell cycling? *Nature* **409**, 844-846 (2001).

323. Clayton, J. D., Kyriacou, C. P. & Reppert, S. M. Keeping time with the human genome. *Nature* **409**, 829-831 (2001).

339. Schultz, J., Copley, R. R., Doerks, T., Ponting, C. P. & Bork, P. SMART: a web-based tool for the study of genetically mobile domains. *Nucleic Acids Res.* **28**, 231-234 (2000).

376. Lander, E. S. & Schork, N. J. Genetic dissection of complex traits. *Science* **265**, 2037-2048 (1994).

388. Collins, F. S. Positional cloning moves from perdition to traditional. *Nature Genet.* **9**, 347-350 (1995).

389. Nagamine, K. *et al.* Positional cloning of the APECED gene. *Nature Genet.* **17**, 393-398 (1997).

390. Reuber, B. E. *et al.* Mutations in PEX1 are the most common cause of peroxisome biogenesis disorders. *Nature Genet.* **17**, 445-448 (1997).

391. Portsteffen, H. *et al.* Human PEX1 is mutated in complementation group 1 of the peroxisome biogenesis disorders. *Nature Genet.* **17**, 449-452 (1997).

392. Everett, L. A. *et al.* Pendred syndrome is caused by mutations in a putative sulphate transporter gene (PDS). *Nature Genet.* **17**, 411-422 (1997).

393. Coffey, A. J. *et al.* Host response to EBV infection in X-linked lymphoproliferative disease results from mutations in an SH2-domain encoding gene. *Nature Genet.* **20**, 129-135 (1998).

394. Van Laer, L. *et al.* Nonsyndromic hearing impairment is associated with a mutation in DFNA5. *Nature Genet.* **20**, 194-197 (1998).

395. Sakuntabhai, A. *et al.* Mutations in ATP2A2, encoding a Ca2+pump, cause Darier disease. *Nature Genet.* **21**, 271-277 (1999).

396. Gedeon, A. K. *et al.* Identification of the gene (SEDL) causing X-linked spondyloepiphyseal dysplasia tarda. *Nature Genet.* **22**, 400-404 (1999).

397. Hurvitz, J. R. *et al.* Mutations in the CCN gene family member WISP3 cause progressive pseudorheumatoid dysplasia. *Nature Genet.* **23**, 94-98 (1999).

398. Laberge-le Couteulx, S. *et al.* Truncating mutations in CCM1, encoding KRIT1, cause hereditary cavernous angiomas. *Nature Genet.* **23**, 189-193 (1999).

399. Sahoo, T. *et al.* Mutations in the gene encoding KRIT1, a Krev-1/rap1a binding protein, cause cerebral cavernous malformations (CCM1). *Hum. Mol. Genet.* **8**, 2325-2333 (1999).

400. McGuirt, W. T. *et al.* Mutations in COL11A2 cause non-syndromic hearing loss (DFNA13). *Nature Genet.* **23**, 413-419 (1999).

401. Moreira, E. S. *et al.* Limb-girdle muscular dystrophy type 2G is caused by mutations in the gene encoding the sarcomeric protein telethonin. *Nature Genet.* **24**, 163-166 (2000).

402. Ruiz-Perez, V. L. *et al.* Mutations in a new gene in Ellis-van Creveld syndrome and Weyers acrodental dysostosis. *Nature Genet.* **24**, 283-286 (2000).

403. Kaplan, J. M. *et al.* Mutations in ACTN4, encoding alpha-actinin-4, cause familial focal segmental glomerulosclerosis. *Nature Genet.* **24**, 251-256 (2000).

404. Escayg, A. *et al.* Mutations of SCN1A, encoding a neuronal sodium channel, in two families with GEFS+2. *Nature Genet.* **24**, 343-345 (2000).

405. Sacksteder, K. A. *et al.* Identification of the alpha-aminoadipic semialdehyde synthase gene, which is defective in familial hyperlysinemia. *Am. J. Hum. Genet.* **66**, 1736-1743 (2000).

406. Kalaydjieva, L. *et al.* N-myc downstream-regulated gene 1 is mutated in hereditary motor and sensory neuropathy-Lom. *Am. J. Hum. Genet.* **67**, 47-58 (2000).

407. Sundin, O. H. *et al.* Genetic basis of total colourblindness among the Pingelapese islanders. *Nature Genet.* **25**, 289-293 (2000).

408. Kohl, S. *et al.* Mutations in the CNGB3 gene encoding the beta-subunit of the cone photoreceptor cGMP-gated channel are responsible for achromatopsia (ACHM3) linked to chromosome 8q21. *Hum. Mol. Genet.* **9**, 2107-2116 (2000).

409. Avela, K. *et al.* Gene encoding a new RING-B-box-coiled-coil protein is mutated in mulibrey nanism. *Nature Genet.* **25**, 298-301 (2000).

410. Verpy, E. *et al.* A defect in harmonin, a PDZ domain-containing protein expressed in the inner ear sensory hair cells, underlies usher syndrome type 1C. *Nature Genet.* **26**, 51-55 (2000).

411. Bitner-Glindzicz, M. *et al.* A recessive contiguous gene deletion causing infantile hyperinsulinism, enteropathy and deafness identifies the usher type 1C gene. *Nature Genet.* **26**, 56-60 (2000).

412. The May-Hegglin/Fechtner Syndrome Consortium. Mutations in MYH9 result in the May-Hegglin anomaly, and Fechtner and Sebastian syndromes. *Nature Genet.* **26**, 103-105 (2000).

413. Kelley, M. J., Jawien, W., Ortel, T. L. & Korczak, J. F. Mutation of MYH9, encoding non-muscle myosin heavy chain A, in May-Hegglin anomaly. *Nature Genet.* **26**, 106-108 (2000).

414. Kirschner, L. S. *et al.* Mutations of the gene encoding the protein kinase A type I-a regulatory subunit in patients with the Carney complex. *Nature Genet.* **26**, 89-92 (2000).

415. Lalwani, A. K. *et al.* Human nonsyndromic hereditary deafness DFNA17 is due to a mutation in non-muscle myosin MYH9. *Am. J. Hum. Genet.* **67**, 1121-1128 (2000).

416. Matsuura, T. *et al.* Large expansion of the ATTCT pentanucleotide repeat in spinocerebellar ataxia type 10. *Nature Genet.* **26**, 191-194 (2000).

417. Delettre, C. *et al.* Nuclear gene OPA1, encoding a mitochondrial dynamin-related protein, is mutated in dominant optic atrophy. *Nature Genet.* **26**, 207-210 (2000).

418. Pusch, C. M. *et al.* The complete form of X-linked congenital stationary night blindness is caused by mutations in a gene encoding a leucine-rich repeat protein. *Nature Genet.* **26**, 324-327 (2000).

419. The ADHR Consortium. Autosomal dominant hypophosphataemic rickets is associated with mutations in FGF23. *Nature Genet.* **26**, 345-348 (2000).

420. Bomont, P. *et al.* The gene encoding gigaxonin, a new member of the cytoskeletal BTB/kelch repeat family, is mutated in giant axonal neuropathy. *Nature Genet.* **26**, 370-374 (2000).

421. Tullio-Pelet, A. *et al.* Mutant WD-repeat protein in triple-A syndrome. *Nature Genet.* **26**, 332-335 (2000).

422. Nicole, S. *et al.* Perlecan, the major proteoglycan of basement membranes, is altered in patients with Schwartz-Jampel syndrome (chondrodystrophic myotonia). *Nature Genet.* **26**, 480-483 (2000).

426. Drews, J. Research & development. Basic science and pharmaceutical innovation. *Nature Biotechnol.* **17**, 406 (1999).

427. Drews, J. Drug discovery: a historical perspective. *Science* **287**, 1960-1964 (2000).

433. Matsunami, H., Montmayeur, J. P. & Buck, L. B. A family of candidate taste receptors in human and mouse. *Nature* **404**, 601-604 (2000).

434. Adler, E. *et al.* A novel family of mammalian taste receptors. *Cell* **100**, 693-702 (2000).

435. Chandrashekar, J. *et al.* T2Rs function as bitter taste receptors. *Cell* **100**, 703-711 (2000).

436. Hardison, R. C. Conserved non-coding sequences are reliable guides to regulatory elements. *Trends Genet.* **16**, 369-372 (2000).

437. Onyango, P. *et al.* Sequence and comparative analysis of the mouse 1-megabase region orthologous to the human 11p15 imprinted domain. *Genome Res.* **10**, 1697-1710 (2000).

438. Bouck, J. B., Metzker, M. L. & Gibbs, R. A. Shotgun sample sequence comparisons between mouse and human genomes. *Nature Genet.* **25**, 31-33 (2000).

446. Feil, R. & Khosla, S. Genomic imprinting in mammals: an interplay between chromatin and DNA methylation? *Trends Genet.* **15**, 431-434 (1999).

447. Robertson, K. D. & Wolffe, A. P. DNA methylation in health and disease. *Nature Rev. Genet.* **1**, 11-19 (2000).

448. Beck, S., Olek, A. & Walter, J. From genomics to epigenomics: a loftier view of life. *Nature Biotechnol.* **17**, 1144-1144 (1999).

449. Hagmann, M. Mapping a subtext in our genetic book. *Science* **288**, 945-946 (2000).

450. Eliot, T. S. in *T. S. Eliot. Collected Poems 1909-1962* (Harcourt Brace, New York, 1963).

Supplementary Information is available on *Nature*'s World-Wide Web site (http://www.nature.com) or as paper copy from the London editorial office of *Nature*.

Correspondence and requests for materials should be addressed to E. S. Lander (e-mail: lander@genome.wi.mit.edu), R. H. Waterston (e-mail: bwaterst@watson.wustl.edu), J. Sulston (e-mail: jes@sanger.ac.uk) or F. S. Collins (e-mail: fc23a@nih.gov).

DNA sequence databases

GenBank, National Center for Biotechnology Information, National Library of Medicine, National Institutes of Health, Bldg. 38A, 8600 Rockville Pike, Bethesda, Maryland 20894, USA

EMBL, European Bioinformatics Institute, Wellcome Trust Genome Campus, Hinxton, Cambridge CB10 1SD, UK

DNA Data Bank of Japan, Center for Information Biology, National Institute of Genetics, 1111 Yata, Mishima-shi, Shizuoka-ken 411-8540, Japan

A Map of Human Genome Sequence Variation Containing 1.42 Million Single Nucleotide Polymorphisms

The International SNP Map Working Group

Editor's Note

This study reveals the first detailed map of the 1.42 million single nucleotide polymorphisms (SNPs) found across the human genome. The data, amassed by The International SNP Map Working Group, provide interesting first glimpses into the patterns of variation found across the human genome. Although the vast majority of human DNA sequences are the same, single base pair changes in the code (SNPs) can affect our response to disease, drugs and environmental factors such as toxins and viruses. This makes SNPs a valuable tool for biomedical research and drug design. SNPs also change little between generations, making them useful for studies of evolutionary history. This map integrates all of the publicly available SNPs with known genes and other genomic features, and was made possible by and was published with the first draft sequence of the human genome.

We describe a map of 1.42 million single nucleotide polymorphisms (SNPs) distributed throughout the human genome, providing an average density on available sequence of one SNP every 1.9 kilobases. These SNPs were primarily discovered by two projects: The SNP Consortium and the analysis of clone overlaps by the International Human Genome Sequencing Consortium. The map integrates all publicly available SNPs with described genes and other genomic features. We estimate that 60,000 SNPs fall within exon (coding and untranslated regions), and 85% of exons are within 5 kb of the nearest SNP. Nucleotide diversity varies greatly across the genome, in a manner broadly consistent with a standard population genetic model of human history. This high-density SNP map provides a public resource for defining haplotype variation across the genome, and should help to identify biomedically important genes for diagnosis and therapy.

INHERITED differences in DNA sequence contribute to phenotypic variation, influencing an individual's anthropometric characteristics, risk of disease and response to the environment. A central goal of genetics is to pinpoint the DNA variants that contribute most significantly to population variation in each trait. Genome-wide linkage analysis and positional cloning have identified hundreds of genes for human diseases[1] (http://ncbi.nlm.nih.gov/OMIM), but nearly all are rare conditions in which mutation of a single gene is necessary and sufficient to cause disease. For common diseases, genome-wide linkage studies have had limited success, consistent with a more complex genetic

包含 142 万个单核苷酸多态性的
人类基因组序列变异图谱

国际 SNP 图谱研究组

编者按

这项研究首次展示了人类基因组中已发现的 142 万个单核苷酸多态性（SNP）的详细图谱。这份由国际 SNP 图谱研究组积累的数据让人们首次目睹了人类基因组的变异图谱。尽管绝大多数的人类 DNA 序列是一致的，但是序列中单个碱基对的改变（SNP）就能够影响我们对疾病、药物和环境因素（例如毒素和病毒）的反应。这使得 SNP 成为生物医药研究和药物设计行业的有力工具。SNP 在不同世代中变化不大，这对于进化史的研究是很有帮助的。这份图谱整合了所有可公开获取的 SNP 与已知基因及其他基因组特征，依据人类基因组第一个草图序列得以完成，并与后者共同发表。

我们描绘了一张遍及人类基因组的包含 142 万个单核苷酸多态性（SNP）的图谱，这张图谱给我们提供了可用序列中 SNP 的平均密度：每 1,900 个碱基一个 SNP。这些 SNP 最初是在两个项目中发现的：SNP 国际联合会和国际人类基因组测序协会的克隆重叠分析。该图谱整合了所有可公开获取的 SNP 与已知基因和其他基因组特征。我们估计有 60,000 个 SNP 在外显子（编码和非翻译区）中，85% 的外显子距离最近的 SNP 5kb 以内。不同基因组间的核苷酸多样性变化很大，但变化方式大致符合人类历史标准群体遗传学模型。高密度的 SNP 图谱可以为定义整个基因组的单体型变异提供公开资源，帮助识别生物医学相关的重要基因，为诊断与治疗提供帮助。

可遗传的 DNA 序列差异导致了表型上的变异，这影响了个体的人体测量特征、疾病的风险和环境应激反应。遗传学的一个核心目标是精确找到在各个性状中对种群变异贡献最显著的 DNA 变异。全基因组连锁分析和定位克隆已经鉴定出人类疾病的数百个基因[1]（http://ncbi.nlm.nih.gov/OMIM），但单个基因的突变足以引起疾病的情况十分罕见。对于常见疾病，全基因连锁研究的成果有限，这与基因结构的复

architecture. If each locus contributes modestly to disease aetiology, more powerful methods will be required.

One promising approach is systematically to explore the limited set of common gene variants for association with disease[2-4]. In the human population most variant sites are rare, but the small number of common polymorphisms explain the bulk of heterozygosity[3] (see also refs 5–11). Moreover, human genetic diversity appears to be limited not only at the level of individual polymorphisms, but also in the specific combinations of alleles (haplotypes) observed at closely linked sites[8,11-14]. As these common variants are responsible for most heterozygosity in the population, it will be important to assess their potential impact on phenotypic trait variation.

If limited haplotype diversity is general, it should be practical to define common haplotypes using a dense set of polymorphic markers, and to evaluate each haplotype for association with disease. Such haplotype-based association studies offer a significant advantage: genomic regions can be tested for association without requiring the discovery of the functional variants. The required density of markers will depend on the complexity of the local haplotype structure, and the distance over which these haplotypes extend, neither of which is yet well defined.

Current estimates (refs 13–17) indicate that a very dense marker map (30,000–1,000,000 variants) would be required to perform haplotype-based association studies. Most human sequence variation is attributable to SNPs, with the rest attributable to insertions or deletions of one or more bases, repeat length polymorphisms and rearrangements. SNPs occur (on average) every 1,000–2,000 bases when two human chromosomes are compared[5,6,9,18-20], and are thus present at sufficient density for comprehensive haplotype analysis. SNPs are binary, and thus well suited to automated, high-throughput genotyping. Finally, in contrast to more mutable markers, such as microsatellites[21], SNPs have a low rate of recurrent mutation, making them stable indicators of human history. We have constructed a SNP map of the human genome with sufficient density to study human haplotype structure, enabling future study of human medical and population genetics.

Identification and Characteristics of SNPs

The map contains all SNPs that were publicly available in November 2000. Over 95% were discovered by The SNP Consortium (TSC) and the public Human Genome Project (HGP). TSC contributed 1,023,950 candidate SNPs (http://snp.cshl.org) identified by shotgun sequencing of genomic fragments drawn from a complete (45% of data) or reduced (55% of data) representation of the human genome[18,22]. Individual contributions were: Whitehead Institute, 589,209 SNPs from 2.57 million (M) passing reads; Sanger Centre, 262,279 SNPs from 1.16M passing reads; Washington University, 172,462 SNPs from 1.69M passing reads. TSC SNPs were discovered using a publicly available panel of 24 ethnically diverse individuals[23]. Reads were aligned to one another and to the available genome

杂性有关。如果每个突变位点的发现对疾病病因学贡献不大，我们就需要更有力的方法。

一个可行的方法是系统地探索出一组数目有限的常规基因变异来研究相关疾病[2-4]。人类群体中大多数变异位点是罕见的，但是少数的常见多态性解释了大量杂合性的存在[3]（也可见于参考文献 5~11）。此外，对人类基因多样性的研究不该受限于个体多态性水平，而且要研究相邻连锁位点观察到的等位基因（单体型）的特异组合[8,11-14]。正因为这些常见的变异是引起种群中大多数杂合性的原因，因此，评价它们在表型性状变异中的潜在影响就十分重要。

如果有限的单体型多态性普遍存在，那么用多态性标记物的密集组合来定义常见的单体型，评估疾病相关的每个单体型，应该会变得切实可行。这些基于单体型的相关研究提供给我们一个重要的优势：无需发现功能型变异，基因组区域可用来测试相关性。标记所需的密度将取决于局部单体型结构的复杂程度，以及这些单体型延伸的范围，这两者均未被很好地界定。

现有的估计（参考文献 13~17）指出，做基于单体型的关联研究需要一个十分密集的标记图谱（30,000~1,000,000 个突变体）。大部分人类序列变异可归因于 SNP，而剩下的则归因于一个或更多碱基的插入或缺失、重复长度多态性和重排。当将两个人类染色体进行比较时，（平均）每 1,000~2,000 个碱基出现一个 SNP[5,6,9,18-20]。对于复杂的单体型分析，SNP 的这种出现频率足够了。SNP 是二等位型的，因此很适合自动化的、高通量基因分型。最后，与更可变的标记如微卫星[21]相比，SNP 有较低的频发突变，这使得它们可以作为人类历史的稳定指标。我们已经绘制了一个具有足够密度的人类基因组 SNP 图谱，用来研究人类单体型结构，从而使未来人类医学和群体遗传学的研究成为可能。

SNP 的鉴定及特性

这张图谱包含 2000 年 11 月公开可获取的所有 SNP。超过 95% 的 SNP 是由 SNP 国际联合会（TSC）和公共人类基因组计划（HGP）发现的。TSC 贡献了 1,023,950 个候选 SNP（http://snp.cshl.org），它们是通过鸟枪测序法测定来自完整的（45% 的数据）或者缩短的（55% 的数据）人类基因组碎片确定的[18,22]。各机构的贡献如下：怀特黑德研究所，从 257 万合格读长中得到 589,209 个 SNP 位点；桑格中心，从 116 万合格读长中得到 262,279 个 SNP 位点；华盛顿大学，从 169 万合格读长中得到 172,462 个 SNP 位点。TSC 的 SNP 位点是从 24 个种族不同个体可公开获取的基因组检测

sequence, followed by detection of single base differences using one of two validated algorithms: Polybayes[24] and the neighbourhood quality standard (NQS[18,22]).

An additional 971,077 candidate SNPs were identified as sequence differences in regions of overlap between large-insert clones (bacterial artificial chromosomes (BACs) or P1-derived artificial chromosomes (PACs)) sequenced by the HGP. Two groups (NCBI/Washington University (556,694 SNPs): G.B., P.Y.K. and S.S.; and The Sanger Centre (630,147 SNPs): J.C.M. and D.R.B.) independently analysed these overlaps using the two detection algorithms. This approach contributes dense clusters of SNPs throughout the genome. The remaining 5% of SNPs were discovered in gene-based studies, either by automated detection of single base differences in clusters of overlapping expressed sequence tags[24-28] or by targeted resequencing efforts (see ftp://ncbi.nlm.nih.gov/snp/human/submit_format/*/*publicat.rep.gz).

It is critical that candidate SNPs have a high likelihood of representing true polymorphisms when examined in population studies. Although many methods and contributors are represented on the map (see above), most SNPs (> 95%) were contributed by two large-scale efforts that uniformly applied automated methods. Random samples of these SNPs have been evaluated by confirmation in the original DNA samples (where possible) to rule out false positives, and in independent population samples to determine allele frequency. The TSC centres and two outside laboratories (Orchid and Cold Spring Harbor Laboratory) successfully genotyped 1,585 TSC SNPs in the 24 DNA samples used for discovery (http://snp.cshl.org); having surveyed all chromosomes in which each SNP could have been identified, any non-polymorphic candidates must represent false positives. In these tests, 1,500 SNPs (95%) were polymorphic, 67 (4%) non-polymorphic (false positives) and 18 (1%) uniformly heterozygous (previously unrecognized repeats). These high validation rates were observed separately for subsets of SNPs discovered by reduced representation shotgun and genomic alignment, and for subsets identified with Polybayes and the NQS. Thus, these algorithms appear to generate few false positive SNPs. The small number (1%) of uniformly "heterozygous" candidate SNPs show that the methods also exclude nearly all low-copy repeats.

The allele frequencies of a set of SNPs have been evaluated[29] in independent populations using pooled resequencing. Samples of TSC ($n = 502$) and overlap SNPs ($n = 774$) were studied in population samples of European, African American and Chinese descent, revealing 82% to be polymorphic in at least one ethnic group at frequencies above the detection threshold of pooled resequencing (~10%). The remaining 18% presumably represent SNPs with a frequency less than 10% in the populations surveyed and false positives. Furthermore, 77% of SNPs had a minor allele frequency of more than 20% in at least one population, and 27% had an allele frequency higher than 20% in all three ethnic groups. TSC and overlap SNPs had similar distributions across the populations, showing that they are comparable in quality and frequency. The high proportion of SNPs with significant population frequency is expected after SNP discovery in two or a few chromosomes, given standard assumptions about human population history[18,29,30].

686

区域发现的[23]。序列进行拼接并与已有基因组序列进行比对，接着用 Polybayes[24] 和周边质量标准（NQS[18,22]）两个有效算法之一进行单个碱基差异性的检测。

额外的 971,077 个候选 SNP 是在 HGP 测序得到的大片段插入克隆（细菌人工染色体（BAC）或者 P1 衍生人工染色体（PAC））的重叠区中发现的序列差异。两个机构（美国国家生物技术信息中心/华盛顿大学（556,694 个 SNP 位点）：邦尼、郭沛恩和谢里；桑格中心（630,147 个 SNP 位点）：马利金和本特利）用两种检测算法对这些重叠区域进行单独的分析。这种方法有助于形成遍及基因组的密集的 SNP 簇。剩下 5% 的 SNP 则是在基于基因的研究中发现的，要么是通过成簇的重叠表达序列标签中单碱基差异性的自动检测[24-28]，要么是通过靶向重测序（见于 ftp://ncbi.nlm.nih.gov/snp/human/submit_format/*/*publicat.rep.gz）。

至关重要的是，检测群体研究发现，候选 SNP 极有可能代表真正的多态性。尽管图谱来源于许多方法以及贡献者（如上所述），但大多数 SNP（＞95%）都是由运用同样自动化方法的两大机构发现的。这些 SNP 的随机样本都经过了原始 DNA 样本（可获得的）的评估来排除假阳性，并且在独立群体样本中检测等位基因的频率。TSC 中心和两个外部实验室（兰花和冷泉港实验室）从 24 个用于研究的样本中，成功地对 1,585 个 TSC SNP 位点进行了基因分型（http://snp.cshl.org）；对所有鉴定到 SNP 的染色体都进行了调研，任何非多态性候选位点都被认定为是假阳性。在这些测试中，1,500 个 SNP（95%）是多态性的，67 个 SNP（4%）是非多态性的（假阳性），而 18 个 SNP（1%）是一致的杂合子（先前无法识别的重复）。这些高验证率分别是在简化鸟枪和基因组比对发现的 SNP 子集以及 Polybayes 和 NQS 鉴定的子集中观察到的。因此，这些算法几乎很少出现假阳性的 SNP。少量（1%）一致的"杂合子"候选 SNP 表明这些方法也几乎排除了所有的低拷贝重复序列。

采用混合重测序的方法，对一组 SNP 在独立群体中的等位基因频率进行了评估[29]。在欧洲人、非洲裔美国人和中国人的人群样本中，研究了 TSC（$n = 502$）和重叠 SNP（$n = 774$）的样本，发现在至少一个族群中，82% 的样本具有多态性，其频率高于混合重测序检测阈值（约 10%）。剩下的 18% 可能代表 SNP 低于 10% 的受访群体以及假阳性。此外，在至少一个群体中，77% 的 SNP 等位基因频率超过 20%，在三个种族群体中，27% 的 SNP 等位基因频率高于 20%。TSC 和重叠 SNP 在各群体间有相似的分布，这表明他们在性质和频率上相似。考虑到关于人类群体历史的标准假设，在两个或少数染色体中发现 SNP 后，预计有高比例的 SNP 伴随显著的群体频率[18,29,30]。

Description of the SNP Map

We mapped the sequence flanking each SNP by alignment to the genomic sequence of large-insert clones in GenBank. These alignments were converted into chromosomal coordinates according to the publicly available genome assemblies of July and September 2000 (http://genome.ucsc.edu). Candidate SNPs were included in the final map only if they mapped to a single location in the genome assembly. Integrated displays of SNPs, genes and other features are available at the ENSEMBL (http://www.ensembl.org), NCBI (National Center for Biotechnology Information; http://www.ncbi.nlm.nih.gov), UCSC (University of California at Santa Cruz; http://genome.ucsc.edu) and TSC (http://snp.cshl.org) websites.

The nonredundant SNP total of 1,433,393 is fewer than the sum of individual submissions (2,067,476) because some SNPs (mainly in regions of BAC overlap) were discovered by more than one effort. Of these, 1,419,190 mapped to unique locations in the 2.7 gigabases (Gb) of assembled human genome sequence, providing an average density of one SNP every 1.91 kb. TSC SNPs, which are more evenly distributed than those from clone overlaps, were found on average every 3.05 kb. SNP density (Table 1) is relatively constant across the autosomes. To characterize the distribution of SNPs, we examined 366,192 SNPs that fell within finished sequence. Most of the genome contains SNPs at high density (Fig. 1): 90% of contiguous 20-kb windows contain one or more SNPs, as do 63% of 5-kb windows and 28% of 1-kb windows. Only 4% of genome sequence falls in gaps between SNPs of > 80 kb, and some of these gaps are covered by SNPs that are discovered but not yet mapped owing to gaps in the genome assembly.

To evaluate the density of SNPs in regions within and surrounding genes, we used the September 2000 release of RefSeq[31]. In total, 14,534 SNPs map to within these 7,000 carefully annotated, non-redundant messenger RNAs, equivalent to about two exonic SNPs per gene (coding and untranslated regions). Extrapolating two exonic SNPs per gene to the approximately 30,000 human genes[32], we estimate there to be 60,000 exonic SNPs in this collection. The density of SNPs in exons (one SNP per 1.08 kb; Table 1) is higher than in the genome as a whole, owing to the contribution of efforts targeted to exonic regions.

We also assessed the distribution of SNPs in the genomic locus surrounding each of the RefSeq mRNAs. We assigned the RefSeq exons to their genomic locations, restricting analysis to the 2,960 RefSeq mRNAs mapping onto finished sequence. As we cannot define the extent of the noncoding (regulatory) regions of each gene, we arbitrarily defined each "gene locus" as extending from 10 kb upstream of the start of the first exon to the end of the last exon. By this definition, 93% of gene loci contain at least one SNP, and 98% are within 5 kb of the nearest SNP; also, 59% of gene loci contained five or more SNPs, and 39% ten or more. Of 24,953 exons, 85% were within 5 kb of the nearest SNP. Thus, most exons should be close enough to at least one SNP for haplotype-based association studies, where the functional variant may be some distance from the SNPs used in the study.

688

SNP 图谱的描述

我们将每个 SNP 的侧翼序列与 GenBank 中的大片段插入克隆基因组序列进行比对。依照 2000 年 7 月和 9 月发布的可公开获取的基因组组装图（http://genome.ucsc.edu），将比对转换成染色体坐标。候选 SNP 只有在基因组组装中被比对到单一位置才能包含在最终图谱中。SNP、基因和其他特征的综合信息可在如下网站获得：ENSEMBL（http://www.ensembl.org）、NCBI（美国国家生物技术中心；http://www.ncbi.nlm.nih.gov）、UCSC（加州大学圣克鲁兹分校；http://genome.ucsc.edu）和 TSC（http://snp.cshl.org）。

非冗余的 SNP 总计有 1,433,393 个，少于各机构提交的总数（2,067,476），这是因为一些 SNP（主要在 BAC 重叠区）被发现的次数多于一次。其中的 1,419,190 个 SNP 在人类基因组 2.7 千兆碱基（Gb）的序列中坐标唯一，平均密度为每 1.91kb 一个 SNP。TSC SNP 比克隆重叠中得到的 SNP 分布更加均匀，其平均密度为每 3.05kb 一个。SNP 密度（表 1）在常染色体间相对恒定。为了描绘 SNP 的分布，我们检查了位于已完成测序区域的 366,192 个 SNP。多数基因组包含高密度 SNP（图 1）：90% 的相邻 20 kb 阅读窗内含有一个或多个 SNP，63% 的 5 kb 阅读窗和 28% 的 1 kb 阅读窗同样如此。只有 4% 的基因组序列位于相距大于 80 kb 的两个 SNP 之间的缺口中，有些缺口被已发现的 SNP 覆盖，但由于基因组组装上的缺陷还没有被绘制出来。

为了评估基因区域内和周围的 SNP 密度，我们采用了 2000 年 9 月发布的参考序列[31]。总体说来，14,534 个 SNP 比对到了 7,000 个精确注释、非冗余的信使 RNA 上，这等同于每个基因约有两个外显子 SNP（编码区和非翻译区）。以此推算到大约 30,000 个人类基因中[32]，我们估计会有 60,000 个外显子 SNP。外显子中 SNP 的密度（每 1.08 kb 一个 SNP；表 1）比全部 SNP 在基因组中的密度要高，这是由把外显子区作为测序靶标导致的。

我们也估算了每个参考序列 mRNA 周围基因座上 SNP 的分布。我们将参考序列外显子分配到它们的基因组位置，将分析限制在已完成序列图谱比对的 2,960 个 mRNA 参考序列上。由于不能界定每个基因非编码（调控）区的大小，我们人为地定义每个“基因座”延伸范围为从第一个外显子起始位置上游 10 kb 到最后一个外显子。通过此定义，93% 的基因座至少包含一个 SNP，而 98% 的基因座在 5 kb 内就有一个 SNP；此外，59% 的基因座包含 5 个或者更多的 SNP，而 39% 拥有 10 个及以上的 SNP。24,953 个外显子中，85% 的外显子在 5 kb 以内有一个 SNP。因此，多数外显子应该至少靠近一个基于单体型关联研究的 SNP，然而功能性变异可能与研究中使用的 SNP 有一定的距离。

Table 1. SNP distribution by chromosome

Chromosome	Length (bp)	All SNPs		TSC SNPs	
		SNPs	kb per SNP	SNPs	kb per SNP
1	214,066,000	129,931	1.65	75,166	2.85
2	222,889,000	103,664	2.15	76,985	2.90
3	186,938,000	93,140	2.01	63,669	2.94
4	169,035,000	84,426	2.00	65,719	2.57
5	170,954,000	117,882	1.45	63,545	2.69
6	165,022,000	96,317	1.71	53,797	3.07
7	149,414,000	71,752	2.08	42,327	3.53
8	125,148,000	57,834	2.16	42,653	2.93
9	107,440,000	62,013	1.73	43,020	2.50
10	127,894,000	61,298	2.09	42,466	3.01
11	129,193,000	84,663	1.53	47,621	2.71
12	125,198,000	59,245	2.11	38,136	3.28
13	93,711,000	53,093	1.77	35,745	2.62
14	89,344,000	44,112	2.03	29,746	3.00
15	73,467,000	37,814	1.94	26,524	2.77
16	74,037,000	38,735	1.91	23,328	3.17
17	73,367,000	34,621	2.12	19,396	3.78
18	73,078,000	45,135	1.62	27,028	2.70
19	56,044,000	25,676	2.18	11,185	5.01
20	63,317,000	29,478	2.15	17,051	3.71
21	33,824,000	20,916	1.62	9,103	3.72
22	33,786,000	28,410	1.19	11,056	3.06
X	131,245,000	34,842	3.77	20,400	6.43
Y	21,753,000	4,193	5.19	1,784	12.19
RefSeq	15,696,674	14,534	1.08		
Totals	2,710,164,000	1,419,190	1.91	887,450	3.05

Length (bp) is from the public Genome Assembly of 5 September 2000. Density of SNPs on each chromosome is influenced by the amount of available genome sequence included in the Genome Assembly, depth of overlap coverage from TSC reads and clone overlaps, and the underlying heterozygosity (Table 2). Data are presented for the entire dataset (All SNPs) and for those from the SNP consortium (TSC SNPs), as the latter are more evenly spaced than those from clone overlaps.

表 1. SNP 在染色体上的分布

染色体	长度 (bp)	所有 SNP		TSC SNP	
		SNP	SNP 间的距离 kb	SNP	SNP 间的距离 kb
1	214,066,000	129,931	1.65	75,166	2.85
2	222,889,000	103,664	2.15	76,985	2.90
3	186,938,000	93,140	2.01	63,669	2.94
4	169,035,000	84,426	2.00	65,719	2.57
5	170,954,000	117,882	1.45	63,545	2.69
6	165,022,000	96,317	1.71	53,797	3.07
7	149,414,000	71,752	2.08	42,327	3.53
8	125,148,000	57,834	2.16	42,653	2.93
9	107,440,000	62,013	1.73	43,020	2.50
10	127,894,000	61,298	2.09	42,466	3.01
11	129,193,000	84,663	1.53	47,621	2.71
12	125,198,000	59,245	2.11	38,136	3.28
13	93,711,000	53,093	1.77	35,745	2.62
14	89,344,000	44,112	2.03	29,746	3.00
15	73,467,000	37,814	1.94	26,524	2.77
16	74,037,000	38,735	1.91	23,328	3.17
17	73,367,000	34,621	2.12	19,396	3.78
18	73,078,000	45,135	1.62	27,028	2.70
19	56,044,000	25,676	2.18	11,185	5.01
20	63,317,000	29,478	2.15	17,051	3.71
21	33,824,000	20,916	1.62	9,103	3.72
22	33,786,000	28,410	1.19	11,056	3.06
X	131,245,000	34,842	3.77	20,400	6.43
Y	21,753,000	4,193	5.19	1,784	12.19
参考序列	15,696,674	14,534	1.08		
总计	2,710,164,000	1,419,190	1.91	887,450	3.05

长度 (bp) 来自 2000 年 9 月 5 日公布的基因组组装信息。每条染色体上 SNP 的密度受基因组组装收录的可用基因组序列的数量、TSC 读长和克隆重叠的覆盖度的深度，以及潜在的杂合性影响（表 2）。表中数据来自整个数据集（所有 SNP）和 SNP 国际联合会（TSC SNP），后者比来自克隆重叠的 SNP 分布更均匀。

Fig. 1. Distribution of SNP coverage across intervals of finished sequence. Windows of defined size (in chromosome coordinates) were examined for whether they contained one or more SNPs. Analysis was restricted to the 900 Mb of available finished sequence.

The density of SNPs obtained at any given location depends upon the methods of SNP discovery contributing at each position (TSC, BAC overlap or targeted), the availability of genome sequence for SNP discovery and mapping, and the rate of nucleotide diversity. Of these, only nucleotide diversity is a fundamental characteristic of the region and population studied. To chart the landscape of human genome sequence polymorphism, we performed a genome-wide analysis of nucleotide diversity.

Analysis of Nucleotide Diversity

Describing the underlying pattern of nucleotide diversity required a polymorphism survey performed at high density, in a single, defined population sample, and analysed with a uniform set of tools. We reanalysed 4.5M passing sequence reads generated by TSC using genomic alignment using the NQS (see Methods). This set contained 1.2 billion aligned bases and 920,752 heterozygous positions. We measured nucleotide sequence variation using the normalized measure of heterozygosity (π), representing the likelihood that a nucleotide position will be heterozygous when compared across two chromosomes selected randomly from a population. π also estimates the population genetic parameter $\Theta = 4N_e\mu$ in a model in which sites evolve neutrally, with mutation rate μ, in a constant-sized population of effective size N_e. For the human genome, π was 7.51×10^{-4}, or one SNP for every 1,331 bp surveyed in two chromosomes drawn from the NIH diversity panel. This value agrees with smaller surveys of human genome variation[18-20].

We next examined the heterozygosity of individual chromosomes (Table 2). The autosomes were quite similar to one another, with 20 of 22 within 10% of the genome-wide average for autosomes (7.65×10^{-4}). Two had more extreme values: chromosome 21 ($\pi = 5.19 \times 10^{-4}$) and

图 1. 已完成序列区间里 SNP 的覆盖分布。检查已定义大小的窗口（在染色体坐标内）是否包含一个或多个 SNP。分析限于 900 Mb 可用的已完成序列。

任何给定位置的 SNP 密度取决于各位点发现 SNP 时所用的方法（TSC、BAC 重叠或者靶向）、基因组序列对于 SNP 发现和定位的可利用性以及核苷酸多样性的比率。这其中，只有核苷酸多样性是区域和群体研究的基本特性。为了绘制人类基因组序列的多态性图谱，我们进行了一个全基因组范围内的核苷酸多样性分析。

核苷酸多样性分析

描述核苷酸多样性的潜在模式需要在高密度、单一的群体样本中进行多态性调查，并且使用一组统一的工具进行分析。我们使用 NQS 方法（见方法）对 TSC 产生的 4.5M 数据进行了重新分析（见方法）。这一组包含了 12 亿对碱基和 920,752 个杂合位点。我们用测量杂合性的标准方法（π）测量核苷酸序列的差异，这代表着当随机从一个群体中选出两条染色体比对时一个核苷酸位置是杂合子的可能性。π 也估算了群体遗传参数 $\Theta = 4N_e\mu$，在模型中其位点进化中立，突变率为 μ，群体有效大小为常量 N_e。对于人类基因组，π 是 7.51×10^{-4}，或者来自 NIH 多样性模型中两个染色体调查得到每 1,331 bp 一个 SNP。这个估值与人类基因组变异的小型调查一致[18-20]。

我们接下来检测了单个染色体的杂合性（表 2）。常染色体彼此十分相似，22 对常染色体中有 20 对在全基因组平均值的 10% 以内（7.65×10^{-4}）。另外两对的值则非常极端：21 号染色体（π = 5.19×10^{-4}），15 号染色体（π = 8.79×10^{-4}）。这些观测结

chromosome 15 ($\pi = 8.79 \times 10^{-4}$). Whether these observations are due to statistical fluctuations or methodological issues, or are biologically meaningful, will require investigation. The most striking difference in heterozygosity is the lower diversity of the sex chromosomes. The lower rate of polymorphism on the X chromosome may be explained by both a lower effective population size (N_e) and lower mutation rate (μ) in $\Theta = 4N_e\mu$. Because the X chromosome is hemizygous in males, the effective population size is three-quarters of that of the autosomes. In addition, μ is higher in male than in female meiosis, with $\mu_{male}/\mu_{female} \approx 1.7/1.0$ (ref. 33). As the X chromosome undergoes male meiosis only 1/3 of the time, the overall rate of mutation in the X chromosome is expected to be 91% that of the autosomes ($\mu_X = 1.23/1.35 = 0.91$). Thus, the diversity of the X chromosome is predicted to be 69% that of the autosomes. The observed heterozygosity of the X chromosome was 4.69×10^{-4}, or 61% of the average value of the autosomes. Thus, the population genetic considerations described above could largely explain the lower heterozygosity on the X chromosome. It is possible that strong selection on the X chromosome (owing to hemizygosity in males) or other factors might partially explain this observation.

Table 2. Nucleotide diversity by chromosome

Chromosome	Heterozygous positions	High-quality bp examined	$\pi(\times 10^{-4})$
1	71,483	92,639,616	7.72
2	81,860	111,060,861	7.37
3	61,190	81,359,748	7.52
4	59,922	74,162,156	8.08
5	56,344	77,924,663	7.23
6	53,864	72,380,717	7.44
7	52,010	68,527,550	7.59
8	44,477	57,476,056	7.74
9	41,329	50,834,047	8.13
10	43,040	52,184,561	8.25
11	47,477	56,680,783	8.38
12	38,607	51,160,578	7.55
13	35,250	43,915,606	8.03
14	35,083	47,425,180	7.40
15	27,847	31,682,199	8.79
16	22,994	27,736,356	8.29
17	21,247	27,124,496	7.83
18	24,711	30,357,102	8.14
19	11,499	15,060,544	7.64
20	22,726	31,795,754	7.15
21	26,160	50,367,158	5.19

果无论是由统计学波动或方法论的问题造成的，还是具有生物学意义，都需要进行研究。杂合性方面最显著的差异是性染色体中较低的多样性。X 染色体的低多态性也许可以用 $\Theta = 4N_e\mu$ 公式中较小的有效群体大小 (N_e) 和较低的突变率 (μ) 来解释。因为 X 染色体在男性中是半合子，其有效群体大小是常染色体的四分之三。此外，男性减数分裂比女性减数分裂时的 μ 更高，$\mu_{\mathrm{male}}/\mu_{\mathrm{female}} \approx 1.7/1.0$（参考文献 33）。由于 X 染色体在男性减数分裂中只占 1/3 的时间，那么 X 染色体的总体突变率应该是常染色体的 91%（$\mu_X = 1.23/1.35 = 0.91$）。因此，X 染色体的多样性预计是常染色体的 69%。观测到的 X 染色体的杂合性为 4.69×10^{-4}，或者说是常染色体平均值的 61%。因此，上述关于群体遗传学的考虑很大程度上可以解释 X 染色体的低杂合性。X 染色体上的强烈选择（由于在男性中是半合子），或者其他因素可能会部分地解释这项观察结果。

表 2. 染色体的核苷酸多样性

染色体	杂合性位置	检查到的高质量 bp	$\pi(\times 10^{-4})$
1	71,483	92,639,616	7.72
2	81,860	111,060,861	7.37
3	61,190	81,359,748	7.52
4	59,922	74,162,156	8.08
5	56,344	77,924,663	7.23
6	53,864	72,380,717	7.44
7	52,010	68,527,550	7.59
8	44,477	57,476,056	7.74
9	41,329	50,834,047	8.13
10	43,040	52,184,561	8.25
11	47,477	56,680,783	8.38
12	38,607	51,160,578	7.55
13	35,250	43,915,606	8.03
14	35,083	47,425,180	7.40
15	27,847	31,682,199	8.79
16	22,994	27,736,356	8.29
17	21,247	27,124,496	7.83
18	24,711	30,357,102	8.14
19	11,499	15,060,544	7.64
20	22,726	31,795,754	7.15
21	26,160	50,367,158	5.19

Continued

Chromosome	Heterozygous positions	High-quality bp examined	$\pi(\times 10^{-4})$
22	17,469	20,478,378	8.53
X	23,818	50,809,568	4.69
Y	348	2,304,916	1.51
Total	920,752	1,225,448,590	7.51

Heterozygosity (π) of each chromosome. The data were filtered to remove repetitive sequences and heterozygosity calculated as described in the methods. Heterozygous positions and high-quality bases examined were counted separately for each pairwise comparison of read to genome, and then summed over each chromosome.

The Y chromosome has the lowest observed heterozygosity of any chromosome. It is divided into two regions: a pseudoautosomal region at either telomeric end that recombines with the X chromosome and is highly heterozygous[34], and the non-recombining Y (NRY). The genome assembly used for this analysis contains only the NRY, which shows very little diversity: 348 SNPs in 2,304,916 bases ($\pi = 1.51 \times 10^{-4}$). These values agree reasonably with previous estimates for NRY[35,36]. The lower diversity of NRY is influenced by a smaller effective population size (20% that of the autosomes), counterbalanced by the higher mutation rate of male meiosis ($\mu_Y = 1.7/1.35 = 1.26 \times$ that of the autosomes). These factors predict that the Y chromosome would have a diversity 31% that of the autosomes, as compared to the observed 20%. Other influences might include selection against deleterious alleles, patterns of male dispersal[35] and a correlation of diversity with recombination rate[19].

To look at diversity on a finer scale, we divided each chromosome into contiguous 200,000-bp bins according to the public Genome Assembly of 5 September 2000. The distribution of heterozygosity among these bins ranges from zero (12 bins, each with zero SNPs over an average of 24,720 bp examined) to 60×10^{-4} (357 SNPs in a bin surveying 58,755 bp). Although 95% of bins display nucleotide diversity values between 2.0×10^{-4} and 15.8×10^{-4}, the pattern is variable (Fig. 2a, b; see also Supplementary Information). One measure of the spread in the data is the coefficient of variation (CV), the ratio of the standard deviation (σ) to the mean (μ) of the heterozygosity π of each individual read. For the observed data, the $CV(\sigma_{observed}/\mu_{observed})$ was 1.93, considerably larger than would be expected if every base had uniform diversity, corresponding to a Poisson sampling process ($\sigma_{Poisson}/\mu_{Poisson} = 1.73$). It was expected that the observed distribution would be much more variable than a Poisson process, because both biochemical and evolutionary forces cause diversity to be nonuniform across the genome. Biological factors may include rates of mutation and recombination at each locus. For example, heterozygosity is correlated with the GC content for each read (Fig. 2c), reflecting, at least in part, the high frequency of CpG to TpG mutations arising from deamination of methylated 5-methylcytosine. Population genetic forces are likely to be even more important: each locus has its own history, with samples at some loci tracing back to a recent common ancestor, and other loci describing more ancient genealogies. The time to the most recent common ancestor at a particular stretch of DNA is variable, and represents the opportunity for sequence divergence; thus, the expected pattern of heterozygosity is more heterogeneous than if every locus shared the same history[37,38].

染色体	杂合性位置	检查到的高质量 bp	$\pi(\times 10^{-4})$
22	17,469	20,478,378	8.53
X	23,818	50,809,568	4.69
Y	348	2,304,916	1.51
总计	920,752	1,225,448,590	7.51

每条染色体的杂合性（π）。数据过滤掉了重复序列，杂合性按照方法里描述的进行计算。杂合位置和高质量碱基的检查是由读长与基因组两两比较分别计算得到的，然后将每条染色体进行合计。

Y 染色体观察到的杂合性比任何一个染色体都低。它分成了两个区：一个是假常染色体区，在与 X 染色体结合的两个端粒末端之一，是高度杂合的[34]；另一个是 Y 染色体非重组区（NRY）。本研究对基因组进行组装的分析只包含 NRY 区，该区域有较低的多样性：2,304,916 个碱基中只有 348 个 SNP 位点（$\pi = 1.51 \times 10^{-4}$）。这些值与之前对 NRY 的估计一致[35,36]。NRY 的低多样性受较小的有效群体大小的影响（常染色体的 20%），这抵消了男性减数分裂时的高突变率（$\mu_Y = 1.7/1.35 = 1.26 \times$ 常染色体的 μ）。这些因素预示与观察到的 20% 相比，Y 染色体将有常染色体 31% 的多样性。其他的影响可能包括对有害等位基因的选择，男性的传播模式[35]以及多样性与重组率的相关性[19]。

为了在更精细的尺度上研究多样性，我们根据 2000 年 9 月 5 日公布的基因组组装结果，把每条染色体分成了连续 200,000 bp 的分箱。这些分箱的杂合性分布变化从 0（12 个分箱平均长度是 24,720 bp，每个分箱有 0 个 SNP）到 60×10^{-4}（该分箱长度是 58,755 bp，有 357 个 SNP）。尽管 95% 的分箱呈现的核苷酸多样性值在 2.0×10^{-4} 到 15.8×10^{-4} 之间，但模式是不同的（图 2a 和 2b；也可见于补充信息）。衡量数据分散性的一种方法是差异系数（CV），即每个个体序列杂合性（π）的标准差（σ）与平均值（μ）之比。对于观察数据，CV 值（$\sigma_{观测}/\mu_{观测}$）是 1.93，比如果每个碱基具有统一的多样性所预期的值要大得多，相当于泊松抽样过程（$\sigma_{泊松}/\mu_{泊松} = 1.73$）。预期观测到的分布将会比泊松过程变化多得多，因为生化和进化力都会导致整个基因组的多样性不均匀。生物因素可能包括每个基因座的突变和重组率。例如，每个序列的杂合性与其 GC 含量相关（图 2c），至少在一定程度上能反映由于甲基化 5–甲基胞嘧啶脱氨引起的 CpG 到 TpG 突变高频发生的原因。群体遗传学力量也许更重要：每个基因座有它自己的历史，一些基因座可以追溯至一个最近的共同祖先，而其他的基因座可能有更多的古老家系。在特定的 DNA 分支上追溯到最近共同祖先的时间是不同的，这代表了序列分化的可能性；因此，相比如果每个基因座都具有相同的历史情况，杂合性的期望模式会更多样[37,38]。

Fig. 2. Distribution of heterozygosity. **a**, The genome was divided into contiguous bins of 200,000 bp based on chromosome coordinates, and the number of high-quality bases examined and heterozygosity calculated for each. A histogram was generated of the distribution of heterozygosity values across all such bins. **b**, Heterozygosity was calculated across contiguous 200,000-bp bins on Chromosome 6. The blue lines represent the values within which 95% of regions fall: 2.0×10^{-4}–15.8×10^{-4}. Red, bins falling outside this range. The extended region of unusually high heterozygosity centred at 34 Mb corresponds to the HLA. **c**, Correlation of nucleotide diversity with GC content of each read (autosomes only). The GC content and heterozygosity of reads from the heterozygosity analysis was calculated after sorting of reads by GC content and separation into 10 bins of equal size. Each bin contains ~150 Mb of aligned, high-quality sequence.

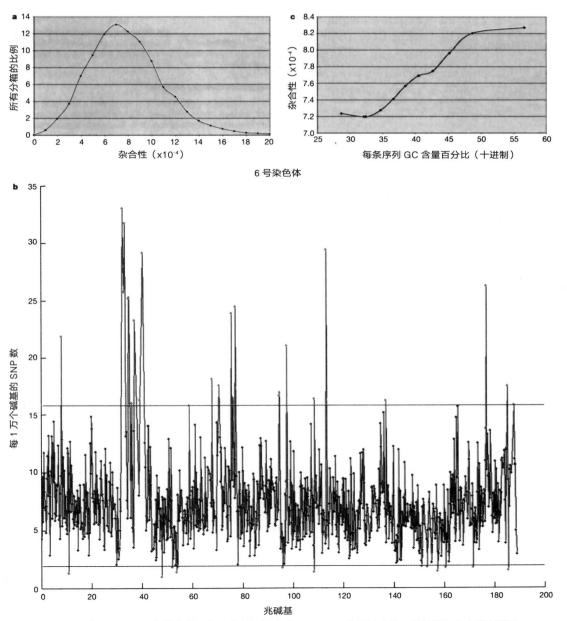

图 2. 杂合性分布。**a**，根据染色体坐标，基因组被分成 200,000 bp 的连续分箱，并计算每个分箱高质量碱基的数目和杂合性。所有这些分箱的杂合性值的分布形成一个直方图。**b**，6 号染色体上所有连续的 200,000 bp 分箱的杂合性。蓝线代表的区间为 $2.0 \times 10^{-4} \sim 15.8 \times 10^{-4}$，95% 的值落在这之间。红色代表落在该范围外面的分箱。相对于 HLA，显著高杂合性的扩展区集中在 34 Mb。**c**，每条序列（只有常染色体）的核苷酸多样性与 GC 含量的相关性。首先将序列按 GC 含量进行排序，然后平均分成 10 个分箱再进行杂合性分析，包括 GC 含量和序列杂合性计算。每个分箱包含约 150 Mb 比对上的高质量的序列。

To assess whether gene history would account for the observed variation in heterozygosity, we compared the observed CV to that expected under a standard coalescent population genetic model. For each read, we adjusted μ on the basis of its per cent GC and length, and simulated genealogical histories under the assumption of a constant-sized population with $N_e = 10,000$. The CV determined under this model ($\sigma_{constant-size}/\mu_{constant-size} = 1.96$) is a close match to the observed data. To estimate standard deviations around these estimates of the CV, it was necessary to consider that tightly linked regions may display correlated histories, and thus are nonindependent. We sampled subsets of the data chosen to minimize correlation among reads (see Methods), providing estimates of the mean and standard deviation of CV for the observed and simulated data (Table 3). These results indicate that the observed pattern of genome-wide heterozygosity is broadly consistent with predictions of this standard population genetic model (for comparison, see an analysis of variation in heterozygosity in the mouse genome)[39]. However, much work will be required to assess additional factors that could influence this distribution: biological factors such as variation in mutation and recombination rates, historical forces such as bottlenecks[40,41], expansions or admixture of differentiated populations, evolutionary selection, and methodological artefacts.

Table 3. Coefficients of variation for the observed data and the Poisson and coalescent models

SNPs per read	Observed	Poisson	Coalescent
0	$8,796 \pm 43$	$8,256 \pm 52$	$8,767 \pm 50$
1	$2,247 \pm 44$	$3,040 \pm 49$	$2,332 \pm 46$
2	668 ± 24	617 ± 24	663 ± 26
3	214 ± 14	99 ± 9	200 ± 15
4	102 ± 10	16 ± 4	66 ± 9
σ/μ	1.94 ± 0.02	1.72 ± 0.02	1.96 ± 0.03

Observed distribution of heterozygosity and comparison to expectation under Poisson and coalescent population genetic models. The autosomes were divided into 200,000-bp bins according to chromosome coordinates and one read randomly selected from each bin. This procedure was chosen to minimize the correlation in gene history of nearby regions, under the simplifying assumption that reads 200,000 bp apart and selected from unrelated individuals will have uncorrelated genealogies. Correlation of gene history does not influence the expected mean value of the CV, but does effect its variance. The random selection of reads and generation of expected distributions were repeated 100 times: presented are the mean and standard deviation of the number of reads in which 0, 1, 2, 3, or 4 SNPs were observed or predicted under each scenario. The Poisson model reports the number of such reads expected to display 0–4 SNPs under Poisson sampling of each read with a heterozygosity adjusted for length and GC content (Fig. 2c). Even in this reduced data set, the Poisson model can be rejected at $P < 10^{-99}$. The coalescent simulation[38] assumed a constant-sized population of effective size 10,000 and free recombination among reads. For each read, μ was scaled according to its length and GC content (Fig. 2c). Each sampled read was assigned a coalescent history from a simulated distribution and the number of SNPs predicted. The coefficient of variation of the estimate of heterozygosity is presented, with the mean and standard deviation of the 100 sampling runs shown.

Regions of low diversity were more prevalent on the sex chromosomes. Whereas only 2.5% of 200,000-bp bins across the genome had $\pi < 2.0 \times 10^{-4}$, 15% of bins on the X chromosome[42] and 89% on the Y chromosome (NRY) had these levels of diversity. Regions

为了评估基因历史能否解释观察到的杂合性的变异，我们将观测到的 CV 与标准的联合群体遗传模型下的预期值进行了对比。对每条序列来说，我们依据 GC 的百分比和长度来调整 μ，并在恒定种群大小 $N_e = 10{,}000$ 的假定条件下模拟系谱历史。这个模式（$\sigma_{\text{恒定大小}}/\mu_{\text{恒定大小}} = 1.96$）下得到的 CV 与观测数据高度匹配。为了评估这些 CV 估值的标准差，必须要考虑紧密相连区域可能表现出相关联的历史，这些区域是非独立的。为了使关联性降到最小，我们抽取了这些数据的子集样本（见方法），并提供了观测和模拟数据 CV 的平均值和标准差（表 3）。这些结果表明观测到的全基因组杂合性的模式与该标准群体遗传学模型的预测大体一致（为了进行比较，请参阅小鼠基因组杂合性变异的分析）[39]。然而，我们还需要做许多工作来评价可能影响分布的其他因素：生物因素如突变和重组率的变异，历史力比如瓶颈[40,41]，不同群体的扩张或混合，进化选择以及方法学误差。

表 3. 观测数据、泊松模型以及联合模型的差异系数

每个读长的 SNP	观测值	泊松模型	联合模型
0	8,796 ±43	8,256 ±52	8,767 ±50
1	2,247 ±44	3,040 ±49	2,332 ±46
2	668 ±24	617 ±24	663 ±26
3	214 ±14	99 ±9	200 ±15
4	102 ±10	16 ±4	66 ±9
σ/μ	1.94 ±0.02	1.72 ±0.02	1.96 ±0.03

观测到的杂合性分布，以及在泊松模型和联合群体遗传模型下的比较结果。依据染色体坐标，常染色体被分成 200,000 bp 的分箱，并随机从每个分箱中选择一条序列。该过程是为了使相邻区域基因座的相关性降到最小，在一种简化思维的假设下，每条序列间隔是 200,000 bp，并且选自不相关的个体，具有不相关的家族系谱。基因史的关联性并不影响 CV 预期的平均值，但会影响它的方差。为了达到期望的分布情况，对序列和世代进行随机选择并重复 100 次；表中呈现的是能观测到的或预测的包含 0、1、2、3 或者 4 个 SNP 位点的序列数量的平均值和标准差。泊松模型报告了这样的序列数量，期望在每次利用泊松抽样抽取序列时，预期能显示 0~4 个 SNP，并且依据长度和 GC 含量对杂合性进行调整（图 2c）。即使在这个简化的数据集中，在 $P < 10^{-99}$ 时，泊松模型仍然可以被拒绝。联合模拟[38]假定了一个具有 10,000 个有效个体的恒定大小的群体，序列之间可以进行自由重组。依据每条序列的长度和 GC 含量来衡量其 μ 值（图 2c）。每个抽样的序列从模拟分布和预测 SNP 的数目中分配一个联合历史。表中呈现的是杂合性估算的差异系数以及 100 次运行的平均值和标准差。

在性染色体上，低多样性区域更普遍。尽管整个基因组中只有 2.5% 的 200,000 bp 分箱的 π 值小于 2.0×10^{-4}，但 X 染色体上 15% 的分箱[42]和 Y 染色体（NRY）上 89%

of low diversity may be explained by the smaller effective population size of the sex chromosomes and the variable underlying distribution of heterozygosity. Strong selection acting on the sex chromosomes in males might also have a role, but this hypothesis requires further testing. Regions of high heterozygosity were also observed. One was found on chromosome 6 (Fig. 2b, centred on 34 Mb), and was confirmed to represent the HLA locus, which has high nucleotide diversity owing to balancing selection[43]. Other regions of varying size were observed on this and other chromosomes (Fig. 2c and Supplementary Information). Some of these highly diverse regions might have also experienced balancing selection, but there are other possible explanations: for example, sampling fluctuations of the coalescent distribution, regions with high rates of mutation and/or recombination, unrecognized duplications in the human genome and sequencing of a rare haplotype by the HGP (to which the TSC reads were compared).

Given the unfinished state of publicly available sequence data and genome assembly, it will be important to reevaluate these estimates as more complete genome sequence becomes available.

Implications for Medical and Population Genetics

We describe a map of publicly available SNPs (as of November 2000), fully integrated with the sequence, physical and genetic maps of the human genome. We anticipate immediate application to studies of human population genetics, candidate-gene studies for disease association, and eventually unbiased, genome-wide association scans. First, the map provides an unprecedented tool for studying the character of human sequence variation. We use these data to describe the first genome-wide view of how human DNA sequence varies in the population, and the public availability of these data should fuel future research into biological and population genetic influences on human genetic diversity.

Second, insights into human evolutionary history will be obtained by using SNPs from the map to characterize haplotype diversity throughout the genome. Human haplotype structure remains largely unexplored, and this map makes it possible to define the extent and variation of haplotype identity, the number and frequencies of common haplotypes, and their distribution among and within existing ethnic groups.

Most practically, where a gene has been implicated in causing disease (by chromosomal position relative to linkage peaks, known biological function or expression pattern), it is desirable exhaustively to survey allelic variation for any association to disease. Using the SNP map, it should be possible to evaluate the extent to which common haplotypes contribute to disease risk. As the speed and efficiency of SNP genotyping increases, such studies will fuel increasingly comprehensive tests of the hypothesis that common variants contribute significantly to the risk of common diseases. To the extent that such studies are successful, they should profoundly affect our understanding of disease, methods of diagnosis, and ultimately the development of new and more effective therapies.

的分箱具有这些多样性水平。这些低多样性的区域可能由性染色体有效种群大小较小以及潜在的杂合性分布不同所致。作用在男性性染色体上的强选择可能也起到一定作用，但这个假说需要进一步的验证。此外还发现了一些高度杂合性的区域。其中一个在 6 号染色体上（图 2b，集中于 34 Mb），并被证实是 HLA 的基因座；由于平衡选择[43]，该区域具有高的核苷酸多样性。在 6 号和其他染色体上观察到大小不一的其他区域（图 2c 及补充信息）。一些高度多样化区域可能经历了平衡选择，但是也有一些其他可能的解释：比如联合模型分布抽样的波动性，带有高突变率和（或）重组率的区域，人类基因组未识别到的重复序列，以及由 HGP 进行的罕见单体型测序（以 TSC 读长作为对比）。

考虑到可公开获取序列数据和基因组组装的未完成状态，当更完整的基因组序列可以获取之时，重新评价这些估算显得尤为重要。

对医学和群体遗传学的影响

我们充分地整合了人类基因组的序列、物理图谱以及遗传图谱，描绘了一张可公开获取的 SNP 图谱（截止 2000 年 11 月）。我们预计该图谱可直接应用于人类群体基因组学研究和疾病相关的候选基因研究，并最终应用于无偏移的全基因组关联扫描。首先，图谱为人类序列差异特性的研究提供了空前的工具。我们用这些数据来描述关于群体中人类 DNA 序列变化的第一个全基因组视图，而这些数据的可公开获取性将促进未来关于生物和群体遗传学对人类遗传多样性的影响的研究。

其次，我们将利用图谱中的 SNP 来洞悉人类进化史，从而描述整个基因组的单体型多样性。人类单体型结构仍然有大部分未被探索，而这张图谱使得对单体型特征的范围和变异，常见单体型的数量和频率，以及它们在现有种群内的分布等的界定变得可能。

最实际的应用就是，当一个基因引起疾病时（通过与连锁峰相关的染色体位置，已知生物学功能或表达模式），可以详尽地调查与疾病有任何相关的等位基因的变异。利用 SNP 图谱，我们可以评估常见单体型促成疾病风险的程度。随着 SNP 基因分型的速度和效率的增加，这样的研究有助于更加全面地检验常见突变显著增加常见疾病风险这一假说。从某种程度上说这些研究是成功的，它们会深刻影响我们对疾病的理解和诊断方法，并最终开发新的更有效的治疗方法。

Methods

SNP identification

Candidate SNPs were identified by detection of high-confidence base differences in aligned sequences. For TSC, sequence reads were filtered to exclude low quality reads and those containing predominantly known repetitive sequence. Sequences were aligned to each other using the reduced representation shotgun (RRS) method, and by genomic alignment (GA) as described[18,22]. For GA of TSC data, reads were compared to available large-insert clones (finished and draft with available PHRAP quality scores) in GenBank. For the analysis of clone overlaps, all available finished and unfinished genomic sequence accessions were aligned. Two methods were used to detect SNPs. The NQS relies upon the sequence trace quality surrounding the SNP base to increase base-calling confidence[18,22]; most data discovered using the NQS was processed using SsahaSNP, an ultrafast, hash-based implementation of the algorithm (Z.N., A. Cox and J.C.M, manuscript in preparation). The second method calculates confidence scores on the basis of a Bayesian analysis of confidence scores[24]. A variety of methods were used to find SNPs in expressed sequence tag (EST) overlaps[24,25,27] and for targeted resequencing; details of the remaining SNPs can be found in the individual dbSNP entries (www.ncbi.nlm.nih.gov/SNP/).

Mapping of SNPs and features

MEGABLAST[44] was used to align TSC SNP flanking sequences to the genomic sequence accessions. A SNP was considered mapped if a high-quality match (99% identity or greater) was found across the available flanking sequence of no less than 270 bp. SNPs that matched more than three accessions with identity > 98% were judged to be possible repetitive regions and set aside. SNP coordinates were generated relative to the OO18 build of the genome assembly (5 September 2000) and the OO15 build (15 July 2000), using the AGP format files provided by D. Haussler (http://genome.ucsc.edu).

The NCBI RefSeq mRNA transcripts[31] were aligned to the Genome Assembly using the NCBI SPIDEY alignment tool. Alignment required > 97% sequence similarity between mRNA and genome sequence; alignments were refined by taking into account the donor/acceptor sites. In cases where CDS annotations were available in the GenBank record, exons of the CDS were aligned within the confines of the mRNA alignment. Regions of known human repeats were annotated directly using RepeatMasker (A. Smit, unpublished).

Nucleotide diversity analysis

To characterize nucleotide diversity, we required a data set in which all data could be analysed both for the number of high-quality bases meeting quality standards for SNP detection, and for

方　　法

SNP 的鉴定

利用比对序列中高置信度碱基的差异进行候选 SNP 的鉴定。对 TSC 来说，将序列读长进行过滤处理，从而排除低质量读长以及那些包含显著已知重复序列的读长。利用简化代表性鸟枪法（RRS）和描述的基因组比对（GA）[18,22] 方法进行序列比对。对 TSC 数据的 GA 而言，序列与 GenBank 中可用的长的插入克隆（包含 PHRAP 质量值的已完成和未完成序列）进行比较。为了分析克隆重叠群，所有可用的完成和未完成基因组序列（含有基因库中编号）均被进行比对。两种方法用来对 SNP 进行鉴定。一种是 NQS 方法，该方法依赖围绕在 SNP 碱基周围序列的质量追踪来增加碱基识别的置信度[18,22]；多数数据使用 NQS 方法都是通过使用 SsahaSNP 软件来进行分析的，SsahaSNP 是一种超快的基于哈希算法实现的 SNP 鉴定工具（宁泽民、考克斯和马利金，稿件准备中）。第二种方法在基于置信评分的贝叶斯分析基础上计算置信评分[24]。我们使用多种方法在表达序列标签（EST）中鉴定了 SNP[24,25,27]并进行靶向测序；剩余 SNP 的信息可以在单独的 dbSNP 条目中找到（www.ncbi.nlm.nih.gov/SNP/）。

SNP 图谱及其特征

利用 MEGABLAST 软件[44]将 TSC SNP 侧翼序列与基因组含有基因库编号的序列进行比对。对于任何一个 SNP 位点，如果发现在可用侧翼序列中不少于 270 bp 的高质量碱基与库中序列相匹配（99% 的一致性或更高），则认为该 SNP 被比对上。如果一个 SNP 匹配三个以上的基因组序列（98% 相似性），那么这个 SNP 定义为重复区，将被去掉。基于 OO18（2000 年 9 月 5 日）和 OO15（2000 年 7 月 15 日）构建的基因组组装结果，使用豪斯勒提供的 AGP 文件格式（http://genome.ucsc.edu）生成 SNP 坐标。

利用 NCBI SPIDEY 比对工具将 NCBI 参考序列中的 mRNA 转录本[31]与基因组组装结果进行比对。比对要求 mRNA 与基因组序列间有 > 97% 的序列相似性；考虑供 / 受体位置对结果进行调整。当 CDS 在 GenBank 中有注释信息时，CDS 的外显子区域在信使 RNA 的范围内进行比对。人类基因组中已知的重复片段区域直接使用 RepeatMasker 软件进行注释（斯米特，未发表）。

核苷酸多样性分析

为了描述核苷酸的多样性，我们需要一个数据集，该数据集里所有的数据都满足 SNP 检测的质量标准中高质量碱基的数量以及 SNP 数量。为了确保分析的均一性，我们只分

the number of SNPs. To ensure homogeneity of analysis, we performed a single analysis of 4.5 million high-quality TSC reads from the Sanger Centre, Washington University in St. Louis and the Whitehead Center for Genome Research. The GC content of these reads was 41%, the same as the genome as a whole[32], and the distribution of read GC content across deciles of the genome (sorted by GC content) was within 10% of the expected value for all bins. The read coverage was well distributed: 88% of contiguous 200,000-bp windows contained over 10,000 aligned bases (5%) surveyed for SNPs (see below). Using a single analytic tool (SsahaSNP, an implementation of the NQS; Z.N., A. Cox and J.C.M, in preparation), these reads were aligned to the available genome sequence (finished and draft with quality scores) and the number of high-quality bases (meeting NQS) and SNPs counted. We limited the analysis to SNPs found by genomic alignment so that the cluster depth of each comparison would be exactly two chromosomes. We precisely measured the target size for SNP discovery by counting the number of positions meeting the NQS. This is desirable because alignments contain positions of both high and low quality, but only those meeting the NQS are candidates for SNP discovery. Where a single TSC read aligned to multiple (overlapping) BACs from the HGP, we averaged the number of SNPs and aligned bp for all pairwise alignments of that read; this weighted evenly those reads mapping to a single BAC and those aligning to a region of overlap. Reads representing repeat loci were excluded using validated criteria[18,22]: alignments of reads to genome were excluded if they were less than 99% identical. The genome was then divided into contiguous bins of 200,000 bp (based on chromosome-relative coordinates). Individual reads were filtered for repeats: any that aligned to more than one bin in the genome assembly were rejected. Finally, heterozygous positions and bases meeting the NQS were counted. As a final filter for regions containing a high proportion of repeats, we reject any bin for which more than 10% of the reads mapping to that bin also mapped to another chromosome. Finally, to avoid statistical fluctuation due to inadequate sampling, we examined only the 88% of bins in which at least 10,000 aligned bases met the NQS and thus could be examined for SNPs.

Coalescent modelling was performed by simulation[38], and assumed a constant-sized population of 10,000 individuals and a mutation rate adjusted for each read on the basis of its GC content (Fig. 2c) and length. To assess the standard deviation around this estimate, the simulation was repeated 100 times. For the observed data, calculating a standard deviation around the CV is difficult owing to the correlation of gene history for closely linked sites. In expectation, this correlation should not alter the mean of the observed coefficient of variation, but does influence its variance. To estimate the variance around the CV for the observed data, we selected 100 reduced data sets, each containing one randomly chosen read from each 200,000-bp bin along the autosomes. In using this approach, we assume that these reads, 200,000 bp apart and sampled from unrelated individuals, have independent genealogies. This random sampling procedure was repeated 100 times to estimate the mean and variance of the observed CV.

The data for the heterozygosity analysis, including the coordinates of each bin, the number of bases examined and number of SNPs identified, is available as Supplementary Information.

(**409**, 928-933; 2001)

析了来自桑格中心、圣路易斯华盛顿大学以及怀特黑德基因组研究中心的 450 万个高质量 TSC 序列。这些序列的 GC 含量是 41%，与整体基因组一致[32]，序列 GC 含量跨基因组十分位数的分布（按 GC 含量分类）在所有分箱预期值的 10% 以内。序列覆盖分布良好：对连续 200,000 bp 窗口区域进行 SNP 分析发现，有 10,000 多个碱基（5%）分布在 88% 的区域中（见下文）。只利用一种分析软件（SsahaSNP，NQS 的一种实现方法；宁泽民、考克斯和马利金，稿件准备中）将这些序列与可用的基因组序列（含有质量值的完成的或未完成的序列）进行比对，计算高质量碱基（符合 NQS）和 SNP 的数目。我们对由基因组比对发现的 SNP 设置限制条件，使每个比较的重叠群深度都正好是两条染色体。通过计算符合 NQS 的位置数量，可以精确计算 SNP 发现区域的目标大小。因为比对信息中包括高质量和低质量碱基的位置，只有那些符合 NQS 的才能作为候选 SNP 位点，这一点是可取的。当单个 TSC 序列比对到来自 HGP 的多个（重叠）BAC 上时，我们对该序列上 SNP 的数目和比对的长度取平均数，这对那些映射到图谱的单一 BAC 和那些与一个重叠区域匹配的序列进行了加权平均。重复基因座上的序列使用如下确认准则进行排除[18,22]：如果与基因组比对的相似性小于 99%，那么该序列被去掉。然后，基因组被分成连续 200,000 bp 的分箱（基于染色体相对坐标）。对每条序列都进行如下重复序列过滤：如果匹配到基因组中多于一个分箱，序列被去掉。最终，计算符合 NQS 的杂合子的位置和碱基数目。最后一步过滤是针对高比例重复区的筛选，当某一分箱中 10% 以上的序列既比对到该分箱中，同时又比对到其他染色体上，那么该分箱被去掉。最终，为了避免由于采样不足引起的统计波动，我们只选择了其中 88% 的分箱进行 SNP 鉴定，这些分箱中至少有 10,000 个比对的碱基符合 NQS。

我们模拟了联合模型[38]，该模型假定了恒定大小为 10,000 个体的群体，并根据 GC 含量（图 2c）和长度对每个序列的突变率进行了调整。将模拟重复 100 次以评估该估算附近的标准差。对于观测到的数据来说，由于紧密相连位点的基因史具有相关性，根据 CV 计算标准差很困难。在预期中，这种相关性应该不会改变观测到的变异系数的均值，但是会影响其方差。为了依据 CV 对观测数据的方差进行估算，我们选定 100 个简化数据集，每个数据集均包含从每 200,000 bp 的常染色体分箱中随机选择的一个序列。运用这种方法，我们假定这些序列相距 200,000 bp 并且从来自不相关的个体中抽样，有独立的家系图谱。该随机抽样过程重复 100 次，以估算观测到的 CV 的平均值和方差。

杂合性分析的数据在补充信息中，这些信息包括每个分箱的坐标、被检查的碱基数目和被鉴定的 SNP 数目。

（杨晶 翻译；胡松年 审稿）

A Map of Human Genome Sequence Variation Containing 1.42 Million Single Nucleotide Polymorphisms

The International SNP Map Working Group[*]
[*] A full list of authors appears at the end of this paper.

Received 28 November; accepted 27 December 2000.

References:

1. Collins, F. S. Of needles and haystacks: finding human disease genes by positional cloning. *Clin. Res.* **39**, 615-623 (1991).

2. Collins, F. S., Guyer, M. S. & Charkravarti, A. Variations on a theme: cataloging human DNA sequence variation. *Science* **278**, 1580-1581 (1997).

3. Lander, E. S. The new genomics: global views of biology. *Science* **274**, 536-539 (1996).

4. Risch, N. & Merikangas, K. The future of genetic studies of complex human diseases. *Science* **273**, 1516-1517 (1996).

5. Li, W. H. & Sadler, L. A. Low nucleotide diversity in man. *Genetics* **129**, 513-523 (1991).

6. Cargill, M. *et al.* Characterization of single-nucleotide polymorphisms in coding regions of human genes [published erratum appears in *Nature Genet.* **23**, 373 (1999)]. *Nature Genet.* **22**, 231-238(1999).

7. Cambien, F. *et al.* Sequence diversity in 36 candidate genes for cardiovascular disorders. *Am. J. Hum. Genet.* **65**, 183-191 (1999).

8. Fullerton, S. M. *et al.* Apolipoprotein E variation at the sequence haplotype level: implications for the origin and maintenance of a major human polymorphism. *Am. J. Hum. Genet.* **67**, 881-900 (2000).

9. Halushka, M. K. *et al.* Patterns of single-nucleotide polymorphisms in candidate genes for blood-pressure homeostasis. *Nature Genet.* **22**, 239-247 (1999).

10. Nickerson, D. A. *et al.* DNA sequence diversity in a 9.7-kb region of the human lipoprotein lipase gene. *Nature Genet.* **19**, 233-240 (1998).

11. Rieder, M. J., Taylor, S. L., Clark, A. G. & Nickerson, D. A. Sequence variation in the human angiotensin converting enzyme. *Nature Genet.* **22**, 59-62 (1999).

12. Templeton, A. R., Weiss, K. M., Nickerson, D. A., Boerwinkle, E. & Sing, C. F. Cladistic structure within the human lipoprotein lipase gene and its implications for phenotypic association studies. *Genetics* **156**, 1259-1275 (2000).

13. Eaves, I. A. *et al.* The genetically isolated populations of Finland and sardinia may not be a panacea for linkage disequilibrium mapping of common disease genes. *Nature Genet.* **25**, 320-323 (2000).

14. Taillon-Miller, P. *et al.* Juxtaposed regions of extensive and minimal linkage disequilibrium in human Xq25 and Xq28. *Nature Genet.* **25**, 324-328 (2000).

15. Kruglyak, L. Prospects for whole-genome linkage disequilibrium mapping of common disease genes. *Nature Genet.* **22**, 139-144 (1999).

16. Collins, A., Lonjou, C. & Morton, N. E. Genetic epidemiology of single-nucleotide polymorphisms. *Proc. Natl Acad. Sci. USA* **96**, 15173-15177 (1999).

17. Reich, D. E. *et al.* Linkage disequilibrium in the human genome. *Nature* (submitted).

18. Altshuler, D. *et al.* An SNP map of the human genome generated by reduced representation shotgun sequencing. *Nature* **407**, 513-516 (2000).

19. Nachman, M. W., Bauer, V. L., Crowell, S. L. & Aquadro, C. F. DNA variability and recombination rates at X-linked loci in humans. *Genetics* **150**, 1133-1141 (1998).

20. Wang, D. G. *et al.* Large-scale identification, mapping, and genotyping of single-nucleotide polymorphisms in the human genome. *Science* **280**, 1077-1082 (1998).

21. Jorde, L. B. Linkage disequilibrium and the search for complex disease genes. *Genome Res.* **10**, 1435- 1444 (2000).

22. Mullikin, J. C. *et al.* An SNP map of human chromosome 22. *Nature* **407**, 516-520 (2000).

23. Collins, F. S., Brooks, L. D. & Chakravarti, A. A DNA polymorphism discovery resource for research on human genetic variation [published erratum appears in *Genome Res.* **9**, 210 (1999)]. *Genome Res.* **8**, 1229-1231 (1998).

24. Marth, G. T. *et al.* A general approach to single-nucleotide polymorphism discovery. *Nature Genet.* **23**, 452-456 (1999).

25. Buetow, K. H., Edmonson, M. N. & Cassidy, A. B. Reliable identification of large numbers of candidate SNPs from public EST data. *Nature Genet.* **21**, 323-325 (1999).

26. Gu, Z., Hillier, L. & Kwok, P. Y. Single nucleotide polymorphism hunting in cyberspace. *Hum. Mutat.* **12**, 221-225 (1998).

27. Irizarry, K. *et al.* Genome-wide analysis of single-nucleotide polymorphisms in human expressed sequences. *Nature Genet.* **26**, 233-236 (2000).

28. Picoult-Newberg, L. *et al.* Mining SNPs from EST databases. *Genome Res.* **9**, 167-174 (1999).

29. Marth, G. T. *et al.* Single nucleotide polymorphisms in the public database: how useful are they? *Nature Genet.* (submitted).

30. Yang, Z. *et al.* Sampling SNPs. *Nature Genet.* **26**, 13-14 (2000).

31. Pruitt, K. D., Katz, K. S., Sicotte, H. & Maglott, D. R. Introducing RefSeq and LocusLink: curated human genome resources at the NCBI. *Trends Genet.* **16**, 44-47 (2000).

32. International Human Genome Sequencing Consortium. Initial sequencing and analysis of the human genome. *Nature* **409**, 860-921 (2001).

33. Bohossian, H. B., Skaletsky, H. & Page, D. C. Unexpectedly similar rates of nucleotide substitution found in male and female hominids. *Nature* **406**, 622-625 (2000).

34. Cooke, H. J., Brown, W. R. & Rappold, G. A. Hypervariable telomeric sequences from the human sex chromosomes are pseudoautosomal. *Nature* **317**, 687-692 (1985).

35. Shen, P. *et al.* Population genetic implications from sequence variation in four Y chromosome genes. *Proc. Natl Acad. Sci. USA* **97**, 7354-7359 (2000).

36. Underhill, P. A. *et al.* Detection of numerous Y chromosome biallelic polymorphisms by denaturing high-performance liquid chromatography. *Genome Res.* **7**, 996-1005 (1997).

37. Tajima, F. Evolutionary relationship of DNA sequences in finite populations. *Genetics* **105**, 437-460 (1983).

38. Hudson, R. R. in *Oxford Surveys in Evolutionary Biology* (eds Futuyma, D. & Antonovics, J.) 1-44 (Oxford Univ. Press, Oxford, 1991).

39. Lindblad-Toh, K. *et al.* Large-scale discovery and genotyping of single-nucleotide polymorphisms in the mouse. *Nature Genet.* **24**, 381-386 (2000).

40. Kimmel, M. *et al.* Signatures of population expansion in microsatellite repeat data. *Genetics* **148**, 1921-1930 (1998).

41. Reich, D. E. & Goldstein, D. B. Genetic evidence for a Paleolithic human population expansion in Africa [published erratum appears in *Proc. Natl Acad. Sci. USA* **95**, 11026 (1998)]. *Proc. Natl Acad. Sci. USA* **95**, 8119-8123 (1998).

42. Miller, R. D., Taillon-Miller, P. & Kwok, P. Y. Regions of low single-nucleotide polymorphism (SNP) incidence in human and orangutan Xq: deserts and recent coalescences. *Genomics* (in the press).

43. Horton, R. *et al.* Large-scale sequence comparisons reveal unusually high levels of variation in the HLA-DQB1 locus in the class II region of the human MHC. *J. Mol. Biol.* **282**, 71-97 (1998).

44. Zhang, Z., Schwartz, S., Wagner, L. & Miller, W. A greedy algorithm for aligning DNA sequences. *J. Comput. Biol.* **7**, 203-214 (2000).

Supplementary Information is available on *Nature*'s World-Wide Web site (http://www.nature.com) or as paper copy from the London editorial office of *Nature*.

Acknowledgements. The SNP Consortium, the Wellcome Trust and the National Human Genome Research Institute funded SNP discovery and data management at Cold Spring Harbor Laboratories, The Sanger Centre, Washington University in St. Louis, and the Whitehead/MIT Center for Genome Research. Work in P.Y.K.'s laboratory is supported in part by grants from the SNP Consortium and the National Human Genome Research Institute. P.Y.K. thanks Q. Li, M. Minton, R. Donaldson and S. Duan for technical assistance. D.M.A. was supported during a phase of this work under a Postdoctoral Fellowship for Physicians from the Howard Hughes Medical Institute. For full list of contributors to TSC programme, see www.snp.cshl.org.

Correspondence and requests for materials should be addressed to D.A. (e-mail: altshul@genome.wi.mit.edu) or D.B. (e-mail: drb@sanger.ac.uk).

* **The International SNP Map Working Group** (contributing institutions are listed alphabetically).

Cold Spring Harbor Laboratories: Ravi Sachidanandam[1], David Weissman[1], Steven C. Schmidt[1], Jerzy M. Kakol[1] & Lincoln D. Stein[1]

National Center for Biotechnology Information: Gabor Marth[2] & Steve Sherry[2]

The Sanger Centre: James C. Mullikin[3], Beverley J. Mortimore[3], David L. Willey[3], Sarah E. Hunt[3], Charlotte G. Cole[3], Penny C. Coggill[3], Catherine M. Rice[3], Zemin Ning[3], Jane Rogers[3], David R. Bentley[3]

Washington University in St. Louis: Pui-Yan Kwok[4], Elaine R. Mardis[4], Raymond T. Yeh[4], Brian Schultz[4], Lisa Cook[4], Ruth Davenport[4], Michael Dante[4], Lucinda Fulton[4], LaDeana Hillier[4], Robert H. Waterston[4] & John D. McPherson[4]

Whitehead/MIT Center for Genome Research: Brian Gilman[5], Stephen Schaffner[5], William J. Van Etten[5,6], David Reich[5], John Higgins[5], Mark J. Daly[5], Brendan Blumenstiel[5], Jennifer Baldwin[5], Nicole Stange-Thomann[5], Michael C. Zody[5], Lauren Linton[5], Eric S. Lander[5,7] & David Altshuler[5,8]

1, Cold Spring Harbor, New York 11724, USA; 2, Building 38A, 8600 Rockville Pike, Bethesda, Maryland 20894, USA; 3, Wellcome Trust Genome Campus, Hinxton, Cambridge, CB10 1SA, UK; 4, 660 S. Euclid Ave, St. Louis, Missouri 63110, USA; 5, 9 Cambridge Center, Cambridge, Massachusetts 02139, USA; 6, Present address: Blackstone Technology Group, Boston, Massachusetts 02110, USA; 7, Department of Biology, Massachusetts Institute of Technology, Cambridge, Massachusetts 02142, USA; 8, Departments of Genetics and Medicine, Harvard Medical School; Department of Molecular Biology and Diabetes Unit, Massachusetts General Hospital, Boston, Massachusetts 02114, USA.

Superconductivity at 39 K in Magnesium Diboride

J. Nagamatsu *et al.*

Editor's Note

By 2001, a variety of materials based on copper oxides that superconduct at temperatures over 130 K had been observed. Here physicist Jun Nagamatsu and colleagues reported their observation of superconductivity at a temperature of "just" 39 K, but in a very different material: the metallic compound magnesium diboride. This work established a new record for the superconducting transition temperature in metallic compounds, for which the previous high had been, since 1973, only 23 K. Later work would show that the behaviour of this compound fits the standard Bardeen–Cooper–Schrieffer theory of superconductivity, although with some peculiarities. Due to the low cost of its constituent elements and fabrication, magnesium diboride has become a widely used superconductor for practical applications.

In the light of the tremendous progress that has been made in raising the transition temperature of the copper oxide superconductors (for a review, see ref. 1), it is natural to wonder how high the transition temperature, T_c, can be pushed in other classes of materials. At present, the highest reported values of T_c for non-copper-oxide bulk superconductivity are 33 K in electron-doped $Cs_xRb_yC_{60}$ (ref. 2), and 30 K in $Ba_{1-x}K_xBiO_3$ (ref. 3). (Hole-doped C_{60} was recently found[4] to be superconducting with a T_c as high as 52 K, although the nature of the experiment meant that the supercurrents were confined to the surface of the C_{60} crystal, rather than probing the bulk.) Here we report the discovery of bulk superconductivity in magnesium diboride, MgB_2. Magnetization and resistivity measurements establish a transition temperature of 39 K, which we believe to be the highest yet determined for a non-copper-oxide bulk superconductor.

THE samples were prepared from powdered magnesium (Mg; 99.9%) and powdered amorphous boron (B; 99%) in a dry box. The powders were mixed in an appropriate ratio (Mg:B = 1:2), ground and pressed into pellets. The pellets were heated at 973 K under a high argon pressure, 196 MPa, using a hot isostatic pressing (HIP) furnace (O₂Dr.HIP, Kobelco) for 10 hours. Powder X-ray diffraction was performed by a conventional X-ray spectrometer with a graphite monochromator (RINT-2000, Rigaku). Intensity data were collected with CuKα radiation over a 2θ range from 5° to 80° at a step width of 0.02°.

Figure 1 shows a typical X-ray diffraction pattern of MgB_2 taken at room temperature. All the intense peaks can be indexed assuming an hexagonal unit cell, with $a = 3.086$ Å and $c = 3.524$ Å. Figure 2 shows the crystal structure of MgB_2 (ref. 5), of which the space

二硼化镁在 39 K 时的超导性

编者按

到 2001 年为止，在温度超过 130 K 的多种基于铜氧化物的材料中已观测到超导性。本文中物理学家永松纯及其同事们报道了在温度"仅仅为"39 K 时观测到的超导性，但这是在一种非常不一样的材料中观测到的：金属化合物二硼化镁。这项工作创造了金属化合物超导转变温度的一个新纪录，因为从 1973 年到此之前，这种转变温度最高只有 23 K。后续的工作表明，尽管存在一些特殊性，这种化合物的性质符合标准的 BCS（巴丁–库珀–施里弗）超导理论。由于原料和制造成本低，二硼化镁已被广泛地用于超导体的实际应用中。

鉴于在提高铜氧化物的超导转变温度上所取得的巨大成就（见参考文献 1 中的综述），其他类型材料的超导转变温度 T_c 可以被提高到何种程度自然而然地引起了人们的关注。现有报道中，非铜氧化物体超导性的 T_c 最高值，在电子掺杂的 $Cs_xRb_yC_{60}$ 中为 33 K（参考文献 2），在 $Ba_{1-x}K_xBiO_3$ 中为 30 K（参考文献 3）。（近期发现空穴掺杂的 C_{60} 超导转变温度 T_c 高达 52 K[4]，尽管那次实验的原本目的是为了揭示超导电流仅局限于 C_{60} 晶体表面，而非检测整体。）本文中报告了二硼化镁（MgB_2）中体超导的发现。磁化和电阻测量表明超导转变温度为 39 K，我们相信这是非铜氧化物体超导的至今为止所确定的最高转变温度。

样品是用粉末状镁（Mg; 99.9%）和粉末状的非晶硼（B; 99%）在干燥箱中制备的。两种粉末以适当的比例（$Mg : B = 1 : 2$）混合，研磨并挤压成圆片。将这些圆片置于热等静压（HIP）炉（$O_2Dr.HIP$，日本神钢集团）中，在 196 Mpa 的高氩压强和 973 K 的温度下加热 10 小时。粉末 X 射线衍射通过带有石墨单色仪的常规 X 射线光谱仪（RINT-2000，日本理学公司）来进行。强度数据利用 Cu 靶的 Kα 辐射采集，2θ 范围从 5° 到 80°，步长宽度为 0.02°。

图 1 为一种典型的在室温下获取的 MgB_2 的 X 射线衍射图。假定一种六方晶胞，其 $a = 3.086$ Å，$c = 3.524$ Å，可以将所有高强度的峰进行标记。图 2 展示了 MgB_2

group is $P6/mmm$ (no.191). As shown in Fig. 2, the boron atoms are arranged in layers, with layers of Mg interleaved between them. The structure of each boron layer is the same as that of a layer in the graphite structure: each boron atom is here equidistant from three other boron atoms. Therefore, MgB_2 is composed of two layers of boron and magnesium along the c axis in the hexagonal lattice.

Fig. 1. X-ray diffraction pattern of MgB_2 at room temperature.　　Fig. 2. Crystal structure of MgB_2.

Magnetization measurements were also performed with a SQUID magnetometer (MPMSR2, Quantum Design). Figure 3 shows the magnetic susceptibility ($\chi = M/H$, where M is magnetization and H is magnetic field) of MgB_2 as a function of temperature, under conditions of zero field cooling (ZFC) and field cooling (FC) at 10 Oe. The existence of the superconducting phase was then confirmed unambiguously by measuring the Meissner effect on cooling in a magnetic field. The onset of a well-defined Meissner effect was observed at 39 K. A superconducting volume fraction of 49% under a magnetic field of 10 Oe was obtained at 5 K, indicating that the superconductivity is bulk in nature. The standard four-probe technique was used for resistivity measurements.

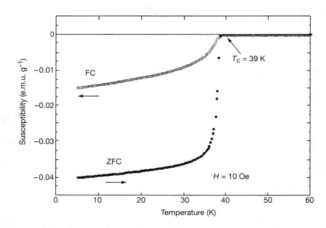

Fig. 3. Magnetic susceptibility χ of MgB_2 as a function of temperature. Data are shown for measurements under conditions of zero field cooling (ZFC) and field cooling (FC) at 10 Oe.

的晶体结构(参考文献 5),空间群为 $P6/mmm$(编号 191)。如图 2 所示,硼原子是按层排列的,镁层交错插入硼层。每一层的硼原子结构与石墨每层的结构相同:其中每个硼原子与其他三个硼原子是等距的。因此,MgB_2 是由两层硼以及一层镁沿六方晶格 c 轴构成的。

图 1. 室温下 MgB_2 的典型 X 射线衍射图

图 2. MgB_2 的晶体结构

磁化强度测量同样是通过超导量子干涉磁强计(SQUID)完成(MPMSR2,Quantum Design)。图 3 显示了 MgB_2 的磁化率($\chi = M/H$,其中 M 为磁化强度,H 为磁场)在零场冷却(ZFC)以及在 10 Oe 的场冷却(FC)条件下随温度变化的曲线。通过测量在磁场中冷却状态下的迈斯纳效应,明确地证实了超导相的存在。在温度为 39 K 时,开始观测到明确的迈斯纳效应。在温度为 5 K 时,10 Oe 磁场下超导体积分数为 49%,这就表明本质上是体超导性。在电阻测量中我们使用的是常规的四探针技术。

图 3. MgB_2 的磁化率 χ 随温度的变化。数据分别表示在零场冷却(ZFC)以及在 10 Oe 的场冷却(FC)条件下的测量结果。

Figure 4 shows the temperature dependence of the resistivity of MgB_2 under zero magnetic field. The onset and end-point transition temperatures are 39 K and 38 K, respectively, indicating that the superconductivity was truly realized in this system.

Fig. 4. Temperature dependence of the resistivity of MgB_2 under zero magnetic field.

(**410**, 63-64; 2001)

Jun Nagamatsu[*], Norimasa Nakagawa[*], Takahiro Muranaka[*], Yuji Zenitani[*] & Jun Akimitsu[*†]
[*] Department of Physics, Aoyama-Gakuin University, Chitosedai, Setagaya-ku, Tokyo 157-8572, Japan
[†] CREST, Japan Science and Technology Corporation, Kawaguchi, Saitama 332-0012, Japan

Received 24 January; accepted 5 February 2001.

References:

1. Takagi, H. in *Proc. Int. Conf. on Materials and Mechanisms of Superconductivity, High Temperature Superconductors VI. Physica C* **341-348**, 3-7 (2000).

2. Tanigaki, K. *et al.* Superconductivity at 33 K in $Cs_xRb_yC_{60}$. *Nature* **352**, 222-223 (1991).

3. Cava, R. V. *et al.* Superconductivity near 30 K without copper: the $Ba_{0.6}K_{0.4}BiO_3$ perovskite. *Nature* **332**, 814-816 (1988).

4. Schön, J. H., Kloc, Ch. & Batlogg, B. Superconductivity at 52 K in hole-doped C_{60}. *Nature* **408**, 549-552 (2000).

5. Jones, M. & Marsh, R. The preparation and structure of magnesium boride, MgB_2. *J. Am. Chem. Soc.* **76**, 1434-1436 (1954).

Acknowledgements. This work was partially supported by a Grant-in-Aid for Science Research from the Ministry of Education, Science, Sports and Culture, Japan and by a grant from CREST.

Correspondence and requests for materials should be addressed to J.A. (e-mail: jun@soliton.phys.aoyama.ac.jp).

图 4 显示了 MgB₂ 在零磁场下电阻率随温度的变化关系。转变温度的起止点分别出现在 39 K 和 38 K，这就表明在该系统中真正实现了超导性。

图 4. 零磁场下 MgB₂ 的电阻率随温度的变化关系

（崔宁 翻译；韩汝珊 郭建栋 审稿）

New Hominin Genus from Eastern Africa Shows Diverse Middle Pliocene Lineages

M. G. Leakey *et al.*

Editor's Note

The story of human evolution is not a linear progress of forms, each passing the baton to its successor. Instead, it is more like a bush, with several coexistent lineages. However, most interpretations of human evolution tend to converge on a single lineage between four and three million years ago, represented by *Australopithecus afarensis*. This model was exploded at the turn of the millennium in this paper by Meave Leakey and colleagues, who describe a 3.5-million-year-old cranium from West Turkana that looked radically different from *A. afarensis*. It had a much flatter and more human-like face, a signal that different lineages ran very deep. The status of this form, *Kenyanthropus platyops*, was soon debated, given the difficulties of reconstructing a skull from many fragments.

Most interpretations of early hominin phylogeny recognize a single early to middle Pliocene ancestral lineage, best represented by *Australopithecus afarensis*, which gave rise to a radiation of taxa in the late Pliocene. Here we report on new fossils discovered west of Lake Turkana, Kenya, which differ markedly from those of contemporary *A. afarensis*, indicating that hominin taxonomic diversity extended back, well into the middle Pliocene. A 3.5 Myr-old cranium, showing a unique combination of derived facial and primitive neurocranial features, is assigned to a new genus of hominin. These findings point to an early diet-driven adaptive radiation, provide new insight on the association of hominin craniodental features, and have implications for our understanding of Plio–Pleistocene hominin phylogeny.

THE eastern African hominin record between 4 and 3 Myr is represented exclusively by a single species, *A. afarensis*, and its possible ancestor, *Australopithecus anamensis*, which are commonly thought to belong to the lineage ancestral to all later hominins[1,2]. This apparent lack of diversity in the middle Pliocene contrasts markedly with the increasingly bushy phylogeny evident in the later hominin fossil record. To study further the time interval between 4 and 3 Myr, fieldwork in 1998 and 1999 focused on sites of this age at Lomekwi in the Nachukui Formation, west of Lake Turkana. New hominin discoveries from Lomekwi, as well as two mandibles and isolated molars recovered previously[3] (Table 1), indicate that multiple species existed between 3.5 and 3.0 Myr. The new finds include a well-preserved temporal bone, two partial maxillae, isolated teeth, and most importantly a largely complete, although distorted, cranium. We assign the latter specimen to a new hominin genus on the basis of its unique combination of primitive and derived features.

东非发现的古人类新属表现出中上新世多样的人类谱系

利基等

编者按

人类演化的故事并不是形式逐个传递的线性变化过程。相反，人类演化是一种灌木式的发展，存在许多并存的谱系。但是许多人试图将人类演化集中到 300 万 ~ 400 万年前的一个谱系上去，即南方古猿阿法种。在千禧年之际，米芙·利基及其同事描述了图尔卡纳湖西岸发现的一件 350 万年前的颅骨，它看上去与南方古猿阿法种形态迥异，这件标本使得这一理论发生了翻天覆地的变革。这件标本有着更扁平且更加像人的脸，这是不同谱系各自深入演化的证据。由于从许多块碎片复原头骨的难度较大，所以肯尼亚扁脸人的地位很快就引起了争论。

大多数关于早期古人类系统发育的解释认为，从早上新世到中上新世，人类只有一个祖先谱系，以南方古猿阿法种最具代表性，它在晚上新世产生了辐射演化。本文中我们报道了在肯尼亚图尔卡纳湖西部发现的新化石，它与同时代的南方古猿阿法种化石显著不同，暗示着古人类的分类学多样性可以上溯到中上新世时期。一具 350 万年的颅骨显示出衍生的面部特征和原始的脑颅特征镶嵌的独特的综合特征，我们将其划分到了一个古人类的新属中。这些发现指向一种早期的受饮食驱动的适应性辐射，为古人类的颅牙特征的相关性提供了新的视角，对我们理解上新世–更新世时期的古人类的系统发育也具有提示性。

在 400 万年前到 300 万年前之间，东非的古人类记录只有一个物种，那就是南方古猿阿法种以及它可能的祖先——南方古猿湖畔种，它们通常被认为是后来所有古人类的祖先[1,2]。中上新世这种明显的多样性缺乏，与后来的古人类化石记录中显著的灌木式系统发育形成了鲜明对比。为了进一步研究 400 万年前到 300 万年前这段时间间隔，于 1998 年和 1999 年进行的野外考察工作主要集中在图尔卡纳湖西部纳丘库伊组的洛梅奎的这一年代的遗址上。在洛梅奎取得的新的古人类发现以及之前发掘的两个下颌骨和游离的臼齿[3]（表 1）暗示着在 350 万年前到 300 万年前之间存在着多个物种。这些新发现包括一个保存完好的颞骨、两块上颌骨部分、游离的牙齿和一块虽然变形但是大部分完整的非常重要的颅骨。由于后一标本独特地结合了原始和衍生的特征，所以我们将其划分到了一个古人类新属中。

717

Table 1. Hominin specimens from the lower Lomekwi and Kataboi Members

KNM-WT	Description	Year	Discoverer	Locality	Measurements (mm)
8556	Mandible fragment: symphysis, right body with RP$_3$–RM$_1$, isolated partial RM$_2$, RM$_3$, LP$_3$	1982	N. Mutiwa	LO-5	RP$_3$, 9.8, 12.4; RP$_4$, 11.3, 12.6; RM$_1$, 13.7, 12.9; RM$_2$, NA, NA; RM$_3$, (17.5), (14.1); LP$_3$, 9.8, 12.5
8557	LM$_{1/2}$	1982	N. Mutiwa	LO-4	NA, (11.5)
16003	RM^3	1985	M. Kyeva	LO-5	13.3, 14.6
16006	Left mandible fragment with M$_2$ fragment and M$_3$	1985	N. Mutiwa	LO-4E	M$_2$, NA, NA; M$_3$, 15.3, 13.1
38332	Partial RM^3 crown	1999	M. Eregae	LO-4E	NA, 14.8
38333	LM$_{1/2}$ crown	1999	M. Eregae	LO-4E	13.1, 12.1
38334	LM$_{1/2}$	1999	M. Eregae	LO-4W	12.1, 11.5
38335	RM$_{1/2}$ crown fragment	1999	M. Eregae	LO-4E	NA
38337	RM$^{1/2}$	1999	R. Moru	LO-4E	11.5, 12.3
38338	Partial RM$^{1/2}$ crown	1999	N. Mutiwa	LO-4E	NA
38339	LM$_{1/2}$ crown	1999	J. Erus	LO-4W	12.8, 12.7
38341	Partial LM$_{2/3}$	1999	G. Ekalale	LO-4E	NA
38342	LM$_{1/2}$ crown	1999	J. Erus	LO-4E	12.8, (11.3)
38343	Right maxilla fragment with I^2 and P^3 roots and partial C; mandible fragment with partial P$_4$ and M$_1$ roots	1998	J. Erus	LO-4W	NA
38344	RM$_{1/2}$ crown	1998	M. Eregae	LO-9	12.8, 12.2
38346	Partial RM$^{1/2}$	1998	M. Mutiwa	LO-5	NA
38347	LdM$_2$ crown	1998	R. Moru	LO-5	11.7, 9.6
38349	RM$_{1/2}$ crown	1998	W. Mangao	LO-5	13.5, 12.6
38350	Left maxilla fragment with P^3 and P^4 roots and partial M^1	1998	B. Onyango	LO-5	LM^1: (10.5), (12.0)
38352	Partial RM$_{1/2}$	1998	W. Mangao	LO-5	NA, 11.5
38355	Partial RM$^{1/2}$ crown	1998	M. Eregae	LO-9	NA
38356	Partial RM$^{1/2}$ crown	1998	M. Eregae & J. Kaatho	LO-9	12.8, NA
38357	RM$_{1/2}$	1998	G. Ekalale	LO-5	12.8, 11.8
38358	Associated RI^2, LM$_2$ fragment, LM$_3$ RM^3 fragment, four crown fragments	1998	G. Ekalale	LO-5	RI^2, 7.5, 7.5, 9.1; LM$_3$, 15.3, 13.2
38359	Associated RM$_1$, RM$_2$	1998	M. Eregae	LO-5	RM$_1$, 12.7, 11.6; RM$_2$, 13.9, 12.2
38361	Associated (partial) germs of I^1, LI^2, RC, LRP^3, LRP^4	1998	R. Moru	LO-5	I^1, NA, (8.0), (11.5); LI^2, 7.6, > 5.9, 8.3; LP^3, (9.3), (12.0)
38362	Associated partial LM$^{1/2}$, RM$^{1/2}$	1998	R. Moru	LO-5	RM$^{1/2}$, 12.9, 14.3
39949	Partial LP$_4$	1998	R. Moru	LO-5	NA
39950	RM$_3$	1998	R. Moru	LO-5	16.0, 14.5
39951	RM$_{1/2}$ fragment	1998	R. Moru	LO-5	NA

表1. 从下洛梅奎段和卡塔博伊段发掘的古人类标本

KNM-WT	描述	年份	发现者	产地	测量（毫米）
8556	下颌骨碎片：联合部、右下颌体带有 $RP_3 \sim RM_1$、游离的部分 RM_2、RM_3、LP_3	1982	N. 穆蒂瓦	LO-5	RP_3, 9.8, 12.4; RP_4, 11.3, 12.6; RM_1, 13.7, 12.9; RM_2, NA, NA; RM_3, (17.5), (14.1); LP_3, 9.8, 12.5
8557	$LM_{1/2}$	1982	N. 穆蒂瓦	LO-4	NA, (11.5)
16003	RM^3	1985	基耶瓦	LO-5	13.3, 14.6
16006	带有 M_2 碎片与 M_3 的左下颌骨碎片	1985	N. 穆蒂瓦	LO-4E	M_2, NA, NA; M_3, 15.3, 13.1
38332	部分 RM^3 齿冠	1999	埃雷加埃	LO-4E	NA, 14.8
38333	$LM_{1/2}$ 齿冠	1999	埃雷加埃	LO-4E	13.1, 12.1
38334	$LM_{1/2}$	1999	埃雷加埃	LO-4W	12.1, 11.5
38335	$RM_{1/2}$ 齿冠碎片	1999	埃雷加埃	LO-4E	NA
38337	$RM^{1/2}$	1999	莫鲁	LO-4E	11.5, 12.3
38338	部分 $RM^{1/2}$ 齿冠	1999	N. 穆蒂瓦	LO-4E	NA
38339	$LM_{1/2}$ 齿冠	1999	埃鲁斯	LO-4W	12.8, 12.7
38341	部分 $LM_{2/3}$	1999	埃卡拉莱	LO-4E	NA
38342	$LM_{1/2}$ 齿冠	1999	埃鲁斯	LO-4E	12.8, (11.3)
38343	有 I^2 和 P^3 齿根与部分 C 的右上颌骨；有部分 P_4 与 M_1 齿根的下颌骨碎片	1998	埃鲁斯	LO-4W	NA
38344	$RM_{1/2}$ 齿冠	1998	埃雷加埃	LO-9	12.8, 12.2
38346	部分 $RM^{1/2}$	1998	M. 穆蒂瓦	LO-5	NA
38347	LdM_2 齿冠	1998	莫鲁	LO-5	11.7, 9.6
38349	$RM_{1/2}$ 齿冠	1998	曼加奥	LO-5	13.5, 12.6
38350	有 P^3 和 P^4 齿根和部分 M^1 的左上颌骨碎片	1998	翁扬戈	LO-5	LM^1: (10.5), (12.0)
38352	部分 $RM_{1/2}$	1998	曼加奥	LO-5	NA, 11.5
38355	部分 $RM^{1/2}$ 齿冠	1998	埃雷加埃	LO-9	NA
38356	部分 $RM^{1/2}$ 齿冠	1998	埃雷加埃 & 卡阿索	LO-9	12.8, NA
38357	$RM_{1/2}$	1998	埃卡拉莱	LO-5	12.8, 11.8
38358	齿列 RI^2、LM_2 碎片、LM_3、RM^3 碎片、4 个齿冠碎片	1998	埃卡拉莱	LO-5	RI^2, 7.5, 7.5, 9.1; LM_3, 15.3, 13.2
38359	齿列 RM_1、RM_2	1998	埃雷加埃	LO-5	RM_1, 12.7, 11.6; RM_2, 13.9, 12.2
38361	I^1、LI^2、RC、LRP^3、LRP^4 齿列（部分）牙胚	1998	莫鲁	LO-5	I^1, NA, (8.0), (11.5); LI^2, 7.6, > 5.9, 8.3; LP^3, (9.3), (12.0)
38362	齿列 $LM^{1/2}$ 部分、$RM^{1/2}$	1998	莫鲁	LO-5	$RM^{1/2}$, 12.9, 14.3
39949	部分 LP_4	1998	莫鲁	LO-5	NA
39950	RM_3	1998	莫鲁	LO-5	16.0, 14.5
39951	$LM_{1/2}$ 碎片	1998	莫鲁	LO-5	NA

Continued

KNM-WT	Description	Year	Discoverer	Locality	Measurements (mm)
39952	LM$_{1/2}$	1998	R. Moru	LO-5	NA
39953	LM$_{1/2}$ fragment	1998	R. Moru	LO-5	NA
39954	Two tooth fragments	1998	R. Moru	LO-5	NA
39955	L$_C$ fragment	1998	R. Moru	LO-5	NA
40000	Cranium	1999	J. Erus	LO-6N	RM^2, 11.4, 12.4
40001	Right temporal bone	1998	P. Gathogo	LO-5	NA

Dental measurements taken as in ref. 34. Mesiodistal crown diameter followed by buccolingual or labiolingual diameter, and for incisors and canines, labial crown height. Values in parentheses are estimates. NA, Not available. L or R in the "Description" column indicates the left or right side. C, upper canine; d, deciduous.

Description of *Kenyanthropus platyops*

Order Primates LINNAEUS 1758
Suborder Anthropoidea MIVART 1864
Superfamily Hominoidea GRAY 1825
Kenyanthropus gen. nov.

Etymology. In recognition of Kenya's contribution to the understanding of human evolution through the many specimens recovered from its fossil sites.

Generic diagnosis. A hominin genus characterized by the following morphology: transverse facial contour flat at a level just below the nasal bones; tall malar region; zygomaticoalveolar crest low and curved; anterior surface of the maxillary zygomatic process positioned over premolars and more vertically orientated than the nasal aperture and nasoalveolar clivus; nasoalveolar clivus long and both transversely and sagittally flat, without marked juga; moderate subnasal prognathism; incisor alveoli parallel with, and only just anterior to, the bicanine line; nasal cavity entrance stepped; palate roof thin and flexed inferiorly anterior to the incisive foramen; upper incisor (I^1 and I^2) roots near equal in size; upper premolars (P^3, P^4) mostly three-rooted; upper first and second molars (M^1 and M^2) small with thick enamel; tympanic element mediolaterally long and lacking a petrous crest; external acoustic porus small. *Kenyanthropus* can be distinguished from *Ardipithecus ramidus* by its buccolingually narrow M^2, thick molar enamel, and a temporal bone with a more cylindrical articular eminence and deeper mandibular fossa. It differs from *A. anamensis*, *A. afarensis*, *A. africanus* and *A. garhi* in the derived morphology of the lower face, particularly the moderate subnasal prognathism, sagittally and transversely flat nasoalveolar clivus, anteriorly positioned maxillary zygomatic process, similarly sized I^1 and I^2 roots, and small M^1 and M^2 crowns. From *A. afarensis* it also differs by a transversely flat midface, a small, external acoustic porus, and the absence of an occipital/marginal venous sinus system, and from *A. africanus* by a tall malar region, a low and curved zygomaticoalveolar crest, a narrow nasal aperture, the absence of anterior facial pillars,

720

KNM-WT	描述	年份	发现者	产地	测量(毫米)
39952	LM$_{1/2}$	1998	莫鲁	LO-5	NA
39953	LM$_{1/2}$ 碎片	1998	莫鲁	LO-5	NA
39954	2 个牙齿碎片	1998	莫鲁	LO-5	NA
39955	L$_C$ 碎片	1998	莫鲁	LO-5	NA
40000	颅骨	1999	埃鲁斯	LO-6N	RM², 11.4, 12.4
40001	右颞骨	1998	加索戈	LO-5	NA

牙齿的尺寸测量方法见参考文献 34。近中远中端齿冠的直径之后是颊舌侧或唇舌侧直径,门齿和犬齿的直径之后是唇侧齿冠高度。圆括号中的数值是估计值。NA,不可用。"描述"栏中的 L 或 R 表示左侧或右侧。C,上犬齿;d,乳齿。

肯尼亚扁脸人的描述

灵长目 Primates LINNAEUS 1758
类人猿亚目 Anthropoidea MIVART 1864
人超科 Hominoidea GRAY 1825
肯尼亚人(新属)*Kenyanthropus* gen. nov.

词源学　考虑了肯尼亚通过其化石遗址发掘出来的许多标本对于理解人类演化的贡献。

属的鉴别特征　这是一个具有以下形态特征的人属:横向的面部轮廓平坦,恰好与鼻骨下方相平;高的颧骨区;颧骨齿槽脊低而弯曲;上颌骨颧突的前表面位于前臼齿之上,比鼻孔和鼻齿槽斜坡的方向更加垂直;鼻齿槽斜坡长,水平方向和矢状方向都很平,没有明显的隆起;适中的鼻下凸颌;门齿槽与双犬齿线平行并且刚刚位于其前面;鼻腔开口呈梯形;颚顶薄,在门齿孔前面向下弯曲;上门齿(I¹ 和 I²)齿根大小几乎相等;上前臼齿(P³、P⁴)大部分是三齿根的;第一和第二上臼齿(M¹ 和 M²)小,牙釉质厚;鼓室部分中间外侧方向上很长,无岩脊;外耳门小。可以通过肯尼亚人的颊舌侧窄的 M²、厚的臼齿釉质以及具有更接近圆柱体的关节隆起和更深的下颌窝的颞骨将其与地猿原始种区别开来。在下面部的衍生形态方面,它与南方古猿湖畔种、南方古猿阿法种、南方古猿非洲种和南方古猿惊奇种都不同,尤其是适中的鼻下凸颌、矢状方向和横向都很平的鼻齿槽斜坡、位于前面的上颌骨颧突、相似大小的 I¹ 和 I² 齿根、小的 M¹ 和 M² 齿冠等。其与南方古猿阿法种的不同之处还有:横向扁平的中面部、小的外耳门以及缺少枕窦/边缘窦系统等;与南方古猿非洲种的不同之处包括:高的颧骨区、低而弯曲的颧骨齿槽脊、狭窄的鼻孔、缺少前面柱、管状的长而无脊的鼓室部分以及小的外耳门等。肯尼亚人缺少在傍人埃

a tubular, long and crestless tympanic element, and a small, external acoustic porus. *Kenyanthropus* lacks the suite of derived dental and cranial features found in *Paranthropus aethiopicus*, *P. boisei* and *P. robustus* (Table 2), and the derived cranial features of species indisputably assigned to *Homo* (For example, *H. erectus s.l.* and *H. sapiens*, but not *H. rudolfensis* and *H. habilis*)[4].

Table 2. Derived cranial features of *Paranthropus*, and their character state in *K. platyops* and *H. rudolfensis*

	Paranthropus aethiopicus	Paranthropus boisei	Paranthropus robustus	Kenyanthropus platyops	Homo rudolfensis
Upper molar size	Large	Large	Moderate	Small	Moderate
Enamel thickness	Hyperthick	Hyperthick	Hyperthick	Thick	Thick
Palatal thickness	Thick	Thick	Thick	Thin	Thin
Incisor alveoli close to bicanine line*	Present	Present	Present	Present	Present
Nasoalveolar clivus	Gutter	Gutter	Gutter	Flat	Flat
Midline subnasal prognathism	Strong	Moderate	Moderate	Weak	Weak
Upper I^2 root to lateral nasal aperture	Medial	Medial	Medial	Lateral	Lateral
Nasal cavity entrance	Smooth	Smooth	Smooth	Stepped	Stepped
Zygomaticoalveolar crest	Straight, high	Straight, high	Straight, high	Curved, low	Curved, low
Anteriorly positioned zygomatic process of maxilla*	Present	Present	Present	Present	Present
Midface transverse contour	Concave, dished	Concave, dished	Concave, dished	Flat	Flat
Malar region	Wide	Wide	Wide	Tall	Tall
Malar orientation to lateral nasal margin	Aligned	Aligned	Aligned	More vertical	More vertical
Facial hafting, frontal trigone	High, present	High, present	High, present	Low, absent	Low, absent
Postorbital constriction	Marked	Marked	Marked	Moderate	Moderate
Initial supraorbital course of temporal lines	Medial	Medial	Medial	Posteromedial	Posteromedial
Tympanic vertically deep and plate-like	Present	Present	Present	Absent	Absent
Position external acoustic porus	Lateral	Lateral	Lateral	Medial	Medial
Mandibular fossa depth	Shallow	Deep	Deep	Moderate	Moderate
Foramen magnum heart shaped	Present	Present	Absent	Absent	Absent
Occipitomarginal sinus	Unknown	Present	Present	Absent	Absent

Hypodigm of *H. rudolfensis* as in ref. 35. See refs 1, 8, 11, 36–40 for detailed discussions of the features.

* Character states shared by *Paranthropus* and *K. platyops*.

塞俄比亚种、傍人鲍氏种和傍人粗壮种（表2）中观察到的一系列牙齿和颅骨衍生特征，还缺少那些无可置疑地被划分到人属的物种（例如广义直立人和智人，但不包括鲁道夫人和能人）所具有的颅骨衍生特征[4]。

表2. 傍人颅骨的衍生特征及其在肯尼亚扁脸人和鲁道夫人中的特征状态

	傍人埃塞俄比亚种	傍人鲍氏种	傍人粗壮种	肯尼亚扁脸人	鲁道夫人
上白齿尺寸	大	大	中	小	中
牙釉质厚度	超厚	超厚	超厚	厚	厚
颚厚度	厚	厚	厚	薄	薄
门齿槽靠近双犬齿线 *	存在	存在	存在	存在	存在
鼻齿槽斜坡	沟状	沟状	沟状	平坦	平坦
中线鼻下凸颌	强	中	中	弱	弱
上 I^2 齿根相对梨状孔位置	中间	中间	中间	侧向	侧向
鼻腔开口	平滑	平滑	平滑	梯形	梯形
颧骨齿槽脊	直而高	直而高	直而高	弯而低	弯而低
位于前方的上颌骨颧骨突 *	存在	存在	存在	存在	存在
中面部横向轮廓	中凹碟形	中凹碟形	中凹碟形	平坦	平坦
颧骨区	宽	宽	宽	高	高
颧骨相对于鼻侧边缘	齐平	齐平	齐平	更垂直	更垂直
面部，额三角	高，存在	高，存在	高，存在	低，缺失	低，缺失
眶后缩狭	明显	明显	明显	中	中
颞骨线的初始上眶路径	中间	中间	中间	中后	中后
鼓室垂直方向深，呈板状	存在	存在	存在	缺失	缺失
外耳门位置	侧向	侧向	侧向	中间	中间
下颌窝深度	浅	深	深	适中	适中
心形枕骨大孔	存在	存在	缺失	缺失	缺失
枕边缘窦	未知	存在	存在	缺失	缺失

鲁道夫人的种型群见参考文献35。对特征的详细讨论见参考文献1、8、11、36～40。
* 傍人和肯尼亚扁脸人共有的特征状态。

Type species. *Kenyanthropus platyops* sp. nov.

Etymology. From the Greek *platus*, meaning flat, and *opsis*, meaning face; thus referring to the characteristically flat face of this species.

Specific diagnosis. Same as for genus.

Types. The holotype is KNM-WT 40000 (Fig. 1a–d), a largely complete cranium found by J. Erus in August 1999. The paratype is KNM-WT 38350 (Fig. 1e), a partial left maxilla found by B. Onyango in August 1998. The repository is the National Museums of Kenya, Nairobi.

Fig. 1. Holotype KNM-WT 40000. **a**, Left lateral view (markers indicate the plane separating the distorted neurocranium and the well-preserved face). **b**, Superior view. **c**, Anterior view. **d**, Occlusal view of palate. Paratype KNM-WT 38350. **e**, Lateral view. KNM-WT 40001. **f**, Lateral view. **g**, Inferior view. Scale bars: **a–c**, 3 cm; **d–g**, 1 cm.

Localities. Lomekwi localities are situated in the Lomekwi and Topernawi river drainages in Turkana district, northern Kenya (Fig. 2). The type locality LO-6N is at 03° 54.03′ north latitude, 035° 44.40′ east longitude.

Horizon. The type specimen is from the Kataboi Member, 8 m below the Tulu Bor Tuff and 12 m above the Lokochot Tuff, giving an estimated age of 3.5 Myr. The paratype is from the lower Lomekwi Member, 17 m above the Tulu Bor Tuff, with an estimated age of 3.3 Myr.

模式种　肯尼亚扁脸人新种。

词源　希腊语中 *platus* 意思是扁平的，*opsis* 意思是面部；因此是指该物种特征性的扁平面部。

种的鉴别特征　与属的特征是一样的。

类型　正模标本是 KNM-WT 40000（图 1a～1d），是由埃鲁斯于 1999 年 8 月发现的一个大部分完整的颅骨。副模标本是 KNM-WT 38350（图 1e），是由翁扬戈于 1998 年 8 月发现的部分左上颌骨。它们都被保存在位于内罗毕的肯尼亚国家博物馆中。

图 1. 正模标本 KNM-WT 40000。**a**，左侧面观（标记表示将变形的脑颅与保存完好的面部分离开来的平面）。**b**，上面观。**c**，前面观。**d**，颚的咬合面观。副模标本 KNM-WT 38350。**e**，侧面观。KNM-WT 40001。**f**，侧面观。**g**，下面观。比例尺：**a**～**c**，3 厘米；**d**～**g**，1 厘米。

产地　洛梅奎遗址位于肯尼亚北部的图尔卡纳地区的洛梅奎和托佩尔纳维河流域（图 2）。LO-6N 典型地点位于北纬 03°54.03′，东经 035°44.40′。

地层　该类型标本是从卡塔博伊段发掘出来的，位于图卢博尔凝灰岩之下 8 米、洛科乔特凝灰岩之上 12 米处，估计其年代为 350 万年。副模标本是在下洛梅奎段发掘出来的，位于图卢博尔凝灰岩之上 17 米处，估计其年代为 330 万年。

Fig. 2. Map showing localities of fossil collection in upper Lomekwi and simplified geology. The boundary between the Kataboi and Lomekwi Members is the base of the Tulu Bor Tuff, indicated as a dashed line through LO-4E and LO-4W. Faults are shown as thick lines; minor faults are omitted. LO-4E and LO-4W are of different shades to distinguish them from each other.

Cranial Description and Comparisons

The overall size of the KNM-WT 40000 cranium falls within the range of *A. afarensis* and *A. africanus*. It is preserved in two main parts, the neurocranium with the superior and lateral orbital margins, but lacking most of the cranial base; and the face, lacking the premolar and anterior tooth crowns and the right incisor roots. Most of the vault is heavily distorted, both through post-mortem diploic expansion and compression from an inferoposterior direction (Fig. 1a, b). The better preserved facial part shows some lateral skewing of the nasal area, anterior displacement of the right canine, and some expansion of the alveolar and zygomatic processes (Fig. 1c–d), but allows for reliable assessment of its morphology.

Only the right M^2 crown is sufficiently preserved to allow reliable metric dental comparisons. It is particularly small, falling below the known ranges of other early hominin species (Fig. 3a). Likewise, the estimated M^1 crown size of KNM-WT 38350 (Table 1) corresponds to minima for *A. anamensis*, *A. afarensis* and *H. habilis*, and is below the ranges for other African early hominins[5-7]. Molar enamel thickness in both specimens is comparable to that in *A. anamensis* and *A. afarensis*. CT scans show that both P^3 and P^4 of KNM-WT 40000 have a lingual root and two well-separated buccal roots. This morphology, thought

图 2. 该地图表示了在上洛梅奎段搜集到的化石的位置和简化的地质情况。卡塔博伊和洛梅奎段间的界线是图卢博尔凝灰岩的基部，用一条穿过 LO-4E 和 LO-4W 的虚线表示。断层用粗线表示；小断层都省略掉了。LO-4E 和 LO-4W 用不同的明暗度表示以相互区分。

颅骨的描述与比较

KNM-WT 40000 颅骨的总大小处于南方古猿阿法种和南方古猿非洲种的范围内。其保存下来了两个主要部分：脑颅，具有眼窝上缘和侧缘、缺少大部分颅底；面部，缺少前臼齿、前部牙齿齿冠和右门齿根。颅顶大部分由于死后板障扩张和来自下后方向的压缩而严重变形了（图 1a 和 1b）。保存较好的面部区域显示出鼻区有些侧斜，右犬齿向前移位以及齿槽和颧骨突有些扩张（图 1c ~ 1d），但是还可以根据它们可靠地估计其形态。

只有右 M^2 的齿冠保存下来的部分足以用来可靠地比较牙齿的尺寸。它非常小，比其他早期的古人类的已知范围还要小（图 3a）。同样地，KNM-WT 38350 的 M^1 的齿冠的估值（表 1）与南方古猿湖畔种、南方古猿阿法种和能人的最小值一致，而比其他的非洲早期古人类的尺寸范围要小[5-7]。两个标本的臼齿釉质厚度都与南方古猿湖畔种和南方古猿阿法种的相当。CT 扫描表明 KNM-WT 40000 的 P^3 和 P^4 都有一个舌侧的齿根和两个完全分离的颊侧齿根。这种形态被认为是人科动物的祖先种才

to be the ancestral hominoid condition[8], is commonly found in *Paranthropus*, but is variable among species of *Australopithecus*. The P^3 of KNM-WT 38350 has three well-separated roots (Fig. 1e). Its P^4 seems to be two-rooted, but the deeply grooved buccal root may split more apically. Relative to M^2 crown size, the canine roots of KNM-WT 40000 are smaller in cross-section at the alveolar margin than in *Ardipithecus ramidus* and *A. anamensis*, similar in size to *A. afarensis*, *A. africanus* and *H. habilis*, and larger than in *P. boisei*. Exposed surfaces and CT scans demonstrate that the I^1 and I^2 roots in KNM-WT 40000 are straight and similar in size. At the level of the alveolar margin the cross-sectional area of the I^2 root is about 90% of that of the I^1 root, whereas this is typically 50–70% in other known hominid taxa.

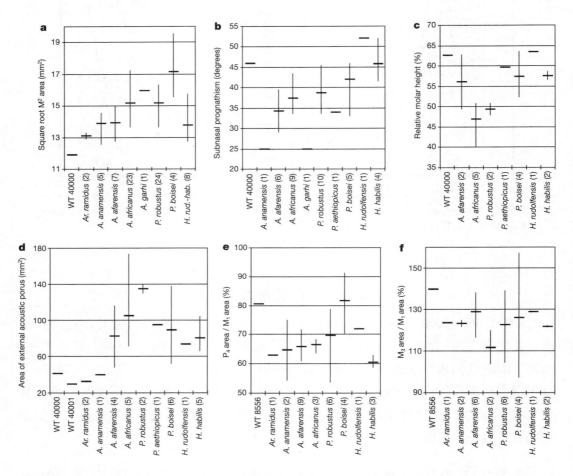

Fig. 3. Mean and range of characters of specified hominins. **a**, Square root of M^2 crown area (buccolingual × mesiolingual diameters). **b**, Angle of subnasal prognathism (nasospinale–prosthion to postcanine alveolar plane). **c**, Malar height[8] relative to orbitoalveolar height (orbitale to alveolar margin aligned with malar surface). **d**, Area of the external acoustic porus (π × long axis × short axis). **e**, Crown area of P_4 relative to that of M_1 × 100. **f**, Crown area of M_3 relative to that of M_1 × 100. All measurements are taken from originals, directly or as given in refs 8, 9, 14, 18, 37, 41–44, except for some South African crania taken from casts. Numbers in parentheses indicate sample size.

具有的特征[8]，通常是在傍人属中发现的，但是在南方古猿的物种中具有较多变异。KNM-WT 38350 的 P³ 具有三个完全分开的齿根（图 1e）。其 P⁴ 看上去似乎具有两个齿根，但是有较深槽的颊侧齿根可能在靠近根尖部分开。相对于 M² 的齿冠尺寸而言，KNM-WT 40000 的犬齿根在齿槽边缘的横截面处比地猿原始种和南方古猿湖畔种的要小，而与南方古猿阿法种、南方古猿非洲种和能人的尺寸相近，比傍人鲍氏种的要大。暴露出来的表面和 CT 扫描证实 KNM-WT 40000 的 I¹ 和 I² 的齿根很直，大小相似。在齿槽边缘水平面上，I² 齿根的横截面面积大约是 I¹ 齿根的 90%，而这一数值在其他已知的人科动物分类单元中多为 50%~70%。

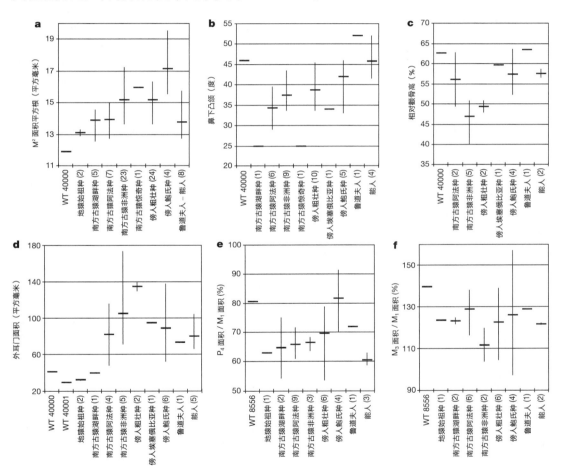

图 3. 特定古人类特征的平均值和范围。**a**，M² 齿冠面积（颊舌侧 × 近中舌侧直径）的平方根。**b**，鼻下凸颌的角度（鼻棘点–齿槽中点与犬齿后部牙齿牙槽平面之间）。**c**，相对于眶齿槽高度（眶最下点到与颧骨表面在一条直线上的齿槽边缘的距离）的颧骨高度[8]。**d**，外耳门的面积（π × 长轴 × 短轴）。**e**，P₄ 的齿冠面积与 M₁ 的齿冠面积之比 × 100。**f**，M₃ 的齿冠面积与 M₁ 的齿冠面积之比 × 100。所有测量值都是直接从原始标本测量得到或者来自参考文献 8、9、14、18、37、41~44 中给出的数据，除了有些南非颅骨的尺寸是根据模型测量的。圆括号中的数字代表标本尺寸。

The incisor alveoli of KNM-WT 40000 are aligned coronally, just anterior to the bicanine line, and the overlying nasoalveolar clivus is flat both sagittally and transversely. There is no canine jugum visible on the preserved left side, reflecting the modest size of the canine root. At 32 mm (chord distance nasospinale to prosthion) the clivus is among the longest of all early hominins. Subnasal prognathism is moderate, expressed by a more vertically orientated clivus than in nearly all specimens of *Australopithecus* and *Paranthropus* (Fig. 3b). The nasal aperture lies in the same coronal plane as the nasoalveolar clivus and there are no anterior facial pillars (Fig. 1a–c). The nasal aperture is small and narrow, in contrast to the large, wide aperture in *A. africanus* and *P. robustus*. The midface of KNM-WT 40000 is dominated by the tall malar region (Fig. 3c) with a low and curved zygomaticoalveolar crest. At a level just below the nasal bones the transverse facial contour is flat (Fig. 1b). In both KNM-WT 40000 and KNM-WT 38350 the anterior surface of the zygomatic process of the maxilla is positioned between P^3 and P^4 (Fig. 1a, d, e), as is commonly seen in *Paranthropus*, but more anteriorly than in most *Australopithecus* specimens[9] or in *H. habilis*. The supraorbital region is *Australopithecus*-like, lacking both a frontal trigon as seen in *Paranthropus*, and a supratoral sulcus as seen in *H. habilis* (but not *H. rudolfensis*). Relative postorbital constriction (frontofacial index) of KNM-WT 40000 is similar to that in *Australopithecus*, *H. rudolfensis* and *H. habilis*, and less than in *P. boisei* (estimated frontofacial index[9] = 70). Its temporal lines converging on the frontal squama have a posteromedial course throughout (Fig. 1b). Around bregma the midline morphology is not well preserved, but the posterior half of the parietals show double, slightly raised temporal lines about 6 mm apart. These contribute posteriorly to indistinct compound temporal/nuchal lines. The original shape of the severely distorted mastoids cannot be reconstructed, but other parts of the left temporal are well preserved. The tubular tympanic lacks a petrous crest and forms a narrow external acoustic meatus with a small aperture. This combination constitutes the primitive hominin morphology, also seen in *Ar. ramidus* and *A. anamensis* (Fig. 3d). The mandibular fossa resembles that of specimens of *A. afarensis* and *A. africanus*. It is moderately deep, and the articular eminence, missing its lateral margin, is cylindrical with a moderately convex sagittal profile. The preserved posterior half of the foramen magnum suggests that it was probably oval in shape, rather than the heart shape seen in *P. boisei* and probably *P. aethiopicus*. Regarding the endocranial aspect, the reasonably well preserved occipital surface lacks any indication of the occipital/marginal venous sinus system characteristic of *A. afarensis*, *P. boisei* and *P. robustus*. Bilateral sulci suggest that the transverse/sigmoid sinus system was well developed. Endocranial capacity is difficult to estimate because of the distorted vault. However, comparing hominin glabella–opisthion arc lengths[8] with that of KNM-WT 40000 (259 mm; an estimate inflated by diploic expansion) suggests a value in the range of *Australopithecus* or *Paranthropus*.

The sex of KNM-WT 40000 is difficult to infer. Interpretation of the canine root size proves inconclusive without a suitable comparative context. The small M^2 crown size could suggest that the specimen is female. However, the close proximity and slightly raised aspect of the temporal lines on the posterior half of the parietals is not seen in known female hominin crania, including the *Paranthropus* specimens KNM-ER 732, KNM-ER 407 and DNH7, and suggests that KNM-WT 40000 could be male.

　　KNM-WT 40000 的门齿齿槽呈冠状排列，刚刚位于双犬齿线的前面，上面的鼻齿槽斜坡在矢状方向和横向上都是平的。在保存下来的左侧没有看到犬齿轭，这反映了犬齿齿根具有最适度的大小。斜坡的长度（从鼻棘点到牙槽中点的弦距离）是 32 毫米，这是所有早期古人类中最长的之一。鼻下凸颌适中，具有比几乎所有南方古猿和傍人属标本都更垂直的斜坡（图 3b）。鼻孔与鼻齿槽斜坡位于同一冠状面上，没有前面柱（图 1a～1c）。鼻孔小而窄，与南方古猿非洲种和傍人粗壮种的大而宽的鼻孔形成对比。KNM-WT 40000 的中面部主要有一个高高的颧骨区（图 3c），颧骨区有一个低而弯曲的颧骨齿槽脊。在刚刚位于鼻骨之下的水平面上，横向的面部轮廓是平的（图 1b）。在 KNM-WT 40000 和 KNM-WT 38350 中，上颌骨颧突的前表面都位于 P^3 和 P^4 之间（图 1a、1d 和 1e），这在傍人中是很常见的，但是比大部分南方古猿标本[9]或能人中的位置要更靠前一些。眶上区域与南方古猿相似，既缺少傍人中所见的额三角，也没有能人（并非鲁道夫人）中所见到的圆枕上沟。KNM-WT 40000 的相对眶后缩狭（额面指数）与南方古猿、鲁道夫人和能人的都相似，而比傍人鲍氏种的（额面指数估计值[9] = 70）要小。其收敛于额鳞部的颞线有一个贯穿后中的路径（图 1b）。前囟周围，中线的形态没有很好地保存下来，但是顶骨的后半部分显示出大约相隔 6 毫米远的、双重的、稍微抬高的颞线。再向后形成了不明确的复合颞/项线。严重变形的乳突的原始形状无法重建出来了，但是左颞骨的其余部分保存完好。管状鼓室缺少岩脊，形成了一个具有小孔的狭窄的外耳道。这种组合构成了原始的古人类形态，在地猿原始种和南方古猿湖畔种中也见到过（图 3d）。其下颌窝与南方古猿阿法种和南方古猿非洲种标本的很像。其深度适中；关节隆起呈圆柱形，侧边缘丢失，有一个凸度适中的矢状面。保存下来的枕骨大孔的后半部分表明，其形状可能是卵圆形，而非傍人鲍氏种中见到（傍人埃塞俄比亚种中也可能见到）的心形。至于颅内方面，保存相当完好的枕骨表面缺少任何南方古猿阿法种、傍人鲍氏种和傍人粗壮种特征性的枕窦/边缘窦系统。双侧沟表明横窦/乙状窦系统很发达。颅容量很难估计，因为颅顶已经变形了。但是，将古人类眉间–枕后点弧长[8]与 KNM-WT 40000 的（259 毫米；由板障扩张获得的估计值）比较，得到的数值处于南方古猿或傍人的范围内。

　　KNM-WT 40000 的性别很难推断。对于犬齿齿根尺寸的说明证明是不确定的，没有适当的可用于比较的方面。小的 M^2 齿冠尺寸能够表明该标本是雌性。但是，在顶骨后半部分颞线极为接近并且较高，这在已知的雌性古人类颅骨（包括傍人标本 KNM-ER 732、KNM-ER 407 和 DNH7）中并没有见到，这一特点表明 KNM-WT 40000 可能是雄性。

With incisor alveoli close to the bicanine line and anteriorly positioned zygomatic processes, the face of KNM-WT 40000 resembles the flat, orthognathic-looking faces of both *Paranthropus* and *H. rudolfensis* cranium KNM-ER 1470. However, KNM-WT 40000 lacks most of the derived features that characterize *Paranthropus* (Table 2), and its facial architecture differs from the latter in much the same way as has been described for KNM-ER 1470 (refs 8, 10). Facial flatness in *Paranthropus* results from the forward position of the anteroinferiorly sloping malar region, whose main facial surface approximates the plane of the nasal aperture, but whose orientation contrasts with the more horizontally inclined nasoalveolar gutter[11]. In KNM-WT 40000 and KNM-ER 1470, it is the flat and orthognathic nasoalveolar clivus that aligns with the plane of the nasal aperture, whereas the anteriorly set, tall malar region is more vertically orientated. KNM-WT 40000 lacks the derived short nasal bones and everted lateral nasal margin of KNM-ER 1470, and is less orthognathic in the midfacial region than this specimen; however, on balance this is the hominin face that KNM-WT 40000 most closely resembles.

Additional Material

The right maxilla fragment KNM-WT 38343A preserves three well-separated P^3 roots, and its damaged canine seems low-crowned when compared with *A. afarensis* canines of similar size and degree of wear. The right temporal bone KNM-WT 40001 lacks the squama and petrous apex, but is otherwise well preserved (Fig. 1f, g). It shows a combination of characters not seen in any other hominin specimen. The projecting mastoid process is rounded, with an anteriorly positioned tip. It has a well-developed digastric fossa in the form of a deep, narrow groove that runs posterolaterally from the stylomastoid foramen, fully demarcating the mastoid process from the adjacent nuchal plane. The tympanic element is long, inferosuperiorly shallow and lacks a petrous crest. The external acoustic porus is the smallest of any known hominin temporal bone (Fig. 3d). The articular eminence is as broad mediolaterally (38 mm) as in *P. aethiopicus* and *P. boisei*, and similar to the largest found in *A. afarensis*. Compared with KNM-WT 40000 the eminence is relatively flat sagittally, and the mandibular fossa is shallow.

The partial mandibles KNM-WT 8556 and KNM-WT 16006 have been assigned to *A. afarensis*[3]. However, KNM-WT 8556 shows a more derived morphology than this species by having a flat, more horizontal post-incisive plane, a more superiorly positioned genioglossal pit, a molarized lower fourth premolar (P_4) and a large M_3 (ref. 3). Indeed, relative to its *Australopithecus*-sized M_1 (refs 5, 6, 12, 13), the P_4 and M_3 crowns of KNM-WT 8556 are enlarged to an extent only seen in *P. boisei* (Fig. 3e, f). All unworn molars in the Lomekwi sample are characterized by low occlusal relief and numerous secondary fissures. Most of the lower molars, including the KNM-WT 16006 M_3, have a well-developed protostylid, a feature that is usually absent in *A. afarensis*, but common in *A. africanus*[14]. The two I^2s are lower crowned than in *A. afarensis*, *A. africanus*[14] and *P. robustus*[14]. Inability to distinguish between first and second molars makes meaningful intertaxon comparisons of these elements difficult.

KNM-WT 40000 的门齿槽靠近双犬齿线，颧突前置，面部与傍人和鲁道夫人颅骨 KNM-ER 1470 的扁平而正颌的面部很像。然而，KNM-WT 40000 缺少大部分表征傍人的衍生特征（表 2），其面部结构与后者不同，而与 KNM-ER 1470 描述过的情况几乎一样（参考文献 8 和 10）。傍人的面部扁平的特点是由于向前下方倾斜的颧骨区的位置向前，其主面部表面接近鼻孔平面，但是其方向与更加水平倾斜的鼻齿槽沟形成对比[11]。在 KNM-WT 40000 和 KNM-ER 1470 中，扁平而正颌的鼻齿槽斜坡与鼻孔平面走向一致，而位于前面的高的颧骨区更加垂直。KNM-WT 40000 缺少 KNM-ER 1470 所具有的衍生的短小的鼻骨和外翻的侧鼻缘，中面部的正颌性比该标本差；但是，总的说来，这是与 KNM-WT 40000 最为相像的古人类面部。

其 他 材 料

右上颌骨碎片 KNM-WT 38343A 保存下来了三个完全分离的 P^3 齿根，当与南方古猿阿法种的具有相似大小和磨损程度的犬齿比较时，发现其损坏的犬齿似乎是低齿冠的。右颞骨 KNM-WT 40001 缺少鳞部和岩部尖，但是同样保存状况很好（图 1f 和 1g）。其显示出在其他古人类标本中所没有看到过的特征的组合。突出的乳突呈圆形，有一个位于前面的尖端。它有一个发达的二腹肌窝，呈深而狭窄的沟状，从茎乳孔向后外侧延伸，完全将乳突与相邻的项面分隔开来。鼓室长，上下方向浅，缺少岩脊。外耳门是现在已知的古人类颞骨中最小的（图 3d）。关节隆起在中外侧像傍人埃塞俄比亚种和傍人鲍氏种的一样宽阔（38 毫米），与南方古猿阿法种中发现的最大值很相似。与 KNM-WT 40000 相比，该隆起在矢状方向上相对平一些，下颌窝很浅。

部分下颌骨 KNM-WT 8556 和 KNM-WT 16006 都被划分到了南方古猿阿法种中[3]。但是，KNM-WT 8556 显示出比该物种更加衍生的形态，具有扁平而更加水平的门齿后平面、位置靠上的颏舌肌窝、臼齿化的下第四前臼齿（P_4）和一个大的 M_3（参考文献 3）。实际上，相对于其尺寸与南方古猿相当的 M_1（参考文献 5、6、12 和 13），KNM-WT 8556 的 P_4 和 M_3 的齿冠扩大到了只有在傍人鲍氏种中才见到过的程度（图 3e 和 3f）。洛梅奎标本中所有没磨损的臼齿都具有的特征是低的咬合面脊纹和许多次级沟纹。大部分下臼齿，包括 KNM-WT 16006 的 M_3，都具有发达的原副尖，这是南方古猿阿法种中通常不具备而南方古猿非洲种中很常见的特征[14]。两颗 I^2 的齿冠都比南方古猿阿法种、南方古猿非洲种[14]和傍人粗壮种[14]的低。无法区分第一和第二臼齿，这使得很难对这些部位在分类单元之间进行有意义的比较。

Taxonomic Discussion

The hominin specimens recovered from the Kataboi and lower Lomekwi Members show a suite of features that distinguishes them from established hominin taxa, including the only contemporaneous eastern African species, *A. afarensis*. Compared with the latter, the morphology of *K. platyops* is more derived facially, and more primitive in its small external acoustic porus and the absence of an occipital/marginal sinus system. These finds not only provide evidence for a taxonomically more diverse middle Pliocene hominin record, but also show that a more orthognathic facial morphology emerged significantly earlier in hominin evolutionary history than previously documented. This early faciodental diversity concerns morphologies that functionally are most closely associated with mastication. It suggests a diet-driven adaptive radiation among hominins in this time interval, which perhaps had its origins considerably earlier. Furthermore, the presence in *K. platyops* of an anteriorly positioned zygomatic process in combination with a small M^1 and M^2 indicates that such characters are more independent than is suggested by developmental and functional models that link such facial morphology in *Paranthropus* with postcanine megadontia[11,15].

At present it is unclear whether the Lomekwi hominin fossils sample multiple species. Apart from the paratype maxilla KNM-WT 38350 with its small molar size and anteriorly positioned zygomatic process, the other specimens cannot be positively associated morphologically with the *K. platyops* holotype. These are therefore not included in the paratype series, and are left unassigned until further evidence emerges. Differences between the tympanic and mandibular fossa morphologies of the KNM-WT 40000 and KNM-WT 40001 temporal bones can perhaps be accommodated within a single species, but their shared primitive characters do not necessarily imply conspecificity. Affiliation of the KNM-WT 8556 mandible with the *K. platyops* types is not contradicted by its molarized P_4, which is consistent with an anteriorly positioned zygomatic process. However, its M_1 is larger than would be inferred from the smaller upper molars of the types, and with a 177 mm^2 crown area it is also larger than any in the combined sample of ten isolated M_1s and M_2s (139–172 mm^2). One isolated $M^{1/2}$ (KNM-WT 38362) is significantly larger than the molars of the *K. platyops* types, whereas another (KNM-WT 38337) is similar in size to the holotype's M^2.

The marked differences of the KNM-WT 40000 cranium from established hominin taxa, both with respect to individual features and their unique combination, fully justify its status as a separate species. It is worth noting that comparisons with *Australopithecus bahrelghazali* cannot be made directly, because this species was named on the basis of the limited evidence provided by an anterior mandible fragment[16]. Specific distinction of *A. bahrelghazali* from *A. afarensis* has yet to be confirmed[17], and Lomekwi specimens differ from *A. bahrelghazali* in symphyseal morphology and incisor crown height.

The generic attribution of KNM-WT 40000 is a more complex issue, in the absence of

734

分类学讨论

从卡塔博伊和下洛梅奎段发掘到的古人类标本显示出一套与已确定的古人类分类单元不同的特征，与唯一的同时代的东非物种——南方古猿阿法种也不相同。与后者相比，肯尼亚扁脸人的面部形态更具有衍生性，其较小的外耳门和枕窦/边缘窦系统的缺失则更加原始。这些发现不仅为分类学上更加多样的中上新世古人类记录提供了证据，而且也表明，更加正颌的面部形态在古人类演化史上出现的时间比之前文件证明的早得多。这一早期的面牙多样性涉及那些功能上与咀嚼关系最密切的形态。它表明在这一时间段的古人类中存在着饮食驱动的适应性辐射，其起源的时间可能更早。此外，肯尼亚扁脸人位置靠前的颧突与小型的 M^1 和 M^2 组合暗示了这些特征更具有独立性，而非发育和功能学模型所倡导的将傍人中的这种面部形态与较大的犬齿后齿联系起来[11,15]。

现在还不清楚洛梅奎古人类化石标本是否包含多个物种。除了副模标本上颌骨 KNM-WT 38350 及其小型臼齿尺寸和前置的颧突外，不能肯定其余标本在形态上与肯尼亚扁脸人正模标本有关。因此这些不被包括在副模标本系列中，直到出现进一步的证据时，才能对这些标本的归属进行判定。KNM-WT 40000 与 KNM-WT 40001 颞骨的鼓室和下颌窝形态之间的差异或许可以被归结为同一个物种内的差异，但是它们共有的原始特征未必意味着同种性。KNM-WT 8556 下颌骨归属于肯尼亚扁脸人类型，与其臼齿化的 P_4 并不冲突，这与前置的颧突是一致的。然而，其 M_1 比根据该类型较小的上臼齿推断出来的要大，齿冠面积达 177 平方毫米，比十颗游离的 M_1 和 M_2 的所有标本中的任何一个（139~172 平方毫米）都大。一颗游离的 $M^{1/2}$（KNM-WT 38362）比肯尼亚扁脸人类型的臼齿要大得多，但是另一个标本（KNM-WT 38337）则与正模标本的 M^2 的大小相似。

KNM-WT 40000 颅骨与已确定的古人类分类单元在个体特征与其特异的结合方面的明显差异，都充分地说明了将其当成一个单独的物种的合理性。值得说明的是，不能直接与南方古猿羚羊河种进行比较，因为该物种是根据一块前下颌骨碎片提供的有限证据而命名的[16]。南方古猿羚羊河种与南方古猿阿法种的特异差别还没有得到证实[17]，洛梅奎标本与南方古猿羚羊河种在下颌联合部的形态和门齿齿冠高度方面有差异。

KNM-WT 40000 属一级别的划分归类是一个更加复杂的问题，对于该属分类的

consensus over the definition of the genus category[4]. The specimen lacks almost all of the derived features of *Paranthropus* (Table 2), and there are no grounds for assigning it to this genus unless it can be shown to represent a stem species. However, the fact that the facial morphology of KNM-WT 40000 is derived in a markedly different way renders this implausible. As KNM-WT 40000 does not show the derived features associated with *Homo*[4] (excluding *H. rudolfensis* and *H. habilis*) or the strongly primitive morphology of *Ardipithecus*[18], the only other available genus is *Australopithecus*. We agree with the taxonomically conservative, grade-sensitive approach to hominin classification that for the moment accepts *Australopithecus* as a paraphyletic genus in which are clustered stem species sharing a suite of key primitive features, such as a small brain, strong subnasal prognathism, and relatively large postcanine teeth. However, with its derived face and small molar size, KNM-WT 40000 stands apart from species assigned to *Australopithecus* on this basis. All it has in common with such species is its small brain size and a few other primitive characters in the nasal, supraorbital and temporal regions. Therefore, there is no firm basis for linking KNM-WT 40000 specifically with *Australopithecus*, and the inclusion of such a derived but early form could well render this genus polyphyletic. In a classification in which *Australopithecus* also includes the "robust" taxa and perhaps even species traditionally known as "early *Homo*"[4], this genus subsumes several widely divergent craniofacial morphologies. It could thus be argued that the inclusion of KNM-WT 40000 in *Australopithecus* would merely add yet another hominin species with a derived face. This amounts to defining *Australopithecus* by a single criterion, those hominin species not attributable to *Ardipithecus* or *Homo*, which in our view constitutes an undesirable approach to classification. Thus, given that KNM-WT 40000 cannot be grouped sensibly with any of the established hominin genera, and that it shows a unique pattern of facial and dental morphology that probably reflects a distinct dietary adaptive zone, we assign this specimen to the new genus *Kenyanthropus*.

Despite being separated by about 1.5 Myr, KNM-WT 40000 is very similar in its facial architecture to KNM-ER 1470, the lectotype of *H. rudolfensis*. The main differences amount to the more primitive nasal and neurocranial morphology of KNM-WT 40000. This raises the possibility that there is a close phylogenetic relationship between the two taxa, and affects our interpretation of *H. rudolfensis*. The transfer of this species to *Australopithecus* has been recommended[4,19], but *Kenyanthropus* may be a more appropriate genus. The identification of *K. platyops* has a number of additional implications. As a species contemporary with *A. afarensis* that is more primitive in some of its morphology, *K. platyops* weakens the case for *A. afarensis* being the sister taxon of all later hominins, and thus its proposed transfer to *Praeanthropus*[1,20]. Furthermore, the morphology of *K. platyops* raises questions about the polarity of characters used in analyses of hominin phylogeny. An example is the species' small molar size, which, although probably a derived feature, might also imply that the larger postcanine dentition of *A. afarensis* or *A. anamensis* does not represent the primitive hominin condition. Finally, the occurrence of at least one additional hominin species in the middle Pliocene of eastern Africa means that the affiliation of fragmentary specimens can now be reassessed. For example, the attribution of the 3.3 Myr old KNM-ER 2602 cranial fragment to *A. afarensis*[21] has been questioned[8],

定义还没有达成一致[4]。标本缺少几乎所有的傍人的衍生特征（表 2），除非可以表明其代表了主干物种，否则没有依据将其划分到该属。但是，KNM-WT 40000 的面部形态的衍生方式如此迥异，使其不可能代表主干物种。鉴于 KNM-WT 40000 并没有显示出与人属（除了鲁道夫人和能人）相关的衍生特征[4]或者地猿的非常原始的形态[18]，其他唯一一个可考虑的属就是南方古猿了。我们同意分类学上保守的、级别敏感的古人类的分类方式，该方式目前将南方古猿认为是一种并系属，在该属中聚集了共有一套关键的原始特征的主干物种，这里所说的关键的原始特征包括较小的脑、强壮的鼻下凸颌和相对大的犬齿后部牙齿等。然而，KNM-WT 40000 具有衍生的面部和小的臼齿，这些将其与划分为南方古猿的物种分开了。它与该类物种共有的全部特征就是其小的脑和鼻骨、眶上区和颞区的一些其他原始特征。因此，没有确定的依据将 KNM-WT 40000 特异性地与南方古猿联系起来，将这样一个衍生但尚属早期的形式包括进来可以很好地使这个属复杂化。在一种分类中，南方古猿也包括"粗壮"的分类单元，甚至可能包括传统意义上称为"早期人属"的物种[4]，该属包含几种差别很大的颅面形态。因此可以这样说，将 KNM-WT 40000 囊括进南方古猿仅会增加另一个具有衍生面部的古人类物种。这等同于将南方古猿用唯一的标准定义，即那些不能被归入地猿或人属的古人类物种，依我们看来，这形成了一个不理想的分类方式。因此，鉴于 KNM-WT 40000 不能明智地与任何已确定的古人类属聚类到一起，以及鉴于其表明了一种独特的面部和牙齿形态模式，该模式可能反映了一个与众不同的饮食适应区，我们将该标本划分到一个新属中，即肯尼亚人。

　　尽管分隔约 150 万年，但是 KNM-WT 40000 在面部结构上与鲁道夫人的选模标本 KNM-ER1470 很相似。主要差异包括 KNM-WT 40000 更加原始的鼻骨和脑颅形态。这提出了一种可能性，即这两种分类单元之间存在密切的系统发育关系，并且影响了我们对鲁道夫人的解释。已经有人建议将鲁道夫人归入南方古猿[4,19]，但是肯尼亚人可能是一个更适合的属。对肯尼亚扁脸人的鉴定具有许多额外的含义。作为与某些形态更加原始的南方古猿阿法种同时代的一个物种，肯尼亚扁脸人削弱了南方古猿阿法种作为所有后来的古人类的姐妹分类单元的理由，以及将其归入 *Praeanthropus* 的建议[1,20]。此外，肯尼亚扁脸人的形态引发了关于分析古人类系统发育时使用的特征的极性的问题。一个例子是该物种的小型臼齿尺寸，这尽管可能是一种衍生性状，但是也可能意味着南方古猿阿法种或南方古猿湖畔种的较大犬齿后部牙齿并不代表原始的古人类状态。最后，在东非的中上新世时期至少出现了另外一个古人类物种，这意味着现在可以重新估计碎片标本的归属了。例如，将 330 万年前的 KNM-ER 2602 颅骨碎片划分为南方古猿阿法种[21]已经被质疑了[8]，现在

and evaluating its affinities with *K. platyops* is now timely.

Geological Context and Dating

KNM-WT 40000 was collected near the contact of the Nachukui Formation with Miocene volcanic rocks in the northern tributary of Lomekwi (Nabetili). It is situated 12 m above the Lokochot Tuff, and 8 m below the β-Tulu Bor Tuff (Fig. 4). Along Nabetili, the Lokochot Tuff is pinkish-grey and contains much clay and volcanic detritus. It is overlain by a volcanic pebble conglomerate, followed by a pale brown quartz-rich fine sandstone that includes a burrowed fine-sandstone marker bed 10–15 cm thick. The Lokochot Tuff is replaced by a thick volcanic clast conglomerate in the central part of Lomekwi. The contact between the fine sandstone and the overlying dark mudstone can be traced from Nabetili to the hominin locality. Locally the mudstone contains volcanic pebbles at the base, and it has thin pebble conglomerate lenses in the upper part at the hominin locality, and also contains $CaCO_3$ concretions. The hominin specimen and other vertebrate fossils derive from this mudstone. Overlying the dark mudstone at the hominin site is a brown mudstone (8 m) that directly underlies the β-Tulu Bor Tuff.

New ^{40}Ar–^{39}Ar determinations on alkali feldspars from pumice clasts in the Moiti Tuff and the Topernawi Tuff, stratigraphically beneath the Lokochot Tuff, were instrumental in re-investigating the lower portion of this section. The new results yield a mean age for the Topernawi Tuff of 3.96 ± 0.03 Myr; this is marginally older than the pooled age for the Moiti Tuff of 3.94 ± 0.03 Myr. Previous investigations[22,23] placed the Topernawi Tuff above the Moiti Tuff, mainly on the basis of the K/Ar ages on alkali feldspar from pumice clasts in the Topernawi Tuff (3.78, 3.71, 3.76 and 3.97 Myr, all ± 0.04 Myr)[23]. The older determination (3.97 Myr) was thought to result from contamination by detrital feldspar. South of Topernawi, however, the Topernawi Tuff has now been shown to underlie the Moiti Tuff, and to be in turn underlain by a tephra informally termed the "Nabwal tuff", previously thought to be a Moiti Tuff correlative. The correct sequence is shown in Fig. 4, and the new ^{40}Ar–^{39}Ar age data on the Moiti Tuff and Topernawi Tuff are provided as Supplementary Information.

正是对其与肯尼亚扁脸人的亲缘关系进行评估的时候。

地质学环境与定年

KNM-WT 40000 是在洛梅奎（纳贝蒂利）北部支流的中新世火山岩与纳丘库伊组接壤部位附近搜集到的。它位于洛科乔特凝灰岩之上 12 米，β 图卢博尔凝灰岩之下 8 米处（图 4）。沿着纳贝蒂利，洛科乔特凝灰岩呈略带粉红的灰色，包含大量黏土和火山碎屑。其上覆盖着火山卵石砾岩，紧接着是淡褐色的富含石英的细砂岩，其中包括挖掘出来的 10~15 厘米厚的细砂岩标准层。洛科乔特凝灰岩在洛梅奎中部被一层厚的火山碎屑砾岩取代了。在细砂岩和覆盖在上面的深色泥岩之间的衔接部分可以从纳贝蒂利一直追踪到古人类遗址处。在当地，泥岩在基部包含火山卵石，在古人类遗址的上半部分有薄层的卵石砾岩透镜体，还含有 $CaCO_3$ 结核。古人类标本和其他脊椎动物化石都是从这层泥岩中发现的。覆盖在古人类遗址深色泥岩上面的是一种褐色的泥岩（8 米），位于 β 图卢博尔凝灰岩的紧下面。

根据在地层学上位于洛科乔特凝灰岩下面的莫伊蒂凝灰岩和托佩尔纳维凝灰岩中的浮岩碎屑的碱性长石确定的 ^{40}Ar–^{39}Ar 新数据，对于重新调查该剖面的下半部分是有帮助的。这些新结果产生的托佩尔纳维凝灰岩的平均年代是 396 万 ±3 万年；这比莫伊蒂凝灰岩的并合年代 394 万 ±3 万年古老的程度有限。之前的调查[22,23] 将托佩尔纳维凝灰岩置于莫伊蒂凝灰岩之上，主要的依据是从托佩尔纳维凝灰岩中的浮岩碎屑得到的碱性长石的 K/Ar 年代（378 万、371 万、376 万和 397 万年，都是 ±4 万年）[23]。确定的年代中较为古老的（397 万年）被认为是长石碎屑的污染造成的。但是，在托佩尔纳维南部，现在表明托佩尔纳维凝灰岩是位于莫伊蒂凝灰岩之下的，而反过来，一种非正式称为"纳布瓦尔凝灰岩"的火山碎屑又位于它的下面，后者之前被认为是莫伊蒂凝灰岩的相关物。正确的地层顺序见图 4 所示，莫伊蒂凝灰岩和托佩尔纳维凝灰岩的新的 ^{40}Ar–^{39}Ar 年代数据在补充信息中给出。

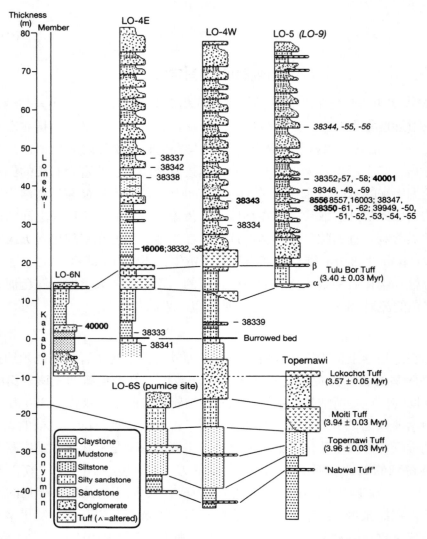

Fig. 4. Stratigraphic sections and placement of hominin specimens at sites in upper part of the Lomekwi drainage, west of Lake Turkana, northern Kenya. Specimen numbers are given without the prefix KNM-WT, and those in bold are discussed in the text. Placement of specimens is relative to the nearest marker bed in the section. Italicized numbers show the relative placement of specimens at LO-9 on section LO-5. The burrowed bed, a useful local marker, is used as stratigraphic datum (0 m). Representative $^{40}Ar-^{39}Ar$ analytical data on the Moiti Tuff and on the Topernawi Tuff are given as Supplementary Information. The date for the Tulu Bor Tuff is taken as the age of the Sidi Hakoma Tuff at Hadar[25], which is consistent with the age of the Toroto Tuff $(3.32 \pm 0.03$ Myr)[45] that overlies the Tulu Bor at Koobi Fora. The age of the Lokochot Tuff is assigned from its placement at the Gilbert/Gauss Chron boundary[24,46]. The tuff formerly thought to be the Moiti Tuff at Lomekwi[22] has been informally called the "Nabwal tuff"[47]. Ages on the Tulu Bor and the Lokochot Tuffs are consistent with orbitally tuned ages of correlative ash layers in Ocean Drilling Program Core 722A in the Arabian Sea[48].

Linear interpolation between the Lokochot Tuff (3.57 Myr old)[24] and Tulu Bor Tuff (3.40 Myr)[25] yields an age of 3.5 Myr for KNM-WT 40000, and 3.53 Myr for the burrowed bed.

图 4. 肯尼亚北部图尔卡纳湖西侧的洛梅奎流域上游区的地层剖面和发现古人类标本的位置。标本号缺省了前缀 KNM-WT，黑体表示的是在正文中讨论的标本。标本的位置是与剖面中最近的标准层对应的。斜体数字表示 LO-9 处的标本在剖面 LO-5 的相对位置。挖掘层是一个有用的局部标志，被用来当作地层基准面（0 米）。对莫伊蒂凝灰岩和托佩尔纳维凝灰岩进行的代表性的 $^{40}Ar–^{39}Ar$ 分析数据作为补充信息给出。图卢博尔凝灰岩的年代根据哈达尔的西迪哈克玛凝灰岩的年代得来[25]，这与覆盖在库比福勒的图卢博尔之上的托罗托凝灰岩的年代（332 万年 ± 3 万年）[45] 一致。洛科乔特凝灰岩的年代根据其在吉尔伯特/高斯年代界线处的位置来判定[24,46]。在洛梅奎处之前认为属于莫伊蒂的凝灰岩[22] 被非正式地称作"纳布瓦尔凝灰岩"[47]。图卢博尔和洛科乔特凝灰岩的年代与阿拉伯海[48]的海洋钻探计划岩芯 722A 中的相关灰层的轨道调谐年代一致。

洛科乔特凝灰岩（357 万年）[24] 与图卢博尔凝灰岩（340 万年）[25] 之间的线性插入得到 KNM-WT 40000 的年代为 350 万年，挖掘层的年代为 353 万年。紧邻挖掘层之下的

KNM-WT 38341 from immediately below the burrowed bed has an age near 3.53 Myr. KNM-WT 38333 and 38339, from between the burrowed bed and the α-Tulu Bor Tuff lie between 3.4 and 3.5 Myr. Other specimens from LO-4, LO-5, and LO-6 lie 16–24 m above the β-Tulu Bor Tuff, with ages near 3.3 Myr. Assuming linear sedimentation between the Tulu Bor Tuff and the Lokalalei Tuff (2.5 Myr)[23], specimens from LO-9 are around 3.2 Myr. The probable error on these age estimates is less than 0.10 Myr.

Palaeogeographically, the mudstone that contained KNM-WT 40000 at LO-6N was deposited along the northern margin of a shallow lake that extended to Kataboi and beyond[26,27]. Laterally discontinuous volcanic pebble conglomerates within the mudstone record small streams draining from hills to the west. Carbonate concretions at the hominin level are probably pedogenic, and indicate regional conditions with net evaporative loss. Other specimens between the burrowed bed and the Tulu Bor Tuff were also preserved in lake-margin environments, as is the case for KNM-WT 38341 that was collected below the burrowed bed. At LO-5, and in the upper part of LO-4E, strata were laid down by ephemeral streams draining the basin margin, principally the ancestral Topernawi, which deposited gravels in broad, shallow channels, and finer grained materials in interfluves. Specimens preserved in floodplain deposits of the ancestral Omo River that occupied the axial portion of the basin include those at LO-9, those less than 6 m above the Tulu Bor Tuff at LO-4E, and KNM-WT 38338. Thus, there is evidence for hominins occupying floodplains of major rivers, alluvial fans, and lake-margin environments 3.0–3.5 Myr ago. There is reasonable evidence that water sources were available to these hominins in channels of the ephemeral streams, and also possibly as seeps or springs farther out into the basin.

Palaeoecology and Fauna

Faunal assemblages from Lomekwi sites LO-4, LO-5, LO-6 and LO-9 indicate palaeoenvironments that were relatively well watered and well vegetated. The relative proportions of the bovids in the early collections from these sites indicate a mosaic of habitats, but with predominantly woodland and forest-edge species dominating[22]. Comparisons of the Lomekwi faunal assemblages with those from the few known hominin sites of similar age, Laetoli in Tanzania, Hadar in Ethiopia and Bahr el Ghazal in Chad, are of interest in view of the different hominin taxa represented. Hadar and Bahr el Ghazal, like Lomekwi, represent lakeshore or river floodplain palaeoenvironments[28,29], whereas Laetoli was not located near a water source; no aquatic taxa nor terrestrial mammals indicative of swamp or grassy wetlands were recovered[30]. The faunal assemblages of all four sites indicate a mosaic of habitats that seems to have included open grasslands and more wooded or forested environments[22,28,29,31,32]; the assemblages differ primarily in the indication of the nature of the dominant vegetation cover.

Although the mammalian faunal assemblage from Lomekwi is more similar to that from Hadar than to that from Laetoli, some mammalian species represented are different.

KNM-WT 38341 的年代接近 353 万年。从挖掘层与 α 图卢博尔凝灰岩之间发掘到的 KNM-WT 38333 和 38339 的年代介于 340 万年到 350 万年之间。从 LO-4、LO-5 和 LO-6 挖掘出来的其他标本位于 β 图卢博尔凝灰岩之上 16~24 米处，年代接近 330 万年。假定图卢博尔凝灰岩与洛卡拉莱伊凝灰岩 (250 万年) [23] 之间存在线性沉积作用，那么从 LO-9 挖掘出来的标本的年代就约为 320 万年。这些年代估计值的可能误差小于 10 万年。

从古地理学角度看，在 LO-6N 处包含 KNM-WT 40000 的泥岩是沿着一个浅湖的北部边缘沉积下来的，这个湖一直延伸到卡塔博伊甚至更远处 [26,27]。在泥岩中的侧面的不连续的火山卵石砾岩记录下了从山丘流到西部的小溪流。在古人类地层中的碳酸盐结核可能是成土的，暗示着具有净蒸发损失的区域性情况。位于挖掘层与图卢博尔凝灰岩之间的其他标本也在湖缘环境中保存下来了，正如 KNM-WT 38341 的情况一样，该标本是在挖掘层之下的地层中搜集到的。在 LO-5，以及 LO-4E 的上半部分，地层由从盆地边缘流出的季节河（主要是原始的托佩尔纳维）沉积而成，它们将砾石在宽阔而浅的河道中沉积下来，细粒的材料在江河分水区沉积下来。原始的奥莫河占据了盆地的轴向部分，在其河漫滩沉积物中保存的标本包括在 LO-9 的那些标本，在 LO-4E 的图卢博尔凝灰岩之上不到 6 米处的标本，以及 KNM-WT 38338。因此，有证据表明，300 万 ~ 350 万年前，有古人类居住在大河的河漫滩、冲积扇以及湖缘环境中。有可靠证据表明，这些古人类可以得到的水源来自季节河的河道，可能还有深入盆地内部的渗流或泉水。

古生态学与动物群

来自洛梅奎遗址 LO-4、LO-5、LO-6 和 LO-9 的动物群组合暗示当时的古环境是相对水源充足、植物茂盛的。从这些遗址搜集到的早期标本中牛科动物的相对比例暗示着生境的镶嵌性，但林地和森林边缘物种占主导地位 [22]。将洛梅奎动物群组合与已知的少数相似年代的古人类遗址（坦桑尼亚的莱托里、埃塞俄比亚的哈达尔和乍得的加扎勒河省）发现的动物群组合相比，从所代表的不同古人类分类单元的视点来看很有趣。哈达尔和加扎勒河省像洛梅奎一样，代表着湖岸或河流河漫滩的古环境 [28,29]，而莱托里并不位于水源附近；没有发现暗示沼泽或多草湿地存在的水生分类单元或陆地哺乳动物 [30]。所有四处遗址的动物群组合都暗示着生境的镶嵌性，它似乎包括开放的草地和更加多树木或多森林的环境 [22,28,29,31,32]；这些动物群组合的主要区别在于优势植被的性质的含义不同。

尽管洛梅奎的哺乳动物群组合与哈达尔的相似性胜过其与莱托里的，但是有些代表性的哺乳动物物种是不同的。在洛梅奎，布鲁姆狮尾狒很常见，并且是主要的

At Lomekwi, *Theropithecus brumpti* is common and is the dominant cercopithecid, as it is elsewhere in the Turkana Basin at this time. This species is generally considered to indicate more forested or closed woodland habitats. In the Hadar Formation, *Theropithecus darti* is the common *Theropithecus* species and is associated with lower occurrences of the water-dependent reduncines and higher occurrences of alcelaphines and/or *Aepyceros*, which indicates drier woodlands and grasslands[33]. Differences in the representation of other common species at the two sites that are less obviously linked to habitat include *Kolpochoerus limnetes*, *Tragelaphus nakuae* and *Aepyceros shungurensis* at Lomekwi, as opposed to *K. afarensis*, *T. kyaloae* and an undescribed species of *Aepyceros* at Hadar (K. Reed, personal communication). The general indication is that the palaeoenvironment at Lomekwi may have been somewhat more vegetated and perhaps wetter than that persisting through much of the Hadar Formation. At both sites more detailed analyses will be essential to further develop an understanding of how subtle temporal changes in the faunal assemblages relate to hominin occurrences.

Note added in proof: If the hominin status of the recently published Lukeino craniodental specimens[49] is confirmed, this would support the suggestion that small molar size is the primitive rather than the derived hominin condition.

(**410**, 433-440; 2001)

Meave G. Leakey[*], Fred Spoor[†], Frank H. Brown[‡], Patrick N. Gathogo[‡], Christopher Kiarie[*], Louise N. Leakey[*] & Ian McDougall[§]

[*] Division of Palaeontology, National Museums of Kenya, P.O. Box 40658, Nairobi, Kenya
[†] Department of Anatomy & Developmental Biology, University College London, WC1E 6JJ, UK
[‡] Department of Geology & Geophysics, University of Utah, Salt Lake City, Utah 84112, USA
[§] Research School of Earth Sciences, The Australian National University, Canberra ACT 0200, Australia

Received 31 January; accepted 16 February 2001.

References:

1. Strait, D. S., Grine, F. E. & Moniz, M. A. A reappraisal of early hominid phylogeny. *J. Hum. Evol.* **32**, 17-82 (1997).

2. Ward, C., Leakey, M. & Walker, A. The new hominid species *Australopithecus anamensis*. *Evol. Anthrop.* **7**, 197-205 (1999).

3. Brown, B., Brown, F. & Walker, A. New hominids from the Lake Turkana Basin, Kenya. *J. Hum. Evol.* (in the press).

4. Wood, B. A. & Collard, M. C. The human genus. *Science* **284**, 65-71 (1999).

5. Leakey, M. G., Feibel, C. S., McDougall, I. & Walker, A. C. New four-million-year-old hominid species from Kanapoi and Allia Bay, Kenya. *Nature* **376**, 565-571 (1995).

6. Leakey, M. G., Feibel, C. S., McDougall, I., Ward, C. & Walker, A. New specimens and confirmation of an early age for *Australopithecus anamensis*. *Nature* **393**, 62-66 (1998).

7. Kimbel, W. H., Johanson, D. C. & Rak, Y. Systematic assessment of a maxilla of *Homo* from Hadar, Ethiopia. *Am. J. Phys. Anthrop.* **103**, 235-262 (1997).

8. Wood, B. A. *Koobi Fora Research Project* Vol. 4 (Clarendon Press, Oxford, 1991).

9. Lockwood, C. A. & Tobias, P. V. A large male hominin cranium from Sterkfontein, South Africa, and the status of *Australopithecus africanus*. *J. Hum. Evol.* **36**, 637-685 (1999).

10. Bilsborough, A. & Wood, B. A. Cranial morphometry of early hominids: facial region. *Am. J. Phys. Anthrop.* **76**, 61-86 (1988).

11. Rak, Y. *The Australopithecine Face* (Academic, New York, 1983).

12. Lockwood, C. A., Kimbel, W. H. & Johanson, D. C. Temporal trends and metric variation in the mandibles and dentition of *Australopithecus afarensis*. *J. Hum. Evol.* **39**, 23-55 (2000).

13. Moggi-Cecchi, J., Tobias, P. V. & Beynon, A. D. The mixed dentition and associated skull fragments of a juvenile fossil hominid from Sterkfontein, South Africa. *Am. J.*

猴科动物，就像当时在图尔卡纳盆地的其他地方一样。该物种通常被认为暗示着更加森林化或者更加封闭的林地生境。在哈达尔组，达提狮尾狒是常见的狮尾狒属的物种，与较少出现的依赖水的苇羚科和经常出现的狷羚科和(或)高角羚属相关，暗示着更加干旱的林地和草地[33]。在这两处遗址，与生境关联不那么明显的其他常见物种的差别包括洛梅奎的 *Kolpochoerus limnetes*、*Tragelaphus nakuae* 和 *Aepyceros shungurensis*，而哈达尔的 *K. afarensis*、*T. kyaloae* 和一种未描述的高角羚属物种(里得，个人交流)与之刚好形成对照。通常认为，与哈达尔组大部分地区长期存在的古环境相比，洛梅奎的古环境可能植被更加丰富，或许也更加潮湿。在这两处遗址，需要进行更加详细的分析以进一步理解动物群组合在时间上的微妙变化如何与古人类出现相关。

附加说明： 如果最近发表的卢凯伊诺颅牙标本[49]的古人类地位得到了证实，那么将支持如下建议，即小型的臼齿尺寸是原始的，而非衍生的古人类特征。

（刘皓芳 翻译；赵凌霞 审稿）

Phys. Anthrop. **106**, 425-465 (1998).

14. Robinson, J. T. The dentition of the Australopithecinae. *Transv. Mus. Mem.* **9**, 1-179 (1956).

15. McCollum, M. A. The robust australopithecine face: a morphogenetic perspective. *Science* **284**, 301-305 (1999).

16. Brunet, M. *et al. Australopithecus bahrelghazali*, une nouvelle espèce d'Hominidé ancien de la région de Koro Toro (Tchad). *C.R. Acad. Sci. Ser. IIa* **322**, 907-913 (1996).

17. White, T. D., Suwa, G., Simpson, S. & Asfaw, B. Jaws and teeth of *A. afarensis* from Maka, Middle Awash, Ethiopia. *Am. J. Phys. Anthrop.* **111**, 45-68 (2000).

18. White, T. D., Suwa, G. & Asfaw, B. *Australopithecus ramidus*, a new species of early hominid from Aramis, Ethiopia. *Nature* **371**, 306-312 (1994).

19. Wood, B. & Collard, M. The changing face of genus *Homo. Evol. Anthrop.* **8**, 195-207 (2000).

20. Harrison, T. in *Species, Species Concepts, and Primate Evolution* (eds Kimbel, W. H. & Martin, L. B.) 345-371 (Plenum, New York, 1993).

21. Kimbel, W. H. Identification of a partial cranium of *Australopithecus afarensis* from the Koobi Fora Formation. *J. Hum. Evol.* **17**, 647-656 (1988).

22. Harris, J. M., Brown, F. & Leakey, M. G. Stratigraphy and paleontology of Pliocene and Pleistocene localities west of Lake Turkana, Kenya. *Cont. Sci. Nat. Hist. Mus. Los Angeles* **399**, 1-128 (1988).

23. Feibel, C. S., Brown, F. H. & McDougall, I. Stratigraphic context of fossil hominids from the Omo Group deposits, northern Turkana Basin, Kenya and Ethiopia. *Am. J. Phys. Anthrop.* **78**, 595-622 (1989).

24. McDougall, I., Brown, F. H., Cerling, T. E. & Hillhouse, J. W. A reappraisal of the geomagnetic polarity time scale to 4 Ma using data from the Turkana Basin, East Africa. *Geophys. Res. Lett.* **19**, 2349-2352 (1992).

25. Walter, R. C. & Aronson, J. L. Age and source of the Sidi Hakoma Tuff, Hadar Formation, Ethiopia. *J. Hum. Evol.* **25**, 229-240 (1993).

26. Brown, F. H. & Feibel, C. S. in *Koobi Fora Research Project*, Vol. 3, *Stratigraphy, artiodactyls and paleoenvironments* (ed. Harris, J. M.) 1-30 (Clarendon, Oxford, 1991).

27. Feibel, C. S., Harris, J. M. & Brown, F. H. in *Koobi Fora Research Project*, Vol. 3, *Stratigraphy, artiodactyls and paleoenvironments* (ed. Harris, J. M.) 321-346 (Clarendon, Oxford, 1991).

28. Johanson, D. C., Taieb, M. & Coppens, Y. Pliocene hominids from the Hadar Formation, Ethiopia (1973-1977): stratigraphic, chronologic and paleoenvironmental contexts, with notes on hominid morphology and systematics. *Am. J. Phys. Anthrop.* **57**, 373-402 (1982).

29. Brunet, M. *et al.* The first australopithecine 2,500 kilometres west of the Rift Valley (Chad). *Nature* **378**, 273-240 (1995).

30. Leakey, M. D. & Harris, J. M. *Laetoli, a Pliocene Site in Northern Tanzania* (Clarendon, Oxford, 1987).

31. Harris, J. M. in *Laetoli, a Pliocene Site in Northern Tanzania* (eds Leakey, M. D. & Harris, J. M.) 524-531 (Clarendon, Oxford, 1987).

32. Kimbel, W. H. *et al.* Late Pliocene *Homo* and Oldowan tools from the Hadar Formation (Kadar Hadar Member), Ethiopia. *J. Hum. Evol.* **31**, 549-561 (1996).

33. Eck, G. G. in *Theropithecus, the Rise and Fall of a Primate Genus* (ed. Jablonski, N. G.) 15-83 (Cambridge Univ. Press, 1993).

34. White, T. D. New fossil hominids from Laetolil, Tanzania. *Am. J. Phys. Anthrop.* **46**, 197-230 (1977).

35. Wood, B. Origin and evolution of the genus *Homo. Nature* **355**, 783-790 (1992).

36. Suwa, G. *et al.* The first skull of *Australopithecus boisei. Nature* **389**, 489-492 (1997).

37. Keyser, A. W. The Drimolen skull: the most complete australopithecine cranium and mandible to date. *S. Afr. J. Sci.* **96**, 189-193 (2000).

38. Kimbel, W. H., White, T. D. & Johanson, D. C. Cranial morphology of *Australopithecus afarensis*: a comparative study based on a composite reconstruction of the adult skull. *Am. J. Phys. Anthrop.* **64**, 337-388 (1984).

39. Walker, A., Leakey, R. E., Harris, J. H. & Brown, F. H. 2.5-Myr *Australopithecus boisei* from west of Lake Turkana, Kenya. *Nature* **322**, 517-522 (1986).

40. Kimbel, W. H., White, T. D. & Johanson, D. C. in *Evolutionary History of the "Robust" Australopithecines* (ed. Grine, F. E.) 259-268 (Aldine de Gruyter, New York, 1988).

41. Asfaw, B. *et al. Australopithecus garhi*: A new species of early hominid from Ethiopia. *Science* **284**, 629-635 (1999).

42. Grine, F. E. & Strait, D. S. New hominid fossils from Member 1 "Hanging Remnant" Swartkrans Formation, South Africa. *J. Hum. Evol.* **26**, 57-75 (1994).

43. Johanson, D. C., White, T. D. & Coppens, Y. Dental remains from the Hadar Formation, Ethiopia: 1974-1977 collections. *Am. J. Phys. Anthrop.* **57**, 545-603 (1982).

44. Tobias, P. V. in *Olduvai Gorge* Vol. 4 (Cambridge Univ. Press, 1991).

45. McDougall, I. K-Ar and ^{40}Ar/^{39}Ar dating of the hominid-bearing Pliocene-Pleistocene sequence at Koobi Fora, Lake Turkana, northern Kenya. *Geol. Soc. Am. Bull.* **96**, 159-175 (1985).

46. Brown, F. H., Shuey, R. T. & Croes, M. K. Magnetostratigraphy of the Shungura and Usno Formations, southwestern Ethiopia: new data and comprehensive reanalysis. *Geophys. J. R. Astron. Soc.* **54**, 519-538 (1978).

47. Haileab, B. *Geochemistry, Geochronology and Tephrostratigraphy of Tephra from the Turkana Basin, Southern Ethiopia and Northern Kenya*. Thesis, Univ. Utah (1995).

48. deMenocal, P. B. & Brown, F. H. in *Hominin Evolution and Climatic Change in Europe* Vol. 1 (eds Agustí, J., Rook, L. & Andrews, P.) 23-54 (Cambridge Univ. Press, 1999).

49. Senut, B. *et al.* First hominid from the Miocene (Lukeino Formation, Kenya). *C.R. Acad. Sci. Paris* **332**,137-144 (2001).

Supplementary information is available on *Nature*'s World-Wide Web site (http://www.nature.com) or as paper copy from the London editorial office of *Nature*.

Acknowledgements. We thank the Government of Kenya for permission to carry out this research and the National Museums of Kenya for logistical support. The National Geographic Society funded the field work and some laboratory studies. Neutron irradiations were facilitated by the Australian Institute of Nuclear Science and Engineering and the Australian Nuclear Science and Technology Organisation. We also thank the Ethiopian Ministry of Information and Culture, the National

Museum of Ethiopia, B. Asfaw, Y. Bayene, C. Howell, D. Johanson, W. Kimbel, G. Suwa and T. White for permission to make comparisons with the early Ethiopian hominins and numerous people including N. Adamali, B. Asfaw, C. Dean, C. Feibel, A. Griffiths, W. Kimbel, R. Kruszynski, K. Kupczik, R. Leakey, D. Lieberman, J. Moore, K. Patel, D. Plummer, K. Reed, B. Sokhi, M. Tighe, T. White, and B. Wood for their help. Caltex (Kenya) provided fuel for the field expeditions, and R. Leakey allowed us the use of his aeroplane. The field expedition members included U. Bwana, S. Crispin, G. Ekalale, M. Eragae, J. Erus, J. Ferraro, J. Kaatho, N. Kaling, P. Kapoko, R. Lorinyok, J. Lorot, S. Hagemann, B. Malika, W. Mangao, S. Muge, P. Mulinge , D. Mutinda, K. Muthyoka, N. Mutiwa, W. Mutiwa, B. Onyango, E. Weston and J. Wynn. A. Ibui, F. Kyalo, F. Kirera, N. Malit, E. Mbua, M. Muungu, J. Ndunda, S. Ngui and A. Mwai provided curatorial assistance. The Leakey Foundation awarded a grant to F.B.

Correspondence and requests for materials should be addressed to M.G.L. (e-mail: meave@swiftkenya.com).

Observation of High-energy Neutrinos Using Čerenkov Detectors Embedded Deep in Antarctic Ice

E. Andrés *et al.*

Editor's Note

Neutrinos are chargeless and almost massless elementary particles. They interact with other matter only through the weak force, and therefore can penetrate large amounts of matter— neutrinos from the Sun are constantly streaming through the Earth. This weak interaction makes them difficult to detect. Here an international team of scientists report a proof-of-concept experiment called AMANDA, in which they set detectors in clear ice in the Antarctic and looked for the characteristic flashes of light emitted when a particle called a muon is created by interaction of a neutrino with an atomic nucleus. A subsequent project using a much larger volume of ice as the detector, called IceCube, is now operating near the South Pole.

Neutrinos are elementary particles that carry no electric charge and have little mass. As they interact only weakly with other particles, they can penetrate enormous amounts of matter, and therefore have the potential to directly convey astrophysical information from the edge of the Universe and from deep inside the most cataclysmic high-energy regions[1]. The neutrino's great penetrating power, however, also makes this particle difficult to detect. Underground detectors have observed low-energy neutrinos from the Sun and a nearby supernova[2], as well as neutrinos generated in the Earth's atmosphere. But the very low fluxes of high-energy neutrinos from cosmic sources can be observed only by much larger, expandable detectors in, for example, deep water[3,4] or ice[5]. Here we report the detection of upwardly propagating atmospheric neutrinos by the ice-based Antarctic muon and neutrino detector array (AMANDA). These results establish a technology with which to build a kilometre-scale neutrino observatory necessary for astrophysical observations[1].

HIGH-ENERGY neutrinos must be generated in the same astrophysical sources that produce high-energy cosmic rays[1]. These sources are a matter of speculation, but are thought to reside in shocked or violent environments such as are found in supernova remnants, active galactic nuclei, and gamma-ray bursters. The interaction of any high-energy proton or nucleus with matter or radiation in the source will produce neutrinos, some of which will have line-of-sight trajectories to Earth. AMANDA detects neutrinos with energies above a few tens of GeV by observing the Čerenkov radiation from muons that are produced in neutrino–nucleon interactions in the ice surrounding the detector

借助南极冰下深处的切伦科夫
探测器观测高能中微子

安德烈斯等

编者按

中微子是无电荷且几乎无质量的基本粒子。它们只能通过弱力与其他物质相互作用，因此可以穿透大量物质——来自太阳的中微子就不断地流经地球。这种弱相互作用使中微子难以被检测。本文中，一个国际科学家团队报告了名为 AMANDA 的概念验证型实验，他们将探测器设置在南极透明的冰层中，并寻找由中微子与原子核相互作用而产生的被称为 μ 子的粒子发出的特征性闪光。随后的冰立方（IceCube）项目使用更大体量的冰作为探测器，目前已在南极附近运行。

中微子是一种不携带电荷且质量极小的基本粒子。由于这类粒子与其他粒子的相互作用很弱，能够穿透大量的物质，因此很可能可以直接传递来自宇宙边缘以及大部分高能激变区域深处的天体物理信息[1]。然而，中微子极强的穿透力也使得对该粒子的探测变得非常困难。在以前的研究中，研究人员通过地下探测器已经探测到来自太阳和附近超新星的低能中微子[2]，以及地球大气中产生的中微子。但是，来自宇宙源的高能中微子通量很低，只能通过更大的、可扩展的探测器才能观测到，比如放置于深水[3,4]或冰[5]中的探测器。本文将报道通过基于冰的南极 μ 子和中微子探测器阵列（AMANDA）对向上传播的大气中微子的探测。这些结果将确立一种技术，可以用于建设千米尺度的中微子天文台，从而用于天体物理的观测[1]。

发射高能宇宙射线的天体物理源也必然产生高能中微子[1]。这些源目前尚属推测，但是一般认为存在于极端剧烈环境中，比如超新星遗迹、活动星系核和伽马射线暴。这些源中，任何高能质子或原子核与物质或辐射相互作用，都会产生中微子，其中一些将具有指向地球的视线径迹。中微子与探测器周围冰层或底下岩床中的核子相互作用可以产生 μ 子。通过探测 μ 子发出的切伦科夫辐射，AMANDA 可以探测到能量高于数十 GeV 的中微子[6]。图 1 给出了我们用于探测切伦科夫辐射的光

or in the bedrock below[6]. This Čerenkov light is detected by an array of photomultiplier tubes (Fig. 1), which are buried deep in the ice in order to minimize the downward flux of muons produced in cosmic-ray interactions in the atmosphere. These muons constitute the main background for AMANDA. To ensure that the detected muons are produced by a neutrino, we use the Earth as a filter and look for upwardly propagating muons that perforce must have been produced by a neutrino that passed through the Earth. From the relative arrival times of the Čerenkov photons, measured with a precision of a few nanoseconds, we can reconstruct the track of the muon. The direction of the neutrino and muon are collinear within an angle $\theta_{\nu\text{-}\mu} \approx 1.5/\sqrt{E_\nu}$ degrees, where E_ν is measured in TeV, thus enabling us to search for point sources of high energy neutrinos.

Fig. 1. The AMANDA-B10 detector and a schematic diagram of an optical module. Each dot represents an optical module. The modules are separated by 20 m on the inner strings (1 to 4), and by 10 m on the outer strings (5 to 10). The coloured circles show pulses from the photomultipliers for a particular event; the sizes of the circles indicate the amplitudes of the pulses and the colours correspond to the time of a photon's arrival. Earlier times are in red and later ones in blue. The arrow indicates the reconstructed track of the upwardly propagating muon.

Upwardly propagating atmospheric neutrinos are a well understood source that can be used to verify the detection technique. The results reported here are from analyses of experimental data acquired in 138 days of net operating time during the Antarctic winter of 1997. At that time the detector consisted of 302 optical modules deployed on ten strings at depths of between 1,500 m and 2,000 m (Fig. 1). The instrumented volume is a cylinder of approximately 120 m in diameter and 500 m in height. An optical module consists of an 8-inch photomultiplier tube housed in a glass pressure vessel. A cable provides the high voltage and transmits the anode current signals to the data acquisition electronics at the surface. Figure 1 also shows a representative event that has satisfied the selection criteria for an upwardly moving muon. The effective detection area for muons varies from about

电倍增管阵列，它们被埋设于冰层深处，以最大限度地减小大气中宇宙射线相互作用产生的 μ 子的向下通量。这些大气 μ 子构成了 AMANDA 的主要背景信号。为了确保探测到的 μ 子确实产生于中微子，我们将整个地球作为一个大过滤器，探测那些一定是由穿过地球的中微子产生的向上传播的 μ 子。探测器探测到的切伦科夫光子的相对到达时间的精度在纳秒量级，我们通过记录这些到达时间可以重建 μ 子的径迹。中微子与 μ 子的方向在夹角 $\theta_{\nu\text{-}\mu} \approx 1.5$ 度$/(E_\nu)^{1/2}$ 内共线，其中 E_ν 单位为 TeV，这可以使我们寻找到高能中微子点源。

图 1. AMANDA-B10 探测器及其光学模块原理图。图中每个小点代表一个光学模块。在内部串，光学模块之间的距离为 20 m(1 到 4)；在外部串，模块之间的距离为 10 m(5 到 10)。不同颜色的圆圈表示某个事例中光电倍增管产生的脉冲，其中圆圈的尺寸大小代表该脉冲的幅度，颜色对应光子到达的时间。较早的时间用红色表示，较晚的时间用蓝色表示。图中箭头表示斜向上运动的 μ 子的重建径迹。

向上传播的大气中微子作为源已经为人们所了解，因此可以用大气中微子验证我们的探测技术。我们分析了在 1997 年南极冬季获取的 138 天净运转时间的实验数据，并将结果在本文中予以报告。当时，实验采用的探测器由 302 个光学模块构成，这些模块埋设为 10 串，深度在 1,500 m 到 2,000 m 之间（图 1）。整个探测器设备是一个圆柱体，其直径大约为 120 m，高度约为 500 m。每个光学模块包括一个封装于玻璃质压力容器中的 8 英寸光电倍增管。一根电缆用于提供光电倍增管所需的高电压，并将阳极电流信号传输到位于地面的数据采集电子设备。图 1 中也给出了一个满足向上运动的 μ 子选择标准的典型事件。根据 μ 子能量的不同，探测系统的有效

3,000 m^2 at 100 GeV to about 4×10^4 m^2 for the higher-energy muons ($\geqslant$ 100 TeV) that would be produced by neutrinos coming from, for example, the same cosmic sources that produce gamma-ray bursts[7].

Because a knowledge of the optical properties of the ice is essential for track reconstruction, these have been studied extensively[8,9]. The absorption length of blue and ultraviolet light (the relevant wavelengths for our purposes) varies between 85 m and 225 m, depending on depth. The effective scattering length, which combines the mean free path λ with the average scattering angle θ through $\lambda/(1 - \langle\cos\theta\rangle)$, varies from 15 m to 40 m. In order to reconstruct the muon tracks we use a maximum-likelihood method, which incorporates the scattering and absorption of photons as determined from calibration measurements. A bayesian formulation of the likelihood takes into account the much larger rate of downward muons relative to the upward signal and is particularly effective in decreasing the chance for a downward muon to be mis-reconstructed as upward. (See refs 6 and 10–13 for more information on optical properties of ice, calibration, and analysis techniques.)

Certain types of events that might appear to be upwardly propagating muons must be considered and eliminated. Rare cases, such as muons that undergo catastrophic energy loss through bremsstrahlung, or that are coincident with other muons, must be investigated. To this end, a series of requirements or quality criteria, based on the characteristic time and spatial pattern of photons associated with a muon track and the response of our detector, are applied to all events that, in a first assessment, appear to be upwardly moving muons. For example, an event that has a large number of optical modules hit by prompt (that is, unscattered) photons, has a high quality. By making these requirements (or "cuts") increasingly selective, we eliminate correspondingly more of the background of false upward events while still retaining a significant fraction of the true upwardly moving muons. Because there is a large space within which the parameters defining these cuts can be optimized, two different and independent analyses of the same set of data have been undertaken. These analyses yielded comparable numbers of upwardly propagating muons (153 in analysis A, 188 in analysis B). Comparison of these results with their respective Monte Carlo simulations shows that they are consistent with each other in terms of the number of events, the number of events in common and, as discussed below, the expected properties of atmospheric neutrinos.

In Fig. 2a, the number of experimental events is compared to simulations of background and signal as a function of the (identical) quality requirements placed on the three types of events: experimental data, simulated upwardly moving muons from atmospheric neutrinos, and a simulated background of downwardly moving cosmic-ray muons. For simplicity in presentation, the levels of the individual cuts have been combined into a single parameter representing the overall event quality. Figure 2b shows ratios of the quantities plotted above. As the quality level is increased, the ratios of simulated background to experimental data, and of experimental data to simulated signal, both continue their rapid decrease, the former toward zero and the latter toward 0.7. Over the same range, the ratio of experimental data to the simulated sum of background and signal remains nearly constant. We conclude that

探测面积范围从 3,000 m² 到 40,000 m²，对应从 100 GeV 到高能 μ 子（≥ 100 TeV）的情形，产生后者的中微子应该来自宇宙源，比如同样产生伽马射线暴的宇宙源[7]。

为了重建中微子的径迹，首先要弄清冰的光学特性。人们对此已进行了广泛的研究[8,9]。根据冰层深度的不同，蓝光和紫外光（我们所用的相关波长）的吸收长度在 85 m 到 225 m 之间变化。由平均自由程 λ 和平均散射角 θ 构成的有效散射长度 $λ/(1 - \langle \cos θ \rangle)$ 为 15～40 m。我们采用最大似然方法重建 μ 子径迹，考虑了通过刻度测量得到的光子的散射和吸收。考虑到向下 μ 子的事例率远远大于向上的信号，对似然值的贝叶斯分析可以有效减小将向下 μ 子错误重建为向上 μ 子的可能性。（参考文献 6 以及 10～13 介绍了更多关于冰的光学特性、刻度以及分析技术。）

在探测过程中，可能存在某些看似是向上传播的 μ 子的伪事件，对这种情况必须予以考虑并剔除。同时，也必须要考虑那些罕见的情况，比如 μ 子经过韧致辐射损失了大部分能量，或者与其他 μ 子同时出现的情况。为此，一系列基于 μ 子径迹预期产生的光子时间和空间特征图样以及基于探测器的响应的要求或者说质量标准在首次评估中用于筛选那些看似是向上运动的 μ 子事件。比如，瞬发（即未被散射）光子触发大量光学模块，该事件就具有较高的品质。通过不断提高选择的标准（或者说"判选"），我们可以相应地剔除更多的向上 μ 子伪事件背景，同时仍然保留大部分真正向上运动的 μ 子。由于构成筛选标准的各参数具有较大的优化空间，我们对相同的实验数据进行了两种不同且互相独立的分析，分别称为 A 分析和 B 分析。A、B 两种分析结果给出的向上运动的 μ 子数目相当，分别为 153 和 188。这两个结果分别与其相应的蒙特卡罗模拟进行比较，发现二者在事件数目、共同事件数目以及如下所述的大气中微子预期特性方面彼此一致。

如图 2a 所示，我们将实验事件的数量与背景和信号的模拟结果作为（相同）品质判据的函数进行了对比，对以下三类事件——实验数据、模拟的大气中微子产生的向上运动的 μ 子、模拟的向下运动的宇宙射线 μ 子背景——进行了分析。为了简化演示，多个筛选标准合并成了一个代表整体事件品质的参数。图 2b 显示了图 2a 绘制的数量间的比值。随着品质水平的增加，模拟背景与实验数据的比值以及实验数据与模拟信号的比值，同时迅速减小，其中前者趋于 0 而后者趋于 0.7。在上述范围内，实验数据与另两者（模拟的背景和信号）之和的比值几乎保持不变。因此，我们得出以下结论：品质筛选标准可以剔除实验数据中误重建的向下运动的 μ the quality requirements have reduced the presence of wrongly reconstructed downward muons in the experimental data to a negligible fraction of the signal and that the experimental data behave in the same way as the simulated atmospheric neutrino signal for events that pass the stringent cuts. The estimated uncertainty on the number of events predicted by the signal Monte Carlo simulation, which includes uncertainties in the high-energy atmospheric neutrino flux, the *in situ* sensitivity of the optical modules, and the precise optical properties of the ice, is $+40\%/-50\%$. The observed ratio of experiment to simulation (0.7) and the expectation (1.0) therefore agree within the estimated uncertainties.

Fig. 2. Experimental data confront expectations. The numbers of reconstructed upwardly moving muon events for the experimental data (Exp) from analysis A are compared to simulations of background cosmic-ray muons (BG) and simulations of atmospheric neutrinos (Atm) as a function of "event quality", a variable indicating the combined severity of the cuts designed to enhance the signal. The comparison begins at a quality level of 4. Cuts were made on a number of parameters including the reconstructed zenith angle ($>$ 100 degrees), maximum likelihood of the reconstruction, topological distributions of the detected photons, and the number of optical modules recording unscattered photons. The optimum levels of the cuts were determined by comparing the relative rejection rates for Monte Carlo simulated neutrino events and background events. **b**, Ratios of the quantities shown in **a**.

子，直至与信号相比达到可以忽略的水平；经过严格筛选后，实验数据与模拟大气中微子信号的行为规律相同。蒙特卡罗模拟预测的信号事件数的估算不确定度为+40%/−50%，该不确定度包括了高能大气中微子通量、光学模块的实地灵敏度以及冰层准确光学特性的不确定度。因此，在上述估算不确定度内，观察到的实验和模拟比值（0.7）与期望值（1.0）相符合。

图 2. 实验数据与期望值比较。A 分析中重建实验数据中向上运动的 μ 子事件的数目（用 Exp 表示），与模拟宇宙射线 μ 子背景（BG）以及模拟大气中微子（Atm），作为"事件品质"的函数进行了比较。其中"事件品质"这一变量表示用于增强信号的若干筛选标准的组合的严格程度。图中对比起始于品质水平 4。筛选标准由若干参量构成，这些参量包括重建天顶角（＞100 度）、重建径迹的最大似然值、探测光子的拓扑分布以及记录未散射光子的光学模块数目。通过比较蒙特卡罗模拟中微子事件和背景事件的相对排斥率，可以确定筛选标准的最佳水平。b 图给出了 a 图中数量的比值。

The shape of the zenith-angle distribution of the 188 events from analysis B is compared to a simulation of the atmospheric neutrino signal in Fig. 3, where the absolute Monte Carlo rate has been normalized to the experimental rate. The variation of the measured rate with zenith angle is reproduced by the simulation to within the statistical uncertainty. We note that the tall geometry of the detector favours the more vertical muons. The arrival directions of the upwardly moving muons observed in both analyses are shown in Fig. 4. A statistical analysis indicates no evidence for point sources in these samples. The agreement between experiment and simulation of atmospheric neutrino signal, as demonstrated in Figs 2 and 3, taken together with comparisons for a number of other variables (to be published elsewhere) leads us to conclude that the upcoming muon events observed by AMANDA are produced mainly by atmospheric neutrinos with energies of about 50 GeV to a few TeV. The background in this event sample is estimated to be $15 \pm 7\%$ events, and is due to misreconstructions.

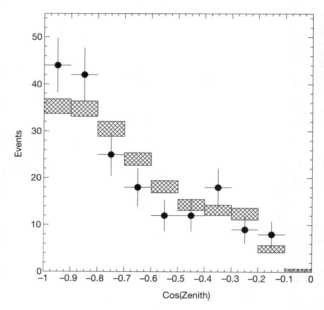

Fig. 3. Reconstructed zenith angle distribution. The data points are experimental data (from analysis B) and the shaded boxes are a simulation of atmospheric neutrino events, the widths of the boxes indicating the error bars. The overall normalization of the simulation has been adjusted to fit the data. The possible effects of neutrino oscillations on the flux and its zenith angle dependence estimated from the Super-Kamiokande measurements[20], are expected to be small in our energy range.

From the consistency of the selected event sample with muons generated by atmospheric neutrinos, and in particular the absence of an excess of high-energy events with a large number of optical modules that had been hit, we can determine an upper limit on a diffuse extraterrestrial neutrino flux. Assuming a hard E^{-2} spectrum characteristic of shockwave acceleration, we expect to reach a sensitivity of order $dN/dE_\nu = 10^{-6} E_\nu^{-2}$ cm^{-2} s^{-1} sr^{-1} GeV^{-1}. This value is low enough to be in the range where a number of models[14-19] predict fluxes, a few of which are larger[15,16]. Most recent estimates are smaller[17-19]. The present level of sensitivity

图 3 给出了 B 分析中 188 个事件的天顶角分布与模拟大气中微子信号的对比，其中蒙特卡罗绝对事例率根据实验值进行了归一化。在统计不确定度之内，测量事例率随天顶角的变化与模拟结果一致。我们注意到，探测器较高的几何尺寸会更利于探测到垂直方向的 μ 子。在 A 和 B 两种分析中，观测到的向上运动的 μ 子的到达方向如图 4 所示。统计分析表明，这些样本尚不足以提供点源存在的证据。图 2 与图 3 已经证明实验与大气中微子信号模拟的一致性；同时对比其他变量（具体研究结果即将发表）的话，我们得出以下结论：AMANDA 观测到的上行 μ 子事件主要是由那些能量介于 50 GeV 到若干 TeV 之间的大气中微子产生。事件样本中的背景事件估计为 15%±7%，这是由于错误的径迹重建造成的。

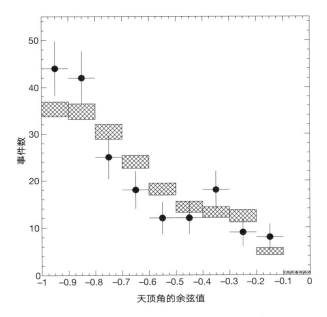

图 3. 重建径迹的天顶角分布。图中数据点是取自分析 B 的实验数据，阴影矩形框表示大气中微子事件的模拟，其中矩形框的宽度代表误差棒。模拟的整体归一化已经经过调整以拟合数据。中微子振荡对通量及通量的天顶角依赖的可能影响可以通过超级神冈实验的测量估算出来[20]，在我们研究的能量范围内，该影响预计很小。

根据筛选的事件样本与大气中微子产生的 μ 子的一致性，特别是触发大量光学模块的高能事件不存在超出的情况下，我们可以确定地外弥散中微子通量的上限。假设激波加速具有 E^{-2} 形式的硬谱特征，那么我们预计灵敏度的量级将达到 $\mathrm{d}N/\mathrm{d}E_v = 10^{-6} E_v^{-2}\ \mathrm{cm}^{-2} \cdot \mathrm{s}^{-1} \cdot \mathrm{sr}^{-1} \cdot \mathrm{GeV}^{-1}$。该值很小，位于很多模型预测的通量范围之内[14-19]，其中一些通量会更大些[15,16]。不过近期的估算值大多数相对更小[17-19]。我们设想可

and the prospects for improving it through longer exposure times and better determination of muon energy illustrate the ability of large-area detectors to test theoretical models that assume the hadronic origin of TeV photons from active galaxies—models which would be difficult to confirm or exclude without the ability to observe high-energy neutrinos.

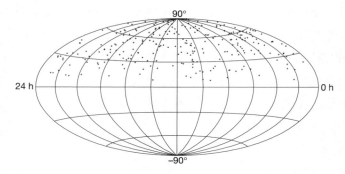

Fig. 4. Distribution in declination and right ascension of the upwardly propagating events on the sky. The 263 events shown here are taken from the upward muons contained in both analysis A and analysis B. The median difference between the true and the reconstructed muon angles is about 3 to 4 degrees.

Searches for neutrinos from gamma-ray bursts, for magnetic monopoles, supernova collapses and for a cold dark matter signal from the centre of the Earth are also in progress and, with only 138 days of data, yield limits comparable to or better than those from smaller underground neutrino detectors that have operated for a much longer period (see refs 10–13).

From 1997 to 1999 an additional nine strings were added in a concentric cylinder around AMANDA-B10. This larger detector, called AMANDA-II, consists of 677 optical modules and has an improved acceptance for muons over a larger angular interval. Data are being taken now with the larger array. Yet the fluxes of very high energy neutrinos predicted by theoretical models[14] or derived from the observed flux of ultra high energy cosmic rays[19] are sufficiently low that a neutrino detector having an effective area up to a square kilometre is required for their observation and study[1,14]. Plans are therefore being made for a much larger detector, IceCube, consisting of 4,800 photomultipliers to be deployed on 80 strings. This proposed neutrino telescope would have an effective area of about 1 km^2, an energy threshold near 100 GeV and a pointing accuracy for muons of better than one degree for high-energy events. In conclusion, the observation of neutrinos by a neutrino telescope deep in the Antarctic ice cap, a goal that was once thought difficult if not impossible, represents an important step toward establishing the field of high-energy neutrino astronomy first envisioned over 40 years ago.

(**410**, 441-443; 2001)

以通过更长时间的曝光以及更好地确定 μ 子的能量来改善灵敏度，目前的灵敏度水平和这些设想说明了大面积探测器检验理论模型的能力。这些理论模型假设活动星系发出的 TeV 能量的光子来源于强子，如果没有观测高能中微子能力，证实或排除这些模型将会非常困难。

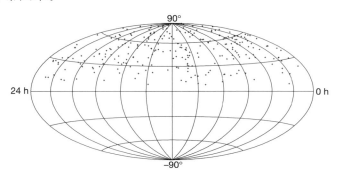

图 4. 向上传播的 μ 子事件在天空中赤纬和赤经上的分布。图中所示的 263 个事件取自 A 和 B 两个分析中包含的共同的上行 μ 子事件。μ 子的真实角度和重建角度之差的中值约为 3～4 度。

寻找来自伽马射线暴的中微子，寻找磁单极子和超新星坍缩，寻找来自地球中心的冷暗物质，这些工作也在进行之中。而且，仅使用 138 天的数据，就可给出与那些已长时间运行的小型地下中微子探测器相媲美或更好的上限（见参考文献 10～13）。

从 1997 年到 1999 年，在 AMANDA-B10 周围的同心圆柱体中又添加了 9 串探测器。这个更大的探测器被称为 AMANDA-II，由 677 个光学模块构成，在更大的角度范围内改善了 μ 子的接收度。目前，这个更巨大的阵列正在采集数据。但是无论是理论模型预言[14]还是由超高能宇宙射线通量观测值推导出的[19]高能中微子通量都是非常低的，以至于为了观测研究这些中微子，探测器的有效面积需要达到一平方千米[1,14]。所以，目前正在计划研制更大的探测器，该探测器被称为冰立方（IceCube），由分布在 80 根串上的 4,800 个光电倍增管构成。这一计划中的中微子探测器将具有 1 km² 大小的有效面积，其探测能量阈值接近 100 GeV，对于高能事件的 μ 子的指向精度优于 1 度。总而言之，通过南极冰盖下的中微子望远镜观测到中微子意味着人们朝 40 多年前就试图建立的高能中微子天文学研究领域迈出了重要的一步，尽管这一设想一度被认为是极难甚至是无法实现的目标。

（金世超 翻译；曹俊 审稿）

E. Andrés[*], P. Askebjer[†], X. Bai[‡], G. Barouch[*], S. W. Barwick[§], R. C. Bay[‖], K.-H. Becker[¶], L. Bergström[†], D. Bertrand[#], D. Bierenbaum[§], A. Biron[☆], J. Booth[§], O. Botner[**], A. Bouchta[☆], M. M. Boyce[*], S. Carius[††], A. Chen[*], D. Chirkin[‖ ¶], J. Conrad[**], J. Cooley[*], C. G. S. Costa[#], D. F. Cowen[‡‡], J. Dailing[§], E. Dalberg[†], T. DeYoung[*], P. Desiati[☆], J.-P. Dewulf[#], P. Doksus[*], J. Edsjö[†], P. Ekström[†], B. Erlandsson[†], T. Feser[§§], M. Gaug[☆], A. Goldschmidt[‖‖], A. Goobar[†], L. Gray[*], H. Haase[☆], A. Hallgren[**], F. Halzen[*], K. Hanson[‡‡], R. Hardtke[*], Y. D. He[‖], M. Hellwig[§§], H. Heukenkamp[☆], G. C. Hill[*], P. O. Hulth[†], S. Hundertmark[§], J. Jacobsen[‖‖], V. Kandhadai[*], A. Karle[*], J. Kim[§], B. Koci[*], L. Köpke[§§], M. Kowalski[☆], H. Leich[☆], M. Leuthold[☆], P. Lindahl[††], I. Liubarsky[*], P. Loaiza[**], D. M. Lowder[‖], J. Ludvig[‖‖], J. Madsen[*], P. Marciniewski[**], H. S. Matis[‖‖], A. Mihalyi[‡‡], T. Mikolajski[☆], T. C. Miller[‡], Y. Minaeva[†], P. Miočinović[‖], P. C. Mock[§], R. Morse[*], T. Neunhöffer[§§], F. M. Newcomer[‡‡], P. Niessen[☆], D. R. Nygren[‖‖], H. Ögelman[*], C. Pérez de los Heros[**], R. Porrata[§], P. B. Price[‖], K. Rawlins[*], C. Reed[§], W. Rhode[¶], A. Richards[‖], S. Richter[☆], J. Rodríguez Martino[†], P. Romenesko[*], D. Ross[§], H. Rubinstein[†], H.-G. Sander[§§], T. Scheider[§§], T. Schmidt[☆], D. Schneider[*], E. Schneider[§], R. Schwarz[*], A. Silvestri[¶ *], M. Solarz[‖], G. M. Spiczak[‡], C. Spiering[☆], N. Starinsky[*], D. Steele[*], P. Steffen[☆], R. G. Stokstad[‖‖], O. Streicher[☆], Q. Sun[†], I. Taboada[‡‡], L. Thollander[†], T. Thon[☆], S. Tilav[*], N. Usechak[*], M. Vander Donckt[#], C. Walck[†], C. Weinheimer[§§], C. H. Wiebusch[☆], R. Wischnewski[☆], H. Wissing[☆], K. Woschnagg[‖], W. Wu[§], G. Yodh[§] & S. Young[§]

[*] Department of Physics, University of Wisconsin, Wisconsin, Madison 53706, USA
[†] Fysikum, Stockholm University, S-11385 Stockholm, Sweden
[‡] Bartol Research Institute, University of Delaware, Newark, Delaware 19716, USA
[§] Department of Physics and Astronomy, University of California, Irvine, California 92697, USA
[‖] Department of Physics, University of California, Berkeley, California 94720, USA
[¶] Fachbereich 8 Physik, BUGH Wuppertal, D-42097 Wuppertal, Germany
[#] Brussels Free University, Science Faculty CP230, Boulevard du Triomphe, B-1050 Brussels, Belgium
[☆] DESY-Zeuthen, D-15735 Zeuthen, Germany
[**] Department of Radiation Sciences, Uppsala University, S-75121 Uppsala, Sweden
[††] Department of Technology, Kalmar University, S-39129 Kalmar, Sweden
[‡‡] Department of Physics and Astronomy, University of Pennsylvania, Philadelphia, Pennsylvania 19104, USA
[§§] Institute of Physics, University of Mainz, Staudinger Weg 7, D-55099 Mainz, Germany
[‖‖] Institute for Nuclear and Particle Astrophysics, Lawrence Berkeley National Laboratory, Berkeley, California 94720, USA

Received 15 September 2000; accepted 25 January 2001.

References:

1. Gaisser, T. K., Halzen, F. & Stanev, T. Particle physics with high-energy neutrinos. *Phys. Rep.* **258**, 173-236 (1995).

2. Totsuka, Y. Neutrino astronomy. *Rep. Prog. Phys.* **55**, 377-430 (1992).

3. Roberts, A. The birth of high-energy neutrino astronomy: A personal history of the DUMAND project. *Rev. Mod. Phys.* **64**, 259-312 (1992).

4. Balkanov, V. A. *et al.* An upper limit on the diffuse flux of high energy neutrinos obtained with the Baikal detector NT-96. *Astropart. Phys.* **14**, 61-67 (2000).

5. Lowder, D. M. *et al.* Observation of muons using the polar ice as a Čerenkov detector. *Nature* **353**, 331-333 (1991).

6. Andres, E. *et al.* The AMANDA neutrino telescope: Principle of operation and first results. *Astropart. Phys.* **13**, 1-20 (2000).

7. Waxman, E. & Bahcall, J. N. High-energy neutrinos from cosmological gamma ray burst fireballs. *Phys. Rev. Lett.* **78**, 2992-2295 (1997).

8. Askjeber, P. *et al.* Optical properties of the south pole ice at depths between 0.8 and 1 km. *Science* **267**, 1147-1150 (1995).

9. Price, B. P. Implications of optical properties of ocean, lake, and ice for ultrahigh-energy neutrino detection. *Appl. Opt.* **36**, 1965-1975 (1997).

10. Wischnewski, R. *et al.* in *Proc. 26th Int. Cosmic Ray Conf., Salt Lake City* Vol. 2 (eds Kieda, D., Salamon, M. & Dingus, B.) 229-232 (1999).

11. Dalberg, E. *et al.* in *Proc. 26th Int. Cosmic Ray Conf., Salt Lake City* Vol. 2 (eds Kieda, D., Salamon, M. & Dingus, B.) 348-351 (1999).

12. Bay, R. *et al.* in *Proc. 26th Int. Cosmic Ray Conf., Salt Lake City* Vol. 2 (eds Kieda, D., Salamon, M. & Dingus, B.) 225-228 (1999).

13. Niessen, P. *et al.* in *Proc. 26th Int. Cosmic Ray Conf., Salt Lake City* Vol. 2 (eds Kieda, D., Salamon, M. & Dingus, B.) 344-347 (1999).

14. Learned, J. G. & Mannheim, K. High-energy neutrino astrophysics. *Ann. Rev. Nucl. Sci.* **50**, 679-749 (2000).

15. Szabo, A. P. & Protheroe, R. J. Implications of particle acceleration in active galactic nuclei for cosmic rays and high-energy neutrino astronomy. *Astropart. Phys.* **2**, 375-392 (1994).

16. Stecker, F. W. & Salamon, M. H. High-energy neutrinos from quasars. *Space Sci. Rev.* **75**, 341-355 (1996).

17. Nellen, L., Mannheim, K. & Biermann, P. L. Neutrino production through hadronic cascades in AGN accretion disks. *Phys. Rev. D* **47**, 5270-5274 (1993).

18. Mannheim, K., Protheroe, R. J. & Rachen, J. P. Cosmic ray bound for models of extragalactic neutrino production. *Phys. Rev. D* **63**, 023003-1–023003-16 (2001).

19. Waxman, E. & Bahcall, J. N. High energy neutrinos from astrophysical sources. An upper bound. *Phys. Rev. D* **59**, 023002-1–023002-8 (1999).

20. Fukuda, Y. *et al.* (Super-Kamiokande Collaboration) Measurement of the flux and zenith-angle distribution of upward through-going muons by Super-Kamiokande. *Phys. Rev. Lett.* **82**, 2644-2648 (1999).

Acknowledgements. This research was supported by the following agencies: US National Science Foundation, Office of Polar Programs; US National Science Foundation, Physics Division; University of Wisconsin Alumni Research Foundation; US Department of Energy; Swedish Natural Science Research Council; Swedish Polar Research Secretariat; Knut and Allice Wallenberg Foundation, Sweden; German Ministry for Education and Research; US National Energy Research Scientific Computing Center (supported by the Office of Energy Research of the US Department of Energy); UC-Irvine AENEAS Supercomputer Facility; Deutsche Forschungsgemeinschaft (DFG). D.F.C. acknowledges the support of the NSF CAREER programme and C.P.d.l.H. acknowledges support from the European Union 4th Framework of Training and Mobility of Researchers.

Correspondence and requests for materials should be addressed to F.H. (e-mail: halzen@pheno.physics.wisc.edu).

Linkage Disequilibrium in the Human Genome

D. E. Reich *et al.*

Editor's Note

By this time, it was known that single nucleotide polymorphisms (SNPs)—the single-letter DNA changes thought to underlie disease susceptibility and individual variation—"travel" together, with one SNP carrying information about its SNP neighbours. So armed with the recent SNP map, geneticist Eric Lander and colleagues set out to see if the method of linkage disequilibrium (LD), where blocks of SNPs are correlated back to an ancestral chromosome, can be used to map disease-causing genes. This study shows, at least in the northern European population tested, that using LD to map disease-related genes might be easier and more practical than had been thought. The results also shed light on human history, suggesting this particular LD pattern might reflect the relatively recent migration of anatomically modern humans.

With the availability of a dense genome-wide map of single nucleotide polymorphisms (SNPs)[1], a central issue in human genetics is whether it is now possible to use linkage disequilibrium (LD) to map genes that cause disease. LD refers to correlations among neighbouring alleles, reflecting "haplotypes" descended from single, ancestral chromosomes. The size of LD blocks has been the subject of considerable debate. Computer simulations[2] and empirical data[3] have suggested that LD extends only a few kilobases (kb) around common SNPs, whereas other data have suggested that it can extend much further, in some cases greater than 100 kb[4-6]. It has been difficult to obtain a systematic picture of LD because past studies have been based on only a few (1–3) loci and different populations. Here, we report a large-scale experiment using a uniform protocol to examine 19 randomly selected genomic regions. LD in a United States population of north-European descent typically extends 60 kb from common alleles, implying that LD mapping is likely to be practical in this population. By contrast, LD in a Nigerian population extends markedly less far. The results illuminate human history, suggesting that LD in northern Europeans is shaped by a marked demographic event about 27,000–53,000 years ago.

TO characterize LD systematically around genes, each of the 19 regions that we studied was anchored at a "core" SNP in the coding region of a gene. The core SNP was chosen from a database of more than 3,000 coding SNPs that had been identified by screening in a multi-ethnic panel (see Methods), subject to two requirements. First, "finished" genomic sequence was available for 160 kb in at least one direction from the core SNP; second, the frequency of the minor (less common) allele was at least 35% in the multi-ethnic panel.

人类基因组中的连锁不平衡

赖希等

编者按

如今众所周知，单核苷酸多态性（SNP）——被认为影响疾病的易感性和个体差异性的 DNA 单个碱基变化——是结伴"旅行"的，即一个 SNP 会携带关于其邻位的信息。因此，结合目前的 SNP 图谱，遗传学家埃瑞克·兰德及其同事着手研究连锁不平衡（LD，即 SNP 的板块都和一个祖先染色体相关联的）的方法能否被用于发现致病基因。本研究显示，至少在北欧人群的测试中，利用 LD 来寻找致病基因也许比预想的要更简单更实际。该结果还可用于阐释人类历史，提示这种独特的 LD 模式可能反映出解剖学上现代人类的迁徙。

随着高密度全基因组单核苷酸多态性（SNP）图谱的获得[1]，人类遗传学的一个核心问题就是现在是否有可能利用连锁不平衡（LD）绘制出致病基因图谱。LD 指的是相邻等位基因之间的相互联系，表现为来自单一祖先染色体的"单体型"。LD 区域的大小一直是争议的焦点。计算机模拟[2]和经验性数据[3]显示 LD 位于常见 SNP 周围，大约只延伸数千个碱基（kb），而其他数据显示其范围更广，在某些情况下可能大于 100 kb[4-6]。一直以来，LD 的系统性图谱难以获得，因为过去的研究都仅仅基于几个（1~3）位点以及不同的人群。本文我们报告一个采用了统一规范，针对 19 个随机选取的基因组区域的大规模实验。结果发现拥有北欧血统的美国人群其 LD 一般从常见等位位点延伸 60 kb，说明在这一群体中进行 LD 图谱的绘制是可行的。相反，在一个尼日利亚人群中，LD 区域的缩短十分明显。这些结果勾画出人类演化历史，提示大约 27,000~53,000 年前的某个重大的人口统计学事件导致了北欧人群中 LD 的形成。

为了系统性地鉴定基因附近的 LD，在我们研究的 19 个区域中，每个区域都在其编码区内锚定了一个"核心"SNP。核心 SNP 选自一个含有超过 3,000 个编码 SNP 的数据库，这些 SNP 从多民族人群筛查中选定（见方法），要求满足以下两个条件。其一，从核心 SNP 起始，至少一个方向上 160 kb 范围内可获得完整基因组序列；其二，次等位基因位点（频率较低的那个位点）在这个多族群数据库中的频率至少为 35%。

We focused on high-frequency SNPs for several reasons. First, they tend to be of high frequency in all populations[7], facilitating cross-population comparisons. Second, LD around common alleles represents a "worst case" scenario: LD around rare alleles is expected to extend further because such alleles are generally young[8] and there has been less historical opportunity for recombination to break down ancestral haplotypes[2]. Third, LD around common alleles can be measured with a modest sample size of 80–100 chromosomes to a precision within 10–20% of the asymptotic limit (see Methods). Last, LD around common alleles will probably be particularly relevant to the search for genes predisposing to common disease[9].

To identify SNPs at various distances from the core SNP, we resequenced subregions of around 2 kb centred at distances 0, 5, 10, 20, 40, 80 and 160 kb in one direction from the core SNP using 44 unrelated individuals from Utah. Altogether, we screened 251,310 bp (see Methods) and found an average heterozygosity of $\pi = 0.00070$, consistent with past studies[1]. A total of 272 "high frequency" polymorphisms were identified (Table 1).

Table 1. Distribution of regions and SNPs within regions

Gene identification*	Chromosome	Local recombination rate (cM Mb⁻¹)†	Span of region in physical map (cR)‡	Number of high-frequency polymorphisms at distances (kb) from core SNPs§						
				1	5	10	20	40	80	160
BMP8‖	1	1.4	60.88–61.04	1	1	1	2	2	1	3
ACVR2B‖	3	1.1	37.27–37.43	2	1	2	3	0	3	1
TGFBI	5	1.4	152.16–152.00	1	3	1	0	1	7	0
DDR1‖	6	–	46.046–45.89	1	4	1	4	2	2	0
GTF2H4	6	–	46.059–46.22	3	3	3	6	2	0	0
COL11A2‖	6	–	48.27–48.43	1	0	1	2	3	1	1
LAMB1‖	7	2.3	106.58–106.42	0	0	5	3	3	2	4
WASL	7	0.5	122.99–122.83	2	1	0	4	2	2	1
SLC6A12	12	3.3	3.62–3.78	2	8	2	1	6	0	0
KCNA1	12	3.3	8.50–8.66	1	1	5	2	1	1	0
SLC2A3	12	2.1	16.33–16.49	1	2	1	1	5	0	2
ARHGDIB‖	12	1.2	21.84–22	3	9	1	2	2	1	2
PCI‖	14	4.3	98.41–98.57	0	7	0	0	4	14	1
PRKCBI	16	1.0	32.50–32.66	0	2	3	0	4	3	0
NFI	17	1.0	38.10–38.26	1	0	2	2	5	1	0
SCYA2‖	17	3.0	40.21–40.37	0	5	1	1	3	1	1
PAI2	18	2.7	64.17–64.01	2	0	2	1	5	2	10
IL17R‖	22	5.9	14.48–14.32	1	1	2	1	2	0	4
HCF2‖	22	2.0	17.91–17.75	1	1	2	2	1	0	3

* Abbreviations from LocusLink (www.ncbi.nlm.nih.gov/LocusLink/list.cgi).

我们着眼于高频率的 SNP 有以下几点原因。首先，它们倾向于在所有人群中高频出现 [7]，这有利于跨人群的比对。其次，常见等位位点附近的 LD 实际代表了一种"最差"的情况：而罕见位点附近的 LD 能够延伸更长，因为这些等位基因通常出现得比较晚 [8]，历史上发生重组而破坏原始单体型的概率也更低一些 [2]。第三，常见等位基因位点附近的 LD 可以通过对 80 ~ 100 个染色体这样一个适中的样本数量测量获得，精度在渐进极限的 10% ~ 20% 之间（见方法）。最后，常见等位基因位点附近的 LD 很可能与寻找常见疾病易感基因更为相关 [9]。

为了确定距离核心 SNP 不同位置的 SNP，我们选取同一方向上距离核心 SNP 0、5、10、20、40、80 和 160 kb 的位置作为中心，对中心附近 2 kb 的子区域进行重测序，样本来自犹他州 44 个不相关的个体。总体来说，我们对 251,310 个碱基对（见方法）进行了上述筛查，发现平均杂合度 $\pi = 0.00070$，与既往的研究一致 [1]。总共检测到 272 个"高频"多态性位点（表 1）。

表 1. 区域分布以及区域内的 SNP

基因代码 *	染色体	局部重组率 $(cM \cdot Mb^{-1})$ †	物理图谱中该区域的范围 (cR)‡	离核心 SNP 不同距离 (kb) 的高频多态位点数目 §						
				1	5	10	20	40	80	160
BMP8‖	1	1.4	60.88 ~ 61.04	1	1	1	2	2	1	3
ACVR2B‖	3	1.1	37.27 ~ 37.43	2	1	2	3	0	3	1
TGFBI	5	1.4	152.16 ~ 152.00	1	3	1	0	1	7	0
DDR1‖	6	–	46.046 ~ 45.89	1	4	1	4	2	2	0
GTF2H4	6	–	46.059 ~ 46.22	3	3	3	6	2	0	0
COL11A2‖	6	–	48.27 ~ 48.43	1	0	1	2	3	1	1
LAMB1‖	7	2.3	106.58 ~ 106.42	0	0	5	3	3	2	4
WASL	7	0.5	122.99 ~ 122.83	2	1	0	4	2	2	1
SLC6A12	12	3.3	3.62 ~ 3.78	2	8	2	1	6	0	0
KCNA1	12	3.3	8.50 ~ 8.66	1	1	5	2	1	1	0
SLC2A3	12	2.1	16.33 ~ 16.49	1	2	1	1	5	0	2
ARHGDIB‖	12	1.2	21.84 ~ 22	3	9	1	2	2	1	2
PCI‖	14	4.3	98.41 ~ 98.57	0	7	0	0	0	14	1
PRKCBI	16	1.0	32.50 ~ 32.66	0	2	3	0	4	3	0
NFI	17	1.0	38.10 ~ 38.26	1	0	2	2	5	1	0
SCYA2‖	17	3.0	40.21 ~ 40.37	0	5	1	1	3	1	1
PAI2	18	2.7	64.17 ~ 64.01	2	0	2	1	5	2	10
IL17R‖	22	5.9	14.48 ~ 14.32	1	2	1	2	1	0	4
HCF2‖	22	2.0	17.91 ~ 17.75	1	1	2	2	1	0	3

* 缩写来自 LocusLink（www.ncbi.nlm.nih.gov/LocusLink/list.cgi）。

† For three regions the genetic and physical maps were inconsistent and no estimates were made.

‡ Span of region within a radiation hybrid map (http://www.ncbi.nlm.nih.gov/genome/seq/HsHome.shtml): 1 Mb ≈ 1 centirad. Position of the core SNP is listed first.

§ Number of SNPs discovered with at least 15 copies of the minor allele (successfully genotyped in at least 32 individuals) and in Hardy-Weinberg equilibrium using a significance criterion of $P < 0.02$.

‖ The ten regions selected for follow-up genotyping.

We measured LD between two SNPs using the classical statistic D′ (see Methods)[10]. D′ has the same range of values regardless of the frequencies of the SNPs compared[11]. Its sign (positive or negative) depends on the arbitrary choice of the alleles paired at the two loci. We chose the pair of SNPs that caused D′ > 0 in Utah so that, in comparisons with other populations, the sign of D′ indicates whether the same or opposite allelic association is present. In a large sample, |D′| of 1 indicates complete LD; 0 corresponds to no LD. The degree of LD needed for effective mapping depends on the details of a particular study[2]. A useful measure is the "half-length" of LD (the distance at which the average |D′| drops below 0.5).

Comparing the 19 randomly selected regions, LD has a half-length of about 60 kb (Fig. 1). Significant *P*-values for LD occur in greater than 50% of cases at distances of ≤ 80 kb. LD therefore extends much further than a previous prediction[2], and our data indicate that, in general, blocks of LD are large. Although the average extent is large, there is great variation in LD across the genomic regions (see also ref. 12), which is apparent in the different rates at which LD declines around the core SNP (Fig. 2). For example, |D′| > 0.5 for at least 155 kb around the *WASL* gene, but for less than 6 kb around *PCI* (Fig. 2). The variability across different genomic regions within the same population sample provides a context for explaining why past empirical studies, each based on one to three regions[3-5], have produced such different results. Large variations in LD are expected because of stochastic factors, such as different gene histories across loci[13]. Differences in recombination rates among regions can also affect the extent of LD. We observe a significant and important correlation ($P < 0.005$) between LD and the estimated local recombination rate (Fig. 2, inset).

Another feature of the data is that, near the range of distances at which LD drops off, there is often considerable variability in |D′| values at neighbouring SNPs (for example, around *IL17R*, *SCYA2*, *TGFBI* and *BMP8* in Fig. 2). Such a wide scatter of LD, even for markers close to each other, has been noted before[14], and is due to the underlying haplotypic structure of LD. SNPs marking sections of chromosome with short extents of correlation are likely to display much lower |D′| values than SNPs marking long haplotypes. In regions of high haplotype diversity, several SNPs may have to be genotyped to have a good chance of tagging most haplotypes. LD-based gene mapping may therefore require clusters of closely spaced SNPs to have maximal power.

† 其中三个区域的基因图谱和物理图谱不一致，因此没有进行估算。

‡ 放射性杂交图谱中的区域范围（www.ncbi.nlm.nih.gov/genome/seq/HsHome.shtml）：1Mb≈1 厘拉德。核心 SNP 的位置列在前。

§ 在至少 15 个次等位位点拷贝（在至少 32 个个体中成功确定基因型）中发现的 SNP 数量，并且在哈迪–温伯格平衡中显著性标准 $P < 0.02$。

‖ 这十个区域用于后续的基因分型。

我们使用经典的 D′ 值量化两个 SNP 之间的 LD（见方法）[10]。不论相比较的 SNP 出现频率如何，D′ 都具有相同的取值范围[11]。其符号（正或者负）取决于两位点间等位位点对的随机选择。我们选择了在犹他州人群中 D′ > 0 的 SNP 对，这样在和其他人群进行比较时，D′ 的符号表示是否存在相同或者相反的等位相关性。在大样本中，|D′| 为 1 表示完全的 LD，0 表示不存在 LD。有效的图谱绘制所需 LD 的程度需要根据具体研究细节确定[2]。一种可行的度量方式是利用 LD 的"半长"（即平均 |D′| 降至 0.5 以下的距离）。

对比这 19 个随机选取的区域，LD 的半长度大约是 60 kb（图 1）。在距离 ≤ 80 kb 的情况下，超过 50% 的样本 LD 的 P 值具有显著性。因此 LD 延伸的距离比先前的预计要长得多[2]，而且我们的数据显示，总体上 LD 区域都相当大。尽管平均尺度很大，整个基因组区域中 LD 的变化也很大（也可见参考文献 12），但很明显在核心 SNP 附近 LD 衰减的速率不同（图 2）。比如，WASL 基因附近，|D′| > 0.5 的区域至少有 155 kb，但是对于 PCI 基因附近则小于 6 kb（图 2）。同一人群中这种不同基因组区域间的变异，可以用来解释为什么过去的经验性研究尽管只是基于 1 到 3 个区域[3-5]，却产生如此多不同的结果。因为存在随机因素，比如不同位点间的基因历史不同[13]，LD 的这种巨大变异是可以预期的。区域间重组率的不同也能影响到 LD 的程度。我们观察到 LD 和预测的局部重组率之间存在显著且重要的相关性（$P < 0.005$）（图 2，右下角插图）。

这些数据的另一个特征是在 LD 急剧下降的区间附近，相邻 SNP 间的 |D′| 值有较大波动（例如，图 2 中 IL17R、SCYA2、TGFBI 和 BMP8 附近）。LD 这种即使在相邻位点也产生大范围波动以前也曾发现过[14]，是由于 LD 潜在的单体型结构引起的。标记染色体区域的 SNP 如果相关性延伸较短，相比于长单体型的 SNP 可能显示出更低的 |D′| 值。在具有高度单体型变化的区域，可能需要多个 SNP 被分型确定才有可能代表大多数的单体型。因此，绘制基于 LD 的基因图谱需要位置关系紧密的 SNP 集合才能达到最大效果。

Fig. 1. LD versus physical distance between SNPs. For each distance from the core SNP (Table 1), we chose the SNP with the largest number of copies of the minor allele for comparison to SNPs at other distances. At a given distance, all comparisons are independent. **a**, Average |D′| values for each distance separation ("Data"; dotted lines indicate the 25th and 75th percentiles), compared with a prediction[2] based on simulations (see Methods). |D′| values for shorter physical distances were calculated by looking within contiguously sequenced stretches of DNA containing at least two SNPs, and picking the two with the most minor alleles. Unlinked marker comparisons are obtained by comparing SNPs in the 40-kb bin in each row of Table 1 to those in the next row. **b**, **c**, Fraction of |D′| values greater than 0.5 (**b**) and proportion of significant (P < 0.05) associations (**c**) between two SNPs separated by a given distance (as assessed by a likelihood ratio test[10]). Bars indicate 95% central confidence intervals. The number of data points used to make the calculations are shown.

Why does LD extend so far? LD around an allele arises because of selection or population history—a small population size, genetic drift or population mixture—and decays owing to recombination, which breaks down ancestral haplotypes[15]. The extent of LD decreases in proportion to the number of generations since the LD-generating event. The simplest explanation for the observed long-range LD is that the population under study experienced an extreme founder effect or bottleneck: a period when the population was so small that a few ancestral haplotypes gave rise to most of the haplotypes that exist today. Our simulations show that a severe bottleneck (inbreeding coefficient $F \geqslant 0.2$) occurring 800–1,600 generations ago (about 27,000–53,000 years ago assuming 25 years per generation) could have generated the LD observed (Fig. 3). In principle, long-range LD could also be generated by population mixture[16], but the degree of LD is much greater than would arise from the mixing of even extremely differentiated populations. An alternative explanation for the observed long-range LD is that the recombination rates in the regions studied might be markedly less than the genome-wide average. This could happen if recombination occurred primarily in well-separated hotspots and our regions fell between them (Fig. 3). However, under this hypothesis, the regions would be expected to show long-range LD in all populations, and this pattern is not observed (see below).

图 1. LD 与 SNP 间的物理距离。对于距离核心 SNP 的不同距离（表 1），我们选择具有次等位基因位点中最大拷贝数目的 SNP 用于与其他距离的 SNP 进行对比。在距离给定的前提下，所有的对比都是独立的。**a**，每个距离间隔的平均 |D'| 值（"数据"；虚线表示 25 和 75 百分位），与模拟推算得出的预期值[2]进行比较（见方法）。更短物理距离的 |D'| 值是通过找出含有至少两个 SNP 的连续 DNA 序列，并且挑选最罕见的两个等位位点计算获得。不连锁的标志是通过对照表 1 每行中每 40 kb 分箱的 SNP 与其下一行进行比较获得的。**b** 和 **c**，在一定距离（通过似然比检验的估算获得[10]）的两个 SNP 之间，|D'| 值超过 0.5(**b**)和具有显著性关联（$P < 0.05$）(**c**)的部分。条形表示 95% 的置信区间。图中显示了计算所用的数据点的个数。

LD 为什么一直在延伸？等位基因附近 LD 的出现是由于自然选择或者种群历史——一个小规模种群，遗传漂变或者种群混合——由于发生了打破祖先单体型的重组而衰减导致的[15]。LD 长度的减小与 LD 产生事件之后世代的数目成比例。对较长 LD 的最简单解释就是我们所研究的人群经历了极端的建立者效应或者瓶颈效应：有一段时间种群太小以至于一些祖先单体型衍生出目前存在的大部分单体型。我们的模拟显示大约 800 ~ 1,600 代以前（大约 27,000 ~ 53,000 年前，假设每代 25 年）发生了一次严重的瓶颈效应（近交相关系数 $F \geqslant 0.2$），由此可能产生了我们观察到的 LD（图 3）。原则上说，长 LD 还能够通过种群混合产生[16]，但 LD 的程度要远远超过极端分化的种群混合而产生的 LD。另一种对长 LD 的解释就是所研究区域的重组率显著低于基因组的平均水平。如果重组主要发生在分离热点区且我们的研究区域刚好落入其中，这种现象可能出现（图 3）。但是，根据这个假设，这些区域应该在所有的人群中都显示长 LD，而事实观察到的并非如此（见下文）。

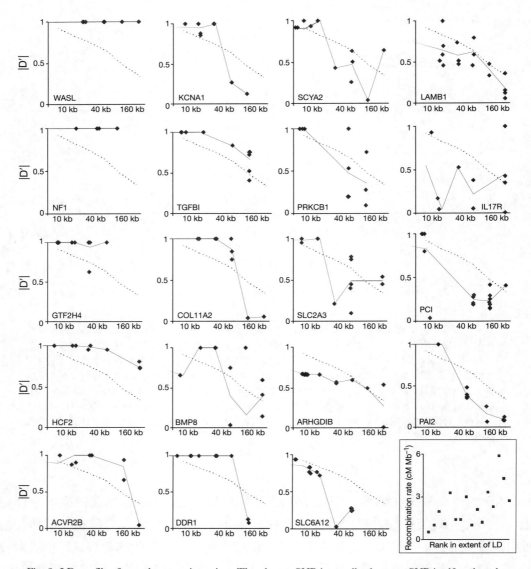

Fig. 2. LD profiles for each genomic region. The chosen SNP is usually the core SNP itself, unless the core SNP could not be readily genotyped or another SNP with more minor alleles had been identified within 1 kb. In both cases, we substituted the closest high-frequency SNP. The chosen SNP is compared with every other high-frequency SNP in the same genomic region. Solid line indicates average |D'| values for each distance for which SNPs were available; for comparison, the dashed line indicates the consensus LD curve from Fig. 1. The extent of LD was calculated by performing a least-squares linear regression to the average |D'| values at each distance from the chosen SNP; more sloped lines indicate less LD. The regions are ordered according to the extent of LD (most extensive LD, top left; least extensive LD, bottom right). Inset (bottom right) shows the rank of each region in terms of LD extent versus the estimated recombination rate per unit of physical distance. For each 160-kb region of interest, we looked for the closest pair of flanking genetic markers from the Marshfield map[34] subject to the condition that they were separated by a non-zero genetic distance on the map. We divided genetic map distance by the physical map distance on the basis of the available draft genome sequence[35]. We analysed the 16 regions for which the genetic and physical map orderings of markers were locally consistent (one-sided Spearman rank correlation, $P < 0.005$).

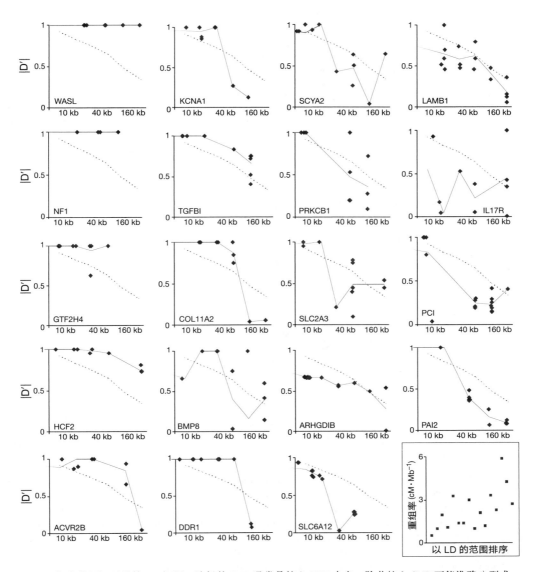

图 2. 每个基因组区域的 LD 概况。选择的 SNP 通常是核心 SNP 本身，除非核心 SNP 不能准确分型或者在 1 kb 范围内发现具有更小的次等位基因频率的 SNP。在这两种情况下，我们都替换成最近的高频率 SNP。所选取的 SNP 与同一个基因组区域的每个其他高频率 SNP 进行对比。实线表示每个距离上可获得 SNP 的平均 |D′| 值；作为对照，虚线表示从图 1 中获得的一致的 LD 曲线。LD 长度的计算是通过对每个距离上选定 SNP 的平均 |D′| 值进行最小二乘线性回归拟合；斜率越大表示 LD 越小。不同区域根据 LD 的长度进行排列（最长的位于左上，最小的位于右下）。插图（右下角）横纵轴分别代表依照 LD 范围大小将各个区域排序而成的各个序列与每一单位物理距离所估算的重组率。对于每个感兴趣的 160 kb 区域，我们根据它们在图谱上被一个非零遗传距离分隔的条件，从马什菲尔德图谱[34]中寻找最近的两侧基因标志。根据可获得的基因草图序列[35]，我们用物理图谱距离来划分基因图谱的距离。我们分析了基因和物理图谱标志顺序局部一致的 16 个区域（单侧斯皮尔曼等级相关性，$P < 0.005$）。

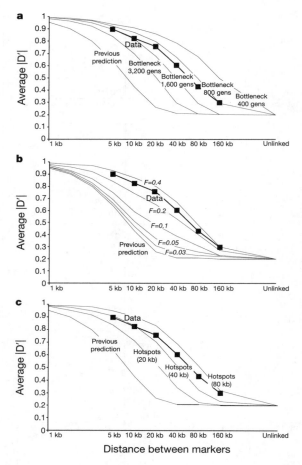

Fig. 3. Effect on LD of assumptions about population history and recombination. **a**, The effect of a population bottleneck instantaneously reducing the population to a constant size of 50 individuals for 40 generations ($F = 0.4$) and occurring 400, 800, 1,600 or 3,200 generations ago. **b**, The effect of bottleneck intensity (F) for a bottleneck that occurred 800 generations ago. **c**, The effect of variation in recombination rate, assuming that all recombination in the genome occurs at hotspots randomly distributed according to a Poisson process with an average density of one every 20, 40 and 80 kb, and with a genome-wide average rate of 1.3 centiMorgans per megabase per generation[35]. Results are compared to a no-hotspot model for the same historical hypothesis. ("Data" refers to the mean $|D'|$ values at each physical distance separation, obtained from Fig. 1a).

To confirm our findings of long-range LD and to investigate the reasons for its occurrence, we next examined a representative subset of SNPs in two additional samples. We first studied another north-European sample (48 southern Swedes) and found LD in a nearly identical pattern to that observed in Utah, both in terms of the overall magnitude of LD and the particular alleles that were associated (indicated by the sign of D') (Fig. 4). The similarity in LD patterns may be due to the same historical event, which occurred deep in European prehistory before the separation of the ancestors of these two groups. This suggests that the long-range LD pattern is general in northern Europeans[3,17].

图 3. 关于种群历史和重组的假设对 LD 的影响。**a**, 按照 400, 800, 1,600 或者 3,200 代以前发生的将人群数量即刻减少到 50 个恒定个体并持续 40 代（$F = 0.4$）的人口瓶颈效应影响。**b**, 一个发生于 800 代前的瓶颈效应强度（F）的影响。**c**, 变异对重组率的影响, 假设基因组中所有的重组发生在热点上且服从泊松过程, 每 20、40 和 80 kb 的平均密度为 1, 并且整个基因组范围内的平均速率是 1.3 厘摩每百万碱基每代[35]。所有结果均和相同的历史事件假设但没有热点的模型进行比较。（"数据"指的是图 1a 中得到的每个物理距离分隔的 |D′| 平均值）。

为了证实我们发现的长 LD 并且研究其出现的原因, 接下来我们在另外两个不同样本中检查了一个有代表性的 SNP 子集。首先我们研究了另一个北欧人群样本（48 名南瑞典人）并且发现无论是总体的 LD 大小还是相关的特定等位基因（由 D′ 结果推测）都和犹他州样本发现的模式几乎一致（图 4）。LD 整体模式的相似性可能是由于群体经历了相同的历史事件。该事件可能发生于史前的欧洲, 彼时两个群体的祖先尚未分离。这提示在北欧人群中长 LD 的模式普遍存在[3,17]。

Fig. 4. LD curve for Swedish and Yoruban samples. To minimize ascertainment bias, data are only shown for marker comparisons involving the core SNP. Alleles are paired such that D' > 0 in the Utah population. D' > 0 in the other populations indicates the same direction of allelic association and D' < 0 indicates the opposite association. **a**, In Sweden, average D' is nearly identical to the average |D'| values up to 40-kb distances, and the overall curve has a similar shape to that of the Utah population (thin line in **a** and **b**). **b**, LD extends less far in the Yoruban sample, with most of the long-range LD coming from a single region, *HCF2*. Even at 5 kb, the average values of |D'| and D' diverge substantially. To make the comparisons between populations appropriate, the Utah LD curves are calculated solely on the basis of SNPs that had been successfully genotyped and met the minimum frequency criterion in both populations (Swedish and Yoruban).

We next studied 96 Yorubans (from Nigeria), believed to share common ancestry with northern Europeans about 100,000 years ago[18]. At short distances, the Nigerian and European-derived populations typically show the same allelic combinations (Fig. 4): D' has the same sign and a similar magnitude, indicating a common LD-generating event tracing far back in human history. However, the half-length of LD seems to extend less than 5 kb (Fig. 4) in the Yorubans. Markedly shorter range LD in sub-Saharan Africa has also been observed in several studies of single regions[19,20] (although two other studies did not show a clear trend[21,22]). Our results indicate that the pattern of shorter LD in sub-Saharan African populations may be general.

Notably, LD in the Nigerians is largely a subset of what is seen in the northern Europeans.

图 4. 瑞典和约鲁巴人的 LD 曲线。为了使确认偏倚最小化，只显示含有核心 SNP 的标志对比数据。等位基因位点进行配对使犹他州人群中 D′ > 0。其他人群中 D′ > 0 说明具有相同方向的等位位点具有相关性，而 D′ < 0 则说明具有相反的关系。**a**，在瑞典人中，平均 D′ 与长达 40 kb 距离的平均 |D′| 值几乎一致，总体曲线的形状也与犹他州人群类似（**a** 和 **b** 中的细线）。**b**，约鲁巴样本中 LD 的长度短一些，其中最长的 LD 来自 *HCF2* 一个单独的区域。即便只有 5 kb，平均 | D′| 值和 D′ 值最终还是发生了分离。为了在两个人群间进行恰当的比较，犹他州人群的 LD 曲线完全基于成功分型并且符合两个人群（瑞典人和约鲁巴人）的最低频率标准的 SNP 进行计算。

随后我们研究了 96 名约鲁巴人（来自尼日利亚），他们被认为在 100,000 年前与北欧人拥有相同的祖先[18]。在短的 LD 中，来自尼日利亚和欧洲的群体都显示出相同的等位基因位点重组（图 4）：D′ 有相同的迹象和类似的大小，说明在人类历史中经历了共同的 LD 产生事件。但是，约鲁巴人中 LD 的半长似乎少于 5 kb（图 4）。数个针对单个区域的研究也发现撒哈拉沙漠以南的非洲人 LD 范围明显缩短[19,20]（尽管另外两个研究没有显示明显的趋势[21,22]）。我们的结果表明撒哈拉沙漠以南非洲人群中更短的 LD 模式可能是普遍存在的。

显然，尼日利亚人的 LD 在很大程度上是观察到的北欧人 LD 的子集。约鲁巴

The Yoruban haplotypes are generally contained within the longer Utah haplotypes, and there is little Yoruban-specific LD (85% of observations of substantial LD ($|D'| > 0.5$) in Yorubans are also substantial and of the same sign in Utah). The vast difference in the extent of LD between populations points to differences owing to population history, probably a bottleneck or founder effect that occurred among the ancestors of north Europeans after the divergence from the ancestors of the Nigerians. The short extent of LD in Nigerians is more consistent with the predictions of a computer simulation study assuming a simple model of population expansion[2].

Could the apparent differences in the extent of LD among populations be due to "ascertainment bias" in the identification of the SNPs? The core SNPs are probably not subject to bias because they were identified in a multi-ethnic population. The neighbouring SNPs were identified in the Utah population and subsequently studied in the other populations, and thus they may be susceptible to ascertainment bias. However, we selected only SNPs with high frequency in Utah and most of these satisfied the high-frequency criterion for use in the other populations (87% in Sweden and 71% in Nigeria). Thus, the inferences about LD are not likely to be much different from what would have been obtained had we used SNPs ascertained in the Yoruban sample. Moreover, the cross-population comparisons (Fig. 4) minimize ascertainment bias because they involve only the core SNP, and because they calculate LD in each population using only the SNPs present in both.

What was the nature of the population event that created the long-range LD? The event could be specific to northern Europe, which was substantially depopulated during the Last Glacial Maximum (30,000–15,000 years ago), and subsequently recolonized by a small number of founders[23,24]. Alternatively, the long-range LD could be due to a severe bottleneck that occurred during the founding of Europe or during the dispersal of anatomically modern humans from Africa[19,20,25,26] (the proposed "Out of Africa" event) as recently as 50,000 years ago. Under the first hypothesis, the strong LD at distances ≥ 40 kb would be absent in populations not descended from northern Europeans. Under the second hypothesis, the same pattern of long-range LD could be observed in a variety of non-African populations. Regardless of the timing and context of the bottleneck, the severity of the event (in terms of inbreeding) can be assessed from our data. To have a strong effect on LD, a substantial proportion of the modern population would have to be derived from a population that had experienced an event leading to an inbreeding coefficient of at least $F = 0.2$ (Fig. 3). This corresponds to an effective population size (typically less than the true population size[15]) of 50 individuals for 20 generations; 1,000 individuals for 400 generations; or any other combination with the same ratio.

Our results have implications for disease gene mapping, suggesting a possible two-tiered strategy for using LD. The presence of large blocks of LD in northern European populations suggests that genome-wide LD mapping is likely to be possible with existing SNP resources[1]. Although the large blocks should make initial localization easier, they may also limit the resolution of mapping to blocks of DNA in the range of 100 kb[27]. Populations

单体型基本上都包含在更长的犹他州单体型中，几乎没有约鲁巴人独有的 LD(85% 约鲁巴人常见的 LD($|D'| > 0.5$)在犹他州人中也很常见，而且具有相同的标志)。不同人群间 LD 长度的明显差别归因于人群历史的差异，北欧人祖先与尼日利亚人祖先分离之后可能发生了瓶颈效应或者建立者效应。尼日利亚人中的短 LD 与基于人群扩张简单模型假设的计算机模拟研究预测结果一致[2]。

这种人群中 LD 的长度有明显差别的现象是否是由于 SNP 鉴定过程中存在的"确认偏倚"导致的？核心 SNP 不太可能受偏倚的影响，因为它们是在多种族人群中鉴定出来的。在犹他州人群中鉴定出的相邻 SNP，随后在其他人群中进行了研究，因此它们有可能受到确认偏倚的影响。但是，我们在犹他州人群中仅仅选择了高频出现的 SNP，其大部分都满足了可以用于其他人群的高频出现的标准(瑞典人群有 87%，尼日利亚人群有 71%)。因而我们现在推断出的 LD 与这些在约鲁巴人群样本中确定出的 SNP 所具有的 LD 不会有太大的差别。此外，跨人群比较使确认偏倚最小化(图 4)，因为这种比较仅仅使用了核心 SNP，还因为仅仅使用了共有的 SNP 来计算每个人群的 LD。

那么产生长 LD 的人群事件的本质是什么？这些事件可能是北欧人特有的，即在末次冰盛期(30,000～15,000 年前)人口的大量减少，随后少量的建立者重新定居[23,24]。另一种可能是，这种长 LD 是由于在欧洲的建立过程中或是 50,000 年前解剖学上的现代人从非洲分离[19,20,25,26](所谓"走出非洲"事件)所产生的严重瓶颈效应。根据第一个假设，长度 ≥ 40 kb 的大型 LD 应该不存在于非北欧后代人群中。根据第二个假设，这类长 LD 应该可以出现于各种非非洲人群中。不考虑这种瓶颈效应的时间和背景，从我们的数据可以推断出该事件的严重程度(以近亲繁殖的程度表示)。如果对 LD 产生巨大影响，很大部分的现代人类将是来自于经历过能导致近交系数至少是 $F = 0.2$ 的严重事件的群体(图 3)。这就相当于一个有效群体(通常小于真实的人口[15])有 50 个个体，经历 20 代繁衍，或 1,000 个个体，经历 400 代繁衍，或是任何相同比例的组合。

我们的结论对疾病的基因图谱绘制具有重要意义，给出了在两个层次上利用 LD 的可能策略。北欧人群中存在大的 LD 板块，说明在现有 SNP 资源下获得基因组水平的图谱是可能实现的[1]。尽管大的 LD 板块可能会使初始的定位变得容易，但是这同时也限制了将图谱的 DNA 解析为 100 kb 大小的分辨率[27]。含有更小 LD with much smaller blocks of LD (for example, Yorubans) may allow fine-structure mapping to identify the specific nucleotide substitution responsible for a phenotype[12]. Our study also has implications for LD as a tool to study population history[19–22]. Simultaneous assessment of LD at multiple regions of the genome provides an approach for studying history with potentially greater sensitivity to certain aspects of history than traditional methods based on properties of a single locus.

Methods

Core SNPs were identified by screening more than 3,000 genes in a multi-ethnic panel of 15 European Americans, 10 African Americans, and 7 East Asians (see ref. 28 for details; a full description of this database will be presented elsewhere). DNA used for sequencing was obtained from the Coriell Cell Repositories. Identification numbers for these Utah samples from the CEPH mapping panel were NA12344, 06995, 06997, 07013, 12335, 06990, 10848, 07038, 06987, 10846, 10847, 07029, 07019, 07048, 06991, 10851, 07349, 07348, 10857, 10852, 10858, 10859, 10854, 10856, 10855, 12386, 12456, 10860, 10861, 10863, 10830, 10831, 10835, 10834, 10837, 10836, 10838, 10839, 10841, 10840, 10842, 10843, 10845 and 10844. We did follow-up genotyping in 48 Swedes (healthy individuals from a case/control study of adult-onset diabetes) and in 96 Yoruban males from Nigeria (healthy individuals from a case/control study of hypertension).

SNPs were discovered by DNA sequencing[28] in the 44 individuals from Utah; we sequenced about 2 kb centred at each distance from the core SNP ≥ 5 kb, with about 1 kb sequenced around the core SNP itself. When no polymorphism of sufficiently high frequency was found, a nearby subregion of about two further kilobases was resequenced; this occurred in only 18% of the cases. Polymorphisms were identified and genotypes were scored automatically using Polyphred[29] and checked manually by at least two different scorers. SNPs in Hardy-Weinberg disequilibrium or showing evidence of breakdown of LD over short physical distances (< 2.5 kb) were triple-checked. Of the 275 high-frequency SNPs (that is, SNPs with at least 15 observed copies of the minor allele), three were discarded because of a Hardy-Weinberg P value of < 0.02; one of the SNPs used in the analysis had a nominally significant P value ($P < 0.05$). To assess the accuracy of scoring, we rescored 26 randomly chosen high-frequency SNPs; only seven discrepancies were found among 1,144 genotypes. For cases in which follow-up genotyping was done, the discrepancy rate was 47 out of 1,484 (3%) between genotypes obtained by both methods.

Genotyping of SNPs was performed by single-base extension followed by mass spectroscopy (Sequenom)[30], fluorescence polarization (LJL Biosystems)[31] or detection on a sequencing gel (Applied Biosystems) . For the ten regions selected for follow-up genotyping (Table 1), we chose at most one "representative" SNP at each distance from the core SNP (each column in Table 1) according to the criterion that it had the highest number of minor alleles of all SNPs at that distance from the core SNP. For other populations, only those SNPs that, when genotyped, had a minimum number of minor alleles were included in studies of LD. For Yorubans, the cutoff was 25 alleles (76% of SNPs met the criterion); for Swedes, the cutoff was 15 alleles (89%). The fact that most of the SNPs we studied in Utah are also present in high frequency in these other populations indicates that the

板块的人群（比如约鲁巴人）则能够进行精细结构的图谱绘制，便于鉴定出造成某种表型的特异性核苷酸替换[12]。我们的研究同时也显示 LD 可以作为研究人群历史的工具[19-22]。同时评估基因组中多个区域的 LD 可以作为研究人群历史的方法，相对于基于单个位点性质的传统方法来说在一些方面具有更高的敏感度。

方　法

　　核心 SNP 是通过对一个多民族人群中超过 3,000 个基因进行筛查确定的，其中包括 15 个欧裔美国人、10 个非裔美国人和 7 个东亚人（详见参考文献 28，此数据库的详细描述将另文表述）。用于测序的 DNA 来自科里尔细胞库。CEPH 图谱标记中这些犹他州人群样本的编号是 NA12344、06995、06997、07013、12335、06990、10848、07038、06987、10846、10847、07029、07019、07048、06991、10851、07349、07348、10857、10852、10858、10859、10854、10856、10855、12386、12456、10860、10861、10863、10830、10831、10835、10834、10837、10836、10838、10839、10841、10840、10842、10843、10845 和 10844。我们对另外 48 个瑞典人（一项成人糖尿病的病例 / 对照研究中的健康个体）和 96 个尼日利亚约鲁巴男性（一项高血压的病例 / 对照研究中的健康个体）进行了基因分型。

　　SNP 是从 44 个犹他州人群个体中用 DNA 测序[28]方法获得的。我们测定了每个距离核心 SNP $\geq$ 5 kb 处周边 2 kb 的序列，同时也对距离核心 SNP 周边 1 kb 区域进行了测序。如果没有足够高频率的基因多态位点，则将周边测序范围再扩大 2 kb；这种情况出现的比例是 18%。多态位点发现以后，就用 Polyphred 软件[29]自动进行基因型的评分，并且至少两个不同的计分人进行手工复查。哈迪-温伯格不平衡中的 SNP 或者在短物理距离（< 2.5 kb）显示 LD 断开证据的 SNP 需要进行三重检查。在这 275 个高频 SNP 中（即 SNP 含有至少 15 个次等位基因位点的可见拷贝），有 3 个由于哈迪-温伯格 P 值 < 0.02 而被舍弃；用于分析的其中一个 SNP 只是在名义上有显著性 P 值（P < 0.05）。为了评分的准确性，我们重新将 26 个随机选取的高频 SNP 进行了评分；在 1,144 个基因型中只发现了 7 处差异。对于进行基因分型的样本，两种方法获得的基因型差异率为 47/1,484（3%）。

　　SNP 的基因分型使用的是单碱基延伸法，随后使用质谱（Sequenom）[30]、荧光偏振（LJL Biosystems）[31]或者测序胶（Applied Biosystems）[32]检测。对于选定进行后续分型的 10 个区域而言（表 1），我们以距离核心 SNP 一定距离的所有 SNP 中出现最多的次等位位点作为标准，选择一个最具代表性的 SNP（表 1 中的每一栏）。对于其他人群，只有那些分型后具有最低数量要求的次等位基因位点才纳入 LD 的研究。约鲁巴人的阈值是 25 个等位基因位点（76% 的 SNP 满足标准）；瑞典人的阈值是 15 个等位位点（89% 的 SNP 满足标准）。我们在犹他州人群中研究的 SNP 大多数也高频存在于其他人群的事实表明，LD 的评估不太可能受

assessment of LD is not likely to be subject to large ascertainment bias.

Heterozygosity[15] (π) was calculated as the average of $2jk/n(n-1)$ for all base pairs screened, with j and k equal to the number of copies of the minor and major alleles, respectively ($n = j + k$). A base was considered screened if it had Phred quality scores[29] of $\geqslant 15$ in $\geqslant 10$ individuals. D' values between markers with alleles A/a and B/b (allele frequencies, c_A, c_a, c_B and c_b; haplotype frequencies, c_{AB}, c_{Ab}, c_{aB} and c_{ab}) were obtained by dividing $c_{AB} - c_A c_B$ by its maximum possible value: $\min(c_A c_b, c_a c_B)$ if $D > 0$ and $\min(c_A c_B, c_a c_b)$ otherwise. An implementation of the expectation maximization algorithm was used to infer haplotype frequencies for pairs of SNPs both for actual and simulated data[33]. A likelihood ratio test was used to assess significance of associations between pairs of SNPs[10].

Computer simulations were based on a model related to that in ref. 2, assuming a population that was constant at an effective size of 10,000 individuals until 5,000 generations ago, when it expanded instantaneously to a size of 100,000,000 (an arbitrary value). This model captures many of the features of more complicated growth, as the effect of population growth on LD is not dependent on the precise details of population growth or the final population size when the growth is moderately fast[2]. Bottlenecks were modelled as described, with the population crashing to a constant size for a fixed number of generations before re-expanding. (The effect of a bottleneck on LD depends primarily on the F-value, the inbreeding coefficient, which is defined as the probability that two alleles randomly picked from the population after the bottleneck derive from the same ancestral allele just before the bottleneck.) Coalescent simulations were used to generate gene genealogies under these models for markers separated by a specified recombination distance (see ref. 13 for a more detailed description of the theory behind these simulations). Simulations were run 2,000 times with sample-size distributions mimicking our data. SNPs were generated by distributing mutations on the simulated gene genealogies at a mutation rate of 6×10^{-5} per generation, under an "infinite alleles"mutation model. The mutation rate was chosen such that the probability of high frequency SNPs in a 2-kb stretch of DNA sequenced in 44 samples (for the model of a simple expansion 5,000 generations ago) was similar to what we observed (about 70%). We also tested mutation rates ten times higher and found that inferences about LD were essentially unchanged.

An extreme hypothesis of population mixture and its effect on LD were assessed in a simulated, mixed population of European Americans and sub-Saharan Africans. For the first simulated mixture, we constructed a mixture of 22 Yorubans and 22 samples from Utah, and used data from the ten core SNPs genotyped in both populations. For the second simulation, we used 26 SNPs from a previous study[7] that had been found to have a minor allele frequency of at least 15% in either African Americans or European Americans; we chose at most one SNP per gene, picking the first listed SNP (in Table A1 of ref. 7) that met our minimum frequency criterion. We found much stronger LD even at 40 kb (56% with $|D'| > 0.5$) (Fig. 1) in our actual data than in the simulated, admixed populations. For the 45 possible pairwise comparisons of the ten core SNPs in the simulated mix of Yoruban and Utah samples, no values of $|D'| > 0.5$ were observed. For the 325 possible pairwise comparisons from the second study, only 11% showed $|D'| > 0.5$. This suggests that admixture probably did not generate the strong signal of LD at long physical distances seen in Utah.

(**411**, 199-204; 2001)

到大量的确认偏倚的影响。

对于所有筛选的碱基对而言，杂合度[15]（π）等于 $2jk/n(n-1)$ 的均值，其中 j 和 k 分别相当于次等位位点和主等位位点的拷贝数，$n=j+k$。如果一个碱基在 ≥ 10 个个体中的 Phred 质量评分[29] ≥ 15，则被认为通过筛选。等位基因 A/a 和 B/b（等位基因频率 c_A、c_a、c_B 和 c_b；单体型频率 c_{AB}、c_{Ab}、c_{aB} 和 c_{ab}）间标志的 D′ 值的计算是将 $c_{AB}-c_Ac_B$ 除以其最大可能值：如果 D > 0，取 c_Ac_b 和 c_ac_B 的较小值，反之则是 c_Ac_B 和 c_ac_b 的较小值。最大期望值算法用来推断实际和模拟数据中成对 SNP 的单体型频率[33]。似然比检验用来评价成对 SNP 之间相关性的显著性[10]。

计算机模拟是基于参考文献 2 中的一个相关模型，模型假设一个种群一直保持稳定在有效群体数量为 10,000 个个体直到 5,000 代，突然扩张到 100,000,000（一个随意假设的值）个个体。在增长速度比较快的情况下，人群增长对 LD 的影响不取决于其增长的准确细节或最终大小[2]，因此该模型具有更复杂增长模式的许多特点。瓶颈效应的模型如前述进行设置，在重新扩张前人群的数量在固定的代数中坍缩至常数值。（瓶颈效应对 LD 的影响主要取决于 F 值，即近交系数，其定义是瓶颈效应后从群体中随机选取的两个等位基因位点来源于瓶颈效应之前同一个祖先位点的可能性。）联合模拟用来生成这些模型设定下的基因谱系以获得特定的重组距离分隔的标志物（有关模拟的详细理论陈述详见参考文献 13）。在样本量的分布类似于我们数据的条件下进行了 2,000 次模拟。SNP 是在突变率为每代 6×10^{-5}，"无限等位位点"突变模型下，通过将突变分布在模拟的基因谱系中产生。突变率的设定是为了保证 44 个样本中所测序的 2 kb 序列中出现高频 SNP 的可能性（对于 5,000 代之前简单扩张的模型）与我们所观察到的类似（大约 70%）。我们也检验了突变率增高至 10 倍以后的情况，发现关于 LD 相关结论没有改变。

对于人群混合的极端假设及其对 LD 的影响是在模拟的、混合了欧裔美国人和南撒哈拉非洲人中进行评估的。对于第一组模拟的混合，我们构建了 22 个约鲁巴人和 22 个犹他州人的混合样本，并且使用两个人群中都进行了分型的 10 个核心 SNP 的数据。对于第二个模拟，我们使用先前研究[7]的 26 个 SNP，已发现无论在非裔美国人还是欧裔美国人中，出现次等位基因位点的频率都不小于 15%；每个基因根据第一个满足我们最小频率标准的 SNP 最多选择一个位点（见参考文献 7 表 A1）。我们发现即便是 40 kb 处，实际数据比模拟的混合人群中的 LD 程度更强（56% 的 |D′| > 0.5）（图 1）。在模拟混合的约鲁巴人和犹他州人样本中 10 个核心 SNP 的 45 种设对比较中，没有看到 |D′| > 0.5 的值。在第二个研究的 325 个可设对比较中，只有 11% 出现 |D′| > 0.5。这说明人群混合可能无法形成像犹他州人群体中所见到的那种在长物理距离上产生 LD 的强信号。

（毛晨晖 翻译；曾长青 审稿）

David E. Reich*, **Michele Cargill***†, **Stacey Bolk***, **James Ireland***, **Pardis C. Sabeti**‡, **Daniel J. Richter***, **Thomas Lavery***, **Rose Kouyoumjian***, **Shelli F. Farhadian***, **Ryk Ward**‡ & **Eric S. Lander***§

* Whitehead Institute/MIT Center for Genome Research, Nine Cambridge Center, Cambridge, Massachusetts 02142, USA
‡ Institute of Biological Anthropology, University of Oxford, Oxford OX2 6QS, UK
§ Department of Biology, MIT, Cambridge, Massachusetts 02139, USA
† Present address: Celera Genomics, 45 West Gude Drive, Rockville, Maryland 20850, USA.

Received 11 December 2000; accepted 13 March 2001.

References:

1. Sachidanandam, R. *et al.* A map of human genome sequence variation containing 1.42 million single nucleotide polymorphisms. *Nature* **409**, 928-933 (2001).
2. Kruglyak, L. Prospects for whole-genome linkage disequilibrium mapping of common disease genes. *Nature Genet.* **22**, 139-144 (1999).
3. Dunning, A. M. *et al.* The extent of linkage disequilibrium in four populations with distinct demographic histories. *Am. J. Hum. Genet.* **67**, 1544-1554 (2000).
4. Abecasis, G. R. *et al.* Extent and distribution of linkage disequilibrium in three genomic regions. *Am. J. Hum. Genet.* **68**, 191-197 (2001).
5. Taillon-Miller, P. *et al.* Juxtaposed regions of extensive and minimal linkage disequilibrium in human Xq25 and Xq28. *Nature Genet.* **25**, 324-328 (2000).
6. Collins, A., Lonjou, C. & Morton, N. E. Genetic epidemiology of single-nucleotide polymorphisms. *Proc. Natl Acad. Sci. USA* **96**, 15173-15177 (1999).
7. Goddard, K. A. B., Hopkins, P. J., Hall, J. M. & Witte, J. S. Linkage disequilibrium and allele-frequency distributions for 114 single-nucleotide polymorphisms in five populations. *Am. J. Hum. Genet.* **66**, 216-234 (2000).
8. Watterson, G. A. & Guess, H. A. Is the most frequent allele the oldest? *Theor. Pop. Biol.* **11**, 141-160 (1977).
9. Lander, E. S. The new genomics: global views of biology. *Science* **274**, 536-539 (1996).
10. Schneider, S., Kueffler, J. M., Roessli, D. & Excoffier, L. Arlequin (ver. 2.0): A software for population genetic data analysis (Genetics and Biometry Laboratory, Univ. Geneva, Switzerland, 2000).
11. Lewontin, R. C. On measures of gametic disequilibrium. *Genetics* **120**, 849-852 (1988).
12. Jorde, L. B. Linkage disequilibrium and the search for complex disease genes. *Genome Res.* **10**, 1435-1444 (2000).
13. Hudson, R. R. in *Oxford Surveys in Evolutionary Biology* (eds Futuyma, D. J. & Antonovics, J.) 1-44 (Oxford Univ. Press, Oxford, 1990).
14. Clark, A. G. *et al.* Haplotype structure and population genetic inferences from nucleotide-sequence variation in human lipoprotein lipase. *Am. J. Hum. Genet.* **63**, 595-612 (1998).
15. Hartl, D. L. & Clark, A. G. *Principles of Population Genetics* (Sinauer, Massachusetts, 1997).
16. Chakraborty, R. & Weiss, K. M. Admixture as a tool for finding linked genes and detecting that difference from allelic association between loci. *Proc. Natl Acad. Sci. USA* **85**, 9119-9123 (1988).
17. Eaves, I. A. *et al.* The genetically isolated populations of Finland and Sardinia may not be a panacea for linkage disequilibrium mapping of common disease genes. *Nature Genet.* **25**, 320-322 (2000).
18. Goldstein, D. B., Ruiz Linares, A., Cavalli-Sforza, L. L. & Feldman, M. W. Genetic absolute dating based on microsatellites and the origin of modern humans. *Proc. Natl Acad. Sci. USA* **92**, 6723-6727 (1995).
19. Tishkoff, S. A. *et al.* Global patterns of linkage disequilibrium at the CD4 locus and modern human origins. *Science* **271**, 1380-1387 (1996).
20. Tishkoff, S. A. *et al.* Short tandem-repeat polymorphism/*Alu* haplotype variation at the *PLAT* locus: Implications for modern human origins. *Am. J. Hum. Genet.* **67**, 901-925 (2000).
21. Kidd, J. R. *et al.* Haplotypes and linkage disequilibrium at the phenylalanine hydroxylase locus, *PAH*, in a global representation of populations. *Am. J. Hum. Genet.* **66**, 1882-1899 (2000).
22. Mateu, E. *et al.* Worldwide genetic analysis of the *CFTR* region. *Am. J. Hum. Genet.* **68**, 103-117 (2001).
23. Housley, R. A., Gamble, C. S., Street, M. & Pettitt, P. Radiocarbon evidence for the Late glacial human recolonisation of northern Europe. *Proc. Prehist. Soc.* **63**, 25-54 (1994).
24. Richards, M. *et al.* Tracing European founder lineages in the Near Eastern mtDNA pool. *Am. J. Hum. Genet.* **67**, 1251-1276 (2000).
25. Reich, D. E. & Goldstein, D. B. Genetic evidence for a Paleolithic human population expansion in Africa. *Proc. Natl Acad. Sci. USA* **95**, 8119-8123 (1998).
26. Ingman, M., Kaessmann, H., Pääbo, S. & Gyllensten, U. Mitochondrial genome variation and the origin of modern humans. *Nature* **408**, 708-713 (2000).
27. Altshuler, D., Daly, M. & Kruglyak, L. Guilt by association. *Nature Genet.* **26**, 135-137 (2000).
28. Cargill, M. *et al.* Characterization of single-nucleotide polymorphisms in coding regions of human genes. *Nature Genet.* **22**, 231-238 (1999).
29. Nickerson, D. B., Tobe, V. O. & Taylor, S. L. PolyPhred: automating the detection and genotyping of single nucleotide substitutions using fluorescence-based sequencing. *Nucleic Acids Res.* **25**, 2745-2751 (1997).
30. Ross, P. Hall, L., Smirnov, I. & Haff, L. High level multiplex genotyping by MALDI-TOF mass spectroscopy. *Nature Biotech.* **16**, 1347-1351 (1998).
31. Chen, X., Levine, L. & Kwok, P. Y. Fluorescence polarization in homogenous nucleic acid analysis. *Genome Res.* **9**, 492-498 (1999).
32. Lindblad-Toh, K. *et al.* Large-scale discovery and genotyping of single-nucleotide polymorphisms in the mouse. *Nature Genet.* **24**, 381-386 (2000).
33. Excoffier, L. & Slatkin, M. Maximum-likelihood estimation of molecular haplotype frequencies in a diploid population. *Mol. Biol. Evol.* **12**, 921-927 (1995).

34. Broman, K. W., Murray, J. C. Sheffield, V. C., White, R. L. & Weber, J. L. Comprehensive human genetic maps: individual and sex-specific variation in recombination. *Am. J. Hum. Genet.* **63**, 861-689 (1998).

35. Lander, E. S. *et al.* Initial sequencing and analysis of the human genome. *Nature* **409**, 860-921.

Acknowledgements. We thank L. Groop for the Swedish samples; R. Cooper and C. Rotimi for the Yoruban samples; and D. Altshuler, M. Daly, D. Goldstein, J. Hirschhorn, C. Lindgren and S. Schaffner for discussions. This work was supported in part by grants from the National Institutes of Health, Affymetrix, Millennium Pharmaceuticals, and Bristol-Myers Squibb Company, and by a National Defense Science and Engineering Fellowship to D.E.R.

Correspondence and requests for materials should be addressed to D.E.R. (e-mail: reich@genome.wi.mit.edu) or E.S.L. (e-mail: lander@genome.wi.mit.edu).

Rapid X-ray Flaring from the Direction of the Supermassive Black Hole at the Galactic Centre

F. K. Baganoff *et al.*

Editor's Note

Although it is generally accepted that there is a black hole with a mass of several million solar masses at the centre of our Milky Way galaxy, there is less light (especially X-rays) coming from the gas swirling into the black hole than standard theory predicts. This led to some uncertainty about what was powering the source of radio emission identified with the Galactic Centre, called Sagittarius A*. Here Frederick Baganoff, lead scientist for one of the instruments on board the Chandra space-based X-ray observatory, and his colleagues report rapid X-ray flares from the Galactic Centre, which imply that the X-rays must be generated within a tiny volume of space. This is consistent with its origin in gas that is falling into the supermassive black hole.

The nuclei of most galaxies are now believed to harbour supermassive black holes[1]. The motions of stars in the central few light years of our Milky Way Galaxy indicate the presence of a dark object with a mass of about 2.6×10^6 solar masses (refs 2, 3). This object is spatially coincident with the compact radio source Sagittarius A* (Sgr A*) at the dynamical centre of the Galaxy, and the radio emission is thought to be powered by the gravitational potential energy released by matter as it accretes onto a supermassive black hole[4,5]. Sgr A* is, however, much fainter than expected at all wavelengths, especially in X-rays, which has cast some doubt on this model. The first strong evidence for X-ray emission was found only recently[6]. Here we report the discovery of rapid X-ray flaring from the direction of Sgr A*, which, together with the previously reported steady X-ray emission, provides compelling evidence that the emission is coming from the accretion of gas onto a supermassive black hole at the Galactic Centre.

OUR view of Sgr A* in the optical and ultraviolet wavebands is blocked by the large visual extinction, $A_V \approx 30$ magnitudes[7], caused by dust and gas along the line of sight. Sgr A* has not been detected in the infrared owing to its faintness and to the bright infrared background from stars and clouds of dust[8]. We thus need to detect X-rays from Sgr A* in order to constrain the spectrum at energies above the radio-to-submillimetre band and to test whether gas is accreting onto a supermassive black hole (see above).

We first observed the Galactic Centre on 21 September 1999 with the imaging array of the Advanced CCD (charge-coupled device) Imaging Spectrometer (ACIS-I) aboard the

银河系中心超大质量黑洞方向上的
快速 X 射线耀发

巴加诺夫等

编者按

尽管人们普遍都接受了在我们的银河系中心存在着一个几百万太阳质量的黑洞这一观点，但是气体旋转着被黑洞吸积所释放的光（尤其是 X 射线）比标准理论所预测的要少。这使得被证认来自于银河系中心人马座 A* 的射电辐射的来源究竟是什么有了一些不确定性。在这篇文章中，弗雷德里克·巴加诺夫（钱德拉空基 X 射线天文台上装载的一架仪器的首席科学家）和他的同事们报道了来自银河系中心的快速 X 射线耀发，这也意味着这些 X 射线肯定是来自于一个很小的空间体积内。这个结论与它是来自于正在被超大质量黑洞吸积的气体的理论相符合。

当前，人们普遍相信大部分星系的中心存在超大质量黑洞[1]。而我们银河系中非常靠近中心（距离约几光年以内）的恒星运动表明银河系中心存在一个质量大约为 2.6×10^6 太阳质量的暗天体（参考文献 2 和 3）。该天体在空间分布上正好与位于银河系动力学中心的致密射电源人马座 A*（Sgr A*）一致，其射电辐射则被认为来源于一个超大质量黑洞吸积物质所释放的引力势能[4,5]。然而，Sgr A* 在各个波段，特别是在 X 射线波段，要暗于预期，这使得人们对上述射电辐射来源产生了一些疑问。直到最近，人们才首次发现了该天体存在 X 射线辐射的强有力证据[6]。在本工作中，我们报告在 Sgr A* 方向发现了快速 X 射线耀发。连同之前发现的稳定 X 射线辐射，这一发现为 Sgr A* 致密射电源的射电辐射来源于银河系中心超大质量黑洞的气体吸积过程提供了极具说服力的证据。

我们在光学和紫外波段对 Sgr A* 的观测受限于视线方向上尘埃和气体产生的显著消光，A_V 约为 30 星等[7]。在红外波段，Sgr A* 没有被探测到，其原因一方面在于它本身暗弱，另一方面在于恒星以及尘埃云的红外背景明亮[8]。因此，为了限制 Sgr A* 的能量在射电到亚毫米波段以上的光谱，并验证气体是否吸积到超大质量黑洞上（见上），我们需要对 Sgr A* 的 X 射线进行探测。

1999 年 9 月 21 日，我们利用安装在钱德拉 X 射线天文台的高级 CCD（电荷耦合器件）成像光谱仪的成像阵列（ACIS-I）[9]对银河系中心进行了首次观测，发现了

Chandra X-ray Observatory[9] and discovered an X-ray source coincident within $0.35'' \pm 0.26''$ (1σ) of the radio source[6]. The luminosity in 1999 was very weak—$L_X \approx 2 \times 10^{33}$ erg s^{-1} in the 2–10 keV band—after correction for the inferred neutral hydrogen absorption column $\mathcal{N}_H \approx 1 \times 10^{23}$ cm^{-2}. This is far fainter than previous X-ray observatories could detect[6].

We observed the Galactic Centre a second time with Chandra ACIS-I from 26 October 2000 22:29 until 27 October 2000 08:19 (UT), during which time we saw a source at the position of Sgr A* brighten dramatically for a period of approximately 10,000 s (10 ks). Figure 1 shows surface plots for both epochs of the 2–8 keV counts integrated over time from a $20'' \times 20''$ region centred on the radio position of Sgr A*. The modest peak of the integrated counts at Sgr A* in 1999 increased by a factor of about 7 in 2000, despite the 12% shorter exposure. The peak integrated counts of the fainter features in the field show no evidence of strong variability, demonstrating that the flaring at Sgr A* is intrinsic to the source.

Fig. 1. Surface plots of the 2–8 keV counts within a $20'' \times 20''$ field centred on Sgr A* at two epochs. The data were taken with Chandra ACIS-I on (**a**) 21 September 1999 and (**b**) 26–27 October 2000. The effective exposure times were 40.3 ks and 35.4 ks, respectively. The spatial resolution is $0.5''$ per pixel. An angle of $1''$ on the sky subtends a projected distance of about 0.04 pc at the galactocentric distance of 8.0 kpc (ref. 30). The peak integrated counts per pixel at the position of Sgr A* increased by a factor of 7 from the first epoch to the second, despite the slightly smaller exposure time ($\sim$12%) in the second epoch. The low-level peak a few arcseconds to the southwest of Sgr A* is the infrared source IRS 13, and the ridge of emission to the northwest is from a string of unresolved point sources. The fainter features in the field are reasonably consistent between the two epochs, considering the limited Poisson statistics and the fact that these stellar sources may themselves be variable; this consistency shows that the strong variations at Sgr A* are intrinsic to the source.

与射电源位置在 $0.35'' \pm 0.26''$（1σ）以内相吻合的一个 X 射线源[6]。根据推断的柱密度为 $N_\mathrm{H} \approx 1 \times 10^{23}$ cm^{-2} 的中性氢吸收进行修正之后，该 X 射线源的光度是非常低的（$2 \sim 10$ keV 波段内，光度 $L_\mathrm{X} \approx 2 \times 10^{33}$ erg · s^{-1}），远比之前各 X 射线天文台的探测极限暗弱[6]。

2000 年 10 月 26 日 22:29 到 2000 年 10 月 27 日 08:19（UT）这段时间里，我们利用钱德拉 ACIS-I 对银河系中心进行了第二次观测。这段时间中，我们看到在 Sgr A* 的位置上有一个在大约 10,000 s（10 ks）的时段内剧烈变亮的源。图 1 显示了以 Sgr A* 射电源为中心的一个 $20'' \times 20''$ 区域内两次观测对时间积分的 $2 \sim 8$ keV 光子计数曲面分布图。尽管曝光时间少了 12%，但是 1999 年的计数曲面分布图上 Sgr A* 位置处的不太大的峰值在 2000 年增加到了大约 7 倍。视场中其他较暗的峰没有明显的光变，表明 Sgr A* 的这个耀发来自其自身的内禀光变。

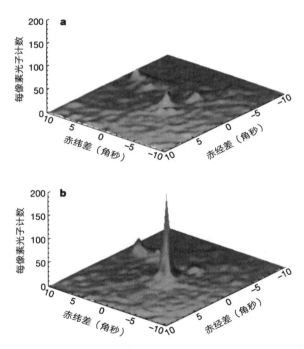

图 1. 两个不同时期以 Sgr A* 为中心的 $20'' \times 20''$ 的天区中 $2 \sim 8$ keV 波段光子计数的曲面分布图。图中所用数据来源于钱德拉 ACIS-I 于 (a) 1999 年 9 月 21 日和 (b) 2000 年 10 月 26 ~ 27 日的观测数据。有效曝光时间分别为 40.3 ks 和 35.4 ks。空间分辨率为每像素 $0.5''$。在距离银心 8.0 kpc 远的位置处（参考文献 30），天空中 $1''$ 的角度约对应 0.04 pc 的投影距离。Sgr A* 位置处每像素的峰值积分光子计数从第一个时期到第二个时期增加到了 7 倍，尽管第二个时期的曝光时间略短（约少 12%）。在 Sgr A* 西南方向外几个角秒处的较低水平的峰值对应的是红外源 IRS 13，而西北方向出现的脊状辐射来源于一串未分辨的点源。考虑到受限的泊松统计，以及这些恒星级天体本身的光度也可能发生变化，两个时期中视场内较暗的特征大致是一致的；这种一致性反映出 Sgr A* 位置处的强烈光变来自于源的内禀原因。

Figure 2 shows light curves of the photon arrival times from the direction of Sgr A* during the observation in 2000. Figure 2a and b shows hard-band (4.5–8 keV) and soft-band (2–4.5 keV) light curves constructed from counts within an angular radius of 1.5″ of Sgr A*. Both bands exhibit roughly constant, low-level emission for the first 14 ks or so, followed by a 6-ks period of enhanced emission beginning with a 500-s event (4.4σ significance using 150-s bins). At 20 ks, flare(s) of large relative amplitude occur, lasting about 10 ks, and finally the emission drops back to the low state for the remaining 6 ks or so. About 26 ks into the observation, the hard-band light curve drops abruptly by a factor of 5 within a span of around 600 s and then partially recovers within a period of 1.2 ks. The soft-band light curve shows a similar feature, but it appears to lag the hard-band event by a few hundred seconds and is less sharply defined.

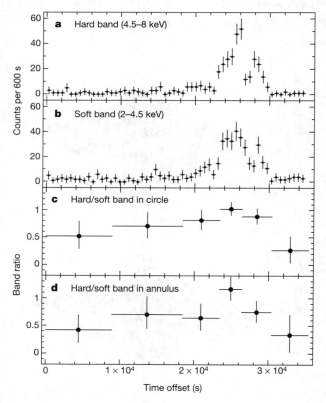

Fig. 2. Light curves of the photon arrival times and band ratios from the direction of Sgr A* on 26–27 October 2000. **a**, Hard-band (4.5–8 keV) counts. **b**, Soft-band (2–4.5 keV) counts. **c**, Hard/soft band ratio within a circle of radius 1.5″. **d**, Hard/soft band ratio within an annulus of inner and outer radii 0.5″ and 2.5″, respectively. The x axis shows the time offset from the start of the observation at 26 October 2000 22:29 (UT). The data are shown with 1σ error bars. The single 2.8-hour period of flaring activity which we have detected so far during a total of 21 hours of observations yields a (poorly determined) duty cycle of approximately 1/8. Our continuing observations of this source with Chandra will permit us to refine this value. During the quiescent intervals at the beginning and end of this observation, the mean count rate in the 2–8-keV band was $(6.4 \pm 0.6) \times 10^{-3}$ counts s^{-1}, consistent with the count rate we measured in

　　图 2 显示了 2000 年观测期间 Sgr A* 方向上关于光子到达时间的光变曲线。图 2a 和 2b 分别显示了根据 Sgr A* 的 1.5″ 角半径范围内的光子计数构建得到的硬 X 射线波段 (4.5 ~ 8 keV) 和软 X 射线波段 (2 ~ 4.5 keV) 的光变曲线。两个波段在最初的大概 14 ks 内都展现出大致稳定的低水平辐射，随后以一个 500 s 的事件作为开始呈现出一个时段为 6 ks 的辐射增强 (以 150 s 分区间，其显著性为 4.4σ)。在 20 ks 的时候，发生相对大幅度的耀发，持续大约 10 ks。在剩余的约 6 ks 里，整体辐射回落到之前较低的水平。在观测到大约 26 ks 的时候，硬 X 射线波段的光变曲线在约 600 s 的时间间隔内突然下降为原来的五分之一，然后在 1.2 ks 的时段内得到了部分的恢复。软 X 射线波段显示了类似的特征，但是似乎要比硬 X 射线波段的事件滞后几百秒，且特征没有那么分明。

图 2. 2000 年 10 月 26 ~ 27 日 Sgr A* 方向上的光子到达时间的光变曲线以及波段比。**a**，硬 X 射线波段 (4.5 ~ 8 keV) 光子计数。**b**，软 X 射线波段 (2 ~ 4.5 keV) 光子计数。**c**，半径为 1.5″ 的圆区域内硬/软 X 射线波段比。**d**，环区域 (内环半径 0.5″、外环半径 2.5″) 内硬/软 X 射线波段比。x 轴表示从 2000 年 10 月 26 日 22:29 (UT) 起算的时间偏移。数据显示了 1σ 的误差棒。目前我们在整个 21 小时的观测中仅探测到一次 2.8 小时的耀发活动，占空比约为 1/8 (结果仍不确定)。我们利用钱德拉对这个源进行后续观测将能够改进这一数值。在本次观测开始和结束的平静状态下，2 ~ 8 keV 波段的平均光子计数率为 $(6.4 \pm 0.6) \times 10^{-3}$ 个/秒，这个结果与我们在 1999 年测量的计数率 $(5.4 \pm 0.4) \times 10^{-3}$ 个/秒相一致。在提

1999, which was $(5.4 \pm 0.4) \times 10^{-3}$ counts s^{-1}. The detected count rate at the peak of the flare was 0.16 ± 0.01 counts s^{-1} within an extraction circle of radius $1.5''$, but this is about 30% less than the true incident count rate owing to pile-up of X-rays in the detector during the 3.2-s integration time for each CCD (charge-coupled device) read out.

The band-ratio time series in Fig. 2c, defined as the ratio of hard-band counts to soft-band counts, suggests that the spectrum "hardened" (that is, became flatter and extended more strongly to higher energies) during the flare. The difference between the band ratio measured at the peak of the flare and the average of the band ratios during the quiescent periods at the beginning and end of the observation is 0.63 ± 0.21 (that is, 3σ). The peak-flare band ratio in Fig. 2c is affected to some extent by the effects of pile-up (see Fig. 2 legend), which would tend to harden the spectrum; however, the band ratios in Fig. 2d, which were computed using the non-piled-up data extracted from the wings of the point spread function, also show evidence for spectral hardening with 2.7σ significance. The sizes of dust-scattering haloes in the Galactic Centre are typically greater than $1'$ (ref. 10), so dust-scattered X-rays from the source contribute a negligible fraction of the emission within the source extraction region that we used; hence dust-scattered X-rays cannot account for the spectral variations. We therefore conclude that the spectral hardening during the flare is likely to be real.

The quiescent-state spectra in 1999 and 2000 and the peak flaring-state spectrum in 2000 are shown in Fig. 3. We fitted each spectrum individually using a single power-law model with corrections for the effects of photoelectric absorption and dust scattering[10]. The best-fit values and 90% confidence limits for the parameters of each fit are presented in the first three lines of Table 1. The column densities for the three spectra are consistent, within the uncertainties, as are the photon indices of both quiescent-state spectra. Next, we fit a double power-law model to the three spectra simultaneously, using a single photon index for both quiescent spectra, a second photon index for the flaring spectrum, and a single column density for all three spectra. The best-fit models for each spectrum from the simultaneous fits are shown as solid lines in Fig. 3; the parameter values are given in the last line of Table 1. Using these values, we derive an absorption-corrected 2–10 keV luminosity of $L_{\mathrm{X}} = (2.2^{+0.4}_{-0.3}) \times 10^{33}$ erg s^{-1} for the quiescent-state emission and $L_{\mathrm{X}} = (1.0 \pm 0.1) \times 10^{35}$ erg s^{-1} for the peak of the flaring-state emission, or around 45 times the quiescent-state luminosity. We note that previous X-ray observatories did not have the sensitivity to detect such a short-duration, low-luminosity flare in the Galactic Centre[6]. The best-fit photon index $\Gamma_{\mathrm{f}} = 1.3^{+0.5}_{-0.6}$ ($\mathcal{N}(E) \propto E^{-\Gamma}$) for the flaring-state spectrum is slightly flatter than, but consistent with, systems thought to contain supermassive black holes[11]. Here E is the energy of a photon in keV, $\mathcal{N}(E)$ is the number of photons with energies in the differential interval E to $E + \mathrm{d}E$, and Γ is the power-law index of the photon number distribution.

取数据的半径为 1.5″ 的圆区域里，耀发峰值处探测的计数率为 0.16±0.01 个/秒。因为在每个 CCD(电荷耦合器件)读出时有 3.2 s 的积分时间，X 射线会在探测器中有堆积效应，因此这个数值比真实的入射光子计数率低大约 30%。

图 2c 显示的波段比(其定义为硬 X 射线波段光子计数与软 X 射线波段光子计数之比)随时间的一连串变化表明在耀发的过程中光谱有"硬化"的现象(即光谱变得更平且更强地延伸到高能端)。耀发时峰值处与观测初期以及末期平静时期的波段比的差别为 0.63±0.21(即 3σ)。图 2c 中的耀发峰的波段比在一定程度上受堆积效应的影响(见图 2 图注)，该效应倾向于使光谱硬化；然而，图 2d 中的波段比利用从点扩散函数的两翼提取的无堆积效应的数据计算得到，它也在 2.7σ 的显著性上显示光谱硬化的证据。银河系中心尘埃散射晕的尺度通常认为大于 1′(参考文献 10)，因此，这个源被尘埃散射的 X 射线对我们用来提取数据的区域内辐射的贡献可以忽略；所以尘埃散射的 X 射线不足以解释所观测到的光谱变化。我们因而得到这样的结论：耀发过程中的光谱硬化很可能是真实的。

图 3 中显示了 1999 年和 2000 年平静状态下的光谱以及 2000 年峰值耀发状态下的光谱。我们利用单一幂律模型对这些光谱逐个进行了拟合，其中对光电吸收和尘埃散射的效应做了修正[10]。表 1 的前三行分别列举了每个拟合的最佳拟合值及其 90% 置信限。三条光谱的柱密度在不确定度范围内是一致的，同时两条平静状态下光谱的光子幂指数也是一致的。随后，我们同时对三条光谱进行双幂律模型拟合，过程中对两条平静状态下的光谱采用一个统一的光子幂指数，对耀发光谱采用另一个光子幂指数，而对三条光谱采用统一的柱密度。图 3 中的实线显示了同时拟合情况下每条谱线的最佳拟合模型；表 1 的最后一行列举了对应的参数值。利用这些结果，我们得到了这个源在 2~10 keV 波段做了吸收修正后的光度：平静状态下 $L_X = (2.2^{+0.4}_{-0.3}) \times 10^{33}$ erg·s^{-1}，耀发状态下的峰值 $L_X = (1.0 \pm 0.1) \times 10^{35}$ erg·s^{-1}(大约是平静状态下的 45 倍)。我们注意到过去的 X 射线天文台的灵敏度不够高，无法探测到银河系中心这样持续时间短、光度低的耀发信号[6]。对于耀发状态下的光谱，其光子幂指数的最佳拟合结果为 $\Gamma_f = 1.3^{+0.5}_{-0.6}$ ($N(E) \propto E^{\Gamma}$)，这个结果比被认为包含超大质量黑洞的系统的理论预言[11]稍平，但仍相互一致。这里，E 是以 keV 为单位的光子能量，$N(E)$ 是能量在 E 到 $E+dE$ 微分区间内的光子数目，Γ 是光子数分布的幂律指数。

Fig. 3. X-ray spectra of the Chandra source at the position of Sgr A*. The data are shown as crosses with vertical bars indicating the 1σ errors in the count rate and horizontal bars the energy range of each bin. The events have been grouped to yield 10 counts per bin. The counts in the 1999 (black) and 2000 (red) quiescent-state spectra were extracted using a source radius of 1.5″. A non-piled-up, peak flaring-state spectrum (green) was extracted from the wings of the point spread function, using an annulus with inner and outer radii of 0.5″ and 2.5″, during the time interval 23.7–26.3 ks after the start of the 2000 observation. The solid lines are the best-fit models for each spectrum, obtained by fitting an absorbed, dust-scattered, double power-law model to the three spectra simultaneously. The best-fit values and 90% confidence intervals for the model parameters are given in the last line of Table 1. The spectra are well-fitted using a single photon index for both quiescent spectra, a second photon index for the flaring spectrum, and a single column density for all three spectra. The column density from the simultaneous fits corresponds to a visual extinction $A_V = 29.6^{+5.0}_{-6.1}$ magnitudes, which agrees well with infrared-derived estimates of $A_V \approx 30$ magnitudes[7]; we thus find no evidence in our X-ray data of excess gas and dust localized around the supermassive black hole. This places an important constraint on the maximum contribution to the infrared spectrum of Sgr A* produced by local dust reprocessing of higher energy photons from the accretion flow. The spectral models used in ref. 6 did not account for dust scattering; hence a higher column density was needed to reproduce the low-energy cut-off via photoelectric absorption alone. We note that there is no sign of an iron $K\alpha$ emission line in the flaring-state spectrum.

Table 1. Spectral fits

Spectrum	$\mathcal{N}_H$	Γ_q	Γ_f	χ^2/ν
1999 quiescent	$5.8^{+1.3}_{-1.4}$	$2.5^{+0.8}_{-0.7}$	...	19/22
2000 quiescent	$5.0^{+1.9}_{-2.3}$	$1.8^{+0.7}_{-0.9}$	...	7.6/12
2000 flaring	$4.6^{+2.0}_{-1.6}$	...	$1.0^{+0.8}_{-0.7}$	12/17
All	$5.3^{+0.9}_{-1.1}$	$2.2^{+0.5}_{-0.7}$	$1.3^{+0.5}_{-0.6}$	45/55

Best-fit parameter values and 90% confidence intervals for power-law models, corrected for photoelectric absorption and dust scattering[10]. $\mathcal{N}_H$ is the neutral hydrogen absorption column in units of 10^{22} H atoms cm^{-2}. Γ_q and Γ_f are the photon-number indices of the quiescent-state and peak flaring-state spectra ($N(E) \propto E^{-\Gamma}$). χ^2 is the value of the fit statistic for the best-fit model, and ν is the number of degrees of freedom in the fit. The parameter values for the spectrum marked "All" were derived by fitting an absorbed, dust-scattered, double power-law model to the three spectra simultaneously (see text and Fig. 3).

图 3. Sgr A* 位置处钱德拉源的 X 射线光谱。数据用交叉十字表示，其中纵向棒代表了光子计数率的 1σ 的误差，而横向棒代表了每个区间的能量范围。这些事件被分组以保证每个区间有 10 个计数。我们在源附近半径为 1.5″ 的范围内从 1999 年（黑色）和 2000 年（红色）的平静状态下的光谱中提取了光子计数，并于 2000 年观测开始的 23.7～26.3 ks 的时间间隔内使用一个环形范围（内环半径 0.5″、外环半径 2.5″）从点扩散函数的两翼中提取了耀发状态下无堆积效应的峰值光谱（绿色）。实线是每条光谱的模型最佳拟合结果，这是基于一个考虑吸收和尘埃散射的双幂律模型对三条光谱同时进行拟合得到的。模型参数的最佳拟合结果以及 90% 置信区间列在了表 1 的最后一行。在对两条平静状态下的光谱采用统一的光子幂指数，对耀发光谱采用另一个光子幂指数并对三条光谱采用统一的柱密度的情况下，我们可以很好地拟合这些光谱。同时拟合所得到的柱密度对应目视波段消光 $A_v = 29.6^{+5.0}_{-6.0}$ 星等，这个结果与从红外数据推断的 $A_v \approx 30$ 星等[7] 相吻合；因此我们在 X 射线数据中并没有发现超大质量黑洞附近存在额外气体和尘埃的证据。局域尘埃会吸收吸积流中更高能量的光子再发出红外辐射，这里得到的结果对这个过程为 Sgr A* 红外光谱所提供的最大贡献给出非常重要的限制。文献 6 中使用的光谱模型没有考虑尘埃散射；因此若只用光电吸收来再现低能端的截断，就需要更高的柱密度。我们注意到，在耀发状态下的光谱中没有铁的 Kα 发射线的迹象。

表 1. 谱线拟合

光谱	N_H	Γ_q	Γ_f	x^2/ν
1999 年的平静状态	$5.8^{+1.3}_{-1.4}$	$2.5^{+0.8}_{-0.7}$	...	19/22
2000 年的平静状态	$5.0^{+1.9}_{-2.3}$	$1.8^{+0.7}_{-0.9}$	...	7.6/12
2000 年的闪耀状态	$4.6^{+2.0}_{-1.6}$	...	$1.0^{+0.8}_{-0.7}$	12/17
总体	$5.3^{+0.9}_{-1.1}$	$2.2^{+0.5}_{-0.7}$	$1.3^{+0.5}_{-0.6}$	45/55

利用考虑了光电吸收和尘埃散射修正[10] 的幂律模型进行拟合的最佳参数值以及 90% 置信区间。N_H 为中性氢吸收柱密度，单位是 10^{22} 个氢原子/cm²。Γ_q 和 Γ_f 分别为平静状态和峰值耀发状态下光谱的光子数指数（$N(E) \propto E^{\Gamma}$）。x^2 是最佳拟合模型的拟合统计值，而 ν 是拟合中自由度的个数。标记为"总体"的光谱的参数值是基于一个考虑吸收和尘埃散射的双幂律模型对三条光谱同时进行拟合得到的（详情见正文和图 3）。

If we view the outburst as a single event, the rise/fall timescales of a few hundred seconds and the 10-ks duration are consistent with the light-crossing and dynamical timescales for the inner part (at less than 10 Schwarzschild radii; $R_S \equiv 2GM/c^2$) of the accretion flow around a black hole of 2.6×10^6 solar masses ; here R_S is the radius of the black-hole event horizon (that is, the boundary at which the escape velocity equals the speed of light, c), G is the gravitational constant and M is the mass of the black hole. Although we cannot strictly rule out an unrelated contaminating source as the origin of the flare (for example, an X-ray binary, for which little is known about such short-timescale, low-luminosity events as we have detected; W. Lewin, personal communication), this explanation seems unlikely, as the characteristic angular scales of the young and old stellar clusters around Sgr A* are 5–20″ (ref. 7), whereas the flaring source lies within 1/3″ of the radio position. These clusters contain up to a million solar masses of stars and stellar remnants[2]; hence it is rather improbable that there would be only one very unusual stellar X-ray source in the image and that it would be fortuitously superposed on Sgr A*. Furthermore, it is not clear that X-ray binaries can be easily formed or long endure near Sgr A*, given the high velocity dispersion and high spatial density of the stars in its deep gravitational potential well[6,12].

Strong, variable X-ray emission is a characteristic property of active galactic nuclei; factors of 2–3 variations on timescales ranging from minutes to years are typical for radio-quiet active galactic nuclei[11]. Moderate- to high-luminosity active galactic nuclei (that is, Seyfert galaxies and quasars) show a general trend of increasing variability with decreasing luminosity[13]. However, this trend does not extend to low-luminosity active galactic nuclei (LLAGN), which show little or no significant variability on timescales less than a day[14]. Assuming the X-ray flare is from Sgr A*, it is remarkable that this source— generally thought to be the nearest and least luminous example of accretion onto a central supermassive black hole—has shown a factor of 45 variation that is an order of magnitude more rapid than the fastest observed variation of similar relative amplitude by a radio-quiet active galactic nucleus of any luminosity class[15]. We note that flares of similar luminosity would be undetectable by Chandra in the nucleus of even the nearest spiral galaxy, M31. LLAGN emit $L_X \gtrsim 10^{38}$ erg s^{-1} (ref. 14), so it should be kept in mind that the astrophysics of accretion onto even the LLAGN may differ substantially from that of Sgr A*. This makes Sgr A* a useful source for testing the theory of accretion onto supermassive black holes in galactic nuclei.

The faintness of Sgr A* at all wavelengths requires that the supermassive black hole be in an extremely quiet phase, either because the accretion rate is very low, or because the accretion flow is radiatively inefficient, or both[5]. A variety of theoretical scenarios, usually based on advective accretion models[16-19], jet–disk models[20], or Bondi–Hoyle models[21,22], have developed this idea. An important prediction of the advective accretion models is that the X-ray spectrum in the Chandra energy band should be dominated by thermal bremsstrahlung emission from hot gas in the outer regions of the accretion flow ($R \gtrsim 10^3 R_S$), but a region this large could not produce the rapid, large-relative-amplitude variations we have seen. Thus, the properties of the X-ray flare are inconsistent with the advective accretion flow models. The low luminosity and short timescales of this event are also inconsistent with

如果我们将爆发看作是一次单一事件，那么一个几百秒的增强/减弱的时标以及 10 ks 的持续时间与一个 2.6×10^6 太阳质量的黑洞周围的吸积流内部区域（小于 10 倍施瓦西半径；$R_S \equiv 2GM/c^2$）的光线穿越以及动力学时标相符合；这里 R_S 是黑洞事件视界的半径（即逃逸速度等于光速 c 的边界），G 是引力常数，而 M 是黑洞质量。尽管我们不能严格地排除此次耀发起源于一个无关的污染源（比如一个 X 射线双星，对于探测到它的这类短时标、低光度的事件，我们知之甚少；与卢因的个人交流），但是这个解释的可能性很低，因为 Sgr A* 周围年轻和年老星团的特征角尺度大约为 5″ ~ 20″（参考文献 7），而耀发源位于射电源位置附近 1/3″ 以内。这些星团包含多达百万太阳质量的恒星以及恒星残迹[2]，因此，在图像中仅出现一个非常特殊的恒星级 X 射线源，且其很偶然地与 Sgr A* 的位置重合，这种概率是相当低的。此外，在 Sgr A* 深引力势阱中[6,12]，恒星拥有高速度弥散以及高空间密度，在这种情况下，X 射线双星能否在 Sgr A* 附近顺利形成或者长时间存活，目前并不清楚。

强且变化的 X 射线辐射是活动星系核的一个特征属性；而射电宁静活动星系核一般会在从分钟到年的时标上产生 2 ~ 3 倍的光变[11]。对于中到高光度活动星系核（即赛弗特星系和类星体）而言，它们大体的趋势是光度越低，光变越大[13]。然而，这种趋势并不能用于描述低光度活动星系核（LLAGN），因为它们在短于一天的时标下几乎没有显著的光变[14]。假设 X 射线耀发来源于 Sgr A*，那么值得注意的是，这个源（一般被认为是最近的而且是最暗的中心超大质量黑洞吸积的例子）展现了一个 45 倍的快速光变，这比拥有类似相对幅度的任何光度级的射电宁静活动星系核观测到的最快光变[15]还要快一个量级。我们注意到，即使是最近的漩涡星系 M31 的核存在类似光度的耀发，钱德拉望远镜也无法探测到。LLAGN 的 X 射线光度为 $L_X \gtrsim 10^{38}$ erg · s^{-1}（参考文献 14），即使是吸积到 LLAGN 上的天体物理过程也可能与吸积到 Sgr A* 上的大不相同，这一点我们也需要牢记在心。因此，Sgr A* 成为检验星系核超大质量黑洞吸积理论的有用的源。

在各个波段 Sgr A* 都非常的暗，这就需要超大质量黑洞处在一个极端宁静的状态，这或者是因为吸积率非常低，或者是因为吸积流的辐射效率低下，又或者两个原因都有[5]。基于径移吸积模型[16-19]、喷流–盘模型[20]或是邦迪–霍伊尔模型[21,22]等，大量理论图景都提出了这一想法。径移吸积模型的一个重要的预言是钱德拉能量波段的 X 射线光谱应当由吸积流外围区域（$R \gtrsim 10^3 R_S$）高温气体的热轫致辐射所主导，但是这样大的区域无法产生我们所看到的快速、相对大幅度的光变。因此，X 射线耀发的性质与径移吸积流模型不相符。这一事件的低光度、短时标特征，也与

tidal disruption of a star by a central supermassive black hole[23].

In all models, the radio-to-submillimetre spectrum of Sgr A* is cyclo-synchrotron emission from a combination of sub-relativistic and relativistic electrons (and perhaps positrons) spiralling around magnetic field lines either in a jet or in a static region within the inner $10R_S$ of the accretion flow. The electron Lorentz factor inferred from the radio spectrum of Sgr A* is $\gamma_e \approx 10^2$. If the X-ray flare were produced via direct synchrotron emission, then the emitting electrons would need $\gamma_e \gtrsim 10^5$. For the 10–100 G magnetic field strengths predicted by the models, the cooling time of the particles would be ~1–100 s. Thus, the approximately 10-ks duration of the flare would require repeated injection of energy to the electrons. On the other hand, if the X-rays were produced via up-scattering of the submillimetre photons off the relativistic electrons, a process called synchrotron self-Comptonization (SSC), then $\gamma_e \approx 10^2$–10^3 would be required, and the cooling time would be of the order of hours, which is consistent with the duration of the flare. The rapid turn-off of the X-ray emission might then be attributed to the dilution of both photon and electron densities in an expanding plasma.

The X-ray spectra of radio-quiet quasars and active galactic nuclei are thought to be produced by thermal Comptonization of infrared-to-ultraviolet seed photons from a cold, optically thick, geometrically thin accretion disk by hot electrons in a patchy corona above the disk[13,24]. The X-ray spectra of these sources generally "soften" (that is, become steeper and extend less strongly to higher energies) as they brighten[15]. In contrast, the extremely low luminosity of Sgr A* precludes the presence of a standard, optically thick accretion disk[5]; hence, the dominant source of seed photons would be the millimetre-to-submillimetre synchrotron photons.

The energy released by an instability in the mass accretion rate or by a magnetic reconnection event near the black hole would shock-accelerate the electrons, causing the synchrotron spectrum to intensify and to extend farther into the submillimetre band. Consequently, the Compton up-scattered X-ray emission would harden as the X-ray intensity increased, exactly as observed. We note that the millimetre-band spectrum of Sgr A* has been observed to harden during one three-week flare[25] and one three-day flare[26], as would be required by the current SSC models for Sgr A* (refs 20, 22).

To test the SSC models, we measured the flux density of Sgr A* at a wavelength of 3 mm with the Millimeter Array at the Owens Valley Radio Observatory, simultaneous with part of the 2000 Chandra measurement. Unfortunately, the available observing window (20:10–02:30 UT) preceded the X-ray flare (04:03–06:50 UT) by a few hours. The observed flux density of Sgr A* was 2.05 ± 0.3 Jy, consistent with previously reported measures[27,28]. Recently, a 106-day quasi-periodicity has been reported in the centimetre band from an analysis of 20 years of data taken with the Very Large Array (VLA)[29]. A weekly VLA monitoring program detected a 30% increase in the radio flux density of Sgr A* beginning around 24 October 2000 and peaking on 5 November 2000. This increase was seen at 2 cm, 1.3 cm, and 7 mm (R. McGary, J.-H. Zhao, W. M. Goss and G. C. Bower, personal communication).

中心超大质量黑洞潮汐瓦解恒星[23]不相符。

在所有模型中，Sgr A* 从射电到亚毫米波段的光谱来源于亚相对论性和相对论性电子（或许还有正电子）组合沿喷流中或者吸积流 $10R_S$ 以内稳定区域中的磁场线旋进所产生的回旋-同步加速辐射。从 Sgr A* 的射电谱推断，其电子的洛伦兹因子 γ_e 约为 10^2。如果 X 射线耀发是通过直接的同步加速辐射产生的，那么发出辐射的电子的洛伦兹因子需要达到 $\gamma_e \gtrsim 10^5$。对于模型所预言的 $10 \sim 100$ G 的磁场强度，粒子的冷却时间大约为 $1 \sim 100$ s。因此只有向电子重复注入能量，才能维持大约 10 ks 的耀发。另一方面，如果 X 射线是通过相对论性电子对亚毫米波光子的向上散射（此过程称为同步加速辐射的自康普顿效应（SSC））产生的，那么就需要 $\gamma_e \approx 10^2 \sim 10^3$，而冷却时间将是小时量级，这与耀发所持续的时间相符。X 射线辐射的快速减弱则可以归因于膨胀等离子体中光子和电子密度的稀释。

射电宁静类星体与活动星系核的 X 射线光谱被认为是由来自冷的、光学厚的、几何薄的吸积盘的从红外到紫外的种子光子被盘上方零散的冕中的热电子热康普顿化产生的[13,24]。这些源的 X 射线谱通常随着亮度的增强会出现"软化"的现象（即光谱变得更陡，更少能延伸到较高能量）[15]。相比之下，Sgr A* 的极低的光度排除了一个标准的、光学厚的吸积盘存在[5]的可能性；因此，种子光子的主要来源将是从毫米波到亚毫米波的同步加速辐射光子。

黑洞附近质量吸积率的不稳定性或者磁重联事件释放的能量将通过激波的方式加速电子，导致同步加速辐射谱增强并进一步延伸到亚毫米波段。因此，正如观测到的，随着 X 射线辐射强度的增加，康普顿向上散射造成的 X 射线辐射将会硬化。我们注意到已经观测到 Sgr A* 毫米波段的光谱在一次历时三周[25]和一次历时三天[26]的耀发过程中发生了硬化，而这正是目前 Sgr A* 的 SSC 模型（参考文献 20 和 22）所要求的。

为了检验 SSC 模型，我们利用欧文斯谷射电天文台的毫米波阵列以及部分钱德拉 2000 年的观测数据对 Sgr A* 在波长为 3 mm 处的流量密度进行了测量。不巧的是，可用的观测时段（20:10 至 02:30 UT）比 X 射线耀发事件（04:03 至 06:50 UT）早了几个小时。观测到 Sgr A* 的流量密度为 2.05 ± 0.3 Jy，这与以前公布的结果[27,28]是一致的。最近报道，甚大阵（VLA）20 年数据[29]分析得到了 Sgr A* 在厘米波段的一个 106 天的准周期性。一个 VLA 的每周监控项目探测到 Sgr A* 的射电流量密度大约从 2000 年 10 月 24 日起开始了一次 30% 的增强，在 2000 年 11 月 5 日达到峰值。这次增强在 2 cm、1.3 cm 以及 7 mm 的波长上看到了（与麦加里、赵军辉、戈斯和

The timing of the X-ray flare and the rise in the radio flux density of Sgr A* suggests that there is a connection between the two events, providing additional indirect support for the association of the X-ray flare with Sgr A* and further strengthening the case that it was produced via either the SSC or direct synchrotron processes. Definitive evidence for these ideas will require detection of correlated variations in the radio-to-submillimetre and X-ray wavebands through future coordinated monitoring projects.

(**413**, 45-48; 2001)

F. K. Baganoff[*], M. W. Bautz[*], W. N. Brandt[†], G. Chartas[†], E. D. Feigelson[†], G. P. Garmire[†], Y. Maeda[†‡], M. Morris[§], G. R. Ricker[*], L. K. Townsley[†] & F. Walter[‖]

[*] Center for Space Research, Massachusetts Institute of Technology, Cambridge, Massachusetts 02139-4307, USA
[†] Department of Astronomy and Astrophysics, Pennsylvania State University, University Park, Pennsylvania 16802-6305, USA
[‡] Institute of Space and Astronautical Science, 3-1-1 Yoshinodai, Sagamihara, 229-8501, Japan
[§] Department of Physics and Astronomy, University of California at Los Angeles, Los Angeles, California 90095-1562, USA
[‖] Department of Astronomy, California Institute of Technology, Pasadena, California 91125, USA

Received 27 April; accepted 2 August 2001.

References:

1. Richstone, D. *et al.* Supermassive black holes and the evolution of galaxies. *Nature* **395** (suppl. on optical astronomy) A14-A19 (1998).

2. Genzel, R., Pichon, C., Eckart, A., Gerhard, O. E. & Ott, T. Stellar dynamics in the Galactic Centre: proper motions and anisotropy. *Mon. Not. R. Astron. Soc.* **317**, 348-374 (2000).

3. Ghez, A. M., Morris, M., Becklin, E. E., Tanner, A. & Kremenek, T. The accelerations of stars orbiting the Milky Way's central black hole. *Nature* **407**, 349-351 (2000).

4. Lynden-Bell, D. & Rees, M. J. On quasars, dust and the Galactic Centre. *Mon. Not. R. Astron. Soc.* **152**, 461-475 (1971).

5. Melia, F. & Falcke, H. The supermassive black hole at the Galactic Center. *Annu. Rev. Astron. Astrophys.* **39**, 309-352 (2001).

6. Baganoff, F. K. *et al.* Chandra X-ray spectroscopic imaging of Sgr A* and the central parsec of the Galaxy. *Astrophys. J.* (submitted); also preprint astro-ph/0102151 at ⟨xxx.lanl.gov⟩ (2001).

7. Morris, M. & Serabyn, E. The galactic center environment. *Annu. Rev. Astron. Astrophys.* **34**, 645-702 (1996).

8. Menten, K. M., Reid, M. J., Eckart, A. & Genzel, R. The position of Sagittarius A*: accurate alignment of the radio and infrared reference frames at the Galactic Center. *Astrophys. J.* **475**, L111-L114 (1997).

9. Weisskopf, M. C., O'Dell, S. L. & van Speybroeck, L. P. Advanced X-Ray Astrophysics Facility (AXAF). *Proc. SPIE* **2805**, 2-7 (1996).

10. Predehl, P. & Schmitt, J. H. M. M. X-raying the interstellar medium: ROSAT observations of dust scattering halos. *Astron. Astrophys.* **293**, 889-905 (1995).

11. Mushotzky, R. F., Done, C. & Pounds, K. A. X-ray spectra and time variability of active galactic nuclei. *Annu. Rev. Astron. Astrophys.* **31**, 717-761 (1993).

12. Davies, M. B., Blackwell, R., Bailey, V. C. & Sigurdsson, S. The destructive effects of binary encounters on red giants in the Galactic Centre. *Mon. Not. R. Astron. Soc.* **301**, 745-753 (1998).

13. Nandra, K., George, I. M., Mushotzky, R. F., Turner, T. J. & Yaqoob, T. ASCA observations of Seyfert 1 galaxies. I. Data analysis, imaging, and timing. *Astrophys. J.* **476**, 70-82 (1997).

14. Ptak, A., Yaqoob, T., Mushotzky, R., Serlemitsos, P. & Griffiths, R. X-ray variability as a probe of advection-dominated accretion in low-luminosity active galactic nuclei. *Astrophys. J.* **501**, L37-L40 (1998).

15. Ulrich, M.-H., Maraschi, L. & Urry, C. M. Variability of active galactic nuclei. *Annu. Rev. Astron. Astrophys.* **35**, 445-502 (1997).

16. Narayan, R., Mahadevan, R., Grindlay, J. E., Popham, R. G. & Gammie, C. Advection-dominated accretion model of Sagittarius A*: evidence for a black hole at the Galactic center. *Astrophys. J.* **492**, 554-568 (1998).

17. Quataert, E. & Narayan, R. Spectral models of advection-dominated accretion flows with winds. *Astrophys. J.* **520**, 298-315 (1999).

18. Ball, G. H., Narayan, R. & Quataert, E. Spectral models of convection-dominated accretion flows. *Astrophys. J.* **552**, 221-226 (2001).

19. Blandford, R. D. & Begelman, M. C. On the fate of gas accreting at a low rate on to a black hole. *Mon. Not. R. Astron. Soc.* **303**, L1-L5 (1999).

20. Falcke, H. & Markoff, S. The jet model for Sgr A*: radio and X-ray spectrum. *Astron. Astrophys.* **362**, 113-118 (2000).

21. Melia, F. An accreting black hole model for Sagittarius A*. II: A detailed study. *Astrophys. J.* **426**, 577-585 (1994).

22. Melia, F., Liu, S. & Coker, R. Polarized millimeter and submillimeter emission from Sagittarius A* at the Galactic center. *Astrophys. J.* **545**, L117-L120 (2000).

23. Rees, M. J. Tidal disruption of stars by black holes of 10^6–10^8 solar masses in nearby galaxies. *Nature* **333**, 523-528 (1988).

鲍尔的个人交流）。X 射线耀发的时间与 Sgr A* 射电波段流量密度的增强的时间相一致，这意味着两个事件之间存在联系，这为本次 X 射线耀发与 Sgr A* 之间的关联提供了额外的间接支持，并且进一步强化了该事件起源于 SSC 或者直接的同步加速辐射过程的情形。要获得这些想法的决定性证据，我们还需要通过未来的协调监测项目探测射电到亚毫米波段与 X 射线波段之间的相关光变。

（刘项琨 翻译；陈阳 审稿）

24. Haardt, F., Maraschi, L. & Ghisellini, G. X-ray variability and correlations in the two-phase disk-corona model for Seyfert galaxies. *Astrophys. J.* **476**, 620-631 (1997).

25. Tsuboi, M., Miyazaki, A. & Tsutsumi, T. in *The Central Parsecs of the Galaxy* (ed. Falcke, H. *et al.*) Vol. 186, 105-112 (ASP Conf. Ser., Astronomical Society of the Pacific, San Francisco, 1999).

26. Wright, M. C. H. & Backer, D. C. Flux density of Sagittarius A at λ = 3 millimeters. *Astrophys. J.* **417**, 560-564 (1993).

27. Serabyn, E. *et al.* High frequency measurements of the spectrum of SGR A*. *Astrophys. J.* **490**, L77-L81 (1997).

28. Falcke, H. *et al.* The simultaneous spectrum of Sagittarius A* from 20 centimeters to 1 millimeter and the nature of the millimeter excess. *Astrophys. J.* **499**, 731-734 (1998).

29. Zhao, J.-H., Bower, G. C. & Goss, W. M. Radio variability of Sagittarius A*—a 106 day cycle. *Astrophys. J.* **547**, L29-L32 (2001).

30. Reid, M. J. The distance to the center of the Galaxy. *Annu. Rev. Astron. Astrophys.* **31**, 345-372 (1993).

Acknowledgements. We thank M. Begelman for useful comments. This work has been supported by a grant from NASA.

Correspondence and requests for materials should be addressed to F.K.B.(e-mail: fkb@space.mit.edu).

Appendix: Index by Subject
附录：学科分类目录

Physics
物理学

Chemistry
化学

Biology
生物学

Astronomy
天文学

Geoscience
地球科学